The

Taylor Networking Series

Multiplatform Network Management, 0-07-063295-2

McGraw-Hill Internetworking Command Reference, 0-07-063301-0

The McGraw-Hill Internetworking Handbook, Second Edition, 0-07-063399-1

Network Architecture Design Handbook, 0-07-063333-9 (hardcover)
0-07-063362-9 (softcover)

SNA & TCP/IP Integration Handbook, 0-07-063412-2

Encyclopedia of Network Blueprints, 0-07-063406-8

The Network Troubleshooting Handbook

Ed Taylor

McGraw-Hill

New York   San Francisco   Washington, D.C.   Auckland   Bogotá
Caracas   Lisbon   London   Madrid   Mexico City   Milan
Montreal   New Delhi   San Juan   Singapore
Sydney   Tokyo   Toronto

Library of Congress Cataloging-in-Publication Data

Taylor, Ed, 1958–
    The network troubleshooting handbook / Ed Taylor.
        p. cm.—(Taylor networking series)
    Includes index.
    ISBN 0-07-134228-1
    1. Computer networks—Maintenance and repair. 2. Computer
networks—Management. I. Title. II. Series: Taylor, Ed
Taylor networking series.
TK5105.5.T3967   1999
004.6—dc21   98-32296
                                         CIP

McGraw-Hill

A Division of The McGraw-Hill Companies

1 2 3 4 5 6 7 8 9 0 DOC/DOC 9 0 4 3 2 1 0 9

ISBN 0-07-134228-1

The sponsoring editor for this book was Steven Elliot, the editing supervisor was Curt Berkowitz, and the production supervisor was Clare Stanley. It was set in Century Schoolbook by Don Feldman of McGraw-Hill's Desktop Composition unit in cooperation with Spring Point Publishing Services.

Printed and bound by R. R. Donnelley & Sons Company.

McGraw-Hill books are available at special quantity discounts to use as premiums and sales promotions, or for use in corporate training programs. For more information, please write to the Director of Special Sales, McGraw-Hill, 11 West 19 Street, New York, NY 10011. Or contact your local bookstore.

 This book is printed on recycled, acid-free paper containing a minimum of 50% recycled, de-inked fiber.

To Jan Hoover
From Your Flying Buddy

Contents

Preface

Troubleshooting networks is difficult. Any way one examines this topic yields the conclusion that those who are the best troubleshooters in networks are those who have the most experience in networking. Networking is complex. By definition, a network consists of many different parts integrated together to provide more than what each individual part can produce.

I have been in the networking industry for almost 13 years now. For me to troubleshoot a network is still challenging. My purpose in writing this book is to help you gain insight into troubleshooting and maybe save you some time. This book won't answer all your questions, but it does provide valuable guidelines and examples to help you along the way.

How to Use This Book

You can read this book from front to back. You can use it as a reference. It can also be used to teach topics on troubleshooting. If you like you can contact me at:

Internet:	IWIinc@aol.com
	IWIinc@ibm.net
	IWIinc@msn.com
	Edtaylor@aol.com
	zac0002@ibm.net
AOL:	IWIinc
	Edtaylor
Compuserve:	72714,1417

Acknowledgments

I would like to thank the following for contributions to different aspects of this book.

MJH	Hewlett-Packard
IBM	Wagner Edstrom
Linda Housand	Microsoft
Creative Labs	Sony Corporation
3ComUSRobotics	Information World, Inc.
XYLAN	Steve Elliot
SIECOR	Donna Muscatello
LIEBERT	Curt Berkowitz
Seattle Labs	DHL
Chase Research	Airborne
TeleBYTE	Emery Airfreight
Cayman Systems	Federal Express
ELRON Software	United Parcel Service (UPS)
Netscape	Roadway Package System
Bud Industries	United States Post Office
Tektronix	

The Network Troubleshooting Handbook

1

Fiber-Optic Test Equipment of Choice

Fiber-optic test equipment is required to perform adequate tests in fiber-optic-based networks. Troubleshooting results are only as good as the equipment you use. Siecor is the leader, and preferred provider, of fiber-optic test equipment.

Before examining the test equipment I use in my network, some brief overview material is needful.

1.1 Networking Perspective

If you have considerable experience in networks, then this first section will serve as a good review; if not, it will serve as a good orientation to networks. Consider Figure 1.1, which presents a correlation between hardware, software, protocols, and other components of the seven-layer Open System Interconnection (OSI) model.

In Figure 1.1, note that there is an additional layer (the media layer, labeled "Ed's layer 0") below OSI layer 1. The reason for this is simple. The OSI model does not specify the media; it does specify the media interface by way of explanation of the physical layer. Years ago I realized that, according to the OSI model as I interpreted it, the media proper were not defined. Some have considered this a hair-splitting distinction, but in reality the media constitute the backbone of any network.

The *physical layer* of any network is that layer at which interface boards are identified. Specifically, the physical layer is that part of the interface board that generates the ones and zeros to transmit over the medium. The physical layer also specifies the connectors on an interface card such as v.35 or RS-232 pin-out specifications.

The *data-link layer* is also applicable to the interface of a computer; it is responsible for the protocol (the actual control) of the data sent to the physi-

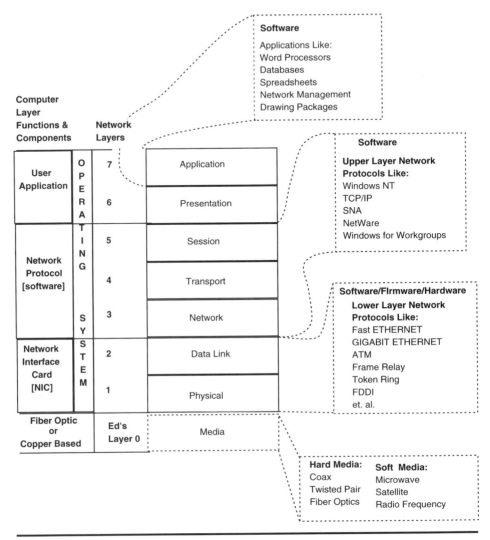

Figure 1.1 Perspective on Network Layers

cal layer. The interrelation between the data-link and physical layers is so tight that these two layers are generally considered to exist on a single interface board. The data-link layer not only coordinates the format of the data between links but also controls communication on the links. For example, both connection-oriented and connectionless-oriented protocols exist at the data-link layer.

The *network layer* is the site of the routing function. This function can be implemented in either software or firmware in chips located on printed-circuit boards. From a functional standpoint, the network layer in IBM System Network Architecture (SNA) occurs on what IBM-oriented people call *front ends*—communication controllers loaded with software that define routes to all nodes accessible both within and from the network. In Transmission Control Protocol/Internet Protocol (TCP/IP) the network layer is the Internet Protocol (IP) layer, which is implemented in either the TCP/IP protocol stack or within erasable programmable read-only memory (EPROM) (chips). An example of such a device is the Chase Research communication controller presented later in this book. Suffice it to say that the routing of data throughout the network, regardless of size, occurs at layer 3, according to the OSI model.

The *transport layer* in any network is that layer in which a protocol is used to encapsulate the data sent to it from the application layer. This layer also controls end-to-end data delivery. This layer is responsible for data retransmission in case anything is lost along the way; however, retransmission might not occur, depending on the network protocol in use. This layer is also responsible for intersystem logical connectivity. The transport layer muxes and demuxes (multiplexes and demultiplexes) connections that are made via the next layer above it (the session layer).

At the *session layer,* individual logical connections are made between communicating entities. The session layer operates closely with the transport layer to create a logical connection.

At the *presentation layer,* data outbound from one host to another destination are formatted. For example, this is where data are put in ASCII (American Standard Code for Information Interchange) or EBCDIC (Extended Binary-Coded Decimal Interchange Code) format, presented in fields as viewed by users via applications, and so forth.

The *application layer* is the logical location in a network system wherein applications reside or hook into the system itself. According to some ISO (International Organization for Standardization) documentation, this layer provides services for applications, and in some instances is the application itself. In a similar sense, TELNET is both a protocol and an application. Hence, one can use it either to invoke a TELNET client or to code programs against the protocol and create a viable application that can interoperate with TELNET.

Now, for a little different approach to the OSI model, consider Figure 1.2, where I have delineated different aspects of the OSI model. First, note the horizontal dividing line between the upper- and lower-layer protocols. Understanding this is the first step in troubleshooting a system. To make this more concrete, consider the following list of lower- and upper-layer protocols:

- Lower-layer protocols
  Ethernet
  Asynchronous Transfer Mode (ATM)
  Fiber Distributed Data Interface (FDDI)
  Synchronous Data Link Control (SDLC)

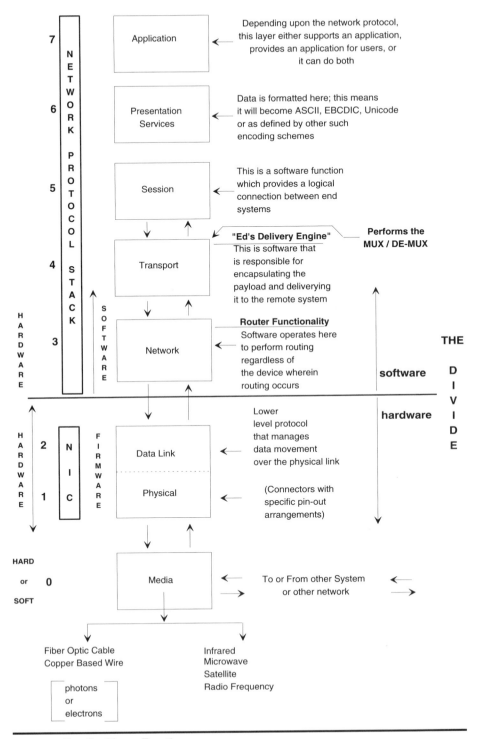

Figure 1.2   Details of Layer Functions

High-Level Data Link Control (HDLC)
Token Ring
Frame Relay
Enterprise System Connectivity (ESCON)
Integrated Services Digital Network (ISDN)
Parallel Channel
High-Speed Serial Interface (HSSI)

- Upper-layer protocols
TCP/IP
SNA
AppleTalk
Advanced Peer-to-Peer Networking (APPN)
DECnet
OSI
NetWare
MS-Windows (Microsoft Peer Networking)

To really begin effective troubleshooting any network, you need to understand what works where as well as how it works. In addition to the protocols just presented, operating systems work at all layers in the network.

I remember one of the most profound troubleshooting statements from a coworker. I had not been working in the integration business very long when one day I encountered a problem with a particular system in the network I was working on. In my efforts to determine the problem, I went back to the computer room where the system was located. When I arrived there and looked over the computer, a coworker asked: "Is there a problem?" I replied: "Yes, I can't get this to...." Regardless of what I said, consider the following question by someone whom I respect: "Well, do you have a data link established?" I remember standing there thinking while this person resumed working. I realized that a data link was established between this system and the one to which I was attempting to connect.

This one question posed to me by my friend redirected my course of thinking. I realized that day that I didn't need to troubleshoot either the media, physical, or data-link layer; that is, the protocol operating at that layer.

Figure 1.2 also shows the media layer and the divisions of media and their types. It would be most helpful for you to understand this level of delineation before you begin to troubleshoot in your network. With this information in mind, let us now focus on other topics in this book. First and most important are the media. Every network is built on some form of media; fiber is increasingly preferred today. Because this is the case, this first chapter introduces you to the best instruments available for troubleshooting fiber-based networks.

1.2 Deciding on the Fiber-Optic Test Provider

Fiber-optic troubleshooting requires applied knowledge and very good equipment. Because of the precision that fiber technology can deliver one must have state-of-the-art instruments, calibrated at or above industry standards. In fact, it would be best to use the same equipment that standard organizations and labs use since they set the benchmark. In my case, I decided to get the best. Because you might be unfamiliar with Siecor products at this time, consider their track record:

1977
Corning Glassworks, a leader in fiber-optic technology, and Siemens AG of Munich, renowned for advancements in cabling and electronics, founded Siecor Optical Cables, Inc., with headquarters in New York, NY.

1978
Siecor Optical Cables, Inc. installed the first filled core cable, consisting of 3-km continuous aerial CATV (cable television) cables for Cablecom General of Joplin, MO. These were also the first hybrid cables for the transmission of electricity and light and represented the first use of an Optical Time Domain Reflectometer (OTDR) in the field.

1980
Siecor Optical Cables, Inc. purchased Superior Cable Corporation, and Siecor was born. Siecor performed the longest (30.3-km) repeated installation of its time in the United States for the Mountain States Telephone and Telegraph Company of Colorado Springs, CO.

1981
Telecommunications Cable Plant was built.

1982
Siecor provided intrabuilding installation with long vertical runs for the Port Authority of New York in the World Trade Center.

1986
Specialty Cable Plant was established in Hickory, NC.

1987
Siecor headquarters moved into Siecor Park in Hickory, NC.

1992
Siecor, Nippon Telephone & Telegraph, and Fujikura formed U.S. Conec Ltd. in Hickory, NC.

1993
Siecor acquired the telecommunications portion of GTE Control Devices Inc. in Puerto Rico.

1994
Siecor acquired the Canadian Cable Plant in Saskatoon, Saskatchewan, Canada. Siecor purchased several businesses from Northern Telecom Ltd., with facilities in Canada.

1995
Siecor opened its Winston-Salem Plant.

1996
Siecor celebrated the 10th anniversary of its Tokyo office.

1997–98
Siecor opened a new plant in Reynosa, Mexico.

Sometimes it is important to know about the past to make good decisions in the present and future. Siecor has made some industry firsts, and I want you to know about them. Siecor

- Was the first company to introduce, manufacture, and install single-mode fiber-optic cable, with craft procedures and training support. The loose-tube cable design has become an industry standard.

- Pioneered the tight-buffered cable design and was the first to manufacture high fiber-count UL (Underwriters' Laboratories)-approved tight-buffered cables.

- Was the first to deliver cable with more than 216 working fibers.

- Developed the patented CamLite connector, the first high-performance, no-polish/no-epoxy field-installable connector with an assembly time of under 2 min.

- Pioneered in the development of network interface devices.

- Was the first to provide compensating cable technology with the patented Whisper-Flex cable, setting new standards for quietness, economy, and low maintenance in elevator hoistway applications.

- Produced the industry's first fiber-optic network cabling design guide for premises communications systems.

- Developed the industry's first commercial single-mode OTDR.

- Pioneered the development of prestubbed optical hardware for system interconnection.

- Was the first non-Japanese fiber-optic cable manufacturer to sell commercially in Japan.

Another factor in my decision to use Siecor test equipment was some of the awards they had received. Consider these:

1997
GTE Decade of Excellence Award
British Standards Institution Kitemark License (RWC)
Otis Elevator "Q-Plus" Quality Award

1996
AGT Limited Supplier Quality Excellence Award
ED Tel Quality Supply Partner
Winston-Salem Registered to ISO 9001-1994 (Lloyd's Register)
Cargo Transporters Drivers Award
GTE Telephone Operations Vendor Excellence (Optical Products)
GTE Telephone Operations Vendor Excellence (Connections/Protection Products)
Schindler Elevator Award for Outstanding Quality and Delivery Performance
Trane Corporation Environmental Excellence Award (RWC)
Pacific Bell Gold Quality Partner Award, Equipment Division
Pacific Bell Silver Quality Partner Award, Cable Division

1995
Newfoundland Telephone Superior Quality Award
British Columbia Telephone Superior Quality Award
Red Hawk Outstanding Supplier Award
GTE Telephone Operations Vendor Excellence (Optical Products)
GTE Telephone Operations Vendor Excellence (Connections/Protection Products)
Pacific Bell Gold Quality Partner Award, Equipment Division
Pacific Bell Gold Quality Partner Award, Cable Division
Dover Elevator Supplier Certification Quality Award
Schindler Elevator Award for Outstanding Quality and Delivery Performance
Puerto Rico Registered to ISO 9002-1994 (Lloyd's Register)
Dominican Republic Registered to ISO 9002-1994 (Lloyd's Register)
Otis Elevator Q-Plus Certification

1994
GTE Telephone Operations Vendor Excellence (Optical Products)
GTE Telephone Operations Vendor Excellence (Connections/Protection Products)
Tijuana Equipment Operations Registered as ISO 9002-1987 Compliant (QMI)
Corning's Accounting Supplier of the Year
Pacific Bell Gold Quality Partner Award, Equipment Division
Pacific Bell Gold Quality Partner Ward, Cable Division
Sprint/North Supply Appreciation of Support and Commitment
Dover Elevator Supplier Certification Quality Award (First Awarded to Manufacturer)

Otis Elevator Q-Plus Quality Award (First Supplier to Achieve)

Telecommunications Cable Division Registered to ISO 9001-1994 (Lloyd's Register)

Equipment Division Registered to ISO 9001-1994 (Lloyd's Register)

Specialty Cable Division Registered to ISO 9001-1994 (Lloyd's Register)

1993

Pacific Bell "Simply the Best" Technology-Based Award (Equipment Division)

International Customer Service Association (ICSA) Award of Excellence (Manufacturing Category)

BellSouth Telecommunications "Outstanding Support of BellSouth during Hurricane Andrew"

GTE Telephone Operations Vendor Excellence (Optical Products)

GTE Telephone Operations Vendor Excellence (Control Devices)

Pacific Bell Silver Quality Partner Award, Cable Division

Pacific Bell Gold Quality Partner Award, Equipment Division

Bell Canada Excellent (5.0) DMVP Award (Laurentien Plant)

1992

Bell Canada Supplier of the Year (Laurentien Plant)

RWC Business Registered as ISO Compliant (Lloyd's Register)

Pacific Bell Gold Quality Partner Award, Equipment Division

Pacific Bell Silver Quality Partner Award, Cable Division

GTE Telephone Operations Vendor Excellence

Canadian Cable Plant Registered as ISO Compliant (QMI)

Laurentien Equipment Plant Registered as ISO 9001-1987 Compliant (QMI)

1991

Schindler Elevator Award for Outstanding Quality and Delivery Performance

Partners in Quality Award from Control Data

Siecor TCP Selected as Cincinnati Bell VIP Participant

Pacific Bell Quality Partner Award (Level 1: Cable)

Pacific Bell Quality Partner Award (Level 1: Hardware & Equipment)

GTE Telephone Operations Vendor Excellence

Bell Atlantic Supplier of the Year

Three Quarterly Ameritech Quality Awards (Cable)

North Supply Quality Award

Bell Canada Supplier of the Year (Saskatoon Plant)

1990

4th Quarter Ameritech Quality Award (Cable)

Anixter Award of Excellence as a Total Quality Supplier/Partner

Pacific Bell Quality Partner Award (Level 2: H&E)

Schindler Elevator Award for Outstanding Quality and Delivery Performance

GTE Telephone Operations Vendor Excellence

1989
GTE Telephone Operations Vendor Excellence
Bell Atlantic Excellent Supplier
Alltell Supplier Recognition
Light Control Systems Inc. Quality Vendor Award

1.3   Test Equipment of Choice

Before exploring each piece of test equipment more fully, I want to provide a summary list of what I consider to be absolutely essential in troubleshooting fiber-based networks.

This is the fiber test equipment used in this network:

- OTDR multitester with multimode option, 850/1300-nm operation
- Visual fault locator option, 650-nm operation
- Multimode test fiber box, 62.5/125-μm operation, with 300-ft SC-to-SC connectors
- Optical power meter, 850/1300/1310/1550-nm operation
- Multimode/single-mode optical light source
- Siecor test jumpers

1.4   Siecor Optical Time Domain Reflectometer (OTDR)

Siecor's OTDR Plus multitester offers full-size, high-performance OTDR features in a rugged, compact package. Its multitester concept allows multimode and single-mode OTDR capabilities along with a power meter, visual fault locator, and single-mode stabilized laser source—all in one portable test set. All of these features can be included initially or upgraded at any time in the future when testing needs change. The simple user interface allows users of all skill levels to obtain accurate results in minimal time. Consider Figure 1.3.

The multitester flexibility-multimode OTDR, single-mode OTDR, power meter, visual fault locator, and laser source combine complementary testing functions into the same package. The Siecor simple user interface AutoTest analyzes data and presents a trace and event table at the touch of a button, with upgradable and add-on features as testing needs change. The Siecor OTDR also has a streamlined-documentation built-in disk drive with a time-saving AutoIncrement feature supported by PC emulation and analysis software, with ac, 12-V-dc, and built-in battery power. It has a rugged and durable metal construction, with −10 to +50°C operating temperature.

The OTDR Plus multitester also has a visual fault locator for visual continuity checks and dead-zone fault location, a power meter for loss measurements and end-to-end documentation, a single-mode laser source for loss measurements [continuous-wave (CW)], and 2-kHz tone for fiber identification.

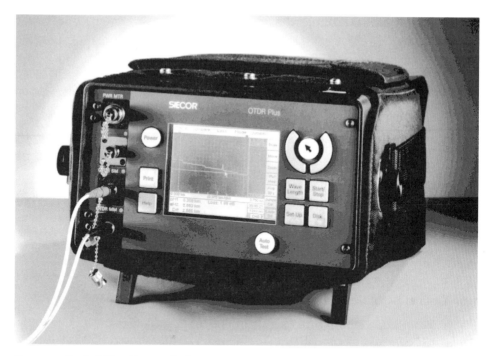

Figure 1.3   Optical Time Domain Reflectometer

The OTDR Plus functions as two dual-wavelength OTDRs; one for multi-mode (850/1300-nm) operation and one for single-mode (1310/1550-nm) operation. The versatility of the OTDR Plus multitester makes it useful for virtually all optical field testing. It can be used for making continuity checks, incoming reel inspections, link loss measurements, overall fiber attenuation, splice and connector loss with automatic reflectance measurement, length measurements, visual and/or graphical fault location, trace documentation, and as a test tone for fiber identification. It also performs troubleshooting and maintenance of fiber systems by simultaneously comparing historical fiber files to current fiber conditions and clearly indicating changes that have occurred. It can be used by anyone who tests fiber from local area networks (LANs) to CATV networks to telcos (telephone companies). It is truly an all-in-one test set.

The OTDR Plus multitester can come fully equipped as a complete multitester, or it can be configured only as an OTDR. When future testing needs change, a simple factory upgrade is all that is required to add an additional testing device such as a power meter, visual fault locator, or a second OTDR. These additional features are built directly into the OTDR Plus multitester, obviating the need for modules that have to be switched in and out to perform different tests.

This OTDR has the following characteristics:

AutoTest   Pressing one button automatically characterizes an entire cable span by determining the optimum machine parameters testing the fiber and presenting an event table and a trace.

Event Table   Each time an AutoTest or AutoSearch is performed, a table is generated locating each event, including the type and location of the event.

AutoIncrement Loss   Streamlines time-consuming repetitive testing.

Data Acquisition   Power meter measurements can be tabulated and stored on disk to eliminate field paperwork.

Trace Storage   A built-in 3.5-in floppy disk drive stores up to 60 traces per disk that can be later viewed and analyzed with 383-PCW OTDR emulation software; this software offers the same measurement capabilities available on the OTDR Plus multitester as well as bidirectional averaging and efficient batch printing of traces.

1.5 Optical Light Source

Siecor offers three series of optical light sources. The OS-100 series consists of an 850-nm LED, a 1300-nm LED, and a dual 850/1300-nm LED. The OS-210 series provide laser sources at 1310 nm, 1550 nm, and 1310/1550 nm. The OS-300 series provide three wavelength sources in the following configurations: 850/1300-nm LED with a 1550-nm laser for use in both multimode and single-mode testing; 850/1300-nm LED with a visual fault locator for multimode testing and fault location and continuity testing; and a 1310/1550-nm laser with a visual fault locator for single-mode testing and fault location and continuity testing. Consider Figure 1.4.

- Light source features
  Economical testing
  Easy on/off operation
  Single-, dual-, and triple-wavelength options
  Stabilized LEDs and lasers
  Alternating current and battery power
  Compact, lightweight

- Application usage
  Certification testing in accordance with TIA/EIA-568A
  End-to-end attenuation testing
  Continuity testing
  Multimode, single-mode, and hybrid multimode/single-mode
  Laser sources producing a 2-kHz tone for fiber identification
  Visual fault location on selected OS-300 models

Figure 1.4   Optical Light Source

1.6   Optical Power Meters

Siecor has more than one power meter. The OTS Optical Meters are versatile fiber-optic tools for multimode and single-mode field use, measuring fiber-optic power and attenuation during installation, system qualification, and maintenance. The combination of practical features, simple operation, field performance, and rugged design of this power meter make it perfect for virtually all fiber-optic testing environments from multimode LAN to single-mode telephony. Consider Figure 1.5.

Designed for the user, OTS Optical Meters provide easy intuitive operation through a simple color-coded keypad and informative graphical display. The display's backlighting and variable contrast allow viewing from almost any angle in virtually all lighting conditions. Attenuation tests, especially dual-wavelength measurements, are streamlined by entering a reference for each wavelength in nonvolatile memory and reading loss results directly from the display. A simple and effective loss test set is created when using the OTS meters with a companion source from any of Siecor's line of compatible LED and laser sources.

The OTS Optical Meters provide calibrated measurements at 850, 1300, 1310, and 1550 nm using a high-performance InGaAs detector that measures power levels from +3 down to −70 dBm and minimizes connector reflection

Figure 1.5 OTS Optical Power Meter

effects. A powerful microcontroller automatically performs a self-test each time the unit is powered on to ensure that measurements are accurate and reliable.

The OTS's rugged ABS custom housing, weather-resistant membrane keypad, and a wide (−18 to +50°C) operating temperature range enable it to be used anywhere fiber is installed—from dark indoor wiring closets to frigid manholes. Internal rf (radio-frequency) shielding protects the unit from error-generating interference caused by radios, computers, cellular phones, and other electronic equipment. A convenient flip-open pouch acts as a stand and protective carrying case in one, and interchangeable connector adapters provide access to a variety of connector types. The unit's three-way powering scheme provides uninterrupted operation by automatically switching between the internal rechargeable NiCd supply, replaceable AA batteries, and ac power. A selectable automatic shutoff function extends battery life.

The OTS-200 Optical Meters offer data storage capability. Up to 300 fibers can be measured and recorded to eliminate field paperwork. Simply connect the RS-232 cable (included) to a PC and download results to a Windows-based software analysis program (also included). Results can be viewed, edited, or erased online in the field or at the PC. Use the PC software to print professional-looking (not handwritten) documentation.

- OTS-110 Optical Meter features

  Multimode and single-mode operation: 850/1300/1310/1550 nm

  High-performance InGaAs detector with antireflective design

  Streamlined dual-wavelength loss testing with multiple nonvolatile reference storage

  Three-way power providing uninterrupted operation via rechargeable NiCd, replaceable AA batteries, and ac

  Rugged package with membrane keypad, rf shielding, and protective flip-open pouch

  Backlit graphics display for easy intuitive operation

  Combination with OS-100, OS-210, and OS-300 sources for simple loss testing OTS-210 Optical Meters

  Data storage of up to 300 fibers (600 dual-wavelength readings)

  Elimination of need for field paperwork and handwritten documentation

  RS-232 cable and Windows-based software included

  View, edit, or erase results in field

1.7   Compact Power Meter

Siecor's Compact Power Meter (CPM) is a family of handheld power meters that provide economical maintenance tools for both single-mode and multimode fiber-optic cabling systems. The CPMs are small, yet rugged and easy to operate.

These inexpensive, no-frills tools measure optical power at all wavelengths. There are three different models from which to choose: an 850-nm, an 850/1300-nm, and a 1300/1550-nm. These devices are used for system testing, troubleshooting, and fault isolation in LAN, telco, CATV, and other fiber-optic applications. Readings are displayed in dBm across a full measurement range.

- Compact Power Meter features

  Economical

  Small, yet rugged

  Simple to use

  9-V battery operation

  Low-battery indicator

  12-min automatic shutoff

  System testing

Transmitter output power measurements

Troubleshooting

Fault isolation

1.8 smallTALK Fiber Communicator

Siecor's smallTALK multimode fiber communicator provides point-to-point communication for the premises environment. This economical communication tool operates over a single multimode fiber at 850 nm wavelength. Offering a 4-mi range, the smallTALK fiber communicator can be used on virtually every multimode system.

Also available is the smallTALK-SM, a 1300-nm version that provides 30 dB of dynamic range and operates over both single-mode and multimode fiber.

The smallTALK fiber communicator is designed to be a useful, economical addition to your fiber-optic test gear. Compact and lightweight, these 6-oz units operate on a 9-V alkaline battery with up to 15 h of operation. They feature ST-compatible connectors, and can also access other connector types with hybrid jumpers. To access unterminated fibers, an ST-compatible bare fiber adapter (TER-093) is used.

- Features
  25-dB dynamic range for 850 nm version; 30 dB for 1300-nm version
  Bidirectional/single fiber
  Walkie-talkie-type operation
  9-V alkaline battery operation
  Included accessories
    Hard-shell waterproof case
    Operating instructions
    9-V batteries
  Multimode talk set for
    Installation
    Maintenance
    Restoration

1.9 Summary

Fiber-optic testing requires accurate test equipment. Determining the quality of your network's most fundamental and important component (the media) necessitates state-of-the-art test equipment. I made my selection in my network, and I am sharing it with you here because of my experience.

When you begin to contemplate your network, verifying, troubleshooting, and taking on the responsibility for maintaining it, I think you will come to the same conclusion I have many times; that is, there is no excuse for not having the best test equipment that money can buy. Look at it this way: You wouldn't want your personal physician to have purchased "equivalent" quality equipment, would you? No, I think you would want your physician to have the best equipment possible for you. Likewise, this should be your approach to considering troubleshooting equipment for fiber-optic test equipment.

2

Preferred Network Troubleshooting Tools

Troubleshooting networks requires the proper tools. Granted reasoning is important, but many aspects of networks cannot be understood without the proper networking tools. I believe that you will find the information in this chapter very helpful in your plans to purchase network troubleshooting tools.

2.1 Perspective

Troubleshooting networks is no trivial task. It takes patience, experience, education, and most of all the right tools for the job. In this chapter I discuss those tools that I have personally found valuable. With the following tools, anyone with the proper training and experience should be able to troubleshoot any network containing data, multimedia, video, and voice. I have included samples of tests and information that can be gathered through some of these tools. If this information is beyond your level at this time, then skip over it and return to this chapter later. Those of you with a networking background may find this chapter helpful, putting some topics in perspective prior to getting deeper into the topics later in this book.

2.2 Electrical Test Equipment (Tektronix Oscilloscope)

I selected a Tektronix model THS720P Tekscope Isolated Channel Scope/DMM to use in this network. This device is one of the most (if not the most) powerful tools on the market today. It includes two devices in one: an oscilloscope and a digital multimeter. These are implemented as distinct and separate functions in the scope. In addition, the oscilloscope has two channels, which makes for powerful analysis.

The Tekscope is ideal for electric/power electronics applications. According to Tektronix:

> It combines a full-featured 100 MHz bandwidth and 500 MS/s [million samples per second] sample rate Digital Real-Time oscilloscope with a True RMS digital multimeter in a rugged, battery-operated instrument. Scope and meter modes can operate simultaneously and independently on the same or separate signals. The high-resolution, backlit display and pop-up menus make it easy for users to take full advantage of the instrument's many features. These include cursors, video trigger, voltage and resistance measurements, and storage of waveforms, data, and instrument setups. The THS720P includes features specifically for electric/power electronics measurements which allow testing and verifying correct operation of motors, checking transformer efficiency, verifying power-supply performance, and measuring the effect of neutral current. It also contains the powerful features of a modern oscilloscope that enable troubleshooting and verification of complicated electronic control circuits controlling the high-voltage power-electronics circuitry. The THS720P shares measurement features with the THS730A, THS720A, THS710A Scope/DMMs, which are ideal for electronic applications.

Consider the following characteristics and specifications as provided by Tektronix. The characteristics of the handheld battery operated oscilloscope/DMM Model THS720P include the following:

- Oscilloscope functions

  Bandwidth: 100 MHz

  Sample rate (each channel): 500 MS/s

  Channels: two

  Sensitivity: 5 mV to 50 V/div (to 500 V/div with 10× probe)

  Position range: 10 div

  Dc gain accuracy: 2%

  Vertical resolution: 8 bits

  Record length: 2500 points

  Time/division range: 5 ns to 50 s/div

  Horizontal accuracy: 200 ppm

  Roll mode: >/= 0.5 s/div

  Autorange: user-selectable

  Trigger modes: auto, normal

  Trigger types: edge, pulse, video, motor, external

  Video trigger formats and field rates: odd field, even field, and line

  Motor trigger: triggers on 3- and 5-level pulse-width-modulated power signal

  External trigger input: 5 MHz TTL (transistor-transistor logic)-compatible

  Harmonics: up to 31st (30 to 450 Hz)

  Waveform processing: add, subtract, multiply, calculate watts $= V \times I$

Waveform storage: 10 waveforms

Acquisition modes: sample, envelope, average, peak detect

Cursor measurements: DELTAVolts, DELTATime, 1/DELTATime (Hz), degree (phase)

Cursor types: horizontal bars, vertical bars, paired (volts at time)

Display system: interpolation; $\sin(x)/x$

Mode: vector, dot, vector accumulate, dot accumulate

Format: YT and XY

- Automatic measurements

Period: frequency

+Width: rise time

−Width: fall time

+Duty cycle: +overshoot

−Duty cycle: −overshoot

High: max

Low: min

Peak-to-peak: amplitude

Mean: root mean square (rms)

Cycle mean: cycle rms

Burst width

- Power measurements

W: true power

VA: apparent power

VAR: reactive power

V: volts (rms, peak)

A: amps (rms, peak)

THD-F: total harmonic distortion as a percentage of the fundamental

THD-R: total harmonic distortion of the rms of the input signal

PF: power factor

DPF: displacement power factor

PHI: phase difference between the voltage and current

- DMM specifications

Dc voltage ranges: 400.0 mV to 880 V

Dc volts accuracy: (0.5% of reading + 5 counts)

True rms ac voltage ranges: 400.0 mV to 640 V

Maximum float voltage: 600 V rms each channel (probe-dependent)

Resolution: 4000 count, 3.75 digits

Ac volts accuracy: (2% of reading + 5 counts)

Resistance ranges: 400.0 Ω to 40.00 MΩ

Resistance accuracy: (0.5% of reading + 2 counts); 40 MΩ—(2% of reading + 5 counts)

Diode test range: 0–2 V

Continuity check: audible tone when <50 Ω

Modes: min, max, DELTAmax-min, avg, hold

Nonvolatile storage: 10 DMM screenshots

External trigger input: 5 MHz TTL-compatible

Vertical zoom capability: 2×, 5×, 10×

dB scale: selectable, referenced from 1 mV to 10 V

dBm scale: selectable, referenced from 50 to 600 Ω

- General specifications

Setups: 10 front-panel setups

Safety certification: UL 3111-1-listed, CSA-certified, complies with EN61010-1

Power: NiCd rechargeable battery pack with ac adapter (both included)

Battery life: ~2 h from full charge

Display: backlit LCD (liquid crystal display)

Display resolution: 320 × 240

- Physical characteristics

Net weight:	1.45 kg (3.2 lb)	
Dimensions	mm	in
Width	177	6.95
Height	217	8.53
Depth	51	2

To provide you with examples of what the Tekscope can do, I took some random readings with it. Consider Figure 2.1, which shows the first sample reading. Note that to the upper right of the figure the scope reads 121.7 V ac. Just beneath that reading it shows channel 1 reading a frequency of 59.99 cycles. Channel 1 also shows the rms reading of 120.1 V.

Now, consider Figure 2.2, which shows a voltage reading of 120.1 V ac. It also shows a frequency reading from channel 1 of 59.99 cycles (Hz). Channel 1 also shows a rms reading of 118 V and a cycle rms reading of 117.8 V.

Figure 2.3 shows another sample voltage reading of 122.1 V ac. Channel 1 is configured to detect the period reading, which is 16.67 ms. Channel 1 also shows a frequency (cycle) of 60. The rms voltage reading is 119.8.

As these illustrations show, the Tekscope is a powerful tool for a wide variety of readings. During your network planning, I recommend determining

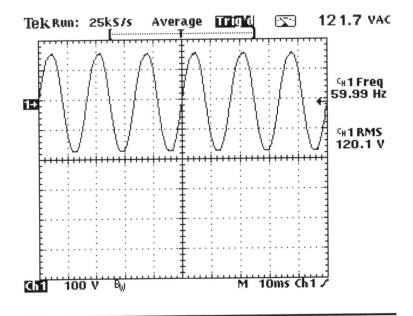

Figure 2.1   Voltage Readings

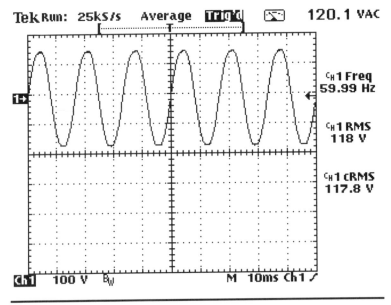

Figure 2.2   Sample Voltage and Frequency Readings

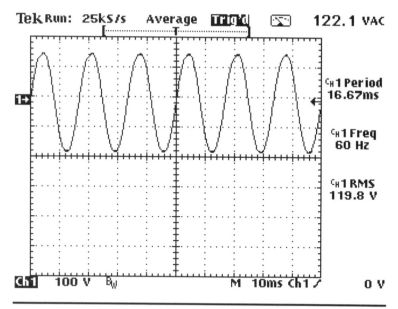

Figure 2.3   Sample Period, Voltage, and Frequency Readings

what devices will be used to collect and maintain power information. Later in this book additional readings are presented by way of the Tekscope THS720P.

Tektronix has a wide offering of scopes and multipurpose meters. For more information, contact them at

Tektronix, Inc.
26600 S.W. Parkway
P.O. Box 1000
Wilsonville, OR 97070-1000
Phone: 1-800-TEK-WIDE
www.tektronix.com

2.3   Temperature Probe (Fluke)

One important aspect of network planning and network maintenance after a network is installed is knowing the temperature of the operating environment. Consider Figure 2.4, which shows an initial reading at the beginning of a business day in the network data center. Note that the temperature reading is displayed in degrees Fahrenheit.

Consider Figure 2.5, which was taken with the same instrument (as shown in Figure 2.4), in the same location, a couple hours after all equipment was powered on and operating. Note that the temperature has risen by approximately 11 degrees.

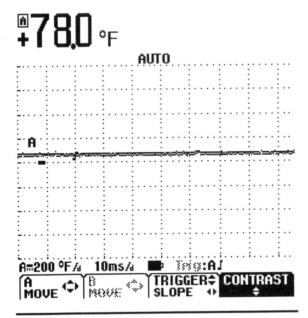

Figure 2.4   Sample Temperature Reading 1

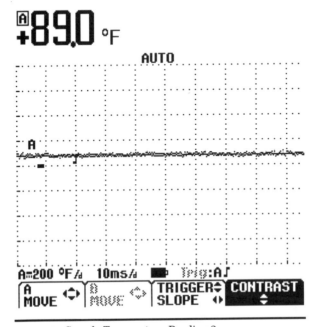

Figure 2.5   Sample Temperature Reading 2

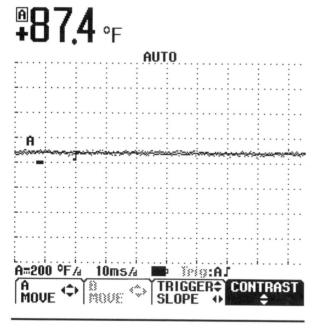

Figure 2.6   Sample Temperature Reading 3

Now consider Figure 2.6, which was taken with the same instrument, in the same place, only at a later time during the same day. Note that the temperature is now 87.4°F. Since the initial reading only a short time earlier in the day, the room temperature has risen by 10 degrees. At the time of this reading no cooling fans, blowers, or air circulation was operating. The room was an average room with normal central air conditioning and ventilation.

Now consider Figure 2.7. Before the middle of the day the room temperature is at a shocking 91.8°F. At this point air blowers and cooling fans were started, with increased airflow to the room where the readings were taken. This temperature is far above the acceptable operating-temperature range.

Normally, the temperature would not reach the level shown in Figure 2.7. However, in certain places where equipment is concentrated in a given area, the area temperature around such equipment can be much higher than the room temperature, say, 15 or 20 ft away in another location in the same room. The significance of these readings should not be overlooked. It proves a point that airflow, cooling, and various air-circulation equipment is important to maintain stable and normal operating temperatures throughout a room in which equipment is concentrated.

This is a good example of why rack-mount cabinets are important. With well-designed rack mount cabinets, equipment can be placed so that the blowers and fans can create a positive airflow and thus maintain temperatures at a level safe for the equipment and personnel working with it.

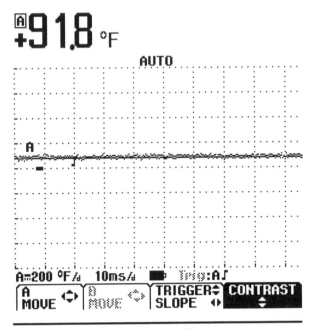

Figure 2.7 Sample Temperature Reading 4

Parallel to the idea of monitoring temperature in an area where equipment is concentrated is another important aspect of network design. In the specifications supplied with their equipment, many vendors recommend that free space be provided around all equipment, to ensure adequate airflow or ventilation. Be sure to ask for this information if it is not stated with each piece of equipment you plan to install in your network.

The instrument used to obtain the temperature here was a Fluke instrument. I recommend that you contact them for more information about their instruments. They can be reached at

Fluke Corporation
P.O. Box 9090
Everett, WA 98206
www.fluke.com

or

Fluke Europe B.V.
P.O. Box 680
7600 AR, Alemelo
The Netherlands

2.4 Network Wire Tester (Microtest)

Testing network wiring is not optional. The information here is from Microtest's Web site. Their information explains their products far better than I could. My purpose here is to convey to you, the reader, the information you will need in troubleshooting your network.

The PentaScanner product family is the handheld certification and diagnostic tool for Category 5 and ISO Class C and D links. PentaScanner products also provide full software compliance with TIA TSB-67 requirements for measurement reporting and analysis (including TSB-67 NEXT sweep and swept attenuation). These tools are designed to be the complete solution for professional cable installers, service providers, and network administrators.

Scanners in the PentaScanner product family incorporate a graphical user interface, backlit display menus, arrow keys, online help, and descriptive menu options that guide you quickly and easily through certifying or troubleshooting cabling systems. Most of the information in this user guide applies to all PentaScanner products. Some information applies only to PentaScanner+ units—this information is noted as such. PentaScanner+ units (with 36-pin connectors) are differentiated from PentaScanner and PentaScanner Cable Admin units (with Modular 8 connectors), where applicable.

2-Way Injector+/2-Way Injector

The 2-Way Injector+ and 2-Way Injector perform wire map, signal generation for attenuation, and end-of-link termination for other measurements. In addition, each measures NEXT at the injector end of the link and reports the results to the scanner. As part of the Autotest, NEXT results are stored for both ends of the link. Data from the injector end of the link can be displayed in any of the Autotest view modes and printed as part of Autotest reports.

Super Injector+/Super Injector

The Super Injector+ and the Super Injector are single direction active injectors and remote test coordinators that work with PentaScanners to verify twisted-pair cable transmission quality. By using the Injector, the scanner can test attenuation, NEXT, and loop resistance, and can provide a wire map for any twisted-pair cable.

Scanner display conventions

The up and down arrows in the display indicate that more information is available by pressing the ↑ or ↓ arrow key. Use the → and ← arrow keys for page-up and page-down navigation, respectively. The paired numbers 12-36 or 12/36 in the display indicate wire pairs. For example, 12 indicates the wire pair on pins 1 and 2; 12-36 indicates two wire pairs tested, the first on pins 1 and 2, and the second on pins 3 and 6.

The PentaScanners include on-line context sensitive help. Just press the HELP key at any time for information about the test that you are performing. By pressing function keys (F1, F2, F3, F4) and arrow keys (↑, ↓ →,←), you can move easily through the HELP text.

CertiFiber

Microtest also has a power fiber-optic test instrument called *CertiFiber*. It is the most advanced handheld certification tool for fiber links, designed to be the complete solution for professional cable installers, service providers, and network administrators. With the push of a button, CertiFiber certifies two multimode fibers simultaneously at both wavelengths.

Rather than merely providing a number, CertiFiber analyzes the fiber link and determines whether cabling and network standards are met. CertiFiber and CertiFiber Remote have an optical source that provides a consistent calibrated dual-wavelength light. The level of light injected into or emerging from the fiber network can be measured at any point so that the performance of fiber-optic transmission paths and equipment can be accessed quickly and accurately.

CertiFiber measures the optical power and at the same time verifies the proper installation and operation of various fiber-optic components such as fiber-optic hub modules, repeaters, and adapter cards. By measuring signal loss, CertiFiber helps you identify faulty patch cables, failing splices, and bad couplers and connectors.

CertiFiber's delay and length measurement capability accurately tests the link's propagation delay, which is then used to calculate length. CertiFiber incorporates a graphical user interface and descriptive menu options that guide you quickly and easily through the completely automated certification. CertiFiber

- Measures loss at 850 and 1300 nm simultaneously—without changing connectors.
- Measures multimode fiber length and propagation delay.
- Saves Autotests under predefined or customized job or project names.
- Tests dual fibers bidirectionally.
- Stores 1000 Autotest results in memory.
- Downloads and prints Autotest results using *free* ScanLink software.
- Interfaces with MT Crimp for professional certification reports and cabling management.
- Certifies a duplex fiber link (two fiber cables) simultaneously.
- Measures optical power loss in the direction of data transmission for both multimode wavelengths on two fiber cables without changing connectors.
- Measures length and propagation delay for a dual-fiber cable.
- Makes bidirectional measurements for duplex fiberlinks.
- Utilizes preprogrammed test templates to easily certify fiber-optic cabling to industry or network standards.
- Pinpoints the margin available on the tested cable above and beyond the pass/fail requirements.

- Stores 1000 Autotests in memory with user-friendly, alphanumeric names, job names, and unique time and date stamps.

- Transmits light continuously or modulated at 2 kHz.

- Downloads stored test results to a computer database for printing and professional record management.

- Includes a custom-tailored, nonremovable impact cover for added protection.

2.5   Internet Advisor: WAN and LAN (Hewlett-Packard)

The Hewlett-Packard Internet Advisor WAN is an integrated hardware package and suite of software applications designed to provide wide area network (WAN) monitoring and data capture, network device and process simulation, and specialized traffic generation, all in a Windows 95 operating environment. The hardware, known as the *HP Internet Advisor,* provides you with the physical interfaces, data acquisition, and hardware processing needed to connect to, and analyze, virtually any wide area network. The Internet Advisor WAN software applications give you the user interface, the data viewing and manipulation tools, and the flexibility to analyze data traffic flow and content on the network.

Types of WAN analysis performed

The Internet Advisor WAN lets you

Quantify line utilization and data throughput.

Identify configuration problems.

Detect transmission errors.

Determine network usage patterns.

Decode and view the actual bit stream.

Log statistics to the hard drive.

These tasks can be performed on network traffic as it occurs (run-time processing) or on captured data after the run (postprocess). Along with the monitoring and data manipulation capability mentioned above, you can

Use the Internet Advisor WAN to simulate network devices and processes.

Perform bit error rate testing (BERT).

Create and transmit specialized network traffic for higher-layer protocol stress tests and loading.

You can monitor the network's response to each of these types of analysis.

WAN analysis

The kind of data displayed and captured, and the kind of simulation and traffic generation performed, are all affected by how the Internet Advisor WAN is configured. You can configure the physical interfaces, set up the Internet Advisor to expect bit streams of various characteristics, define filters and counters to screen out or accept data and count data events, and set the necessary parameters to decode the bit stream in a specific way. You can also view, filter, and search data that has been stored to the buffer or to a file. The parameters for simulation, traffic generation, and BERT can also be easily set for specific protocols, traffic patterns, and test situations. Any of the configurations you set up can be saved as part of captured data or they can be saved individually and used again to speed your network analysis activity. Supplied tests that configure the Internet Advisor for you are also available in the cascaded menus in the Windows 95 desktop.

Software and hardware processing

The analysis capability is accessed via a user-friendly Windows 95 user interface. Complex configurations are made easy, and network traffic and related statistics are displayed in easy-to-read tabular and graphical formats. For every user interface component, online help is available.

The Internet Advisor WAN hardware consists of a ruggedly packaged IBM-compatible personal computer enhanced by high-speed data acquisition hardware, data communication physical interfaces, and Reduced Instruction Set Computer (RISC)-based hardware processing.

The Internet Advisor WAN can monitor, capture data, simulate, and generate traffic at rates ranging from 50 bits per second (bps) to 2 megabits per second (Mbps), including full-bandwidth T1 and Conference of European Postal and Telecommunications Administrations (CEPT) E1 rates (and fractional rates of each). The physical interfaces supported are built-in RS-232/v.24, RS-449/v.36, and v.35 ports, and interchangeable ISDN Basic Rate S/T, T1, CEPT E1, and Digital Data Service (DDS) 4-Wire interface modules. Because the Internet Advisor WAN uses the software for display and the dedicated processor for analysis, network traffic and statistics are immediately displayed on the screen, and high-speed simulation, traffic generation, and BERT can be performed.

WAN protocols and technologies supported

The Internet Advisor WAN consists of seven distinct applications, each associated with a specific WAN protocol or test scenario. These applications are typically launched by selecting a supplied test from the WAN Analysis menu (in the Windows 95 desktop), or from the run command. These applications are as follows:

Frame Relay: This application analyzes Frame Relay at layer 2. All Layer Management Interface (LMI) versions are decoded automatically, and you can choose to look at X.25, bit-oriented protocols (BOPs), Point-to-Point Protocol (PPP), or traditional LAN protocols encapsulated at layers 3 and 4. You can also monitor Frame Relay traffic carried on one or more ISDN B channels when the T1/E1 or Basic Rate Interface (BRI) S/T and U interface modules are installed. Traffic generation can be performed with this application, and a number of Frame Relay simulations are available.

X.25: This application analyzes Link Access Procedure Balanced (LAPB) at layer 2, X.25 at layer 3, and Frame Relay, PPP, or traditional LAN protocols encapsulated at layers 4 and/or 5. You can also monitor X.25 traffic carried on one or more ISDN B channels when the T1/E1 or BRI S/T and U interface modules are installed. Traffic generation can be performed with this application, and a number of X.25 call placement simulations are available.

Bit-oriented protocols (BOPs): This application allows you to analyze layer 2 BOPs such as LAPB, Link Access Procedure—D Channel (LAPD), HDLC, SDLC, CiscoSLE, and those defined by Request for Comments (RFCs) 1662 and 1663. You can choose to analyze encapsulated X.25, Frame Relay, PPP, or traditional LAN protocols at layers 3 and 4. You can also monitor BOP traffic carried on one or more ISDN B channels when the T1/E1 or BRI S/T and U interface modules are installed. Traffic generation is available for HDLC, and an HDLC PING simulation test can be run.

Point-to-Point Protocol (PPP)—Synchronous and Asynchronous: This application lets you analyze Sync and Async PPP carried on layer 2 BOPs defined by RFCs 1662 or 1663. No traffic generation or simulation is available.

ISDN: This application lets you analyze LAPD at layer 2, and Q.931 and/or X.25 at layer 3 on the ISDN D channel only (to monitor B-channel traffic, use one of the other applications). This application requires the Basic Rate S/T (or S/T and U) Interface module to be installed for BRI analysis and either the T1 or CEPT E1 module for Primary Rate Interface (PRI) analysis. This is a monitor-only application.

ATM DXI: This application lets you monitor ATM DXI (Data Exchange Interface) traffic and Common Part Convergence Sublayer AAL 3/4 traffic that occurs on a v.35 link between a data terminal equipment (DTE) device (such as a router) and an ATM digital services unit (DSU) [or other data communications equipment (DCE) device]. You can also monitor other WAN protocols such as Frame Relay, X.25, BOPs, and PPP as well as encapsulated LAN protocols on layers 3 and above. However, if you want to analyze ATM User Network Interface (UNI) traffic, you will need to use the Internet Advisor ATM application.

Bit Error Rate Testing (*BERT*): Independent of any layer 2 protocol, you can perform physical layer/medium analysis using the Internet Advisor BERT application.

Sample Internet Advisor information

```
*************************************************************
     HEWLETT-PACKARD INTERNET ADVISOR

     Node Discovery measurement
      Run started on Aug 14, 1998 @ 16:41:25
      Run stopped on Aug 14, 1998 @ 16:45:41
      19 nodes observed
     Display format: Observed Nodes
     Print:    All displayed records
*************************************************************
* New address observed on network
# Known address observed on network
~ New address-name mapping; no traffic observed
> Selected record
    Address        Layer      Type/ID      Comment/Name
    _____  _____  _____  _____

> ANGEL
*. Ibm——45-43-F3   Ethernet
*. 220.100.100.41    IP
* 00000000-0060944543F3 IPX   0001   ANGEL
* 00000001-0060944543F3 IPX
*> ADMINISTRATOR       NetBIOS       ADMINISTRATOR
* ANGEL          NetBIOS         ANGEL
* INFO.COM        NetBIOS         INFO.COM

> ANNE
*> Kingston-30-CB-C6    Ethernet
*> 220.100.100.132    IP       ANNE
* 00000000-00C0F030CBC6 IPX   0001   ANNE
* 00000001-00C0F030CBC6 IPX
* __MSBROWSE__        NetBIOS        __MSBROWSE__
*> ADMINISTRATOR       NetBIOS      ADMINISTRATOR
* ANNE          NetBIOS     ANNE
* INFO          NetBIOS      INFO
* INet~Services    NetBIOS       INet~Services
* IS~ANNE         NetBIOS      IS~ANNE_____

> CHEROKEE
*> Kingston-30-C2-9E   Ethernet
*> 220.100.100.139     IP       CHEROKEE
* 00000000-00C0F030C29E IPX    0001  CHEROKEE
* 00000001-00C0F030C29E IPX
* ADMINISTRATOR        NetBIOS       ADMINISTRATOR
* CHEROKEE          NetBIOS       CHEROKEE
*> IBMPCC$$POSTERR        NetBIOS      IBMPCC$$POSTERR
* INFO.COM       NetBIOS        INFO.COM

> FATBOY
*< Kingston-30-C2-4A  Ethernet
*> 220.100.100.121    IP
```

```
*> 00000000-00C0F030C24A IPX
*> FATBOY          NetBIOS      FATBOY


> HOLLYWOOD
*> Kingston-1C-78-4D  Ethernet
*> 220.100.100.144    IP
*> 00000000-44455354616F IPX    0001    INFO.COM
* HOLLYWOOD         NetBIOS      HOLLYWOOD
* INFO.COM          NetBIOS      INFO.COM
*> JAN            NetBIOS       JAN


> INFO.COM              User
*> WstDigt—3A-B8-EC  Ethernet
*> 220.100.100.108    IP     BRAINS
*> 00000001-0000C03AB8EC IPX   0001    BRAINS
*> BRAINS          NetBIOS     BRAINS


> LITTLE MAN
*> WstDigt—C5-08-F3   Ethernet
*> 220.100.100.32     IP     LITTLE MAN
*> 00000000-0000C0C508F3 IPX
*> INFO           NetBIOS      INFO
* LITTLE MAN         NetBIOS     LITTLE MAN


> MONY
*> WstDigt—4E-B5-EC   Ethernet
*> 220.100.100.19     IP     MONY
*> 00000000-0000C04EB5EC IPX   0001    INFO.COM
*> MONY           NetBIOS     MONY


> MUSCLE
*> Kingston-30-C2-43   Ethernet
*> 220.100.100.10     IP     MUSCLE
*> 00000001-000000000001 IPX   0001    INFO.COM
*> ADMINISTRATOR      NetBIOS      ADMINISTRATOR
* MUSCLE           NetBIOS     MUSCLE


> RENEGADE
*> Kingston-30-98-B3   Ethernet
*> 220.100.100.79     IP     RENEGADE
* 00000000-00C0F03098B3 IPX    0001   RENEGADE
* 00000001-00C0F03098B3 IPX
*> ADMINISTRATOR      NetBIOS      ADMINISTRATOR
* INFO.COM          NetBIOS      INFO.COM
* RENEGADE          NetBIOS      RENEGADE


> RICK
*> Kingston-30-C0-AB   Ethernet
*> 220.100.100.147    IP     RICK
* 00000000-00C0F030C0AB IPX    0001    RICK
* 00000001-00C0F030C0AB IPX
*> ADMINISTRATOR      NetBIOS      ADMINISTRATOR
* INFO.COM          NetBIOS      INFO.COM
* RICK            NetBIOS     RICK


> SILO-1
*> Axis—-32-41-35  Ethernet
*> 220.100.100.175    IP     SILO-1
* INFO           NetBIOS     INFO
*> SILO-1          NetBIOS     SILO-1
```

```
> SILO-2
*> Axis—-32-41-3F  Ethernet
*> 220.100.100.180   IP        SILO-2
* INFO              NetBIOS    INFO
*> SILO-2           NetBIOS    SILO-2

> SPEEDY
*> WstDigt—CF-08-F3   Ethernet
*> 220.100.100.111    IP
*> SPEEDY             NetBIOS     SPEEDY

> THE-HOSTAGE
*> 00-60-08-98-1D-33  Ethernet
*> 220.100.100.172    IP
*> 00000000-006008981D33 IPX
*> THE-HOSTAGE        NetBIOS      THE-HOSTAGE

> THE-KID
*> 00-00-D1-0F-E2-9B   Ethernet
*> 220.100.100.77      IP          THE-KID
*> ADMINISTRATOR       NetBIOS         ADMINISTRATOR
* INFO.COM      NetBIOS         INFO.COM
* THE-KID       NetBIOS         THE-KID

> *new HP—2108A0
*> HP——-21-08-A0   Ethernet

> *new Wellf1E88F10
*> WellfleetE8-8F-10   Ethernet

> *new Wellf1E88F1B
*> WellfleetE8-8F-1B   Ethernet
```

Another example of what the HP Internet Advisor can do is provide lower-layer protocol measurements. An example of Ethernet Vital Signs Measurement is presented in Table 2.1. Many other measurements can be made with the Internet Advisor; those are presented later in this book.

HP Internet Advisor LAN

The HP Internet Advisor LAN family of products includes Ethernet, Fast Ethernet, Token Ring, and FDDI Advisors. The hardware for the different Advisors can be any of the following:

A streamlined portable Internet Advisor—built-in Ethernet or Token Ring with an optional Fast Ethernet or FDDI undercradle

An Internet Advisor—WAN with a LAN undercradle

A ruggedized transportable Network Advisor (and attachable modules)

Advisor PC cards for Ethernet or Token Ring

Whatever form the hardware takes, all Internet Advisors consist of measurements and applications to help you monitor, analyze, and troubleshoot your network. There are many different applications that run on the Internet

TABLE 2.1   Ethernet Vital Signs Measurement

	Threshold	Current	Average	Peak	Total
NETWORK COUNTS (Pre-Filter)					
Utilization %	30	0.01	0.10	1.04	
Frames	5000	2	9	62	675
Local coll	35	0	0	0	0
Late coll	0	0	0	0	0
Remote coll	35	0	0	0	0
Rem late coll	0	0	0	0	0
Bad FCS	0	0	0	0	0
Runt	0	0	0	0	0
Misaligns	0	0	0	0	0
BUFFER COUNTS (Post-Filter)					
Utilization %	40	0.01	0.11	1.04	
Frames	700	2	9	61	675
Runts (good FCS)	0	0	0	0	0
Jabbers	0	0	0	0	0
Jabber (bad FCS)	0	0	0	0	0
Dribble frms	35	0	0	0	0
Broadcasts	25	0	0	5	99
Multicasts	2	1	0	5	78
Buff Overwrites	100	0	0	0	0

Start Time: Aug 14 98 @ 16:57:42
Sample Time: Aug 14 98 @ 16:59:39

Advisor LAN. The basic operation of typical measurements are involved in monitoring, troubleshooting, and analyzing your networks. Most measurements and techniques are similar across all network types. Where the procedure or measurements differ, an example is given for each.

Online help is built into the Internet Advisor LAN. You can find specific information on the tests you are running in the area of the Internet Advisor LAN you are in. There is also an online glossary of terms.

The Internet Advisor LAN has six main or top-level windows from which you can run measurements, generate node lists, set up filters, monitor events, and diagnose network problems. The top-level windows are as follows:

Measurements

Setup

Node List

Filters

Utilities

Event Log

The Internet Advisor LAN Quick Reference Card shows keyboard shortcuts and a map of the top-level windows to help you find the different functions at a glance.

Measurements window. The main purpose of the Measurements window is to let you select and run various measurements. These Measurements report information about your network, help you troubleshoot network problems, or show you the contents of packets on the network. The Measurements window organizes measurements using a hierarchy of categories and subcategories similar to the way that DOS uses directories and subdirectories to organize files. General categories of measurements include the following:

Expert Analyzer

Statistics

Decodes

Commentators

Stimulus/Response Tests

Network Discovery

Screen Snapshots

Troubleshooters

Demo Tools

Expert Analyzer. The Expert Analyzer window is a measurement that gives you an overview of the health of an Ethernet, Fast Ethernet, Token Ring, or FDDI network. The Expert Analyzer automatically opens and runs specialized versions of other Internet Advisor LAN measurements, and then uses the results from these tests to present the data in graphical and numerical form. In addition to the data displayed in the Expert Analyzer window, you can drill down to see more detailed information in additional windows.

Statistics. The Internet Advisor LAN statistical measurements show you important information about a Ethernet, Fast Ethernet, FDDI, or Token Ring network's overall performance or about particular nodes or stations. For example, the Ethernet, Fast Ethernet, FDDI, and Token Ring Summary Stats measurements use graphs, gauges, and pie charts to show information about the network's overall performance. Some of the information they show are the percentage of the network's capacity being used, the number and type of errors occurring, the mix of protocols on the network, and the number of stations or nodes on the network.

You can choose four of the items from the Summary Stats window to plot together in the Trends Graphical display, or you can list four of the items in the Trends Tabular display. This lets you detect correlations between the items. In addition to the data presented in the Summary Stats window, you can get more detailed information by drilling down to additional statistical windows. There are several graphical and tabular node statistics measurements that identify critical users on the network, such as the nodes that are generating the most traffic (top talkers) or the nodes that are generating the most errors (top error sources).

The Vital Signs measurements provide a tabular list of significant events that may be preludes to network performance degradation or network failure. There are Vital Signs measurements for Ethernet, Fast Ethernet, Token Ring, FDDI, AppleTalk, DECnet, Novell, OSI, TCP/IP, and Virtual Networking System (Vines) protocols.

The Ethernet, Fast Ethernet, FDDI, and Token Ring top talker measurements list up to 50 nodes generating the most frames and how many bytes and frames each is sending and receiving. Figure 2.8 shows the most active nodes talking on the network. It also provides statistical information to interpret the load each node is generating on the network.

The Internet Advisor can perform the top talker function with Fast Ethernet and Ethernet as well. Fast Ethernet, Ethernet Top Error Sources, FDDI Top Error Sources, and Token Ring Top Error Reporters measurements list up to 50 nodes generating the most errored frames and how many and what type of errors they are generating.

The Node Stats (for Fast Ethernet and Ethernet) and the Station Stats (for Token Ring or FDDI) graphically show you, in either bar or pie chart form, a variety of statistical information about 20 nodes or stations. For example, you can configure the Token Ring Station Stats measurement to show the 20 sta-

Ethernet Top Talkers				
Node	**Frames Xmt**	**Bytes Xmt**	**Frames Rcv**	**Bytes Rcv**
WstDigt--4E-B5-EC	5467	6979356	1010	106432
WstDigt--CF-08-F3	1118	131558	5664	7061009
Kingston-30-C2-43	312	37563	205	41635
Kingston-30-C2-9E	173	79255	127	13681
WellfleetE8-8F-1B	166	10624	166	10624
Kingston-30-98-B3	127	28528	130	17086
00-60-08-98-1D-33	85	10475	72	10267
WstDigt--3A-B8-EC	74	7380	68	6651
Kingston-30-C2-4A	68	11157	58	7387
00-00-D1-0F-E2-9B	50	7363	46	5819
Ibm------45-43-F3	28	2428	32	4526
Kingston-30-C0-AB	27	2204	35	5576
Kingston-30-CB-C6	16	2534	0	0
WstDigt--C5-08-F3	9	1934	0	0
Kingston-1C-78-4D	7	748	7	712
Axis-----32-41-35	5	1618	0	0
Axis-----32-41-3F	5	1618	0	0
WellfleetE8-8F-10	5	1730	0	0
HP-------21-08-A0	4	256	1	182
01-80-C2-00-00-00	0	0	166	10624
Broadcast	0	0	156	22678
03-00-00-00-00-01	0	0	36	4064

Figure 2.8 Network Example of Top Talkers

tions sending source routed broadcasts, all stations broadcasts, functional address frames, and source routed frames.

The Protocol Statistics measurement graphically shows statistical information for up to 20 protocols running on your network. You can look at data-link layer protocols, the IP stack, AppleTalk stack, Banyan Vines stack, DECnet stack, OSI stack, or Novell stack protocols. The measurement shows you number of frames, number of bytes, number of errors, and average frame length for each discovered protocol.

Decodes. The Internet Advisor LAN provides a set of decodes for many Ethernet, Fast Ethernet, FDDI, and Token Ring protocols such as 802.2, Apollo Domain, AppleTalk, Banyan Vines, DECnet, Novell, Xerox Network Standard (XNS), 3COM, SNA, TCP/IP, and IBM PC.

Decode measurements interpret the data in frames according to a protocol so that you can examine the contents of the frames. There are three decode formats:

1. The summary format shows a one-line overview of each decoded frame.

2. The detailed format shows the decode for each field of each frame.

3. The data format shows the raw hexadecimal data.

When the Decodes category is selected, you can choose a stack decode measurement which shows all the protocols working in the selected networking environment. For example, in the Novell Stack Decode, fields in the Internetwork Packet Exchange (IPX), SPX, and Netware Core Protocol (NCP) protocols are all decoded and displayed. You can also select an individual layer protocol decode that decodes only the selected protocol. When you start a decode measurement, a window opens, showing the data in the detailed format. From the detailed display, you can open windows that show the same data in the summary format and the data format.

Commentators. These measurements identify high-level significant network events. These events may be signs of network performance degradation or network failure. You can get more detailed information about a particular event by double-clicking the left mouse button on the event. Doing this opens another window which describes the event and offers advice on how to resolve the problem.

Commentators let you identify network problems without sifting through pages of decodes. Commentators can be configured to comment on events in the following protocols:

AppleTalk   TCP/IP
Banyan Vines   Internet Control Message Protocol (ICMP)
OSI   Novell
TCP/IP   IBM Lan Manager
DECnet

Stimulus/Response. These are measurements such as traffic generators and server lists that perform a specific test by transmitting onto the network and listening for responses. For example, a Nearest Server measurement can query the network to find the nearest server of a type you specify.

Network Discovery. These measurements search for physical and network addresses. Node Discovery, Automatic Baseline, and Server lists are examples of Network Discovery measurements.

Screen Snapshots. Screen Snapshots (Fast Ethernet, Ethernet, and Token Ring Internet Advisor LANs) are a convenient way to position and start several measurements simultaneously. After you open the snapshot, you configure the measurements you want to run, size the windows, and position them. Then, when you run the snapshot, those same measurements open, size, position, and run.

Troubleshooters. This category contains many different troubleshooting measurements. These measurements are custom-designed snapshots that have been configured to start several useful measurements. The online help for the custom snapshots explains how to add filters and use these troubleshooters as a basis for your own customized snapshots.

Demo Tools. These measurements let you run demonstrations that show the features of the statistics measurements. Also, you can use a Demo to generate traffic on the network to demonstrate other measurements.

Setup window. The Setup window lets you set global parameters that affect the way measurements run.

Data Source. The Data Source field in the Setup window can be set to Network Under Test, Capture Buffer, or Advisor Data File. The choice you make determines whether measurements will capture data from the network or analyze data already in the capture buffer or data from a file.

Network Interface. The Network Interface field determines what type of network you can test and what measurements you can run. For example, if you choose Ethernet, you can run only Ethernet measurements.

Capture Buffer Control. The Capture Buffer Control parameters let you control the Internet Advisor LAN's capture buffer. You can select the buffer mode you want. In Continuous mode, data fill the buffer until you stop the measurement, which means that once the buffer is full, newer data overwrite the oldest data. In Stop When Full mode, the measurement stops as soon as the buffer is full. You can also select the buffer size you want.

Finally, you can select whether to use partial packet store (packet slicing). Enabling partial packet store causes the Internet Advisor LAN to capture only the first portion of each packet. This lets you store more packets for a given buffer size. If you enable partial packet store, you can select the partial packet size. If you decide to use partial packet store (packet slicing), remember that it can affect other measurements and their outcome.

Ethernet, Fast Ethernet, FDDI, or Token Ring Parameters. Depending on the selection you make for the Network Interface field (Ethernet, Fast Ethernet, FDDI, or Token Ring), you can enter parameters to configure the Internet Advisor LAN for that interface. The Fast Ethernet and Ethernet Media Connection parameter tells the Internet Advisor LAN which one of the Internet Advisor LANs Ethernet connectors (MII, TX, FX, AUI, or ThinLAN/10Base2) is connected to the network.

Depending on the Media Connection you select for Fast Ethernet, you can select between 10 and 100 megabytes per second (MB/s) for Line Speed. The Line Mode parameter lets you choose whether the Internet Advisor is connected as a node on the network or is connected in a Monitor mode. With Fast Ethernet, the Line Mode parameter also lets you select between Half Duplex (HDX) and Full Duplex (FDX).

FDDI parameters are Connection Type and Connection Mode. They configure the ports for attaching the Internet Advisor LAN to an FDDI network. You can also specify a Target Token Rotation Time, and choose whether to monitor Link Confidence Test frames.

Token Ring parameters enable you to decide whether to participate in the ring. If you choose not to participate in the ring, the Internet Advisor LAN passively monitors the network and inserts into the ring, but you cannot perform measurements that transmit such as Traffic Generator or Request Station ID. You can also select the appropriate line speed [4 or 16 megabits per second (Mbps)] depending on the type of Token Ring to which you are connected.

Finally, you can select whether to have early token release. Early token release causes the Internet Advisor LAN to release the token immediately after it transmits the last bit of a frame. You can select early token release only with 16 Mb/s line speed.

Advisor Physical Address. The Advisor Physical Address field in the Setup window contains the Internet Advisor LAN's unique physical layer address. This address can be modified.

Transmit Password. All measurements which transmit on the network require a password when the Transmit Password field is set to Required. After the password is entered correctly, the value of this field changes to Entered, and all transmitting measurements run without prompting for the password until this field is changed to Required again. Check your HP Internet Advisor documentation for the factory-set password.

Node/Station List window. In the Node/Station List window, you can create a node list (symbolic name table) so that you can use meaningful names rather than hexadecimal addresses to identify the nodes or stations on your network. The Node Discovery Measurement for Ethernet, the Station Discovery Measurement for Token Ring, and the Station Discovery Measurement for

FDDI can automatically create a node list for you. You can obtain online help with each one of these measurements for more information about creating node lists.

The node list is a global database that can be used by the Internet Advisor LAN measurements to provide name/address mapping. For each node, you can identify the general type of node, add comments about the node, and identify address information about the node. You can add new nodes to the list, modify information about an existing node in the list, and delete nodes from the list.

Filters window.   The purpose of filters is to control which frames the Internet Advisor LAN captures or excludes when you are testing a network. Filters can also be used to stop the Internet Advisor LAN when a specified frame is encountered on the network.

The Internet Advisor LAN is supplied with many basic Ethernet, Fast Ethernet, FDDI, and Token Ring filters. To create a new filter, you modify one of these provided filters or another filter you have created and save the changes to a new filter name. To use a filter, you activate it.

Utilities window.   The Utilities window contains a list of system utilities. These utilities provide functionality that is not directly related to running measurements:

- File Manager lets you perform common file management tasks such as copying, deleting, printing, and renaming files, and creating and deleting subdirectories.

- PC Configuration lets you control whether the internal LCD display or an external display is used. It also lets you control whether the PRINT SCREEN key is disabled or sends output to a printer or a file.

- Autostart lets you specify the Internet Advisor LAN's power-on state and whether any measurements are automatically run at power-on.

- Version Information shows you what version of software and hardware your Internet Advisor LAN has.

- Install Application displays a list of available applications that may be installed. Select an application to display dialog boxes that guide you through the installation.

- Proxy Port Setup lets you support decodes and protocol statistics for non-standard proxy ports. Network firewalls may use nonstandard proxy ports, especially for the World Wide Web. Select this item to display dialog boxes that prompt you for the proxy port information. After a proxy port is set up, the Decodes display the specified protocol on the specified proxy port.

- Exit to DOS lets you leave the Internet Advisor LAN mode and go to either Windows 95 or to a DOS menu.

Event Log window.   The Event Log provides high visibility of events occurring on the network and in the Internet Advisor LAN. Events are occurrences that are especially significant or noteworthy.

The Event Log is a file on the Internet Advisor's hard disk. Events are logged until the file is full; then as a new event is logged, the oldest event is removed from the file and that space is reused. You can turn the Event Log on or off. While it is on, all events are stored on disk. While off, only instrument events are logged to the disk. Errors, or events, that require immediate notification and user interaction open a dialog box.

There are six categories of events:

1. *Protocol events:* when connections are established

2. *Threshold events:* the number of collisions that exceeded a given threshold

3. *Topology events:* when a ring insertion occurred or a node was unreachable

4. *Fault events:* when a broadcast storm occurred or there is a defective cable

5. *Instrument events:* a measurement starts or stops, data capture occurred, and system errors occurred

6. *All events:* includes all the other categories

2.6   Network Communication Software (Seattle Lab)

Seattle Lab is a company that provides very powerful and useful software for Windows 95, Windows 98, and Windows NT networks. One of the best software tools available to use with Windows NT is the TELNET Server offered by Seattle Lab. This software runs as a normal software process in the NT environment. Once configured and operational, it works just like TELNET servers on any UNIX-oriented or other host that has a full-blown TCP/IP stack.

Consider Figure 2.9, which shows the logon prompt generated from TELNET server on ANNE (the host in my network; see also Figure 2.12). Note that it has been customized, and can present any message you like.

Figure 2.10 shows the login message as well as the login prompt and the password prompt.

Figure 2.11 shows the message reflected back to the original system to which a TELNET client was fired against the TELNET server on ANNE. Note that Figure 2.11 shows ANNE "pinging" THE-HOSTAGE. The response from THE-HOSTAGE is typical TCP/IP operation.

Now consider Figure 2.12, which shows a logical view of the network and the connections made possible via the TELNET server operating on ANNE. Note that two lines indicate bidirectional data transfer from BRAINS to ANNE. Also, note the logical connection established between ANNE and THE-HOSTAGE. Actually, the information generated from THE-HOSTAGE

```
U - GOT - ME !!  Ed said: You can Login now !!!
logon:
```

Figure 2.9 TELNET Server Prompt

```
U - GOT - ME !!  Ed said: You can Login now !!!
logon: renegade
password: ******
```

Figure 2.10 TELNET Server Prompt

```
C:\>ping THE-HOSTAGE

Pinging THE-HOSTAGE [220.100.100.172] with 32 bytes of data:

Reply from 220.100.100.172: bytes=32 time<10ms TTL=128
Reply from 220.100.100.172: bytes=32 time<10ms TTL=128
Reply from 220.100.100.172: bytes=32 time<10ms TTL=128
Reply from 220.100.100.172: bytes=32 time<10ms TTL=128

C:\>
```

Figure 2.11 TELNET Server Prompt

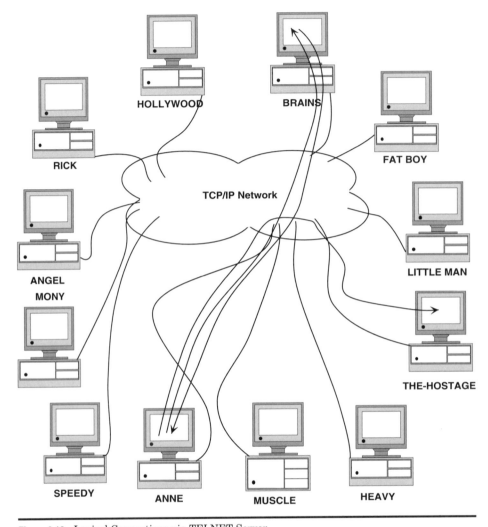

Figure 2.12 Logical Connections via TELNET Server

is redirected back to BRAINS via the TELNET server connection established between ANNE and BRAINS.

This type of operation is powerful and possible from remote settings. The TELNET server part of TCP/IP has been left out of Windows NT for whatever reason, but Seattle Lab provides the much-needed piece to accomplish tasks previously not easily achieved.

2.7 Summary

Network troubleshooting involves more than thought; it involves having the right tools for the right job. The tools I presented in this chapter are the most powerful network troubleshooting tools available in the industry. These tools are discussed from various angles later throughout this book; however, I recommend that you contact the individual companies which offer each of these troubleshooting tools.

3

Knowledge Required to Troubleshoot Networks Effectively

Troubleshooting networks presupposes an understanding of many different aspects of technology and pieces of equipment in which this technology is implemented. This chapter presents information that is required to do troubleshooting, regardless of the size of the network. For example, to troubleshoot some basic aspects of networks requires an understanding of topologies and actual media used to connect different pieces of equipment. This information presented in this chapter may not be as "attractive" as what you may think troubleshooting should be, but the bottom line of troubleshooting is that one must understand the abstract nature of technology.

First, it is important to understand the meaning of the terms *physical* and *logical*. In the context of networking, *physical* (anything) is generally agreed on as being something actual with regard to its existence. On the other hand, *logical,* as the term is used in networking, has a meaning other than sound reasoning. In fact, something logical in networking may not at all resemble logic as one would associate it with reason. In networking, logical generally means an association between some function—abstract as it may be—and something actual. Consider Figure 3.1, which shows a logical connection between two hosts mapped over physical transmission line C. This mapping could have occurred over line B or A as well.

Another example of interpreting the use of physical or logical is the protocols used in Windows NT networking. For example, in NT networking there are bindings (associations) between services or protocols and network adapters. These associations could be regarded as a logical mapping of a service or protocol to a particular network adapter. In other words, there is a logical link between a service and/or protocol to an adapter.

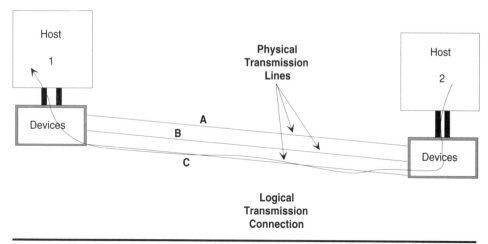

Figure 3.1 Physical and Logical Connections

The examples presented in this chapter and further information presented later in this book provide sufficient insight as to how physical and logical are interpreted. In some cases, the interpretation of these terms is context-dependent.

3.1 Network Topologies

Topology refers to the structure of a network. Most networks can be described by physical and logical characteristics. As explained in this section, some examples that represent a network are not the same as the network when seen in reality. For a network to exist, something physical must be present, but a logical network (or multiple logical networks) may be mapped to the physical network.

Bus topology

One aspect of a bus network is the common medium that connects multiple devices together. Physically, bus networks are considered to exist in one central location. Consider Figure 3.2, which depicts logical views of older-style (Figure 3.2*a*) and current-style (Figure 3.2*b*) bus networks. Fundamental to the bus network is a single medium, which may be coaxial or fiber-optic cable. Each host connects to the network via a transceiver, and each end of the medium is terminated. To a certain degree Figure 3.2 is a popular representation of bus networks. Figure 3.2 is best described as a logical view of a bus topology.

In reality, when a bus topology is implemented, it rarely, if ever, appears as shown in Figure 3.2, because the computer cables and the hub or switch used

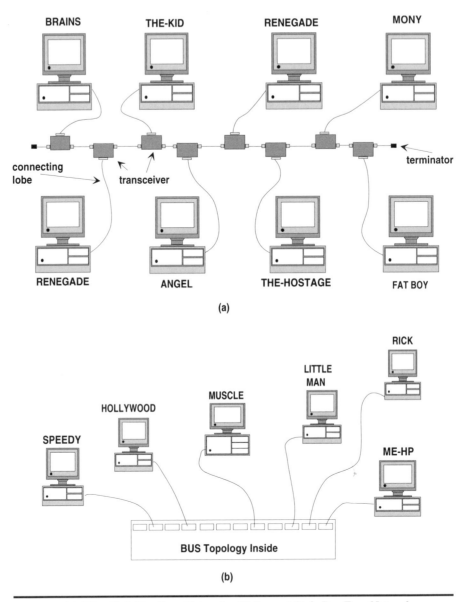

Figure 3.2 (*a*) Older-Style Bus-Type Network   (*b*) Current-Style Bus-Type Network

to connect the different systems may be dispersed over greater distances, not located in the same physical room. Furthermore, the wires used to connect the systems to the hub or switch may be hidden in ductwork, behind walls, or otherwise. Figure 3.2 also presents a highlighted view of the actual communications bus within a hub. It shows a bus with respect to the ports in which actual devices connect.

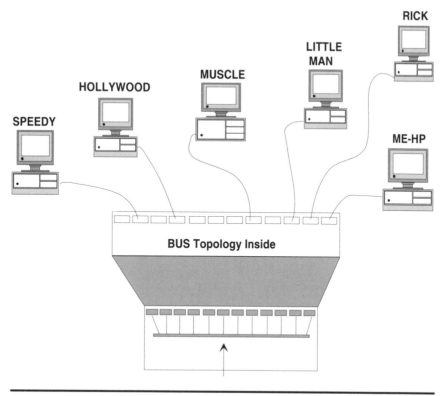

Figure 3.3   Inside View of Current Bus-Type Network Implementations

Figure 3.3 shows a highlighted view of the hub/switch, ports, internal bus, and devices connected to the hub or switch. This illustration best represents the overall idea behind bus technology as it is implemented with actual pieces of hardware.

Star topology

Two star networks are represented in Figure 3.4. A star implementation uses a central processor or hub to which multiple hosts are connected (Figure 3.4*a*). It may appear similar to a ring topology but without an internal ring (Figure 3.4*b*). Basic to the operation of this topology is that data are routed through the central processor.

Figure 3.5 shows a variation of the star topology. This illustration shows a physical device that might initially appear to be in a star-type configuration; however, close examination reveals that it operates with a ring functionality inside.

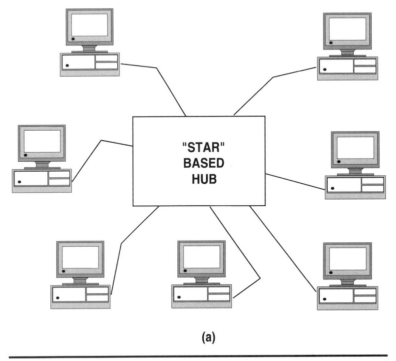

(a)

Figure 3.4 (a) Physical View of a Star Implementation

Ring topology

Figure 3.6 is a physical view of ring technology. Actually, ring technology is physically implemented with the appearance of a star implementation (topology). Ring topology is implemented through what is called a *media access unit* (MAU). Devices connect to a MAU via a cable from their interface card, and internally, the MAU is a ring (actually a dual ring). MAUs are generally rectangular and have no external appearance of a ring. The ring itself is inside, connecting each port.

Most MAUs have ring-in (RI) and ring-out (RO) connecting points. These connecting points exist in order to daisy-chain multiple MAUs, thus increasing the number of devices that can be added to a ring.

Tree topology

Tree topologies appear as shown in Figure 3.7. This is a flexible topology. Certain protocols could make this type of network

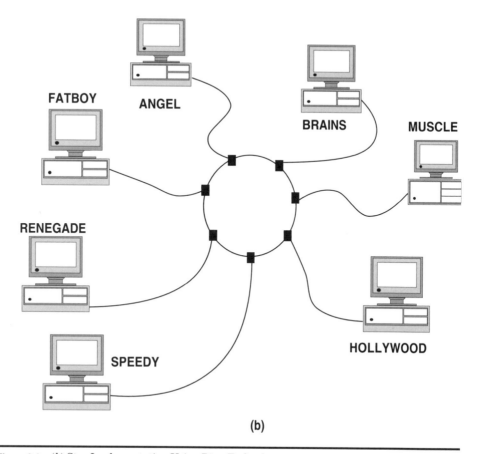

(b)

Figure 3.4   (*b*) Star Implementation Using Ring Technology

easily segmented to isolate users or to streamline the functionality of communications in the network.

3.2   Network Media

Networks use transmission media to communicate; this is common to all networks. The issue here is what type of medium is used to connect network devices. There are two categories of media: hard and soft.

Hard media

Twisted-pair cable.   *Hard media* include various types of distinctly different media. The simplest example of hard media is twisted-pair cable, as shown in Figure 3.8. Twisted-pair cabling is normally copper-stranded cable, with shielding on each stranded group. However, some twisted-pair cables are col-

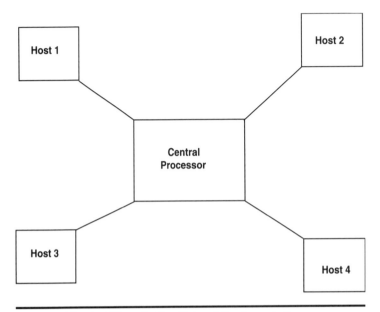

Figure 3.5 Physical View of a Star Network Implementation

lectively compounded together and benefit from a shield and an outer jacket housing all the individual shields.

Twisted-pair cable is measured by gauge. The lower the gauge number, the larger the cable physically and the more current it can support. Interpreting cable gauge is not arbitrary; formal definitions apply. For example, 20-gauge or higher cabling is typically found in networking systems, whereas 10- or 8-gauge twisted-pair cable, which is about the width of an ordinary pencil, is commonly used in electrical wiring, as it can accommodate considerable electrical voltage and current.

All twisted-pair cabling, regardless of size, is fundamentally similar with respect to electric current, specifically, resistance. The electrical capacity of twisted-pair cables (either ac or dc) is proportional to the length of the cable. The greater a cable's length, the greater its resistance, and hence the greater its signal loss.

Tables listing the amount of resistance incurred with different gauges of cable are available, but I have witnessed two scenarios: (1) cases where signal loss was so great, as a result of cable length, that devices at the far end of the cable were not functional; and (2) ironically, the converse.

I have participated in wiring of a terminal with twisted-pair cable that far exceeded the specifications for that cable, and the terminal worked. The only answer to this paradox must be that the maximum distance was not exceeded. The precise point (length) at which a cable begins to experience significant signal loss is contingent on at least two factors: the device driving the cable and the cable size. Another factor is the environment in which the cable is placed.

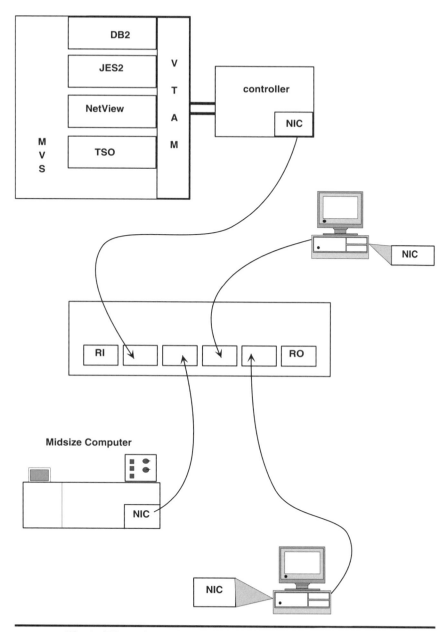

Figure 3.6   Physical View of a Media Access Unit

Coaxial cable.   This type of cable is prevalent in many networks today, including cable television (CATV) installations. Figure 3.9 depicts a coaxial cable.
Coaxial cable has an outside covering called a *jacket*. Immediately inside the
jacket is a *shield*, which is generally a fine wire wrapped around its inner
component; the shield typically serves as ground. Just inside the shield is a

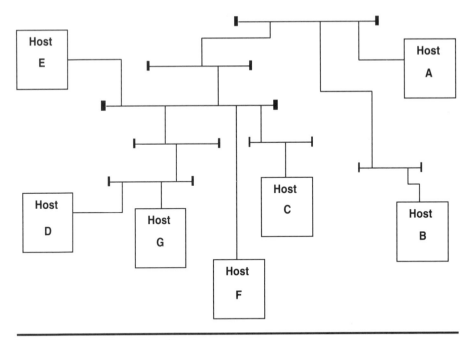

Figure 3.7 Logical View of Tree Structure

Figure 3.8 Twisted-Pair Cabling

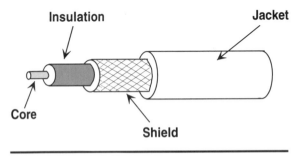

Figure 3.9 Coaxial Cable

plastic material that serves as insulation. Inside the insulated material is the core (the actual cable). The core is usually solid copper cable.

Coaxial cable also has a means of measurement. Its rating differs from that of twisted-pair cable, but the two are somewhat similar. The larger the core, the greater the length a cable can be implemented. However, coaxial cable differs from twisted pair.

Because of its inherent design, coaxial cable has good resistance to outside interference. The cable core is insulated, shielded, and jacketed.

Fiber-optic cable.   Fiber-optic cable appears as shown in Figure 3.10. Fiber cable has an outer covering called a *sheath.* Inside some cables have strands of string or strengthening components. Next, as Figure 3.10 shows, is the cladding. *Cladding* is glass or other transparent material surrounding the optical fibers. Inside the cladding is the *core,* the part of the cable that carries the signal.

Fiber-optic cable is distinctly different from any form of copper cable; it does not emit any electromagnetic properties, nor is it sensitive to these properties. Fiber can span distances much greater than can copper-based cable before a signal loss factor is significant. However, length is not the only factor in the computation of signal loss in fiber-optic cable; the refractive index is also important. The *refractive index* is the ratio of the speed of light in a vacuum to the speed of light in a material such as optical fibers. *Pulse dispersion,* another factor in the equation used to calculate bandwidth and hence data loss, is the spreading of pulses as they traverse fiber cable.

Fiber also has a rule for measurement. Numbers used to indicate the size of fiber reflect the core size and the cladding size; for instance, a rating of 50/125 or 62.5/125 would mean 50 μm core with 125 μm cladding or 62.5 μm core with 125 μm cladding (measured from side to side). There are other sizes and types of fiber; however, fiber is used to move photons, not electrons.

Soft media

Soft media in fact use hard, tangible components, but they move data through means other than cable.

Satellite communication.   Satellite communication utilizes satellites in orbit around the earth. These satellites are *geosynchronous,* orbiting earth at

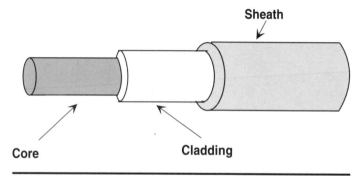

Figure 3.10   Fiber-Optic Cable

approximately 36,000 km above the equator, and remaining stationary. Hence, they are synchronous with the earth's revolutions. These satellites remain in a fixed position, thus permitting signals to be transmitted to and from earth stations. Figure 3.11 illustrates this type of communication.

Satellite communication is interesting in concept. Three satellites positioned 120° apart can cover the entire earth, from a communications standpoint. In satellite communication, transmitters and receivers are located at the origination and destination points. *Satellite communication,* by definition, implies that a transmission delay will occur. The delay may be measured in seconds or fractions of seconds, but it nevertheless occurs.

Infrared. Infrared communication, which uses different hardware and frequency bands for communication to occur, is a *line-of-sight* method of communication, meaning that if anything interferes with it (physically), the signal is impaired. At the time of this writing, infrared LANs are beginning to appear in the marketplace. Figure 3.12 conveys the idea behind infrared communication. In this example two devices are communicating. This could be implemented in physical plants where distances are long and clear between two points where communication needs to occur.

Microwave. Microwave communication is similar to satellite communication in that transmitters and receivers must be located at the origin and destination points. Microwave communications however do not use orbiting devices in communications; however, they use line-of-sight communication. Figure 3.13 illustrates this idea.

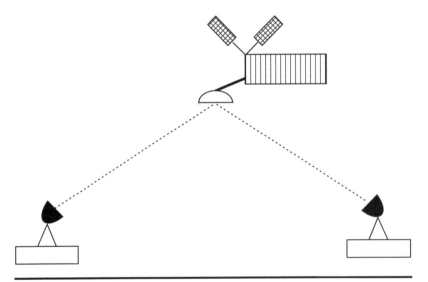

Figure 3.11 Satellite Communications

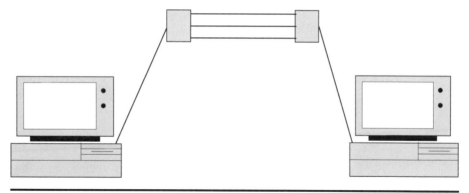

Figure 3.12   Conceptual View of Infrared Communication

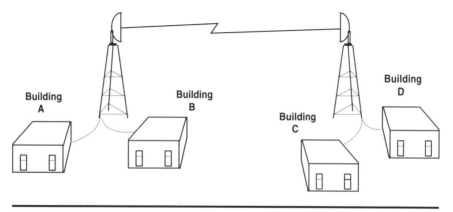

Figure 3.13   Conceptual View of Microwave Communication

Microwave communication is possible between sites approximately 25 to 30 km apart. Distance of microwave communication is restricted primarily because of the curvature of the earth. However, transmitter and receiver tower height also affects this equation. Obviously the terrain affects the equation as well. Microwave communication is popular in metropolitan areas and provides an effective means for signal transmission to various locales outside a metropolitan area. Microwave communication is not only effective technically but also cost-effective.

3.3   Physical Communication Link Configurations

Physical links used in data communications can take on a variety of possibilities. Certain technologies in this book use different technological implementations to achieve their purposes. This section explores some of the popular implementations.

Figure 3.14 Point-to-Point Communication

Figure 3.14 illustrates *point-to-point communication,* meaning communication or connection between two or more points. This type of connection can be categorized as either switched or dedicated.

Figure 3.15 depicts a switched point-to-point connection. A switched communication line is best described as being in use when needed and not in use when not needed; hence the term *switched.* An excellent example of this is the ordinary telephone, which is used only when necessary.

A dedicated point-to-point communication line may appear as either scenario shown in Figure 3.16. The top configuration could represent communication between two hosts (A and B) in one physical location with a line *dedicated* between the two. In the second scenario, depicting communication between hosts C and D, a modem is used and what might appear to be a switched connection is also used. The difference between this connection and

Figure 3.15 Switched Point-to-Point Communication

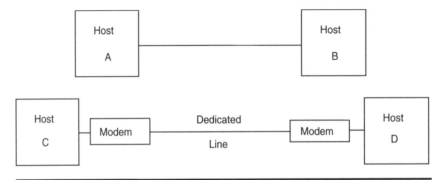

Figure 3.16 Dedicated Point-to-Point Communication

a switched one is that in this scenario, the line is dedicated. Analogously, the modems do not release the line; rather, the signal is maintained. This type of connection is typically referred to as a *leased line* because of the requirement for a circuit to accommodate this service. Leased connections are common in the United States with commercial companies.

Figure 3.17 depicts a multipoint or multidrop line. In this example there is one host (host A) with a communication line attached and multiple devices (devices A to D) connected to the line. This is simple to understand. It is similar to a street with houses. At any given time the host may communicate with a device *downstream* or vice versa. In this form of communication, there is one single path for data flow and multiple device accessibility. Scenarios similar to Figure 3.17 are generally nonswitched.

Figure 3.18 depicts a ring or loop communication line configuration. These normally operate in what is considered a nonswitched configuration, but in some implementations devices can be removed and inserted into the line without disrupting other devices on the line.

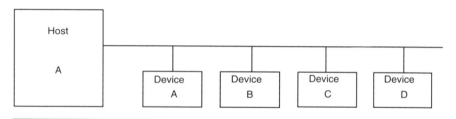

Figure 3.17 Multipoint Communication Line

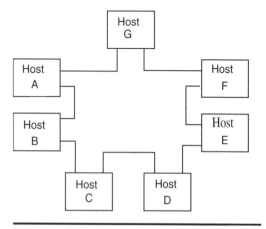

Figure 3.18 Ring or Loop Communication Line

3.4   Signal Characteristics

Communication between entities is achieved through signals of some sort. This is true with both humans and machines. Humans normally use speech, whereas networks, computers, and internetworking devices use electrical or optical signals. These signals have many characteristics, and the type of signal—electrical or optical—determines (to a degree) the characteristics of that signal.

This section explores signals and their characteristics. The details presented are intended as a source of information needed for work at fundamental layers within a network.

Signal types

A signal can be defined or characterized in many ways; however, for purposes of discussion here, the difference between analog and digital signals is explained.

Analog   An analog signal can be described by what it is not. It is in neither ON nor OFF state, is neither positive nor negative, nor is it in some other diametrically opposed condition or position. An example would be a dimmer switch used in electrical lighting to vary light intensity without full intensity or with the light completely off (unless the latter two states of intensity are desired).

Digital   A digital signal is best defined as being in either an ON or an OFF state and with no in-between point. In data communications a digital signal is a binary 1 or 0.

Signaling methods

There are two signaling methods: baseband and broadband. Baseband signaling uses digital signal techniques for transmission; broadband, analog. Baseband signaling has a limited bandwidth in general whereas broadband signaling has a large bandwidth potential.

Signaling characteristics

Signals, either analog or digital, are based on fundamental trigonometric functions. Thus, understanding some fundamental principles yields the ability to evaluate waveforms.

A baseline for evaluating waveforms is rooted in the cartesian coordinate system. This system of measurement is mathematically unique for defining or locating a point on a line, on a plane, or in space. Fundamental to this coordinate system are numbered lines that intersect at right angles. See Figure 3.19. This coordinate system along with other aspects of trigonometry are used in signaling. Here the focus is on certain characteristics of signals.

Signals in computers, networking, or data communications can be categorized as either analog or digital. Consequently, using this coordinate system along with other tools, it is possible to explain the signals.

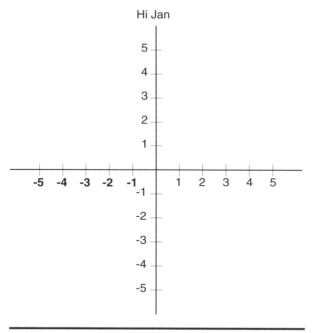

Figure 3.19 Cartesian Coordinate System

Analog and digital commonalities

Both analog and digital signals have commonalities. Each can be evaluated by amplitude, frequency, and phase.

Amplitude. The *amplitude* of a signal refers to its height in respect to a baseline. Height may be a positive or negative voltage. The baseline is a zero-voltage reference point. This amplitude value is proportional to the movement of the curve about the X axis of the coordinate system.

Frequency. *Frequency* is the number of cycles a wave makes per second. Specifically, frequency is measured in hertz (Hz), which is also known as a unit of frequency. A *cycle* is a complete signal revolution from zero to the maximum positive voltage past zero to the maximum negative voltage, then back to zero. In the coordinate system this is a complete revolution from 0 to 360°. Figure 3.20 shows an example of signal characteristics, particularly one cycle. Figure 3.20 shows one cycle and the signal in respect to time and amplitude as well as frequency.

Phase. *Phase* is normally measured in degrees representing the location of a waveform. Phase is also measured as the relative duration of a signal with respect to another signal. A change in phase without change in frequency or amplitude results in a scenario such as that depicted in Figure 3.21. In

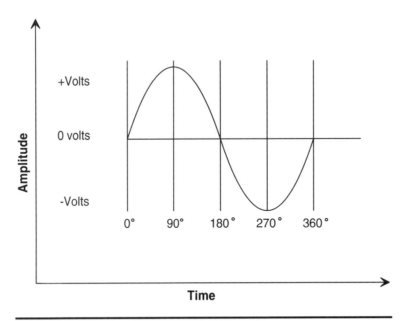

Figure 3.20 Signal Characteristics

Figure 3.21 three waveforms are present: A, B, and C. In this example waveform A has a 20° phase angle or leads waveform B by 20 degrees. Determination of the leading waveform is derived by visually ascertaining which waveform crosses the X (abscissa; horizontal) axis first; in this case it is waveform A. Waveform C, on the other hand, is lagging waveform A by 20°.

Figure 3.22 shows an example of two signal waveforms (better known as *sine waves*) that have the same frequency but are out of phase with respect to each other.

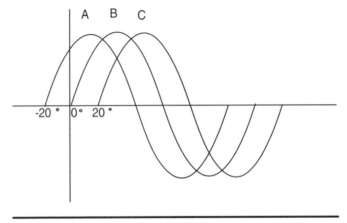

Figure 3.21 Example of a Phase Angle

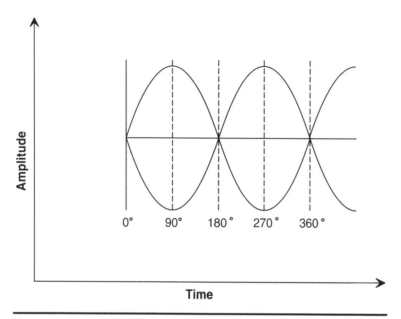

Figure 3.22   Phase Differentiation

In general, signals transmitted over a medium are subject to varying frequencies. Phase can be regarded as the distance a waveform is from its point of origin [zero degrees (0°)]. This is particularly important when examining transmission characteristics of encoded signals. Encoded signaling characteristics are explained later; however, the significance of this information becomes real when one uses different measuring scopes to troubleshoot a line with varying frequencies.

Period.   A *period* is best described as the length of a cycle. It is defined as time required by signal transmission of a wavelength.

Waveforms

Waveforms exist in many forms. Two are discussed here: the sine wave and the square wave.

Sine wave.   A *sine wave* is a periodic wave. Characteristically, this is a wave's amplitude based on the sine of its linear quantity of phase or time. See Figure 3.23.

Square wave.   A *square wave* is a wave with a square shape. It has the same characteristics as the sine wave (see Figure 3.24), except that it has a square appearance rather than the wave appearance of the sine wave.

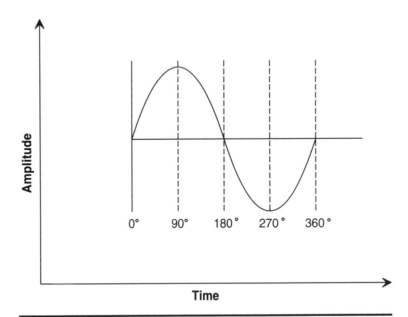

Figure 3.23 Example of a Sine Wave

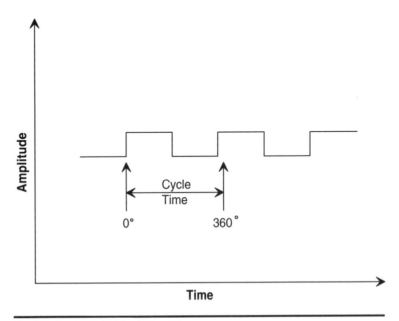

Figure 3.24 Example of a Square Wave

3.5   How to Use Data Representation in Troubleshooting

It is important to be able to perform manual conversions of data representations in any system, such as a computer or a network. As humans, we live in an analog world; however, it seems that the majority of businesses in technologically advanced countries attempt to convert all business transactions and methods of maintaining information to binary form.

All things emanate from a point of singularity. However, the reality of daily life lends to perceptions of shades of gray, so to speak. At the smallest particles of existence, binary reality exists. This becomes problematical when attempts are made to convert most aspects of life which are analog to the native sense perception into digital forms. At the most fundamental aspects of computers and modern technology is the conversion from analog to digital. Invariably, this conversion involves tables used to correlate *something* to *something*. Consequently, if one understands conversion methods and ratios of correlation, then one has incredible power over that system because all else is built on top of it.

Data representation can take different forms: binary, hexadecimal, decimal, and octal. Data representation can also be explained categorically.

Binary

Binary data representation uses ones (1s) and zeros (0s) to represent alphanumeric characters within computer systems. Another way of approaching binary representation is by way of the *American Standard Code for Information Interchange* (ASCII), a method of data representation that uses 128 permutations of arrangements of ones and zeros. This means that with a computer using an ASCII character set letters, numbers, control codes, and other keyboard symbols have a specific binary relationship. Consider the following examples which show the correlation of a letter or number in the ASCII character set and its binary equivalent:

Letter or number	Binary value
A	01000001
a	01100001
E	01000101
2	00110010
3	00110011
7	00110111
T	01010100
t	01110100
"	00100010
-	00101101

This is an example showing that each time a key is pressed on a keyboard, the equivalent binary value is generated (a string of ones and zeros). This value is represented inside the computer as a voltage. That voltage is direct current (dc).

Computers for the most part are digital, that is, either a 1 or 0. Hence, converting letters, numbers, or control codes to a numeric value is straightforward. When it comes to how computers work with data representation, consider what I told my friend Isaac: "Computers do not negotiate; they are binary." At the most fundamental place within computers, data representation is a method similar to being in an OFF or ON state.

A *bit* is a single digit, either one or zero. A byte is 8 bits. Hence, in the previous example a single letter or number is represented by a combination of ones and zeros. The binary numbering system is based on powers of 2 and is counted from right to left. The significance of this is that binary digits are determined by their positions in how they are noted. Consider the following:

Powers of two	Value
2×0	1
2×1	2
2×2	4
2×3	8
2×4	16
2×5	32
2×6	64
2×7	128
2×8	256
2×9	512
2×10	1024
2×11	2048
2×12	4096

Most people who have had some form of education would probably think I made a mistake showing that 2×0 is equivalent to 1! However, note what is being conveyed. I am explaining powers of 2 and each correlating value. This is not multiplication. Try to avoid superimposing previous knowledge onto something new; in this case the mental tabula rasa is the best way to begin learning with computing.

With the previous example, one byte is 2×0, which is eight binary digits (either 1s or 0s, or some variation thereof). Following are more examples of how this correlates to keys one presses on a keyboard, or how letters and numbers are generated prior to representation in visual form.

Letters or numbers	Binary value
Ed	01000101 01100100
$	00100100

The two examples here—Ed and $—are shown with the corresponding binary value to the right. It is possible to convert binary numbers into shorthand. Popular methods of doing this are hexadecimal and octal.

Hexadecimal

Hexadecimal (Hex) refers to a numbering scheme that uses a base 16 for counting. Hex is a shorthand notation for expressing binary values of characters. Consider the following example:

Hexadecimal value	Decimal value
0	0
1	1
2	2
3	3
4	4
5	5
6	6
7	7
8	8
9	9
A	10
B	11
C	12
D	13
E	14
F	15

The following example correlates a character with a binary representation and Hex expression of that value.

Letter/number	Binary	Hex value
A	01000001	41
a	01100001	61
E	01000101	45
2	00110010	02
3	00110011	03
7	00110111	07
T	01010100	54
k	01101011	6B
m	01101101	6D
z	01111010	7A

As this example indicates, it is easier to represent the letter *z* by Hex value 7A than by its binary representation.

The *octal* representation uses base 8 for whole numbers and decimals. Of these systems, binary and Hex are most common, and understanding this binary representation is helpful with other data-communication concepts.

A final word about data representation. IBM uses Extended Binary-Coded Decimal Interchange Code (EBCDIC) for representing data, alphanumerics, and control codes. EBCDIC uses an arrangement of 256 ones and zeros to make this possible. And, it should be noted that ASCII and EBCDIC are not one-for-one interchangeable.

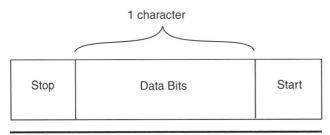

Figure 3.25 Example of an Asynchronous Frame

Converting binary to Hex

The ASCII character set includes representation of arrangements of 128 variations with ones and zeros to represent letters, numbers, and special characters used in many computers. As shown in the previous examples, correlations can be made between a letter, its binary value, its hexadecimal value, and its decimal value.

Since the hexadecimal system is based on a power of 16, no letters higher in the alphabet above F are used. Therefore, a binary value of 010101000, for instance, yields a hexadecimal value of A8. Another example could be a binary value of 10101010 yielding a hexadecimal value of AA.

3.6   Transmission Characteristics

Communication is achieved through signals of some sort. This is true with humans or machines. Humans normally use speech, whereas networks, computers, and internetworking devices use electrical or optical signals. These signals have many characteristics. These and other topics are presented here.

Asynchronous transmission

Asynchronous transmission, also called "start/stop" transmission, is characterized by character-oriented protocols. The rationale for this is that data are transmitted asynchronously and timed by the start and stop bits of the frame, primarily the start bit. Consider Figure 3.25, which depicts a start bit, data bits, and a stop bit. In asynchronous transmission, the start bit notifies the receiving entity that data bits follow. Likewise, the stop bit signifies end-of-data bits.

A problem with this method of communication exists if the last data bit and the stop bit are the same. If this occurs, the receiving entity is confused. Ironically, whether the last data bit and the stop bit are the same is relatively unimportant because this is overcome with *parity,* which is achieved by the originating entity counting the number of bits and appending the outgoing character as necessary to achieve even or odd parity. The receiver, on the other hand, calculates for parity against 7 data bits and compares it to the parity bit received (the parity bit is the eighth bit transmitted). If the parity sent and the computation on behalf of the receiver do not match, an error has occurred.

Terms normally used with parity are *odd* and *even*; they reflect an accurate representation of the transmission. However, the terms *mark* and *space,* referring to parity as the bit setting of 1 and 0, respectively, are sometimes used as well.

The term *asynchronous serial communication* is a misnomer. In fact, the start bit actually synchronizes the following bits, whereas synchronous serial communication is synchronized by bytes. Both are synchronized; asynchronous synchronization is performed on bits while synchronous synchronization is typically performed at the byte level, as is explained below. The bottom line is that, theoretically, more overhead occurs with asynchronous communication than with synchronous communication.

Synchronous transmission

Basic to synchronous transmission is the intent to reduce the overhead inherent in *asynchronous* transmission and to provide more efficient error detection and correction. Two categories of synchronous protocols are described here: byte- and bit-oriented.

Byte-oriented protocols. An example of a byte-oriented protocol used in synchronous transmission is IBM's Binary Synchronous (BISYNC) Protocol. Introduced by IBM in 1967, it appears as shown in Figure 3.26. Figure 3.26 shows the beginning field as the synchronization (SYN) character. This precedes all data, and a synchronization (SYN) control character may even be inserted in the middle of a long message to ensure synchronization.

The start-of-text (STX) character indicates that data immediately follow. Data codes supported in BISYNC are ASCII, EBCDIC, and a 6-bit transparent code. The end-of-text character (ETX) follows data. If a BISYNC transmission is lengthy and divided into segments, only the last segment will have a ETX indicator. The block check character (BCC) can be either a longitudinal redundancy check (LRC) or a cyclic redundancy check (CRC).

The byte-oriented protocol BISYNC is not as dominant now as it was in the 1970s. Its code dependence and transparency implementation are not sufficiently flexible to support popular demands today.

S Y N	S T X	DATA	E T X	B C C

Figure 3.26 Byte-Oriented Protocol for Synchronous Transmission

Bit-oriented protocols. Two examples of bit-oriented protocols transmitted synchronously are High-Level Data Link Control (HDLC) and Synchronous Data Link Control (SDLC). Figure 3.27 shows an example of a SDLC frame.

The beginning and ending flags have reserved values, which are always 01111110 (7E). The address field in the SDLC frame contains addresses. The control field (CF) in the frame indicates what type frame it is: control, information, or supervisory. The data field contains the data being transmitted. The frame check sequence (FCS) is implemented for determining whether errors in transmission have occurred. The last field is the ending flag.

SDLC supports code transparency because it was designed into the protocol. The result of this architecture is good performance with low overhead.

Synchronization of these byte- and bit-oriented protocols is achieved by performing error checks on larger blocks of data, resulting in lower overhead.

How to interpret bandwidth

Bandwidth is an interesting topic. Depending on the company in which the conversation is held, one could find many different aspects of discussion. For example, many think of a connection ability between two given points, A and B. This is an appropriate consideration for bandwidth. However, before examining this line of discussion for bandwidth, we need to define the term *channel,* which means the medium used for transmission—data, voice, or even multimedia. A channel can also be defined as a path along which data can be moved, or a path for passage of analog or digital signals.

Bandwidth is also the difference between the highest frequency and lowest frequency with which signals can be sent simultaneously across the channel. Bandwidth directly reflects data transfer rate of the channel. Obviously the higher the bandwidth, the higher the data rate. This poses an interesting scenario. Say that a given channel has bandwidth value of X. That number, whatever it is, is fixed. Not true. Consider implementing a compression algorithm for the data to be moved through the channel. Assume that this algorithm operates on an 8-to-1 ratio. Usually this means that the amount of data denoted as a quantity of one (1) going through a channel is actually eight (8) because of the compression algorithm.

In most instances today networks of all sorts employ algorithms to compress data so that more can move through a channel. Many different com-

F l a g	Address	Control	Data	Frame Check Sequence	F l a g

Figure 3.27 Bit-Oriented Protocol Used in SDLC

pression utilities are available today, and some are even shipped with systems in a preload package.

Understanding bandwidth encompasses more than how much data can move through a channel. In some instances a bandwidth problem exists on either end of a given channel. If the channel contains a fiber medium, either end will generally have a problem either with continuing to provide data to feed the channel or vice versa, continuing to receive the amount of data passing through the channel.

Still another twist on bandwidth is evident in network devices. Some vendors provide network devices that operate as a concentrator or hub, and then pass data to a processor. Figure 3.28 illustrates an example of this idea. This illustration depicts multiple devices connected to a hub and the hub connected to a processor. There is nothing inherently wrong with this configuration or implementation; however, when discussing bandwidth, one must discuss the bandwidth ability of the hub's backplane. Bandwidth of the device channels to the hub is one matter; the capabilities of the backplane of this hub are entirely different. To not discuss bandwidth of the hub's backplane and its link to the processor is to address only one side of the bandwidth equation.

How to interpret channel capacity

Channels can be categorized as either voice, data, narrowband, wideband or broadband, and by a wide variety of other terms. With growing migration to fiber channels and with encoding and compression techniques, a channel can be exploited in ways not thought of only a few decades ago.

Generally, a channel is the "pipe" that moves data from point A to point B. The term itself is generic; however, IBM uses the term in a proprietary sense when referring to their Byte, Block, and Selector channels. They also use the term to refer to ESCON (fiber) channels.

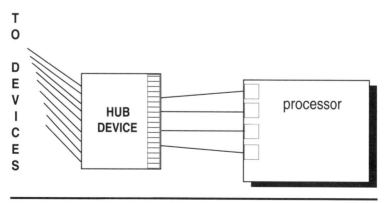

Figure 3.28 Interpreting Various Aspects of Bandwidth

From a different perspective, some think of channels as referring to television, while still others use the term to refer to nonvisible channels such as microwave and radio frequency. Also, some online service providers now use the term *channel* to refer to accessible parts of their networks that can be easily identified such as weather or news.

Serial transmission

Another transmission characteristic is how data are moved from one entity to another. *Serial communication* is bit by bit. An example of this is fiber-optic-based data transfer. In this example photons are moved in serial fashion through the medium. Figure 3.29 is an example of serial transmission of the letter T through a medium. This translates into a binary representation of 01010100.

Parallel transmission

Parallel transmission is movement of data along a channel path in byte form. An example of this is IBM's parallel channels. The essence of parallel transmission is moving data in bytes rather than sequential bits. Figure 3.30 illustrates an example of parallel data transfer.

Simplex transmission

Simplex transmission is a reference to the direction that data can move at any given instance. Simplex transmission is best exemplified by analogy of a radio station broadcasting and multiple receivers detecting the signal. Hence, direction of data flow is one-way only.

Half-duplex transmission

This reference to direction of data flow means that data can flow in either of two directions, but only one direction at a time. An analogy of this is courteous communication between individuals. Normally, one speaks while another

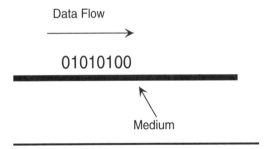

Figure 3.29 Serial Transmission

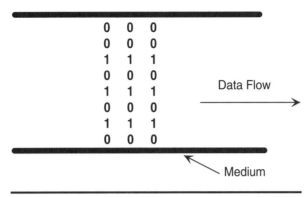

Figure 3.30 Parallel Transmission

listens; then the reverse happens. Unfortunately, this does not have to be the case with humans, but it does with technology.

Full-duplex transmission

This direction of data flow is both directions at the same time. The implication here is that simultaneous data transfer can occur and be interpreted by both parties. Each entity can send and receive at the same time.

3.7 Modulation Techniques

When data are transmitted over a channel via a modem, modulation is involved. *Modulation* is simply the conversion of digital signals into analog signals. Conversely, when this signal arrives at the destination, the modem performs reverse modulation, if you will; it performs *demodulation*.

Three modulation techniques are popular: *amplitude modulation* (AM), which varies the amplitude of a signal without changing its frequency or phase; *frequency modulation* (FM), which changes the frequency to reflect the change is binary state but maintains the amplitude; and *phase modulation* (PM), which varies the phase of the wave to reflect the binary value.

Amplitude modulation

Amplitude modulation is the use of a single carrier frequency to convert the digital signals to analog. Figure 3.31 shows the high wave amplitude to indicate a binary one and a low wave amplitude to indicate a binary zero.

Frequency shift key modulation

Frequency shift keying (FSK) uses a constant-amplitude carrier signal along with two additional frequencies to allow differentiation between a mark and a

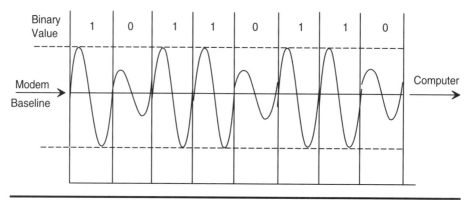

Figure 3.31 Amplitude Modulation

space. Consider Figure 3.32. This type of modulation technique is not prevalent among higher-speed modems because of its simplicity. Higher baud rates require different modulation techniques.

Differential phase shift key modulation

This type of modulation technique uses a phase angle comparison of an input signal to the prior *di-bit* (where each phase angle represents two bit values). Consider Figure 3.33, which shows the comparison of the wave pattern and the square-wave interpretation thereof. Actually, the modulation technique is a comparison-based modulation technique. Some medium-speed modems use this technique.

Phase shift key modulation

In this method of modulation, the phase of the signal is shifted at the baseline (transition point). Consider Figure 3.34. This type of modulation is com-

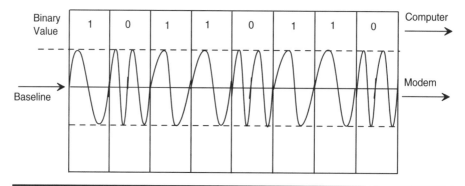

Figure 3.32 Frequency Shift Key Modulation

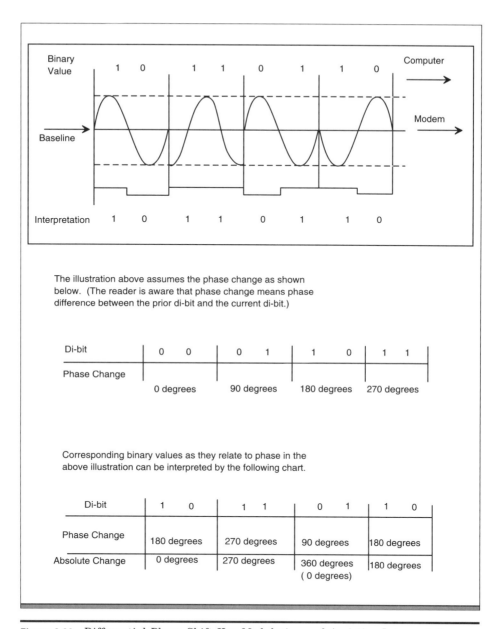

Figure 3.33 Differential Phase Shift Key Modulation and Assisting Interpretation Information

parative in nature to a degree. It uses a phase shift relative to a fixed reference point. A modem using this type of modulation has an oscillator inside to determine a signal phase angle as it enters the modem. (An *oscillator* is basically a component that generates an alternating signal, continuously. Its voltage, or current, periodically varies relative to time.)

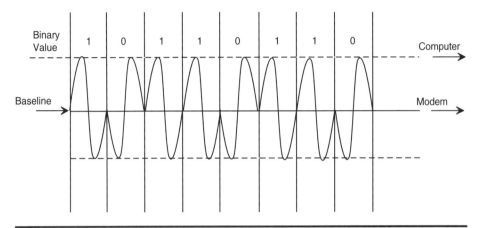

Figure 3.34 Phase Shift Key Modulation

3.8 Encoding Techniques

The term *encoding* refers to how signals are introduced onto the medium and how signals appear on the medium when examined. This idea is reflected in Figure 3.35, which shows an example of *non-return-to-zero encoding,* a type of encoding scheme that uses each signal change to represent a bit.

Figure 3.36 illustrates *Manchester encoding,* a type of encoding scheme that changes the polarity each bit time. Note in Figure 3.36 that each bit time has a change in polarity. This method of encoding results in good clocking performance and is widespread throughout LAN technology.

Other encoding schemes include *differential Manchester encoding,* which is a form of Manchester encoding that uses the previous bit time as a base reference point for interpretation of the signal. *Return to zero* is another scheme that utilizes two signals to represent one bit change. It is similar to Manchester encoding in that polarity is changed each bit time.

Popular interface standards

Interface standards include popular terms such as RS-232, v.35, T1, and X.21. These interfaces and many others are prevalent throughout the marketplace. There are entire books devoted to explaining these and other interfaces.

Physical layer interfaces have protocols to transfer data the same as do the higher layers within a network. A particular interface specification identifies the protocols of its operation. Some examples are described in the following paragraphs.

RS-232. RS-232-D is the follow-on to RS-232-C. The fundamental difference between the two is that RS-232-D is parallel to the v.24, v.28, and ISO 2110 specifications. The RS-232 standard comes from the Electronics Industry

Bit
Time
⟶   0   1   1   0   1   0

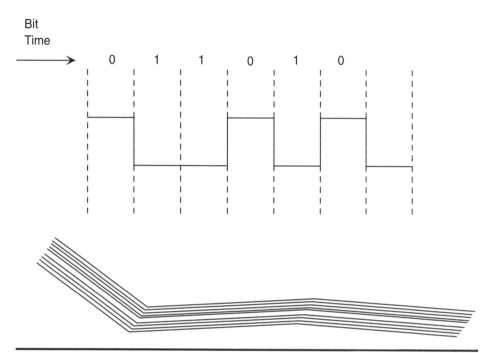

Figure 3.35 Non-Return-to-Zero Encoding

Bit
Time
⟶   0   1   0   1   1   0

0 Volts

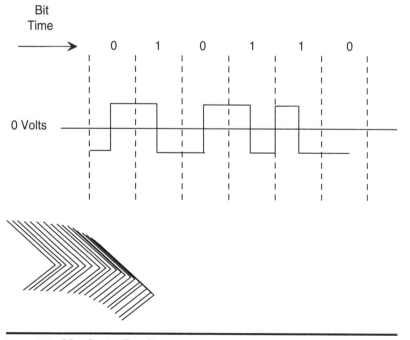

Figure 3.36 Manchester Encoding

Association (EIA). It specifies the pin-outs of a 25-pin cable used for serial communications. Although most of them are not used for typical modem installations used with PCs, the 25 pins are nevertheless assigned.

V.35. This specification comes from the CCITT. It specifies modem operation of 48 kilobits per second (kbps). It is typically implemented at 56 kbps, however.

T1. T1 interfaces have the capability to move data up to 1.54 Mbps. T1 lines comprise 24 channels, each using 8 bits per channel. The result is that one T1 line uses a twisted-pair cable for 24 voice signals. The result is a ratio of 24 to 1.

X.21. This CCITT specification is flexible in that different signaling rates are supported. For example, a given DTE and DCE may differ with respect to adherence to specifications. X.21 calls for synchronous operations with public data networks. An example of this scenario is X.25 using X.21 as the interface.

Many other interfaces exist. To list them here would require the remainder of the book; the purpose is only to orient you into what happens at the physical layer. Regardless of the vendor, interfaces are designed to provide a link between systems or between a system and the medium. The interface standard used may be vendor specific, but in most cases vendors adhere to the guidelines that the services providers offer.

A final note about interfaces. They do not have to be physical in the sense that they are used to bridge cables or some tangible medium. For example, wireless networks require interfaces between network devices, transmitters, and receivers.

3.9 Multiplexing

The purpose of multiplexing is to achieve maximum utilization of a channel. Multiplexing can be accomplished a variety of ways; however two popular ones are explained here.

Frequency division multiplexing

Frequency division multiplexing (FDM) means multiplexing of frequencies. This type of multiplexing can be readily used with analog transmission because frequencies are divided then multiplexed onto the medium. Consider Figure 3.37, which shows one medium and three devices connected to the medium. Each device transmits on a different frequency; in this hypothetical example the frequencies are 1, 2, and 3. These hypothetical frequencies could realistically be 10 to 14 kHz, 5 to 9 kHz, and 0 to 4000 kHz. The premise of a FDM multiplexer is that each device uses a range of frequencies and that the

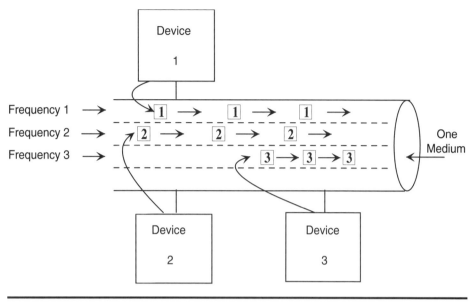

Figure 3.37 Frequency Division Multiplexing

frequencies remain within that range. The point is that bandwidth of the medium is utilized effectively to accommodate multiple users communicating with different frequencies.

Time division multiplexing

Time division multiplexing (TDM) means multiplexing data via time. Figure 3.38 illuminates this idea. Time division multiplexing is the utilization of the medium by time-slicing devices attached to the multiplexer. Its premise for operation is time-based data transfer. In Figure 3.38 three devices are attached to the multiplexer and the multiplexer itself multiplexes signals from devices 1, 2, and 3 to maximize the channel. Although not shown, on the receiving end of the data path is another multiplexer which demultiplexes the data to their destination point.

Types of multiplexers

There are various types of multiplexers. For example, a network-based multiplexer may provide services for a variety of devices each utilizing different transfer speeds. T1 multiplexers operate at T1 speeds (1.54 Mbps). Another type of T1 multiplexer is the fractional T1, which supports fractions of the T1 speeds, which are increased in 56- or 64-kbps increments. Normally, 1 to 23 circuits can be derived from a fractional T1.

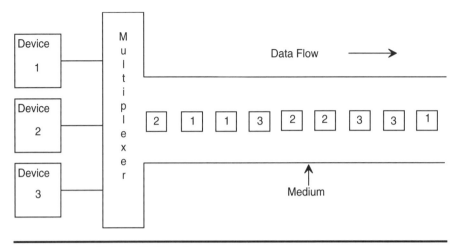

Figure 3.38   Time Division Multiplexing

3.10   Measuring Bandwidth

At the physical layer within a network, numerous topics must be considered. A number of well-written books focus on exactly this level within a network. Information here is focused and concise. These topics provide sufficient reference information and at the end of the book, references for additional information are provided.

Bit rate

The *bit rate* is the number of bits transmitted per second; this term is generally used with modems.

Baud rate

The *baud rate* is a measurement of number of times per second a change occurs in amplitude, frequency, or phase of a wave; one baud is equivalent to a change in one of these parameters. To calculate the number of bits per second, the following rule can be used. Determine the number of bits that equal one baud. This information usually is obtained through documentation sources from modem suppliers or by knowing the specifications for the modem and referencing this specification. Next, multiply the number of bauds per second that a modem can perform; this product will equal the number of bits per second for that modem:

The number of bauds per second × 1 bit per baud (or the appropriate amount according to specifications) = the number of bits per second.

Practical bandwidth measurements

Many interpret the term *bandwidth* as focusing on and understanding the size of the channel ("pipe") between one or more points. To understand bandwidth requires a total (holistic) approach to networks and systems. Bandwidth analysis includes a comprehensive approach. For example, it includes examination of backplane throughput capabilities for devices throughout a network, consideration of computing device front-end drivers for channels from one point to another, and actual application capabilities regarding user support. It also includes operating system's analysis for user (either human or mechanical, i.e., computer programs) capacity. Total (holistic) bandwidth analysis also includes other factors of networks and computing systems.

An example of a total perspective for bandwidth considerations includes analysis of interface boards and buses used in fiber-based networks. It matters little whether fiber links exist between any given points or if there is an input/output (I/O) bottleneck in the interface cards that drive the fiber connections.

One rule of thumb to remember is that even if fiber connections are used extensively in a network, the maximum throughput capacity may be limited by the actual computing device or devices using these fiber links. In addition, it is best to remember that signal loss and degradation due to impairment also affects overall network speed. Another way to examine this concept is to remember that the fastest part of any network is the slowest component.

Total component examination for bandwidth capacity is the most accurate way to determine the speeds which can be ascribed to any network. Evaluation of signal transmission is also important in understanding bandwidth. The following section addresses the topic of signal transmission.

3.11   Signal Transmission

Signal transmission involves a number of topics. As discussed previously, types of signals, how they are transmitted, the bandwidth used, the way data are represented, and a variety of other topics surround the topic of transmission.

Signal distortion is no trivial matter. It occurs in most transmissions. For example, when lines originally designed for voice transmission are used for data transmission, some distortion can occur. Distortion can be filtered out by the human ear when it occurs during a voice conversation between two or more parties speaking over a given medium. This happens frequently; we become used to the "noise" or distortion, and unless it is sufficiently extreme to cause difficulty interpreting another's words, it is typically dismissed. This is not always possible when data are transmitted. Because data are generally transmitted via machines of some sort, they have preprogrammed methods of dealing with distortion.

Delay is a type of distortion. Delay is the time it takes for a signal to arrive at its destination from its point of origin. Frequently, this type of delay is called *propagation delay*. It may seem trivial to discuss delay in light of how rapidly current technology can transmit and receive signals, but consider the following. For example, if a signal is generated in Dallas and is routed through local switches, then transmitted to a satellite, and then received in Paris, a considerable delay time is incurred. Although the delay may be only in the millisecond or second range, it is quite important. Propagation delay is becoming more of a concern today because of how technology is being implemented. For example, TCP/IP is the backbone protocol in the Internet. TCP/IP and certain devices encounter difficulty when delays occur in transmission of data packets from point A to point B. When significant delay is introduced to the transmission, some devices cannot convey a data stream, and thus reliable transmission fails. This is a significant topic for concern in many technical arenas today.

Harmonic distortion is an older term for a type of distortion. When a frequency is transmitted through a medium, other harmonics can be measured as a result of the main tone in the medium; these are generally referred to as *second* and *third harmonics*.

Nonlinear distortion is a current way to evaluate what has been traditionally viewed as harmonic distortion. A nonlinear distortion measurement is the value obtained from monitoring paired frequencies and the harmonics associated with them. The net effect of nonlinear distortion is the introduction of other symbols of some measurable magnitude that appear in low magnitude. This type of distortion is similar to harmonic distortion, but it has a twist to it that is sufficiently different so that it can be compensated for, thus improving line quality.

Jitter is another type of distortion. This term refers to phenomena in which a signal is moved around the center of an axis on which it is being transmitted. Jitter is a frequency-oriented noise or distortion. Jitter has caused a common type of distortion with analog signals. In the world of digital signal transfer, jitter causes problems with clocking an incoming signal on the receiving end of transmission.

Crosstalk is another form of distortion. It occurs with analog signals when the lines carrying them are too close and there is literally crosstalk: a "bleeding" onto the other signal. Technically, this is a form of induction that occurs generally between two wires or other types of equipment in close proximity.

Fading is another form of distortion where a signal becomes progressively weaker. Generally, this is due to atmospheric conditions. In microwave and satellite transmission, distortion is an effect of the atmosphere. Rain, snow, ice, and other atmospheric phenomena such as ozone and particulates create distortion of signals transmitted through space. Different times of the year and even different seasons affect some signals differently.

There are other types of distortions. Interference frequently results when signal transmission occurs regardless of whether the signal is transmitted over a physical line, through space, or by other means. These types of distortion are examples of the difficulties encountered with signal transmission. Degradation of signals is not a trivial topic; in fact, it is a core topic to those entities who provide services that carry signals from place to place.

3.12   Summary

This chapter has provided significant information for those who need to understand practical information in working with network blueprints.

Signal characteristics are common to all signals. This is a fundamental way to analyze fundamental operation in any network. Signal types and methods need to be understood to operate certain devices (both hardware and software) in network operation and maintenance.

Data representation is also critical to working with network blueprints. More than ever, data representation is important. When some networks were EBCDIC or ASCII in their native form, it was not too important to understand the fundamentals of data representation conversion. Today integrated networks have brought forth the need to understand data representation; thus, interpretation of information through analyzers and network test equipment requires a higher level of understanding network fundamentals.

Transmission characteristics of signals is important as well. Transmission characteristics accompany all transmission methods used in networking blueprints today. Focusing on understanding transmission characteristics enhances the understanding of the overall interpretation of information obtained about networks.

Measuring bandwidth in all networks is an increasingly important topic of conversation. The information presented in this chapter may encourage you to focus on the overall approach to this topic. It should be used against the backdrop of understanding other topics in this and later chapters.

Modulation methods or techniques are equally important to understand for application of practical knowledge. Modulation affects the overall throughput of any network. The information presented here is applicable in most networks on the market today.

Much information is required to work with network blueprints today. Networks today are not as simple as they were in the 1980s. One must be aware of the diversity of the different vendor equipment as well as the interaction between implementations in diverse geographic locations. This chapter has been the starting place for information provided in the rest of this book.

Network design has evolved in the past 20 years to emerge as an important aspect in the technological arena. When local area networks began to take off in the early 1980s, design and planning was mostly after the fact. Network design was rudimentary, involving mainly what device would be located where. During the mid to late 1980s, this emphasis began to shift.

Because of rapid invention, creation, manufacturing, consumer awareness, and consumption, most technology was deployed without much planning.

Certainly this is not true in every case or with large networks, but it does reflect the norm of operation for medium- to small-size environments where technology was utilized. In the timeframe from the early to mid 1990s, a shift began to occur in the technical community concerning the planning or design of networks.

By the mid 1990s sources of all types such as newspapers, employment agencies, and consulting firms had identified a person with a set of skills that reflected the title of *network architect*. Little consensus exists even today regarding the exact role or function of a network architect. Designing a network involves many different disciplines. In a sense, designing a network is every bit as complex as—or perhaps more complex than—the architect's task in designing a building.

Beginning in this chapter, a variety of informative tools were presented for the reader to begin to grasp in order to develop good troubleshooting skills. The best place to begin is with the basics; in this case, that means addressing those ideas that need adjustment, removal, or deeper consideration.

How to Troubleshoot Network Devices

Before examining the details for troubleshooting network devices, some information needs to be understood in order to ensure a common framework of understanding.

Network equipment, such as repeaters, bridges, routers, brouters, switches, or gateways, can be analyzed with respect to the layers in which they operate. Today many areas of functionality have become blurred because of such levels of high integration. In fact, I don't know of a network that is not integrated to some degree.

Prior to 1983 or so, some of the devices presented in this chapter did not exist; or if they did, it was in secluded technological implementations. In fact, the 1980s may well go down in history as the decade of design and development of internetworking devices. One would only need glance at some of the trade journals and weeklies that began to dominate the industry to realize that something was going on; the question was *what*.

So many specialized devices were designed and brought to market during the 1980s that a naming problem prevailed, and still does to some degree. This part of the book explores and explains the major networking devices that exist today. But first let us consider an example.

In the 1970s the term *gateway* was used to mean what the term *router* means today. Unfortunately, depending on the context, the term *gateway* may have an elusive meaning. Nevertheless, in this chapter separate sections are devoted to routers, gateways, brouters, and similar with detailed definitions and descriptions of each of these network components.

The 1990s may well go down in the record books as the decade of assimilation, then disintegration, respectively. The 1970s were literally individualistic in regard to computer vendors and their products as they were brought to market. The 1980s, as mentioned previously, were fraught with the development of integration devices and then the initial stages of integration of various sorts of equipment. Early on in the 1990s there was assimilation of diverse equipment with hopes of "seamless" operation of equipment; later in the 1990s many seamless operations became just that—unraveled at the seams! But wait, the next millennium promises demise of integration intents. It could well be that the first years of the next millennium may reveal to the masses exactly how difficult and complex technology really is; and this author believes that it will also reveal to the masses just how "dumb" technology is. What I mean here is this—every computer, software program, or whatever is no greater than its maker; it is fundamental ignorance to believe that artificial intelligence will surpass human intelligence. Computers and networks merely do things faster, but not better, than humans do; after all, computers were created by humans. Consider the remainder of this chapter to be the basis for distilling your thoughts on how to integrate this information into your environment, and hence troubleshoot your own network.

4.1 Device Perspective

Assimilation of disjointed facts into a meaningful level of knowledge is the beginning of intelligence. Here, information about different network devices and functionality with regard to transmission and processing is the focus. Consider Figure 4.1, which shows transmission methods and layers. Note that hard and soft media methods are presented. Actually, the fiber, copper wire, satellite, microwave, and infrared transmission methods use the media layer and the physical layer. Technically, some operational function to the methods of transmission extends to the data-link layer. This is an overview of these transmission methods, but more focus is needed here—specifically, on network devices that work at these layers.

4.2 Equipment Perspective

Different types of equipment are used in network integration. Most networks have the devices listed in this section, and additional information is presented later in this chapter.

Repeaters

Repeaters are devices that operate at the physical layer compared to the OSI model. They are generally considered the simplest network devices. They perform one basic function: to repeat a signal. The signal may be electrical or optical, but never both simultaneously.

The basic purpose of a repeater is to extend the distance of something. It may be a network, devices connected together, or even processors—however, the term *repeater* is seldom used to refer to the latter implementation.

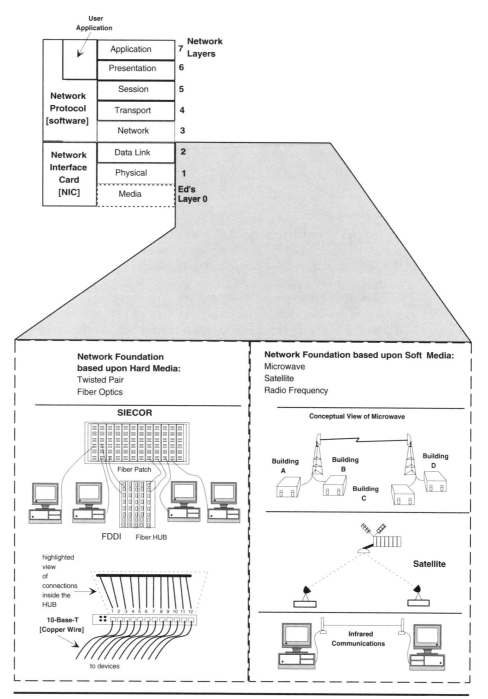

Figure 4.1   Transmission Methods and Layers

Bridges

Bridges operate at layers 1 and 2 (physical and data-link layers) of the OSI model. A bridge may be described in numerous ways. For example, some bridges operate with *like* lower-layer protocols, while others can work with *unlike* lower-layer protocols. They may also be described by their operations. Some bridges can operate only in a single physical environment, while others can operate in remote environments over switched or leased lines. Other ways of characterizing bridges can be how they perform their bridge functions. Some may perform source routing, while others may be capable of what is called *learning*.

Router

Almost no definition is needed here, but for the sake of clarity, one will be given. Routers *route!* This may seem to be the most profound statement in the book, but it is true. Routers can be characterized as to what and how they route, however.

First, it is best to note that routers operate at layer 3 (network) of the OSI model. This becomes significant when multiprotocol routers are explained. Routers route data from one location to another. This may be on another floor in a high-rise office building, or it may be halfway across the United States.

One way of examining routers is to ask which upper-layer protocol it supports. This is what routers do: route upper-layer network protocols. On the other hand, multiprotocol routers *route* multiple upper-layer protocols. This does not mean that they perform any protocol conversion; it merely means that they route multiple protocols to the target location.

Brouter

The *brouter* is a hybrid device. It can perform bridge and routing functions. Often the functionality of a brouter is vendor-specific. Depending on the device, some can perform bridging and routing functions at the same time.

Servers

Many types of specialized servers are available today. Interestingly, I have had numerous conversations with individuals who referred to a router as a "server." I suppose that such interchangeability of terms does have a point in the broadest sense of the word; routers do *serve,* but the question is *what.*

Servers today are available in many varieties. For example, there are file, print, terminal, and communication servers, to name only a few. And to be honest, there are probably others on the market that I am not aware of that fit a niche outside those listed here.

Generally, servers are devices that concentrate on performing a single function. For example, the file server is probably the easiest to understand at first glance. Most file servers perform the function of maintaining files and making them available for requesting parties on an as-needed basis. The importance behind this idea is that it removes the redundancy of each participating individual having his or her own hard disk. It also serves another function of making files accessible to others who may need access to them if authority is granted.

Gateways

Gateways, the most complex components in the network device category, perform protocol translation and operate at layer 3 and higher layers of the OSI model. Gateways can operate at all layers in a network, meaning that they perform protocol conversion at all seven layers.

The basic purpose of gateways is to interconnect heterogeneous networks. They are required to do this or perform the functionality thereof. Networks that are not architecturally identical or compatible require protocol conversion at all or some of the seven OSI layers. The only remaining issue is *where* this will be performed.

Protocol-specific devices

Some vendors who have proprietary standards require a specific device from themselves or a licensed manufacturer's copy. For example, consider IBM's ESCON lower-layer protocol. It is fiber-based and uses highly specialized equipment. IBM sells repeaters for ESCON and other reputable companies to whom it has agreed to license the technology to create such devices.

The same is true with devices which operate with upper-layer protocols. For example, some gateways can be implemented to operate at layers 3 and above in a network. If so, this is done via software. Again, depending on the vendor, contingencies may exist. One thing is for sure—at the time of this writing many network devices *are not* plug and play.

4.3   Repeater Details

Repeaters are the simplest of networking devices. Their primary purpose is simply to regenerate a signal received from input and correct the signal to its original state for output. In short, repeaters provide signal amplification and also the retiming required to connect the connected segments.

How repeaters are implemented

Local area networks utilizing Ethernet as a lower-layer protocol can use a variety of cabling types. Examples are copper-stranded twisted-pair cabling, thicknet coaxial cable, thinnet coaxial cable, and even fiber-optic cabling. By definition, thicknet coaxial cable has a resistance of 75 Ω and is generally RG-50, RG-58, or RG-59. Thinnet cable is 75 Ω and typically RG-6, RG6a, or

RG-225. Many Ethernet implementations use what is considered thicknet coaxial cable for a network backbone.

Single-port repeater

A single-port repeater actually operates with two segments: (1) the one it takes a signal from to boost and pass to the next segment and (2) a multiport repeater. Figure 4.2 is a flowchart of a physical plant with three departments: orders, parts, and shipping. Note that three repeaters are used to connect the different Ethernet-based LANs in each department.

In Figure 4.2 the configuration is such that all hosts in any department can communicate with one another because logically there is only one network, rather than three physical networks. This type of repeater implementation is straightforward and connects one cable segment to another cable segment. However, there is yet another type of repeater.

Multiport repeater

A *multiport repeater* has one input and multiple outputs. Consider Figure 4.3, which illustrates a good example of how a multiport repeater can be implemented using two different methods of Ethernet technology. This is especially beneficial using multiple point-to-point connections. Figure 4.3 shows a 10BaseT connection through a media access unit. This, in turn, makes multi-

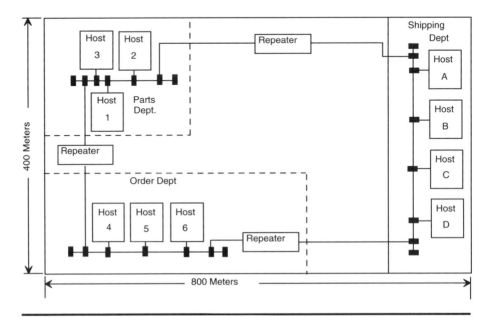

Figure 4.2   Repeater Implementation

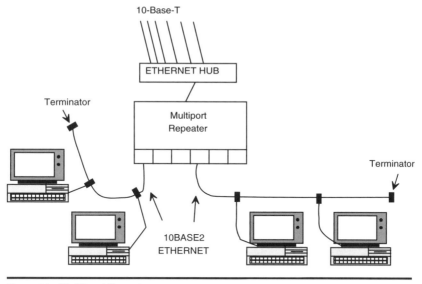

Figure 4.3   Multiport Repeater

ple connections via 10Base2 (10 Mbps) using baseband signaling with a maximum segment length of 200 m.

Smart repeaters

Smart repeaters can perform packet filtering. In reality this is a hybrid device and is very similar to a bridge in functionality. This device operates by capturing packets destined for another segment, but the repeater waits to transmit the packet(s) until congestion in the network is cleared. Ironically, this type of repeater can have an inverse effect with the connecting segments by creating a higher level of collision.

Optical repeaters

Repeaters that *repeat* optic signals do the same as those which operate with electronic signals; they repeat the signal. IBM has a particular fiber-optic channel extender link: the model 3044. According to the system selection guide, it is used in environments to extend the distances of the traditional nonfiber media to that which fiber media can obtain.

Other vendors offer repeaters that repeat optical signals over long distances; however, in the traditional sense of copper-stranded cabling, fiber can operate without a repeater in many instances.

Conclusions

Repeaters are the simplest of all networking devices. They perform signal amplification and retiming for the segments connected. Repeaters can be used with electrical and optical signals; however, they are more popular with electrical signals because of the nature of electrical signals.

Single-port and multiport repeaters are available. Single-port repeaters are used to connect two segments of cabling. Multiport repeaters take a single segment and provide the ability for multiple segments to connect.

Smart repeaters are really hybrid devices and are not considered repeaters in the traditional sense; rather, they fit into devices known as *bridges.*

4.4   Bridge Details

Bridges operate at layers 1 and 2 of the OSI model. They work with lower-layer protocols. Bridges are more complex than repeaters if for no other reason than the fact that they function with two layers of protocols.

Network operation

Bridges can serve multiple functions in a network environment. Some of these functions are vendor-specific; however, companies that sell bridges typically offer products that perform most basic functions. However, because of the diversity in what a bridge can do, vendors differ in their offerings. This sounds almost like a circuitous conversation, but there is hope! The point is that all bridges I have worked with have certain commonalities, but some are capable of performing specialized functions.

Bridge operation

As mentioned previously, bridges operate at the physical and data-link layers. Figure 4.4 shows where this occurs by illustrating an example of two hosts and a bridge connecting them together. Figure 4.5, a detailed view of bridge functions, shows two physical interfaces, one for host A and the other for host B. Note that there is only one data-link layer because this is where bridging is performed.

Functional advantages

In many real-world scenarios multiple LANs operate throughout a given entity, such as a corporation or government agency. When this is the case, it is not uncommon for multiple higher-level protocols to be implemented at higher levels in the networks. Since some upper-layer protocols have limited capability with others, the use of a bridge can be advantageous to connect multiple networks, assuming that they use the same lower-layer protocol. Another advantage of bridges is in certain situations where they may be a better

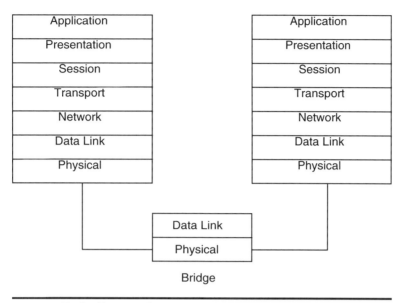

Figure 4.4   Bridge Functionality

choice than a router. Bridges are also relatively cheaper and easier to install. Other advantages of bridges are

- Many bridges can connect networks of different speeds.
- They are easily managed.
- Many can be adapted to an environment as it grows.

   Bridges also have some disadvantages. Common ones are

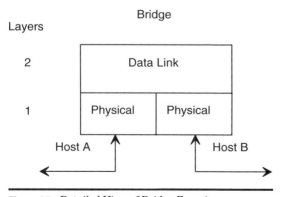

Figure 4.5   Detailed View of Bridge Functions

- Bridges can be installed in such a way that physically, in reality, the net result is one logical network; consequently, sometimes troubleshooting can be difficult when problems arise.

- In some implementations, such as a cascaded topology, a problem can occur with fast protocols because of delay factors.

- Bridges are transparent to end systems. For this reason, and because of the potential delays encountered relative to the number of bridges, the actual limit could be indirectly imposed on the number of bridges utilized.

- Bridges could potentially impede the use of some applications over the Internet. An example of this scenario could be multiple copies of the same application operating with, unfortunately, the same naming or addressing scheme.

Practically speaking, bridges are good network devices when used for the right need.

Bridge functions

Bridges can be described in various ways. Three ways are the focus of this section: forwarding, filtering, and learning. *Forwarding* is passing a frame toward its ultimate destination. *Filtering* operates by discarding frames where their destination is not. *Learning* is a function that a bridge performs when it does not receive a positive response in return for comparing a frame to its host's table. These functions are explained in the following paragraphs.

Forwarding.   Forwarding is best explained by examining Figure 4.6, which shows two LANs: A and B. LAN A has SPEEDY, LITTLEMAN, THE-KID, MONY, and HOLLYWOOD connected. They are known on the LAN as A1, A2, A3, and so forth. A bridge connects both LANs. LAN B has multiple systems connected to it, two of which are B4 and B5. Note that the highlighted table to the right of the bridge used to "know" which hosts are located on which LAN. In the bridge's table host 5 is shown to be on LAN B. The bridge intercepts the frame because it knows that its target is on LAN B. The packet is still broadcast on LAN A as well, but it is "spent" timewise in a matter of fractions of a second; therefore it does not stay on LAN A.

Filtering.   Figure 4.7 consists of two LANs and a bridge connecting them. Figure 4.7 portrays an example of the filtering function of a bridge. Note the frame leaving host 1 destined for host 3—on LAN A. The frame is captured by the bridge and compared against the bridge's table. After the bridge performs its compare function, it discards the frame. Host 3 receives the frame destined for it.

Learning.   Bridges are said to "learn" about a host (e.g., a computer or other device) when a frame is received by a bridge and the bridge does not have the

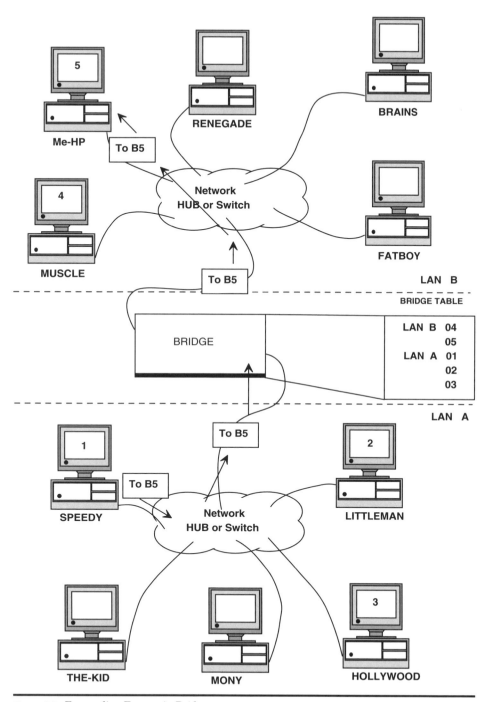

Figure 4.6 Forwarding Frames in Bridges

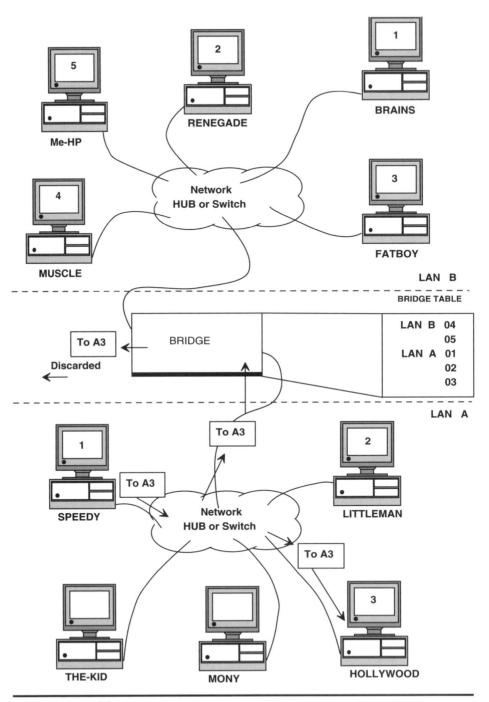

Figure 4.7 Frame Filtering

address of that device in its table. If not, the bridge dynamically updates its table and then "knows" about this device; therefore, the bridge is considered to have learned of a device. Consider Figure 4.8, which shows two LANs and a bridge connecting them together. Assume that host 3 has recently been added to the LAN. Now assume that host 3 wants to communicate with host 5 on the other LAN. The bridge knew the location of host 5 and also knew the location of host 3 because it learned its address, both host and network address. Now, any of the hosts on LAN 2 can communicate with any hosts on LAN 1.

Examination of bridges by protocol

Bridges can also be characterized by protocol. This makes sense because they work with lower-layer protocols. The simplest approach to understanding how bridges work with different protocols is to focus on how a bridge operates with these protocols.

Like protocols. Different vendors support various protocols with their bridges. Some of the most popular ones include Ethernet and Token Ring.

Ethernet. Ethernet is a popular lower-layer protocol and is widely used throughout the marketplace. It is common for LANs to be created in departments; then, over time, realization of multiple disparate LANs becomes apparent. Multiple LANs can be connected together by bridges, thereby creating one logical network while still permitting independence of departments. Consider Figure 4.9, which shows three departments performing distinctly different functions. However, these departments need to share files for purposes of creating documents, informing potential customers of products soon to be released, and general communication.

Token Ring. Token Ring is another popular lower-layer protocol. Like Ethernet, multiple upper-layer protocols can operate above it. Figure 4.10 demonstrates how multiple Token Rings can be connected, thus creating a single logical network.

Note in Figure 4.10 that both 4 and 16 MB/s Token Ring speeds are used. Many popular bridge vendors offer solutions that fit such a scenario.

Figure 4.10 shows three floors of a corporation. Each floor houses a different department. The first floor is the collection department; the second, the billing department; and the third, the central data center for this corporation. Each floor has considerable flexibility. Token Ring is considered a "self-healing" technology, and therefore hosts can be inserted and removed from the network at will. Likewise, any given floor can be removed from the 16-MB/s corporate backbones. This scenario provides independence and flexibility and is characteristically very dynamic.

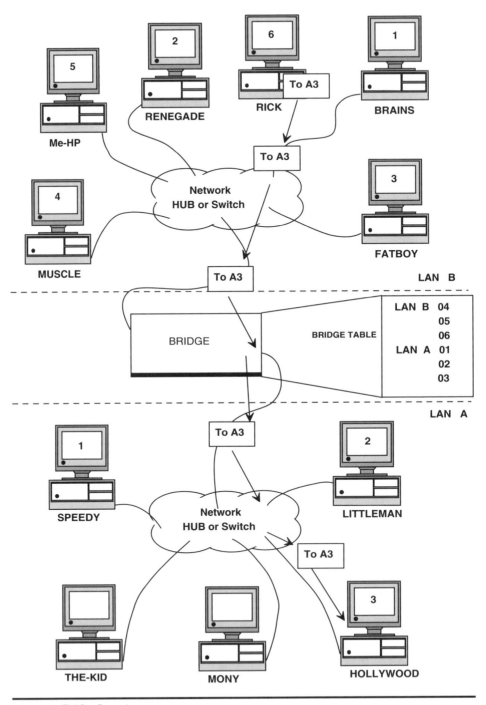

Figure 4.8 Bridge Learning

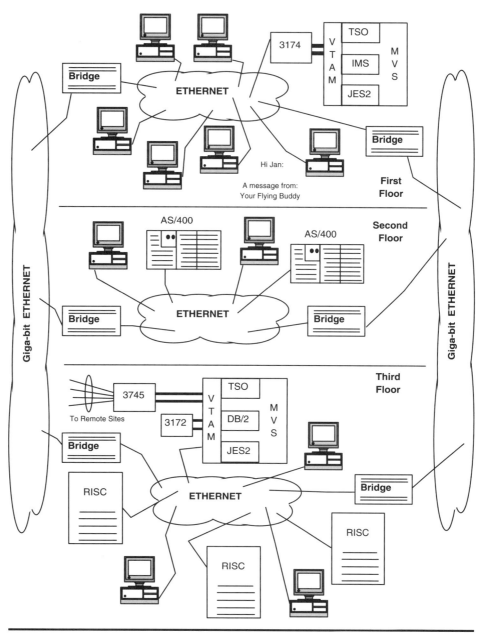

Figure 4.9   Ethernet Bridge

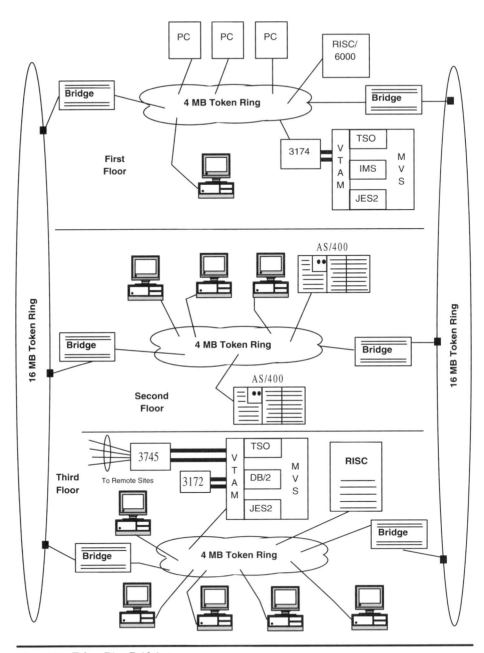

Figure 4.10 Token Ring Bridging

Unlike protocols. Bridges can also perform lower-layer protocol conversion. Many reputable vendors have such devices. In fact, these devices have become a commodity in a comparatively short amount of time.

Ethernet-to-Token Ring. An Ethernet–Token Ring bridge operates bidirectionally. Users on an Ethernet network can communicate with users on a Token Ring network and vice versa. Figure 4.11 illustrates an example of such an environment. Figure 4.11 shows three Ethernet-based LANs, a 16-MB Token Ring backbone, a 4-MB Token Ring LAN with multiple hosts, and two large SNA environments connected to another 16-MB Token Ring. This configuration makes for interoperability among all hosts possible. However, some additional components such as software and possible configuration changes may be required.

Some bridges support protocols beyond those shown in Figure 4.11. However, most bridge vendors support these protocols. These sample implementations are examples of real installations.

Analysis of bridge location

Another way bridges can be examined is with respect to their support for local and remote operations. Some examples of various bridge implementations are presented here.

Local bridging. Bridges are good devices to use in this type of environment as a general rule. They permit segmentation but also connectivity of LANs at the same time. Consider Figure 4.12, which shows engineering, marketing, and documentation departments. They each have a LAN and each are connected via a bridge; one between engineering and marketing and the other between marketing and documentation. A twofold benefit is realized.

First, all three departments can communicate with any hosts in any of the other departments; thus enterprisewide connectivity is achieved. Second, isolation of departmental computing can be maintained on each network LAN because of the way bridges operate (this aspect of bridges is explained shortly). Third, a degree of load balancing can be realized as a result of this scenario.

Remote bridging. *Remote bridging* bridges geographically remote networks. Consider Figure 4.13, which shows the site of a remote bridge implementation. Both LANs need to communicate. Now, with the advent of remote Ethernet bridging, these LANs can communicate. The connectivity between the two sites could be a switched or a leased line with speeds of generally 56 kbps or higher. However, if a switched line is used, this implies bandwidth on demand, and consequently there are some requirements for bridging this type of environment. The result is that users on both networks view all hosts as located on one LAN.

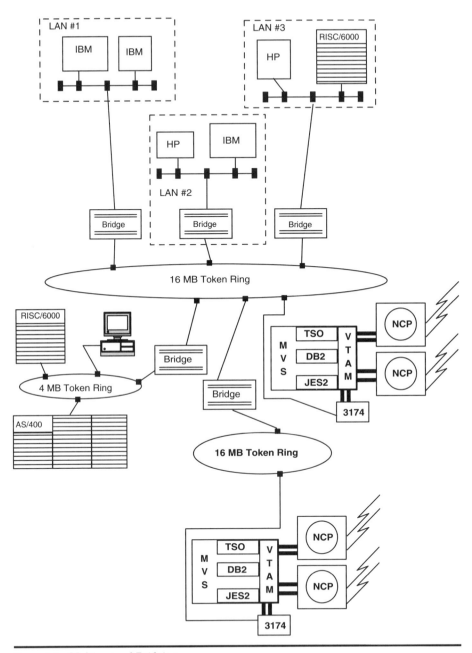

Figure 4.11 Multiprotocol Bridging

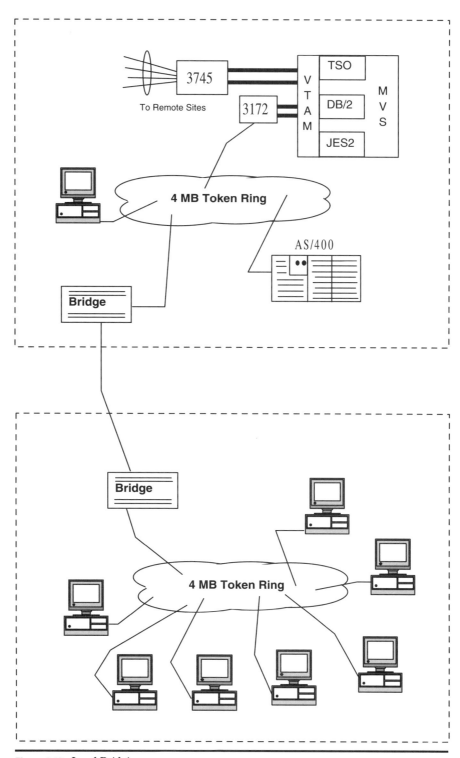

Figure 4.12 Local Bridging

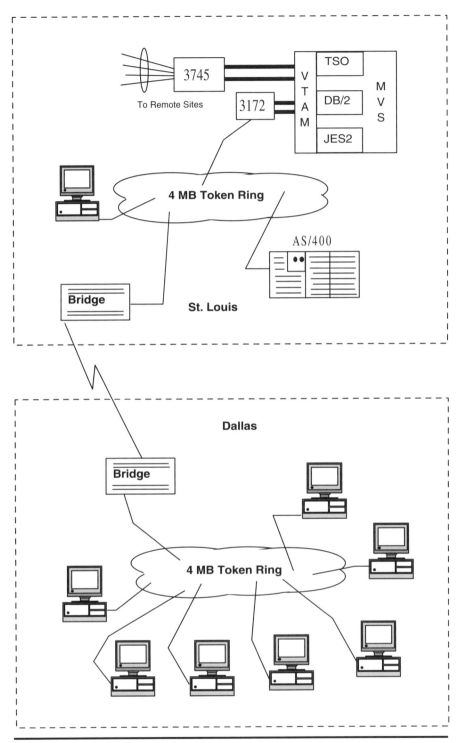

Figure 4.13 Remote Bridging

Both local and remote bridging can be performed with Token Ring networks. Bridges supporting the respective protocols are required. Depending on the vendor offering, other network protocols may be supported as well.

Some vendors offer redundant line support for remote bridges. Others offer data compression on the fly; depending on the vendor, some algorithms can achieve approximately a 4:1 ratio. This is effective utilization of bandwidth. Some vendors also offer network management support for their devices. These and other aspects of a bridge should be discussed with a vendor whose forte is bridges.

Author's comment. Remote bridging is similar to other aspects of internetworking technology. One question always remains: "Where is the bottleneck?" I am not implying that remote Ethernet, Token Ring, or other protocol bridging will result in a bottleneck; however, I do intend to raise this question because in data communications a bottleneck always exists. The question is where and to what degree. It may or may not have anything to do with bridging, routing, or gateways; but it nevertheless is present.

Source routing and transparent bridges

Attention is required to the way bridges obtain routing information. "Routing" is somewhat of a misnomer in this context. Bridges do not route in the sense that a router does, but they do have to pass frames from a source toward their destination point, wherever that may be. Source routing needs explanation.

Source routing. In *source routing* (an IBM function), the route to the destination is determined before data leave the originating point. Sometimes this function is called *source route bridging* (SRB). This type of routing is dominant among IBM Token Ring networks.

Frame contents. Understanding source routing is easily achieved by understanding the contents of the IBM Token Ring frame contents. Figure 4.14 shows the structure and contents of the media access control (MAC) frame. Figure 4.14 shows the IBM Token Ring frame, the highlights of the routing control field, and the highlights at bit level of the routing control field.

This frame itself differs from the IEEE 802.5 frame in that the Token Ring frame has a routing information field. Here we explore that field and its contents.

Segment numbers. The first component in the routing information field is the routing control subfield. It contains information that is used in the routing function and is explained in greater detail later. Segment number subfields follow the routing control subfield.

Each segment number reflects two pieces of information. Segment numbers consist of a ring number and a bridge number. Each ring is a LAN, and each

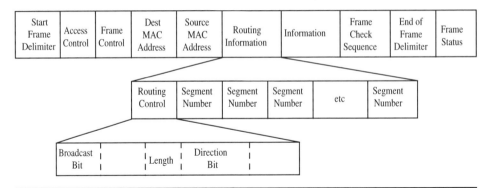

Figure 4.14 IBM Token Ring Frame

LAN has a number associated with each ring. Each bridge used is assigned a number. The combination of the ring and bridge number creates a segment number. If multiple rings are connected via bridges, then multiple segment subfields exist, as shown in Figure 4.14.

Routing control subfield. The routing control subfield has two significant pieces of information: the broadcast bit and the direction bit. The *broadcast bit* indicates what type frame it is—that is, a broadcast or nonbroadcast frame. The *direction bit* indicates which way the frame is going. It is either en route from the original source to the destination or vice versa. This is important because the setting of this bit dictates how the segment number bits are interpreted.

Transparent bridges. The working definition of transparent bridges is that they learn which hosts are reachable across the data link by observing the frames as they pass. This type of bridge is also known as a "spanning tree" bridge.

This type bridge forwards frames as discussed previously in this chapter. It also maintains and updates a table of MAC addresses of the hosts which are reachable across the link used to attach multiple rings. This type of bridge is also sometimes known as a "learning" bridge.

A transparent bridge implementation was used in an earlier figure, but for the reader's convenience it is also used in Figure 4.15.

Source routing theory of operation. We will now see how IBM source routing operates. Two types of frames can exist in an IBM Token Ring network: non-broadcast and broadcast frames.

Nonbroadcast frame. The term *nonbroadcast* is virtually the same as *multi-cast*. If there is a difference, it is minimal. What is important is how non-broadcast frames are handled in a multiring environment. Consider Figure 4.16.

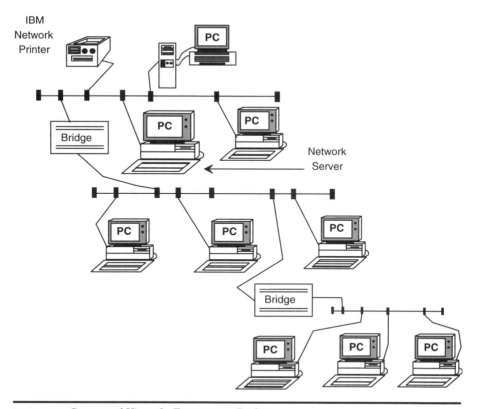

Figure 4.15   Conceptual View of a Transparent Bridge

A nonbroadcast frame reveals the significance of the segment numbers discussed previously. Assume that host A on ring 1 is the source host and the destination host is host G on ring 2. Note that bridge X connects rings 1 and 2 directly. In this case bridge X recognizes its bridge number and ring number. The bridge simply copies the frame from ring 1 onto ring 2. At the same time, bridge Z receives the same frame. It examines its bridge number and its ring number; no match is made, so the frame is discarded.

Broadcast frames.   Source routing is implemented by two types of MAC addresses via broadcast frames, according to IBM. One type of MAC frame contains a certain value that is received by all hosts on the ring on which that host exists. This frame is a frame containing a special hexadecimal value. Figure 4.17 illustrates this concept. Figure 4.17 illustrates the frame by the H6 box shown as received by all hosts on the ring from which it originated. The H6 box indicates that that is its destination. However, note that two rings are connected by a bridge and that the H6 frame is not repeated onto ring 2.

The other type of MAC frame contains an address that is considered a broadcast address. It has a Hex value different from that in the example

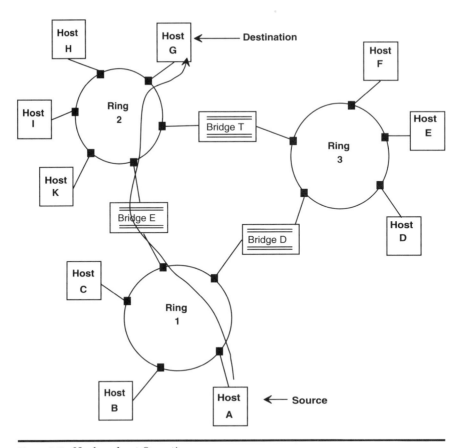

Figure 4.16 Nonbroadcast Operation

shown in Figure 4.17. The broadcast frame is sent to all hosts, all rings, and hence all bridges connecting them. Figure 4.18 shows this environment.

Referring to Figure 4.18, assume that host 8 on ring B sends a broadcast frame. It is received by all hosts, each ring, and consequently each bridge. Operationally it works as follows. Host 8 sends the frame. Bridge D copies the frame, then adds its bridge number and the number associated with ring C. At the same time the frame reaches bridge T. Bridge T copies the frame, and adds its bridge number along with the number for ring A. The frame then passes to bridge E; bridge E copies it, then adds its bridge number and ring C's number. The process is complete, but a question remains: "Why do this?"

When many hosts exist, isolation of networks must be achieved but total connectivity between LANs is required; Figure 4.17 demonstrates how to do this. It provides multiple paths to any given ring; the more rings, the more reason to have redundancies in paths.

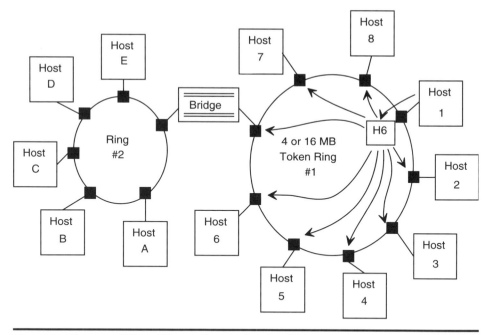

Figure 4.17   Conceptual View of Frame Contained on One Ring

Discovering routes.   The process of discovering routes is twofold. First, assume that a source wants to communicate with a destination host. The source host will initially attempt to send a frame on the ring (the source host) on which it is located. If no positive response is encountered, then another process is used.

A source host sends a route discovery frame to a destination host whose address the source host knows; the question is how to get there. Assume that multiple rings are attached to the ring where the source host is located. Each bridge attaching these rings copies the frame from the source, inserts its segment information, then passes the frame on. Once the frames have reached all connected rings and bridges, they begin returning to the source host. If the destination host is located, it inserts routing information into the original route discovery frame and sends it back to the source. Multiple frames may return to the source. When this happens, the source determines the route for additional frames to be sent to the destination host.

Concluding thoughts on bridges

Bridges operate at the lower two layers relative to the OSI model. They can serve a variety of functions. For example, bridges can be used to merge multiple LANs into one virtual network. Another strength of bridges is that they can perform protocol conversion on LANs at the lower two layers. Bridges can

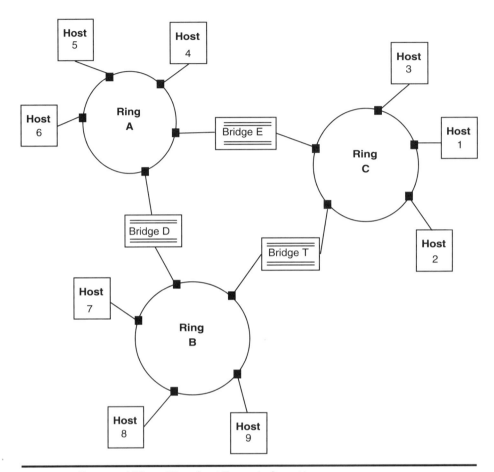

Figure 4.18 Conceptual View of Broadcast Frame in Operation

convert Ethernet to Token Ring and vice versa. Some vendors offer bridges that support FDDI bridging.

Transparent bridges perform three basic functions: forwarding, filtering, and learning. This simply means that when a transparent bridge receives frames, it forwards them, filters those which are not destined for another ring to which it (the bridge) is attached, and then learns of hosts throughout the network(s) within which it operates and stores this information in tables that are, in turn, used for routing purposes.

Source routing is a function of another type of bridge. IBM uses source routing, and the MAC frame contains a field for insertion of routing information. This type of bridge operates by including the destination address into the frame along with the source address. Source routing bridges also perform different types of frame broadcasting.

Bridges can be used to effectively manage sites where multiple Token Ring networks exist and the need for redundancy also exists. Because Token Ring technology is considered self-healing, it is easy to remove and add hosts and devices to these networks.

Bridges also offer advantages to Ethernet-based LANs, particularly where multiple Ethernet LANs are geographically dispersed. Remote bridges can create a virtual LAN environment where users "think" they are all attached to the same network in the same physical location.

Implementing bridges remotely should be evaluated and modified according to the load in respective sites, the bandwidth available through the link, and other operational considerations.

Many well-known vendors offer good products to achieve a desired result.

4.5   Router Technology

Routers operate at layer 3 relative to the OSI model. Routers route upper-layer protocols. They do not perform protocol conversion, assuming that they are a router in the conventional sense. Routers, like bridges, can be examined from different angles. This section explores those angles.

Router technology functions

An explanation is in order concerning the term *router*. This is especially true for those who may be new to networking devices. Sometimes different groups and individuals use terms in loose ways, and confusion can result.

The routing function can be defined as getting data from point *A* to point *B,* wherever that may be. This concept can be traced back to the 1970s, when networking technology began to sprout. Those working in the Internet community were involved with networks that were sometimes located in different cities. At any rate, multiple networks existed, and the desire arose to connect to networks and connect networks together.

As an outgrowth of this desire, devices were developed to perform this function. At the time they were generally referred to as *gateways.* Yes, gateway. An obvious question is why? The *American Heritage Dictionary,* defines *gateway* as "**1.** An opening, as in a wall or fence, that may be closed by a gate. **2.** A means of access." I believe the informal consensus at the time probably favored definition 2.

Taking a number of points into consideration, it is understandable why devices that performed a routing function were called *gateways.* Unfortunately, the confusion surrounding this term still exists today. Taking the definition of gateway as a means of access to explain the function of a device that permitted connectivity of networks *was* reasonable. These devices did, in fact, provide such a function. And, beyond this, these devices routed information to various networks and locations. With this in mind, coupled with the mindset of the day during the 1970s, it is plausible that the term *gateway* was used. But, technology changes.

Today an entire industry exists around network devices. In fact, a part of this book is devoted to explaining some of these devices. I do not believe that in the 1970s most technically oriented individuals could envision the explosive technological growth of the 1980s with such specialized devices. It may have been conceivable, but not to a detailed level that hindsight provides today. Hence, the dilemma continues.

The terms *routers* and *gateways* are constantly used in various media, and at best the meanings are skewed. For the record, routers route; period. They may perform other peripheral functions, but the focus of routers is simply to route data.

Gateways, on the other hand, perform protocol conversion between heterogeneous networks at layer 3 and above at a minimum and can perform protocol conversion at all seven layers between two networks. Gateways perform protocol conversion; routers do not. Interestingly, some gateways can perform routing functions because of their architectural nature, but they do not necessarily have to. In fact, this is a vendor-specific offering.

The point of this section is to emphasize that discussing internetworking with different people can result in confusion if clarification of terms is not agreed on. Many who have worked for years with TCP/IP-, UNIX-, and Internet-related issues still use the term *gateway* to convey the function of a router. I have often wondered what term they use to refer to the device used to integrate heterogeneous networks. It would seem that a catch 22 situation exists.

Another comment about routers and terminology is appropriate here. There are different types of routers, which are discussed in this chapter, and not all routers perform the same functions; many functions are vendor-specific. There are a number of prominent router vendors on the market today that sell effective equipment. The point is to understand your needs and obtain the appropriate fit to meet those needs.

How routers work

There are multiple types of routers which perform different functions. Some of the terms used for router functions tend to overlap in some instances with other identified functions. Routers can be explained in terms of the geographic distance they support—local or remote. They can also be explained by the upper-layer protocols supported and their interface support.

Router operation is based on tables of possible networks and routes. These tables are utilized to indicate the path to a given network. Router tables do not locate device addresses such as some type bridges are capable of performing. Functionally, routers exploit the information available to them to determine the most expedient route. Another unique aspect about routers is that they receive data addressed to them by hosts or other routers. Route determination is somewhat contingent on the upper-layer protocol. For example, TCP/IP uses routing algorithms that differ from those of SNA-based networks. In this respect routers are protocol-dependent. Some routers are simple and function with one protocol; however, other types of routers can manipulate multiple protocols, and hence the term *multiprotocol routers*.

The remainder of this chapter explores various aspects about routers and specifics of how they operate in certain environments. Similar to bridges, routers have become a basic commodity in internetworking technology.

Dependency of routers

Routers are protocol-dependent. They operate at network layer 3 relative to the OSI model. Consider Figure 4.19, which illustrates an example of two hosts identified by OSI layers with a router operating between them.

As the figure shows, the physical and data-link layers are also part of the router; therefore, these aspects must be taken into consideration.

Some large routers (in terms of what they support) offer a wider variety of physical layer interface support. More than a few reputable router vendors offer fine products that support such interfaces as the following:

RS-232

V.35

AUI

X.21

HISSI

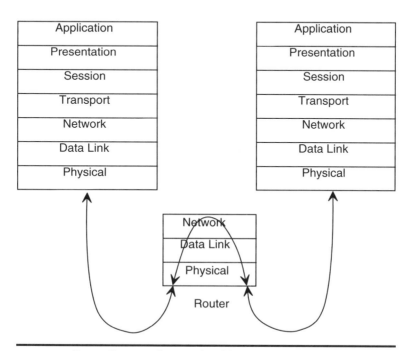

Figure 4.19 Router Operator Compared to OSI Layers

RS-449

Serial

Additionally, lower-layer protocols must be supported as well. These also vary according to the vendor and the router. Some examples of popular protocols supported are

Ethernet

Token Ring

SDLC

HDLC

FDDI

X.25

Routing occurs at the network layer. If you have read other chapters in this book, you are aware that upper-layer network protocols operate differently. For example, the way TCP/IP performs routing is different from the way SNA or APPN performs routing. Consequently, these upper-layer protocols drive the router decision to a certain degree. This is so because multiprotocol routers exist and support routing of multiple upper-layer protocols.

When routing is implemented, it brings together two or more networks. The consequence of this from the user's standpoint is that it is transparent except for possible time-zone inconveniences, but those issues are easily overcome. In essence, the use of routers provides an end-to-end solution. The remainder of the chapter focuses on some examples of different upper-layer protocol routing as well as aspects of routing in general.

How routers are implemented

Routers can be implemented locally or used in an environment where multiple networks exist in different geographic locations and need to exchange data.

Local implementation. Figure 4.20 depicts a scenario in which routers are used within the same physical facility. Figure 4.20 shows a single physical site with three distinct Ethernet LANs. Note that a router is the common denominator of them. The result of this configuration is that any of the LANs can communicate directly with any hosts shown via the Internet protocol. All LAN hosts have TCP/IP as their upper-layer protocol. By removing the router, connectivity between all three LANs would not be achieved, or other means would have to be implemented to achieve the same results.

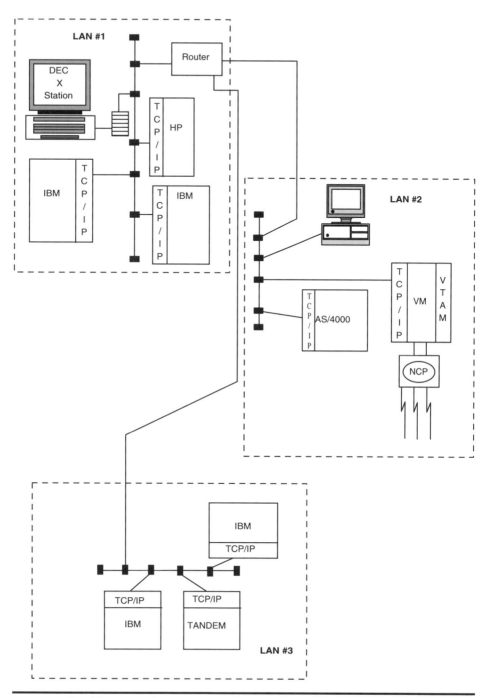

Figure 4.20   Local Router Implementation

This particular implementation is straightforward, flexible, and relatively inexpensive. Additionally, the router fits into the management method that is common among TCP/IP networks. This example can take on many variations because of the flexibility with routers. In a sense, they can be customized to meet site-specific needs fairly easily. The primary reason for this is because routers maintain routing tables within them that can be customized to accommodate diverse situations.

Metropolitan implementation.   The notion of a metropolitan implementation may not be popular, but it is frequently a solution that meets many needs. Consider Figure 4.21, which shows headquarters in Dallas, where master files, statements, accounts receivables, and other operational functions are performed. However, because the agency prospered, it has four satellite offices (A, B, C, and D). All four satellite offices are located within 35 mi from the headquarters in Dallas.

Because data must be sent to and from the satellite office and headquarters, this router solution satisfies the needs here. In fact, the router in the Dallas office can route data from satellite office A to satellite office B, if configured appropriately.

Similar to the example of a local implementation of a router, this metropolitan router implementation is popular because the links between all sites are not considered long distance and therefore significant saving is the result.

Remote continental U.S. routing.   Remote routing is a popular solution for many corporations that are geographically dispersed and in different time zones. Figure 4.22 demonstrates this idea. Figure 4.22 shows facilities in Chicago, Memphis, Dallas, and San Francisco. These sites differ in function and, to some degree, type of equipment. But through the use of routers, the site in San Francisco can send data to Memphis or any of the sites connected in this virtual network via the router solution.

International routing.   International routing is similar in theory to routing multiple sites in the United States. However, time considerations warrant attention, and the type of work to be done between all connected sites must be determined. It is also important to know the peak traffic times in all locations and correlate them; this will help in performance tuning. Consider Figure 4.23.

The significance of the international scenario versus the local, metropolitan, or even in the continental United States is the issue of time-zone differences. Merely coordinating a time for staff to represent each site is difficult because of the time difference.

Another reason for routing is business-related. If a company performs significant amounts of processing, the best place to do this is where it is most cost-effective while achieving the original goals. With distributed processing and exploitation of network devices such as routers, this can be accomplished.

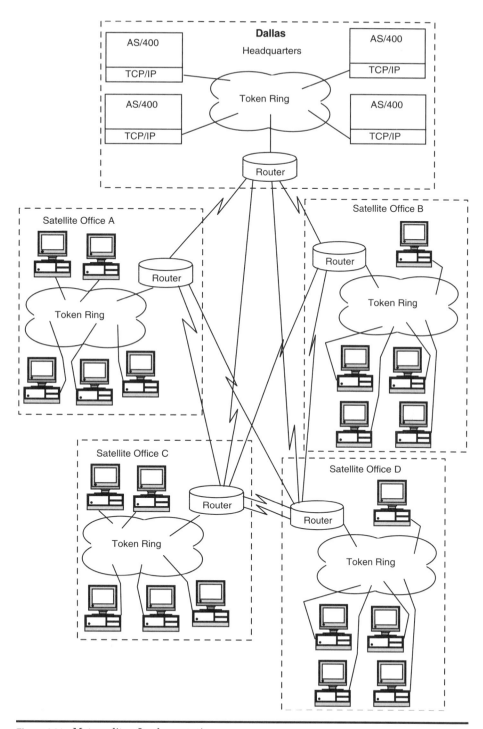

Figure 4.21 Metropolitan Implementation

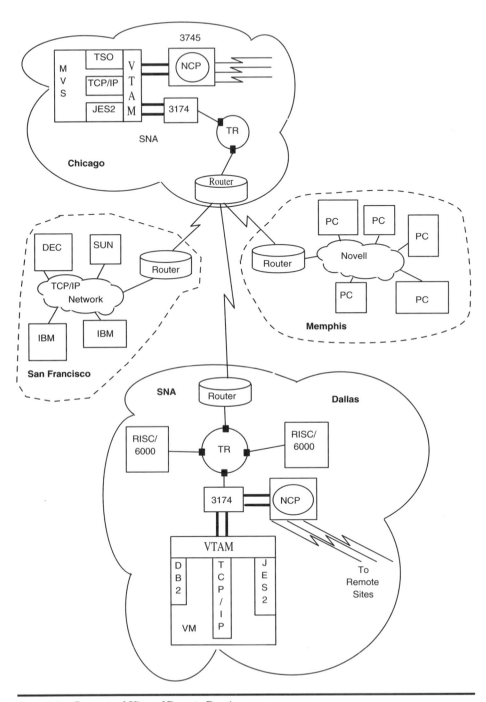

Figure 4.22 Conceptual View of Remote Routing

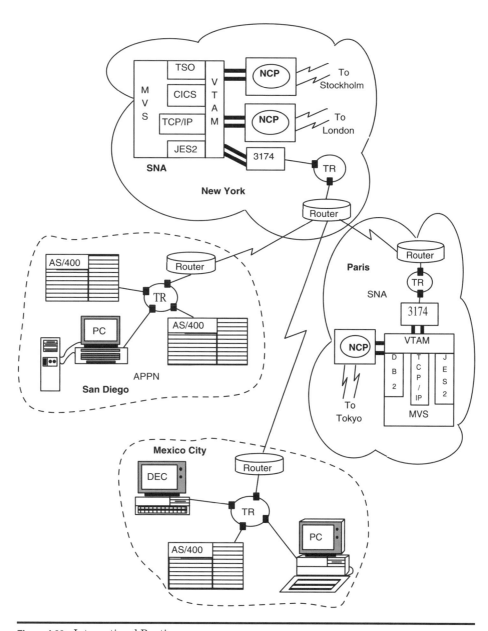

Figure 4.23 International Routing

Routing types

Multiple methods are used in routing. Technically, routing schemes can be categorically defined. Different vendor network protocols tend to route differently, but some common threads among the different protocols remain.

Central routing.   In centrally based routing, a central repository of routing information is maintained. Conceptually, this appears as illustrated in Figure 4.24, where multiple locations are shown connected in a myriad of combinations. Moving data from one location to another can be accomplished via multiple routes. However, the centralized routing node in Dallas maintains the routing tables.

Here each router informs the centralized node of the potential routing of a local environment. This information is arranged into tables and distributed to each router participating within the network, and the central routing node determines the route capabilities.

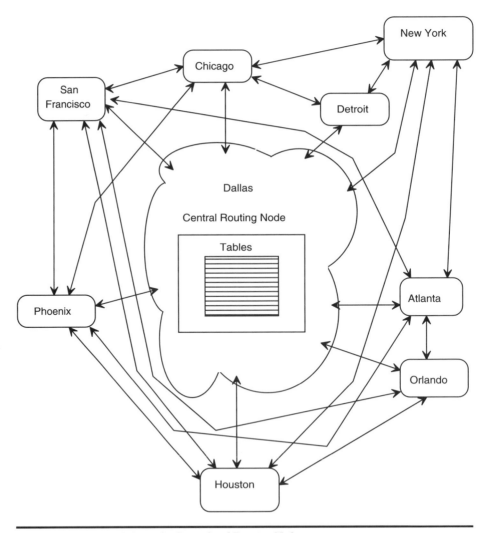

Figure 4.24 Conceptual View of a Centralized Routing Node

Noncentralized routing.   In *noncentralized routing,* the routing algorithm is not located in a central routing node. Figure 4.25 is a conceptual view of this. Figure 4.25 is interesting, to say the least! However, it does convey the notion of noncentralized routing. In this environment each router informs its *neighbor* of valid routes. The significant point of the figure is that each router determines the route as the packet arrives. Also, this type of implementation is constantly changing as changes are made to individual routes. Each time a change is made, updates occur.

Static routing.   This type of routing is where tables and routes are made via network management functions. By definition, this means that static routing must be performed when the network is nonoperational from a user perspective. The simplest way to explain this is that no changes are performed while the network is operational. This means that the routes are therefore *fixed.* Consider Figure 4.26.

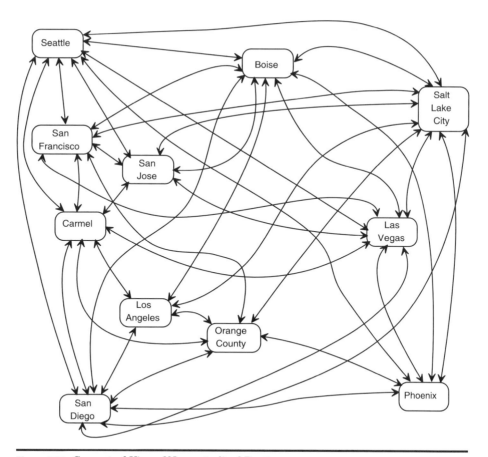

Figure 4.25 Conceptual View of Noncentralized Routing

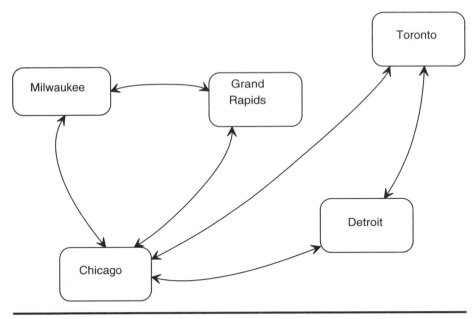

Figure 4.26 Conceptual View of Static Routing

Interpretation of the notion of static routing is easy when considering Figure 4.26. As the lines drawn between the cities indicate, a routing path is available. Note paths that are *not* available. It is not possible to route directly to Toronto from Grand Rapids without going through Chicago, and this implies that a routing table for this configuration is predetermined. Also, routing from Detroit to Grand Rapids is not possible without going through Chicago.

This example can be changed once the network is offline, but while the network is operational, no changes can be made. Hence, it derives its name, static routing.

These are examples of routing technology. Other methods of routing are possible; some of these are protocol-dependent. In order to provide an example, two different protocols are shown in light of their routing schemes.

SNA routing. To a considerable degree, routing in SNA is performed on the front end (the communications controller). The Network Control Program (NCP) inside has the routes defined and utilizes this software to exploit the hardware and gear involved in the routing process. Consider Figure 4.27, which illustrates an example of predefined routes. In each city—Boise, ID; Orange County, CA; Chicago, IL; and Houston, TX—the hosts are configured to route data through the indicated connections. For example, note there is no direct connection between Chicago and Orange County. Does this mean that they cannot pass data? Not necessarily; because Boise and Houston are con-

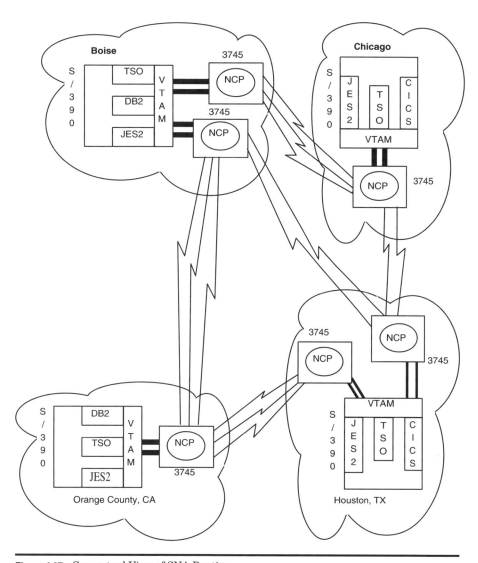

Figure 4.27 Conceptual View of SNA Routing

nected to both Chicago and Orange County, they could be configured to route data between those locations to destinations as well as to the ones to which they are physically attached.

In this example, line speed, data compression, type of line (dedicated or switched), and other data-communication issues are relatively unimportant because the point in this example is that even though a physical connection may or may not exist directly between two entities, routing may still be achieved. This is a matter of software, and obviously some physical route must exist, but beyond this it is a matter of configuration.

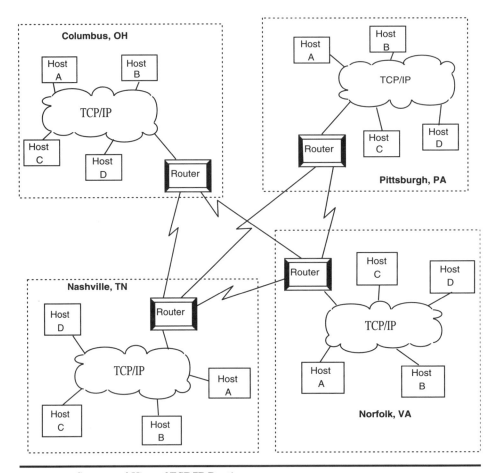

Figure 4.28 Conceptual View of TCP/IP Routing

TCP/IP routing. Routing in TCP/IP is performed by IP; routing itself is a complex task. Figure 4.28 shows an example of TCP/IP networks and routers connecting them. Figure 4.28 shows TCP/IP networks in Columbus, OH, Pittsburgh, PA, Norfolk, VA, and Nashville, TN. These locations are connected via routers. Note that all routers are physically linked and also that each LAN's hosts have the same names and could be given the same addresses. What differentiates them is the fact that they are located on different networks; therefore there are no naming or addressing conflicts.

In this example, it is the Internet Protocol (IP) software in conjunction with one of the routing protocols that makes routing possible. The routing protocols could be either the Router Information Protocol (RIP), the Open Shortest Path First (OSPF), or other protocols. Obviously, a routing device is required; nevertheless, it is the combination of IP and the routing protocol that makes this process happen.

Maintaining routing tables is a separate issue here. This could be done via the `/etc/networks` and `/etc/hosts` files or the Domain Name System (DNS). Most likely it will be the latter because of the power behind its operation.

These examples of how different network protocols perform routing suffice to show that in a heterogeneous networking environment, routing is not a simple matter. Consider the routing issues involved in the Internet!

Demand routing. This topic has moved into the forefront of routing in the past few years (at the time of writing). The idea of bandwidth-on-demand routing is as its name implies; in plain English, the router uses the line when it needs it and does not keep it *dedicated*. Consider the following examples showing the three phases of this routing.

Figure 4.29 shows two networks; one in Monterey, CA and the other in Birmingham, AL. Figure 4.29 shows two multiple-vendor networks with multiple hosts attached to each. It also indicates that no link is established between the two locations. This is important because it means that *no* dedicated line exists and that some degree of money is involved—typically savings.

Figure 4.30, on the other hand, shows a different scenario. Figure 4.30 shows the same environment as in Figure 4.29, but this time a link is established between the routers. Also, it indicates that host A in Monterey is communicating with host C in Birmingham. Figure 4.31 shows how the environment appears once communication is complete.

This example of a bandwidth-on-demand router may well fit the needs of many situations. More than one or two vendors have such devices available today. One consideration for this device is to weigh the consequences of purchasing such a device versus having a router with a dedicated line. Determining the amount of usage should dictate which would be the better solution; and my philosophy is that the *customer* should make the decision.

Router benefits

Routers provide a variety of capabilities that are advantageous to networking of different types. With the influx of growth of LANs since the late 1980s, routers are sometimes the best solution to meet needs of a given situation.

Segment isolation. A major advantage routers provide is the ability to split a large network into smaller, more easily manageable ones. This is important because the number of LANs as well as the specialized devices attached to them is increasing. Figure 4.32 illustrates how routers can be used to create a more manageable LAN environment.

Figure 4.32 portrays a single-backbone LAN. It is apparent that it is crowded and is difficult to manage. Many different types of traffic are passed across a single backbone. This puts a load on the network and consequently causes performance degradation.

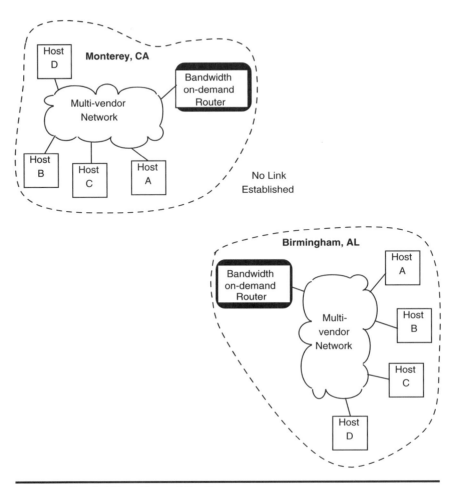

Figure 4.29 Bandwidth-on-Demand Routing

Figure 4.33 depicts the same equipment implemented differently. In Figure 4.33 multiple LAN segments have been created, and a real sense of load balancing is the result. Note the three routers that tie the segments together. They are able to control the passage of packets to the correct segment or keep packets on a given segment and thus avoid impeding performance. Another advantage is the ability that this configuration provides. With this arrangement a given segment can be removed from other segments if changes need to be made or other management-related functions that would affect other LAN segments are required.

Multiprotocol support. Many vendors who sell routers have routers that support multiple lower-layer protocols quite effectively. Since the IEEE 802.X protocols call for delineation of the data-link layer, it is possible to mix and match a variety of lower-layer protocols. Consider Figure 4.34, which demon-

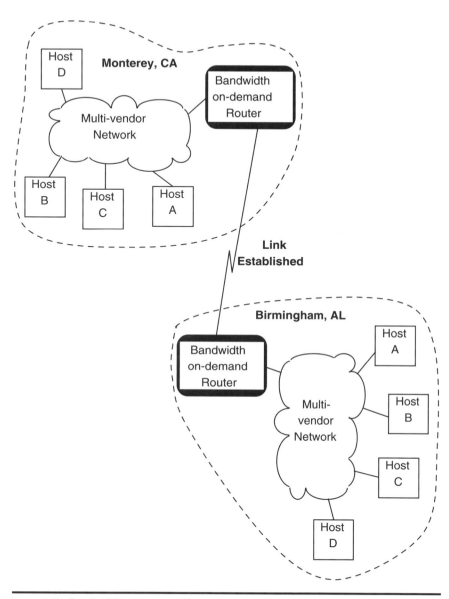

Figure 4.30 Bandwidth-on-Demand Routing

strates different networks with unlike lower-layer protocols and interface connections. However, because of the versatility of routers, they came to be merged into the router as shown in this sketch.

Scalable architecture.   Another feature offered by some router vendors is a scalable architecture. For example, some routers can provide basic needs for one protocol and also be potentially upgradable to support other types of

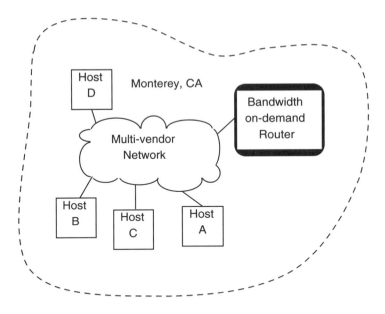

No Link
Established

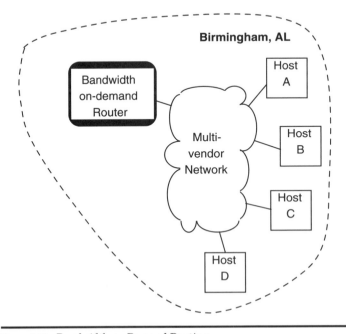

Figure 4.31   Bandwidth-on-Demand Routing

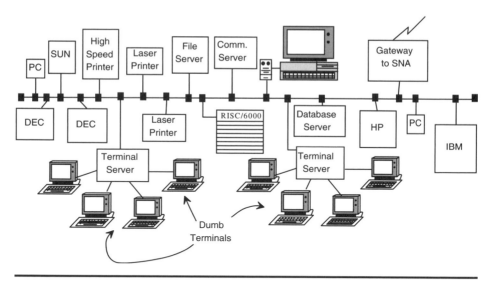

Figure 4.32   Single-Backbone LAN

lower-layer protocols. Network topologies are a factor in routers. Some router vendors offer routers that have the flexibility to change and expand to interoperate with topologies that change over time.

Other advantages of routers include price and performance, flexibility to support local and/or remote sites simultaneously, and be amenable to network management technologies such as the Simple Network Management Protocol (SNMP). Routers also provide what is considered an intelligent link between networks. They can also protect against network failure by their ability to isolate networks. These and other features offered by router vendors make routers an attractive solution for internetworking requirements.

Multiprotocol routers

Recently much attention has been given to multiprotocol routers. Many vendors have brought such devices to market. A multiprotocol router supports multiple upper- and lower-layer protocols. By definition, this is a complex task for only one device. Also, regardless of which vendor supplies a multiprotocol router, it must be a *robust* device to function when multiple protocols are being routed at the same time. These are technical facts, not opinions. Think of it. One device that can route IP, IPX (Internetwork Packet Exchange), SNA, DECnet, and AppleTalk must be a powerful and well-architected machine.

Some of the following protocols are supported by various multiprotocol routers. After reading the list, it is reasonable to conclude that multiprotocol routers must be robust.

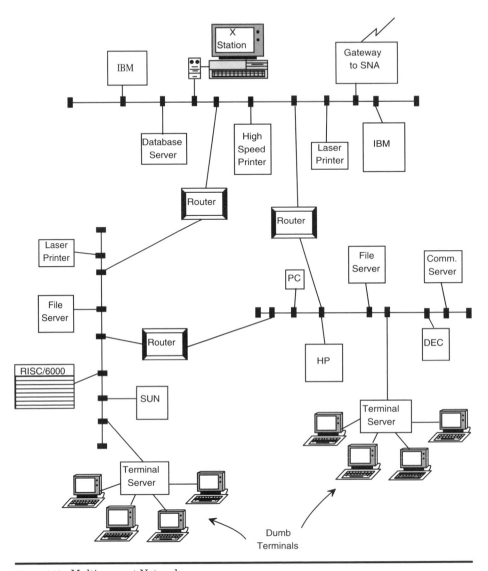

Figure 4.33 Multisegment Network

Physical-layer protocols

RS-232

RS-422

RS-449

V.24

V.35

V.36

X.21

Physical layers specified by IEEE 802.X:

Data-link protocols

SDLC by IBM

Ethernet v.2 by DIX

X.25 by CCITT

PPP as in RFCs 1171 and 1172

MAC and LLC (Logical Link Control) IEEE protocols

Frame Relay by CCITT and ANSI

Upper-layer protocols

SNA

TCP/IP

AppleTalk

NetWare

OSI

DECnet

XNS

NetBIOS (Basic Input/Output Operating System)

Routing-layer-protocol-specific

Internet Protocol (IP)—TCP/IP

Internetwork Datagram Protocol (IDP)—XNS

Datagram Delivery Protocol (DDP)—AppleTalk

Connectionless Network Protocol (CNLP)—OSI

SNA

DECnet

Conceptual examples.   On the basis of the preceding information, some examples showing multiprotocol routing follow. Consider Figure 4.35, which shows an example of three multiprotocol routers, three networks, and the backbone Frame Relay network. Since the multiprotocol routers support data-link layer protocol connectivity among networks 1, 2, and 3 is possible.

Figure 4.36 is a different example of a multiprotocol router implementation. In Figure 4.36, mixed lower-layer protocol networks are supported by multiprotocol routers, thus making data exchange among them possible.

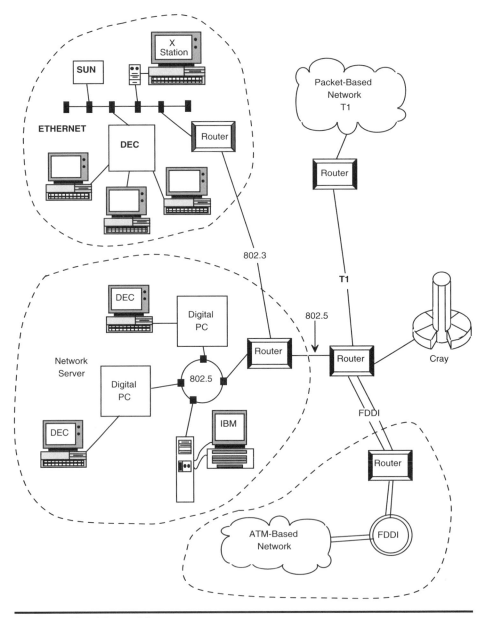

Figure 4.34   Mixed-Protocol Support

Figure 4.37 shows an example of two NetWare and TCP/IP networks integrated using a multiprotocol router. In this figure the routers are interconnected together, thus making the NetWare and TCP/IP networks physically and logically connected. Since NetWare supports TCP/IP, a degree of interoperability can be achieved via this arrangement.

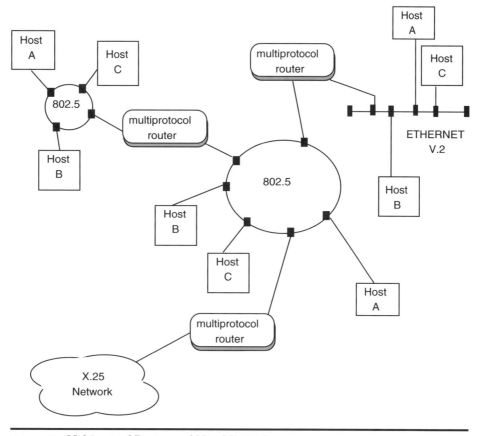

Figure 4.35   Multiprotocol Routers and Mixed Protocols

A variety of implementations can be achieved with multiprotocol routers. The number of permutations that can be obtained with multiprotocol routers is also considerable.

IBM, Bay Networks, Cisco, and other vendors offer multiprotocol routers to the marketplace today.

Router conclusions

Routers are complex devices and in some form or other have been around for at least two decades (at the time of writing). In the late 1960s and 1970s the device that performed router functions was called a *gateway,* and even now this term is still sometimes used to refer to a router. In the networking community today, legitimate devices that perform router functions are available, and they are named as such. There are also devices called *gateways*; they, too, perform a specific function, and generally this is not routing.

There are many types of routers. Some support different upper-layer protocols and are protocol-specific in their implementation. Others support differ-

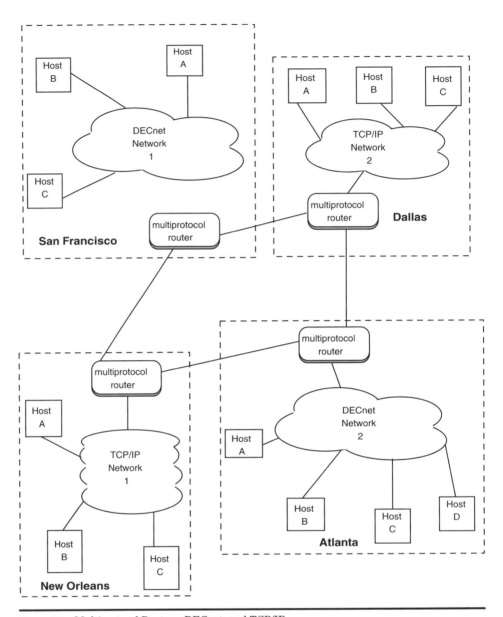

Figure 4.36 Multiprotocol Routers, DECnet, and TCP/IP

ent lower-layer protocols and are specific to that end. Any given router generally supports multiple physical layer interfaces as well as multiple data-link
layer protocols.

Routers serve multiple purposes. From a geographic perspective routers
can be used to satisfy internetworking needs. Some routers are used in what
are considered metropolitan implementations where there are major facilities

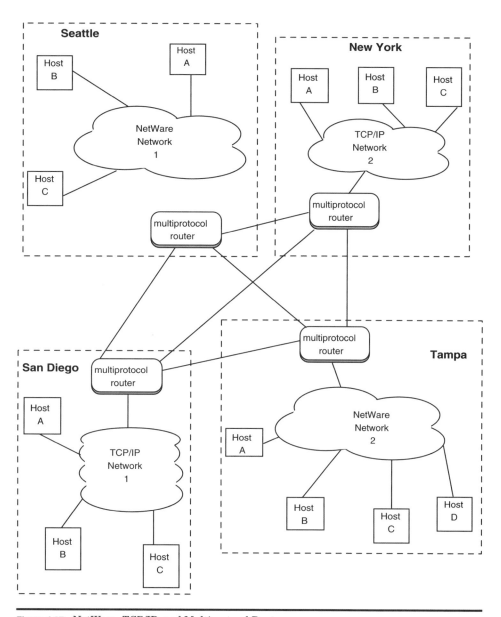

Figure 4.37 NetWare, TCP/IP, and Multiprotocol Routers

and satellite offices within a reasonable proximity. Remote routers can be used to solve integration issues of geographically dispersed networks. The same holds true for what is considered internal routing.

Different types of routing are possible. Centralized routing focuses the routing tables within a centralized processing device. Noncentralized routing implements a strategy where routers exchange information about those

routers with which they operate. In static routing, routing tables are predetermined; in other words, the tables and paths for routing are determined
and configured when the network is nonoperational from a user's perspective.

Two examples of different approaches to routing were presented earlier.
SNA routes data primarily via its front-end processor by way of the Network
Control Program (NCP), but this appears to be changing. This seems to be
the case because of announcements and products that are now capable of performing functions that not too long ago were considered a front-end-proces-
sor-type function. Additionally, with the SNA networking blueprint, many
areas are now in a state of flux.

TCP/IP was cited as an example of how routing is achieved. The software
components that are involved in this process were explained. The versatility
of the TCP/IP protocol stack makes it possible for multiple possibilities to be
considered for implementation.

A type of router arrived on the market in the late 1990s that differentiates
it from some of its predecessors. The bandwidth-on-demand router, described
earlier in this chapter, offers an alternative to a dedicated line for two geographically distant sites that need a router for intermittent connectivity, that
is, on demand.

Multiple advantages are realized for those sites where they are implemented. For example, segment isolation is possible with the implementation of a
router. This is significant because troubleshooting and maintenance are
easier with a segmented network than with a single-backbone network where
crowding exists. Those routers that offer multiprotocol support at the upper
and lower layers offer greater flexibility for growing environments. Some
scalable routers are available on the market today. For example, immediate
needs can be met with the ability to expand and increase support through the
router as these needs arise.

A multiprotocol router has a tall order to achieve many functions at the
same time. As mentioned earlier, a router that supports so many different
protocols at the physical interface, data-link, and upper-layer protocol layers
must be vigorous in its processing capabilities.

Routers may be a part of an integration equation when multiple protocols
are used, but they may not meet all the needs possible. As was stated early
on in this chapter, routers route.

4.6 Gateways

Gateways are the focus of this section. Explanation of the function of this network device is the central purpose. Clarification of the term, implementation
of a gateway in different networks, and other topics are covered.

The Internet community has used the term in a general rather than specific sense. As mentioned earlier in this chapter, the term has been used to convey a device that performed functions of what is known as a router today.

Inadvertently, ambiguity of the meaning of this term began to arise in the
1980s, probably because during the 1980s an influx of numerous types of net-

working devices were developed and brought to market. As a result, the terms *router* and *gateway* became definable according to the functions they performed. A clear distinction was identifiable between devices that performed router functions and gateway functions.

Gateway operation

By definition, gateways operate at layer 3 (network) and above, at a minimum. However, a gateway can operate at all seven layers if necessary. Examine Figure 4.38.

A gateway performs protocol conversion between unlike networks. The key issues are which layers require protocol conversion for integration to be achieved and where the protocol conversion process is performed. Integration of heterogeneous networks is the purpose of a gateway. This is its sole purpose, but it can perform other functions as well.

Currently many good literature sources of information on networking devices are available. Many of these sources are nonbiased, meaning that they conduct research about products and make this available to the public through different avenues. Multiple sources I use list devices such as gateways, routers, bridges, and brouters by category, typically listing the vendor and their product names and functions. In many cases those products listed under gateways are not, in fact, gateways. To be fair, after examining some of the products I am referring to, it seems valid to list the product under the gateway category by referring to the product function as given in the *American Heritage Dictionary* under gateway definition 2 (as a means of access).

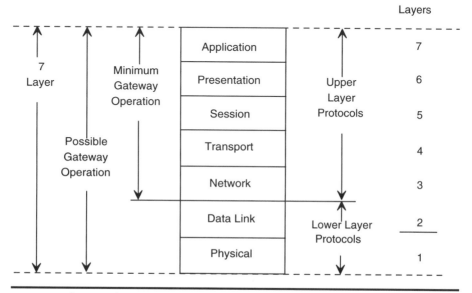

Figure 4.38 Gateway Operation Correlated with OSI Layers

A clear example of this is how a device that permits non-X.25 networks into an X.25-protocol-based network is categorized as a gateway. X.25 is considered a lower-layer protocol, even though it operates at part of layer 3 relative to the OSI model functions. The point is that to classify a device that permits other networks into a X.25-based network as a gateway indicates hairsplitting in meaning. However, this classification could be correct.

For example, consider a Token Ring–based network with TCP/IP used as the upper-layer protocols. Then, contemplate the X.25 network using something other than TCP/IP as an upper-layer network protocol. If this is the case, the device that performs this function is in fact a gateway. If, on the other hand, the device does not perform such a function, what is the device called? An interesting question, but nevertheless important.

Technical details of gateways

Gateways operate with protocols; the question is with which ones and at what layers relative to the OSI model. This section describes gateways and different protocol environments.

Internet gateways. The Internet comprises numerous individual networks connected together to form the collective whole (the Internet). Figure 4.39 illustrates an example of three networks in three different cities that portray this idea. Figure 4.39 shows each of the networks connected via a router. Traditionally, these routers would have been considered gateways. Indeed, in 1983 the Department of Defense announced that anyone desiring to connect to the Internet must use TCP/IP as the protocol. This drew a line in the sand, so to speak, and since that time connecting to the Internet has been a direct TCP/IP-to-TCP/IP connection or some variation thereof requiring gateway functionality between the connecting entity and the Internet.

A typical way to connect to a service provider that offers connectivity to the Internet is via a multihome host. Figure 4.40 is an enhanced view of the Dallas site as shown in Figure 4.39. In Figure 4.39, at the Dallas site it appears that all hosts are connected to the router and are able to connect to the Internet. Figure 4.40 shows reality. All networks and hosts are connected to an Ethernet network which has a multihomed host. One side of the host attaches to the local Ethernet and the other, to the router, which, in turn, connects to the San Francisco and Chicago networks.

SNA gateways. SNA gateways function so that connectivity can be achieved between SNA and a different environment. Consider Figure 4.41, which shows a DECnet network connected to an SNA network via an SNA/DECnet gateway. This example shows SNA protocols used in the SNA environment and DECnet protocols used in the DEC environment. In this case both upper- and lower-layer protocols have to be converted. In the DECnet Ethernet is used as a lower-layer protocol. The upper layers are DECnet-oriented. In the

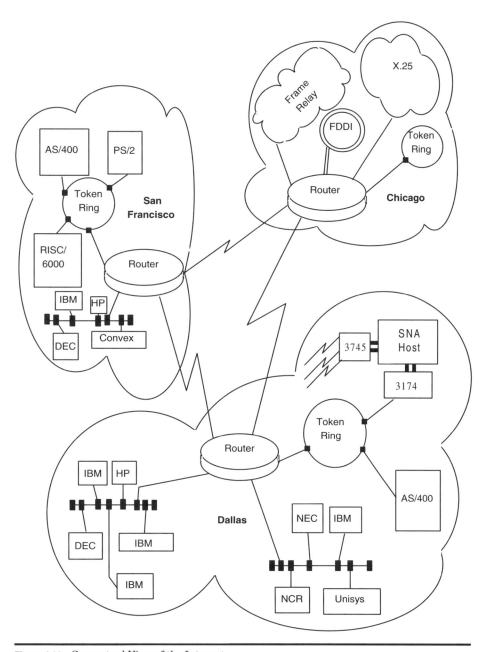

Figure 4.39 Conceptual View of the Internet

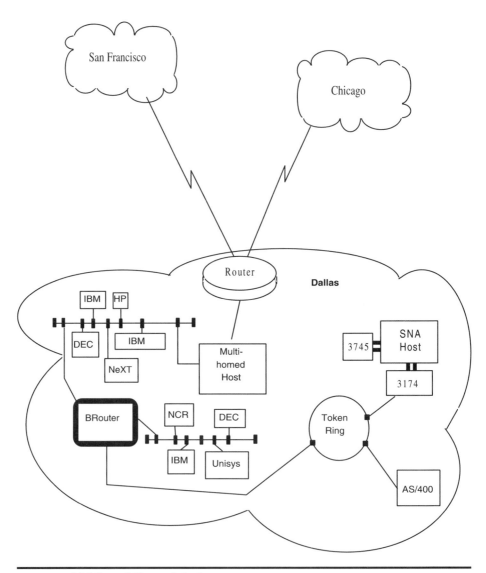

Figure 4.40 Multihomed Host and the Internet

SNA environment SDLC is the lower-layer protocol used on the front-end processor (FEP) and SNA is the upper-layer protocol.

OSI gateways. OSI defines all seven layers. As a protocol it provides different functions at various layers. However, many OSI gateways provide access into an OSI-oriented environment where one or more applications are used. Figure 4.42 shows an example of an OSI-based gateway. It is interesting that OSI gateways are portrayed as oriented at applications. In Figure 4.42 a

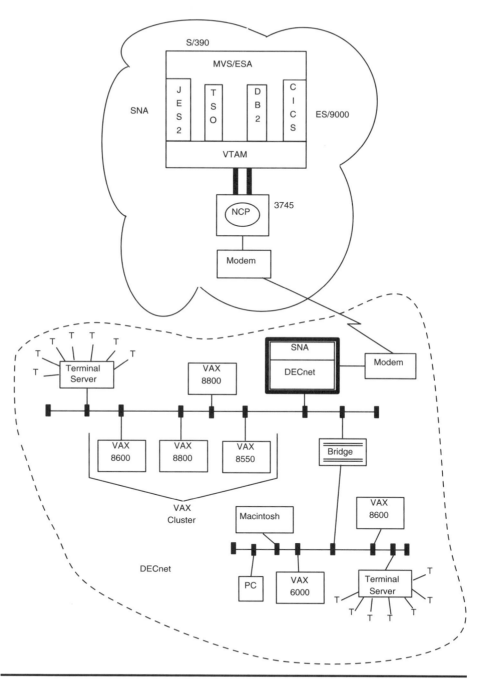

Figure 4.41 SNA/DECnet Gateway

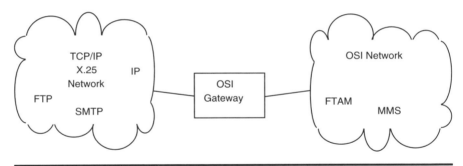

Figure 4.42   OSI-Based Gateway

TCP/IP network is using X.25 and has File Transfer Protocol (FTP) and Simple Mail Transfer Protocol (SMTP) as standard applications. On the other hand, the OSI network has a complete OSI protocol stack implemented and File Transfer and Access Management (FTAM) along with Message Handling Service (MHS) is available.

This scenario implies the exchange between mail systems (SMTP and MHS) and file transfers between (FTP and FTAM). These applications are distinctly different and require interconversion.

DECnet gateway. A *DECnet gateway* is a device that permits networks or devices that are using non-DECnet protocols and converts them into DECnet requirements. Figure 4.43 shows an example of a scenario such as this, where a sizable DECnet environment and also an APPN network composed of AS/400 hosts use a 5250 data stream. This is significant because the DECnet network utilizes an ASCII data stream. In this particular instance, both the protocol and the data stream must be converted in both directions for successful work to be achieved.

AppleTalk gateways. AppleTalk-based networks use this protocol for the upper layers in the network. Figure 4.44 shows a conceptual example of this; note that there is a gateway between an AppleTalk-based network and a TCP/IP-based network. There are multiple devices on the AppleTalk-based network, and they interoperate with the hosts on the TCP/IP-based network. The gateway is required because of the difference in upper-layer protocols.

Bidirectional functionality. Gateways operate between heterogeneous networks. Some exceptions may apply, but most gateways provide bidirectional communication between networks. The degree to which this is possible is vendor-dependent. Since some *gateways* perform specific functions, it is difficult to explain the many variations of this concept without performing a vendor analysis, and that is not the purpose of this chapter or book.

Gateway in light of previous information. Other types of gateways exist; some provide peer-level communication and are highly specialized. Review of

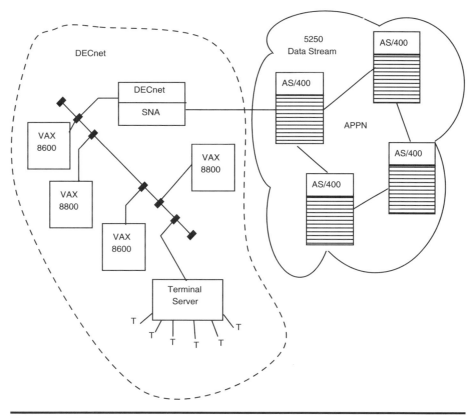

Figure 4.43 DECnet Gateway

industry magazines provides multiple examples of how the term *gateway* is used. This term has been used to convey communication capabilities with UNIX, X.25, SNA, DECnet, and other protocols and environments. All meanings of a term should be given with respect to each context if the term has multiple interpretations. Some vendors use the term *gateway* to define products that give their environment or products the ability to operate with environments such as UNIX, X.25, SNA, or DECnet.

The point here is that UNIX and SNA are not parallel. UNIX is an operating system. SNA is a network protocol. X.25 is considered a data-link layer protocol, but in reality it operates at part of layer 3, the network layer. If the term *gateway* is used to describe products, or their ability to communicate with a different environment, then a comparative analysis should give equal weight to all meanings or contexts. To use a familiar phrase, comparing apples to apples should be the order of the day. Any explanation of the functionality of a device that provides interoperability between devices or networks should be in context.

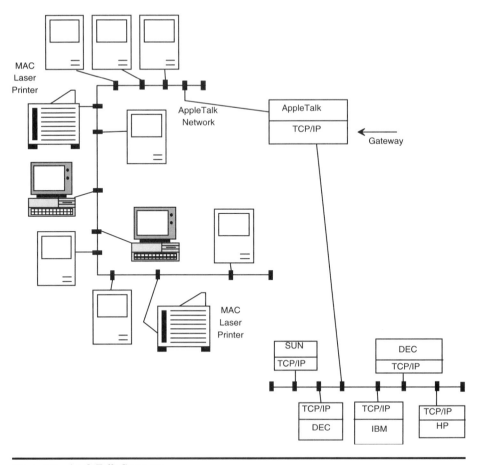

Figure 4.44   AppleTalk Gateway

For example, to call a device that connects heterogeneous networks a *gateway* and use that same term to refer to a device that connects devices or environments to a particular operating system or lower-layer protocol reflects incongruent usage of the term. In fact, it does not matter what operating system is used in many network protocol implementations. What matters is the networking protocols used. This is entirely different from an operating system. For example, with SNA at least three bona fide operating systems exist. In DECnet at least two are noted. OSI can operate with multiple operating systems.

An example is in order here. Consider TCP/IP, which can operate under operating systems such as

UNIX

VMS

OS/2

MS-DOS

MVS/ESA

VM

Apple

OS/400

Additionally, TCP/IP can operate with multiple data-link layer protocols. The following are examples of this:

Ethernet

FDDI

X.25

Token Ring

802.X series of protocols

Understanding these issues should indeed be considered prior to purchase of a gateway. Actually, it would be best to ask any vendor you are working with to explain explicitly their *gateways'* functionality in such a way that *no* ambiguity exists.

SNA-TCP/IP gateways

A finite number of upper- and lower-layer protocols exist and have been explained in this book. As a result, it is possible to identify popular networking protocols in light of their percentage in the worldwide marketplace.

SNA is probably the most dominant vendor network protocol in the world. TCP/IP is probably the most dominant non-vendor-specific protocol in the world. However, an incredible number of vendors support TCP/IP or offer it as a network protocol. DECnet has a considerable amount of the market share as well. The same can be said about NetWare; it is also prevalent. AppleTalk also has a considerable marketshare. OSI is gaining marketshare as time passes.

Estimating a percentage these networking protocols command in terms of marketshare is difficult because the market has been, and is, in such a state of flux. One thing is certain, though—these protocols are dominant. In terms of gateways, the SNA-based gateway certainly has a considerable marketshare. Of this type of gateway, TCP/IP and DECnet are probably the most significant protocols that are integrated into SNA via gateways.

SNA and TCP/IP have received considerable attention since the early 1990s. It seems that TCP/IP has penetrated many institutions and companies that have traditionally been SNA-based. Interestingly, even DEC systems support TCP/IP. This means that DEC customers have an option for protocol use; they can use either TCP/IP, DECnet, or OSI as it is supported in the DEC environment. In this section, however, the focus is on SNA and TCP/IP gateways.

There are many types of SNA-TCP/IP gateway implementations. Most possibilities are presented here. From a user perspective, the question is which best meets their needs.

Hardware gateways.   Hardware gateways almost always operate at all seven layers within an SNA-TCP/IP network. Figure 4.45 shows an example of this type of gateway. The illustration shows three locations: Dallas, Hattiesburg, and San Diego. The office in San Diego was recently acquired because of a recommendation from Jan. Cindy, however, is responsible for all corporate operations, including those in Hattiesburg, where Kelly is responsible for daily operations.

The final result is a hardware gateway in the San Diego office. This provides interoperability between the San Diego office and both the Dallas and Hattiesburg offices. This arrangement provides users in the Hattiesburg office opportunities to use files on hosts in the San Diego office.

This type of gateway is required because the San Diego office has an Ethernet-based TCP/IP network. In Dallas and Hattiesburg, SNA is the network protocol and native lower-layer protocols are used. Consequently, this means that, in order for a gateway to integrate San Diego and the SNA offices, Ethernet and TCP/IP must be converted into SNA and the appropriate lower-layer protocol. The most cost-effective solution in this case is a hardware-based gateway.

In this example both upper- and lower-layer protocol conversion is performed on the hardware gateway. Data translation may or may not be performed on the gateway. Data translation in this case is contingent on how the vendor implements this type of hardware gateway.

This example of an Ethernet-based TCP/IP network connected to multiple SNA networks is a common scenario in the internetworking community today. A significant number of vendors provide gateways such as this.

TCP/IP on an SNA host.   In a different SNA-TCP/IP solution, TCP/IP is loaded onto an SNA host. When this is the case, TCP/IP is GENned as a TCP/IP application. Figure 4.46 depicts this scenario. TCP/IP operates as a VTAM application in Figure 4.46. Just because TCP/IP runs as a VTAM application does not mean that it does not perform protocol conversion. In fact, when SNA and TCP/IP are integrated, protocol conversion and data translation always take place; the only question is *where*. In this example protocol conversion does have to be performed on the host. Data translation may or may not be performed on the host. The location of data translation is contingent on a number of factors, primarily what type of remote logon and file transfer mechanism are used.

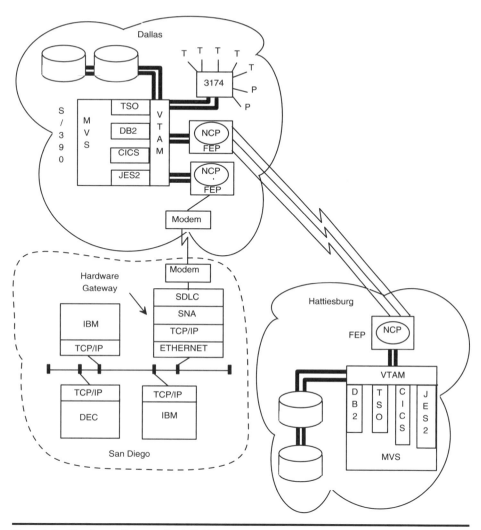

Figure 4.45   Hardware Gateway Installation

Offload.   IBM has what it calls an *offload option*. This is where TCP/IP is
loaded on an SNA host, but offloaded onto a 3172 interconnect controller and
then only the customer-requested applications running on the host itself.
Figure 4.47 illustrates this. Figure 4.47 shows TCP/IP on the host, on the
3172, and on disk. So, where is it? TCP and IP have been offloaded onto the
3172 processor. Those applications selected can function where TCP/IP is
indicated on the hosts, and the remainder of the TCP/IP suite that is not
needed is on hard disk. This type of implementation is versatile. As Figure
4.47 shows, even a remote TCP/IP network (shown as LAN 1) can be integrated into the TCP/IP network connected to the 3172 processor via a remote
Ethernet bridge.

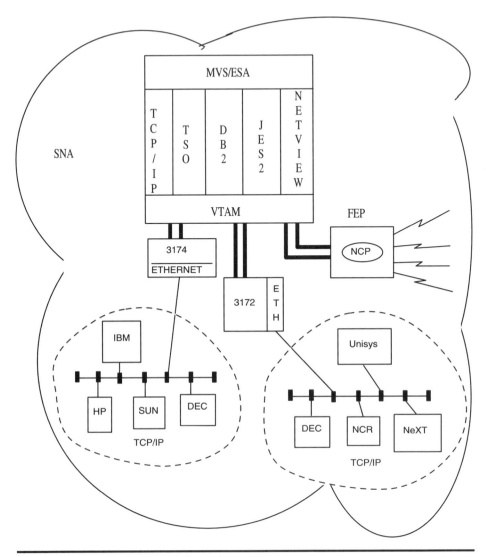

Figure 4.46   TCP/IP as a VTAM Application

Software gateway.   A software gateway is program code that operates on a workstation. Figure 4.48 shows an example of this. In this example a RISC/6000 implements gateway software. It is used to connect the TCP/IP network in Paris to the SNA network in New York. Note that the TCP/IP network does not necessarily indicate a data link. The significance of this is that software gateway code can operate on a number of different vendors' hardware. Here, the gateway software is operating on an IBM RISC/6000.

In this type of implementation the data-link layer protocols are left to the host to resolve. In this case the RISC/6000 supports a very wide variety of data links; in fact, the question with this machine is which one a customer wants to

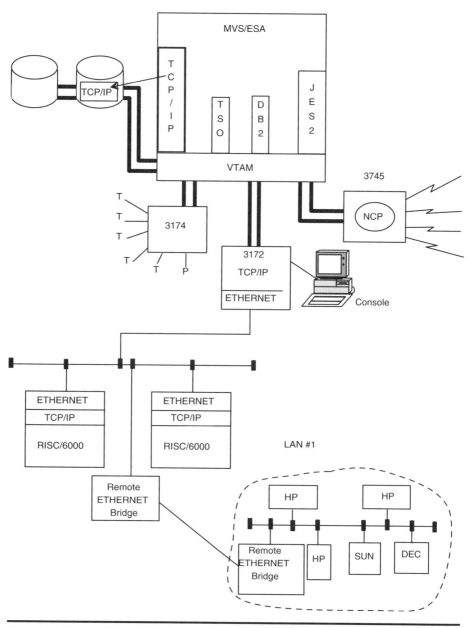

Figure 4.47   TCP/IP with an Offload Option

use, not which ones it can support. The RISC/6000 host has one of the most robust data-link layer protocol support subsystems on the market today.

The significance of this example is that the software gateway code operates as any other started task in the AIX (IBM's UNIX for the RISC/6000) environment. Therefore, the workstation does not have to be dedicated; however, it

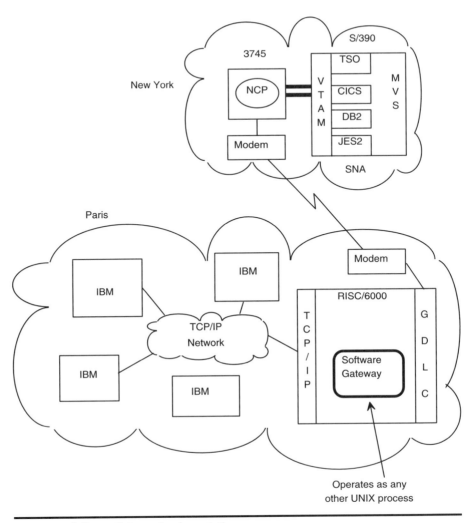

Figure 4.48 Software Gateway Implementation

could be if so desired. Another interesting fact about this type of solution is that some software vendors who supply gateway code can support more than 1000 logical units (LUs). In fact, some software gateway vendors have code that can operate on considerably small workstations. Some software gateway vendors support only certain vendor hardware, so it is best to determine which vendor hardware is supported by a potential software gateway supplier.

PC interface cards and software. Another way to integrate SNA and TCP/IP is to use interface boards and software with PCs. Consider Figure 4.49, which may illustrate the best solution if this type of configuration is similar. However, it is just one of the four types mentioned previously. In the example

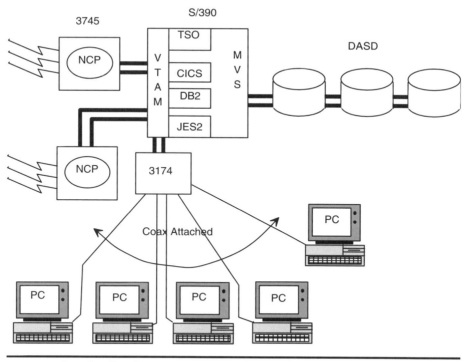

Figure 4.49 Interface Boards

shown in Figure 4.49, there are multiple PCs on site where the S/390 host is located. The PCs have interface boards, software inside, and are attached by coaxial cable to the 3174 establishment controller.

As the previous five examples have shown, there are various ways to integrate SNA and TCP/IP. The last example depicted multiple PCs with interface boards attached to a local 3174. Indeed, multiple methods are currently available to bring together SNA and TCP/IP.

Gateway usage

To achieve interoperability between SNA and TCP/IP, protocol conversion and data translation must be performed. The only question is where these functions will be performed. The previous section provided examples of where protocol conversion was performed—primarily upper-layer protocols. However, it did not indicate where data translation occurs or what user-oriented functions are supported.

Remote logon. In SNA and TCP/IP, much of the traffic is considered inbound, that is, to the SNA host. Any logon from a TCP/IP-based network to an SNA network is considered a remote logon, even if the network is in the same room with the SNA host. When SNA and TCP/IP are integrated via a gateway, the issue of data translation is paramount. The SNA arena supports multiple data streams, but the one used interactively is a 3270 data stream. This is significant because 3270 data streams are based on an EBCDIC character set. Most traditional data streams in TCP/IP networks have been based on the ASCII character set. There are numerous ways to solve this one issue of data translation. Consider Figure 4.50, which shows a Sun (Sun Microsystems) user invoking a TELNET client native to the TCP/IP stack on that host. The user executes the client against the TELNET server on the gateway between the network in Salt Lake City and Boise. The first part of the connection establishes a logical link between the Convex host and the gateway, and is labeled A. The second portion of the connection, labeled B, is

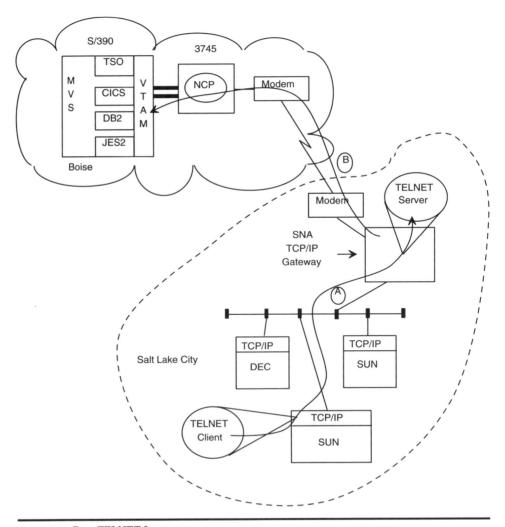

Figure 4.50 Raw TELNET Logon

established from the gateway to VTAM on the S/390 host. The Convex user *thinks* that one logical connection exists between their terminal and VTAM. This type of connection is called a "raw" TELNET because the TELNET client out of the native TCP/IP stack is used to establish a logical connection. In this case data translation is performed on the gateway, regardless of whether it is a hardware or software gateway.

Figure 4.51 presents another example of how a remote logon can be achieved. Figure 4.51 shows a TCP/IP-based network in New York and an SNA network in Ottawa. Note the TN3270 client application shown on the

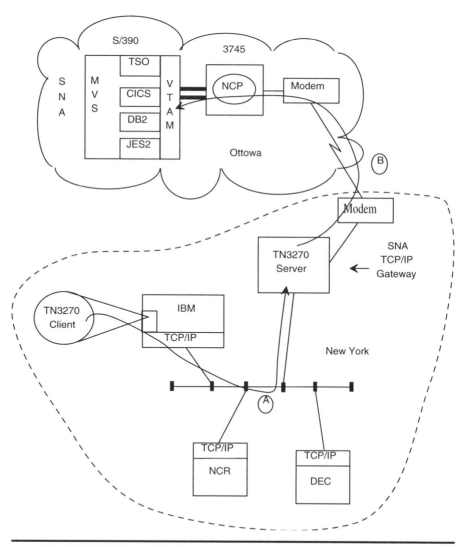

Figure 4.51   TN3270 Client and Gateway

IBM host in the New York network. It indicates, via logical connection A, that it connects to the TN3270 server on the gateway connecting the two networks. The second part of the connection between New York and Ottawa is shown via connection B. In this case data translation occurs on the IBM host.

This is so because TN3270 client applications are designed to output a 3270 data stream. The fact that it is TCP/IP- and Ethernet-based is insignificant because data formatting is performed at the presentation layer within a network. By the time any data reach the physical interface of the host, they are represented in binary data. Hence, what is shipped across the Ethernet is Ethernet frames.

However, for a TN3270 application to operate, one of two conditions must be met. Either a TN3270 server must be present as shown on the gateway in Figure 4.51 or the SNA-based host must have TCP/IP on it to enable the TELNET server native to that stack to respond to the request of the TN3270 client. Figure 4.52 illustrates this. In Figure 4.52 a TN3270 client application is present on the Unisys (Unisys Corp.) host. A user invokes it against the SNA host attached to the TCP/IP-based Ethernet network. Note that the TN3270 client application is executed against the TCP/IP stack running as a VTAM application on the SNA-based host. Why would this be done? When this type of scenario is implemented, it operates this way because within the TCP/IP stack running as a VTAM application, a TELNET server exists by default. Consequently, the data stream inbound to the SNA hosts is 3270 (no conversion needed), and this saves CPU cycles, and CPU cycles cost money.

Other proprietary methods support a remote logon from a TCP/IP-based network and an SNA network. Since these are proprietary, they may or may not coincide with industry standards.

File transfers.   File transfers can be interactive or programmatic. The former implies human intervention whereas the latter does not. Both are discussed here.

Interactive.   There are numerous methods of performing file transfers between SNA environments and TCP/IP networks. A common way to do this is via FTP. Figure 4.53 shows an example of an SNA network, a TCP/IP network, and a gateway connecting them together. Note that the FTP client has been invoked on the Sun host and is executed against the FTP server native to the TCP/IP stack running as a VTAM application. As this figure shows, file XYZ is written from the DASD (Direct Access Storage Device) in the SNA environment to the Sun disk.

Another method for file transfer between SNA and TCP/IP environments includes support for the IND$FILE program that IBM has supported. Figure 4.54 is an example of this. Figure 4.54 shows a DEC user invoking a program that supports the IND$FILE program by TSO (Time Sharing Option) and CICS (Customer Information Control System) under VTAM. As the figure

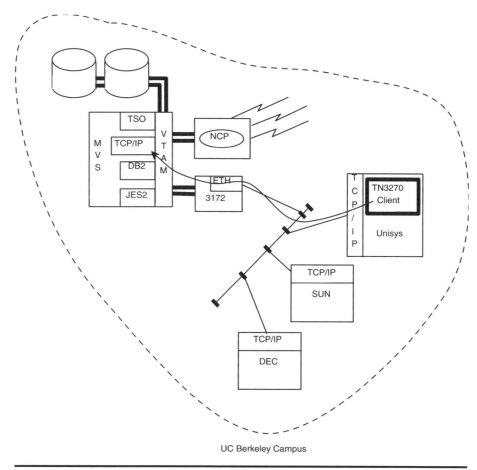

Figure 4.52 TN3270 Client and Host

shows, file XYZ is moved from DASD on the MVS hosts to a disk connected directly to the DEC host.

Programmatic. Files can be transferred programmatically. There are various reasons for this capability. Some companies need to download files at night when little or no operations are being performed within the company. Others need programmatic file transfers because of the nature of the interacting entities. Figure 4.55 best depicts this scenario. Figure 4.55 presents an example of two different types of file transfers being performed. On the left portion of the drawing a LU6.2 file transfer is shown using a hardware gateway with proprietary LU6.2 library support on the gateway itself and the host. To the right side of the figure, socket communication is being performed where socket programming with CICS is communicating with a socket-based User Datagram Protocol (UDP) program on host C in the figure.

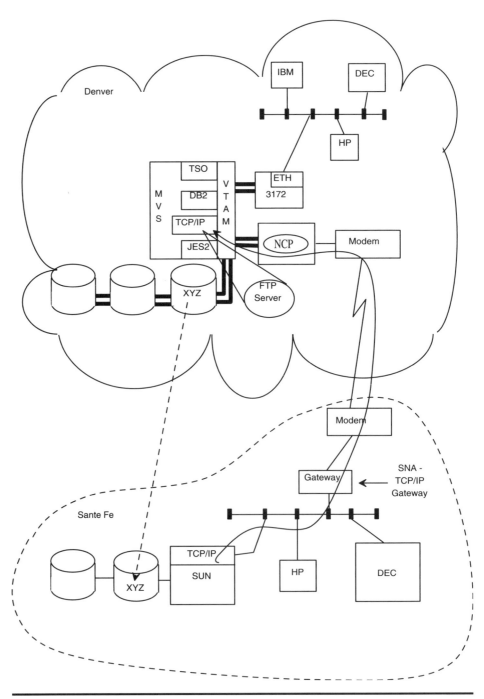

Figure 4.53 FTP Client

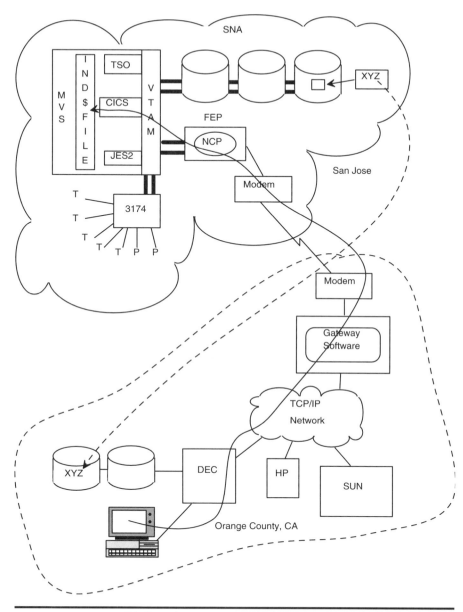

Figure 4.54   IND$FILE File Transfer

Mail.   Mail support between SNA and a TCP/IP environment is best depicted by Figure 4.56, which shows an SNA network in Oak Harbor, WA and a TCP/IP network in Portland, OR. An SNA-TCP/IP gateway is used to connect the two networks. This particular gateway supports SMTP to PROFS mail and vice versa. As a result, those in Oak Harbor can send mail to those users on the network in Portland. All users in their respective networks view mail in the native format they are accustomed to using. Some vendors have such support for gateways; some do not.

Management support. The notion of network management is a topic in and of itself; however, it is important to know if network devices to be integrated into an internetworking arena support the network management used to manage that (those) network(s). SNA and TCP/IP networks connected together via a gateway indicate that the gateway should support network management for SNA and TCP/IP. In addition, it should have management capabilities in and of itself, meaning that it should be manageable as a separate entity. Figure 4.57 is an example of network management on both sides of the gateway.

Figure 4.57 shows SNMP as TCP/IP network management. It also shows NetView as SNA network management. No particular management is shown for the gateway itself because this is vendor-specific. However, the gateway should have some functional management capabilities that permit systems personnel access to information from the gateway if needed.

Working conclusions about gateways

The term *gateway* means different things to different groups of individuals. However, the *American Heritage Dictionary* does define how the term is used in English. Use of the term in the 1970s with the Internet community took on the meaning of routing. The term did connote an entryway, but technically speaking, it was used to convey what the term *router* means today.

Different types of gateways are marketed today. Gateways to permit connectivity into DECnet, TCP/IP, NetWare, SNA, OSI, and AppleTalk can all be purchased. Gateways perform protocol conversion by default because this is what makes them gateways. Gateways can operate at layer 3 and above relative to the OSI model, or they can operate at all layers within a network.

SNA- and TCP/IP-based gateways are quite popular today. These two environments include a considerable amount of the internetworking community around the world. Other network protocols have marketshare as well, but even the Digital Equipment Corporation (DEC) supports TCP/IP for those who want to use it with DEC hosts. DEC also supports OSI.

There are multiple types of gateways. There are hardware- and software-based gateways. Regarding TCP/IP and SNA, TCP/IP can be loaded as a VTAM application and operated in this way, or it can be offloaded onto a 3172 interconnect controller. Other possibilities may be available in the near future.

Gateways are used to bring together heterogeneous networks. When this is achieved, multiple user oriented tasks can also be achieved. For example, remote logons, file transfers (both interactive and programmatic), and elec-

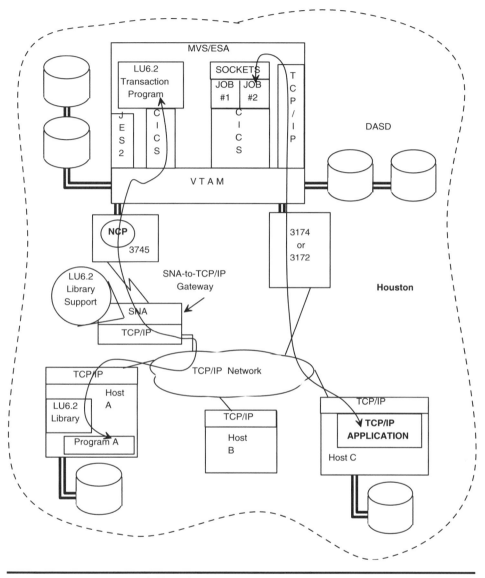

Figure 4.55 Programmatic File Transfers

tronic mail (email) can be exchanged; network management can be utilized; and customized offerings may be provided by some vendors.

Gateways are available in a variety of packaging and support a variety of different end-user applications and systems-oriented tasks. It is best to check with a specific vendor to determine what is supported by a given gateway.

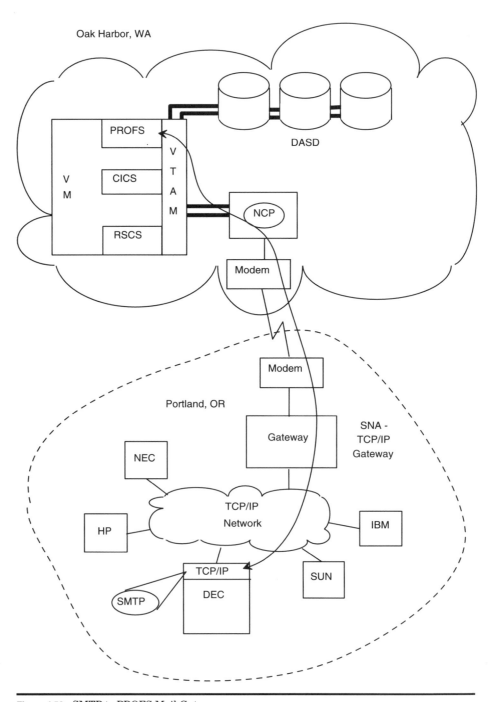

Figure 4.56 SMTP to PROFS Mail Gateway

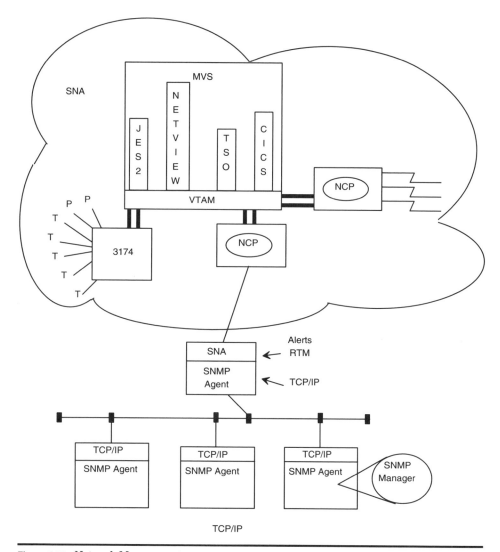

Figure 4.57 Network Management

4.7 Server Implementations

The term *server* is a often used generically. However, today there are many highly specialized types of servers. Even so, the term is still used loosely to refer to devices such as gateways, routers, and other function-specific network devices. This section explains some popular servers that perform a specific function.

Servers, in the general sense, can be basically any network device. Servers have come of age and are categorized into the functions they perform.

Function

Typically, a server provides specific functions to the whole network or at least a significant portion of it. One point of clarification is in order. Some level of confusion still abounds about the notion of client/server. *Client* programs can be invoked manually or programmatically, and either way they always initiate something. *Servers,* on the other hand, always answer a client's request.

In the context used here, the term *server* means something different. *Servers,* as a network device, do in a sense provide requests to clients. However, network servers normally provide some functions that separate their function from a server program. For example, a *file server* is a dedicated host with disks dedicated to storing files. These files are used by multiple users throughout the network, and therefore centralized storage of common files removes the need for vast amounts of disk space for each user. So, in this sense a server assumes a meaning different from the notion of client/server networking, which connotes peer-oriented communication.

The philosophy behind a *server* is that it performs some function in a centralized manner rather than having that function distributed throughout a network or tied to particular hosts. The growth of servers of all types seems to be the result of networks providing a single commonality among hosts of all types, including PCs. With the proliferation of networks in the 1980s, the notion of delegating functions such as printing to a designated printer seemed to make more sense than each host having a printer when in reality this may not be required.

File servers

File servers are devices (hardware and software) that function as a centralized network disk storage that authorized users on a network can access. These devices can be configured to perform multiple tasks.

One function that a file server can perform is file storage. This is advantageous because one centralized server can be the central repository for all files. Conceptually, the idea of a file server on a network would appear as shown in Figure 4.58. In Figure 4.58 multiple PCs are connected to a NetWare network along with a file server that contains the files required by the PC users. In this type of configuration any PC can access the server to retrieve a file or store a file onto it.

Figure 4.59 depicts a detailed view of the PC users and their operations with the file server. In Figure 4.59, PC users 1, 2, and 4 are accessing the file server. All of them are retrieving the different files they are working with on their respective PCs. This is possible because of the multitasking capabilities, storage ability, and configuration of the file server. In this example the file server appears to be a single disk to each user. All users *think* they have their own hard disks. In reality the configuration is such that a virtual drive is created and each PC is configured to point to this disk (server).

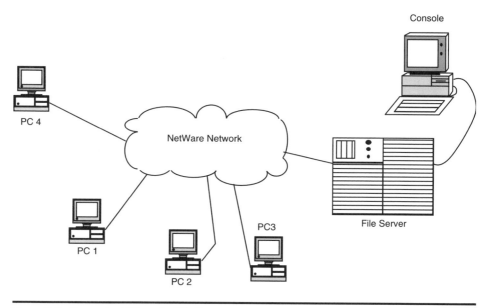

Figure 4.58 Conceptual View of a File Server

Program storage. A file server can also function as a disk that holds the master copy of the software package. For example, the Microsoft Word network edition software package can be purchased and loaded onto a server where multiple users can utilize it, and immediate savings are realized because purchase of multiple packages of the software program is not required. Consider Figure 4.60, which shows PC users 2 and 4 using the Microsoft Word software package based on the file server. Neither user is aware of the other's work because of the nature of the network configuration and how the software package operates. This is a straightforward example of how a network can be utilized to save money. Four users are on this NetWare network, and each has access to the Microsoft Word software. Only one copy of the software was purchased rather than four.

Another example of program storage is exemplified in Figure 4.61. Examine it. In Figure 4.61 a database is loaded onto the file server, and five users are connected to the network. In this example the software package happens to be a database package. Note that PC user 3 is working on Mr. Taylor's file, PC user 1 is manipulating the IWI file, and PC user 4 is changing Mr. May's file. These separate functions are occurring concurrently. The same file and record locking functions that are standard to most database programs are also in force in the network edition of this database version.

Other functions are possible with a file server such as operating multiple programs simultaneously with multiple users performing different functions. The key issue in such an environment is that the file server must be powerful

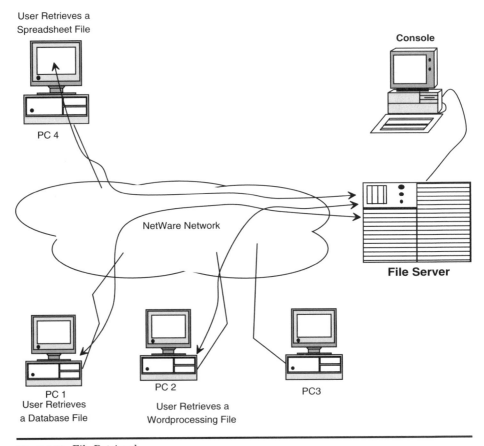

Figure 4.59 File Retrieval

and—depending on the number of users, the programs being used, and the size of files—a large amount of disk space is almost a must.

Communication servers

Communication servers perform basically one role—they provide communication-related functions. These functions vary depending on the communication server.

Modem pools. One function a communication server can perform is to house multiple modems, permitting access via various lines and speeds. Consider Figure 4.62, which is a logical view of a communication server and the network with a DEC, IBM, RISC/6000, and two PCs attached. To the users of these hosts, the communication server logically appears as part of the network—just as another resource.

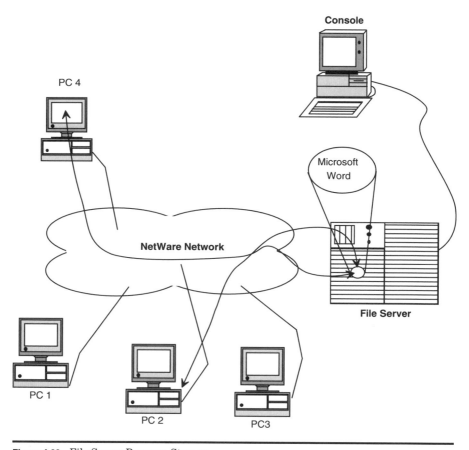

Figure 4.60   File Server Program Storage

Figure 4.63 portrays a physical view of the network showing more detail on the line speeds and connections to the hosts themselves.

Notice in Figure 4.63 that the DEC host has a T1 link, the Unisys host has a switched 56-kbps line, the IBM host has a 56-kbps leased line, and the two PCs have access to a dual modem with a 56-kbps switched line.

Consumer tip.   Many vendors are listed in charts and magazine listings under the heading of *communication servers*. The following names and functions are examples:

Multiprotocol Concentrator

X.25 Communications Interface

Video Mux

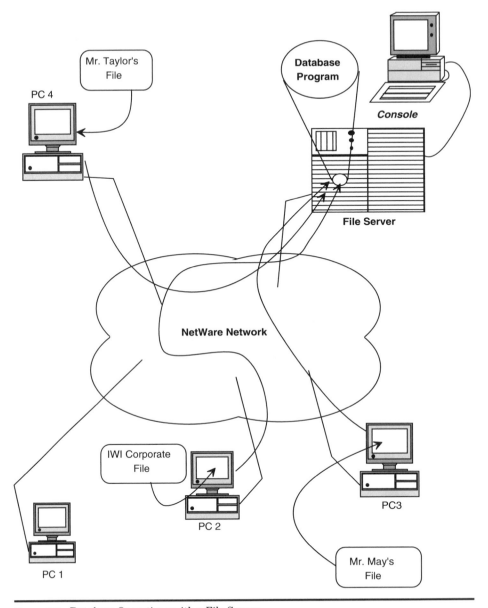

Figure 4.61   Database Operations with a File Server

Multiprotocol Communication Server

Fax Plus

Remote Access Server

Modem Server

Asynchronous LAN Gateway

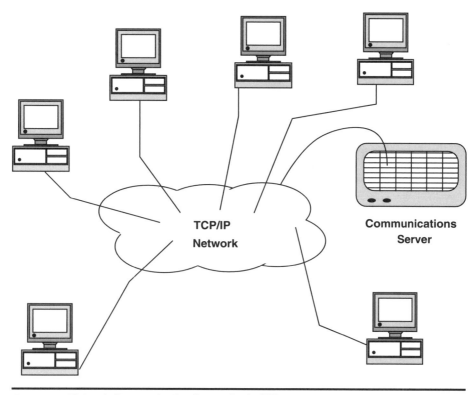

Figure 4.62   Network Communication Server: Logical View

I believe the point is clear if you read the list. Because the category *communication server* has such broad meanings, research is required to understand what is meant. Some communication servers are highly specialized, so much so that they are vendor-specific and the device may operate only with a given vendor's equipment. This is helpful when reading about *communication servers.*

Study the following terms and concepts. These are presented here, in this chapter, to better equip you to understand the overall topics in this chapter.

Autobaud

This term is relatively easy to understand because it does what the name implies. It literally automatically selects the highest baud rate that the destination modem is capable of performing. Generally, the autobaud process is like bidding. Some modems attempt to move up to the highest speed that either modem will support. However, this is not always the case; this is the reason for autobaud. If one modem supports a higher baud rate than the other, the higher-baud-rate modem will come down to the slower speed if the higher speed modem can autobaud. This, however, can differ with ven-

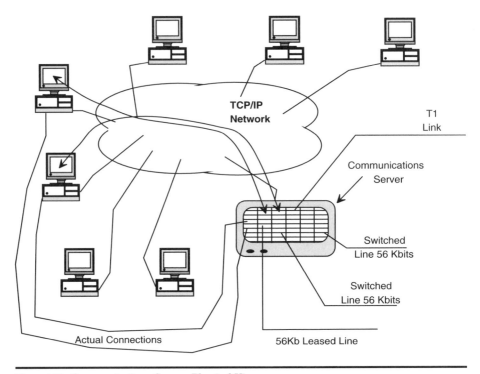

Figure 4.63 Communications Server: Physical View

dors, but the term *autobaud* is generally agreed on. It is preferable to have an autobaud modem in most cases because of its versatility.

Line conditioning

The networks on which modems operate experience interference by default in many instances. As the baud rate increases with higher-speed modems, so does the tendency to incur errors as a result. One problem related to this is amplitude distortion. This is where the signal strength itself varies independently of noise of the line itself. In order to compensate for this phenomenon, most modems have circuitry built into them to make property adjustments so that the signal is not too disproportional.

The equalizer

This is an important aspect about modems even though it is not a prevalent topic! Modems operating at baud rates in excess of approximately 2400 baud have an equalizer built into them. The purpose of this equalizer is to serve the function of a filter. This filter is unusual because its phase characteristics and amplitude are inversely proportional to the ones encountered on the lines on which the modem operates. Additionally, equalizers perform a function to correct for propagation delay causing distortions.

Modulation information

When data are transmitted over a line via a modem, modulation is involved, as was explained earlier in this book. However, additional details are pertinent here in view of the subject. *Modulation* is simply the conversion of digital signals into analog signals. Conversely, when this signal arrives at the destination, the modem performs reverse modulation, if you will; it performs *demodulation*.

Print server

Reference to a print server may indicate one of two possible entities. One is a general reference to a printer attached to a network where all users with network accessibility can use it; in this instance it is generally referred to as a *standalone printer*. Another use of this reference is where a printer is attached to a network host and its print jobs are queued from that host and then sent to the printer. In this instance the printer appears to be attached to the network directly, when in fact it is attached to a network host. This example is loosely referred to as a *network printer*. Interestingly, there is little difference between the phrases, but the implementation differs radically.

Standalone printer. Network printers have existed for some time. The concept is not new; however, it has been brought to the forefront recently. Figure 4.64 is an example of a network printer. Figure 4.64 shows multiple hosts attached to a bus-based Ethernet. Any of these hosts can use the network printer because it is attached to the network and is addressable.

Figure 4.65 shows the highlight of the Ethernet Network Module (NM) attached to the side of a Hewlett-Packard printer. In this example, the NM makes it possible for the printer to be a standalone network device. Note that the NM attaches one end to the network transceiver and the other to the parallel port on the printer.

In fact, the arrangement shown in Figure 4.65 makes the printer such that *any* host that can access the network can use this printer to print. This means that utilization of communication servers and other devices make remote location computing *and* local network printing possible.

Figure 4.65 shows an example of a standalone printer. In most instances this scenario implies small quantities of on-board memory, and thus printer queue bottlenecks are likely. Generally, they are proportional to the number of users attempting to use the printer at any given point in time.

Network printer. In this example a printer is attached to a host but appears to be attached to the network, but its jobs are spooled to it via a host on the net-

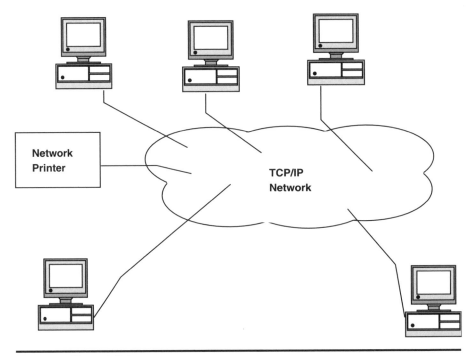

Figure 4.64 Network Printer

work. Consider Figure 4.66. Note that multiple workstations are shown in Figure 4.66. Even though they do not have a printer attached to their own workstations, they can print on the network printer via the IBM computer to which the printer is physically attached. However, as mentioned previously, the printer appears to be attached to the network itself.

There are other variations of network printing. One such example is given in Figure 4.67. Figure 4.67 depicts printing in an SNA environment. Note that two terminals are connected to the 3174 to which the 3287 printer is attached. These local terminals can print just as do those in the New Orleans and New York offices. However, the printing occurs at the headquarters office on Mystic Trail.

Network printing has a variety of meanings. It is not uncommon for the meaning to be associated with a given vendor network protocol. Nevertheless, the bottom line is that multiple users are using the printer in contrast to each individual user having a dedicated printer.

Terminal server

Terminal servers have grown from rarely used devices to commodity items in less than a decade. The fundamental philosophy of terminal servers is the implementation of multiple "dumb" terminals concentrated into one device. Figure 4.68 illustrates this concept.

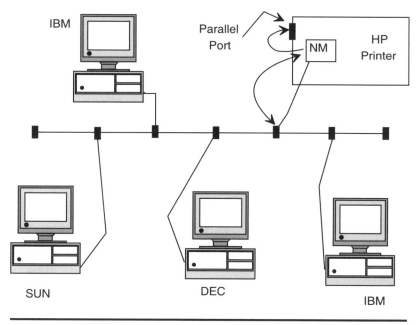

Figure 4.65   Network Module Highlight

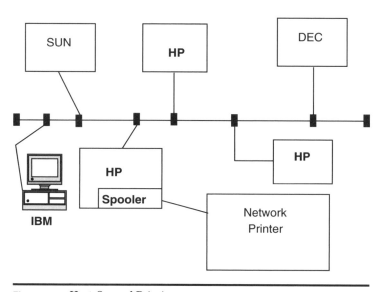

Figure 4.66   Host-Queued Printing

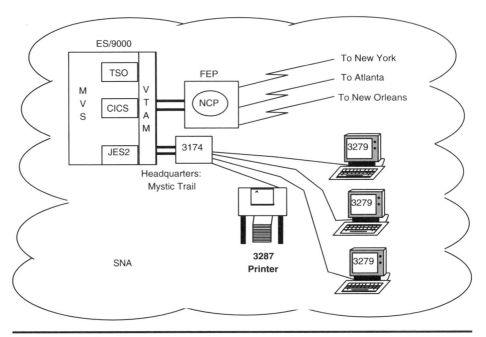

Figure 4.67   SNA Printing

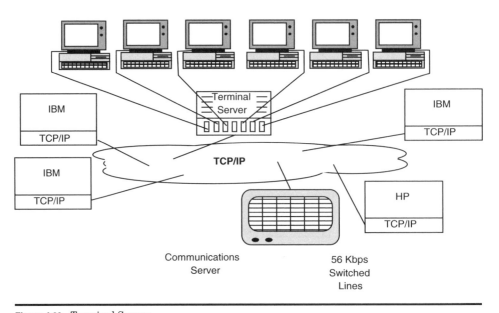

Figure 4.68   Terminal Server

Figure 4.68 shows multiple hosts, communications server, terminal server, and six dumb terminals. The use of the term "dumb" is defined technically as a device with little intelligence. I suppose this has always been the case, but in networking devices intelligence is measured by levels or degrees.

Figure 4.68 is a TCP/IP-based network. The terminal server has a TCP/IP complement inside in programmable read-only memory (PROM) on the motherboard. Hence, the terminal server has a degree of intelligence. Many vendors make terminal servers, and most can be configured to accommodate terminals or a modem or two.

The result of a TCP/IP-based terminal server is that dumb terminals can be used. The significance behind this is that they cost considerably less than PCs or terminals with a higher level of intelligence. Ironically, what was considered a dumb terminal in the early 1990s is entirely different from what is now considered dumb.

Basically there are two categories of dumb terminals: those which have the basics such as DCE, DTR (data terminal ready), DTE, parity, and other fundamental parameters and those which may have a set of programmable function keys, multiple ports, printer capability, and built-in calendars. As you may have concluded, the price differs between these two terminal categories as well.

Interestingly, terminal servers are available with a variety of ports. Most terminal servers have anywhere from six to nine, with a console port for superuser (maintenance) functions. Terminal servers are a very cost-effective method of meeting the needs of network users. A dumb terminal and a terminal server are basically limitless (with the exception of graphics capabilities, and somewhere the ability to perform this function is probably being attempted). Figure 4.69 depicts what is actually a minor task.

In Figure 4.69 shows multiple network devices on the TCP/IP-based network. In short, the figure includes a terminal server with two terminals attached; a modem attached to the terminal server; and IBM, DEC, RISC/6000, Unisys, Sun, and IBM hosts. Additionally, the PC is in a location remote from the network. The remote PC user can access the network by dialing the number of the modem indicated in Figure 4.69.

A sequence of five functions is performed by the *dumb* terminal user (no pun intended), user 1. These five functions are as listed:

A Function A is the dumb terminal user (user 1) invoking the TELNET client inside the terminal server against the IBM host. The native TELNET server in the TCP/IP stack on the IBM answers the TELNET client request.

B User 1 invokes the TELNET client on the IBM against the 3172 attached to the MVS host. The MVS host has TCP/IP running as an offload option, but as default, a VTAM application. Hence when user 1 invokes the TELNET client against the TELNET server on the MVS host, user 1 sees the VTAM banner screen.

C User 1 performs a logon to the ISPF editor under the control of TSO. The line-mode option is selected and user 1 invokes the FTP client resident on the MVS host.

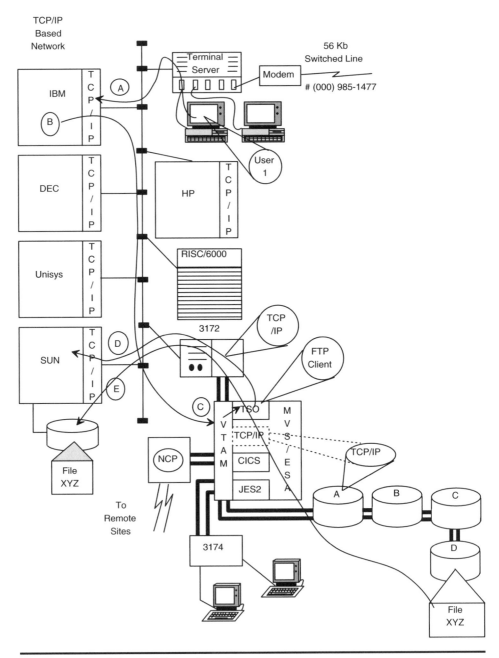

Figure 4.69 Typical Terminal Server Operation

D   Even though TCP and IP is operating on the 3172, the TELNET and FTP applications are running indirectly as VTAM applications. Hence, user 1 can execute an FTP client against the Sun host.

E   Function E is where user 1 moves a file from MVS disk D to the Sun host.

This operation, shown in Figure 4.69, is, in reality, in heterogeneous environments. In fact, I have performed this exact operation so many times that I have lost count. The questions that arise as a result of such usage is that terminal server users generally require some time to accustom themselves to these operations. However, once they are accustomed to such an environment, the working power within it is unbelievable.

Concluding thoughts

Server is a generic term used loosely in the marketplace to refer to a specific device. Depending on the context, the meaning differs. After examining three lists in publications listing *servers,* I concluded little continuity exists aside from broad categories such as those mentioned here. Servers have a distinct function and philosophy; ascertaining exactly what this is should be the goal of customers purchasing servers of any kind.

The *file server* is a specific device that can be used to store files or programs or both depending on the product—either hardware or software. File servers can be cost-efficient if implemented appropriately. File servers can be used interactively or programmatically; either use depends on the need and sophistication of the network environment and the human users.

Communication servers are devices that generally operate with data-communication-related products. Many operate with modems. Some offer modem pooling exclusively. This term is as vague as the use of other server terms. Some communication servers have the ability to perform multiplexing functions, or interfaces into certain network environments.

Many communication servers lend themselves to modem support functions. Modems are complex in their own right. The term *autobaud* means that a modem is capable of regulating operating speed relative to the target modem. Line conditioning is a factor of telephone line communications. Most modems have circuitry built into them to compensate for this phenomenon. Equalizers are special filters used to adjust for phase differentiation.

Modulation is a topic in its own right, but is important when discussing modems and communication with modems. Four types of modulation techniques were explained: amplitude, frequency shift keying, differential phase shift keying, and phase shift keying. Modems use specific modulation techniques, and the impact of these techniques on modem operation is important.

Print servers are also network devices. In short, this is a printer that usually *serves* the entire network. Two categories of printers are identifiable: (1) the type with a network interface card attached, which is considered a stand-alone printer—this type of print server generally has limited memory (even though this is a relative term) and (2) a network printer, whose configuration is such that the printer is connected to a host and the host generally has a spooling mechanism with enough memory to accommodate the network users. This is obviously the ideal case; in reality, differences do exist.

Terminal servers are network devices that have received more attention since the early 1990s. Theoretically, with a terminal server, multiple dumb terminals are connected to a single device that provides network accessibility. "Dumb" terminal is a technical reference to a terminal that has limited software or firmware intelligence. Some dumb terminals are more intelligent than others.

Terminal servers differ with respect to network protocols, but in principle they achieve the same function; they provide access to a network. Contrasted to a terminal server is a PC or a terminal attached directly to a host. As Figure 4.69 depicted, the power behind a dumb terminal and terminal server is typically limited only by the user behind it.

4.8   Network Troubleshooting Technology

Troubleshooting any network device presupposes that you understand the operation of the device and its environment. For this reason, the topics were presented in this chapter. Is there any set list of questions one can ask for troubleshooting network devices? Can a chart be constructed to troubleshoot devices? I have heard these and many similar questions.

First, let me tell you that no reasonable approach to troubleshooting network technology can be a mere list of questions. The people I know who can best troubleshoot technology are those who have a wide experience, are open-minded, and think unconventionally. To assume that a simple list of questions given to a "rookie" in the technological community will produce "identified problems" is blissful naivete. It can, and I have seen cases where this approach worked. However, the best rule of thumb is to keep in mind a list of questions and then learn to think through technology and scenarios that lend themselves to problem areas. Then you will be better prepared to troubleshoot those areas.

Consider the following list of questions that will help you in the early phases of troubleshooting technology. The list is broad, and will apply to most situations involving network technology. I am presenting it here for you to consider as a set of general guidelines only; I recommend that you make additions to it or remove those questions that do not apply to your situation.

1. What geographic area is served by the technology?

2. Is the technology serving this area in the same physical location?

3. Does the problem you are working with lend itself to isolation of equipment in a certain geographic location?

4. List all the hardware you are aware of that relates to the problem.

5. List all the software related to the problem.

6. List the symptoms of the problem.

7. Can the location where the problem area is be isolated from the remainder of the network?

8. Is it possible to segment the network?

9. If the problem is communication-related, can you isolate the telecommunication lines so that each of them can be tested?

10. If you suspect the problem to be hardware-related, do you have a piece of hardware to replace the suspect piece(s)?

11. Is it possible to set up an environment in which each piece of equipment duplicating the problem can be tested?

12. How long have the symptoms or problems existed?

13. Have any changes occurred in the past day, 2 days, 3 days, week, or month?

14. Do you have testing equipment such as a protocol analyzer, volt-ohm-milliammeter, and so forth?

15. Can you obtain any trace information about network traffic in which this device has been installed?

Many, many other questions can be added to this list. The purpose of this list is to get you thinking. Later in this book other questions are presented which are more pointed and focused on various topics.

4.8 Summary

Networks are complex. The saying goes that the network is the computer. This is true. However, networks today are increasingly difficult to troubleshoot and fix when they break down. Technologically speaking, we have come to a point in time where the technology has outstripped the human ability to keep up with it from a collective sense. It is increasingly difficult to find people who understand the technology well enough to troubleshoot it.

Good troubleshooting practices begin with understanding the technology. Having a checklist is helpful but does little more than produce paperwork unless one understands its purpose. Consider the information presented in the remainder of the book to assist you in troubleshooting your network.

5

Troubleshooting Terms and Reference Information

This chapter includes a wide variety of information for one reason—over the years I realized that this information is needed when you are troubleshooting networks. I have hand-picked each section in this chapter and put it together in such a way to provide you a powerful wealth of information.

5.1 Electrical Terminology

If you are new to electricity, you could be concerned or a little scared. My first comment is don't lose your respect for electricity because if you do, and become careless, you could damage your computer or any electronic system. This is one chapter that should be read carefully. Yes, the rest of the book is serious too, but this chapter is especially serious. I recommend caution at every turn when you work with any electrical device, particularly with topics presented here.

To understand and work with electricity, one needs to understand some basic terminology and concepts. After these are understood, one can apply one's practical knowledge. Consider the terminology presented here to begin with.

alternating current (ac) An electric current that is continually varying in value and reversing its direction of flow at regular intervals, usually in a sinusoidal manner. Each repetition from zero to a maximum in one direction and then to a maximum in the other direction and back to zero, is called a *cycle.*

ac frequency The speed at which an ac voltage or current waveform repeats itself. Frequency is measured in hertz (Hz).

amperage The amount of current in amperes (A).

ampere   A practical unit of electrical current. Once ampere of current is 6.24×10^{-18} electrons passing one point in 1 s. It equals 1 C/s. This is the result of 1 V across a resistance of 1 Ω.

apparent power   The product of current and voltage, expressed as kVA. It is the real power (kW) divided by the power factor (PF).

atom   The smallest particle into which an element can be divided and still retain the chemical properties of that element.

balanced current   A current flowing in the two conductors of a balanced line so that, at every point along the line, they are equal in magnitude and opposite in direction.

balanced line   A transmission line consisting of two conductors which are capable of being operated so that the voltages of the two conductors at any transverse plane are equal in magnitude and opposite in polarity with respect to ground. The currents in the two conductors are then equal in magnitude and opposite in direction.

balanced voltages   Voltages that are equal in magnitude and opposite in polarity with respect to ground. They are also called *push-pull voltages.*

brownout   Normally, a voltage reduction initiated by the utility to counter excessive demand on its electric power generation and distribution system.

conductor   A material that serves as a conduit for electric current easily because it offers little electrical resistance. Some examples of conductors are tin, metals, salt water, aluminum, copper, gold, nickel, and platinum.

current   In electricity, the flow of electrons, or the movement thereof, through a conductive material. This is the flow of electrons or holes measured in amperes (A) or in fractions of an ampere such as milliamperes (mA), microamperes (μA), nanoamperes (nA), or picoamperes (pA). Current can be induced by the application of an electric field through a conductor or by changing the electric field either through a conductor or across a capacitor (which is known as *displacement current*).

direct current (dc)   An electric current that flows in one direction.

electric field   The region around an electrically charged body in which other charged bodies are acted on by an attracting or repelling force.

electricity   A fundamental quantity realized in nature that consists of electrons and protons either at rest or in motion. Electricity at rest (not in motion) has an electric field which possesses potential energy and can exert force. Electricity in motion (not at rest) has the characteristics of an electric or magnetic field that possesses potential energy and can exert force.

electron   An elementary atomic particle that carries the smallest negative electric charge. It is highly mobile and orbits the nucleus of an atom.

frequency   The number of complete cycles per unit of time for a periodic quantity such as alternating current, sound waves, or radio waves. The frequency, represented by the letter f, of 1 cycle per second is 1 Hz.

harmonic   A sinusoidal component of a periodic wave, with a frequency that is an integral multiple of the fundamental frequency. The frequency of the second harmonic is twice that of the fundamental frequency or the first harmonic. Also called *harmonic component* and *harmonic frequency.*

harmonic analysis   Any method for identifying and evaluating the harmonics that make up a complex form of voltage, current, or some other varying quantity.

hertz   The SI (Système International d'Unités) unit of frequency, equal to 1 cycle per Web second.

impedance   The total opposition offered by a component or circuit to the flow of an alternating or varying current. It is represented by the letter Z. Impedance is expressed in ohms (Ω) and is the combination of resistance R and reactance.

inductance   The property of a circuit or circuit element that opposes a change in current flow. Inductance causes current changes to lag behind voltage changes. Inductance is measured in henrys, millihenrys, and microhenrys (H, mH, μH). It is represented by the letter L.

kilo   One thousand.

kVA   One thousand voltamperes. A unit for rating devices. The number is derived by multiplying the output in amperes by its operating voltage.

linear   Referring to a relationship in which one function is directly proportional to another function, providing a straight sloping line when plotted on a graph.

magnetic field   Any space or region that a magnetic force exerts on moving electric charges. This field can be produced by a current-carrying coil or conductor, by a permanent magnet, or by the earth itself.

nonlinear   Anything with this characteristic is not directly proportional to its complement.

nonlinear element   An element in which an increase in applied voltage does not produce a proportional increase in current.

nonlinear load   A load for which the relationship between voltage and current is not a linear function. An example of nonlinear loads could be fluorescent lighting and uninterruptible power supply (UPS) systems. These types of loads cause abnormal heating and voltage distortion.

ohm   The SI unit of resistance and impedance. The electric resistance between two points of a conductor when a constant of potential difference of 1 V applied to these points produces a current of 1 A in the conductor, meaning that the conductor is not the seat of any electromotive force.

period   The time required for one complete cycle of a regularly repeated series of events.

photon   A quantum of electromagnetic radiation equal to Planck's constant multiplied by the frequency in hertz. Electromagnetic radiation can be considered as photons of light, X rays, gamma rays, or radio rays.

power   The time rate of doing work or the speed in which work is done. This is represented by the letter P and is measured in watts (W).

power factor   The extent to which the voltage zero differs from the current zero. In ac circuits inductances and capacitances cause a point where the voltage wave passes through zero to differ from the point at which the current wave passes through zero. One complete cycle is 360°; consequently, the difference between zero points (e.g., voltage and current) can be expressed in an angle. The power factor is the cosine of the angle between zero points and is expressed as a decimal fraction of 0.8, or 80 percent. The power factor is the ratio of kW to kVA. The kW equals the kVA times the power factor.

proton An elementary particle that has a positive charge equal in magnitude to the negative charge of the electron. The atomic number of an element indicates the number of protons in the nucleus of each atom of that element. The rest mass of a proton is 1.67×10^{-24} g or 1836.13 times that of an electron.

reactance The opposition to the flow of alternating current by pure inductance or capacitance in a circuit, expressed in ohms (Ω). This is the component of impedance that is not due to resistance.

resistance The opposition that a device or material offers to the flow of direct current, measured in ohms, kilohms, or even megohms. In ac circuits, resistance is the real component of impedance.

root mean squared (rms) The square root of the average of the squares of a series of related values. The effective value of an alternating current, corresponding to the dc value that will produce the same heating effect. The rms value is computed as the square root of the average of the squares of the instantaneous amplitude for one complete cycle. For a sine wave, the rms value is 0.707 times the peak value. Unless otherwise specified, alternating quantities are assumed to be rms values. The rms value is also referred to as the *effective value*; in simpler terms, this is the effective value of voltage, current, and power when these parameters are expressed with such.

sag An ac power-line undervoltage condition that lasts more than ⅟₆₀th of a second. A condition lasting longer than this is referred to as a *brownout*.

sinusoidal Varying in proportion to the sine of an angle or time function. An ordinary alternating current is considered sinusoidal.

spike A short-duration transient whose amplitude considerably exceeds the average amplitude of the associated pulse or signal.

surge A long-duration overvoltage or overcurrent condition.

time The measure of a duration of an event. The fundamental unit of time is the second.

transient A sudden, very brief spike of high voltage on a power line caused by lightning, electrostatic discharge, or power-line switching.

unbalanced line A transmission line that conducts voltage on its two conductors that are not equal with respect to ground.

volt The SI unit of voltage or potential difference. The difference in electrical potential between two points of a conducting wire carrying a constant current of 1 A when the power dissipated between these points is equal to 1 W.

voltampere The unit of apparent power in an ac circuit that contains reactance. Apparent power is equal to the voltage in volts multiplied by the current in amperes, without considering phase.

watt The watt is the unit of electric power. It gives rise in 1 second to the energy of 1 joule. In an ac circuit, the true power is effective volts multiplied by effective amperes, then multiplied by the circuit power factor.

wave A propagated disturbance whose intensity at any point in the medium is a function of time, and whose intensity at a given instant is a function of the position of the point. A wave can be electric, electromagnetic, acoustic, or mechanical.

5.2 Practical Information

If you read many books, you probably realize that some of them have little practical value. I am attempting to provide you with practical information in this book. I realize that many of you do not have a background in electricity. However, the information provided in this chapter, and those that follow, will help you in your network planning.

Wire

There are many types of wire. The focus of this section is on electrical wire, specifically, wire sizes and types. Understanding electrical wire is easy. The smaller the American Wire Gauge (AWG) number, the bigger the wire and hence, the more voltage and current it can accommodate. For example, many common table lamps have a 14- to 18-gauge wire. Standard AWG wire sizes are as follows:

26	8
24	6
22	4
20	3
18	2
16	1
14	0
12	00
10	000

A 26-gauge wire is very small; in fact, it is smaller than wire in most telephone cords that connect a handset to the base. Much of the 10BaseT wire is between 20- and 24-gauge. As mentioned previously, many ordinary table lamps are wired with 14- to 18-gauge wire. Some extension cords that can be purchased in discount stores are 14- to 18-gauge. These are considered general-purpose.

Most houses are wired with 12-gauge wire; some use 10-gauge. A 12-gauge wire for an extension cord would be considered adequate for many shop-type purposes. Many outdoor-use extension cords are 12-gauge, and 10-gauge wire is fairly heavy-duty. Going up in capability and down in numeric order are 8-, 6-, 4-, 2-, and 0-gauge. Wire sizes under 10 become increasingly large and can carry significant voltage and current. Remember, voltage and current are two different things. Let me illustrate this. Consider Figure 5.1. As I write this, I am listening to an ordinary AM/FM radiocassette player that operates on

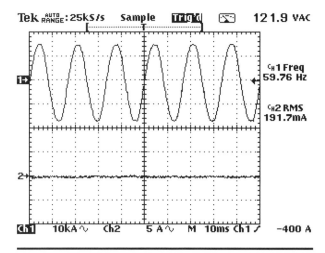

Figure 5.1 AM/FM Radio Voltage and Current Readings

120-V-ac or batteries. Figure 5.1 shows the voltage, frequency, and amperage that the radio uses. Technically, the voltage and frequency are what is available at the wall outlet. The amperage reading is what the radio is using to operate. Note that the amperage draw as indicated from channel 2 is 191.7 mA. This is not very much, and rightfully so—it is simply a desktop radio. You may be thinking this is odd. But wait! Consider Figure 5.2, which shows the readings I took from my microwave oven! Yes, I took the microwave from the kitchen counter and brought it into the lab (Linda said it would be OK!). I connected it to the test outlet; no other device was connected except the

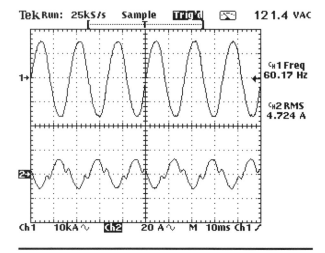

Figure 5.2 Microwave Oven Voltage and Current Readings

Tektronix THS720P power analyzer. Note the voltage, frequency, and amperage readings. The microwave is drawing 4.724 A as shown by channel 2, indicated in the lower portion of the figure. This illustration is the snapshot on initial power-on of the microwave. Now consider Figure 5.3, which shows the reading of the microwave oven, and this time the current draw is 7.764 A. This reading was taken with the microwave in operation, not just after initial power-on. It sustains a significant current draw.

These illustrations are important because they show the difference in device current requirements. Remember, amperage is how much current a device uses. Yes, this is a loose definition, but stay with me. Current is

the flow of electrons, notated by (A) or in fractions of an ampere such as milliamperes (mA), microamperes (μA), nanoamperes (nA), or picoamperes (pA). Current can be induced by the application of an electric field through a conductor or by changing the electric field through a conductor or by changing the electric field across a capacitor (which is known as displacement current).

The measure of current (the amperage draw) is technically "how much" electricity a given device uses. For example, the AM/FM radio obviously uses less electricity than the microwave, as Figures 5.1 and 5.2 show. How can this be? Don't they both use 120 V ac? The measure of how much electricity is used is generally referred to as *current*. Technically the current draw is referred to in amperage or amperes (A). Now, the greater the current or the higher the amperage rating, the more electrons are flowing through a wire. The more electrons flowing through a wire, the hotter the wire becomes. Consequently, the more amperes required for a given device to function, the larger wire size required to deliver that number of amperes.

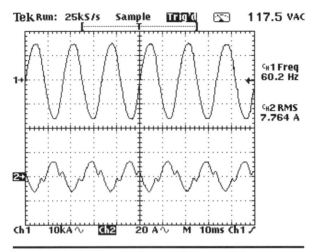

Figure 5.3 Microwave Oven Voltage and Current Readings

Most wire sizes have an amperage rating. *Ampacity* refers to the amount of amperes a given wire can accommodate. Generally, the smaller the wire size in number (e.g., 6 or 2), the more amperes the wire can accommodate. Different tables apply when measuring wire size and ampacity. Whether the wire (also called the *conductor*) is single or multiple, operating in free air, or otherwise factors into the capacity of the wire. The following illustrates the current-carrying capacity of two or three conductors. The measurement shown reflects the AWG number for a Neoprene jacket. Consider the following as a general reference:

2 or 3 conductors

AWG	Current capacity
22	6
20	8
18	14
16	18
14	25
12	30
10	40
8	55
6	75
4	95
3	110
2	130
1	150
0	170
00	195
000	225
0000	260

One factor not presented in this chart is distance. The length of wire always—let me repeat, always—factors into the equation of current draw. The longer the wire run, the greater (larger) wire size needed to deliver X number of amperes. Think about this; it makes sense. Amperage is the movement of electrons. Whenever the length of something is extended, more resistance enters into the equation. Consider the following real-world example I encountered in 1986.

In December 1986 the religious group I was affiliated with at the time was planning to put on a Christmas special. During preparation for the musicians, speakers, singers, etc., we moved considerable electrical equipment to a new location. During setup of the public address (PA) equipment the person "directing the show" realized we needed an extension cord to provide electricity to the PA equipment. This person proceeded to obtain an extension cord and began connecting everything together. The second day of setup I realized this person had used three, 100-ft, 14-gauge extension cords to supply electricity to the power amplifier for the PA equipment. I knew from former education and experience that this was not going to work; the voltage drop was too great at that distance. I tried to inform the person "directing the show" of the problem; he wouldn't do anything after I told him (I think he thought I was too young to understand). I finally told him: "Go ahead, the power amps will roll over and go belly-up." He looked at me askance and went on with final touches. This person was also notorious for doing things on the fly (meaning no trial runs). So, the presentation began and about two minutes into the beginning, guess what happened? That's right, the power amps went belly-up. The voltage drop was too great.

Why the personal story? A couple of reasons. First, sensitive equipment such as computers and power amplifiers are very sensitive to voltage drops, whether as a result of a wire that is too long or for some other reason. Second, just because you have access to an extension cord does not mean that your equipment, whatever it is, will operate correctly. The previous chart of wire size and ampacity indicated that a 20-gauge wire could accommodate 8 A. I doubt this is the case if the 20-gauge wire is 400 ft long! See what I mean?

Still another factor that comes into play with the wire size and ampacity is the number of conductors. For example, some wire has only one conductor, some two, some three, some four, and so forth. This factors into the equation as well.

Still another consideration is the temperature. This factors into the equation, as different types of wire shielding work differently according to temperature. Consider the following information:

Material type	Operating temperature range
Crosslinked polyethylene	−55 to 150
Hermetic	−60 to 125
Hypalon	−30 to 105
EPDM	−60 to 150
Neoprene	−30 to 90
PVC	−35 to 105
Silicone, braided	−75 to 200
Silicone, braidless	−75 to 200
Teflon	−100 to 260

Temperature readings are in Celsius. To convert degrees Celsius into degrees Fahrenheit, multiply by 1.8 and add 32 to the Celsius reading.

The information presented here is from one particular wire vendor; however, other wire vendors refer to wire by type as well and the specifications may differ.

Wire used in houses and commercial buildings is typically ROMEX. This is a stiff outer jacket used to wrap the wire. Inside, each conductor is insulated and the earth ground is typically wrapped in a form of heavy-gauge paper. In contrast, many ordinary extension cords consist of type SJ cable. This type jacket is not as stiff as that of ROMEX (plastic-coated cable). It is relatively flexible. Two other types of cable jackets are SO and SO-W, which are more pliable, like rubber. Most of them are oil- and water-resistant. This type jacketing is used in many commercial-grade extension cords.

In summary, the important considerations to remember with wire are

1. Wire size and length determine current capacity.

2. Wire has a voltage rating.

3. The smaller the wire number, the larger the wire.

4. The number of conductors affects the ampacity.

5. The longer the cable length, the greater the resistance and voltage drop.

5.3   xDSL Terminology

ABCD parameters   A term used to refer to a 2×2 matrix description of the input voltage and current-to-output voltage and the current relationship of a dual-port network.

access network   A portion of a public switched network that connects access nodes to individual subscribers. An access network is predominantly passive, copper-based, twisted-pair wiring.

algorithm-specific signal processor (ASSP)   An integrated circuit designed to perform specific algorithm functions.

alternate mark inversion (AMI)   A baseband-oriented line coding scheme that alternates data symbol parity for adjacent ones (1s).

amplifier nonlinearity   The nonlinear amplifier input/output relationship.

analog front end (AFE)   The part that converts digital signal processing circuits to an analog signal. An analog/digital front-end consists primarily of an ADC and DAC.

analog-to-digital converter (ADC)   An analog integrated circuit that samples, measures, and holds analog signals for digital signal processing.

application-specific integrated circuit (ASIC)   A component designed for specific application functions in contrast to more general-purpose components.

asymmetric digital subscriber line (ADSL)   A technology implemented in modems and subscriber lines that have enhanced throughput. Transmission ranges from 1.5 to 9 Mbps downstream (to what is generally known as the *subscriber*) and from 16 to 800 kbps upstream (both of which will depend on the line distance).

asymptotic coding gain   A value derived when the signal-to-noise ratio (SNR) of value begins to near infinity.

Asynchronous Transfer Mode (ATM)   A high-speed cell-based transmission protocol that can be run over ADSL.

ATM passive optical network   ATM technology implemented over a passive optical network.

attenuation   A signal loss caused by a transmission medium operating at a particular frequency.

ATU-C and ATU-R   An ADSL transmission unit, either central or remote. The device is located at the end of the ADSL line and stands between the line and the first item of equipment in the subscriber premises or telephone switch.

automatic gain control (AGC)   A part of the AFE which manipulates the signal levels received to adequate levels for the input of the ADC.

background noise   Unwanted sounds or other forms of interference with a signal; it is considered to be random, in front of, and also external to the receiver of the intended signal.

balance condition   A state in which a hybrid circuit achieves effective separation between transmitted and received signals.

baseband signals   Data symbols sent to a channel without any form of modulation.

baud rate equalizer   An adaptive channel equalizer operating at the symbol of a baud rate.

Bessel filter   A filter whose frequency response is best defined according to Bessel specifications.

biphase line code   A baseband line code with different phases for zeros and ones.

bipolar with 8-zero substitution line coding   A baseband line code in which ones and zeros are encoded with different (opposite) parities; consequently, every consecutive eight zeros is replaced with a special non-all-zero sequence of zeros.

bit error rate (BER)   A measurement that reflects performance. It is usually in the terms of the number of errors per second or a transmission system.

bit stuffing   The process of inserting an extra bit to correct the frame size.

Bose, Chaudhuri, and Hocquenghem Code (BCH)   A class of cyclic codes which is easily defined and implemented.

brickwall filter   A frequency filter response with a no-loss passband, infinite-loss stopband, and no transition between them.

bridged tap   A pair of twisted-pair cables attached to the telephone subscriber loop; they are unused.

capacitance   The capacity of electrical energy storage in positive and negative charges.

carrier serving area   An area served by a local exchange carrier of the regional Bell Telephone operating company using digital loop carrier technology. The carrier serving area also serves as a design guideline for limiting the length of carrier loops to accommodate digital telephone transmission equipment.

carrierless AM/PM system   A variation of the passband quadrature amplitude modulation (QAM) line code.

central office   A telephone company site used to terminate subscriber loop and which maintains telephone backbone infrastructure.

channel capacity   Reference to the maximum throughput capacity of a particular medium (commonly referred to as a *channel* in the particular sense).

clipping noise   Unwanted interference by peaking DAC or ADC signals.

code book   The reference book of mappings between input information sequences and the output codewords.

companding   A prescribed method of compression of large-amplitude signals to increase the dynamic range of a voice encoder through what is considered nonuniform quantization.

complementary metal oxide semiconductor   A circuit, typically found on the motherboard of computers, composed of n and p (negative and positive) semiconductor material.

conductance   The capacity of electrical energy storage in the strength electromagnetic fields.

convolution code   A coding mechanism in which output codewords depend on input information sequences as well as the state of the encoder.

core network   The combination of switching offices and transmission plant connecting switch offices together. In the United States the core networks are linked by several competing interexchange networks.

crosstalk noise   An unwanted signal carried over adjacent telephone lines, commonly within the same subscriber loop.

cyclic code   A code in which a codeword changes by only one digit when increasing from one number to the next-higher number in a given sequence. Binary code is a type of cyclic code.

dc resistance   Opposition at a direct current or zero frequency.

differential channel capacity   The channel capacity within a unit of frequency. The differential channel capacity is a derivative of the conventional channel capacity. It can be used to examine the frequency characteristic aspect of a channel.

differential hybrid circuit   A hybrid circuit that deliberately connects to ADC with DAC and differential input and output, respectively.

digital loop carrier (DLC) system   A high-throughput digital transmission system developed to connect centralized offices to a remote terminal. A DLC system can be implemented using existing twisted-pair telephone subscriber loops or optical fiber cables.

digital signal processor   A programmable semiconductor circuit capable of implementing multiple signal processing algorithms.

digital signal 0   A 64-kbps representation of voice.

digital signal 1   Representation of 24 voice channels bundled into a 193-bit frame and transmitted at a rate of 1.544 Mbps. This unframed version is 192 bits at a rate of 1.536 Mbps.

digital signal 1 (DS1) circuit   The first level of the North American digital hierarchy with a nominal rate of 1.544 Mbps.

digital subscriber line   The original name for the physical layer of the Basic Rate Access (ISDN) channel. The DSL implements a 2B1Q baseband line code with a transmission throughput of 160 kbps. In the DSL environment, modems on both ends of a twisted-pair wire deliver ISDN basic rate access.

digital subscriber line access multiplexer   A device that takes a number of ADSL lines and concentrates them into a single ATM line.

digital-to-analog converter (DAC)   An analog integrated circuit that takes in a group of binary digits.

discrete Fourier transform   Operation implemented with a fast Fourier transform (FFT) algorithm using digital hardware.

discrete multitone (DMT) system   A multicarrier line code whose modulation and demodulation are implemented using the inverse fast Fourier transform and fast Fourier transform, respectively. The twisted-pair channel intersymbol interference of a DMT system is mitigated by dividing the transmission spectrum into many subchannels.

discrete time domain   A time domain in which signal values are designed to change only at discrete sampling instances, referred to as *periodic intervals*.

distribution area   The area which is generally served by what some call a remote terminal; however, the nature of the term "remote" is relative to the context thereof.

distribution cable   A part of the telephone infrastructure that connects the feeder cables to the drop wires.

double-Barker code   Code involving word synchronization where contents are the double-bit assignment of a Barker code. This double-Barker code is defined for the HDSL frame structure.

drop wire   A telephone wire (typically) that connects distribution cable to a piece of subscriber equipment.

dual-tone multifrequency   A method used for telephone touch dialing.

echo canceler   The digital signal processing circuitry that implements components required to perform cancellation in the unit.

echo cancellation   The transmit signal separation that is received from the signal through the use of an adaptive filter.

echo path impulse response   A time domain impulse response of the echo path gauged from the time of transmission to the time of reception.

echo path transfer function   The frequency domain description of the echo path.

echo return loss   The amount of loss as measured on the echo path.

embedded operations channel   A virtual communication channel that is embedded in the physical layer for intertransceiver and network maintenance purposes.

Exclusive-or operation   The binary operation that returns a 1 only when one of its two operations is a 1.

far-end crosstalk noise   The unwanted distribution of signals across one end of the twisted-pair telephone loop.

fast Fourier transform   An efficient digital implementation of the Fourier transform that converts a time domain signal to its frequency domain equivalent.

feedback filter   The filter of a DFE. This filter cancels the ending portion of a channel impulse response using recovered data symbols. A feedback filter can be implemented only at the baud rate.

feeder distribution interface   A twisted-pair telephone loop plant interface point between feeder and distribution cables.

feeder network   The part of a public switched network that connects access nodes to the core network.

feedforward filter   The portion of a DFE known as the *FFF*; it compensates for channel distortion with a linear equalization approach. The FFF is implemented at multiples of baud rates.

finite impulse response filter   A device that has a finite number of delay and multiplication elements. Its output is the convolution of input and filter coefficients.

Fourier transform   A linear transform based on the sinusoidal expansion of a signal.

fractionally spaced equalizer   A channel equalizer operating on multiples of the signaling rate.

frequency division duplex system   A system in which channels transmit in opposite directions separated by frequency divisions.

Galois field   A closed algebraic field describing encoding and decoding operations.

Gaussian distribution   A bell-shaped statistical distribution function.

general adaptive FIR filter   A semiprogrammable Fourier infrared semiconductor circuit for the implementation of DSL transceivers.

guard period   A period used in a DMT system to elevate the effect of channel distortion.

hamming distance   The minimum number of bits that differ between every pair of codewords.

high-data-rate digital subscriber line (HDSL)   A telephone line in which modems operate on both ends of the line (twisted pair), delivering T1 or E1 speeds.

hybrid fiber coax   A system where fiber is used in a distribution point that is close to the subscriber; then the signal is converted to the subscriber premises over coaxial cable.

impedance   The relationship between the applied voltage and the induced current of an electrical device.

impulse noise   Short-duration, high-magnitude noise whose occurrence does not follow the normal distribution.

inductance   Measurement of the amount of energy stored in the magnetic field format.

Integrated Service Digital Network (ISDN)   A digital network with integrated services, switch, and maintenance functions.

intelligent network architecture A general telephone networking concept that coordinates trunk, network, service, and management capabilities.

intersymbol interference Interference between adjacent data symbols caused by channel distortion.

inverse discrete Fourier transform The discrete version of the inverse of Fourier transform. It is usually implemented with the IFFT algorithm using digital hardware.

inverse fast Fourier transform (IFFT) An efficient digital implementation of the inverse Fourier transform that converts a frequency domain signal to its time domain equivalent.

IPC converter An ISDN-to-Plain Old Telephone System (POTS) converter, which converts an ISDN interface to a POTS interface.

LC **ladder** This is an analog filter structure in which inductance and capacitance are connected in an alternate cascading fashion.

least mean-square algorithm An algorithm commonly used for adaptive filters because of its simplicity and robustness.

least significant bit The bit that determines the presence of the zero power of two terms in a binary polynominal representation.

line termination The Central Office side of the DSL transceiver defined for the ISDN Basic Rate Access channel.

linear channel equalizer A channel equalizer with only received signals as its input.

linear echo canceler An canceler dealing only with a linear echo path.

load coils Inductance coils used in telephone loops to improve the transmission performance of the voice band channel.

local exchange carrier A local telephone access and service provider in the United States, such as Pacific Bell and GTE in Los Angeles.

lookup table A map of the input/output logic relationship stored in memory or described by a table instead of a logic expression.

loopback A direct connection between the transmit path and the receive path. Loopback can be used for testing purposes or to describe the direct connection between the transmit clock and the clock recovered from the received signal.

magnitude The amplitude of a signal.

Manchester line code A line code that maps a data bit of 1 into a pulse containing both a positive level and a negative level and a data bit of 0 into the same pulse with inverted polarity.

minimum mean-square error An optimization objective to minimize the average power of error.

modified duobinary line code A baseband line code in which each data symbol is followed by its negative replica after a two-symbol delay.

most significant bit The bit that determines the presence of the highest power of the two terms in a binary polynomial representation.

near-end crosstalk noise   Crosstalk noise emanating from near-end transmitters.

near-maximum-likelihood algorithm   A receiver algorithm whose performance is close to that of a maximum-likelihood algorithm, but with a simplified implementation.

network interface device   A telephone company–supplied module for interconnection between the telephone subscriber loop and in-house wiring at the loop entry point.

network termination   The subscriber side of a DSL transceiver defined for an ISDN Basic Rate Access channel.

noise   Generally considered to be random signals with no detectable information.

noise floor   The background noise level across a frequency band.

nonlinear echo canceler   An echo canceler capable of accommodating an echo path with a certain degree of nonlinearity.

nonlinearity   The input/output value deviations for digital-to-analog and analog-to-digital conversions.

Nyquist shaping filter   A digital FIR filter that introduces no intersymbol interference at particular periodic sampling points.

Operation, Administration, Maintenance, and Provisioning Channel   An embedded utility channel for carrying out auxiliary functions.

optical carrier 3   An optical fiber line carrying 155 Mbps payload. This designation is used in the United States; however, it is generally acknowledged worldwide.

optical network unit (ONU)   A form of access node that converts optical signals that are transmitted over fiber and then electrical signals that can be transmitted by coaxial cable or twisted-pair cable to suscribers.

parity check code   An encoding method for which the coding redundancy consists of the parity check bits of message bits.

passband signals   Line codes that are modulated by a cosine- and/or sine-wave carrier frequency.

peak-to-peak average voltage ratio   Measurement for the dynamic range of a line signal.

peak-to-peak voltage   The voltage measured from the highest reading to the lowest reading; both readings represent the "peak" of the signal, both positive and negative.

phase   The starting angle of a sinusoidal signal.

phase delay   The starting-time shift of a sinusoidal signal.

phase-invariant Trellis codes   Trellis codes that preserve the angular information of data symbols.

phase-locked loop   A feedback loop with a very tight bandwidth that can be used to track the clock signal.

Plain Old Telephone Service   Colloquial term for the telephone service (primarily in the United States) that many people became accustomed to in the latter part of the twentieth century.

post–cursor channel impulse response   The portion following the peak of an impulse response.

power spectrum density   The power density signal at different frequencies.

pre–cursor channel impulse response   The portion preceding the peak of an impulse response.

private branch exchange (PBX)   A telephone switch for private business applications.

propagation constant   The attenuation and phase shift of a cable with terminations.

Public Switched Telephone Network   The portion of the telephone network in the United States that is switched and connects central offices.

pulse code modulation   A pulse-width representation of a baseband multilevel signal. In other words, the magnitude of a signal is translated.

pulse duration modulation   A pulse-width representation of a baseband multilevel signal. The magnitude of a signal is translated into the width of a fixed-height pulse.

quadrature amplitude modulation (QAM) line code   A line code generated through the modulation in phase and quadrature data symbols with cosine and sine phases of a carrier frequency.

quadrature phase shift keying signals   A passband signal generated through modulation of complex symbols with four different angles of a carrier frequency.

quantization noise   The noise generated when converting an analog signal to a digital one via rounding to the nearest signal level.

rate adaptive asymmetric digital subscriber line   A version of ADSL in which modems test the line at the start of use and adapt their operating speed to the fastest line speed that the line itself can handle.

rate conversion filters   A digital filter that has different input and output data rates.

RC-**balanced network**   A network, or hybrid circuit, in which resistors and capacitors are of equal magnitude or strength. Inductance is not a factor in this circuit.

receiver front-end noise   A combination of background and electronic noise at the input of a transceiver.

Reed–Solomon code   A class of nonbinary BCH codes with features for easy code definition and implementation.

resolution   The accuracy of a digital circuit.

ring trip   The disconnection of ringing voltage from the loop when the called party picks up the telephone.

rolloff   A point at which the energy of a spectrum or magnitude of the transfer function is reduced by a certain amount.

sigma-delta modulation   An ADC technique that trades high processing speed for high resolution.

signal-to-noise ratio (SNR)   A measurement indicating the quality of a signal in relation to the unwanted noise on the channel.

single-ended hybrid circuit   A hybrid circuit that effects connection to a single-ended line driver.

superframe format   A data synchronization structure built on data synchronization frames of a lower hierarchy.

symmetrical digital subscriber line   An HDSL over the POTS network using a single telephone line. The name has not been adopted by standards groups, but it is used generically by different people in the technical community.

synchronization word   A bit or symbol pattern designed for the synchronization of data frames.

syndrome vector   A decoder-derived vector that has a pattern unique to particular (discrete) error sequences.

T1 line   A specially equipped telephone line in the United States that can deliver transmission throughput capability at T1 speeds (1.544 Mbps nationally; ≤2.048 Mbps internationally).

time compression multiplex transmission   Transmission opposite in direction to that achieved via a time division multiplex.

timing recovery   A mathematical algorithm used to derive the clock from the received signal.

transfer function   The frequency response of a linear system or a linear channel.

transmit power density   Reference to transmission of power at a particular frequency.

transmit symbol pulse shape   Defined for baseband code as a time domain mask to ensure interoperability among different computer equipment is possible.

Trellis code modulation   A combination of selected code and bit symbol mapping in order to achieve an improvement on coding gain with no significant bandwidth intrusion.

Unger NEXT model   A simple linear NEXT model based on computer simulation results.

variable frame structure   A frame structure with a length which can be altered to accommodate symmetric transmission in opposite directions.

very high-data rate digital subscriber line   A modem for twisted-pair access where data rates range from the 12.9 to 52.8 Mbps at a maximum distance of about 1000 to 4500 ft.

very large-scale integrated circuit   A high-density circuit in which signal processing has been incorporated.

voltage-controlled crystal oscillator   An accurate oscillator whose frequency can be altered by different voltages.

5.4   Fiber-Optic Terminology

Aramid yarn   A component which provides a tensile strength and support to fiber bundles.

attenuation The decrease of signal power magnitude between points; a term that expresses the total loss of an optical system.

attenuation coefficient The rate of power loss with respect to the distance along the fiber, which is usually measured in decibels per kilometer at a specific wavelength.

buffer tubes Cylindrical coverings that house optical fibers to protect them.

bundle A group of optical fibers shrouded with a jacket or buffer tube.

cable assembly Fiber-optic cable with connectors on each end.

cable bend radius The minimum bend when installing fiber-optic cable.

central member The innermost component in bulk cable. In many instances it serves as a strengthening component and often consists of steel, fiberglass, or glass-reinforced plastic.

cladding The material surrounding the core part of the fiber cable.

coating Material on a fiber while in the drawing process; this protects it from handling and environmental factors.

composite cable Cable containing fiber and copper media [referred to in the National Electric Code (770)].

core The center part of the optical fiber by which light is emitted.

decibel That unit which is used to measure light signals. One decibel (dB) is equal to one tenth the common logarithm of the ratio of the two levels.

dielectric A nonmetallic, nonconductive mechanism. Glass fibers and other gizmos are considered dielectrics.

dispersion Cause of bandwidth limitations in a fiber.

ferrule A rigid tube used to protect and align fiber in a given connector.

fiber A thin filament of glass; an optical component of core and cladding that is capable of carrying pulses from light.

fiber bend radius The maximum radius to which a fiber can bend before increased risk of breakage or increase in attenuation.

fusion splice A joint at which a permanent juncture occurs; characterized by the formation of a single fiber.

graded index A type of fiber design in which the refractive index of the particular core is lower than toward the outside of the fiber core and increases toward the center thereof. The result, therefore, is the bending of light rays inward, thus allowing them to travel faster in the lower-index-of-refraction region.

hybrid cable A fiber cable that contains two or more different types of fiber such as 625-μm multimode and single-mode fiber.

index matching fluid A fluid with an index of refraction close to that of glass that reduces reflections caused by a refractive-index difference.

kilometer (km) A metric unit of measurement equivalent to 3281 ft.

laser diode   Light amplified by the emission of radiation. This is light generated at around 780, 1310, or ~1550 nm.

light-emitting diode   A semiconductor used to transmit light.

loose-tube cable   A type of cable design with coated fibers in a tube.

mechanical splicing   The joining of two fibers to enable a continuous signal.

mode field diameter   The coding of information onto a carrier frequency which includes amplitude, frequency, and/or phase modulation.

multimode fiber   An optical waveguide (fiber) in which light can traverse in multiple modes. The typical core/cladding size is 62.5/125 μm.

nanometer (nm)   A unit of measurement equal to one-billionth of a meter.

Optical Time Domain Reflectometer   An instrument (proprietary to Siecor) used to measure the quality of light transmission through fiber-optic cable. It functions by sending a light pulse through a fiber cable, providing a graph of the backlight pattern of light.

pigtail   An optical fiber that has a connector installed on only one end.

reflectance   The ratio of power reflected to the incident power at a connector or other component or device; it is usually measured in decibels.

tight-buffered cable   A type of cable in which each glass fiber is buffered tightly by a protective thermoplastic coating to a diameter of 900 μm.

wavelength   The distance between two successive points of an electromagnetic waveform; it is usually measured in nanometers.

5.5   Significant Internet Events

Many have asked me about the history of the Internet. Countless times I have mentioned its history, including significant events that relate to it in one way or another. This section provides a general reference to some significant Internet dates and events.

1957   Advanced Research Project Agency (ARPA) is formed.

1961   First paper on packet-switching technology is published.

1962   Significant paper on packet-switching networks with no single point of failure is published.

1965   Two systems are linked together (one at MIT, the other in Santa Monica, CA).

1966   ARPANET has its first plan.

1967   ARPANET publishes the first paper reflecting its design.

1968   Packet-switched network design is proposed to ARPA.

1969   ARPANET is commissioned by Department of Defense (DoD) to do research networking. The first machine-to-machine message is sent between a system at UCLA and the Stanford Research Institute.

1970   The ALOHA network is created.

1971	A total of 15 systems now exist on the ARPANET.
1972	Specification of TELNET (RFC 318) and the first email software are written.
1973	The first international connections are made to ARPANET; that is, University College of London. The FTP (RFC 454) is presented.
1974	The design of Transmission Control Protocol (TCP) is written by Cerf and Kahn.
1976	UNIX-to-UNIX-Copy program is created at AT&T.
1977	The email specification (RFC 733) is written.
1979	ARPA sets up the Internet Configuration Control Board (ICCB).
1981	The Because It's Time network (BITnet) is started.
1982	External Gateway Protocol standard is written (RFC 827). DoD proclaims TCP/IP as the standard protocol for its use.
1983	The ARPANET converts from the Network Control Program to TCP/IP protocol.
1984	MILNET becomes part of the Defense Data Network. The Berkeley version 4.2 of the UNIX operating system is released. The Internet Architecture Board replaces the ICCB. The Domain Name System is introduced and the number of hosts connected to the Internet is over 1000.
1985	The Information Sciences Institute at USC (University of Southern Calif.) becomes responsible for Domain Name System management.
1986	The National Science Foundation Network (NSFnet) creates a 56-kbps backbone. The Network News Transfer Protocol is created.
1987	The number of Internet hosts exceeds 10,000.
1988	Internet Relay Chat is created by J. Oikarinen of Finland.
1989	The number of Internet hosts breaks 100,000. The first commercial email relays through the Internet and MCI (Media Control Interface) is achieved.
1990	The ARPANET ceases to exist. The first commercial Internet service provider, known as *world.std.com,* comes into existence. The Archie protocol is released.
1991	The Wide Area Information Server (WAIS) is released. The World Wide Web (WWW) is released by CERN Institute for Particle Physics (Geneva). Gopher is released.
1992	Chartering of the Internet Society (ISOC) occurs. The World Bank goes online. The number of hosts on the Internet breaks 1,000,000.
1993	The InterNIC is created to provide specific Internet services such as registration, information, and directory/database information. The U.S. White House and the United Nations go online.
1994	Information World, Inc. is incorporated. The WWW becomes the most popular service on the Internet. Multiple radio broadcasts begin on the Internet.
1995	The new NSFnet is created with a very high speed backbone. The WWW goes beyond FTP traffic on NSFnet. Domain Name registration fees begin. America Online, CompuServe, and Prodigy begin offering Internet access. The Canadian government goes online.
1996	First acknowledged serious security breaches occur at the CIA (U.S. Central Intelligence Agency), Department of Justice, and Air Force. First severe meltdown of Internet service providers due to overloads occurs.

1997   The first 2000th RFC is reached. The American Registry for Internet Numbers (ARIN) is established. Information World, Inc. bypasses $2 million in its initial corporate equipment investment.

1998   The notion of electronic postage stamps on the Internet becomes reality. Information World, Inc. achieves its first successful email presentation. Information World, Inc. offers video over its network to its customers.

5.6   How to Use Internet Troubleshooting Tools

This information presented here is the same as that which you can find on the Internet, with the exception that it is easier to read. Some of the most commonly available TCP/IP and Internet tools and utilities allow users to access the wide variety of information on the network, such as determining whether a particular host is up to viewing a multimedia thesis on foreign policy. This section also describes discussion lists accessible from the Internet, ways to obtain Internet and TCP/IP documents, and some resources that help users weave their way through the Internet. This information is presented as a helpful tutorial for individual self-learning, a step-by-step laboratory manual for a course, or the basis for a site-specific user's manual. It is intended as a basic guide only, and the reader will be referred to other sources for more detailed information.

Nomenclature

The following sections provide descriptions and detailed examples of several TCP/IP utilities and applications, including the reproduction of actual sessions using these utilities (with some extraneous information removed). Each section describes a single TCP/IP-based tool, its application, and, in some cases, how it works. The text description is usually followed by an actual sample session.

The sample dialogs presented below were obtained from a variety of software and hardware systems, including AIX (IBM's Advanced Interactive eXecutive) running on an IBM RS/6000, Linux on an Intel 486, MultiNet TCP/IP over VMS on a VAX (DEC's Virtual Access eXtension), and FTP Software's OnNet (formerly PC/TCP) running on a DOS/Windows PC. Although the examples below can be used as a guide to using and learning about the capabilities of TCP/IP tools, the reader should understand that not all of these utilities may be found at all TCP/IP hosts nor in all commercial software packages. Furthermore, the user interface for different packages will be different and the actual command line may appear differently than shown here; this will be particularly true for graphical user interfaces (GUIs) running over Windows, X-Windows, OS/2, or Macintosh systems. Windows-based sessions are not shown here because most GUI-based TCP/IP packages obscure some of the detail that is essential for understanding what is really happening when you click on a button or drag a file. The Internet has many exciting things to offer, but standardized interfaces to the protocols is not yet one of them!

In the descriptions below, commands are shown in a Courier font [as in PostScript (Adobe Systems, Inc.) and HTML (HyperText Markup Language) versions]; items appearing in square brackets ([ ]) are optional, the vertical bar (|) means OR, parameters appearing with no brackets or within curly brackets ({ }) are mandatory, and parameter names that need to be replaced with a specific value are shown within angle brackets (< >) (they would be italic in PostScript and HTML versions). In the sample dialogs, user input is denoted with asterisks (**) in the margin (this would be in bold in PostScript and HTML versions).

Information about Internet hosts and domains

There are several tools that let you learn information about Internet hosts and domains. These tools provide the ability for an application or enable a user to perform host name/address reconciliation (NSLOOKUP), determine whether another host is up and available (PING), learn about another host's users (Finger), and learn the route that packets will take to another host (Traceroute).

NSLOOKUP. NSLOOKUP is the name server lookup program that is shipped with many TCP/IP software packages. A user can use NSLOOKUP to examine entries in the Domain Name System (DNS) database that pertain to a particular host or domain; one common use is to determine a host system's IP address from its name or the host's name from its IP address. The general form of the command to make a single query is

```
nslookup [IP_address|host_name]
```

If the program is started without any parameters, the user will be prompted for input; the user can enter either an IP address or host name at that time, and the program will respond with the name and address of the default name server, the name server actually used to resolve each request, and the IP address or host name that was queried. The exit function is used to quit the NSLOOKUP application.

Three simple queries are shown in the example below:

1. Requests the address of the host named *www.hill.com,* the World Wide Web server at Hill Associates. As it turns out, this is not the true name of the host, but an alias. The full name of the host and the IP address are listed by NSLOOKUP.

2. Requests the address of host *syrup.hill.com,* which is the same host as in the first query. Note that NSLOOKUP provides a "nonauthoritative" answer. Since NSLOOKUP just queried this same address, the information is still in its cache memory. Rather than send additional messages to the name server, the answer is one that it remembers from before; the

server didn't look up the information again, however, so it is not guaranteed to still be accurate (because the information might have changed within the last few milliseconds!).

3. Requests the name of the host with the given IP address. The result points to the Internet gateway to Australia, *munnari.oz.au.*

One additional query is shown in the dialog below. NSLOOKUP examines information that is stored by the DNS. The default NSLOOKUP queries examine basic address records (called "A records") to reconcile the host name and IP address, although other information is also available. In the final query below, for example, the user wants to know where electronic mail addressed to the *hill.com* domain actually gets delivered, since *hill.com* is not the true name of an actual host. This is accomplished by changing the query type to look for mail exchange (MX) records by issuing a set type command (which must be in lowercase). The query shows that mail addressed to *hill.com* is actually sent to a mail server called *mail.hill.com.* If that system is not available, mail delivery will be attempted first to *mailme.hill.com* and then to *netcomsv.netcom.com*; the order of these attempts is controlled by the "preference" value. This query also returns the name of the domain's name servers and all associated IP addresses.

The DNS is beyond the scope of information here, although more information about the concepts and structure of the DNS can be found in RFCs 1034 and 1591. The help command can be issued at the program prompt for information about NSLOOKUP's more advanced commands.

```
  **SMCVAX$ nslookup
  Default Server: ns1.ner.bbnplanet.net
  Address: 192.52.71.5
**> www.hill.com
  Name:  syrup.hill.com
  Address: 199.182.20.3
  Aliases: www.hill.com
**> syrup.hill.com
  Non-authoritative answer:
  Name: syrup.hill.com
  Address: 199.182.20.3
**> 128.250.1.21
  Name: munnari.OZ.AU
  Address: 128.250.1.21
**> set type=MX
**> hill.com
  hill.com preference = 20, mail exchanger = mail.hill.com
  hill.com preference = 40, mail exchanger = mailme.hill.com
  hill.com preference = 60, mail exchanger = netcomsv.netcom.com
  hill.com nameserver = nameme.hill.com
  hill.com nameserver = ns1.noc.netcom.net
  hill.com nameserver = ns.netcom.com
  mail.hill.com internet address = 199.182.20.4
  mailme.hill.com internet address = 199.182.20.3
  netcomsv.netcom.com internet address = 192.100.81.101
  ns1.noc.netcom.net internet address = 204.31.1.1
```

```
  ns.netcom.com internet address = 192.100.81.105
**> exit
  SMCVAX$
```
= = = = = = =

Packet Internetwork Groper (PING).   This is one of the most widely available tools bundled with TCP/IP software packages. PING uses a series of Internet Control Message Protocol (ICMP) Echo messages to determine whether a remote host is active or inactive, and to determine the round-trip delay in communicating with it.

A common form of the PING command, showing some of the more commonly available options that are of use to general users, is

```
ping [-q] [-v] [-R] [-c Count] [-i Wait] [-s PacketSize] Host
```

where

-q = quiet output; nothing is displayed except summary lines at start-up and completion

-v = verbose output, which lists ICMP packets that are received in addition to echo responses

-R = record route option; includes the RECORD_ROUTE option in the Echo Request packet and displays the route buffer on returned packets

-c Count = the number of Echo Requests to be sent before concluding test (default is to run until interrupted with a control-C)

-i wait = the number of seconds to wait between sending each packet (default = 1)

-s PacketSize = the number of data bytes to be sent; the total ICMP packet size will be PacketSize+8 bytes due to the ICMP header (default = 56, or a 64-byte packet)

Host = IP address or host name of target system

In the first example below, the user PINGs the host *thumper.bellcore.com*, requesting that six (-c) messages be sent, each containing 64 bytes (-s) of user data. The display shows the round-trip delay of each Echo message returned to the sending host; at the end of the test, summary statistics are displayed.

In the second example, the user PINGs the host *smcvax.smcvt.edu,* requesting that 10 messages be sent in quiet mode (-q). In this case, a summary is printed at the conclusion of the test and individual responses are not listed. Older versions of the PING command, which are still available on some systems, had the following general format:

```
ping [-s] {IP_address|host_name} [PacketSize] [Count]
```

In this form, the optional -s string tells the system to continually send an ICMP Echo message every second; the optional PacketSize parameter specifies the number of bytes in the `Echo` message (the message will contain `PacketSize-8 bytes` of data; the default is 56 bytes of data and a 64-byte message); and the optional `Count` parameter indicates the number of `Echo` messages to send before concluding the test (the default is to run the test continuously until interrupted).

```
= = = = = = = = = = = = = = = = = = = = = = = = = = = = = = = = = = = = =
**syrup:/home$ ping -c 6 -s 64 thumper.bellcore.com
PING thumper.bellcore.com (128.96.41.1): 64 data bytes
72 bytes from 128.96.41.1: icmp_seq = 0 ttl = 240 time = 641.8 ms
72 bytes from 128.96.41.1: icmp_seq = 2 ttl = 240 time = 1072.7 ms
72 bytes from 128.96.41.1: icmp_seq = 3 ttl = 240 time = 1447.4 ms
72 bytes from 128.96.41.1: icmp_seq = 4 ttl = 240 time = 758.5 ms
72 bytes from 128.96.41.1: icmp_seq = 5 ttl = 240 time = 482.1 ms
-- thumper.bellcore.com ping statistics --
6 packets transmitted, 5 packets received, 16% packet loss
round-trip min/avg/max = 482.1/880.5/1447.4 ms
**syrup:/home$ ping -q -c 10 smcvax.smcvt.edu
PING smcvax.smcvt.edu (192.80.64.1): 56 data bytes
-- smcvax.smcvt.edu ping statistics --
10 packets transmitted, 8 packets received, 20% packet loss
round-trip min/avg/max = 217.8/246.4/301.5 ms
= = = = = = = = = = = = = = = = = = = = = = = = = = = = = = = = = = = = =
```

Finger. The Finger program may be used to find out who is logged in on another system or to obtain detailed information about a specific user. This command has also introduced a brand new verb; fingering someone on the Internet is not necessarily a rude thing to do! The Finger User Information Protocol is described in RFC 1288. The most general format of the Finger command is

```
finger [username]@host_name
```

The first example below shows the result of fingering an individual user at a remote system. The first line of the response shows the username, the user's real name, and their process identifier, application, and terminal port number. Additional information may be supplied at the option of the user in "plan" and/or "project" files that they supply; these files are often named `PLAN.TXT` or `PROJECT.TXT`, respectively, and reside in a user's root directory (or somewhere in an appropriate search path).

The second example shows the result of fingering a remote system. This lists all the processes currently running at the fingered system or other information, depending on how the remote system's administrator set up the system to respond to the Finger command.

```
= = = = = = = = = = = = = = = = = = = = = = = = = = = = = = = = = = = = =
**C:> finger kumquat@smcvax.smcvt.edu
[smcvax.smcvt.edu]
KUMQUAT Gary Kessler     KUMQUAT not logged in
Last login Fri 16-Sep-2000 3:47PM-EDT
= = = = = = = = = = = = = = = = = = = = = = = = = = = = = = = = = = = = =
```

Traceroute. Traceroute is another common TCP/IP tool, this one allowing users to learn about the route that packets take from their local host to a remote host. Although used often by network and system managers as a simple, yet powerful, debugging tool, Traceroute can be used by end users to learn something about the ever-changing structure of the Internet.

The classic Traceroute command has the following general format (where "#" represents a positive integer value associated with the qualifier):

```
traceroute [-m #] [-q #] [-w #] [-p #]    {IP_address|host_name}
```

where   -m = the maximum allowable TTL value, measured as the number of hops allowed before the program terminates (default = 30)

-q = the number of UDP packets that will be sent with each time-to-live setting (default = 3)

-w = the amount of time, in seconds, to wait for an answer from a particular router before giving up (default = 5)

-p = the invalid port address at the remote host (default = 33434)

The Traceroute example below shows the route between a host at St. Michael's College (*domain smcvt.edu*) and a host at Hill Associates (*www.hill.com*), both located in Colchester, VT, but served by different Internet service providers (ISPs).

1. St. Michael's College is connected to the Internet via BBN Planet; since the mid-1980s, BBN operated the NSF's regional ISP, the New England Academic and Research Network (NEARNET), which was renamed in 1994. The first hop, then, goes to St. Mike's BBN Planet gateway router (*smc.bbnplanet.net*). The next hop goes to another BBN Planet router (denoted here only by IP address since a name was not assigned to the device), until the packet reaches the BBN Planet T3 backbone.

2. The packet takes two hops through routers at BBN Planet's Cambridge (MA) facility and is then forwarded to BBN Planet in New York City, where the packet takes four more hops. The packet is then forwarded to BBN Planet in College Park (MD).

3. The packet is sent to BBN Planet's router at MAE-East, MFS Datanet's Network Access Point (NAP) in Washington, DC. [MAE stands for Metropolitan Area Exchange, and is a Fiber Distributed Data Interface (FDDI) ring interconnecting routers from subscribing ISPs.] The packet is then forwarded to NETCOM, Hill Associates' ISP.

4. The packet now travels through NETCOM's T3 backbone, following links from Washington, DC to Chicago to Santa Clara (CA), to San Jose (CA).

5. The packet is now sent to the Hill Associates router (again, a system designated only by an IP address since the NETCOM side of the router was not named) and then passed to the target system. The host's real name is

not *www.hill.com,* but *syrup.hill.com.* The original version of Traceroute works by sending a sequence of User Datagram Protocol (UDP) datagrams to an invalid port address at the remote host. Using the default settings, three datagrams are sent, each with a Time-To-Live (TTL) field value set to one. The TTL value of 1 causes the datagram to "time out" as soon as it hits the first router in the path; this router will then respond with an ICMP Time Exceeded Message (TEM) indicating that the datagram has expired. Another three UDP messages are now sent, each with the TTL value set to 2, which causes the second router to return ICMP.

This process continues until the packets actually reach the other destination. Since these datagrams are trying to access an invalid port at the destination host, ICMP Destination Unreachable Messages are returned indicating an unreachable port; this event signals the Traceroute program that it is finished! The Traceroute program displays the round-trip delay associated with each attempt. (Note that some current implementations of Traceroute use the `Record-Route` option in IP rather than the method described above.)

As an aside, Traceroute did not begin life as a general-purpose utility, but as a quick-and-dirty debugging aid used to find a routing problem. The code (complete with comments!) is available by anonymous FTP in the file `traceroute.tar.Z` from the host ftp.ee.lbl.gov.

```
= = = = = = = = = = = = = = = = = = = = = = = = = = = = = = = = = = = = =
**SMCVAX$ traceroute www.hill.com
traceroute to syrup.hill.com (199.182.20.3), 30 hops max, 38 byte
packets
 1. smc.bbnplanet.net (192.80.64.5) 10ms 0ms 0ms
 2. 131.192.48.105 (131.192.48.105) 0ms 10ms 10ms
 3. cambridge1-cr4.bbnplanet.net (199.94.204.77) 40ms 40ms 50ms
 4. cambridge1-br1.bbnplanet.net (4.0.1.205) 30ms 50ms 50ms
 5. nyc1-br2.bbnplanet.net (4.0.1.121) 60ms 60ms 40ms
 6. nyc2-br2.bbnplanet.net (4.0.1.154) 60ms 50ms 60ms
 7. nyc2-br2.bbnplanet.net (4.0.1.154) 60ms 40ms 50ms
 8. nyc2-br1.bbnplanet.net (4.0.1.54) 70ms 60ms 30ms
 9. collegepk-br2.bbnplanet.net (4.0.1.21) 50ms 50ms 40ms
10. maeeast.bbnplanet.net (4.0.1.18) 200ms 170ms 210ms
11. fddi.mae-east.netcom.net (192.41.177.210) 60ms 50ms 70ms
12. t3-2.was-dc-gw1.netcom.net (163.179.220.181) 70ms 60ms 50ms
13. t3-2.chw-il-gw1.netcom.net (163.179.220.186) 70ms 80ms 80ms
14. t3-2.scl-ca-gw1.netcom.net (163.179.220.190) 140ms 110ms 160ms
15. t3-1.sjx-ca-gw1.netcom.net (163.179.220.193) 120ms 130ms 120ms
16. 198.211.141.8 (198.211.141.8) 220ms 260ms 240ms
17. syrup.hill.com (199.182.20.3) 220ms 240ms 219ms
SMCVAX$
= = = = = = = = = = = = = = = = = = = = = = = = = = = = = = = = = = = = =
```

Two fundamental tools

The two most basic tools for Internet applications are TELNET and the File Transfer Protocol (FTP). TELNET allows a user to login to a remote host over a TCP/IP network, while FTP, as the name implies, allows a user to move files between two TCP/IP hosts. These two utilities date back to the very early days of the ARPANET.

TELNET. TELNET is TCP/IP's virtual terminal protocol. Using TELNET, a user connected to one host can log in to another host, appearing as a directly attached terminal at the remote system; this is TCP/IP's definition of a virtual terminal. The general form of the TELNET command is

```
telnet [IP_address|host_name] [port]
```

As shown, a TELNET connection is initiated when the user enters the TELNET command and supplies either a host_name or IP_address; if neither is given, TELNET will ask for one once the application begins.

In the example below, a user of a PC uses TELNET to attach to the remote host *smcvax.smcvt.edu.* Once logged in via TELNET, the user can do anything on the remote host that would be possible if connected via a directly attached terminal or via modem. The commands that are subsequently used are those available on the remote system to which the user is attached. In the sample dialog below, the user attached to SMCVAX will use basic VAX/VMS commands:

- The dir command lists the files having a COM file extension.
- The mail command enters the VMS MAIL subsystem; the dir command here lists waiting mail.
- PING checks the status of another host.

When finished, the logout command logs the user off the remote host; TELNET automatically closes the connection to the remote host and returns control to the local system.

It is important to note that TELNET is a very powerful tool, one that may provide users with access to many Internet utilities and services that might not be otherwise available. Many of these features are accessed by specifying a port number with the TELNET command, in addition to a host's address, and knowledge of port numbers provides another mechanism for users to access information with TELNET.

The information here presents TCP/IP and Internet utilities that require local client software, such as Finger, Whois, Archie, and Gopher. But what if your software does not include a needed client? In some cases, TELNET may be used to access a remote client and provide the same functionality. This is done by specifying a port number with the TELNET command. Just as TCP/IP hosts have a unique IP address, applications on the host are associated with an address, called a *port.* Finger, for example, is associated with the well-known port number 79. In the absence of a Finger client, TELNETing to port 79 at a remote host may provide the same information. You can finger another host with TELNET by using a command such as

```
telnet net host_name 79
```

Other well-known TCP port numbers include 25 (Simple Mail Transfer Protocol), 43 (whois), 80 (HyperText Transfer Protocol), and 119 (Network News Transfer Protocol).

Some services are available on the Internet using TELNET and special port numbers. A geographic information database, for example, may be accessed by TELNETing to port 3000 at host *martini.eecs.umich.edu,* and current weather information is available at port 3000 at host *downwind.sprl.umich.edu.*

```
= = = = = = = = = = = = = = = = = = = = = = = = = = = = = = = = = = = = =
**C:> telnet BRAINS.INFO.COM
   FTP Software PC/TCP tn 3.10 01/24/95 02:40
   Copyright(c)1986-1995byFTP Software,Inc. All rights reserved
   - Connected to St. Michael's College -
   **Username: hewey
   **Password: dewey
   St. Michael's College VAX/VMS System.
   Node: Brains
   Last interactive login on Monday, 16-SEP-2000 15:47
   Last non-interactive login on Wednesday, 6-MAR-2000 08:19
   You have 1 new Mail message.
   Good Afternoon User Taylor. Logged in on 17-SEP-2000 at 1:10 PM.
   User [GUEST,Taylor] has 3225 blocks used, 6775 available, of 10000
   authorized and permitted overdraft of 100 blocks on $1$DIA2
   To see a complete list of news items, type: NEWS DIR
   To read a particular item, type NEWS followed by the name of the item
   you wish to read.
   **SMCVAX$ dir *.com
   Directory $1$DIA2:[GUEST.TAYLOR]
   BACKUP.COM;24   24 16-JUL-2000 16:22:46.68 (RWED,RWED,RE,)
   DELTREE.COM;17  3 16-JUL-2000 16:22:47.58 (RWED,RWED,RE,)
   EXPANDZ.COM;7   2 22-FEB-2000 10:00:04.35 (RWED,RWED,RE,)
   FTSLOGBLD.COM;3     1 16-JUL-2000 16:22:48.57 (RWED,RWED,RE,)
   FTSRRR.COM;2    1 16-JUL-2000 16:22:48.73 (RWED,RWED,RE,)
   LOGIN.COM;116   5  1-DEC-2000 09:33:21.61 (RWED,RWED,RE,)
   FATBOY.COM;6    1 16-JUL-2000 16:22:52.06 (RWED,RWED,RE,)
   SYLOGIN.COM;83  8 16-JUL-2000 16:22:52.88 (RWED,RWED,RE,RE)
   SYSTARTUP.COM;88    15 16-JUL-2000 16:22:53.21 RWED,RWED,RE,)
   WATCH_MAIL.COM;1    173 10-MAY-2000 09:59:52.65 (RWED,RWED,RE,)
   Total of 10 files, 233 blocks.
   **SMCVAX$ mail
   You have 1 new message.
   **MAIL> dir
   NEWMAIL
   # From    Date   Subject
   1 IN%"ibug@plainfield. 15-SEP-1996 ANNOUNCE: Burlington WWW
   Conference
   **MAIL> exit
   **SMCVAX$ ping kestrel.hill.com /n = 5
   PING HILL.COM (199.182.20.24): 56 data bytes
   64 bytes from 199.182.20.24: icmp_seq = 0 time = 290 ms
   64 bytes from 199.182.20.24: icmp_seq = 1 time = 260 ms
   64 bytes from 199.182.20.24: icmp_seq = 2 time = 260 ms
   64 bytes from 199.182.20.24: icmp_seq = 3 time = 260 ms
```

```
64 bytes from 199.182.20.24: icmp_seq = 4 time = 260 ms
----KESTREL.HILL.COM PING Statistics----
5 packets transmitted, 5 packets received, 0% packet loss
round-trip (ms) min/avg/max = 260/266/290
**SMCVAX$ logout
TAYLOR  logged out at 15-SEP-2000 13:17:04.29
Connection #0 closed
C:>
```

= =

File Transfer Protocol (FTP).   FTP is one of the most useful and powerful TCP/IP utilities for the general user. FTP allows users to upload and download files between local and remote hosts. Anonymous FTP, in particular, is commonly available at file archive sites to allow users to access files without having to preestablish an account at the remote host.

TELNET might, in fact, be used for this purpose, but TELNET gives the user complete access to the remote system; FTP limits the user to file transfer activities.

The general form of the FTP command is

```
ftp [IP_address|host_name]
```

An FTP session can be initiated in several ways. In the example shown below, an FTP control connection is initiated to a host (the Defense Data Network's Network Information Center) by supplying a host name with the FTP command; optionally, the host's IP address in dotted-decimal (numeric) form could be used. If neither host name nor IP address is supplied in the command line, a connection to a host can be initiated by typing open host_name or open IP_address once the FTP application has been started.

The remote host will ask for a username and password. If a bona fide registered user of this host supplies a valid username and password, then the user will have access to any files and directories to which this username has privilege. For anonymous FTP access, the username *anonymous* is used. Historically, the password for the anonymous user (not shown in actual use) has been *guest,* although most systems today ask for the user's Internet email address (and several sites attempt to verify that packets are coming from that address before allowing the user to log in).

The help ? command may be used to obtain a list of FTP commands and help topics available with your software; although not always shown, nearly all TCP/IP applications have a help command. An example of the help for FTP's type command is shown in the sample dialog. This command is a very important one, by the way; if transferring a binary or executable file, be sure to set the type to image (or binary on some systems).

The dir command provides a directory listing of the files in the current directory at the remote host; the UNIX ls command may also usually be used. Note that an FTP data transfer connection is established for the transfer of the directory information to the local host. The output from the dir command will show a file listing that is consistent with the native operating system of the remote host. Although the TCP/IP suite is often associated with UNIX, it can (and does) run with nearly all common operating systems. The directory information shown in the sample dialog happens to be in UNIX format and includes the following information:

- *File attributes.* The first character identifies the type of file entry as a directory (d), link or symbolic name (1), or individual file (-). The next nine characters are the file access permissions list; the first three characters are for the owner, the next three for the owner's group, and the last three for all other users. Three access privileges may be assigned to each file for each of these groups: read (r), write (w), and execute (x).

- Number of entries, or hard links, in this structure. This value will be a 1 if the entry refers to a file or link, or will be the number of files in the listed directory.

- File owner.

- File owner's group.

- File size, in bytes.

- Date and time of last modification. If the date is followed by a time stamp, then the date is from the current year.

- Filename.

After the directory information has been transferred, FTP closes the data transfer connection.

The command cd is used to change to another working directory, in this case the rfc directory (note that file and directory names may be case-sensitive). As in DOS, cd .. will change to the parent of the current directory. The CWD command successful is the only indication that the user's cd command was correctly executed; the show-directory (may be truncated to fewer characters, as shown) command, if available, may be used to see which working directory you are in.

Another dir command is used to find all files with the name rfc173*.txt; note the use of the * wildcard character. We can now copy (download) the file of choice by using the get (or receive) command, which has the following general format:

```
get remote_file_name local_file_name
```

FTP opens another data transfer connection for this file transfer purpose; note that the effective data transfer rate is 93.664 kbps. FTP's put (or send) command allows uploading from the local host to the remote. The put command is seldom available when using anonymous FTP.

Finally, we terminate the FTP connection by using the close command. The user can initiate another FTP connection using the open command or can leave FTP by issuing a `quit` command. The `quit` command can also be used to close a connection and terminate a session.

It is important to note that different FTP packages have different commands available and even those with similar names may act differently. In the example shown here (using MultiNet for VMS), the `show` command will display the current working directory; in FTP Software's OnNet, `show` will display a file from the remote host at the local host. Some packages have nothing equivalent to either of these commands.

```
= = = = = = = = = = = = = = = = = = = = = = = = = = = = = = = = = = = =
  **SMCVAX$ ftp INFO.IWI.COM
  SMCVAX.SMCVT.EDU MultiNet FTP user process 3.4(111)
  Connection opened (Assuming 8-bit connections)
  <*****Welcome to the IWI Network Information Center*****
  <*****Login with username "anonymous" and password "guest"
  **Username: anonymous
  <Guest login ok, send "guest" as password.
  **Password: TAYLOR <--- Not displayed
  <Guest login ok, access restrictions apply.
  **INFO.IWI.OCM> help type
  TYPE
  Set the transfer type to type.
  Format
  TYPE type
  Additional information available:
  Parameters Example Restrictions
  **TYPE Subtopic? parameters
  TYPE
  Parameters
  type
  Specify a value of ASCII, BACKUP, BINARY, IMAGE or LOGICAL-BYTE.
  Use TYPE ASCII (the default) for transferring text files.
  Use TYPE BACKUP to set the transfer type to IMAGE and write the local
  file with 2048-byte fixed length records. Use this command to trans-
  fer VAX/VMS BACKUP save sets.
  Use TYPE BINARY to transfer binary files (same as TYPE IMAGE).
  Use TYPE IMAGE to transfer binary files (for example, .EXE).
  Use TYPE LOGICAL-BYTE to transfer binary files to or from a TOPS-20
  machine.
  **TYPE Subtopic?
  **Topic?
  **NIC.DDN.MIL> dir
  <Opening ASCII mode data connection for /bin/ls.
  total 58
drwxr-xr-x 2 nic 1    512 Sep 16 23:00 bcp
drwxr-xr-x 2 root 1    512 Mar 19 1996 bin
drwxr-xr-x 2 nic 1   1536 Jul 15 23:00 ddn-news
drwxr-xr-x 2 nic 1    512 Mar 19 1996 demo
drwxr-xr-x 2 nic 1    512 Mar 25 14:25 dev
drwxr-xr-x 2 nic 10   512 Mar 19 1996 disn_info
drwxr-xr-x 2 nic 1    512 Sep 17 07:01 domain
drwxr-xr-x 2 nic 1    512 Mar 19 1996 etc
lrwxrwxrwx 1 nic 1      3 Mar 19 1996 fyi -> rfc
drwxr-xr-x 2 nic 10  1024 Sep 16 23:00 gosip
drwxr-xr-x 2 nic 1    512 Mar 19 1996 home
drwxr-xr-x 2 nic 1    512 Mar 19 1996 lost+found
```

```
lrwxrwxrwx 1 nic 1    8 Mar 19 1996 mgt->ddn-news
drwxr-xr-x 2 nic 1    1024 Sep 13 12:11 netinfo
drwxr-xr-x 4 nic 1    512 May 3 23:00 netprog
drwxr-xr-x 2 nic 1    1024 Mar 19 1996 protocols
drwxr-xr-x 2 nic 1    512 Mar 19 1996 pub
drwxr-xr-x 3 140 10    512 Aug 27 21:03 registrar
drwxr-xr-x 2 nic 1    29696 Sep 16 23:00 rfc
drwxr-xr-x 2 nic 1    5632 Sep 9 23:00 scc
drwxr-xr-x 2 nic 1    1536 Sep 16 23:00 std
drwxr-xr-x 2 nic 1    1024 Sep 16 23:00 templates
drwxr-xr-x 3 nic 1    512 Mar 19 1996 usr
<Transfer complete.
   1437 bytes transferred at 33811 bps.
   Run time = 20. ms, Elapsed time = 340. ms.
   **NIC.DDN.MIL> cd rfc
   <CWD command successful.
   **NIC.DDN.MIL> show
   <"/rfc" is current directory.
   **NIC.DDN.MIL> dir rfc173*.txt
   <Opening ASCII mode data connection for /bin/ls.
-rw-r--r-- 1 nic 10   156660 Dec 20 1994 rfc1730.txt
-rw-r--r-- 1 nic 10   11433 Dec 20 1994 rfc1731.txt
-rw-r--r-- 1 nic 10   9276 Dec 20 1994 rfc1732.txt
-rw-r--r-- 1 nic 10   6205 Dec 20 1994 rfc1733.txt
-rw-r--r-- 1 nic 10   8499 Dec 20 1994 rfc1734.txt
-rw-r--r-- 1 nic 10   24485 Sep 15 1995 rfc1735.txt
-rw-r--r-- 1 nic 10   22415 Feb 8 1995 rfc1736.txt
-rw-r--r-- 1 nic 10   16337 Dec 15 1994 rfc1737.txt
-rw-r--r-- 1 nic 10   51348 Dec 15 1994 rfc1738.txt
-rw-r--r-- 1 nic 10 102676 Dec 21 1994 rfc1739.txt
<Transfer complete.
   670 bytes transferred at 26800 bps.
   Run time = 10. ms, Elapsed time = 200. ms.
   **INFO.IWI.COM> get rfc1739.txt primer.txt
   <Opening ASCII mode data connection for rfc1739.txt (102676 bytes).
   <Transfer complete.
   105255 bytes transferred at 93664 bps.
   Run time = 130. ms, Elapsed time = 8990. ms.
   **INFO.IWI.COM> quit
   <Goodbye.
   SMCVAX$
= = = = = = = = = = = = = = = = = = = = = = = = = = = = = = = = = = = = = = =
```

User database lookup tools

Finding other users on the Internet is an art, not a science. Although there is a distributed database listing all the 16+ million hosts on the Internet, no similar database yet exists for the tens of millions of users. While many commercial ISPs provide directories of the users of their network, these databases are not yet linked. Some of the tools available for finding users on the Internet are discussed in the following paragraphs.

WHOIS/NICNAME.   WHOIS and NICNAME are TCP/IP applications that search databases to find the name of network and system administrators, RFC authors, system and network points of contact, and other individuals who are registered in appropriate databases. The original NICNAME/WHOIS protocol is described in RFC 954.

WHOIS may be accessed by TELNETing to an appropriate WHOIS server and logging in as *whois* (no password is required); the most common Internet name server is located at the Internet Network Information Center (InterNIC) at *rs.internic.net*. This specific database contains only Internet domains, IP network numbers, and domain points of contact; policies governing the InterNIC database are described in RFC 1400. The MILNET database resides at *nic.ddn.mil,* and PSI's White Pages pilot service is located at *psi.com.*

Many software packages contain a WHOIS/NICNAME client that automatically establishes the TELNET connection to a default name server database, although users can usually specify any name server database that they want.

The accompanying dialogs show several types of WHOIS/NICNAME information queries. In the session below, we request information about an individual (Ed Taylor) by using WHOIS locally, a specific domain (*hill.com*) by using NICNAME locally, and a network address (199.182.20.0) and high-level domain (*com*) using TELNET to a WHOIS server.

Consider the following example:

```
= = = = = = = = = = = = = = = = = = = = = = = = = = = = = = = = = = = = = = =
**SMCVAX$ whois taylor,ed
Taylor, Ed (DET) edtaylor@IWI.com
Information World, Inc.
8601 Mystic Trail
Suite S
Fort Worth, TX 76118
Record last updated on 02-Nov-99.
SMCVAX$
**C:> nicname MGT
[198.41.0.5]
Domain Name: HILL.COM
**C:> telnet rs.internic.net
SunOS UNIX 4.1 (rs1) (ttypb)
*********************************************************************
* --InterNIC Registration Services Center --
*
* For wais, type:       WAIS <search string> <return>
* For the *original* whois type: WHOIS [search string] <return>
* For referral whois type:   RWHOIS [search string] <return>
*
*********************************************************************
Please be advised that use constitutes consent to monitoring
(Elec Comm Priv Act, 18 USC 2701-2711)
  **[vt220] InterNIC > whois
  InterNIC WHOIS Version: 1.2 Wed, 18 Sep 96 09:49:50
  **Whois: 199.182.20.0
  Hill Associates (NET-HILLASSC)
  17 Roosevelt Highway
  Colchester, VT 05446
  Netname: HILLASSC
  Netnumber: 199.182.20.0
  **Whois: com-dom
```

```
     Commercial top-level domain (COM-DOM)
     Domain Name: COM
     Domain servers in listed order:
A.ROOT-SERVERS.NET          198.41.0.4
H.ROOT-SERVERS.NET          128.63.2.53
B.ROOT-SERVERS.NET          128.9.0.107
C.ROOT-SERVERS.NET          192.33.4.12
D.ROOT-SERVERS.NET          128.8.10.90
E.ROOT-SERVERS.NET          192.203.230.10
I.ROOT-SERVERS.NET          192.36.148.17
F.ROOT-SERVERS.NET          192.5.5.241
G.ROOT-SERVERS.NET          192.112.36.4
     **Would you like to see the known domains under this top-level domain?
     n
     **Whois: exit
     **[vt220] InterNIC > quit
     Wed Sep 18 09:50:29 1996 EST
     Connection #0 closed
     C:>
= = = = = = = = = = = = = = = = = = = = = = = = = = = = = = = = = = = = = =
```

KNOWBOT.   KNOWBOT is an automated username database search tool that is related to WHOIS. The Knowbot Information Service (KIS), operated by the Corporation for National Research Initiatives (CNRI) in Reston, VA, provides a simple WHOIS-like interface that allows users to query several Internet user databases (White Pages services) all at one time. A single KIS query will automatically search the InterNIC, MILNET, MCImail, and PSI White Pages Pilot Project; other databases may also be included.

KNOWBOT may be accessed by TELNETing to host *info.cnri.reston.va.us*. The help command will supply sufficient information to get started. The sample dialog below shows use of the query command to locate a user named Steven Shepard; this command automatically starts a search through the default set of Internet databases.

```
 = = = = = = = = = = = = = = = = = = = = = = = = = = = = = = = = = = = = = =
**C:> telnet info.cnri.reston.va.us
      Knowbot Information Service
KIS Client (V2.0). Copyright CNRI 1990. All Rights Reserved.
   KIS searches various Internet directory services to find someone's
street address, email address and phone number.
   Type 'man' at the prompt for a complete reference with examples.
   Type 'help' for a quick reference to commands.
   Type 'news' for information about recent changes.
   Please enter your email address in our guest book...
   **(Your email address?) > s.shepard@hill.com

   **> query shepard, steven
   Trying whois at ds.internic.net...
   The ds.internic.net whois server is being queried:
   Nothing returned.
   *The rs.internic.net whois server is being queried:
   Shepard, Steven (SS2192) 888-888-5215
   Shepard, Steven (SS1302) axisteven@com.COM
   Trying mcimail at cnri.reston.va.us...
```

```
Trying ripe at whois.ripe.net...
Trying whois at whois.lac.net…
No match found for .SHEPARD,STEVEN
**> quit
KIS exiting
Connection #0 closed
C:>
```
= =

Information servers

File transfer, remote login, and electronic mail remained the primary applications of the ARPANET/Internet until the early 1990s. But as the Internet user population shifted from hard-core computer researchers and academics to more casual users, easier-to-use tools were needed for the Net to become accepted as a useful resource. That means making things easier to find. This section discusses some of the early tools that made it easier to locate and access information on the Internet.

Archie.   Archie, developed in 1992 at the Computer Science Department at McGill University in Montreal, allows users to find software, data, and other information files that reside at anonymous FTP archive sites; the name of the program, reportedly, is derived from the word *archive,* and not from the red-headed comic-strip character. Archie tracks the contents of several thousand anonymous FTP sites containing millions of files. The Archie server automatically updates the information from each registered site about once a month, providing relatively up-to-date information without unduly stressing the network. Archie, however, is not as popular as it once was, and many sites have not updated their information; as the examples below show, many of the catalog listings are several years old.

Before using Archie, you must identify a server address. The sites below all support Archie; most (but not all) Archie sites support the server command which lists all known Archie servers. Because of the popularity of Archie at some sites and its high processing demands, many sites limit access to non-peak hours and/or limit the number of simultaneous Archie users. Available Archie sites include:

archie.au	*archie.rediris.es*
archie.edvz.uni-linz.ac.at	*archie.luth.se*
archie.univie.ac.at	*archie.switch.ch*
archie.uqam.ca	*archie.ncu.edu.tw*
archie.funet.fi	*archie.doc.ic.ac.uk*
archie.th-darmstadt.de	*archie.unl.edu*
archie.ac.il	*archie.internic.net*
archie.unipi.it	*archie.rutgers.edu*
archie.wide.ad.jp	*archie.ans.net*

archie.kr   *archie.sura.net*

archie.sogang.ac.kr

All Archie sites can be accessed using Archie client software. Some Archie servers may be accessed using TELNET; when TELNETing to an Archie site, log in as *archie* (you must use lowercase) and hit ENTER if a password is requested.

Once connected, the help command assists users in obtaining more information about using Archie. Two more useful Archie commands are `prog`, used to search for files in the database, and `whatis`, which searches for keywords in the program descriptions.

In the accompanying dialog, the set `maxhits` command is used to limit the number of responses to any following `prog` commands; if this is not done, the user may get an enormous amount of information. In this example, the user issues a request to find entries related to `dilbert`; armed with this information, a user can use anonymous FTP to examine these directories and files.

The next request is for files with `tcp/ip` as a keyword descriptor. These responses can be used for subsequent `prog` commands.

Exit Archie using the EXIT command. At this point, TELNET closes the connection and control returns to the local host.

Additional information about Archie can be obtained by sending email to Bunyip Information Systems (*archie-info@bunyip.com*). Client software is not required to use Archie, but can make life a little easier; some such software can be downloaded using anonymous FTP from the `/pub/archie/clients/` directory at `ftp.sura.net` (note that the newest program in this directory is dated June 1994). Most shareware and commercial Archie clients hide the complexity described in this section; users usually connect to a preconfigured Archie server merely by typing an Archie command line.

```
= = = = = = = = = = = = = = = = = = = = = = = = = = = = = = = = = = = = = =
  **C:> telnet archie.unl.edu
   SunOS UNIX (crcnis2)
   **login: archie
   **Password:
   Welcome to the ARCHIE server at the University of Nebraska -  Lincoln
   # Bunyip Information Systems, 1993
   **unl-archie> help
   These are the commands you can use in help:
   . go up one level in the hierarchy
   ? display a list of valid subtopics at the current  level
   <newline>
   done, ^D, ^C quit from help entirely
   <string> help on a topic or subtopic
   Eg.
 "help show"
 will give you the help screen for the "show" command
 "help set search"
 Will give you the help information for the "search" variable.
 The command "manpage" will give you a complete copy of the archie
 manual page.
   **help> done
```

```
**unl-archie> set maxhits 5
**unl-archie> prog dilbert
# Search type: sub.
# Your queue position: 2
# Estimated time for completion: 00:20
Host ftp.wustl.edu (128.252.135.4)
Last updated 10:08 25 Dec 1993
Location: /multimedia/images/gif/unindexed/931118
FILE  -rw-r-r- 9747 bytes 19:18 17 Nov 1993  dilbert.gif
**unl-archie> whatis tcp/ip
RFC        1065
Structure and identification of management information for
TCP/IP-based internets. 1988 August; 21 p. (Obsoleted by RFC 1155)
RFC        1066    McCloghrie, K.; Rose, M.T.
Management Information Base for network management of TCP/IP-based
internets. 1988 August; 90 p. (Obsoleted by RFC 1156)
RFC        1085    Rose, M.T. ISO presentation
services on top of TCP/IP based internets. 1988 December; 32  p.
RFC        1095    Warrier, U.S.; Besaw, L. Common
Management Information Services and Protocol over TCP/IP  (CMOT). 1989
April; 67 p. (Obsoleted by RFC 1189)
RFC        1144    Jacobson, V. Compressing TCP/IP
headers for low-speed serial links. 1990 February; 43 p.
RFC        1147    Stine, R.H.,ed. FYI  on a network
management tool catalog: Tools for monitoring and debugging TCP/IP
internets and interconnected devices.   1990 April; 126 p. (Also
FYI 2) RFC        1155    Rose, M.T.; McCloghrie, K.
Structure and identification of management information for
TCP/IP-based internets. 1990 May; 22 p. (Obsoletes RFC 1065)
 RFC        1156    McCloghrie, K.; Rose, M.T. Management Information
Base for network management of TCP/IP-based internets. 1990 May;
91 p. (Obsoletes RFC 1066)        RFC        1158  Rose, M.T.,ed.
Management
 Information Base for network management of TCP/IP-based internets:
MIB-II. 1990 May; 133 p.
RFC        1180    Socolofsky, T.J.;  Kale, C.J.
TCP/IP tutorial. 1991 January; 28 p.
RFC        1195    Callon, R.W. Use of OSI
IS-IS for routing in TCP/IP and dual environments. 1990 December; 65 p.
RFC        1213    McCloghrie, K.; Rose,M.T.,eds.
Management Information Base for network management of TCP/IP-based
internets:MIB-II. 1991 March; 70 p. (Obsoletes RFC 1158)
log_tcp       Package to monitor tcp/ip connections
ping       PD version of the ping(1) command.  Send ICMP
ECHO requests to a host on the network (TCP/IP) to see whether it's
reachable or not
**unl-archie> exit
# Bye.
Connection #0 closed
C:>
```

= =

Gopher. The Internet Gopher protocol was developed at the University of Minnesota's Microcomputer Center in 1991, as a distributed information search and retrieval tool for the Internet. Gopher is described in RFC 1436 [1]; the name derives from the University's mascot.

Gopher provides a tool so that publicly available information at a host can be organized in a hierarchical fashion using simple text descriptions, allowing files to be perused using a simple menu system. Gopher also allows a user to view a file on demand without requiring additional file transfer protocols. In addition, Gopher introduced the capability of linking sites on the Internet, so that each Gopher site can be used as a stepping stone to access other sites and reducing the amount of duplicate information and effort on the network.

Any Gopher site can be accessed using Gopher client software (or a WWW browser). In many cases, users can access Gopher by TELNETing to a valid Gopher location; if the site provides a remote Gopher client, the user will see a text-based, menu interface. The number of Gopher sites grew rapidly between 1991 and 1994, although growth tapered with the introduction of the Web; in any case, most Gopher sites have a menu item that will allow you to identify other Gopher sites. If using TELNET, log in with the username *gopher* (this must be in lowercase); no password is required.

In the sample dialog below, the user attaches to the Gopher server at the Internet Network Information Center (InterNIC) by TELNETing to *ds.inter-nic.net*. With the menu interface shown here, the user merely follows the prompts. Initially, the main menu will appear. Selecting item 3 causes Gopher to seize and display the InterNIC Registration Services (NSI) menu; move to the desired menu item by typing the item number or by moving the pointer (⟶) down to the desired entry using the DOWN-ARROW key on the keyboard, and then hitting ENTER. To quit the program at any time, press key q (quit); keys ? and u will provide help or go back up to the previous menu, respectively. Users may also search for strings within files using the / command or download the file being interrogated using the D command.

Menu item 1 within the first submenu (selected in the dialog shown here) is titled "InterNIC Registration Archives." As its submenu implies, this is a place to obtain files containing the InterNIC's domain registration policies, domain data, registration forms, and other information related to registering names and domains on the Internet.

```
= = = = = = = = = = = = = = = = = = = = = = = = = = = = = = = = = = = = =
**SMCVAX$ telnet ds.internic.net
 UNIX(r) System V Release 4.0 (ds2)
 **login: gopher
 ***************************************************************
 Welcome to the InterNIC Directory and Database Server.
 ***************************************************************
 Internet Gopher Information Client v2.1.3
  Home Gopher server: localhost
--> 1.  About InterNIC Directory and Database
        Services/
    2.  InterNIC Directory and Database Services
        (AT&T)/
    3.  InterNIC Registration Services (NSI)/
    4.  README
    Press ? for Help, q to Quit
    **View item number: 3
--> 1. InterNIC Registration Archives/
    2.  Whois Searches (InterNIC IP, ASN, DNS, and
        POC Registry) <?>
```

```
        Press ? for Help, q to Quit, u to go up a menu
        **View item number: 1
--> 1. archives/
    2. domain/
    3. netinfo/
    4. netprog/
    5. policy/
    6. pub/
    7. templates/
        Press ? for Help, q to Quit, u to go up a menu
        **q
        **Really quit (y/n) ? y
        Connection closed by Foreign Host
        SMCVAX$
= = = = = = = = = = = = = = = = = = = = = = = = = = = = = = = = = = = = = = =
```

VERONICA, JUGHEAD, and WAIS. The problem with being blessed with so much information from FTP, Archie, Gopher, and other sources is exactly that—too much information. To help users locate the system on which their desired information resides, a number of other tools have been created.

VERONICA (Very Easy Rodent-Oriented Netwide Index to Computerized Archives) was developed at the University of Nevada at Reno as an Archie-like adjunct to Gopher. As the number of Gopher sites quickly grew after its introduction, it became increasingly harder to find information in gopher-space since Gopher was designed to search a single database at a time. VERONICA maintains an index of titles of Gopher items and performs a keyword search on all the Gopher sites that it has knowledge of and access to, obviating the need for the user to perform a menu-by-menu, site-by-site search for information. When a user selects an item from the menu of a VERONICA search, "sessions" are automatically established with the appropriate Gopher servers, and a list of data items is returned to the originating Gopher client in the form of a Gopher menu to enable the user to access the files. VERONICA is available as an option on many Gopher servers.

Another Gopher adjunct is JUGHEAD (Jonzy's Universal Gopher Hierarchy Excavation And Display). JUGHEAD supports keyword searches and the use of logical operators (AND, OR, and NOT). The result of a JUGHEAD search is a display of all menu items which match the search string, which are located in the University of Manchester and UMIST Information Server, working from a static database that is re-created every day. JUGHEAD is available from many Gopher sites, although VERONICA may be a better tool for global searches.

The Wide Area Information Server (WAIS, pronounced "ways") was initiated jointly by Apple Computer, Dow Jones, KMPG Peat Marwick, and Thinking Machines Corp. It is a set of freeware, shareware, and commercial software products for a wide variety of hardware and software platforms, which work together to help users find information on the Internet. WAIS provides a single interface through which a user can access many different information databases. The user interface allows a query to be formulated in

English, and the WAIS server will automatically choose the appropriate data-bases to search. Further information about WAIS can be obtained by reading the WAIS FAQ, from host *rtfm.mit.edu* in file `/pub/usenet/news.answers/wais-faq`.

5.7   The World Wide Web

HyperText Transfer Protocol (HTTP) is an application-level protocol for dis-tributed, collaborative, hypermedia information systems. HTTP has been in use by the WWW global information initiative since 1990. The first version of HTTP, HTTP/0.9, was a simple protocol for raw data transfer across the Internet. HTTP/1.0 improved the protocol by allowing messages to be in the format of MIME (Multipurpose Internet Mail Extensions)-like messages, con-taining metainformation about the data transferred and modifiers on the request/response semantics. However, HTTP/1.0 does not sufficiently take into consideration the effects of hierarchical proxies, caching, the need for persistent connections, and virtual hosts. In addition, the proliferation of incompletely implemented applications calling themselves "HTTP 1.0" has necessitated a protocol version change to enable two communicating applica-tions to determine each other's true capabilities.

An explanation is offered here about the HTTP protocol known as HTTP 1.1. This protocol is more stringent than HTTP/1.0 in order to ensure reliable implementation of its features. Practical information systems require more functionality than simple retrieval, including search, front-end update, and annotation. HTTP allows an open-ended set of methods that indicate the pur-pose of a request. It builds on the discipline of reference provided by the Uniform Resource Identifier (URI), as a location (URL) or name (URN), for indicating the resource to which a method is to be applied. Messages are passed in a format similar to that used by Internet mail as defined by MIME.

HTTP is also used as a generic protocol for communication between user agents and proxies and gateways to other Internet systems, including those supported by SMTP, NNTP, FTP, Gopher, and WAIS protocols. In this way, HTTP allows basic hypermedia access to resources available from diverse applications.

Terminology

This specification uses a number of terms to refer to the roles played by par-ticipants in, and objects of, the HTTP communication.

connection   A transport layer virtual circuit established between two programs for the purpose of communication.

message   The basic unit of HTTP communication, consisting of a structured sequence of octets matching the syntax defined in section 4 and transmitted via the connection.

request   An HTTP request message.

response   An HTTP response message.

resource   A network data object or service that can be identified by a URI. Resources may be available in multiple representations (e.g., multiple languages, data formats, size, resolutions) or vary in other ways.

entity   The information transferred as the payload of a request or response. An entity consists of metainformation in the form of entity-header fields and content in the form of an entity-body.

representation   An entity included with a response that is subject to content negotiation. There may exist multiple representations associated with a particular response status.

content negotiation   The mechanism for selecting the appropriate representation when servicing a request. The representation of entities in any response can be negotiated (including error responses).

variant   A resource may have one, or more than one, representation(s) associated with it at any given instant. Each of these representations is termed a *variant*. Use of the term *variant* does not necessarily imply that the resource is subject to content negotiation.

client   A program that establishes connections for the purpose of sending requests.

user agent   The client which initiates a request. These are often browsers, editors, spiders (Web-traversing robots), or other end-user tools.

server   An application program that accepts connections in order to service requests by sending back responses. Any given program may be capable of being both a client and a server; our use of these terms refers only to the role being performed by the program for a particular connection, rather than to the program's capabilities in general. Likewise, any server may act as an origin server, proxy, gateway, or tunnel, switching behavior based on the nature of each request.

origin server   The server on which a given resource resides or is to be created.

proxy   An intermediary program which acts as both a server and a client for the purpose of making requests on behalf of other clients. Requests are serviced internally or by passing them on, with possible translation, to other servers. A proxy must implement both the client and server requirements of this specification.

gateway   A server which acts as an intermediary for some other server. Unlike a proxy, a gateway receives requests as if it were the origin server for the requested resource; the requesting client may not be aware that it is communicating with a gateway.

tunnel   An intermediary program which is acting as a blind relay between two connections. Once active, a tunnel is not considered a party to the HTTP communication, although the tunnel may have been initiated by an HTTP request. The tunnel ceases to exist when both ends of the relayed connections are closed.

cache   A program's local store of response messages and the subsystem that controls its message storage, retrieval, and deletion. A cache stores cachable responses in order to reduce the response time and network bandwidth consumption on future, equivalent requests. Any client or server may include a cache, although a cache cannot be used by a server that is acting as a tunnel.

cachable   A response is cachable if a cache is allowed to store a copy of the response message for use in answering subsequent requests. Even if a resource is cachable, there may be additional constraints on whether a cache can use the cached copy for a particular request.

firsthand   A response is firsthand if it comes directly and without unnecessary delay from the origin server, perhaps via one or more proxies. A response is also firsthand if its validity has just been checked directly with the origin server.

explicit expiration time   The time at which the origin server intends that an entity should no longer be returned by a cache without further validation.

heuristic expiration time   An expiration time assigned by a cache when no explicit expiration time is available.

response age   The time since the response was sent by, or successfully validated with, the origin server.

freshness lifetime   The length of time between the generation and expiration time of a response.

fresh   A response is fresh if its age has not yet exceeded its freshness lifetime.

stale   A response is stale if its age has passed its freshness lifetime.

semantically transparent   A cache behaves in a "semantically transparent" manner, with respect to a particular response, when its use affects neither the requesting client nor the origin server, except to improve performance. When a cache is semantically transparent, the client receives exactly the same response (except for hop-by-hop headers) that it would have received had its request been handled directly by the origin server.

validator   A protocol element (e.g., an entity tag or a `Last-Modified` time) that is used to ascertain whether a cache entry is an equivalent copy of an entity.

HTTP operation

The HTTP protocol is a request/response protocol. A client sends a request to the server in the form of a request method, URI, and protocol version, followed by a MIME-like message containing request modifiers, client information, and possible body content over a connection with a server. The server responds with a status line, including the message's protocol version and a success or error code, followed by a MIME-like message containing server information, entity metainformation, and possible entity-body content.

Most HTTP communication is initiated by a user agent and consists of a request to be applied to a resource on some origin server. In the simplest case, this may be accomplished via a single connection (v) between the user agent (UA) and the origin server (O).

```
request chain ---------->
UA ----------v---------- O
<--------- response chain
```

A more complicated situation occurs when one or more intermediaries are present in the request/response chain. There are three common forms of intermediary: proxy, gateway, and tunnel. A *proxy* is a forwarding agent, receiving requests for a URI in its absolute form, rewriting all or part of the message, and forwarding the reformatted request toward the server identified by the URI. A *gateway* is a receiving agent, acting as a layer above some other server(s) and, if necessary, translating the requests to the underlying server's protocol. A *tunnel* acts as a relay point between two connections without changing the messages; tunnels are used when the communication needs to pass through an intermediary (such as a firewall) even when the intermediary cannot understand the contents of the messages.

```
request chain ---------------->
UA ---v--- A ---v--- B ---v--- C ---v--- O
<--------------- response chain
```

This excerpt shows three intermediaries (A, B, and C) between the user agent and origin server. A request or response message that travels the whole chain will pass through four separate connections. This distinction is important because some HTTP communication options may apply only to the connection with the nearest, nontunnel neighbor, only to the endpoints of the chain, or to all connections along the chain. Although the diagram is linear, each participant may be engaged in multiple, simultaneous communications. For example, B may be receiving requests from many clients other than A, and/or forwarding requests to servers other than C, at the same time that it is handling A's request.

Any party to the communication which is not acting as a tunnel may employ an internal cache for handling requests. The effect of a cache is that the request/response chain is shortened if one of the participants along the chain has a cached response applicable to that request. The following illustrates the resulting chain if B has a cached copy of an earlier response from O (via C) for a request which has not been cached by UA or A.

```
request chain ---->
UA ---v--- A ---v--- B ----------- C ----------- O
<----- response chain
```

Not all responses are usefully cachable, and some requests may contain modifiers which place special requirements on cache behavior. In fact, there are a wide variety of architectures and configurations of caches and proxies currently being experimented with or deployed across the World Wide Web; these systems include national hierarchies of proxy caches to save transoceanic bandwidth, systems that broadcast or multicast cache entries, organizations that distribute subsets of cached data via CD-ROM, and so on. HTTP systems are used in corporate intranets over high-bandwidth links, and for access via PDAs with low-power radio links and intermittent connectivity. The goal of HTTP 1.1 is to support the wide diversity of configurations already deployed while introducing protocol constructs that meet the needs of those who build Web applications that require high reliability and, failing that, at least reliable indications of failure.

HTTP communication usually takes place over TCP/IP connections. The default port is TCP 80, but other ports can be used. This does not preclude HTTP from being implemented on top of any other protocol on the Internet, or on other networks. HTTP only presumes a reliable transport; any protocol that provides such guarantees can be used; the mapping of the HTTP 1.1 request and response structures onto the transport data units of the protocol in question is outside the scope of this specification.

In HTTP 1.0, most implementations used a new connection for each request/response exchange. In HTTP 1.1, a connection may be used for one or more request/response exchanges, although connections may be closed for a variety of reasons.

Uniform Resource Identifiers (URIs)

URIs have been known by many names: WWW addresses, Universal Document Identifiers, Universal Resource Identifiers, and finally the combination of Uniform Resource Locators (URLs) and Uniform Resource Names (URNs). As far as HTTP is concerned, URIs are simply formatted strings which identify—via name, location, or any other characteristic—a resource.

General syntax

URIs in HTTP can be represented in absolute form or relative to some known base URI, depending on the context of their use. The two forms are differentiated by the fact that absolute URIs always begin with a scheme name followed by a colon.

```
URI = (absoluteURI | relativeURI) [ "#" fragment ]
absoluteURI = scheme ":" *( uchar | reserved )
relativeURI = net_path | abs_path | rel_path
net_path = "//" net_loc [ abs_path ]
abs_path = "/" rel_path
rel_path = [ path ] [ ";" params ] [ "?" query ]
path = fsegment *( "/" segment )
fsegment = 1*pchar
segment = *pchar
params = param *( ";" param )
param = *( pchar | "/" )
```

```
scheme = 1*( ALPHA | DIGIT | "+" | "-" | "." )
net_loc = *( pchar | ";" | "?" )
query = *( uchar | reserved )
fragment = *( uchar | reserved )
pchar = uchar | ":" | "@" | "&" | " = " | "+"
uchar = unreserved | escape
unreserved = ALPHA | DIGIT | safe | extra | national
escape = "%" HEX HEX
reserved = ";" |"/"|"?"| ":" | "@" | "&" | " = " | "+"
extra = "!" | "*" | "'" | "(" | ")" | ","
safe = "$" | "-" | "_" | "."
unsafe = CTL | SP | <"> | "#" | "%" | "<" | ">"
national = <any OCTET excluding ALPHA, DIGIT, reserved,
           extra, safe, and unsafe>
```

The HTTP protocol does not place any a priori limit on the length of a URI. Servers *must* be able to handle the URI of any resource they serve, and *should* be able to handle URIs of unbounded length if they provide GET-based forms that could generate such URIs. A server *should* return 414 (Request-URI Too Long) status if a URI is longer than the server can handle. Servers should be cautious about depending on URI lengths above 255 bytes, because some older client or proxy implementations may not properly support these lengths.

HTTP URL

The http scheme is used to locate network resources via the HTTP protocol. This section defines the scheme-specific syntax and semantics for HTTP URLs.

```
http_URL = "http:" "//" host [ ":" port ] [ abs_path ]
Host     = A legal Internet host domain name or IP address (in dotted-
           decimal form)
Port     = *DIGIT
```

If the port is empty or not given, port 80 is assumed. The semantics are that the identified resource is located at the server listening for TCP connections on that port of that host, and the Request-URI for the resource is abs_path. The use of IP addresses in URLs *should* be avoided whenever possible (see RFC 1900). If the abs_path is not present in the URL, it *must* be given as "/" when used as a Request-URI for a resource.

URI comparison. When comparing two URIs to decide whether they match, a client *should* use a case-sensitive octet-by-octet comparison of the entire URIs, with these exceptions:

- A port that is empty or not given is equivalent to the default port for that URI
- Comparisons of host names *must* be case-insensitive
- Comparisons of scheme names *must* be case-insensitive
- An empty `abs_path` is equivalent to an `abs_path` of "/"

Characters other than those in the `reserved` and `unsafe` sets are equivalent to their "`%`" HEX HEX encodings.

For example, the following three URIs are equivalent:

http://abc.com:80/~ smith/home.html

http://ABC.com/%7Esmith/home.html

http://ABC.com:/%7esmith/home.html

Character sets.   HTTP uses the same definition of the term *character set* as that described for MIME. This term is used in this document to refer to a method used with one or more tables to convert a sequence of octets into a sequence of characters. Note that unconditional conversion in the other direction is not required, in that not all characters may be available in a given character set and a character set may provide more than one sequence of octets to represent a particular character. This definition is intended to allow various kinds of character encodings, from simple single-table mappings such as US-ASCII to complex table switching methods such as those that use ISO 2022's techniques. However, the definition associated with a MIME character-set name *must* fully specify the mapping to be performed from octets to characters. In particular, use of external profiling information to determine the exact mapping is not permitted. This use of the term *character set* is more commonly referred to as a *character encoding*. However, since HTTP and MIME share the same registry, it is important that the terminology also be shared.

HTTP character sets are identified by case-insensitive tokens. The complete set of tokens is defined by the Internet Assigned Numbers Authority (IANA) Character Set Registry.

`charset` = token

Although HTTP allows an arbitrary token to be used as a `charset` value, any token that has a predefined value within the IANA Character Set Registry *must* represent the character set defined by that registry. Applications *should* limit their use of character sets to those defined by the IANA Registry.

HTTP Status-Line.   The first line of a `Response` message is the `Status-Line`, consisting of the protocol version followed by a numeric status code and its associated textual phrase, with each element separated by SP characters. No CR or LF is allowed except in the final CRLF sequence.

Status-Line = HTTP-Version SP Status-Code SP Reason-Phrase CRLF

HTTP Status-Code and Reason-Phrase. The Status-Code element is a three-digit integer result code of the attempt to understand and satisfy the request. The Reason-Phrase is intended to give a short textual description of the Status-Code. The Status-Code is intended for use by automata and the Reason-Phrase is intended for the human user. The client is not required to examine or display the Reason-Phrase.

The first digit of the Status-Code defines the class of response. The last two digits do not have any categorization role. There are five values for the first digit:

- *1xx: Informational*—request was received, process is continuing.

- *2xx: Success*—the action was successfully received, understood, and accepted.

- *3xx: Redirection*—further action must be taken in order to complete the request.

- *4xx: Client Error*—the request contains faulty syntax or cannot be fulfilled.

- *5xx: Server Error*—the server failed to fulfill an apparently valid request.

The individual values of the numeric status codes defined for HTTP 1.1, and an example set of corresponding Reason-Phrases, are presented below. The reason phrases listed here are only recommended—they may be replaced by local equivalents without affecting the protocol.

```
Status-Code = "100"    ; Continue
        | "101" ; Switching Protocols
        | "200" ; OK
        | "201" ; Created
        | "202" ; Accepted
        | "203" ; Non-Authoritative Information
        | "204" ; No Content
        | "205" ; Reset Content
        | "206" ; Partial Content
        | "300" ; Multiple Choices
        | "301" ; Moved Permanently
        | "302" ; Moved Temporarily
        | "303" ; See Other
        | "304" ; Not Modified
        | "305" ; Use Proxy
        | "400" ; Bad Request
        | "401" ; Unauthorized
        | "402" ; Payment Required
        | "403" ; Forbidden
        | "404" ; Not Found
        | "405" ; Method Not Allowed
        | "406" ; Not Acceptable
        | "407" ; Proxy Authentication Required
```

```
       | "408" ; Request Time-out
       | "409" ; Conflict
       | "410" ; Gone
       | "411" ; Length Required
       | "412" ; Precondition Failed
       | "413" ; Request Entity Too Large
       | "414" ; Request-URI Too Large
       | "415" ; Unsupported Media Type
       | "500" ; Internal Server Error
       | "501" ; Not Implemented
       | "502" ; Bad Gateway
       | "503" ; Service Unavailable
       | "504" ; Gateway Time-out
       | "505" ; HTTP Version not supported
       | extension-code
  Extension-code = 3DIGIT
  Reason-Phrase = *<TEXT, excluding CR, LF>
```

HTTP status codes are extensible. HTTP applications are not required to understand the meaning of all registered status codes, although such understanding is obviously desirable. However, applications *must* understand the class of any status code, as indicated by the first digit, and treat any unrecognized response as being equivalent to the x00 status code of that class, with the exception that an unrecognized response *must not* be cached. For example, if an unrecognized status code of 431 is received by the client, it can safely assume that there was something wrong with its request and treat the response as if it had received a 400 status code. In such cases, user agents *should* present to the user the entity returned with the response, since that entity is likely to include human-readable information which will explain the unusual status.

10 Status-Code definitions

Each `Status-Code` is described below, including a description of which method(s) it can follow and any metainformation required in the response.

Informational 1xx. This class of status code indicates a provisional response, consisting only of the `Status-Line` and optional headers, and is terminated by an empty line. Since HTTP 1.0 did not define any 1xx status codes, servers *must not* send a 1xx response to an HTTP 1.0 client except under experimental conditions.

100—Continue The client may continue with its request. This interim response is used to inform the client that the initial part of the request has been received and has not yet been rejected by the server. The client *should* continue by sending the remainder of the request or, if the request has already been completed, ignore this response. The server *must* send a final response after the request has been completed.

101—Switching Protocols The server understands and is willing to comply with the client's request, via the `Upgrade` message header field, for a change in the application protocol being used on this connection. The server will switch protocols to those defined by the response's `Upgrade` header field immediately after the empty line which terminates the 101 response. The protocol should be switched only when it is advantageous to do so. For example, switching to a newer version of HTTP is advantageous over older versions, and switching to a real-time, synchronous protocol may be advantageous when delivering resources that use such features.

Successful 2xx. This class of status code indicates that the client's request was successfully received, understood, and accepted.

200—OK The request has succeeded. The information returned with the response is dependent on the method used in the request; for example

GET—an entity corresponding to the requested resource is sent in the response.

HEAD—the entity-header fields corresponding to the requested resource are sent in the response without any message-body.

POST—an entity describing or containing the result of the action.

TRACE—an entity containing the request message as received by the end server.

201—Created The request has been fulfilled and resulted in a new resource being created. The newly created resource can be referenced by the URI(s) returned in the entity of the response, with the most specific URL for the resource given by a `Location` header field. The origin server *must* create the resource before returning the 201 status code. If the action cannot be carried out immediately, the server should respond with 202 (Accepted) response instead.

202—Accepted The request has been accepted for processing, but the processing has not been completed. The request *may* or *may not* eventually be acted upon, as it *may* be disallowed when processing actually takes place. There is no facility for re-sending a status code from an asynchronous operation such as this. The 202 response is intentionally noncommittal. Its purpose is to allow a server to accept a request for some other process (perhaps a batch-oriented process that is run only once per day) without requiring that the user agent's connection to the server persist until the process is completed. The entity returned with this response *should* include an indication of the request's current status and either a pointer to a status monitor or some estimate of when the user can expect the request to be fulfilled.

203—Non-Authoritative Information The returned metainformation in the entity-header is not the definitive set as available from the origin server, but is gathered from a local or a third-party copy. The set presented *may* be a subset or superset of the original version. For example, including local annotation information about the resource *may* result in a superset of the metainformation known by the origin server. Use of this response code is not required and is appropriate only when the response would otherwise be 200 (OK).

204—No Content The server has fulfilled the request but there is no new information to send back. If the client is a user agent, it *should not* change its document view from that which caused the request to be sent. This response is primarily intended to allow input for actions to take place without causing a change to the user agent's active document view. The response *may* include new metainformation in the form of entity-headers, which *should* apply to the document currently in the user agent's active view. The 204 response *must not* include a message-body, and thus is always terminated by the first empty line after the header fields.

205—Reset Content The server has fulfilled the request and the user agent *should* reset the document view which caused the request to be sent. This response is primarily intended to allow input for actions to take place via user input, followed by a clearing of the form in which the input is given so that the user can easily initiate another input action. The response *must not* include an entity.

206—Partial Content The server has fulfilled the partial GET request for the resource. The request must have included a Range header field indicating the desired range. The response *must* include either a Content-Range header field indicating the range included with this response, or a multipart/byteranges Content-Type including Content-Range fields for each part. If multipart/byteranges is not used, the Content-Length header field in the response *must* match the actual number of OCTETs transmitted in the message-body. A cache that does not support the Range and Content-Range headers *must not* cache 206 (Partial) responses.

Redirection 3xx. This class of status code indicates that further action needs to be taken by the user agent in order to fulfill the request. The action required *may* be carried out by the user agent without interaction with the user if and only if the method used in the second request is GET or HEAD. A user agent *should not* automatically redirect a request more than five times, since such redirections usually indicate an infinite loop.

300—Multiple Choices The requested resource corresponds to any one of a set of representations, each with its own specific location, and agent-driven negotiation information (section 12) is being provided so that the user (or user agent) can select a preferred representation and redirect its request to that location. Unless it was a HEAD request, the response *should* include an entity containing a list of resource characteristics and location(s) from which the user or user agent can choose the one most appropriate. The entity format is specified by the media type given in the Content-Type header field. Depending on the format and the capabilities of the user agent, selection of the most appropriate choice may be performed automatically. However, this specification does not define any standard for such automatic selection. If the server has a preferred choice of representation, it *should* include the specific URL for that representation in the Location field; user agents *may* use the Location field value for automatic redirection. This response is cachable unless indicated otherwise.

301—Moved Permanently The requested resource has been assigned a new permanent URI and any future references to this resource *should* be done using one of the returned URIs. Clients with link editing capabilities *should* automatically re-link references to the Request-URI to one or more of the new references returned by the server, where possible. This response is cachable unless indicated otherwise. If the new URI is a location, its URL *should* be given by the location field in the response. Unless the request method was HEAD, the entity of the response *should* contain a short hypertext note with a hyperlink to the new URI(s). If the 301 status code is received in response to a request other than GET or HEAD, the user agent *must not* automatically redirect the request unless it can be confirmed by the user, since this might change the conditions under which the request was issued. When automatically redirecting a POST request after receiving a 301 status code, some existing HTTP/1.0 user agents will erroneously change it into a GET request.

302—Moved Temporarily The requested resource resides temporarily under a different URI. Since the redirection may be altered on occasion, the client *should* continue to use the `Request-URI` for future requests. This response is cachable only if indicated by a `Cache-Control` or `Expires` header field. If the new URI is a location, its URL *should* be given by the `Location` field in the response. Unless the request method was HEAD, the entity of the response *should* contain a short hypertext note with a hyperlink to the new URI(s). If the 302 status code is received in response to a request other than GET or HEAD, the user agent *must not* automatically redirect the request unless it can be confirmed by the user, since this might change the conditions under which the request was issued. When automatically redirecting a POST request after receiving a 302 status code, some existing HTTP/1.0 user agents will erroneously change it into a GET request.

303—See Other The response to the request can be found under a different URI and *should* be retrieved using a GET method on that resource. This method exists primarily to allow the output of a POST-activated script to redirect the user agent to a selected resource. The new URI is not a substitute reference for the originally requested resource. The 303 response is not cachable, but the response to the second (redirected) request *may* be cachable. If the new URI is a location, its URL *should* be given by the `Location` field in the response. Unless the request method was HEAD, the entity of the response *should* contain a short hypertext note with a hyperlink to the new URI(s).

304—Not Modified If the client has performed a conditional GET request and access is allowed, but the document has not been modified, the server *should* respond with this status code. The response *must not* contain a message-body. The response *must* include the following header fields:

Date

`ETag` and/or `Content-Location`, if the header would have been sent in a 200 response to the same request

`Expires`, `Cache-Control`, and/or `Vary`, if the field-value might differ from that sent in any previous response for the same variant

If the conditional GET used a strong cache validator, the response *should not* include other entity-headers. Otherwise (i.e., the conditional GET used a weak validator), the response *must not* include other entity-headers; this prevents inconsistencies between cached entity-bodies and updated headers. If a 304 response indicates an entity not currently cached, then the cache *must* disregard the response and repeat the request without the conditional. If a cache uses a received 304 response to update a cache entry, the cache *must* update the entry to reflect any new field values given in the response. The 304 response *must not* include a message-body, and thus is always terminated by the first empty line after the header fields.

305—Use Proxy The requested resource *must* be accessed through the proxy given by the `Location` field. The `Location` field gives the URL of the proxy. The recipient is expected to repeat the request via the proxy.

Client Error 4xx. The 4xx class of status code is intended for cases in which the client seems to have erred. Except when responding to a HEAD request, the server *should* include an entity containing an explanation of the error situation, and whether it is a temporary or permanent condition. These status codes are applicable to any request method. User agents *should* display any included entity to the user.

If the client is sending data, a server implementation using TCP should be careful to ensure that the client acknowledges receipt of the packet(s) containing the response, before the server closes the input connection. If the client continues sending data to the server after the close, the server's TCP stack will send a reset packet to the client, which may erase the client's unacknowledged input buffers before they can be read and interpreted by the HTTP application.

400—Bad Request The request could not be understood by the server due to malformed syntax. The client *should not* repeat the request without modifications.

401—Unauthorized The request requires user authentication. The response *must* include a WWW-Authenticate header field containing a challenge applicable to the requested resource. The client *may* repeat the request with a suitable Authorization header field. If the request already included Authorization credentials, then the 401 response indicates that authorization has been refused for those credentials. If the 401 response contains the same challenge as the prior response, and the user agent has already attempted authentication at least once, then the user *should* be presented the entity that was given in the response, since that entity *may* include relevant diagnostic information.

402—Payment Required This code is reserved for future use.

403—Forbidden The server understood the request, but is refusing to fulfill it. Authorization will not help and the request *should not* be repeated. If the request method was not HEAD and the server wishes to make public why the request has not been fulfilled, it *should* describe the reason for the refusal in the entity. This status code is commonly used when the server does not wish to reveal exactly why the request has been refused, or when no other response is applicable.

404—Not Found The server has not found anything matching the Request-URI. No indication is given of whether the condition is temporary or permanent. If the server does not wish to make this information available to the client, the status code 403 (Forbidden) can be used instead. The 410 (Gone) status code *should* be used if the server knows, through some internally configurable mechanism, that an old resource is permanently unavailable and has no forwarding address.

405—Method Not Allowed The method specified in the Request-Line is not allowed for the resource identified by the Request-URI. The response *must* include an Allow header containing a list of valid methods for the requested resource.

406—Not Acceptable The resource identified by the request is only capable of generating response entities which have content characteristics not acceptable according to the accept headers sent in the request. Unless it was a HEAD request, the response *should* include an entity containing a list of available entity characteristics and location(s) from which the user or user agent can choose the one most appropriate. The entity format is specified by the media type given in the `Content-Type` header field. Depending on the format and the capabilities of the user agent, selection of the most appropriate choice may be performed automatically. However, this specification does not define any standard for such automatic selection. HTTP 1.1 servers are allowed to return responses which are not acceptable according to the accept headers sent in the request. In some cases, this may even be preferable to sending a 406 response. User agents are encouraged to inspect the headers of an incoming response to determine if it is acceptable. If the response could be unacceptable, a user agent *should* temporarily stop receipt of more data and query the user for a decision on further actions.

407—Proxy Authentication Required   This code is similar to 401 (Unauthorized), but indicates that the client *must* first authenticate itself with the proxy. The proxy *must* return a `Proxy-Authenticate` header field containing a challenge applicable to the proxy for the requested resource. The client *may* repeat the request with a suitable `Proxy-Authorization` header field.

408—Request Timeout   The client did not produce a request within the time that the server was prepared to wait. The client *may* repeat the request without modifications at any later time.

409—Conflict   The request could not be completed due to a conflict with the current state of the resource. This code is allowed only in situations where it is expected that the user might be able to resolve the conflict and resubmit the request. The response body *should* include enough information for the user to recognize the source of the conflict. Ideally, the response entity would include enough information for the user or user agent to fix the problem; however, that may not be possible and is not required. Conflicts are most likely to occur in response to a `put` request. If versioning is being used and the entity being `put` includes changes to a resource which conflict with those made by an earlier (third-party) request, the server *may* use the 409 response to indicate that it can't complete the request. In this case, the response entity *should* contain a list of the differences between the two versions in a format defined by the response `Content-Type`.

410—Gone   The requested resource is no longer available at the server and no forwarding address is known. This condition *should* be considered permanent. Clients with link editing capabilities *should* delete references to the `Request-URI` after user approval. If the server does not know, or has no facility to determine, whether the condition is permanent, the status code 404 (Not Found) *should* be used instead. This response is cachable unless indicated otherwise. The 410 response is primarily intended to assist the task of Web maintenance by notifying the recipient that the resource is intentionally unavailable and that the server owners desire that remote links to that resource be removed. Such an event is common for limited-time, promotional services and for resources belonging to individuals no longer working at the server's site. It is not necessary to mark all permanently unavailable resources as "gone" or to keep the mark for any length of time—that is left to the discretion of the server owner.

411—Length Required   The server refuses to accept the request without a defined `Content-Length`. The client *may* repeat the request if it adds a valid `Content-Length` header field containing the length of the message-body in the request message.

412—Precondition Failed The precondition given in one or more of the request-header fields evaluated to false when it was tested on the server. This response code allows the client to place preconditions on the current resource metainformation (header field data) and thus prevent the requested method from being applied to a resource other than the one intended.

413—Request Entity Too Large The server is refusing to process a request because the request entity is larger than the server is willing or able to process. The server may close the connection to prevent the client from continuing the request. If the condition is temporary, the server *should* include a `Retry-After` header field to indicate that it is temporary and after what time the client may try again.

414—Request-URI Too Long The server is refusing to service the request because the `Request-URI` is longer than the server is willing to interpret. This rare condition is likely to occur only when a client has improperly converted a POST request to a GET request with long query information, when the client has descended into a URL "black hole" of redirection (e.g., a redirected URL prefix that points to a suffix of itself), or when the server is under attack by a client attempting to exploit security holes present in some servers using fixed-length buffers for reading or manipulating the `Request-URI`.

415—Unsupported Media Type The server is refusing to service the request because the entity of the request is in a format not supported by the requested resource for the requested method.

Server Error 5xx. Response status codes beginning with the digit 5 indicate cases in which the server is aware that it has erred or is incapable of performing the request. Except when responding to a HEAD request, the server *should* include an entity containing an explanation of the error situation, and whether it is a temporary or permanent condition. User agents *should* display any included entity to the user. These response codes are applicable to any request method.

500—Internal Server Error The server encountered an unexpected condition which prevented it from fulfilling the request.

501—Not Implemented The server does not support the functionality required to fulfill the request. This is the appropriate response when the server does not recognize the request method and is not capable of supporting it for any resource.

502—Bad Gateway The server, while acting as a gateway or proxy, received an invalid response from the upstream server that it accessed in attempting to fulfill the request.

503—Service Unavailable The server is currently unable to handle the request because of a temporary overload or maintenance of the server. The implication is that this is a temporary condition which will be alleviated after some delay. If known, the length of the delay may be indicated in a `Retry-After` header. If no `Retry-After` is given, the client *should* handle the response as it would for a 500 response. The existence of the 503 status code does not imply that a server must use it when becoming overloaded. Some servers may wish to simply refuse the connection.

504—Gateway Timeout   The server, while acting as a gateway or proxy, did not receive a timely response from the upstream server it accessed in attempting to complete the request.

505—HTTP Version Not Supported   The server does not, or refuses to, support, the HTTP protocol version that was used in the request message. The server is indicating that it is unable or unwilling to complete the request using the same major version as the client other than with this error message. The response *should* contain an entity describing why that version is not supported and what other protocols are supported by that server.

The World Wide Web (WWW) is thought (erroneously) by many to be the same thing as the Internet. But the confusion, in many ways, is justified; by early 1996, the WWW accounted for over 40 percent of all of the traffic on the Internet. In addition, the number of hosts on the Internet prefixed *www* has grown from several hundred in mid-1994 to 17,000 in mid-1995 to 212,000 in mid-1996 to over 410,000 by early 1997. The Web has made information on the Internet accessible to users of all ages and computer skill levels. It has provided a mechanism so that nearly anyone can become a content provider. According to some, growth in the number of WWW users is unparalleled by any other event in human history.

The WWW was developed in the early 1990s at the CERN Institute for Particle Physics in Geneva, Switzerland. The Web was designed to combine aspects of information retrieval with multimedia communications, unlike Archie and Gopher, which were used primarily to index text-based files. The Web allows users to access information in many different types of formats, including text, sound, image, animation, and video. WWW treats all searchable Internet files as hypertext documents. *HyperText* is a term which merely refers to text that contains pointers to other text, allowing a user reading one document to jump to another document for more information on a given topic, and then return to the same location in the original document. WWW hypermedia documents are able to employ images, sound, graphics, video, and animation in addition to text.

To access WWW servers, users must run client software called a *browser*. The browser and server use the HyperText Transfer Protocol (HTTP). WWW documents are written in the HyperText Markup Language (HTML), a simple text-based formatting language that is hardware and software platform–independent. Users point the browser at some location using a shorthand format called a *Uniform Resource Locator* (URL), which allows WWW servers to obtain files from any location on the public Internet using a variety of protocols, including HTTP, FTP, Gopher, and TELNET.

Mosaic, developed in 1994 at the National Center for Supercomputer Applications (NCSA) at the University of Illinois at Urbana–Champaign, was the first widely used browser. Because it was available at no cost over the Internet via anonymous FTP, and had a version for Windows, Mac, and UNIX systems, Mosaic was probably the single reason why the Web attracted so many users so quickly. The most commonly used browsers today include

1. Netscape Navigator (*http://www.netscape.com*)
2. Microsoft's Internet Explorer (*http://www.microsoft.com*)
3. NCSA Mosaic (*http://www.ncsa.uiuc.edu/SDG/Software/Mosaic/*)

The WWW is ideally suited to a windows environment, or other point-and-click graphical user interface (GUI). Nevertheless, several text-based Web browsers do exist, although their usefulness is limited if trying to obtain graphical images, or audio or video clips.

Uniform Resource Locators

As more and more protocols have become available to identify files, archive and server sites, newslists, and other information resources on the Internet, it was inevitable that some shorthand would arise to make it easier to designate these sources. The common shorthand format is the Uniform Resource Locator. The following list provides information on how the URL format should be interpreted for the protocols and resources:

file://host/directory/file-name identifies a specific file. For example, the file *htmlasst* in the *edu* directory at host *ftp.cs.da* would be denoted, using the full URL form, as *<URL:file:///ftp.cs.da/edu/htmlasst>*.

ftp://user:password@host:port/directory/file-name identifies an FTP site (e.g., *ftp://ftp.eff.org/pub/EFF/Policy/Crypto/**).

gopher://host:port/gopher-path identifies a Gopher site and menu path; a 00 at the start of the path indicates a directory and 11 indicates a file (e.g., *gopher://info.umd.edu:901/00/info/Government/Factbook92*).

http://host:port/directory/file-name?searchpart identifies a WWW server location (e.g., *http://info.isoc.org/home.html*).

mailto:e-mail_address identifies an individual's Internet mail address (e.g., *mailto:s.shepard@hill.com*).

telnet://user:password@host:port/ identifies a TELNET location (the trailing "/" is optional) (e.g., *telnet://envnet:henniker@envnet.gsfc.nasa.gov*).

User directories on the Web

While finding users on the Internet remains somewhat like alchemy if using the tools and utilities mentioned earlier, the Web has added a new dimension to finding people. Since 1995, many telephone companies have placed national White and Yellow Page telephone directories online, accessible via the World Wide Web.

For a while, it seemed that the easiest and most reliable approach to finding people's email address on the Internet was to look up their telephone number on the Web, call them, and ask for their email address! More recently, however, many third parties are augmenting the standard telephone directory with an email directory. These services primarily rely on users voluntarily registering, resulting in incomplete databases because most users don't know about all of the services. Nevertheless, some of the personal directory services available via the Web with which email addresses (and telephone numbers) can be found include:

Four11 Directory Services (*http://www.Four11.com/*)

Excite (*http://www.excite.com/Reference/locators.html*)

People Search (*http://www.yahoo.com/search/people/*)

In addition, the Knowbot Information Service (KIS), CNRI's automated username database search tool described earlier in this chapter, is also available on the Web, at *http://info.cnri.reston.va.us/kis.html.* Users can select several options for the KIS search, including the InterNIC, MILNET, MCImail, and Latin American Internic databases; UNIX Finger and WHOIS servers; and X.500 databases.

Other service accessible via the Web

Many of the other utilities described earlier in this chapter can also be accessed via the WWW. In general, the Web browser acts as a viewer to a remote client rather than requiring specialized software on the user's system.

Several sites provide DNS information, obviating the need for a user to have a local DNS client such as NSLOOKUP. The hosts *http://ns1.milepost.com/dns/* and *http://sh1.ro.com/~mprevost/netutils/ dig.html* are among the best DNS sites, allowing the user to access all DNS information. The site *http://www.bankes.com/nslookup.html* allows users to do multiple, sequential searches at a given domain. Other Web sites providing simple DNS name/address translation services include

http://rhinoceros.cs.inf.shizuoka.ac.jp/dns.html

http://www.engin.umich.edu/htbin/DNSquery

http://www.lublin.pl/cgi-bin/ns/nsgate

http://www.trytel.com/cgi-bin/weblookup

PING is another service available on the Web. The *http://sh1.ro.com/~mprevost/netutils/ping.html* page allows a user to select a host name, number of times to PING (1–10), and number of seconds between each PING (1–10), and returns a set of summary statistics. Other Web-based PING sites include *http://www.net.cmu.edu/bin/ping* (sends 10 PINGs, and reports the times and minimum/maximum/average summary statistics) and *http://www.uia.ac.be/cc/ping.html* (indicates whether the target host is alive).

Traceroute is also available on the Web. Unfortunately, these servers trace the route from their host to a host that the user chooses, rather than from the user's host to the target. Nevertheless, interesting route information can be found at *http://www.net.cmu.edu/bin/traceroute*. Traceroute service and a list of a number of other traceroute sites on the Web can be found at *http://www.lublin.pl/cgi-bin/trace/traceroute*.

Access to Archie is also available via the WWW, where your browser acts as the graphical interface to an Archie server. To find a list of Archie servers, and to access them via the Web, point your browser at *http://www.yahoo.com/Computers_and_Internet/Internet/FTP_Sites/Searc hing/Archie/*.

Finally, even Finger can be found on the World Wide Web; check out *http://sh1.ro.com/~mprevost/netutils/finger.html*.

5.8   Internet Discussion Lists and Newsgroups

Among the most useful features of the Internet are the discussion lists that have become available to allow individuals to discuss topics of mutual concern. Discussion list topics range from scuba diving and home brewing of beer to AIDS research and foreign policy. Several, naturally, deal specifically with the Internet, TCP/IP protocols, and the impact of new technologies. Most of the discussion lists accessible from the Internet are unmoderated, meaning that anyone can send a message to the list's central repository and the message will then be automatically forwarded to all subscribers of the list. These lists provide very fast turnaround between submission of a message and delivery, but often result in a lot of messages (including inappropriate junk mail, or "spam"). A moderated list has an extra step; a human list moderator examines all messages before they are forwarded to ensure that the messages are appropriate to the list and not needlessly inflammatory!

Users should be warned that some lists generate a large number of messages each day. Before subscribing to too many lists, be sure that you are aware of local policies and/or charges governing access to discussion lists and email storage.

Internet discussion lists

Mail can be sent to almost all Internet lists at an address with the form *list_name@host_name*.

The common convention when users want to subscribe, unsubscribe, or handle any other administrative matter is to send a message to the list administrator; do not send administrivia (administrative trivia) to the main list address! The list administrator can usually be found at *list_name-REQUEST@host_name*.

To subscribe to a list, it is often enough to place the word *subscribe* in the main body of the message, although a line with the format `subscribe` `list_name your_full_name` will satisfy most mail servers. A similar message may be used to get off a list; just use the word *unsubscribe* followed by the list name. Not every list follows this convention, but it is a safe bet if you don't have better information!

LISTSERV. A large set of discussion groups is maintained using a program called *LISTSERV,* a service provided widely on BITNET and EARN, but also available to Internet users. A LISTSERV user's guide can be found on the Web at *http://www.earn.net/lug/notice.html*. Mail can be sent to most LISTSERV lists at an address with the form *list_name@host_name*.

The common convention when users want to subscribe, unsubscribe, or handle any other administrative matter is to send commands in a message to the LISTSERV server; do not send administrivia to the main list address! The list server can usually be found at *LISTSERV@host_name*.

LISTSERV commands are placed in the main body of email messages sent to an appropriate list server location. Once you have found a list of interest, you can send a message to the appropriate address with any appropriate command, such as

`subscribe list_name your_full_name`	Subscribe to a list.
`unsubscribe list_name`	Unsubscribe from a list.
`help`	Get help and a list of commands.
`index`	Get a list of LISTSERV files.
`get file_name`	Obtain a file from the server.

Majordomo. Majordomo is another popular list server for Internet discussion lists. The Web site *http://www.greatcircle.com/majordomo/* has a large amount of information about Majordomo. Mail is sent to Majordomo lists using the same general address format as above: *list_name@host_name*.

The common convention when users want to subscribe, unsubscribe, or handle any other administrative matter is to send a message to the Majordomo list server; do not send administrivia to the main list address! The Majordomo server can usually be found at *MAJORDOMO@host_name*. Majordomo commands are placed in the main body of e-mail messages sent to an appropriate list server location. Available commands include

`help`	Get help and a list of commands.
`subscribe list_name your_e-mail`	Subscribe to a list (email address is optional).
`unsubscribe list_name your_e-mail`	Unsubscribe from a list (email address is optional).
`info list`	Sends an introduction about the specified list.
`lists`	Get a list of lists served by this Majordomo server.

Usenet. Usenet, also known as *NETNEWS* or *Usenet news,* is another information source with its own set of special interest mailing lists organized into newsgroups. Usenet originated on UNIX systems but has migrated to many other types of hosts. Usenet clients, called *newsreaders,* use the Network News Transfer Protocol and are available for virtually any operating system; several Web browsers, in fact, have this capability built in. While Usenet newsgroups are usually accessible at Internet sites, a prospective Usenet client host must have appropriate newsreader software to be able to read news. Users will have to check with their local host or network administrator to find out what Usenet newsgroups are locally available, as well as the local policies for using them.

Usenet newsgroup names are hierarchical in nature. The first part of the name, called the *hierarchy,* reflects the general subject area. There are two types of hierarchies, called *mainstream* and *alternative*; the total number of newsgroups is in the thousands. The *news.announce.newusers* newsgroup is a good place for new Usenet users to find a detailed introduction to the use of Usenet, as well as an introduction to its culture.

Usenet mainstream hierarchies are established by a process that requires the approval of a majority of Usenet members. Most sites that receive a NET-NEWS feed receive all of these hierarchies, which include

comp	Computers
misc	Miscellaneous
news	Network news
rec	Recreation
sci	Science
soc	Social issues
talk	Various discussion lists

The alternative hierarchies include lists that may be set up at any site that has the server software and disk space. These lists are not formally part of Usenet and, therefore, may not be received by all sites getting NETNEWS. The alternative hierarchies include

alt	Alternate miscellaneous discussion lists
bionet	Biology, medicine, and life sciences
bit	BITNET discussion lists
biz	Various business-related discussion lists
ddn	Defense Data Network
gnu	GNU lists
ieee	IEEE information
info	Various Internet and other networking information
k12	K-12 education
u3b	AT&T + 3B computers
vmsnet	Digital's VMS operating system

How to find discussion lists and newsgroups

Armed with the rules for signing up for a discussion list or accessing a news-group, how does one find an appropriate list given one's interests? There are tens of thousands of email discussion lists on the Internet. One List of Lists may be found using anonymous FTP at *ftp://sri.com/netinfo/interest-groups.txt*; the List of Lists can be searched using a Web browser by going to *http://catalog.com/vivian/interest-group-search.html*. Other places to look are the Publicly Accessible Mailing Lists index at *http://www.neosoft.com/internet/paml/byname.html* and the LISZT Directory of E-Mail Discussion Groups at *http://www.liszt.com*.

To obtain a list of LISTSERV lists, send email to *listserv@bitnic.cren.net* with the command lists global in the body of the message. Alternatively, look on the Web at *http://www.tile.net/tile/listserv/index.html*. The Web site *http://www.liszt.com* has a Mailing Lists Database of lists served by LISTSERV and Majordomo.

There are also thousands of Usenet newsgroups. One Usenet archive can be found at *gopher://rtfm.mit.edu/11//pub/usenet/news.answers*; see the */active-newsgroups* and */alt-hierarchies* subdirectories. Usenet news may also be read at *gopher://gopher.bham.ac.uk/11/Usenet*. A good Usenet search facility can be found on DejaNews at *http://www.dejanews.com/*; messages can also be posted to Usenet newsgroups from this site.

Note that there is often some overlap between Usenet newsgroups and Internet discussion lists. Some individuals join both lists in these circumstances or, often, there is cross-posting of messages. Some Usenet newsgroup discussions are forwarded onto an Internet mailing list by an individual site to provide access to those users who do not have Usenet available.

Internet documentation

To fully appreciate and understand what is going on within the Internet community, users might wish to obtain the occasional Internet specification. The main body of Internet documents is Requests for Comments (RFCs), although a variety of RFC subsets have been defined for various specific purposes. The sections below describe the RFCs and other documentation, and how to get them.

The Internet Engineering Task Force (IETF) is the guiding body for Internet standards; their Web site is *http://www.ietf.org*. The IETF operates under the auspices of the Internet Society (ISOC), which has a Web site at *http://www.isoc.org*. For complete, up-to-date information on obtaining Internet documentation, go to the InterNIC's Web site at *http://ds.internic.net/ds/dspg0intdoc.html*. For information on the organizations involved in the IETF standards process, see RFC 2028. For information on the relationship between the IETF and ISOC, see RFC 2031.

5.9 Requests for Comments (RFCs)

RFCs are the body of literature comprising Internet protocols, standards, research questions, hot topics, humor (especially those dated April 1), and general information. Each RFC is uniquely issued a number which is never reused or reissued; if a document is revised, it is given a new RFC number and the old RFC becomes obsolete.

Announcements are sent to the RFC-DIST mailing list whenever a new RFC is issued; anyone may join this list by sending email to *majordomo@zephyr.isi.edu* with the line `subscribe rfc-dist` in the body of the message.

RFCs may be obtained through the mail (i.e., postal service), but it is easier and faster to get them online. One easy way to obtain RFCs online is to use RFC-INFO, an email-based service to help users locate and retrieve RFCs and other Internet documents. To use the service, send email to *rfc-info@isi.edu* and leave the `Subject:` field blank; commands that may go in the main body of the message include

`help`	Help file.
`help: ways_to_get_rfcs`	Help file on how to get RFCs.
`RETRIEVE: RFC Doc-ID: RFCxxxx`	Retrieve RFC xxxx; use all four digits.
`LIST: RFC`	List all RFCs.
`[options] (…[matching the following options])`	
`  KEYWORDS: xxx`	Title contains string xxx.
`  AUTHOR: xxx`	Written by xxx.
`  ORGANIZATION: xxx`	Issued by company xxx.
`  DATED-AFTER: mmm-dd-yyyy`	
`  DATED-BEFORE: mmm-dd-yyyy`	
`  OBSOLETES: RFCxxxx`	List RFCs obsoleting RFC xxxx.

Another RFC email server can be found at the InterNIC. To use this service, send an email message to *mailserv@ds.internic.net,* leaving the `Subject:` field blank. In the main body of the message, use one or more of the following commands:

`help`	Help file
`file /ftp/rfc/rfcNNNN.txt`	Text version of RFC NNNN
`file /ftp/rfc/rfcNNNN.ps`	PostScript version of RFC NNNN
`document-by-name rfcNNNN`	Text version of RFC NNNN

Primary RFC repositories can be found at the following:

Host address	Directory
ds.internic.net	*rfc*
nis.nsf.net	*internet/documents/rfc*
nisc.jvnc.net	*rfc*
ftp.isi.edu	*in-notes*
wuarchive.wustl.edu	*info/rfc*
src.doc.ic.ac.uk	*rfc*

ftp.ncren.net	*rfc*
ftp.sesqui.net	*pub/rfc*
nis.garr.it	*mirrors/RFC*
funet.fi	*rfc*
munnari.oz.au	*rfc*

To obtain an RFC via anonymous FTP, connect to one of the RFC repositories listed in the preceding tabular list using FTP. After connecting, change to the appropriate RFC directory (as shown in the preceding list) using the cd command. To obtain a particular file, use the get command:

`GET RFC-INDEX.TXT local_name`	RFC index
`GET RFCxxxx.TXT local_name`	Text version of RFC xxxx
`GET RFCxxxx.PS local_name`	PostScript version of RFC xxxx

The RFC index, or a specific reference to an RFC, will indicate whether the RFC is available in ASCII text (`.txt`) or PostScript (`.ps`) format. By convention, all RFCs are available in ASCII, while some are also available in PostScript where use of graphics and/or different fonts adds more information or clarity; an increasing number are also being converted to HTML. Be aware that the index file is very large, containing the citing for over 2000 documents. Note that not all RFCs numbered below 698 (July 1975) are available online.

Finally, the InterNIC's Web site at *http://ds.internic.net/ds/dspg1int-doc.html* contains the RFC index and a complete set of RFCs. More information about Web-based RFC servers can be found at *http://www.isi.edu/rfc-editor/rfc-sources.html*.

The sample dialog below, although highly abbreviated, shows a user obtaining RFC 1594 (Answers to Commonly asked "New Internet User" Questions) using email and anonymous FTP.

```
= = = = = = = = = = = = = = = = = = = = = = = = = = = = = = = = = = = = = =
**SMCVAX$ mail
**MAIL> send
**To: in%"rfc-info@isi.edu"
Subject:
Enter your message below. Press CTRL/Z when complete, CTRL/C to quit
**retrieve: rfc
**doc-id: rfc1594
**^Z
**MAIL> exit
**SMCVAX$ ftp ds.internic.net
**Username: anonymous
**Password:
**NIC.DDN.MIL> cd rfc
**NIC.DDN.MIL> get rfc1594.txt rfc-1594.txt
**NIC.DDN.MIL> exit
SMCVAX$
= = = = = = = = = = = = = = = = = = = = = = = = = = = = = = = = = = = = = =
```

Internet standards

RFCs describe many aspects of the Internet. By the early 1990s, however, so many specifications of various protocols had been written that it was not always clear which documents represented standards for the Internet. For that reason, a subset of RFCs have been designated as STDs to identify them as Internet standards.

Unlike RFC numbers that are never reused, STD numbers always refer to the latest version of the standard. UDP, for example, would be completely identified as STD-6/RFC-768. Note that STD numbers refer to a standard, which is not necessarily a single document; STD 19, for example, is the NetBIOS Service Protocols standard comprising RFCs 1001 and 1002, and a complete citation for this standard would be STD-19/RFC-001/RFC-1002.

The availability of new STDs is announced on the RFC-DIST mailing list. STD-1 always refers to the latest list of Internet Official Protocol Standards. The Internet standards process is described in RFC 2026 and STD notes are explained in RFC 1311.

STDs can be obtained as RFCs via anonymous FTP from any RFC repository. In addition, some RFC sites (such as *ds.internic.net*) provide an STD directory so that STD documents can be found in the path `/STD/xx.TXT,` where `xx` refers to the STD number.

STDs may also be obtained via the RFC-INFO server using the `RETRIEVE:` `STD` and `Doc-ID:` `STDxxxx` commands. Also, check out the InterNIC's Web site at *http://www.internic.net/std/* for the STD index and a complete set of STDs.

For Your Information documents

The For Your Information (FYI) series of RFCs provides Internet users with information about many topics related to the Internet. FYI topics range from historical to explanatory to tutorial, and are aimed at the wide spectrum of people that use the Internet. The FYI series includes answers to frequently asked questions by both beginning and seasoned users of the Internet, an annotated bibliography of Internet books, and an explanation of the Domain Name System.

Like the STDs, an FYI number always refers to the latest version of an FYI. FYI 4, for example, refers to the answers to commonly asked questions by new Internet users; its complete citation would be FYI-4/RFC-1594. The FYI notes are explained in FYI 1. FYIs can be obtained as RFCs via anonymous FTP from any RFC repository. In addition, some RFC sites (such as *ds.internic.net*) provide an FYI directory so that FYI documents can be found in the path `/FYI/xx.TXT,` where `xx` refers to the FYI number. FYIs may also be obtained via the RFC-INFO server using the `RETRIEVE:` `FYI` and `Doc-ID:` `FYIxxxx` commands. Also, check out the InterNIC's Web site at *http://www.internic.net/fyi/* for the FYI index and a complete set of FYIs.

Best Current Practices

Standards track RFCs are formally part of the IETF standards process, subject to peer review, and intended to culminate in an official Internet Standard. Other RFCs are published on a less formal basis and are not part of the IETF process. To provide a mechanism of publishing relevant technical information which it endorsed, the IETF created a new series of RFCs, called the *Best Current Practices* (BCP) series. BCP topics include variances from the Internet standards process and IP address allocation in private networks.

Like the STDs and FYIs, a BCP number always refers to the latest version of a BCP. BCP 5, for example, describes an IP address allocation plan for private networks; its complete citation would be BCP-5/RFC-1918. The BCP process is explained in BCP 1.

BCPs may also be obtained via the RFC-INFO server using the `RETRIEVE: BCP` and `Doc-ID: BCPxxxx` commands. Also, check out the RFC Editor's Web site at *http://www.isi.edu/rfc-editor/* for the BCP index and a complete set of BCPs.

RARE Technical Reports

RARE, the Réseaux Associés pour la Recherche Européenne (Association of European Research Networks), has a charter to promote and participate in the creation of a high-quality European computer communications infrastructure for the support of research endeavors. RARE member networks use Open Systems Interconnection (OSI) protocols and TCP/IP. To promote a closer relationship between RARE and the IETF, RARE Technical Reports (RTRs) have also been published as RFCs since summer 1993.

RTRs may also be obtained via the RFC-INFO server using the `RETRIEVE: RTR` and `Doc-ID: RTRxxxx` commands. Also, check out the InterNIC's Web site at *http://www.internic.net/rtr/* for the RTR index and a complete set of RTRs. Finally, RTRs may be obtained via anonymous FTP from *ftp://ftp.rare.nl/rare/publications/rtr/*.

Browsing the Internet

There are several books that will help you get started finding sites on the Internet. But, much more timely and up-to-date information can be found on the Internet itself, using such search tools as

Yahoo (*http://www.yahoo.com*)

Excite (*http://www.excite.com*)

Lycos (*http://www.lycos.com*)

WebCrawler (*http://www.webcrawler.com*)

Altavista (*http://altavista.digital.com*)

Several other sources cite locations from which to access specific information about a wide range of subjects using such tools as FTP, TELNET, Gopher, and WWW. One of the best periodic lists, and archives, is through the Scout Report, a weekly publication by the InterNIC's Net Scout Services Project at the University of Wisconsin's Computer Science Department. To receive the Scout Report by email each week, join the mailing list by sending email to *listserv@lists.internic.net*; place the line `subscribe scout-report your_full_name` in the body of the message to receive the text version, or use `subscribe scout-report-html your_full_name` to receive the report in HTML. The Scout Report is also available on the Web at

http://www.cs.wisc.edu/scout/report

http://rs.internic.net/scout/report

anonymous FTP at ftp://rs.internic.net/scout/

Another list is Yanoff's Internet Services List, which may be found at *http://www.spectracom.com/islist/* or *ftp://ftp.csd.uwm.edu/pub/inet.services.txt*. Another one is at *http://www.together.net/~kessler/gck_site.html*. If you are looking for Internet-specific information, one good starting point is *http://www.yahoo.com/Computers_and_Internet/Internet/*. The InterNIC is another valuable resource, with their Scout Report and Scout Toolkit (*http://rs.internic.net/scout/toolkit*).

There is also a fair amount of rudimentary tutorial information available on the Internet. The InterNIC cosponsors The 15 Minute Series (*http://rs.internic.net/nic-support/15min/*), a collection of free, modular, and extensible training materials on specific Internet topics. ROADMAP96 (*http://www.ua.edu/~crispen/roadmap.html*) is a free, 27-lesson Internet training workshop over email.

Acronyms and abbreviations related to the Internet

ASCII	American Standard Code for Information Interchange
BCP	Best Current Practices
BITNET	Because It's Time Network
DDN	Defense Data Network
DNS	Domain Name System
EARN	European Academic Research Network
FAQ	Frequently Asked Questions list
FTP	File Transfer Protocol
FYI	For Your Information series of RFCs
HTML	HyperText Markup Language
HTTP	HyperText Transport Protocol
ICMP	Internet Control Message Protocol

IP	Internet Protocol
ISO	International Organization for Standardization
NetBIOS	Network Basic Input/Output System
NIC	Network Information Center
NICNAME	Network Information Center name service
NSF	National Science Foundation
NSFNET	National Science Foundation Network
RARE	Réseaux Associés pour la Recherche Européenne
RFC	Request for Comments
RARE	Reseaux Associes pour la Recherche Europeenne
RTR	RARE Technical Reports
STD	Internet Standards series of RFCs
TCP	Transmission Control Protocol
TTL	Time to Live
UDP	User Datagram Protocol
URL	Uniform Resource Locator
WAIS	Wide Area Information Server
WWW	World Wide Web

References

RFC 1436	*The Internet Gopher Protocol*
RFC 1866	*HyperText Markup Language,* 2.0
RFC 1945	*HyperText Transfer Protocol,* HTTP/1.0
RFC 1738	*Uniform Resource Locators* (URLs)
RFC 2026	*Internet Standards Process,* rev. 3
RFC 954	*NICNAME / WHOIS*
RFC 2028	*The Organizations Involved in the IETF Standards Process*
RFC 2031	*IETF-ISOC Relationship*
RFC 977	*Network News Transfer Protocol*
RFC 1150	*F.Y.I. on F.Y.I.: Introduction to the F.Y.I. Notes*
RFC 1034	*Domain Names—Concepts and Facilities*
RFC 1591	*Domain Name System Structure and Delegation*
RFC 792	*Internet Control Message Protocol*
RFC 2000	*Internet Official Protocol Standards*
RFC 1311	*Introduction to the STD Notes*
RFC 1818	*Best Current Practices*
RFC 959	*File Transfer Protocol* (FTP)
RFC 854	*TELNET Protocol Specification*

RFC 1180   *TCP/IP Tutorial*

RFC 1400   *Transition and Modernization of the Internet Registration Service*

RFC 1288   *The Finger User Information Protocol*

5.10   TELNET Options

For convenience, all the TELNET Options are collected here with both their state and status.

Protocol	Name	Number	State	Status	RFC	STD
TOPT-BIN	Binary Transmission	0	Std	Rec	856	27
TOPT-ECHO	Echo	1	Std	Rec	857	28
TOPT-RECN	Reconnection	2	Prop	Ele	...	
TOPT-SUPP	Suppress Go Ahead	3	Std	Rec	858	29
TOPT-APRX	Approx Message Size Negotiation	4	Prop	Ele	...	
TOPT-STAT	Status	5	Std	Rec	859	30
TOPT-TIM	Timing Mark	6	Std	Rec	860	31
TOPT-REM	Remote Controlled Trans and Echo	7	Prop	Ele	726	
TOPT-OLW	Output Line Width	8	Prop	Ele	...	
TOPT-OPS	Output Page Size	9	Prop	Ele	...	
TOPT-OCRD	Output Carriage-Return Disposition	10	Prop	Ele	652	
TOPT-OHT	Output Horizontal Tabstops	11	Prop	Ele	653	
TOPT-OHTD	Output Horizontal Tab Disposition	12	Prop	Ele	654	
TOPT-OFD	Output Formfeed Disposition	13	Prop	Ele	655	
TOPT-OVT	Output Vertical Tabstops	14	Prop	Ele	656	
TOPT-OVTD	Output Vertical Tab Disposition	15	Prop	Ele	657	
TOPT-OLD	Output Linefeed Disposition	16	Prop	Ele	658	
TOPT-EXT	Extended ASCII	17	Prop	Ele	698	
TOPT-LOGO	Logout	18	Prop	Ele	727	
TOPT-BYTE	Byte Macro	19	Prop	Ele	735	
TOPT-DATA	Data Entry Terminal	20	Prop	Ele	1043	
TOPT-SUP	SUPDUP	21	Prop	Ele	736	
TOPT-SUPO	SUPDUP Output	22	Prop	Ele	749	
TOPT-SNDL	Send Location	23	Prop	Ele	779	
TOPT-TERM	Terminal Type	24	Prop	Ele	1091	
TOPT-EOR	End of Record	25	Prop	Ele	885	
TOPT-TACACS	TACACS User Identification	26	Prop	Ele	927	
TOPT-OM	Output Marking	27	Prop	Ele	933	
TOPT-TLN	Terminal Location Number	28	Prop	Ele	946	
TOPT-3270	Telnet 3270 Regime	29	Prop	Ele	1041	
TOPT-X.3	X.3 PAD	30	Prop	Ele	1053	
TOPT-NAWS	Negotiate About Window Size	31	Prop	Ele	1073	
TOPT-TS	Terminal Speed	32	Prop	Ele	1079	
TOPT-RFC	Remote Flow Control	33	Prop	Ele	1372	
TOPT-LINE	Linemode	34	Draft	Ele	1184	
TOPT-XDL	X Display Location	35	Prop	Ele	1096	
TOPT-ENVIR	Telnet Environment Option	36	Hist	Not	1408	
TOPT-AUTH	Telnet Authentication Option	37	Exp	Ele	1416	
TOPT-ENVIR	Telnet Environment Option	39	Prop	Ele	1572	
TOPT-TN3270E	TN3270 Enhancements	40	Prop	Ele	1647	
TOPT-AUTH	Telnet XAUTH	41	Exp			
TOPT-CHARSET	Telnet CHARSET	42	Exp		2066	

Protocol	Name	Number	State	Status	RFC	STD
TOPT-RSP	Telnet Remote Serial Port	43	Exp			
TOPT-COMPORT	Telnet Com Port Control	44	Exp		2217	
TOPT-EXTOP	Extended-Options-List	255	Std	Rec	861	32

5.11 Summary

The information provided in this chapter has presented terms, trouble-shooting tools such as WWW information, RFC information, and so forth. This information helps me all the time; that is, I use this information currently to troubleshoot my network. For this reason, I know that it will help you, too.

6

Troubleshooting Electrical Aspects of Your Network

Network components require electrical power. Power is fundamental. I know of few, if any, devices that operate with networks that do not require electricity to operate. During my years working with network professionals, I realized that many of these people do not understand some fundamental principles of electricity. I decided to cover basic topics in this chapter, beginning with some electrical principles and facts, and then helping the reader understand how they are meaningful to everyday work with networks. Then I decided to cover power conditioning in this chapter, prior to what I call the core of the book, because if there is a single focal point in all networks, it surely is power. Let me put this in perspective.

Look around you. If you are in an office environment, all the better. Now consider that I have just discovered the circuit breaker box supplying electricity to your office. Now suppose that I have turned all of them off. Got any idea what is going on now in your office? Not much. You can't print, compute, or use anything that relies on electrical power. Power is fundamental. Yes, I am aware of solar-powered calculators and other such devices as well as battery-driven notebook computers and cell(ular) phones that run on batteries, but without doubt the core of your business relies on electricity for daily operations.

Electricity is taken for granted for the most part, and this is unfortunate. Electricity is an artificially created force in the way it is harnessed and used today in our modern world. However, electricity is not available in equal quantity and quality worldwide. In most places where business is conducted in some form or fashion, however, some degree of electricity is available. But remember that electricity is human-made in the way it is used in the business community, but technically it does exist in nature as a fundamental characteristic of the universe.

I am exaggerating a little here to make a point. Those who understand the critical role of power in networks, computers, and modern offices realize that all operations revolve around *power*; likewise, the converse is true. Without power, or proper power conditioning and backup, operations come to a halt in a hurry. Consequently, in this chapter basic electrical principles are presented for those unfamiliar with electricity. Other parts of this chapter include sample electrical readings and how to interpret them, and important information about power conditioning and aspects of it.

6.1 Electrical Fundamentals

As mentioned at the beginning of Section 5.2, understanding the basic principles of electricity will help you in the practical aspects of planning your network and, as mentioned in Section 5.1, will help you safeguard your system against faulty wiring and other electrical problems once it is up and running.

Site wiring

Houses, commercial buildings, and the majority of building facilities in modern cities today are already wired for electricity, and the wiring schemes in many of these structures are similar. This might seem like an overgeneralization; however, consider a highlighted overview of my house as an example. Figure 6.1 shows a voltage reading of 122.2 V ac. I took this reading inside the load center where the wire connects to a breaker supplying the outlets in

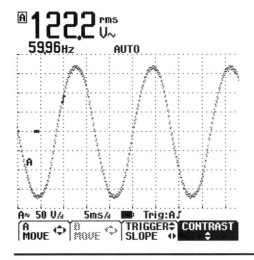

Figure 6.1 Voltage and Cycle Reading at Breaker 1

my dining room. It is simply a typical reading; most likely the reading of this line taken at a dining room outlet fed by it would yield the same results.

Now consider Figure 6.2, which shows 244.3 V and a 59.97 Hz reading. I took this voltage measurement at the lines feeding my house load center. Now consider Figure 6.3, which shows a highlighted view (observed from the attic) of the load center, the garage, kitchen, dining room, hallway, porch, front door, and other structural components. Note that the load center is in the garage. I have illustrated two ac outlets in the dining room, and this is a fairly accurate representation of their physical location. I show a stove and refrigerator in the kitchen. Note that the stove is wired to the load center and appears to be 220 V ac. Now note that the wire going to the stove appears to be larger (4-gauge) than that going to the outlets (12-gauge). (As mentioned earlier, wire size and gauge are inversely proportional.) The refrigerator is wired directly to the load center as well and is 120 V ac, and 6-gauge wire is used. The ac outlets are 120 V. A significant point here is that many of the outlets in the house are wired in parallel; meaning multiple outlets running from a single breaker. Why is this important? Because the wiring pattern is similar in the commercial world. Granted, in the commercial world more dedicated outlets do exist, but the primary reason for this is to save money. Why are you not surprised? Unless you custom-build, most builders will install the outlets and other wiring components in general conformance to standards in the industry and to electrical code. Note also in the illustration that the stove, the heater, and the air-conditioning system each have dedicated outlets.

Consider Figure 6.4, which shows a detailed view of the load center. Note three leads coming from the electric meter: two 120-V ac feeds and one neutral lead. The illustration shows the cable going to the dining room outlet,

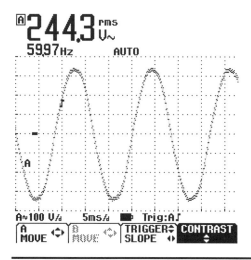

Figure 6.2 Input Voltage Reading from Electric Company

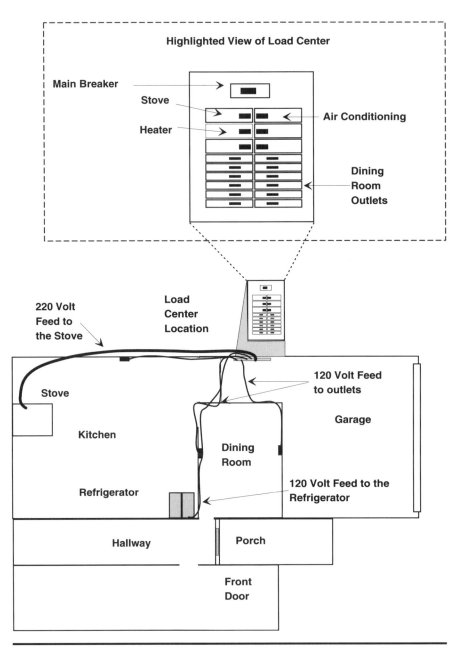

Figure 6.3 Overview on House Wiring

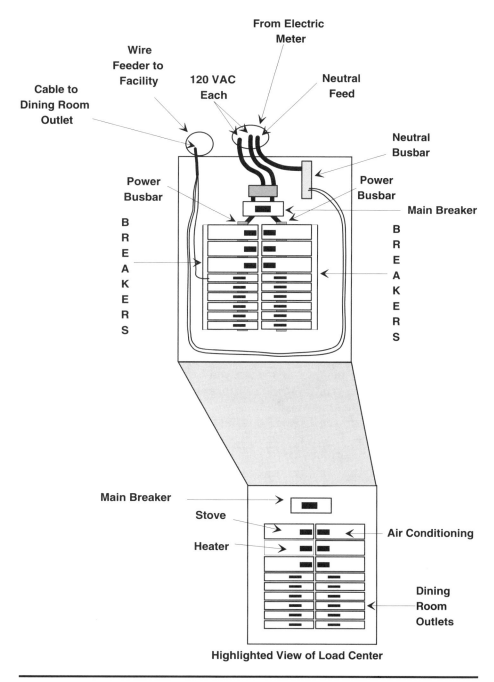

Figure 6.4 Detailed View Inside Load Center

and the hot lead connects to a breaker, while the neutral and ground connect to the neutral busbar as shown. Beneath the breakers shown in this figure, two busbars carry the voltage. Also observe the single main circuit breaker at the top of the load center. This breaker is the single *switch* used to turn on or off the feed to the entire house. Most load centers are similar to this. Although they differ when working with much higher voltage, there are commonalities.

Consider Figure 6.5, which shows the voltage reading at the top of the busbar where the hot feeds enter the load center from the electric meter. Note that I got a reading of 243.7 V at this location.

So, what is the purpose in this? First, to illustrate some fundamental concepts that you may not have been exposed to in traditional network or computer coursework; second, to emphasize that electricity is serious business and if you are not trained in electricity, it is best to consult a licensed electrician; and third, to illustrate that not all outlets or even lighting, for that matter, have dedicated circuits. Also, most of the wiring in my house is 12-gauge ROMEX wire, which is quite large for use in a house, but considering the various loads that network equipment can generate, one might need a larger wire. Why does this matter? Well, consider what would happen if you plugged two microwave ovens into the same 20-A circuit. At 7.764 A per microwave, as shown in Figure 5.3, you would be far beyond a 50 percent utilization of that breaker. Odds are that one more device on that breaker would overload it. Just remember this when you begin working with laser or thermal printers, which tend to draw significant current, both at start-up and during the cycles of heating the drum.

I also presented the material for you to consider with respect to your work premises. If you think of it with the perspective I have shown here, you'll have a healthier view of your environment.

Harmonics

Why harmonics? Well, harmonics evaluation reveals the quality of power. Depending on your worksite, this could be very significant, because the more sensitive the equipment, the more susceptible it is to harmonic distortion. Remember the definition of *harmonics:* a sinusoidal component of a periodic wave, with a frequency that is an integral multiple of the fundamental frequency. The frequency of the second harmonic is twice that of the fundamental frequency or the first harmonic. This is also called the *harmonic component* and *harmonic frequency*. Remember also that *harmonic analysis* refers to any method used to identify and evaluate the harmonics (frequencies) that make up a complex form of voltage, current, or some other varying quantity. Consider Figure 6.6, which shows channels 1 and 2 monitored on the Tektronix Tekscope. This is a voltage harmonic reading from the fundamental harmonic to the 11th. Notice the rms harmonic is 117.9 V while the rms voltage is 118 V ac. Now consider Figure 6.7, which shows the amperage

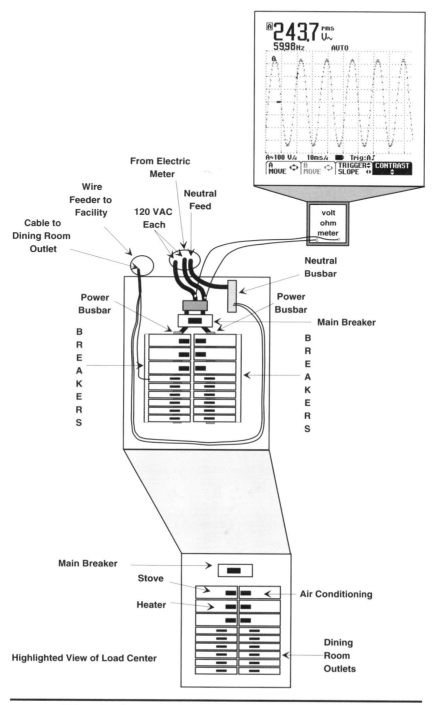

Figure 6.5 Voltage Reading from Electric Meter

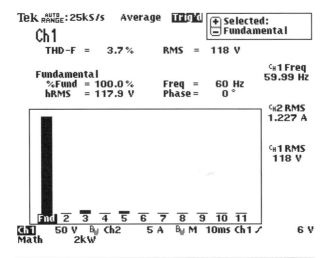

Figure 6.6 Voltage Harmonics of the Feed to the Printer

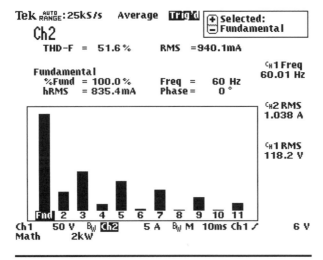

Figure 6.7 Amperage Harmonics of the Printer

harmonics while the network printer is at idle after a number of pages have been printed. The rms amperage reading is 1.038 A as indicated for channel 2, while the rms harmonic amperage reading is 835.4 mA. Note that the scope has also calculated the rms voltage from channel 1 and it reads 118.2 V ac.

Consider Figure 6.8, which shows the odd harmonics of the voltage reading from the fundamental harmonic to the 21st. This level of detail is quite helpful for those who need to analyze their power quality. Clean power is important, and ascertaining the harmonic values of various readings is important in power evaluation.

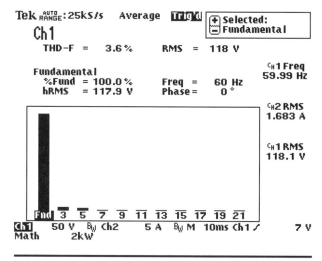

Figure 6.8 Odd Harmonics

Ground loops

If your background is not in electricity or electronics, you might not be familiar with *ground loops,* which occur when multiple grounds have a potential difference between them. The significance of this is to be aware that you can incur grounding from network cabling and through your electrical wiring. Hopefully the twain don't conflict.

Ground loops can eat away at your bandwidth by injecting distortion into a line and, if they are severe, can cause power quality degradation. So, what do you do? Well, just be aware that all electrical equipment, wherever it is located, can potentially pick up grounding. It is best to check the grounding of your telco wiring and network cabling, and to check for stray wires that could create such an environment.

I encourage you to obtain early on in your project information such as the electrical requirements you have (what to consider and how to calculate these are given in the following section), wiring of the existing facility, estimates (if possible) for power quality, and information for planning purposes on the grounding of the facility in which your equipment will operate.

6.2 How to Calculate Your Power Requirements

I am presenting fundamental information here. I recommend that you contact a certified electrician to assist you in determining exactly what your requirements are.

Equipment category and list

First, it is a good idea to categorize your equipment. The categories I derived and worked from are

- Printers
- Computers
- Peripherals
- Required 90 percent of the time
- Required 50 percent of the time
- Required less than 50 percent of the time
- Equipment in multiple locations
- Equipment in one location
- Number of downtime hours you can afford
- Amount of money you can afford to lose

This list is where I began categorizing to plan for power requirements. If you do not have an inventory list yet, start one. If you are starting in the middle of a network already established, then begin first by inventorying the equipment you currently have. For instance, how many computers and monitors do you have? Then move on to the printers you have; how many are networked, and how many are standalone? Is it feasible for all or some of them to use the same power source? List your peripherals as well. It would be a very good idea to access the original vendor documentation and/or reference the information on the equipment label and document the electrical and environmental requirements.

Now, list the equipment required 50 and 90 percent of the time. In other words, if a PC is used all day every day in your environment, then list it under the 90 percent column. On the other hand, if you have a system that is used occasionally, then list it appropriately.

It is also wise to list the equipment you have, or will have, by the location where it will be installed. This is important because networks generally span multiple facilities, sometimes in multiple locations. As a result, you may be required to purchase multiple types of equipment in order to get the coverage you need.

Another important issue is to estimate how much money can you afford to lose if your equipment is "cooked" by way of a lightning bolt. Don't laugh. I know some people who lost equipment because they did not plan ahead and prepare for this scenario.

Similar to losing equipment is the number of hours you can lose in lack of productive work (downtime). How many work-hours can you afford to lose? If you have 25 people, all using a computer, and you lose an entire day, this equates to 25 worker-days.

Specific calculations and UPS requirements

First, determine whether you have one- or three-phase equipment. Most of you will have one-phase. Be sure that you obtain what is considered steady-state operating amperage. This is not the circuit breaker rating, surge current, or inrush current. Use this number in the amperage portion of the equation. If you do not calculate for steady-state current, erroneous conclusions may result. In order to determine the amount of UPS (uninterruptible power supply) coverage, use the following equation:

$$\mathrm{kVA} = \frac{\mathrm{V} \times \mathrm{A}}{1000}$$

Then subtract the number you arrive at, which should be about 20 to 50 percent more than this, to calculate the approximate size you need. Now, reflect back to the Liebert UPS rating shown above as the kVA rating. This is oversimplified, but you need to remember this. As the Liebert documentation rightfully indicates, you would be better served by load-balancing your equipment through the use of three-phase UPS protection and then determining the size UPS on the basis of the largest load. This topic is significant and goes well beyond the scope of the purpose here; I recommend contacting a certified electrician to help you with three-phase power.

6.3   Types of Power Protection

Another topic in the realm of electricity that you need to understand is which devices perform which functions when it comes to power protection. Here are some of the basic types of power protection and their purpose.

Surge protectors

Surge protectors do exactly that; they protect against power surges. Spikes (sudden voltage increases) are typically inhibited with surge protection devices. This is probably the minimum level of protection you need. Even home computers should have this minimum level of protection.

Voltage regulators

Voltage regulators have the ability to maintain a certain voltage and current level for the device drawing on the electrical source. A voltage regulator is a good device to use with printers, especially laser printers.

Uninterruptible power supply (UPS)

A UPS device is prepared to provide interim power. UPSs are not a solution to power outages; they are an interim solution to bridge the time gap between power failure and power restoration. Large UPSs may provide a considerable number of minutes or even hours of uptime. However, UPS use presupposes that power from the electric company will be restored or that alternative power supply will be provided from a source such as a generator.

Generators

Generators create or *generate* electricity. They are typically used as alternative power sources in case the main source of power fails. If sufficiently large, a generator can generate electric power indefinitely—assuming that you can provide the diesel or gasoline to keep it operating. Generators are typically reserved for use in large commercial settings.

Switch gear

Transfer switch gear is used to change the source of electrical power to a generator. *Parallel switch gear* is used in settings where multiple generators are used in parallel with the other. This is advanced technology and not for novices. Generators, transfer switches, and paralleling UPSs are complex implementations that are almost always found in complex commercial settings, such as hospital complexes.

6.4   Where to Perform Electrical Tests

Your network has specific places where you can perform tests on the electrical aspect of your network. Consider Figure 6.9, which shows some of the equipment I have used in my network. Note the logical arrangement of the network equipment. The figure shows numerous workstations, storage equipment, servers, network UPS devices, and other network equipment. Each piece of equipment can be tested at the point where it plugs into the outlet to draw ac power. Also, if you have the proper device, and the know-how, you can measure the electrical harmonics and amperage at these locations as well.

Now, consider Figure 6.10, which shows the electrical load center, wiring to the network UPS, and some equipment used in my network. Note that four test points (Figure 6.10, points A to D) have been isolated:

A. The first test point for ac power, quality, and load is at the load center itself.

B. Test records should indicate the readings at the UPS busbar in which the cable connecting it to the load center is located.

C. Another test reading should indicate where the output busbar connections are made on the output side of the UPS.

D. Tests should also be made where each piece of equipment connects to the cable extending electrical power from the UPS (see lower right portion of diagram).

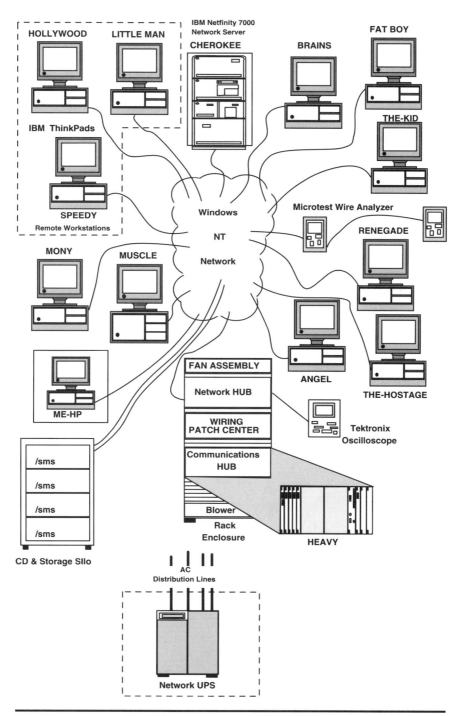

Figure 6.9 UPS for the Network

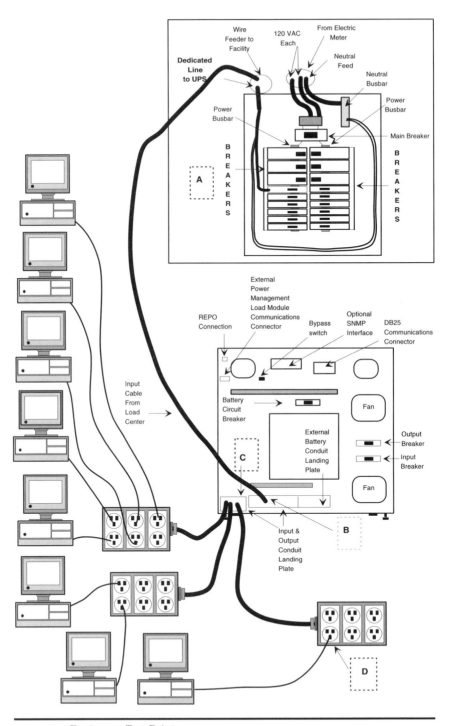

Figure 6.10 Equipment Test Points

DEVICE	DATE	TIME	VOLTAGE		FREQUENCY	AMPS	NOTES
			RMS	Peak-to-Peak			

Figure 6.11 Sample Electrical Recording Chart

After testing the electrical signals, you should record and log these readings for recordkeeping purposes. Figure 6.11 shows an example of the records that should be kept. Figure 6.11 shows a sample chart for keeping electrical readings. Note that the device, date, time, and other information can be included with this. Each device on your network should have something similar to this in order to maintain good records for an adequate baseline. Consider Figure 6.12, which shows sample readings from an electrical source feeding some peripheral systems in my network.

Figure 6.13 shows a sample reading of voltage harmonics on the same line as indicated in Figure 6.12. Figure 6.13 presents one aspect of examining power for quality's sake. It shows the harmonics of voltage from the fundamental to the 11th.

Figure 6.14 shows the fundamental harmonics as they relate to the amperage draw against this particular line. These readings are typical of what you should acquire for each device on your network. I recommend keeping printouts like these for future reference if needed; also, initial readings should be recorded in order to establish a baseline.

Consider Figure 6.15, which is a mathematical calculation for the voltage on a given line feeding some equipment in my network. Notice that the rms voltage reading is shown, as well as the frequency, power factor, average wattage, and other indicators of the electrical draw on this particular outlet.

Consider Figure 6.16, which is similar to Figure 6.15. Figure 6.16 shows the same readings as Figure 6.15, but the values differ. The significance of these two like readings is the time difference between them.

While you are acquiring this level of information about equipment in your network, remember to take some readings at different times and indicate the

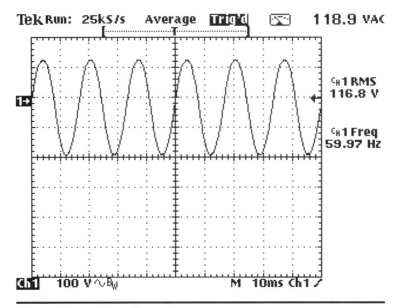

Figure 6.12 Sample Readings

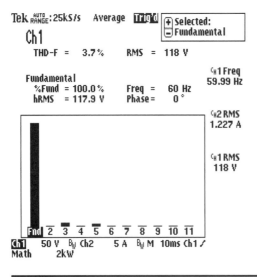

Figure 6.13 Voltage Harmonics from 1 through 11

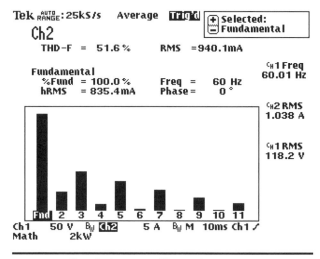

Figure 6.14   Sample Amperage Harmonics

Tek ᴬᵁᵀᴼ_ᴿᴬᴺᴳᴱ:25kS/s   Average   Trig'd

Math

$W = 1.875$ w $PF = 0.09$

$VA = 21.75$ va $DPF = 0.56$ ᶜʜ1 RMS
115.7 V

$VAR = 21.67$ var $\theta = -56°$

ᶜʜ1 Freq
60 Hz

	Average	Minimum	Maximum
W	1.875 w	1.875 w	1.875 w
VA	24.89 va	21.27 va	35.9 va
VAR	24.82 var	21.19 var	35.85 var
V	115.7 v	115.6 v	115.8 v
A	215.2 mA	184 mA	310.1 mA

Ch1   50 V   ʙ_w Ch2   5 A   ʙ_w M 10ms Ch1 ⁄
Math   2kW

Figure 6.15   Sample of Mathematical Readings

time on the readings for your records. This will greatly assist you if a past history of network functionality is needed later.

6.5   Troubleshooting Questions

Sometimes the hardest place to work is the beginning; for that reason, I am supplying some questions here to assist in your initial work in troubleshooting electrical aspects of your network. Please bear in mind that you should

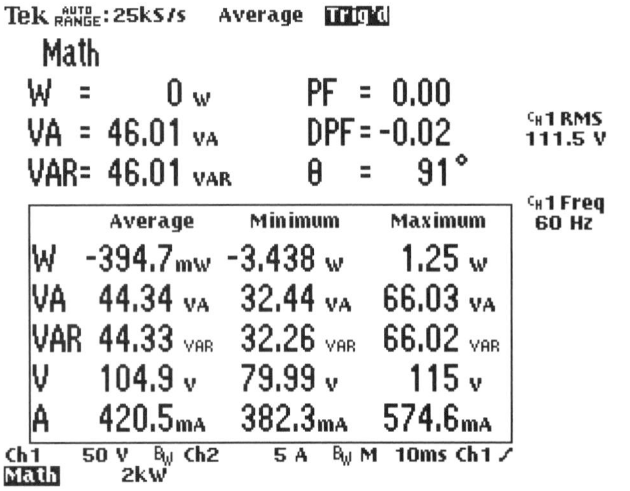

Tek ᴬᵁᵀᴼ₍ᴿᴬᴺᴳᴱ₎:25kS/s   Average   [Trig'd]

Math

W =   0 w   PF = 0.00
VA = 46.01 va   DPF = -0.02   ᶜᴴ1 RMS
VAR= 46.01 var   θ =   91°   111.5 V

	Average	Minimum	Maximum
W	-394.7mw	-3.438 w	1.25 w
VA	44.34 va	32.44 va	66.03 va
VAR	44.33 var	32.26 var	66.02 var
V	104.9 v	79.99 v	115 v
A	420.5ma	382.3ma	574.6ma

ᶜᴴ1 Freq
60 Hz

Ch1   50 V Bᵥ Ch2   5 A   Bᵥ M 10ms Ch1 ∕
Math   2kW

Figure 6.16 Sample Mathematical Reading 2

always consult with a certified electrician. Ignorance in electrical matters can be costly, so be careful.

1. Is the current power problem isolated to your facility?

2. Is the current power problem isolated to your floor or area?

3. Do you know of any significant event that has happened in the past few minutes, hours, or days that could have affected your current power problem?

4. Do you have a baseline recording of all electrical equipment on your network?

5. Are the records you have on file about your network equipment up to date?

6. Have any additions and/or deletions of equipment to your network occurred since you made the last inventory of electrical baseline?

7. Have you checked your load center (electrical breaker box)?

8. Are all the breakers operating as they should?

9. Have you isolated the problem to a device?

10. Have you contacted your electrician?

11. If you have isolated the problem, can you turn the breakers off until your electrician arrives?

12. If you have isolated the problem to a specific device, do you have a volt-ohm-milliammeter to check the outlet providing electricity to the device failed?

Many other questions may apply to your environment; it is difficult to make a clear-cut list that applies to each and every site. Please remember to use caution when you do anything with electricity. The information provided here is intended only to get you started in the right direction.

6.6 Summary

Electrical requirements in a network are often taken for granted. Understanding the terminology and instruments used to obtain information about your electrical environment is helpful. This chapter presented some basic information for you to use as a reference to begin considering the electrical needs for your network environment. I again recommend great caution when you work with electricity; it is not to be played with.

7

Network Troubleshooting Case Study: Part 1 (General)

The easiest way for me to describe network troubleshooting to you is to present a real network, explain its components, and then discuss troubleshooting. This, and the following chapters, present a real network—the one in my lab—and also some troubleshooting techniques.

This chapter begins by presenting the logical network design I created before obtaining any equipment. After the design is explained, further sections in this and the following chapters explain the network components and troubleshooting techniques.

I began with this network design the same way I have all others: literally at the drawing board. I use a marker board to work out my ideas. It can take days, sometimes weeks, for me to sift through the requirements, my thoughts, and variations of what equipment is needed and how it fits into the overall design scheme.

The network design explained here and later in the book is based more on principle than a given piece of technology. The purpose of the network design here is to meet current needs and sustain growth; in other words, the original design intent of this network is to do what I want it to do now and be flexible enough to change and accommodate growth in the near future. It is designed for use as a backdrop for some troubleshooting techniques and not according to anyone else's criteria. It is my private "Internet," and it is 100 percent compatible with the real Internet.

Before examining the components of the network, consider the logical network design as shown in Figure 7.1, which shows numerous network components. Some are not shown as clearly, such as network interface cards or par-

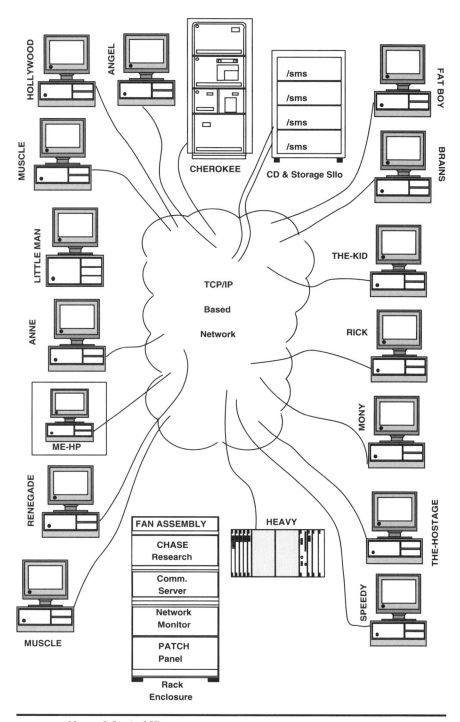

Figure 7.1   Network Logical View

ticular wiring. However, Figure 7.1 does show the overall logical design of the network. Close inspection of the figure may tend to imply a single point of failure in a given place, but redundancies have been built into it.

The reason this is the logical network design is because it was driven by user requirements. This network enables users to exchange files, email, and remote logons to systems such as servers, and even use network printing. The remaining sections in this chapter explain the components of the network.

7.1 Component Overview

Before examining each component, a list is provided here to describe the network components. It includes the major components I selected for use in this network.

Network component list

- Electrical wiring infrastructure
  Thomas & Betts
  Pass & Seymour
  General Cable
- Copper-based wiring (Thomas & Betts)
- Fiber-optic backbone (Siecor)
- Rack enclosures (Great Lakes Cabinets)
- Network UPS (Liebert)
- Network backbone (XYLAN)
- Network printer (IBM)
- Network communication server (Chase Research)
- xDSL Network Router (Cayman Systems)
- Network data communication software (Tactical Software)
- Enterprise support software (Seattle Lab)
- Media converters and special network devices (TELEBYTE)
- Network storage silo (SMS Data Products Group)
- DiscPort PRO and DiscView PRO Software (Microtest)
- Network server (IBM Netfinity 7000)
- Microsoft Windows 95 and 98
- Microsoft Windows NT
- Commercial desktop computers (IBM)
- Remote workstations (IBM ThinkPads)

- 3Com USRobotics enterprise network hub
- Multimedia devices (Creative Labs)
- Ethernet adapters and SCSI interface boards (Adaptec)
- Network security and virus protection software (McAfee)
- Network tape drive (Sony)
- Cables (serial, parallel, SCSI, gender changers, SCSI terminators, IEEE 1284–compliant printer cables, etc.) (Belkin)
- Infrared network device (JetEye)
- Power protection (Tripp-Lite)

These components, and other presented later, have been put together to make the network possible.

7.2 Electrical Infrastructure

Because I designed the network infrastructure, I used equipment from the following vendors to make it possible:

- Thomas & Betts
- Pass & Seymour LeGrand
- Carol Cable

I literally designed this network from the ground up! Since I designed, specified, selected, and installed all equipment, I include this information here to provide you an opportunity to gain perspective on the complexities of the underlying infrastructure. Networks, worldwide, have an underlying infrastructure which is often taken for granted.

Because of the complexity of the network, I designed the data center to be partitioned into two main load centers. First, the lighting and ordinary wall outlets are wired as normal commercial wiring environments. Consider Figure 7.2, which shows the load center I designed for the lighting, wall outlets, and heating, ventilation, and air conditioning (HVAC) for the facility.

Figure 7.3 shows the load center for the data center and computer room where the computer and network equipment is located. Figure 7.3 shows a highlighted view of the site load center and also the feed to the data center. Now, consider Figure 7.4, which shows the second load center in the same location (part of the facility) as the data center. Note that it has 100-A breakers. This load center is separate from the one feeding the site; that is, this load center and the site load center are wired in parallel, that is not interdependent. Figure 7.4 shows the four-quad division of components in the data center. This four-way division is for organizational reasons. Note the UPS located in the middle of the data center. At the end of the raised floor, both

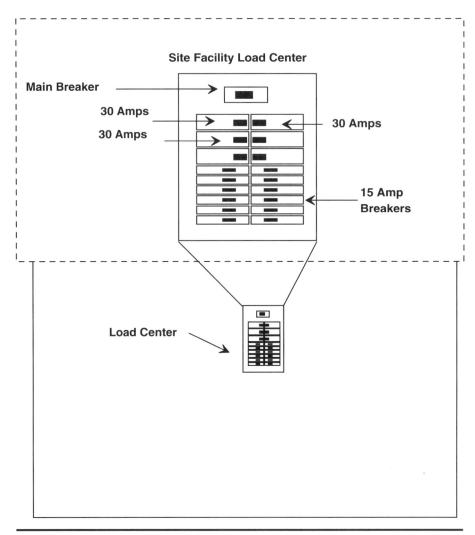

Figure 7.2 Load Center for Site

conditioned and nonconditioned power outlets are available for lines feeding computer rooms 1 and 2.

Consider Figure 7.5, which puts all the electrical components in perspective. Note that, as in Figure 7.4, the data center load center draws feed from the same location as the site load center. This figure illustrates computer room 1 with both conditioned and nonconditioned power along with the data center. A highlighted rear view of the UPS is also presented; note the remote emergency power-off (REPO) mechanism in the upper left area of this inset.

Because I worked at such a level of detail—creating the electrical infrastructure design and installing all the electrical components—I had to select

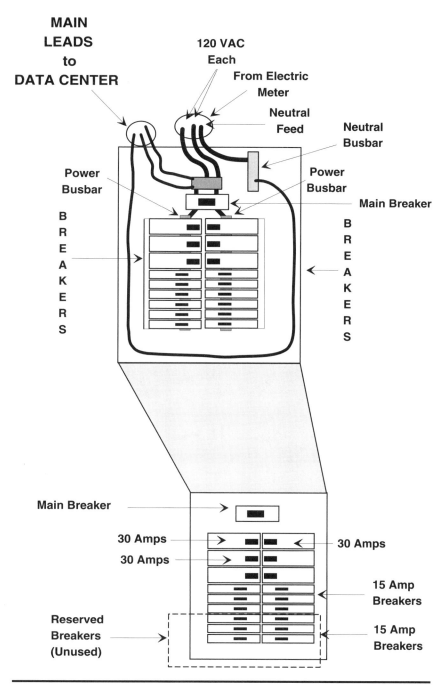

Figure 7.3 Highlighted View of Site Facility Load Center and Feed to Data Center

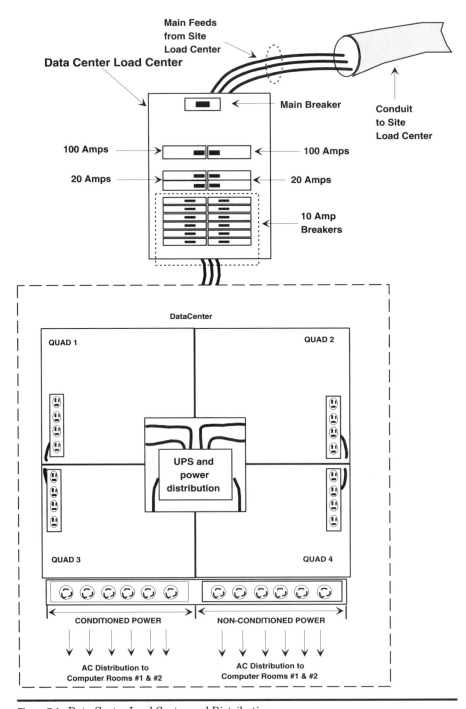

Figure 7.4 Data Center Load Center and Distribution

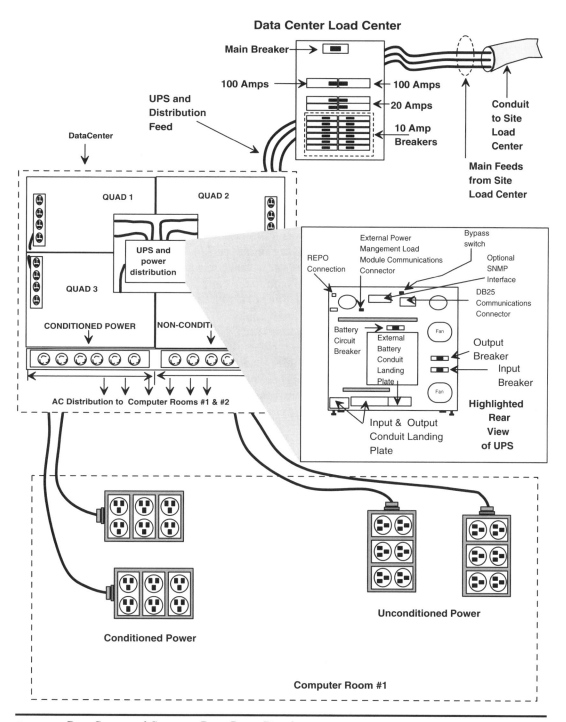

Figure 7.5   Data Center and Computer Room Power Distribution

one or more vendors for those components needed. Here are some of the components I obtained and put together to make this network possible:

Four-gang outlet boxes	Circuit breakers
Four-gang cover plates	Wire strippers
Twisted-pair patch cables	Ring terminals
Load centers	Zinc clamp connectors

Figure 7.6 shows a more detailed view of the overall electrical infrastructure in relation to systems supported. Thomas & Betts components were integral to this infrastructure. In fact, the Thomas & Betts equipment is more fundamental to network operation than the network equipment itself: the computers, hubs, and the like. The reason for this is simple; every network requires an electrical and structural environment. I am not aware of any operational networks built in a sandpile on an island.

Electrical components, including plugs, receptacles, flange outlets, pin-and-sleeve connections, and connectors, were required for this network. After considering two different electrical component suppliers. I chose Pass & Seymour products, which, to my knowledge, are the highest-grade electrical components in the industry.

Each time an electrical connection is effected, resistance occurs. The greater the resistance, the greater the electrical loss. The better the connection (where connections are made), the more smoothly electrical current can flow. In addition, the use of higher-quality components in electrical connections ensures a safer electrical infrastructure.

I used the following Pass & Seymour products in this network:

- Commercial-grade duplex receptacles

- Boot connectors

- L830 receptacles

- L830 connectors

- Pin-and-sleeve connectors

For further information, contact Pass & Seymour at

Pass & Seymour Legrand
50 Boyd Avenue
Syracuse, NY 13209
Phone: 800-776-4035

In addition, electrical wiring itself is a significant part of the network backbone. I used ROMEX, SO, and SW wire in this network. Wire sizes varied from 4- to 12-gauge being the smallest used. I decided to obtain wire from General Cable, which was able to meet all the needs of my network. It was for this reason that I also selected Carol Cable; not all wire providers can supply large gauges of wire in various forms such as SO and SW types.

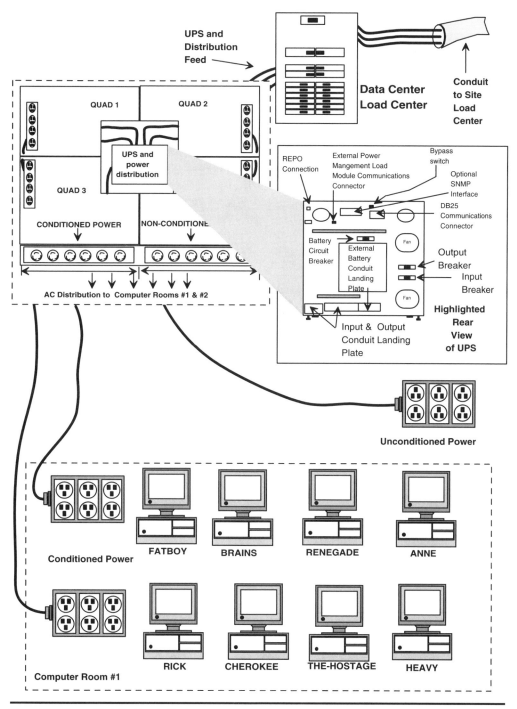

Figure 7.6 Power Distribution to Systems

I recommend that you contact General Cable to let them assist you in your electrical wiring needs. They can be reached at

General Cable
#4 Tessener Drive
Highland Heights, KY 41076
Phone: 800-424-5666

All computers and network equipment require some form of artificially generated power. Hence, the electrical infrastructure is fundamental and essential to the network. Few consider this level of detail unless they are designing a building with architectural engineers. Most networks designed and installed are built into facilities that already exist; this fact must be considered in the entire equation.

7.3 Copper-Based Wiring Infrastructure

An integral piece of the network is the copper-based network wiring backbone. I decided to use ALL-LAN for this network, as it is of superior quality. I used the following components to create the copper-based backbone:

- ALL-LAN network cable
- ALL-LAN patch panel
- ALL-LAN jacks
- ALL-LAN wall plates
- ALL-LAN to RJ-45 patch cables

Consider the specifications of ALL-LAN cable. It features rugged shielded construction for reliable operation. The horizontal or "home run" cable for the ALL-LAN Interconnection System is a 4-pair, 24-AWG solid copper core wire. Each pair is individually foiled and the cable has an overall braid, a construction that allows high-frequency signals to be transmitted without noticeable signal corruption or degradation. ALL-LAN cable has been characterized up to 300 MHz. This cable accommodates all existing systems while allowing for the anticipated bandwidth of future systems. Cable specifications include the following:

Thomas & Betts jacket type	Cable no.	Impedance and # pairs	AWG gauge
Plenum	PWCS-300N4-95	100 Ω, 4-pair	24
PVC	PWCS-300V4-95	100 Ω, 4-pair	24
Patch	PWCS-300A6-95	100 Ω, 4-pair	26
LSH	PWCS-300L3-95	100 Ω, 4-pair	23
Patch	PWCS-300A4-95	100 Ω, 4-pair	24

The copper-based network backbone utilizes ALL-LAN cable as indicated. This cable is characterized by a high-frequency bandwidth ability. The cable itself is jacketed with PVC, then aluminum shielding, and then four pairs of twisted-pair wire are wrapped with aluminum shielding. The intense shielding of each pair of cables makes the high bandwidth possible.

Some further specifications of the ALL-LAN cable include the following information: channel and link performance significantly beyond existing Cat5 (Category 5) specifications, including superior ACR performance at frequencies 30 to 300 MHz (<16 dB), and EMC-compliant in all protocols through 300 MHz and beyond without using multilevel encoding non-RJ-45-based connectivity. ALL-LAN cable has a low profile: $0.650 \times 0.695 \times 1.525$. It is a full $360°$ connector shielding with a cable jack that has only three components. It is easy to field-install, and the integral strain relief accommodates cable of up to 0.320 IDCs compatible with 23 to 26 AWG wire. It has a unique latch with damage free unmating at pullout forces greater that 30 lb. Its durability is greater than 2500 cycles. Figure 7.7 provides some additional cable specifications.

Consider Figure 7.8, which shows more statistics displaying the attenuation of the ALL-LAN cable.

Figure 7.9 shows additional information about ALL-LAN cable with regard to NEXT and attenuation. ALL-LAN cable was used from the devices to the hubs; that is, PCs, servers, printers, and all the connections were made with ALL-LAN cable. The main network patch panel is an ALL-LAN panel with ALL-LAN connectors and cabling. It serves the primary network wiring backbone.

Figure 7.10 shows still another example of some statistical information with ALL-LAN cable. Figure 7.10 shows ALL-LAN-correlated data with respect to the Cat5 basic link limit rate. It further presents ALL-LAN in perspective to the performance of standard Cat5.

Thomas & Betts provided the information shown in Figures 7.7 through 7.10. They have knowledgeable representatives who were more than able to answer the questions I brought in the preparation for my network. I recommend that you contact them for more information about ALL-LAN products:

www.tnb.com

Thomas & Betts

7.4 Fiber-Optic Backbone (Siecor)

Early on in the network design phase I decided that the core network backbone would be fiber-based. Multiple reasons for this factored into my decision. First, fiber provides the highest bandwidth capability in existence today. Before you disagree, hear me out!

Moving data, or whatever, through a network is possible in only one of two ways: by electrons or photons. I know, you are thinking: "Gee, Ed, you sure do

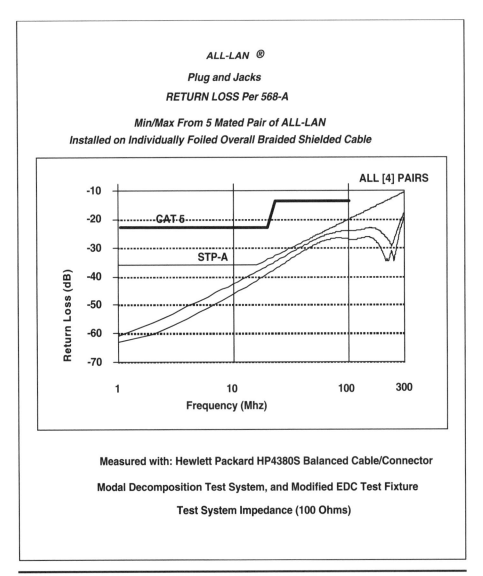

Figure 7.7   ALL-LAN Cable Specifications

exaggerate a bit." Yes, I do, when it is applicable. Answer this: At the most fundamental level in networks, are data not represented by either electrical charges of some sort or by light pulses? Is this not true? If it is—and it is regardless of whether you agree—then the most fundamental infrastructure in any network is the media and how "data" are moved through these media.

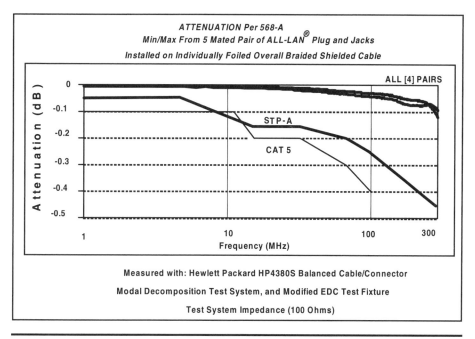

Figure 7.8   ALL-LAN Cable Statistics

Everything digital—whether that is data, voice, video, or whatever—is represented in binary form; that is, by either a one or a zero. Since this is true, these binary representations are represented by either an electronic charge or a light pulse or the absence thereof. At this point in time, fiber is the most powerful delivery mechanism available. The bandwidth capability of fiber is very high, and fiber serves as an excellent vehicle for delivering data, voice, video, and multimedia. I chose Siecor as the vendor because of their wide variety of fiber offerings. I also selected fiber for the following reasons:

1. Fiber is flexible and will accommodate future network growth or upgrades.

2. Fiber is not susceptible to electrical, radio, or magnetic interference.

3. Fiber is secure; one cannot tap fiber without being intrusive.

4. Fiber is relatively inexpensive.

These are only a few reasons why fiber is the best choice for networking backbones. In fact, it is far superior to copper-based wire; however, some copper-based wiring will still be needed for some time to come.

Siecor has the best and most versatile products in the marketplace today. The products presented here are a very small sample of what Siecor offers. Consider Figure 7.11, which shows a message transfer part (MTP) module. This module is compact in size and houses six SC duplex connectors on the

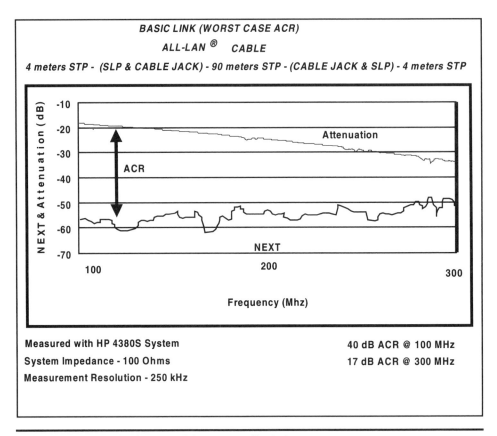

Figure 7.9 ALL-LAN Cable NEXT and Attenuation Statistics

front. The rear has an MTP connector. The fiber cable that fits this connector is very small but durable. The beauty behind this MTP module is its portability, total cost of ownership, and extremely high degree of integration capability. Further illustrations will make these points clear.

In Figure 7.12, which shows an example of an MTP implementation, multiple hosts are connected to the MTP module. In the housing along with the MTP modules SC duplex modules are shown. This level of flexibility makes troubleshooting the fiber backbone easy. With the SC connectors, a local patch is easily achieved. Both MTP and the pair of SC modules are mounted into the rack-mount housing that fits into a standard 19-in rack-mount cabinet.

Now consider Figure 7.13, which shows three distinct locations (labs) in one physical site. Note that physical location 1 has two MTP modules and is connected to two MTP modules in physical location 2. Likewise, physical location 3 is a mirror-image of number 1.

Physical location 2 is the central patch room. In addition to the MTP modules, the Siecor patch panel resides there as well. The benefit of this arrangement is considerable and is discussed later in greater detail.

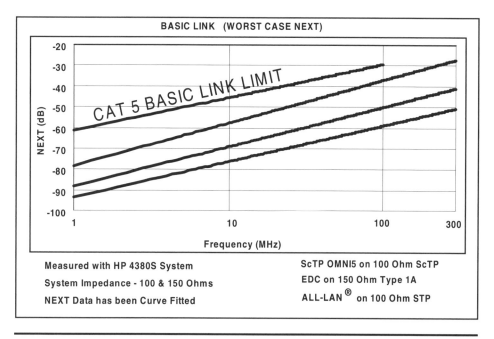

Figure 7.10   ALL-LAN Basic Link (Worst Case NEXT)

I also selected Siecor to provide fiber because of the breadth of their products and the people behind them. I recommend that you contact them and let them help you in network environment, whether you are building it from scratch, making additions, or attempting to troubleshoot your existing environment. You can reach them at

Siecor Corporation
P.O. Box 489
Hickory, NC 28604-0489
www.siecor.com

7.5   Rack Enclosures (Great Lakes Cabinets)

Network design includes a wide variety of equipment. The size and type of network design you build will determine to some degree what components you will use. Most networks include rack-mount equipment. The network I designed and built required multiple cabinets. Consider Figure 7.14.

I selected Great Lakes Cabinets because these cabinets are of lightweight steel construction but are very durable. The significance of these features cannot be understated. When six or more rack cabinets are used to house network equipment, the total weight of these cabinets becomes a factor to consider.

Great Lakes Cabinets have standard offerings comparable to those of other cabinetmakers such as either pullout shelves or stationary shelves. However,

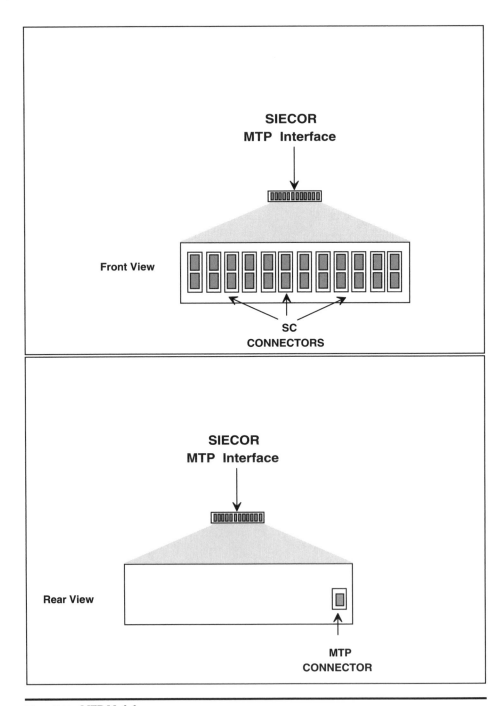

Figure 7.11 MTP Module

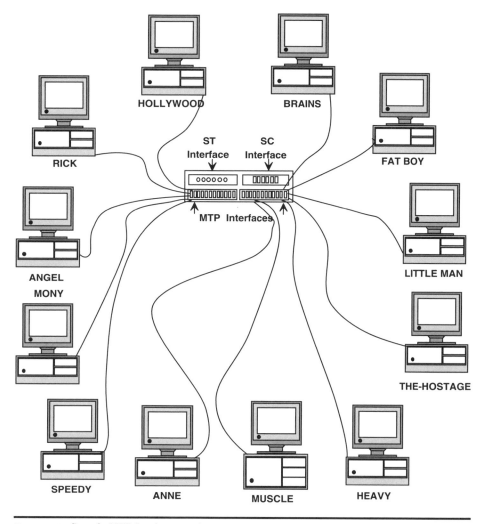

Figure 7.12 Sample MTP Implementation

the unique selection of metal and the design make the shelves easy to work with but also very durable, with a high weight-bearing capacity. As shown later in this book, two Great Lakes Cabinets I used in this network design have IBM monitors and other equipment on a single shelf. This is significant because of the shear weight.

The Great Lakes cabinets used in this network were configured with the following:

- Removable side panels
- Six-position power strip
- Dual-packaged blowers

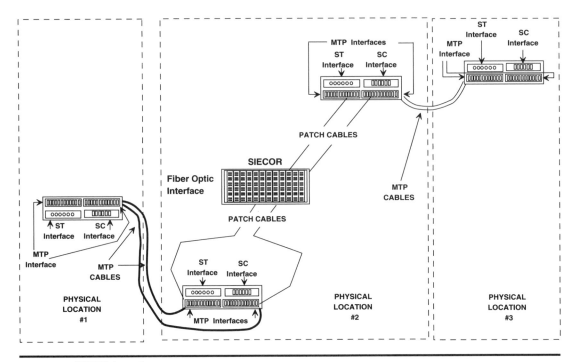

Figure 7.13 MTP Integration

- Front and rear mounting adjustments
- Front and rear sliding mounting adjustments
- Fan trays with nine 75CFM fans
- Filler panels (3.50 and 1.5 in)
- Single-sided cable organizer
- Plexiglass doors
- Gray color with highlighted black trim
- Vented steel rear door

Another aspect I like about these cabinets is the interior, with side accessibility to reach around installed components. In these cabinets there is actually more internal space between the side panel and the rack-mount space. This enhances maneuverability with mounted equipment. Also, these cabinets have a considerably larger opening (vent) in the bottom for airflow.

7.6 Network UPS (Liebert)

Much research went into the power (surge) protection part of this network's design. Early on it was determined a significant size UPS was needed to meet

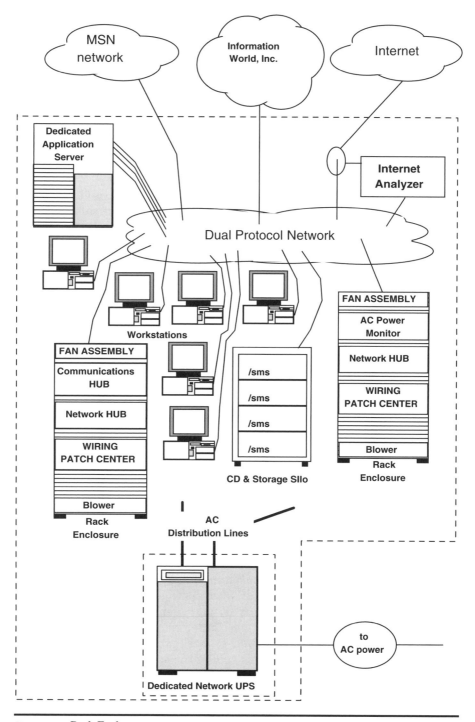

Figure 7.14   Rack Enclosures

the requirements. After evaluating numerous UPSs from various vendors, Liebert was chosen.

Liebert is the best in power protection, at least this author thinks so. I have worked closely with Liebert equipment of all sizes in numerous data centers throughout the United States and abroad. Liebert has been around for decades and will be around for decades to come. The company is established, has considerable market penetration, well-trained and tenured employees, well-built and well-furnished physical plants, and (from my experience) committed personnel at every level of the corporation. Liebert defines quality. Consider the following firsthand evidence. The large cooling systems Liebert offers are built in their facility. Liebert has certified on-site welders who build each frame by hand—that's right, no mass production here in the sense of assembly line and robots. The significance of this transcends the entire production cycle.

For the needs in my network, I selected a 15-kVA Liebert UPS Station S. Consider Figure 7.15, which shows much of the equipment and the Liebert UPS; however, some additional equipment could not be shown in this illustration. The nice thing about the Liebert UPS is its quality; from packaging to the documentation, everything is done right.

Devices built at Liebert are traced with an accompanying piece of paper with each employee's stamp during the production process. This signature literally follows the device to the end of the production cycle. During the production cycle there are numerous checkpoints (quality-control points). If for any reason a product does not meet a certain preset standard, that product is literally stopped and does not continue until the problem is resolved.

Another aspect of Liebert's quality assurance is how they build their products. Liebert starts with raw elements. They don't work with prefabricated stuff; however, there is one noted exception. One printed circuit board (PCB) is assembled in another location and included with a certain product at Liebert's facility. However, these PCBs undergo testing to verify predefined standards.

Liebert's attention to detail is incredible. Their painting process is not what most would think—it has been fine-tuned to a mixture between art and science. On some products they bake a powder onto the panels. This production process is monitored not only for quality but also for control of paint substances to ensure that contamination does not leave the paint room.

A notable aspect of Liebert's attention to detail is the way their production floor is operated. There is no management—that's right; people work with (not for) other people to meet order requirements. It is the first team implementation I have observed to work well. Most team criteria are based on averaging; Liebert's teams exploit the strength of each person. Change is driven by workers, not management.

Liebert uses technology where technology makes sense. For example, they implement a computer-controlled metal cutter. This enables them to compute the maximum number of cuts from a given piece of metal. This is an effective

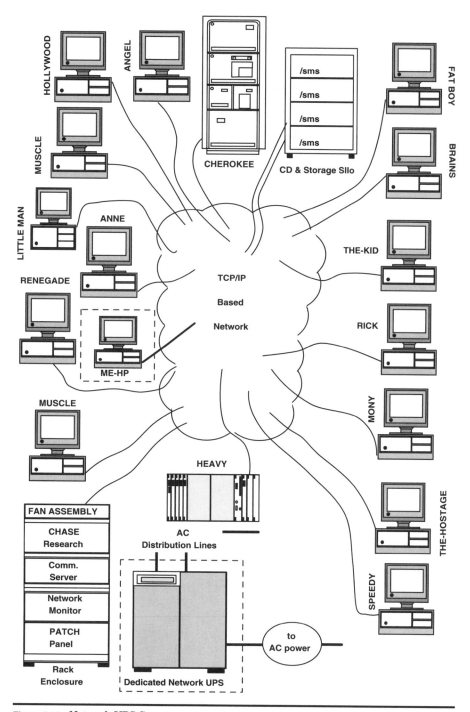

Figure 7.15 Network UPS Support

way to reduce production cost: employ people where they excel and machines where they excel. This information is important for anyone who considers investing significant money into a device that is to serve network needs for a considerable time to come.

A Liebert UPS Station S was selected to meet the needs of this network. This line of UPS equipment can meet a wide variety of needs in networks and ranges from 3.5 to 18 kVA in apparent power. In this instance, I selected a 15-kVA UPS. The capability of this system can meet the needs of all the network equipment I built and have explained in this book.

For further information, contact Liebert at

www.liebert.com
Liebert Corporation
1050 Dearborn Drive
P.O. Box 29186
Columbus, OH 43229
Phone: 614-841-5924

Liebert Corporation
Globe Park, Marlow
Buckinghamshire SL7 1YG
United Kingdom
Phone: +44 1628 403200

Liebert Corporation
19/F Causeway Bay Plaza 1
489 Hennessy Road
Causeway Bay, Hong Kong
Phone: 852.2.572.2201

7.7 Network Backbone (XYLAN)

Because of the nature of the network, I decided to use a switch. I needed a switch that could support Ethernet, Token Ring, ATM, and FDDI. XYLAN had just what I needed, and it is straightforward technology (easy to work with).

The Omni-9wx chassis supports the new high-density wide switching modules in addition to thin versions of switching modules. It contains nine slots for Management Processor Module (MPM), FCSM, and switching modules. Slots are numbered from 1 to 9 starting with the leftmost slot. Slots for two power supplies are located at the bottom of the chassis. A separate, removable fan tray containing four fans is located above the power supply module bays. Consider Figure 7.16, which illustrates the switch I used in my network. Its performance, backed with the product quality of the company's personnel, make it the backbone switch of choice for networks in my opinion, and remember—this author has been working with networks for a few years!

However, a fully loaded Omni-9wx weighs nearly 100 lb. Therefore, if you are rack-mounting the chassis, you should use a rack-mount shelf instead of

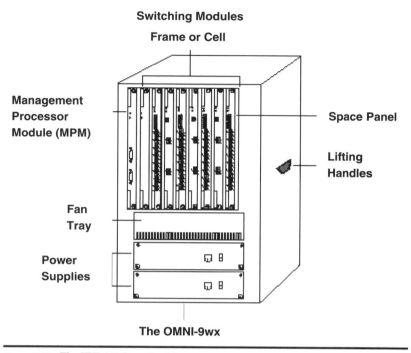

Figure 7.16 The XYLAN OmniSwitch

only brackets. Using a shelf will ensure that the weight of the chassis can be supported. In addition, the Omni-9wx contains side handles to facilitate lifting and installation. Wide modules are standard for high-density Ethernet and ATM modules. Wide versions of previously thin modules are available for all switching modules. If thin versions of the modules are installed, a spacer panel must be used to fill the extra space between modules.

The Omni-9wx chassis uses the MPM 1GW, which must be installed in either slot 1 or 2. If the MPM 1GW is installed in slot 2, you can install a switching module in slot 1. If it is installed in slot 1, a switching module can be installed in slot 2. When dual-redundant MPM 1GWs are installed, one of them must be installed in slot 1 and the other in slot 2.

The Omni-9wx backplane is functionally the same as the Omni-9x backplane, but it has been modified to fit the larger chassis unit. It supports the 13.2-Gbps ATM cell-switching matrix, the 640/960-Mbps frame-switching bus, and the 120-Mbps management bus. The chassis may be configured as a pure LAN switch (only frame-switching modules), a pure ATM switch (only cell-switching modules), or a hybrid LAN/ATM switch (mixture of frame- and cell-switching modules).

The ease of use with the switch I selected is reflected in the well-designed menu shown in Figure 7.17. The system itself is easy to configure, and the menu is easy to navigate for whatever work is needed at the time.

```
********************************************************************************
Xylan OmniSwitch - Copyright (c) 1994-1998 Xylan Inc.
All rights reserved.
OmniSwitch is a trademark of Xylan Corporation
registered in the United States Patent and Trademark Office.
System Name:   Taylor's Switch
Primary MPM
Command Main Menu
-------------- ----------------------------------------------------------------------------
File Manage system files
Summary Display summary info for VLANs, bridge, interfaces, etc.
VLAN VLAN management
Networking Configure/view network parameters such as routing, etc.
Interface Enter the Physical Interface Configuration/Parameter sub-menu
Security Configure system security parameters
System View/set system-specific parameters
Services View/set services parameters
Switch View/set any to any switching parameters
Help Help on specific tasks
Diag Display diagnostic commands
Exit (Logout) Log out of this session
? Display contents of current menu
Main File Summary VLAN Networking
Interface Security System Services Help
```

Figure 7.17   The XYLAN Menu

OmniSwitch failure-resistant features

The OmniSwitch has several features that provide redundancy and reliability. The switch backplane actually contains no active components. Every module contains its own processors, and redundancy can be added to all critical components.

1. *Redundant Management Processor Module (MPM)*. When two MPMs are installed, they serve as the primary and secondary MPMs. In the event of a failure of the primary MPM, the secondary one automatically takes over the management role for the OmniSwitch.

2. *Redundant power supplies.* The OmniSwitch's power supplies can support a fully configured unit. When operating with two power supplies, load sharing is automatic. In the event of failure on one of the supplies, the redundant power supply is capable of powering the OmniSwitch without

any loss of data. If power to one supply fails, the switch will automatically notify the network manager and keep running with no loss of data.

3. *Hot replaceable modules.* All modules, including redundant MPMs, can be removed and reinserted while the unit is operational.

4. *Hot swappable power supplies.* Power supplies can be removed and inserted while the unit is operational. You can add or replace a power supply at any time.

5. *Dual ac inputs.* Each power supply has its own power cord. If dual power supplies are installed, a loss of power due to a circuit breaker malfunction on one power supply will not affect the other power supply.

6. *Temperature alarm.* Special hardware in the switch detects overtemperature conditions and immediately notifies the network manager.

7. *Flash memory.* All operating software and configuration information is stored in nonvolatile flash memory. You can download new software revisions while the OmniSwitch is operational. No mechanical disk drive is used for storage.

8. *Extensive LED indicators.* Each OmniSwitch module contains an extensive array of LED indicators that allow you to get a quick glance at the board's health, port states, port activity, collisions, beacons, and many other status indicators.

Switch modules

Switch modules are available for Ethernet, ATM, FDDI, CDDI, Token Ring, and WAN interfaces. A variety of connector, speed, and signalling options is available for each network interface type. Each switching module port is assigned a dedicated amount of bandwidth. For example, a 10-Mbps Ethernet module contains ports that each provide the full 10 Mbps of bandwidth. Likewise, an ATM OC-3 module contains ports that each provide the full 155 Mbps of bandwidth. Translations are provided for all interfaces contained in an OmniSwitch chassis. For example, if your OmniSwitch contained Ethernet, Token Ring, and ATM switching modules, then all devices from all three network interfaces would be able to communicate through the OmniSwitch.

Since the OmniSwitch employs a distributed architecture, each switching module you add increases the processing and memory power of the entire switch. The Management Processor Module (MPM) handles central functions such as software storage, VLAN MAC learning, routing, and SNMP/User Interface management. But the MPM passes off much of the processing and memory functions to individual switching modules. Switching modules perform software filtering, translations between dissimilar network interfaces (e.g., Token Ring and Ethernet, Ethernet and ATM, ATM and Frame Relay), and hardware-based switching. Each switching module contains at least one

RISC processor, RAM for software storage, application-specific integrated circuits (ASICs) for performing hardware-based switching, and content-addressable memory (CAM) for storing the MAC addresses of source devices. A MAC address for a single source device needs to be stored only once in the CAM of the switching module that received the original frame. The memory on each switching module can be leveraged over an entire switch since all switching modules can communicate with one another. Each module's CAM is capable of storing up to 1024 MAC addresses, and you can optionally add CAM to boost the total addresses stored by the module to 4096.

All switching modules provide front-panel LEDs that provide a quick view of the status of the board, ports, connections, and traffic. All switching modules may be hot-swapped as long as you reinsert a module of the same type. The following lists the available switching modules:

Ethernet (10-Mbps) modules

- ESM-C-12: twelve 10BaseT connections using RJ-45 ports
- ESM-C-8: eight 10BaseT connections using RJ-45 ports (discontinued)
- ESM-F-8: eight 10BaseFL connections using fiber (ST) ports
- ESM-T-12: one Telco connector supporting 12 UTP or STP (unshielded or shielded twisted-pair) ports
- ESM-U: universal Ethernet module supporting six connections that may be a combination of AUI (attachment unit interface; full- or half-duplex), RJ-45, fiber, or BNC (bayonet coaxial) ports.

High-density and 10/100 Ethernet modules

- ESM-100C-12: twelve autosensing 10/100-Mbps connections using RJ-45 ports
- ESM-100FM-8: eight 100BaseFX connections using multimode fiber (SC) ports
- ESM-C-16: sixteen 10BaseT connections using RJ-45 ports
- ESM-C-32: thirty-two 10BaseT connections using RJ-45 ports
- ESM-FM-16W: sixteen 10BaseFL connections using multimode fiber (ST) ports

Fast Ethernet (100-Mbps) modules

- ESM-100C: four or eight 100BaseTX connections using RJ-45 ports
- ESM-100C-FD: one or two full-duplex 100BaseTX connections using RJ-45 ports
- ESM-100FX-FD: one or two full-duplex 100BaseFX fiber connections (single- or multimode) using SC connectors
- ESM-100C-5: five 100BaseTX connections using RJ-45 ports (one of the five ports supports full-duplex operation)
- ESM-100CFX-5: one fiber 100BaseFX connection and four 100BaseTX connections

The fiber port supports full-duplex operation and can be configured with single- or multimode connectors.

ATM access modules

- ASM-155FX: one- or two-port fiber single- or multimode OC-3 modules
- ASM2-155FX: one- or two-port fiber single- or multimode OC-3 switching module (a higher-performance version of the ASM-155FX)
- ASM-155C: one- or two-port UTP OC-3 modules
- ASM2-622F: one-or two-port fiber single- or multimode OC-12 switching modules
- ASM2-622FR: two- or four-port redundant fiber single- or multimode OC-12 switching module (each port pair includes a primary and backup port)
- ASM-DS3: One- or two-port DS-3 modules
- ASM-E3: one- or two-port E3 modules
- ASM-CE: one ATM uplink port (OC-3, DS-3, or E3), two T1/E1 ports, and two serial ports supporting ATM circuit emulation

FDDI/CDDI modules

- FSM-M: one or two DAS connections over multimode fiber
- FSM-S: one or two DAS connections over single-mode fiber
- FSM-SH: one or two DAS connections over single-mode fiber using Category 2 high-powered laser optics
- FSM-C: four or eight RJ-45 ports for CDDI
- FSM-M-C: one FDDI DAS connection and four CDDI ports

Token Ring modules

- TSM-C-6: six-port UTP or STP station connections (discontinued)
- TSM-F-6: six-port fiber that supports station, lobe, ring-out, and ring-in/ring-out connections
- TSM-CD-6: six-port UTP or STP that supports station or lobe connections
- WSM-S: two, four, or eight serial ports that support the Frame Relay or PPP protocol
- WSM-FT1/E1: one or two T1/E1 ports and one or two serial ports that support the Frame Relay or PPP protocol
- WSM-BRI: one USP (universal serial port) and one ISDN-BRI port that support Frame Relay or PPP

Much more information can be obtained about XYLAN's products. They have an excellent line of products that span the entire gamut of networking from workgroup to enterprise.

7.8   Network Printer (IBM)

An IBM printer was selected as the network printer. In terms of performance, price, and maintenance cost, the IBM network printer model 17 is probably the best printer on the market for networks of this scale and a little larger. The following features and functions factored into the author's decision to use the IBM model 17. Before examining all features and functions of this printer, consider the first list of *standard* ones:

17 pages per minute	4 MB of RAM (optional to 66 MB)
600×600 resolution	Automatic language switching with options
≤5 addressable input trays	Automatic I/O switching
PCL5e standard language (PostScript, IPDS, SCS optional)	Standard parallel with two network interface slots

The following options were added to the printer to make it capable of meeting the needs of all users on the network:

75-envelope feeder	PostScript language option level 2
Ethernet interface	500-sheet second paper tray
Token Ring interface	Duplex unit
24 MB of RAM	10-bin secured mailbox unit

This printer arrived on a pallet weighing in at approximately 250 lb (entire pallet weight). The specification weight of the printer alone is 40.9 lb (18.6 kg). With all options installed, the dimensions are 31 in height, 25 in front to back, and 17 in wide. (These are my measurements, which include space for rear cabling, etc., and are approximations; with cabling attached, the printer weighs ~65 lb.)

The printer was chosen because of its flexibility and power. It supports both IPDS and SCS character strings. This is valuable because should the network need a system which uses either of these character strings for printing, the printer itself will be capable of handling it.

Intelligent Printer Data Stream (IPDS) is used between an IBM host and a printer; generally this refers to an SNA environment. This data stream is used with an all-points-addressable printer. IPDS can intermix text and graphics—both vector- and raster-based. An SCS character string is a protocol used with printers and certain terminals in the SNA environment. Logical units LU1 and LU6.2 can use this data stream. One unique aspect of this data stream is its lack of data flow control functions. The significance of the model 17 printer chosen for this network should not be overlooked. This means that when the need arises for a host running MVS and VTAM, the *current* printer can be used with it. Here again is another example of architecting success into the network.

Because the printer is on the network, all network users can take advantage of it, such as off-site users who desire to work on the network from a remote location, and print something to someone and ensure that the document will be secure. Figure 7.18 shows a remote user connecting via a switched line to the network. The "network" in this example is viewed as the equipment in the rack enclosure. However, the network includes all devices participating in it. This example shows the remote user working with a file on the NT server. The NT server then sends the file to the printer. The printer prints it and sends it to bin 3, where the bin 3 owner must enter a code to receive the print.

Users on site where the printer is installed have free access to it, with the exception of those who require secured access through the mailbox feature.

Author's comment

The IBM model 17 printer arrived on a pallet as described previously. From time of delivery until the printer was operational, 1 worker-day elapsed. It took about 2 h to unpack the printer and read the material IBM recommended before setup. Assembling the various components (accessories) for the printer was easy. IBM designed the printer so that minimal tools are needed to install it. More than likely, you, like myself, will require more time to configure it and integrate the network workstations and servers than for actual printer setup.

IBM has a wealth of information that can assist you in your network plans. You can reach IBM at

www.ibm.com
International Business Machines
Department M7FE, Bldg. 003G
P.O. Box 190
Boulder, CO 80301

7.9   Communications Server (Chase Research)

I needed a communications server in this network and decided to use Chase Research's product because of its rich features and quality support personnel.

IOLAN+ is a feature-rich Ethernet TCP/IP communications server which enables serial devices to be connected directly to LANs. The serial devices can be terminals, printers, modems, bar-code readers, or any other RS-232 device.

Feature summary

TCP/IP protocols, including TELNET, Rlogin, PPP, and Serial Line Internet Protocol (SLIP) are supported by the IOLAN+; it also supports terminals, printers, modems, and any other RS-232 device, and has fast (115.2-kbps) port speeds. Other features include

Dial-in Internet/intranet remote access

UNIX and Windows NT/95 dial-out modem pooling for UNIX and Windows NT/95

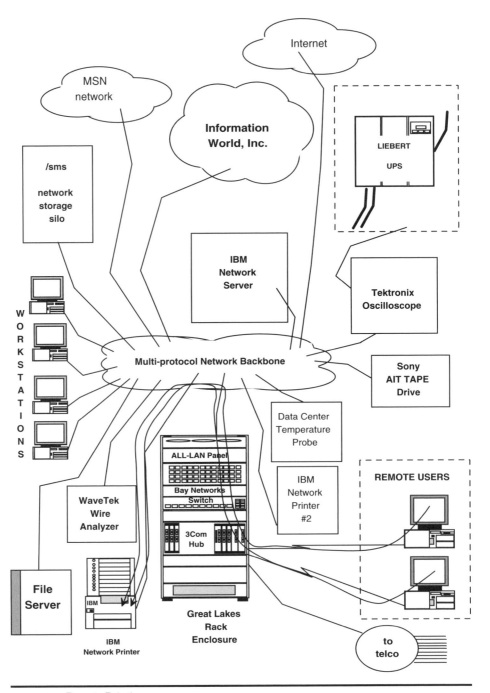

Figure 7.18 Remote Printing

Autosense Ethernet with RJ-45, BNC, and AUI

19-in rack-mount or desktop

Dial-on-demand IP routing

Flash memory for simple upgrade

Universal power supply 90 to 250 V for worldwide use

48-V power supply option for telecommunications operation

Surge protection on all signals on all ports

Easy-to-use menus

4, 8, or 16 ports

Lifetime warranty

Applications

IOLAN+ is used wherever serial devices need to be connected to LANs. IOLAN+'s architecture features the flexibility to address a wide variety of applications, from workgroup computing to remote access. Typical areas of application include

POS (point-of-sale) and warehousing systems

Internet service providers

Banking and other financial front-desk systems

Corporate remote access server for home or mobile workers

UNIX terminal and printer workgroups

Modem pools for dial-in and dial-out

Reverse TELNET access for nonnetworked computer systems

Multiplexing RS-232 data over Ethernet and TCP/IP WANs

Console server for remote management of any hardware with console ports

Dial-out features (Chase DialOut/IP), available for Windows NT systems.

Architecture

IBM industry-standard connectivity is built around TCP/IP protocols to ensure open-systems compatibility. IOLAN+ operates on standard Ethernet networks with Autosense between BNC, RJ-45, and AUI physical connectors.

Flash memory is used for storing the operating firmware and configuration information. The latest versions of firmware are easily downloaded. Setup information can be saved to a local host for backup purposes.

The built-in power supply will operate in most countries by sensing between 50 and 60 Hz and voltage ranges between 90 and 250 V-ac. A 48-V-dc power supply for rack mounting is optional and is used in telecommunications environments.

Performance

IOLAN+ has the performance you need to handle a diverse range of high-speed devices. IOLAN+ can transmit and receive data at speeds of up to 115.2 kbps. This allows high-performance devices to function at their full speed.

To achieve this high speed and to maintain a high throughput, IOLAN+ utilizes the performance of RISC-based CD1865 intelligent universal asynchronous receiver-transmitters (UARTs) in combination with highly tuned firmware.

Easy installation

IOLAN+ setup can be performed in a matter of minutes using a simple menu interface. A quick start requires that only the IP address be set. Initial setup can be done on a directly connected console. IOLAN+ also supports Bootstrap Protocol (BOOTP) and Reverse Address Resolution Protocol (ARP) for set-up across the LAN.

IOLAN+ will assist you in stepping through the additional configuration options, including port profiles, remote sites, security, and PPP configuration.

Reliability

All serial ports have built-in surge protection devices to protect the unit from electrical damage. ISO9001 standards adherence results in superior quality and IOLAN+ comes with a lifetime warranty (as does every Chase product).

Terminals and printers

Terminal services include powerful multisessions and a user menu. Ports can be configured individually for dedicated connections to a predefined host, enhancing security and simplicity. Alternatively, a preconfigured host table or DNS support can be used.

Printers can be configured as local [fixed teletype displays (TTYs)] on a UNIX host with Chase-supplied utilities. Alternatively, RCP or LPD protocols can be used, enabling IOLAN+ to act as a remote print queue for UNIX and NT hosts. Printer hunt groups can also be configured.

Remote access

IOLAN+ provides remote access to a LAN for terminal or PC connections. Dial-in access can be from a terminal or a terminal emulator such as Hyperterminal, with IOLAN+ providing TELNET and rlogin services allowing host system access. PPP access (such as from the Windows 95 Dial-up Adapter) is autodetectable on all ports, and dial-in PCs can use Internet services such as a browser, FTP, or TELNET. Windows file and print sharing is also supported via a WINS server set up on the IOLAN+. Windows NT domain services show up in the "network neighborhood" of the client PC. User authentication allows users to be restricted to specific services (TEL-

NET/PPP) or hosts (TELNET), and also provides user-based IP address assignment. User profiles are maintained on a central host, which can be a RADIUS server. IOLAN+ logging also records calls for billing.

Modem pooling

All ports provide simultaneous dial-in and dial-out and modems can be shared by UNIX and Windows NT and 95 systems on the LAN. UNIX TTY ports and Windows COM ports can be redirected to the IOLAN+ using a combination of Chase utilities and reverse TELNET settings. Modems can be dedicated to certain users, or shared reducing the total number of phone lines.

Network routing

IP routing connections between LANs can be configured on any port. Dedicated connections, or dial-on-demand PPP connections can be used. The IOLAN+ can route to any vendors PPP service (including an ISP) or another IOLAN+ . The modems can be shared with dial-in and dial-out users.

Security

A dual-password system for remote access security can be used. Password protection levels can be set per port. Login scripts and automatic Printer Access Protocol (PAP) negotiations are supported. First-level passwords are validated by the IOLAN+, while user passwords are authenticated against a central host (which can be a RADIUS server). One host can support multiple IOLAN+ servers. Administration is protected by a third password level.

Management

Local console or TELNET access is possible from anywhere on the LAN; this important facility allows easy remote configuration and diagnostics. IOLAN+ supports SNMP (Simple Network Management Protocol) with MIB (Management Information Base) II, Character MIB, Sessions MIB, and Chase-specific enterprise variables. An extensive statistics system allows monitoring of the IOLAN+, providing information such as network activity by protocol, port connect time, idle time, throughput average, and total per port.

IOLAN+ and dial-out capability

An IOLAN+ and Windows NT or Windows 95 system coupled with the dial-out capability makes for a powerful combination enabling work such as

Branch connections: Enable the main office of a retail or food chain to call into its branch locations nightly to collect accounting data.

Private networks: Dial-out to private networks not on the Internet, especially financial institutions and credit checks.

Internet connects: Allow ISP connections by enabling all networked users access to modems, especially in small offices.

Chase DialOut/IP enables Windows workstations on your network to make outbound dial-up connections using modems attached to an IOLAN+. With DialOut/IP, your dial-in remote access server can now dial-out to branch locations, ISPs, and other network-based services. This allows better use of resources since all modems can be banked onto a central IOLAN+, and all workstations can access the modems as if they were attached locally.

DialOut/IP is a Windows COM port redirector for TCP/IP networks providing transparent access to networked modems for most Windows applications. DialOut/IP creates new "virtual COM ports" in Windows that appear to have directly connected modems. Windows client programs (including Windows Dial-up Networking), which assume the presence of a local modem, can now share pooled modems on your TCP/IP network.

The main reason for implementing shared dial-out solutions with DialOut/IP is economics. By using a modem pool to share modems for dial-out purposes, it is possible to achieve significant savings when individual desktop phone lines and modems are eliminated. Another widespread reason for dial-out with shared modems is that central equipment is easier to configure and maintain.

Technical specification

RS-232 ports: 4, 8, or 16, DB-25 or RJ-45 (RS-422 optional)

Network: Ethernet DIX and 802.3

Protocols: TCP/IP, TELNET, rlogin, raw or reverse TELNET, PPP, SLIP, CSLIP, LPD, RCP, DNS, WINS

Management: SNMP, MIB II, Character and Chase Enterprise variables, TELNET, console port

Menu languages: English, French, German, Italian, and Spanish

Speed range: serial—50 bps to 115.2 kbps

Modem support: full bidirectional

Serial port signals: CTS, RTS, DSR, DTR, DCD, RX, TX

Network connector: AUI, BNC, and RJ-45 Autosense

Processor: 80C186, 25 MHz

Memory: 1 MB of DRAM, 512 kB of flash memory

UARTs: CD1865 intelligent

Power supply: 50/60 Hz, 90 to 250 V ac, optional 48-V-dc rack

Warranty: lifetime

You can reach Chase Research at one of the following addresses:

Chase Research PLC
7 Cedarwood, Chineham Business Park
Basingstoke RG24 8WD, United Kingdom
Phone: +44 (0)1256 352260
Fax: +44 (0)1256 810159
http://www.chaser.co.uk
email: *info@chaser.co.uk*

Chase Research GmbH
Zettachring 6
D-70567 Stuttgart, Germany
Phone: +49 (0)711 7287 155
Fax: +49 (0)711 7287 156
email: *info@chaser.de*

Chase Research Inc
Suite 100, 545 Marriott Drive
Nashville, TN 37214 (USA)
Phone: +1 615 872 0770
Fax: +1 615 872 0771
email: *info@chaser.com*
http://www.chaser.com

Chase Research China
Room 329, Hua Tong Building
19A Che Gong Zhuang Xi Road
Haidian District, Beijing 100044
People's Republic of China
Phone/fax: +86 10 6848 3355
e-mail: *infochina@chaser.co.uk*

7.10 xDSL Router (Cayman Systems)

Because of the nature of the network, I needed a powerful router for the Ethernet portions. Because of its sheer quality and performance, I chose Cayman technology. This author thinks Cayman is one of the best xDSL vendors in the market today. In fact, their information says it best. The following information is from the Cayman Systems Web page on the Internet.

Cayman Systems was founded in 1987 to develop internetworking products that helped integrate workgroup networks of Macintosh computers into enterprise networks based on emerging technology standards such as Ethernet and TCP/IP. Between 1988 and 1994, thousands of Cayman customers worldwide deployed over 40,000 Cayman GatorBoxes and GatorStars to provide Macintosh users with point-and-click access to TCP/IP-based networks.

By 1995, the role of the Macintosh and AppleTalk networking within large organizations had diminished substantially, as Windows-based PCs replaced most Macintoshes and the Internet protocols became the basis for enterprise intranets. With its traditional market greatly reduced, Cayman began evaluating emerging markets to address. Anticipating that the Internet would soon become a strategically important medium for many information-oriented small businesses, Cayman decided in late 1995 to focus on developing next-generation Internet-access solutions for the small-office market.

Next-generation Internet access

Cayman's definition of "next-generation Internet access" for small offices is Internet service that offers four key benefits:

1. *Speed:* To make the Internet an integral part of small-business operations means eliminating the hassles and sluggishness of dial-up networking, and providing small offices with the same performance enjoyed by larger firms with dedicated Internet connections.

2. *Ease of use:* Small offices rarely have an in-house networking expert. A true next-generation Internet-access solution for the small office–home office (SOHO) market should be as plug-and-play as possible. Connect it to the network, plug it in, point your Web browser to it, and provide it with the address of the upstream gateway. The next-generation Internet-access router should transparently manage all TCP/IP addressing issues on the small-office network.

3. *"Always on" (aka "IP Dialtone"):* Emerging Internet-access technologies like xDSL and cable modems are "next-generation" both because they're fast and are "always on." High-speed Internet connections that are "up" around the clock allow small businesses to take advantage of services such as push technology, virtual private networks, videoconferencing, extranets, and Internet telephony—the same emerging services that larger companies are now evaluating as potential sources of competitive advantage.

4. *Affordability:* While established technologies such as T1 lines, CSU/DSUs (channel/digital services units), Internet firewalls, and midrange routers offer all of these benefits today, they do so at prices that put these benefits out of reach for the vast majority of small offices. To bring the potential of the next-generation Internet access to the mainstream small-office market, the price of the Internet-access device needs to fall below the $1000 threshhold, and then eventually converge with the price levels associated with consumer electronics.

Cayman products

In developing products to meet the requirements of next-generation Internet access for the small-office market, Cayman is focusing on two principal Internet-access technologies: digital subscriber line technology (xDSL) and cable modems.

As these technologies progress from proprietary technologies toward interoperable standards, customers will want to avoid locking themselves into proprietary implementations that become obsolete as standards emerge, so Cayman has chosen to develop two types of next-generation Internet-access routers: (1) routers with integrated xDSL or cable modems and (2) standalone routers designed to connect to an external xDSL modem, cable modem, or dial-up modem.

With or without integrated modems, all Cayman routers meet the key criteria of high-performance operation, affordability, and unmatched ease of use. Cayman's 2E and LR line of routers are designed to connect small-office Ethernet networks to external dial-up modems and next-generation modems, respectively. The Cayman DSL series incorporates ADSL, HDSL, and SDSL modems; during 1998 the Cayman DSL Series will become interoperable with xDSL equipment for the Telco Central Office produced by leading vendors like Alcatel, Ascend, PairGain, Paradyne, and Westell. And future Cayman routers will incorporate standard cable-modem technology based on the recently developed MCNS standard, allowing small-office Ethernet networks to share cable modems for high-speed, always-on Internet access.

Service and support

All Cayman routers have been designed to minimize the need for technical support. For most users, installing and configuring a Cayman router will take less than 10 min. Once installed, Cayman routers don't require network management, and are designed to recover automatically from power outages or temporary network disconnections.

For customers who require technical assistance, Cayman offers free telephone-based technical support and a 30-day money-back guarantee as part of the Cayman SafetyNet Program.

Future products

As next-generation Internet access based on xDSL and cable-modem technology enters the mainstream small-office market over the next few years, Cayman will develop additional features and services for its routers that take advantage of the high bandwidth and "always on" attributes of these technologies. Like all Cayman products intended for the small-office market, these future products will be designed to deliver state-of-the-art performance, affordability, and unmatched ease of use.

Overview

The Cayman DSL Series of Ethernet-to-Internet routers combines high-speed xDSL wide area networking technology with full-featured TCP/IP routing and Cayman's industry-leading Swift-IP Internet-addressing software to deliver state-of-the-art Internet access for small offices. The Cayman DSL small-office routers are compatible with the implementations of emerging xDSL technologies developed by a variety of leading suppliers of equipment for the Telco Central Office (CO) and ISP Point of Presence (POP), including PairGain Technologies, Alcatel Telecom, Paradyne, Westell/Amati, Ascend Communications, and others.

HDSL and SDSL

The Cayman DSL Series supports symmetric xDSL technologies such as HDSL and SDSL to deliver high-speed data networking over a single pair of copper phone lines at the same speed in both the upstream and downstream directions.

Cayman's HDSL and SDSL routers can be used as Customer Premises Equipment (CPE) to connect a small-office Ethernet network to DSL Access Multiplexers in the Telco Central Office. Alternatively, the Cayman HDSL or SDSL routers can be connected to each end of an unconditioned copper circuit (sometimes referred to as a dry pair) up to 12,000 ft in length that connects the small-office network directly to the ISP Point of Presence for affordable, high-speed Internet access.

The Cayman DSL 1000 small-office router features an integrated HDSL modem running at 768 kbps and is compatible with HDSL-based CO equipment from PairGain Technologies. The Cayman DSL 1400 provides an integrated SDSL modem running at 1.544 Mbps and is compatible with the Ascend SDSL interface card for the Max TNT.

ADSL

The Cayman DSL Series also supports asymmetrical xDSL technologies such as CAP RADSL and DMT RADSL. Cayman's ADSL routers connect a small-office network to DSL Access Multiplexers at the CO or POP, and provide Internet access at speeds of up to 8 Mbps downstream, and up to 1 Mbps upstream.

The Cayman DSL 2000 router includes an integrated CAP RADSL modem, and is compatible with Paradyne's GlobeSpan technology. The Cayman DSL 3000 incorporates a DMT RADSL modem, and is compatible with DMT-based ADSL equipment provided by Alcatel Telecom.

Transparent Internet addressing

The Cayman DSL Series' Swift-IP functionality combines support for the Dynamic Host Configuration Protocol (DHCP), Domain Name Service (DNS) protocol, and Network Address Translation (NAT) to eliminate the hassle of assigning, configuring, and managing Internet addresses. PCs and Macintoshes can be connected to or removed from the small-office Ethernet and Swift-IP automatically handles all IP addressing issues.

Best of all, Swift-IP saves Internet-access charges by transparently allowing up to 250 simultaneous users on the Ethernet network to share one Internet address and one xDSL port on the DSL Access Multiplexer at the Telco Central Office (CO) or the ISP's Point of Presence (POP). For campus internetworking solutions, Swift-IP allows workgroup Internet addresses to be statically assigned or dynamically allocated using DHCP.

Built-in security and cross-platform management

The Cayman DSL Series' Swift-IP technology makes the Cayman DSL router the only device on the small-office LAN visible to the outside world. This basic firewalling capability shields the small-office Ethernet network from intrusion by unauthorized users across the Internet.

Because the Cayman DSL Series of small-office routers feature embedded Web server technology, they can be securely monitored and managed from any standard Web browser running on a PC, Macintosh, UNIX workstation, or other platform. No proprietary management software needs to be installed on any PC or workstation. The Cayman DSL Series also supports remote management via TELNET, SNMP monitoring, and network-based downloads of software upgrades.

Full-fledged support

The Cayman DSL Series is backed by Cayman's full-fledged SafetyNet Support Program, which features free access to telephone-based technical support, "migration pricing" for product upgrades, a one-year hardware warranty, a 24-h "hot swap" hardware replacement service, and a 30-day money-back guarantee.

The Cayman DSL 1000 Internet-access router is equipped with an integrated two-wire HDSL modem, has a 768-kbps data rate, and is compatible with PairGain Central Office equipment. The Cayman DSL 1001 Internet-access router has an integrated four-wire HDSL modem and a 1.544-kbps data rate and is compatible with PairGain Central Office equipment.

I recommend that you contact Cayman at

Cayman Systems
100 Maple Street
Stoneham, MA 02180
Phone: 800-473-4776 or 781-279-1101
Fax: 781-438-5560
www.cayman.com

7.11   Network Communication Software (Tactical Software)

Because of the extensive outbound needs of multiple users on the network, network communication software from Tactical Software was selected to meet these needs.

COM/IP is a software package that lets your serial communications applications use TCP/IP connections. Your applications see what appears to be a modem on a COM port. The only necessary change to your applications is to configure them to dial IP network addresses instead of telephone numbers. In effect, your applications place a call using TCP/IP networking. Here, we refer to these connections as *network calls.*

This naturally raises the question of what is on the other end of a network call. Technically, the answer is anything that accepts a TCP/IP network socket connection. In practical terms, this usually means a TELNET server, SMTP server, or any other server software that listens for TCP/IP socket connections. The latter includes servers as diverse as bulletin boards, financial information services, and custom-built server applications. The bottom line is that, when considering your potential use of COM/IP, you must also determine whether the software at the other end is also network-capable.

Although it is a less common use, COM/IP is also able to receive network calls. This means that you can use COM/IP to network-enable a client application that usually waits for a modem to indicate a ring with an incoming call.

COM/IP includes a Hayes-compatible modem emulator that responds to standard modem commands and standard S-register settings. Additionally, the modem emulator supports a set of special COM/IP S registers that are used to configure COM/IP itself. There are sections in the configuration chapter that describe the operation of all S registers supported by COM/IP.

How COM/IP works

Here is a somewhat simplified summary of how COM/IP provides access to networked modem pools. When you install COM/IP, you create one or more new virtual COM ports. Unlike your other COM ports, these ports don't control serial hardware—they just appear to do so. On Windows NT or 95 you can also create Windows modem devices that use virtual COM ports instead of real COM ports. These modem devices are not to be confused with the modem emulator built into COM/IP. Windows modem devices are often used by certain Windows applications to simplify their interactions with various brands of modems. For each virtual COM port, you adjust its configuration with an initialization string (called the *Init String*), much like that of a real modem. The special COM/IP S registers are modified by the Init String if necessary. One of the key settings of the COM/IP S registers is the selection of TELNET protocol versus a raw socket connection. You then configure Windows client programs to use a virtual COM port directly or through a Windows modem device that uses a virtual COM port.

When your client program uses the modem or the virtual COM port, COM/IP sees that the COM port has been opened, processes the Init String, and then begins processing input from the client application. Usually, the first action of the client application is to initiate a network call. When your client program closes the COM port, COM/IP terminates the network call. The application at the other end of the network call may also terminate the connection.

For more information about Tactical Software Products, you can contact them at

Tactical Software
P.O. Box 805
Hollis, NH 03049
Phone: 888-482-2879   (toll-free)
www.tactical-sw.com

7.12   Network Email and Maintenance Software (Seattle Lab)

Considering the nature of the network and devices functioning on it, I selected Seattle Lab because of the robust nature of their software tools.

Seattle Lab is a server company. The servers are industrial-strength, enterprisewide, and mission-critical. Large companies depend on the fact that Seattle Lab servers never go down. Many of the world's largest enterprises use their TELNET-based products to take care of remote systems. They know that Seattle Lab's servers are the one piece of software they can count on for maintaining their systems.

Seattle Lab manufactures and provides the best communications servers for Windows. Their flagship product, SLmail, a powerful and easy-to-use email server for Windows 95 and NT, has helped thousands of businesses, schools, government agencies, nonprofit organizations, and individuals host a mail domain and become first-class communicants on the Internet. SLmail is the premier email server for Windows NT. The award-winning software functions as a post office for virtually all popular Internet mail clients. SLmail includes all the powerful features you need to start sending email in minutes.

One of the first companies in the world to actually make its living on the Internet, Seattle Lab today sells, delivers, and supports its software via its World Wide Web site. Full-featured versions of all Seattle Lab products are available for download, allowing prospective customers to thoroughly test the software and ensure that it is the best solution for their needs before they purchase Seattle Lab products.

Founded in 1989, Seattle Lab develops the best communication servers available on the market today. Seattle Lab's engineers are now building a new communications architecture for the next decade and millennium.

Emurl, Seattle Lab's Web-based email host, extends all the functionality of email over the World Wide Web. With emurl installed on your Web server, all you need for email is a Web browser. SLnet, the Seattle Lab TELNET server for Windows NT, is the ideal remote administration tool for Windows NT. SLnet turns your Windows NT machine into a true multiuser application server, allowing multiple users to access a Windows NT server and simultaneously run a variety of DOS, OS/2, and POSIX (Portable Operating System Interface for Computer Systems) character-based applications.

SLink is the terminal service for Windows NT and provides the link between serial devices and Windows NT. SLink allows access to any TELNET server for such devices as bar-code readers, time clocks, and cash registers.

Seattle Lab recognizes that with the awesome explosion of the Internet, servers are gaining a more central role in computing. Some of the impetus for a return to server-based computing has been afforded by emphasis on "total cost of ownership." Buying a PC and putting software on it is only the beginning of a very expensive process! The connectivity afforded by Internet protocols has allowed enterprises to completely reorganize themselves around their information technology using server-based architecture.

As enterprises reform themselves around their communications technologies, it will become more important that the software be robust, easy-to-use, and scalable. All Seattle Lab software products meet those requirements. The most notable product quality is ease of use. Products from Seattle Lab "just work."

Seattle Lab listens closely to their customers to create software that provides complete solutions that are easy to use and manage. Their customers include universities, government agencies, and companies around the world, from the tiniest sole proprietorships operating out of home offices to mega-billion-dollar corporations. Seattle Lab is represented by hundreds of resellers worldwide and has OEM agreements with many major companies.

Everything Seattle Lab builds is open, including the architecture they design. They designed built-in hooks throughout their products for third-party developers to use. They use the same interfaces they publish for other developers to use.

The Seattle Lab Internet Engineering Task Force (IETF) sets the standards for interoperability in this networked world. These standards ensure customers the safety and security of knowing they will never be trapped in a single-vendor corner, because Internet-standard products work with each other. Seattle Lab is committed to Internet standards. They build all their products around Internet RFCs, and pride themselves on their commitment to interoperability.

Seattle Lab products don't run only on Windows NT. They are designed for Windows NT. Their products are optimized for the Microsoft architecture. Since 1992 they have concentrated exclusively on the Microsoft architecture. Their customers trust Seattle Lab to ensure that their systems will thrive in a software future led by Microsoft.

Seattle Lab is committed to building new server architecture. One of the first pieces of software development optimized for Microsoft Windows NT 5.0 and built entirely as components in the Component Object Model (COM), this new server architecture offers power, reliability, and—above all—adaptability that is unmatched by any other server products developed for Windows NT.

Seattle Lab is now working on server applications that will function as PC replacements. Emurl is the first product in their line of Web-based servers. Emurl, which delivers full email functionality via the Web, replaces the need for a PC-based email client. Using Emurl, you can read, write, reply to, forward, and store your email in folders from anywhere you can find a Web browser, regardless of whether you have your PC at hand.

Functionality formerly delivered by client applications on the PC will now be delivered by server applications over the network, much like Emurl's functionality. Look for more such highly capable servers from Seattle Lab to move even more PC functionality to the server.

For additional information, contact

Seattle Lab, Inc,
9606 NE 180th Street
Bothell, WA 98011
Phone: 425-402-6003
http://www.seattlelab.com

7.13   Media Converters and Special Network Devices (TELEBYTE)

The size and contents of my network compelled me to select a company like TELEBYTE to do business with. My needs lent themselves toward copper-to-fiber converters and short-haul modems, among other items.

TELEBYTE has such a wide variety of products, and so many of their products are required to make a network complete, that I decided to list them for you here:

TELEBYTE short-haul modems and line drivers

SHM Chart	*Short Haul Modem Selection Guide*
Model 72A	Optically Isolated Short Haul Modem
Model 75	Dual Short Haul Optically Isolated Modem—Rack Mounted
Model 76	Rack Mount Card Cage
Model 77	Sync-Async Short Haul Modem—Rack Mounted
Model 78X	T1/E1 Fiber Optic Modem
Model 79	Dual Short Haul Optically Isolated Modem with Control Signals—Rack Mounted
Model 91	Synchronous Short Haul Modem—Opto Isolated, Daisy Chained
Model 92	Sync-Async Short Haul Modem
Model 201	Auto Powered Line Driver
Model 203	Two Wire Groundless Short Haul Modem
Model 209	Micro Short Haul DB9 Modem
Model 214	Fast Wire Short Haul 2 Wire-Transformer Isolated Modem

Model 221	Auto Powered Line Driver with LCD Display
Model 224	Short Haul Modem with Control Signals & LCD Display
Model 225	Transformer Isolated Multi-Drop Modem with LCD Display
Model 226	Handshaking Modem with LCD Display
Model 227	Speed Link Line Driver with High Speed LCD Display
Model 270	High Speed Fiber Optic Line Driver for Model 570
Model 271	Fiber Optic Auto Powered Line Driver—RS-232
Model 274	Si-Fi, Single Fiber, Sync/Async Short Haul Modem
Model 278X	Card Mounted T1/E1 Fiber Optic Modem
Model 420	Synchronous High Speed Short Haul Modem
Model 431	V.35, Two Wire, Synchronous High Speed Short Haul Modem
Models 681, 682	HDSL modems
Model 8225	DIN Rail Mounted—Multi-Dropped Short Haul Modem
Model 8241	Point to Point Fiber Optic Din Rail Mounted Modem
Model 8242	Multi-Point Fiber Optic Din Rail Mounted Modem
Model 8321	RS-485 Opto Isolated Link Extender in DIN Rail Format
Model 8361	RS-422 Short Haul Modem Isolated in Din Rail Enclosure
Model 8362	Optically Isolated Short Haul Modem in DIN Rail Enclosure

Fiber-optic products

Model 78X	T1/E1 Fiber Optic Modem
Model 270	High Speed Fiber Optic Line Driver for Model 570
Model 271	Fiber Optic Auto Powered Line Driver—RS-232
Model 272	Optoverter RS-422 to Fiber Optic Line Driver
Model 273	Four Channel Fiber Optic Multiplexer
Model 274	Si-Fi, Single Fiber, Sync/Async Short Haul Modem
Model 276	RS-485 to Fiber Optic Line Driver
Model 277	RS-232, RS-422, RS-485 to Multimode Fiber Optic Modem
Model 278	Fiber Optic Short Haul Modem—Full Duplex and 2 Control Signals
Model 278X	Card Mounted T1/E1 Fiber Optic Modem
Model 279	Single Mode to Multimode Converter
Model 370	LAN-Spreader, AUI to Fiber Optic Converter
Model 371	10Base-T to Fiber Optic Converter
Model 372	100Base-T to Fiber Converter
Model 373	10Base-T to Multi-Mode Fiber Optic Converter
Model 374	10Base-T to Single Mode Fiber Optic Transceiver
Model 381	2 Channel Wave Length Division Multiplexer
Series 2200	Fiber Optic Card Cage
Model 2277	Rack Mount Multi-Interface Fiber Optic Modem

Model 3786	PC Desk 10Base-T Transceiver
Model 8241	Point to Point Fiber Optic Din Rail Mounted Modem
Model 8242	Multi-Point Fiber Optic Din Rail Mounted Modem
Model 8277	DIN Rail Multi-Interface Fiber Optic Modem

Multiplexers

Model 31	Port Miser—Port Sharing Device
Model 273	Four Channel Fiber Optic Multiplexer
Model 381	2 Channel Wave Length Division Multiplexer
Model 570	Quick Mux Eight Port Multiplexer
Model 575	Super Mux Four Port Multiplexer

Interface converters

IC Chart	*Interface Converter Selection Guide*
Model 62½	EIA-530 to RS-232 Interface Converters
Model 62-4PS	Power Supply for 62½ , 62⅞
Model 63-2SA	RS-232 to RS-422 Interface Converter—Full Duplex
Model 63¾	RS-232 to RS-422 Interface Converter—Full Duplex and 3 Controls
Model 65A	RS-232 to Current Loop Converter
Model 121	Dual RS-232 to RS-422 Interface Converter—Rack Mount
Model 122	Dual RS-232 to RS-422/RS-485 Rack Mounted Interface Converter
Model 234	RS-232 Modem Eliminator
Model 235	V.35 Modem Eliminator
Model 236	G.703 to RS-232/V.35 Interface Converter
Model 240	Universal RS-232 to V.35 Interface Converter
Model 242	X.21 to RS-232 Interface Converter
Model 243	Universal X.21 to EIA 232 Interface Converter
Model 245	Opto Isolated Superverter RS-422/RS-485 to RS-232
Model 253	Non-Powered RS-232 to RS-422 9 Pin Interface Converter
Model 256	Non-Powered RS-232 to RS-422 Interface Converter with LCD Display
Model 260	RS-232 to RS-422 Interface Converter
Model 261	RS-232 to RS-422 Interface
Model 263	Non-Powered RS-232 to RS-422 Interface Converter, 10-kV Protected
Model 265	Opto Isolated RS-232 to RS-422 Interface Converter
Model 267½	Card Mounted EIA-530 to RS-232 Interface Converter
Model 267¾	Card Mounted EIA-530 to RS-232 Interface Converter

Model 272	Optoverter RS-422 to Fiber Optic Line Driver
Model 276	RS-485 to Fiber Optic Line Driver
Model 277	RS-232, RS-422, RS-485 to Multimode Fiber Optic Modem
Model 278	Fiber Optic Short Haul Modem—Full Duplex and 2 Control Signals
Model 279	Single Mode to Multimode Converter
Model 285	Superverter RS-422/RS-485 to RS-232
Model 287	RS-232 to RS-422 Opto Isolated Interface Converter (nonpowered)
Model 290	RS-422/RS-485 Concentrator—Wiring Hub
Model 365	Multimode RS-422/RS-485 to RS-232 Interface Converter and Display
Model 366	RS-232 to RS-485 2 Wire Interface Converter with LCD Display
Model 370	LAN-Spreader, AUI to Fiber Optic Converter
Model 371	10Base-T to Fiber Optic Converter
Model 372	100Base-T to Fiber Converter
Model 373	10Base-T to Multi-Mode Fiber Optic Converter
Model 374	10Base-T to Single Mode Fiber Optic Transceiver
Model 1510	Power Adapter—DC to DC Converter, 18–36 Volts to 12 Volts
Model 2277	Rack Mount Multi-Interface Fiber Optic Modem
Model 3786	PC Desk 10Base-T Transceiver
Model 8277	DIN Rail Multi-Interface Fiber Optic Modem
Model 8321	RS-485 Opto Isolated Link Extender in DIN Rail Format
Model 8322	RS-232 to RS-485 Optically Isolated Interface Converter
Model 8323	RS-232 to RS-422 Optically Isolated Interface Converter
Model 8365	Multimode RS-422/RS-485 to RS-232 Interface Converter

Isolation products

Model 72A	Optically Isolated Short Haul Modem
Model 75	Dual Short Haul Optically Isolated Modem—Rack Mounted
Model 79	Dual Short Haul Optically Isolated Modem with Control Signals—Rack Mounted
Model 91	Synchronous Short Haul Modem—Opto Isolated, Daisy Chained
Model 214	Fast Wire Short Haul 2 Wire-Transformer Isolated Modem
Model 245	Opto Isolated Superverter RS-422/RS-485 to RS-232
Model 248	V.35 Opto Isolator/Driver
Model 265	Opto Isolated RS-232 to RS-422 Interface Converter
Model 268	RS-232 Opto Isolation Module
Model 269	RS-232 Opto Isolation Module—High Voltage ($\leq$4000 V ac)
Model 281	RS-422 Opto Isolation Module
Model 282	Async RS-232 Opto Isolator/Driver

Model 287   RS-232 to RS-422 Opto Isolated Interface Converter (nonpowered)
Model 8321   RS-485 Opto Isolated Link Extender in DIN Rail Format
Model 8322   RS-232 to RS-485 Optically Isolated Interface Converter
Model 8323   RS-232 to RS-422 Optically Isolated Interface Converter
Model 8361   RS-422 Short Haul Modem in DIN Rail Enclosure
Model 8362   Optically Isolated Short Haul Modem in DIN Rail Enclosure
Model 8381   RS-422 Opto Isolator

LAN products

Model 370   LAN-Spreader AUI to Fiber Optic Converter
Model 372   100Base-T to Fiber Converter
Model 373   10Base-T to Multi-Mode Fiber Optic Converter
Model 374   10Base-T to Single Mode Fiber Optic Transceiver, 1310 μm
Model 466   LAN Communications Server
Model 3786   PC Desk 10Base-T Transceiver
Model 8021nx   RS-485 DIN Rail Mounted Surge Suppressor
Model 8022   RS-232 DIN Rail Mounted Surge Suppressor
Model 8022nx   RS-422 and RS-485 DIN Rail Mounted Surge Suppressor

Test equipment

Model 451   ISDN Wideband Wireline Simulator
Model 452   T1 Wireline Simulator
Model 453   Extended Wideband Local Loop Simulator
Model 456   Loop Simulator Interface, Noise Source
Model 904   PC Notebook Comscope Protocol Analyzer via Serial Port
Model 905   Parallel Comcsope Protocol Analyzer via Serial Port

Port sharing

Model 335   RS-232 8 Port Digital Sharing Unit
Model 576   Code Activated Switch

Lightning and surge protection

L/S Chart   *Lightning and Surge Protector Selection Charts*
Model 22/2256 Lightning Sponge—Short Haul Modems/RS-232
Model 22NX   Lightning Sponge—RS-422 and RS-485
Model 22PX   Lightning Sponge—Dial up Telephone Lines
Model 22T1   Lightning Sponges for T1 & 56KB Telco Lines
Model 24   Lightning Sponge (for RS-232 Cables)—3 Lines

Model 27a	Lightning/Surge Protector
Model 29	DB9 Lightning/Surge Suppressor—9 Lines, PC Compatible
Model 2356	High Speed Lightning Protectors—UL 1459 Compliant
Model 8021nx	RS-485 DIN Rail Mounted Surge Suppressor
Model 8022	RS-232 DIN Rail Mounted Surge Suppressor
Model 8022nx	RS-422 and RS-485 DIN Rail Mounted Surge Suppressor

DIN rail-mounted products

Models 8000–8002	DIN Rail Accessories
Model 8003	Rack Mounted DIN Rail Rack Adapter
Model 8321	RS-485 Opto Isolated Link Extender in DIN Rail Format
Model 8021nx	RS-485 DIN Rail Mounted Surge Suppressor
Model 8022	RS-232 DIN Rail Mounted Surge Suppressor
Model 8022nx	RS-422 and RS-485 DIN Rail Mounted Surge Suppressor
Model 8225	DIN Rail Mounted—Multi-Dropped Short Haul Modem
Model 8241	Point to Point Fiber Optic Modem
Model 8242	Multipoint Fiber Optic Modem
Model 8277	DIN Rail Multi-Interface Fiber Optic Modem
Model 8321	RS-485 Opto Isolated Link Extender in DIN Rail Format
Model 8322	RS-232 to RS-485 Optically Isolated Interface Converter
Model 8323	RS-232 to RS-422 Optically Isolated Interface Converter
Model 8324	RS-232 to RS-485 2 Wire Converter
Model 8361	RS-422 Short Haul Modem in DIN Rail Enclosure
Model 8362	Optically Isolated Short Haul Modem in DIN Rail Enclosure
Model 8365	Multimode RS-422/RS-485 to RS-232 Interface Converter
Model 8381	RS-422 Opto Isolator

WAN products

Model 464	Internal ISDN Terminal Adapter
Model 466	LAN Communications Server
Model 480	Ultra High Speed Serial I/O Card
Model 683	HDSL Super Router
Model 2500T1	T1 Multiprotocol Router
Model 5501	Single-Port Frame Relay Access Device (FRAD) with Integral DSU/CSU
Model 9000	Super Rate Digital Network CSU/DSU
Model 9015	56K DSU/CSU
Model 9020	Fractional T1 DSU/CSU

Software

Office WEB	Software for high-speed, dial-up Internet access for local area networks
Office 3	Software for high-speed, dial-up Internet access for local area networks
Office MS	Software for high-speed, dial-up Internet access for local area networks

XDSL

Model 453	Extended Wideband Local Loop Simulator
Model 456	Loop Simulator Interface, Noise Source
Models 681, 682	HDSL modems
Model 683	HDSL Super Router

Card cages

Model 76	Rack Mount Card Cage
Series 2200	Fiber Optic Card Cage

T1/E1 products

Model 78X	T1/E1 Fiber Optic Modem
Model 278X	Card Mounted T1/E1 Fiber Optic Modem
Model 452	T1 Wireline Simulator
Model 2500T1	T1 Multiprotocol Router
Model 9020	Fractional T1 DSU/CSU

Technical references

ASCII Chart	Protecting Control Systems from Lightning
AUI	Ethernet Transceiver (AUI) Interface
V.35	V.35 Interface
Parallel	Parallel Interface (Centronics Type)
RS-232	RS-232 Interface
Port-232	PC Com Port—232
RS-449	RS-449 Interface
EIA-449	EIA-449 Secondary Interface
PC Mono	PC Monochrome Monitor Interface
PC Color	PC Color Monitor Interface
PS/2	PS/2 Monitor Interface
EIA-530	EIA-530 Interface Reference
Schemes	Common Unshielded Twisted Pair Data and Voice Wiring Schemes

TELEBYTE has a wealth of products and resources and is one of the best sources for such technology and information. You can contact them at

TELEBYTE Technology, Inc.
270 Pulaski Road
Greenlawn, NY 11740-1616
Phone: 800-835-3298
www.telebyteusa.com

7.14 Network Storage Silo (SMS Data Products Group)

In the early phase of network design I determined that SMS data products had the best solution for network storage. The primary driving force behind the decision was ease of use. Consider Figure 7.19, which shows the SMS network server with the following components:

28-bay rack	1 Jaz drive
25 CD-ROM drives	1 Axis StorPoint module
1 Barracuda hard-disk drive	1 NetWare connectivity module
1 CD-ROM recorder	

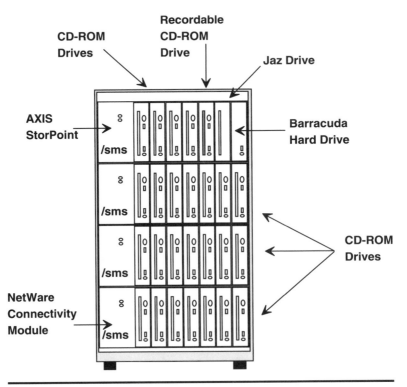

Figure 7.19 SMS Network Storage Silo

Technically, the 28-bay tower from SMS can be configured anyway you want it when ordering. For example, it could have three recordable CDs, four Barracuda hard drives, and multiple Jaz drives. Or, it could have 28 CD-ROM drives. I selected the configuration because of the power behind this array with regard to network implementation.

More information is provided in the remaining chapters on how I configured the SMS tower for my network, but remember that the simplicity of SMS products is one aspect that makes them powerful assets to a network.

SMS has other products, too many to mention here; however, I have presented the information below which was provided by SMS Data Products Group.

Millennia Series S70028

The Millennia Series S70028 comes with 28 CD-ROM drive cells in a single frame using four Series 700 chassis that can be integrated with connectivity modules for Novell, Windows NT, and the Web. The core of the Millennia Series is the Series 700 chassis: a robust, standards-based platform that can be preconfigured as an S70028 with the features listed below. Each 7-drive rack chassis can be separated into four individual towers, and the following characteristics apply:

Network direct connectivity modules for any network

Scales up from 28 to 196 drives

Swappable drives, LAN connectivity modules, and power supplies

Locking door

3-year advanced replacement warranty

UL- and FCC-B-certified

- *Standard SCSI:* S70028S—a preconfigured SCSI server attached workgroup enclosure consisting of four Series 700 chassis and 28 standard CD-ROM drive cells.

- *Network direct for Novell:* S70028NOV—a Novell network direct 28 CD-ROM drive cell enclosure using four Series 700 towers with a Novell connectivity module; comes complete with everything needed to install and access CD-ROMs on your network; Token Ring version part number S70028NOVTR.

- *Network direct for Windows NT:* S70028NT—a Windows NT network direct 28 CD-ROM drive cell enclosure using four Series 700 towers with a Windows NT connectivity module; comes complete with everything needed to install and access CD-ROMs on your network; Token Ring version part number S70028NTTR.

NETower for Windows NT

NETowers use a built-in AXIS StorPoint Connectivity Module for Windows NT, WFW, Banyan Vines, UNIX, LAN Manager, and OS/2 environments. Other particulars are

1. *Features:* Plugs directly into network node; no software required; multiple CDs as 1-drive letter; no dedicated file server necessary; works with Token Ring or Ethernet; CD-ROM license metering; no SCSI interface card to install; allows unlimited users; SCSI 12× speed drives; RJ-45 and AUI connections; easy installation.

2. *Easy sharing of CD-ROMs:* The NETower allows several users to access CDs at the same time. No more changing disks and no need to search for disks around the office. Up to seven CD-ROM drives per NETower.

3. *Security and license:* User access can be controlled by password. Can also restrict the number of users.

4. *Versatility, portability, and ease of use:* Designed for mixed LAN environment—can be used simultaneously from Windows, OS/2, DOS, and UNIX; location-independent—can be placed anywhere on the network, and does not need a file server; quick to install and easy to use—no special drivers or software needed, configuration and management done via already existing application tools, and 12× speed CD-ROM drives are supported through use of 32-bit RISC processor technology.

5. *Protocols and file systems supported:* Protocols—SMB, NetBIOS/NetBEUI, NFS, TCP, UDP, IP, RARP, BOOTP, SNMP, HTTP, FTP; file systems—High Sierra (HSF), ISO 9660.

In addition, NETowers come with a 1 year warranty, universal power supply, and a powerful cooling-fan. The FCC-B, UL, and CUL listing labels indicate quality and safety.

SMS AXIS StorPoint Connectivity Module

This is a serverless solution for Windows NT and UNIX CD-ROM networking. The AXIS StorPoint CD/T provides a flexible and cost-effective solution for sharing CD-ROM disks over networks, making all CDs easily accessible to all users at all times.

This module attaches directly to the network without involving any file server or additional software. The AXIS StorPoint CD/T is a CD-ROM server that enables users to access and share CD-ROMs over the network. No more changing of disks or searching for them around the office. Place it where needed and connect up to seven CD-ROM drives and up to 56 disks to each unit.

The AXIS StorPoint makes the SMS tower easy to use on any network. The CDs appear as shared disks to all users. AXIS StorPoint CD/T can be used with NetWare, UNIX, Windows (including Windows NT and 95), OS/2, and

WWW/intranet simultaneously. It is easily set up using platform-independent Web-based management.

The AXIS StorPoint is file-server-independent. AXIS StorPoint CD/T installs and operates completely independent of any file server. This approach allows peer-to-peer communication between the client and the CD-ROM server, which keeps the network traffic to a minimum, giving users direct, fast, and familiar access to all CDs.

It can also function as an Internet/intranet Web server. A built-in WWW server makes it possible to access the CDs using any WWW browser (e.g., Internet Explorer or Netscape Navigator). Put Web pages on a CD-ROM for a quick WWW site.

The AXIS StorPoint technical specifications include:

Network systems	Simultaneous operation in the Novell (NetWare 3.11, 3.12, and 4.10), Windows (Windows 95, Windows NT, Windows for Workgroups), Microsoft LAN Manager (LAN Manager 1) network environments.
File systems and protocols	Simultaneous operation of the NetWare (NCP over IPX); Windows, OS/2 [SMB over NetBIOS and TCP/IP, SMB over NetBIOS and NetBEUI (NetBIOS Extended User Interface)]; UNIX (NFS over UDP/IP, TCP, ARP, RARP, B) file systems.
CD-ROM standards	ISO 9660, High Sierra (HSF), Multisession, ISO 9660 Rock Ridge.
Installation	NetWare—shows up as a NetWare file server; mount with NetWare tools; all CDs can be mounted under one drive letter; Windows—shows up as an NT server; mount in Explorer or File Manager.
Network management	SNMP MIB-II and private enterprise MIB, platform independent configuration and status monitoring via standard Web browser.
Software updates	Flash memory allows central and remote software updates over the network using FTP over TCP/IP.
Security	The server unit can be User/Group access-controlled by password, and the number of users, specified in unit resident database, can be restricted. NetWare: encrypted passwords. Authorization via file server, including NDS.
Performance	Network throughput up to 900 kB/s.
Logical connection	Ethernet—IEEE 802.2, IEEE 802.3, SNAP, DIX, and Ethernet II frame types simultaneously; Token Ring—IEEE 802.2, IEEE 802.3 (with early token release support for 16 Mbps) frame types simultaneously.
Network attachment	Ethernet—10BaseT (twisted-pair) and 10Base2 (thin); Token-Ring—STP (media type 1/DB9) and UTP (media type 3/RJ-45).

Hardware   CPU—32-bit RISC processor; flash memory—2 MB;
                                        RAM—2 MB, 32 MB of cache expansion.

RAID: The S700HDA

The S700HDA, the cornerstone of your future data storage architecture, offers a universal, standards-based storage platform for hard-disk, CD-ROM, DVD, and tape storage devices delivered on multiple and redundant SCSI and Fiber Channel Data I/O paths. It also offers the following:

1. *High availability:* Beyond hot swap, the S700HDA provides automatic hot-spare failover. RAID (redundant array of independent disks) levels 1, 0/1, and 5 can be configured on the fly. Superior physical fault tolerance with active/active automatic failover power and cooling is provided. Logical fault tolerance is further enhanced with real-time predictive failure sensing and reporting for each drive.

2. *High performance:* Utilizing advanced Adaptec parity and calculating and caching technology, data are mobilized faster than in native OS and server manufacturer "RAID-like" solutions. For blazing speed, parity calculations are performed via a coprocessor accelerator on a separate yet parallel data I/O path. SCSI channels support data transfer rates up to 40 MB/s. FC-AL backplane options will support 100 MB/s burst rates and beyond.

3. *High capacity:* The S700HDA chassis meets the cooling and vibration isolation requirements of both current and future drive densities. The S700HDA is always available with the latest drive densities for the maximum storage capacity per array. As storage densities of drives double each year, the capacity of this subsystem will keep pace.

4. *Low cost:* Utilizing the latest storage technologies, the S700HDA is not bound by the cost structures of legacy systems. The S700HDA's fresh and modular approach delivers advanced storage features at prices comparable to that of just the raw drives included with servers and legacy subsystems.

5. *Storage management:* The S700HDA array management software is the command center for the network manager. Monitor and command the enterprise's storage subsystem from any workstation.

6. *Array reconfiguration:* Reconfiguration is merely a point and click away, simply highlight the drives from the graphical interface. Bar graphs instantly show data protection and performance tradeoffs among the RAID levels you select. Multiple arrays, spares, and banks of spares can be configured both within each chassis and across subsystems.

7. *Viewing of array and device information:* On a single screen, physical and logical array configurations, individual channel, and PCI host information are provided. Capacities, availability, and predictive failure data are instantly displayed.

8. *Monitoring of array activity:* Color-coded messages and charts alert the system administrator of all array activity. Status indicators depict all active fault-tolerant and critical states. Real-time predictive failure sensing and analysis allows disks to be replaced before failure.

Other features and benefits are

- Active hot spare
  Enables fast rebuild of a failed disk
  No user intervention required

- Active/active power supplies and cooling fans
  Improve data integrity
  Improve data availability
  Eliminate single point of failure

- Swappable and field-replaceable drives
  Minimal downtime when replacing failed drives
  Easily upgrade to the latest hard-disk capacities

- RAID coprocessor
  Offloads parity calculations and controlled tasks
  Frees the CPU for other I/O tasks

- Racks mounts instantly
  Standard 19-in rack
  Easy data management and expandability

- 3-year advanced replacement warranty: replacement products shipped overnight

- Scalable storage capacity
  Expand on initial investment
  Storage capacity grows with network requirements

- Unlimited, toll-free technical support
  Fast response
  Assured of support for the life of the product

- Compatible with Windows NT and Novell

- FCC-B-approved and UL-listed

7.15 DiscPort PRO and DiscView PRO Software (Microtest)

In this section we discuss two software products offered by Microtest that are designed to facilitate CD-ROM loading and network sharing.

DiscPort PRO XL

The SMS DiscPort PRO is the high-performance CD-ROM networking solution that enables NetWare and Windows NT workgroups to share up to 14 CD-ROM devices simultaneously.

Your CD-ROM sharing solution should keep up with the demands of your growing network. If you're looking for Windows NT and NetWare compatibility, increased speed and performance—look no further than DiscPort PRO, the CD-ROM networking solution for workgroups that offers speed and compatibility in one. With DiscPort PRO, you can access CD devices as easily as accessing an application on a file server.

DiscPort PRO and CD sharing. DiscPort PRO is easy to install and requires no TSRs (terminate-and-stay-resident programs) or client software on your workstations. Attach DiscPort PRO anywhere on your Thin Ethernet or 10BaseT network, and install DiscView PRO management software. Attach up to 14 CD-ROM devices per DiscPort PRO and load your CD-ROM titles. DiscPort PRO supports 8X CD-ROM drives on your 10-Mbps Ethernet network and works with popular CD-ROM drives, towers, and disk changers. And as your network grows, it's easy to add more DiscPort PROs and other Microtest Workgroup products or enterprise solutions. All Microtest CD-ROM Networking products work together seamlessly.

One product, DiscPort PRO, supports both NetWare and Windows NT networks. Easy to install, DiscPort PRO plugs into any network connection. It includes two (2) SCSI ports, providing network users simultaneous access to as many as 14 CD-ROM devices per DiscPort PRO. It lets you physically place CDs within workgroups, allowing local control of and access to CD-ROM libraries. It also includes DiscView PRO graphical user interface (GUI), making DiscPort PRO easy to manage and use, and it supports multiple protocols, including IPX/SPX and TCP/IP. DiscPort PRO works seamlessly with additional DiscPort PROs or other Microtest workgroup and enterprise solutions.

Also, *only one DiscPort PRO device supports NetWare and Windows NT Networks*. Whether you're running NetWare, Windows NT, or a combination of the two, DiscPort PRO works with both operating systems. Administrators will find sharing CD-ROMs effortless with DiscView PRO software, Microtest's CD-ROM management interface. DiscView PRO includes SmartLaunch, the totally transparent user Interface that allows users to access CD-ROM titles with point-and-click simplicity. DiscView PRO supports ISO 9660, HFS (Macintosh), CD-Bridge and Photo CDs on NetWare, and ISO 9660 on Windows NT. DiscView PRO allows CD-ROM sharing using as little as 6K (kilobytes) of RAM per CD, auto mounts and shares CDs instantly, and offers dynamic security and support for volume sets. CD-ROMs can appear as subdirectories under a single volume, so there is no need to map and unmap numerous drive letters.

DiscPort PRO comes complete with DiscView PRO, Windows-based software for easy CD-ROM installation, management, and use. DiscView PRO also

- Allows your networked CD-ROMs to appear as subdirectories of a single drive letter—no need to map and unmap numerous DOS drive letters.

- Integrates NetWare and NT security, caching, and usage statistics for your CD-ROMs.

- Integrates with NetWare Directory Services (NDS) and NT Domains.
- Instantly mounts and shares CD-ROM titles.
- Provides cache control for managing server resources.
- Offers drag-and-drop CD-ROM management.
- Offers dynamic security and dynamic volume sets for easy management.

DiscView PRO's SmartLaunch provides any user easy access to entire libraries of CD-ROMs. SmartLaunch:

- Automatically prepares and mounts your CD-ROMs—users can access titles with point-and-click simplicity.
- CD format support includes ISO 9660 (NT), ISO 9660, HFS (Macintosh), CD-I/Bridge, and Photo CDs.
- Allows easy access by DOS, Windows, Macintosh, UNIX, and OS/2 clients to CD-ROMs attached to DiscPort PRO.

Specifications are as follows:

- SCSI port
  Two (2) High Density Mini-D connector
  One (1) MiniD-to-SCSI 50 pin cable included
  SCSI II protocol
- File server requirements
  Novell NetWare 3.11 or higher with 8 MB of RAM or Windows NT 3.51 (Intel-based) with 16 MB of RAM
- Ethernet compatibility
  Thin Ethernet RG-58 A/U BNC, and 10BaseT
- Twisted-pair RJ-45 connectors
  IPX: 802.2, 802.3, Ethernet II, or SNAP frame types
  TCP/IP: Ethernet II frame types
- Workstation requirements
  Windows 3.1 or higher recommended
  At least 4 MB recommended for Windows users
  Macintosh users running System 6.0.7 or higher
  Novell NetWare for Macintosh installed

7.16   Network Cable Tester (WaveTek LANPro XL; Lantek Pro)

An integral part of installing and maintaining networks is having accurate information about the components used in the network. During the planning phase I determined that the best instrument to use in this network is the Lantek Pro XL cable tester.

Some of the features of the Lantek Pro XL include

- Autotest time 25 s
- Dual NEXT
- Autotest suites (reporting pass/fail for each)
  Line mapping
  Length
  Dc loop Ω
  Attenuation
  Dual NEXT
  ACR
  Average impedance
  Return Loss
  Delay
- Cable expert
- TDR (impedance vs. length)
- Average noise [for EMI, RFI (electromagnetic, radio-frequency interference)]
- Test storage: 500
- Graphical display 160×160 (pixels)
- Flash EEPROM
- Cable types supported: 150*
- AutoSave/AutoPrint

WaveTek has another instrument, the LanTEK Pro, which can also be used for cable testing. Its features include

- Autotest time 30 s
- Dual NEXT
- Autotest suites (reporting pass/fail for each)
  Line mapping
  Length
  Dc loop Ω
  Attenuation
  Dual NEXT
  ACR
  Average impedance

---

*Includes, but is not limited to, UTP and STP for Categories 3–5, ISO (Class B–D), CATV, and user-specified cabling. Specifications subject to change.

Return loss

Delay

- Cable expert
- TDR (impedance vs. length) (not included)
- Average noise (for EMI, RFI) (not included)
- Test storage: 500
- Graphical display 160 × 160
- Flash EEPROM
- Cable types supported—150*
- AutoSave/AutoPrint

The Lantek Pro Series meets or exceeds all TIA requirements for LevelII testing.

Electrical specifications

- Line map
- 8-wire pin connectivity, cable destination and shield continuity
- Dc resistance
  Range: 0 to 400 Ω autoranging
  Accuracy: ±(1 percent + 2 Ω)
  Resolution: 0.1 Ω
- Length
  Range: 0 to 610 m (0 to 2000 ft)
  Accuracy: ±(3 percent + 3 ft + NVP uncertainty)
  Resolution: 0.1 m (0.33 ft)
  Propagation rate: 0.5 0.99c + 0.01

- Impedance
  Range: 0 to 400 Ω
  Accuracy: ±(3 percent + 1 ms)
  Resolution: 0.1 m (0.33 ft)

- Capacitance
  Range: 0 pF to 100 nF
  Accuracy: ±(2 percent + 20 pF)
  Resolution: 1 pF/min

---

*Includes, but is not limited to, UTP and STP for Categories 3–5, ISO (Class B–D), CATV, and user-specified cabling. Specifications subject to change.

- Average (wideband) noise
  Range: 0 to 1 VRMS
  Bandwidth: 50 Hz to 30 MHz
  Resolution: 10 mV
- Attenuation
  Swept frequency range: 1 to 102 MHz
  Frequency steps: TIA TSB-67
  Full range: 0 to 70 dB
  Dynamic range: 50 dB at 1 MHz to 30 dB at 100 MHz (log curve)
  Accuracy: ± 1.0 dB at channel or basic link
  Resolution: 0.1 dB
- Near-end crosstalk
  Swept frequency range: 1 to 102 MHz
  Frequency steps: TIA TSB-67
  Full range: 70 dB
  Dynamic range: 70 dB at 1 MHz to 45 dB at 100 MHz (log curve)
  Residual NEXT: 55 dB at 100 MHz
  Accuracy: ± 1.6 dB at basic link limit
  Resolution: 0.1 dB
- Delay
  Range: 0 to 4000 ms
  Accuracy: $\pm$(3 percent + 1 ms)
  Resolution: 0.1 ns
- Average impedance
  Range: 0 to 400 Ω
  Accuracy: $\pm$(3 percent+ 1 Ω)
  Resolution: 1 Ω
- Return loss
  Swept frequency range: 1 to 102 MHz
  Dynamic range: 30 dB
  Accuracy: ± 0.1 dB
  Resolution: 0.1 dB

Environmental specifications

- Operating temperature range: 0–50°C
- Temperature coefficient: $0.1 \times$ spec/°C
- Storage temperature range: -20 to $+ 70$°C
- Relative humidity: 5–90%, noncondensing

Mechanical specifications

- Display handset

  Dimensions: $10 \times 4.25 \times 2.5$ in ($250 \times 108 \times 64$ mm)

  Weight: 1.75 lb (800 g)

- Remote handset

  Dimensions: $10 \times 4.25 \times 2.5$ in ($250 \times 108 \times 64$ mm)

  Weight: 1.6 lb (728 g)

- Charging bay

  Dimensions: $3.15 \times 9.65 \times 3.75$ in ($80 \times 245 \times 95$ mm)

  Weight: 2.5 lb (1137 g)

  Input power: 110 V $\pm$ 10 percent or 240 V + 10 percent

  50 or 60 Hz

  Output power: 9 V dc, 300 MA

- Battery management

  Display handset: 8 h typical

  Remote handset: 14 h typical

  Recharging time: 3 h or less

7.17 Network Server (IBM Netfinity 7000)

An IBM Netfinity 7000 was selected for this network, especially because of its specifications and the performance it can deliver. This server provides the critical function in the network I designed, implemented, and explained here in this text. The actual configuration I used in this network is presented later in this book.

The Netfinity 7000 is available in tower (rack) (THO series) and cabinet (TMO series) models. For numerous reasons, I selected the cabinet system. To provide you with the most accurate information about this system, I am presenting the IBM Netfinity 7000 specifications here:

Standard features

Processor	200-MHz Pentium Pro processor: 8651-RM0, 8651-RH0, 8651-TM0, and 8651-TH0 models; 200 MHz standard with two dual-processor complexes. One of the four ZIF (zero insertion force) sockets on the two processor complexes is populated, leaving room for up to three 200-MHz Pentium Pro processors to be added via 387-pin ZIF sockets.
L2 cache	8651-RH0 and 8651-TH0: 1 MB write-back set associate cache integrated on each Pentium Pro processor. 8651-RM0 and 8651-TM0: 512 kB of write-back

	set associate cache integrated on each Pentium Pro processor.
Memory	All models: 256-MB ECC DIMMs (4 × 64 MB), 12 sockets available. A maximum system memory of 4 GB can be achieved via 16 × 256-MB DIMMs. All memory DIMMs installed into one standard memory card with 16 sockets (2 banks of 8 sockets). Memory DIMMs are parity with ECC implemented by the memory controller.
Memory controller	ECC
Hard drive	Hard Drive 8651-RM0 , 8651-RH0, 8651-TM0, and 8651-TH0 models: open bay. A maximum internal disk capacity of 54.6 GB can be achieved via 6 × 9.1-GB Wide Ultra-SCSI hot-swap hard-disk drives; 4.51-GB Wide Ultra SCSI hot-swap hard-disk drives are also supported.
SCSI controller	All models: 2 × 7880 Wide Ultra SCSI PCI controllers. Optional: IBM ServeRAID II Ultra SCSI Adapter.
Architecture	PCI/EISA; I2O-ready dual PCI bus.
Slots (10 total)	Slot 1: full-size, 32-bit PCI
	Slot 2: full-size, 32-bit PCI
	Slot 3: full-size, 32-bit PCI
	Slot 4: full-size, 32-bit PCI
	Slot 5: full-size, 32-bit PCI
	Slot 6: full-size, 32-bit PCI
	Slot 7: full-size, 32-bit EISA (Extended Industry Standard Architecture) or 16-bit ISA (Industry Standard Architecture)
	Slot 8: full-size, 32-bit EISA or 16-bit ISA
	Slot 9: full-size, 32-bit EISA or 16-bit ISA
	Slot 10: full-size, 32-bit EISA or 16-bit ISA, Advanced System Management Adapter
Bays	Total 18 bays; 12 bays support hot-swap disks. Bank A: 6 × 3.5-in bays, SL, access, hot-swap.
	Bank B: 6 × 3.5-in bays, SL, access, hot-swap; 6 device bays, 5 × 5.25-in bays, HH, access, one bay used by CD-ROM drive; 1 × 3.5-in bays, SL, access, 1.44-MB diskette drive
System management	All models: one Advanced System Management Adapter
BIOS	512 kB of EEPROM, Plug-and-Play BIOS support
Power supply	All models: two standard 400 W, hot-swap power supplies. Optional: hot-swap 400 W redundant power supply option, which backs up the two standard

	power supplies, installs in third power supply bay. All power supplies are PFA-enabled.
Cooling	All models: three hot-swap fans. The three cooling fans provide redundancy. If one fan fails, the system will continue to operate safely for a period of time with only two fans.
Diskette drive	3.5 in, 1.44 MB.
CD-ROM	All models: front-tray loading. 8× IDE (1200 kbps transfer rate and 120 ms access time).
Keyboard	8651-TM0 and 8651-TH0 models: basic 101-key. 8651-RM0 and 8651-RH0 models: optional.
Mouse	8651-TM0 and 8651-TH0 models: IBM two-button mouse, 400 dpi (dots per inch). 8651-RM0 and 8651-RH0 models: optional.
Graphics and video resolution	Integrated RAMDAC with 262,144 color palette supporting SVGA with 512 kB of DRAM. Up to 1024 × 768 with 16 colors at 72 Hz.
Ports	Two 9-pin serial, UART 16550A maximum 56 kbps, one parallel (ECP/EPP, IEEE 1284, 2 Mbps), keyboard, mouse, SVGA, and two Wide Ultra SCSI PCI ports.
Security	The System Configuration Utility (SCU) is used to enable keyboard timer, disable keyboard and mouse inputs, enable power-on/reset administrator password, and disable writing to diskette drive. A mechanical lock on the front door of the system limits access to drive bays (tower models). Cover-intrusion switches on the top and the front covers provide cover-intrusion alarm warnings. An optional Netfinity Security Cover III can be installed to prevent unauthorized access to external cabling, adapter connectors, and ports on the backplane (tower models).
Supported operating systems	Microsoft Windows NT 3.51/4.0 Workstation, Microsoft Windows NT 3.51/4.0 Server, Novell NetWare 3.12/4.1/4.11/4.1 SMP, IBM OS/2 Warp 3.0, IBM OS/2 Warp 3.0 with Win-OS/2, IBM OS/2 Warp Connect 3.0, IBM OS/2 SMP V2.11, IBM OS/2 Warp Server V4, IBM OS/2 Warp Server Advanced V4 (includes SMP enhancements), IBM OS/2 LAN Server 4.0 Entry, IBM OS/2 LAN Server 4.0 Advanced, SCO UnixWare 2.x, SCO Open Server 5.0, SCO Open DeskTop/Open Server 3.0, and SunSoft Solaris 2.5.
Standard software	IBM ServerGuide, IBM Netfinity Manager 5.1, QAPlus/PRO, IBM AntiVirus, APC PowerChute Plus, and Lotus Domino 4.51 (single-processor edition).

Support	IBM TechConnect, IBM Netfinity Start Up Support, and IBM HelpCenter.
Warranty	Three-year on-site limited warranty: IBM on-site repair, 8:00 A.M. to 5:00 P.M. Monday through Friday, with 8-h average response time.
Weight and dimensions	Tower models (8651-TM0 and 8651-TH0): weight 120 lb, $h \times w \times d$ (height $\times$ width $\times$ depth) = 19.0 $\times$ 19.0 $\times$ 26 in. Rack model (8651-RM0, 8651-RH0): weight 120 lb, $h \times w \times d$ = 19.0 $\times$ 16.5 $\times$ 24 in (11 units required for a rack installation).

Legal notices

1. The MHz reading measures internal clock speed only, not application performance. Many factors affect application performance.

2. When referring to hard-drive capacity, MB stands for million bytes and GB stands for billion bytes. Total user-accessible capacity may vary depending on operating environments.

3. For terms and conditions or copies of IBM's limited warranty, call 800-772-2227 in the United States. Limited warranty includes International Warranty Service in those countries where this statement of product is sold by IBM or IBM Business Partners (registration required).

4. Energy Star compliance: The EPA, as a matter of policy, does not endorse any particular company or its products.

5. Battery life (and recharge times) will vary depending on screen brightness, applications, features, power management, battery conditioning, and other references. CD-ROM or hard-disk drive usage may also have a significant impact on battery life.

6. Actual specifications may vary slightly depending on features and components.

7. Unless otherwise indicated, prices shown are estimated reseller prices to end users. Reseller prices may vary. IBM reserves the right to change prices and product specifications and to discontinue marketing products without notice.

Netfinity Manager

IBM Netfinity Manager gives you total control over your entire Intel-based systems environment. It makes systems management easier by automating many processes. For example, you can monitor systems usage, log events, and be alerted in the event of a problem. You have the tools to manage what you want, when you want, wherever you are.

- Schedule asset management. Set up routines to back up key systems, poll clients and servers for configuration information, and more.

- Head off problems before they start with Predictive Failure Analysis alerting and configuration information.

- Reduce time and distance with remote access through IBM Netfinity Manager software and the Advanced System Management Adapter.

- Set up a remote Help Desk. Take action to correct client and server system problems remotely.

- Manage with remote control over the World Wide Web. Connect to your servers and clients on any standard browser for total control.

- Link to TME10, SMS, OpenView, and more.

- Complete your total information technology management with integration with your system of choice.

- Manage your clusters with ease from a single console with IBM Netfinity Cluster Management for Microsoft Cluster Server (when available).

- Integrate your multiplatform, multiprotocol systems management solution easily.

- Reduce total cost of ownership by controlling many of the costs of operating your networked systems.

- Maintain high availability and prevent problems with the IBM Advanced System Management Adapter's remote monitoring and control capabilities.

Netfinity Manager supports many of the industry's most popular PC operating systems, including Windows NT, Windows 95, Windows 3.1, Novell NetWare, OS/2, and network protocols such as NetBIOS, IPX, SNA (LU6.2), TCP/IP, and serial. Netfinity Manager also provides these functions over an Internet connection with a Web browser.

With Netfinity Manager as the foundation for IBM's System Management solution, you can help your business realize true, long-term success through comprehensive control.

Hardware and software information

The following is a list and chart of correlating information as it relates to the Netfinity:

Applications	High-speed networking adapters
Cables	Peripheral devices
Clustering products	Storage devices
SCSI controllers	Token Ring LAN adapters
Ethernet LAN adapters	System upgrades
Fast Ethernet LAN adapters	Wide area networking

Applications

Product	Manufacturer	Part number	Product description
Backup	Seagate	BackupExecNT	Backup Exec for Windows NT Server 6.1
Backup	Seagate	BackupExecNW	Backup Exec for Netware Server 7.0
Backup	Cheyenne	OS2-SO17-PRO	Arcsolo for OS/2 (version 1.7)
Backup	Cheyenne	ARCserveSCO-20A	ARCserve/Open for SCO v2.0A
Backup	Cheyenne	NT-AS60EE	ARCserve for Windows NT 6.0
Backup	Cheyenne	N3-AS60-EE	ARCserve 6.0 for NetWare
Backup	IBM	84H3129	ADSM for OS/2 2.1 Network Enabler
Backup	Seagate	ALEO-220SY	Sytos Autoloader v2.2 for OS/2
Backup	Seagate	PREO-220SY	Sytos Premium for OS/2 2.2
Communication	IBM	EagleCommSrv	IBM Communication Server
Database	IBM	41H2114	DB2/2 (OS/2) v2.1.1
Database	IBM	EagleDBSrv	Database Server
Database	Microsoft	SQL Server6.0	SQL Server (Back Office)
Database	Oracle	Oracle7NW	Oracle 7 Database (NW)
Database	Oracle	WrkGrpEntOS_2	Workgroup Enterprise OS/2
Firewall	Checkpoint	CPFireWall	Firewall
Groupware	IBM	EagleNotesSrv	Lotus Notes Server
Groupware	Lotus	Notes4.xNT	Notes 4.1 for Microsoft Windows NT
Groupware	Lotus	Notes4.xNW	Notes 4.1 for Novell NetWare
Groupware	Lotus	Notes4.xOS2	Notes 4.1 for IBM Warp Server
Groupware	Lotus	Domino4.5NT	Notes Domino Server 4.5 for Microsoft Windows NT
Groupware	Lotus	Domino4.5NW	Notes Domino Server 4.5 for Novell NetWare
Groupware	Lotus	Domino4.5OS	Notes Domino Server 4.5 for OS/2
High Availability	Adaptec	Duralink	Duralink Redundant Network Link
Internet Server	IBM	EagleInetSrv	IBM Internet Server
Internet Server	Netscape	Suitespot3.0	Suitespot Server 3.0
Network Management	IBM	PCSServices	IBM Netfinity 4.x Services OS/2,NW,NT
Network Management	IBM	PCSMgmt	IBM Netfinity 4.x Mgmt (OS/2,NW,NT)
Network Management	Intel	LDM2NW	Intel LAN Desk Manager 2.5 NW & NT
Network Management	Microsoft	SMS 1.1	Systems Management Server (Back Office)

Cables

Product	Manufacturer	Part number	Product description
SCSI	IBM	76H5400	IBM Third Channel Cable
SCSI	IBM	94G7421	Netfinity PCI SCSI Controller to Bulkhead
SCSI	IBM	01K8017	IBM 0.8 mm to 68-pin SCSI Adapter
SCSI	IBM	70G9857	PC Server F/W to F/W External SCSI Cable
SCSI	IBM	70G9858	PC Server F/W to Fast External SCSI Cable

Clustering

Product	Manufacturer	Part number	Product description
Clustering	Microsoft	MCS1.0	MS Cluster Server 1.0
Clustering	IBM	94G7584	IBM Shared Disk Convenience Kit
Clustering	IBM	01k8018	IBM Netfinity Cluster Pack by Vinca
Clustering	IBM	94G6620	PC Server High Availability Solution for OS/2 Warp
Clustering	IBM	94G6621	PC Server High Availability Solution for Windows NT
Clustering	IBM	94G6622	PC Server High Availability Solution for NetWare

Controllers

Product	Manufacturer	Part number	Product description
UltraSCSI	Adaptec	AHA-3940AUW	PCI Fast/Wide Ultra SCSI Adapter
SCSI-2/RAID	DPT	PM3334UW_3	SmartRAID IV SCSI Raid Adapter (3 Channel)
SSA/RAID	IBM	32H3811	IBM SSA RAID PCI Adapter
SSA/RAID	IBM	96H9835	IBM SSA RAID Cluster Adapter
UltraSCSI	Adaptec	AHA-2940UW	PCI Fast/Wide Ultra SCSI-2 Adapter
UltraSCSI	Adaptec	AHA-2940U	PCI Fast Ultra SCSI-2 Adapter
UltraSCSI	IBM	76H5401	IBM ServeRAID II 8 MB/Battery-Backup Cache
UltraSCSI	IBM	76H3584	ServeRaid II Ultra SCSI Adapter
UltraSCSI	IBM	76H5407	PCI Ultra Wide SCSI Adapter

Ethernet LAN adapters

Product	Manufacturer	Part number	Product description
Ethernet	IBM	13H9237	PCI Ethernet

Fast Ethernet LAN adapters

Product	Manufacturer	Part number	Product description
Fast Ethernet	IBM	25H3501	10/100 ISA Ethernet
Fast Ethernet	Intel	PILA8465B	EtherExpress PRO/100 LAN
Fast Ethernet	Olicom	OC-2325	Fast Ethernet PCI/II 10/100
Fast Ethernet	3Com	3C905-TX	Fast EtherLink XL PCI
Fast Ethernet	Adaptec	ANA-6911_TX	Cogent 10/100 PCI Fast Ethernet
Fast Ethernet	Adaptec	ANA-6944A_TX	Cogent PCI Quartet 10/100 4-Port Ethernet
Fast Ethernet	IBM	86H2432	100/10 Ethernet PCI
Fast Ethernet	Intel	PILA8480	EtherExpress PRO/100 Server
Fast Ethernet	Olicom	OC-2326	Fast Ethernet PCI/II 10/100
Fast Ethernet	SMC	SMC9332BDT	EtherPower 10/100 32-bit
Fast Ethernet	SMC	SMC9432TX	EtherPower II 10/100 32-bit

High-speed networking products

Product	Manufacturer	Part number	Product description
ATM	3Com	3C975-F	ATMLink PCI-155 ATM
ATM	Fore	PCA-200EPC	ForeRunner PCA-200EPC PCI
ATM	Madge	32-01	Collage 155 ATM Adapter (Fiber)
FDDI	SysKonnect	SK5541	PCI FDDI Adapter (SAS-MIC)
FDDI	SysKonnect	SK5544	PCI FDDI Adapter (DAS)
ATM	IBM	85H9035	Turboways 25 PCI ATM APE-Bridge Adapter

Networking hardware (peripheral devices): routers, switches, and hubs

Product	Manufacturer	Part number	Product description
Ethernet	IBM	8224	8224 Ethernet Hub
Ethernet	IBM	8237	8237 Ethernet Hub
Token Ring	IBM	8238	8238 Token Ring 16-Port Hub
External	IBM	2210-14T	2210-T14 25-MB ATM Router
External	IBM	2210-12E	2210-E12 Router
External	IBM	2210-12T	2210-T12 Router
Router/Int	Sourcecom	Incarda_P	Incarda/P Server-Based Router Adapter
ATM	IBM	42H0525	Turboways 25 ISA Adapter
Keyboard	IBM	76H0109	104-Key Standard Keyboard (Raven Black)
Keyboard	IBM	13H6705	101-key Enhanced Keyboard with Trackpoint II (Black)
Monitor	IBM	6540-0x0	G42P Monitor (14 in, 48 kHz)
Monitor	IBM	6540-02x	G42L Monitor (14 in, 48 kHz)
Monitor	IBM	6541-02x	G51L Monitor (15 in, 54 kHz)
Monitor	IBM	6542103	G40 Color Monitor 14 in
Monitor	IBM	6543303	G50 Color Monitor 15 in
Monitor	IBM	6553503	P50 Color Monitor 6553
Monitor	IBM	6544403	G70 Color Monitor 17 in
Monitor	IBM	6554673	P70 Color Monitor 6554
Monitor	IBM	6553-5xx	P50 Color Monitor 6553
Mouse	IBM	13H6690	Enhanced Mouse (Pearl White)
Mouse	IBM	13H6714	Enhanced Mouse (Raven Black)
Monitor	IBM	6546-x0x	G52P Monitor (15 in, 69 kHz)
Monitor	IBM	6547-x1x	G72S Monitor (17 in, 69 kHz)
Monitor	IBM	6547-x0x	G72P Monitor (17 in, 69 kHz)
Monitor	IBM	6546-x1x	G52S Monitor (15 in, 69 kHz)
Printer	HP	C3155A#ABA	Laserjet 5P
Printer	IBM	4772001	4772 Universal Financial Printer
Rack	IBM	9306900	IBM Netfinity Rack
Upgrade Kit	IBM	94G7424	Tower to Rack Conversion Kit
Upgrade Kit	IBM	94G7425	Rack to Tower Conversion Kit

Storage devices

Product	Manufacturer	Part number	Product description
Enclosure	IBM	7133-020	7133-020 SSA—Storage Enclosure— Rack Mountable
Enclosure	IBM	3519R01	3519—Rack Drawer Enclosure

Product	Manufacturer	Part number	Product description
Enclosure	IBM	7133-600	7133-600—SSA Storage Enclosure—Floor Standing
Enclosure	IBM	3517001	3517-001—SCSI Multi-Storage Enclosure
Enclosure	IBM	3517002	3517-002—SCSI Multi-Storage Enclosure
Enclosure	IBM	3527001	3527—IBM SSA Entry Storage Subsystem
Enclosure	IBM	3518001	3518—PC Server Enterprise Expansion Enclosure
Enclosure	IBM	35201RU	IBM Netfinity EXP10 Rack Storage Enclosure
Enclosure	Symbios-Logic	DS-20E	Metastor RAID Storage Enclosure (Desktop)
Enclosure	Symbios-Logic	RM-20E	Metastor RAID Storage Enclosure (Rack)
HDD/HS	IBM	27H1062	4.51-GB SL F/W SSA Hot-Swap HDD
HDD/HS	IBM	05J6413	2.25-GB SSA Hot-Swap HDD II
HDD/HS	IBM	05J6414	4.51-GB SSA Hot-Swap HDD II
HDD/HS	IBM	94G7429	4.51-GB Wide Ultra SCSI Hot-Swap HDD
HDD/HS	IBM	94G7430	9.1-GB Wide Ultra SCSI Hot-Swap HDD
HDD/HS	IBM	21H8734	9.1-GB SL F/W SSA Hot-Swap HDD
Repeater	IBM	94G7426	Netfinity SCA Backplane Repeater Adapter Kit
Repeater	IBM	94G7585	IBM SCSI-2 F/W Enhanced Repeater Card
Tape Library	Exabyte	EXB-220	EXB-220 Tape Library
Tape	IBM	76H0485	20/40-GB 8-mm Internal SCSI Tape Drive
Tape	IBM	01K1174	35/70-GB External DLT Tape Drive
Tape Library	IBM	3447106	DLT Tape Library (Rack—5U)
Tape	IBM	00K7900	35/70-GB Internal DLT Tape Drive
Tape Library	IBM	3449356	8-mm Tape Library (Rack—15U)
Tape	Quantum	TH5AA-YF	DLT4000 40GB External SCSI-2 Tape Drive
Tape Library	IBM	3449355	8-mm Tape Library (Tower)
Tape Library	IBM	3447105	DLT Tape Library (Desktop)

Token Ring LAN adapters

Product	Manufacturer	Part number	Product description
Token Ring	IBM	04H8095	AutoLANStreamer PCI T/R
Token Ring	IBM	41H8900	PCI Token Ring Adapter
Token Ring	Madge	51-02	Smart 16/4 PCI Ringnode
Token Ring	Olicom	OC-3137	Token Ring PCI/II 16/4 Adapter

System upgrades

Product	Manufacturer	Part number	Product description
DIMM	IBM	94G7384	64-MB FPM ECC DIMM (4-8Mx72) 60-ns Memory Upgrade Kit
DIMM	IBM	94G7385	128-MB FPM ECC DIMM (4-16Mx72) 60-ns Memory Upgrade Kit
DIMM	IBM	94G7386	256-MB FPM ECC DIMM (4-32Mx72) 60-ns Memory Upgrade Kit
UPS	IBM	94G3135	APC Smart-UPS 1000
UPS	IBM	94G3136	APC Smart-UPS 1400
Security	IBM	94G7427	IBM Netfinity Security Cover III
Service	IBM	94G5570	Advanced Systems Management Adapter
Service	IBM	94G5571	Advanced Systems Management Power Unit
Service	IBM	94G7578	Advanced Systems Management Adapter
Hot-Plug	IBM	94G7150	400W Hot-Swap Redundant Power Supply
PP200MHz	IBM	94G6678	PC Server SMP 200-MHz Upgrade
Card	IBM	94G7387	Netfinity 200-MHz/1-MB Processor Card
PP200MHz	IBM	94G7147	Netfinity SMP 200-MHz/1-MB L2 Cache
UPS	IBM	94G6674	APC Smart-UPS 1400RMB (120 V)
UPS	IBM	94G6675	APC Smart-UPS 1400RMiB (230 V)
UPS	IBM	94G6676	APC Smart-UPS 3000RMB (120 V)
UPS	IBM	94G6677	APC Smart-UPS 3000RMiB (230 V)

Wide area networking

Product	Manufacturer	Part number	Product description
Modem/Bank	Digital	70001183	T1 Modem Bank (6-24 v.34 Modems)
Modem/Ext	Hayes	08-02349	Optima 28.8 v.34/v.FC Modem
Modem/Ext	USRobotics	001224-0	Courier v.Everything with v.34
SDN/Ext	3COM	3C871	ISDN External Digital Modem
Asynch	Digital	70001169	C/X16 System PCI DB25
ISDN/LAN	Ascend	P25-1UBR	Pipeline 25 ISDN Modem (Ethernet Attach)
ISDN/Int	Digital	77000372	Datafire-U S1 Server ISDN Adapter
Multiprotocol	Digital	70001270	Sync/570i PCI (with v.35 cable)
Multiprotocol	IBM	85X2706	ARTIC Realtime Interface Coprocessor
Multiprotocol	IBM	61G3862	ARTIC Multiport
Multiprotocol	IBM	06H3890	ARTIC Multiport 8-Port RS-232 with 1 MB
Multiprotocol	IBM	39H8058	ARTIC960/PCI
Multiprotocol	IBM	33F8791	ARTIC Multiport Model 2
Multiprotocol	Software Group	570PCI-NH	Netcom Highway (570 PCI)
X.25	IBM	71G6460	ARTIC X.25 ISA Interface Coprocessor

Information summary

Networks that utilize a server, especially an application or file server, require a server that is reliable, powerful, and expandable. The Netfinity 7000 used in this network is robust and expandable. Additional information about its configuration and use is presented in subsequent chapters.

I recommend that you contact IBM for the most recent information about the servers they offer. They can be reached at

ww.ibm.com
International Business Machines Corp.
One Old Orchard Road
Armonk, NY 10504
Phone: 914-765-1900
Fax: 914-288-1147

7.18 Microsoft Windows 95 and 98

Software used in this network includes Windows 95 and Windows 98 operating systems. Both work well with all the hardware and software integrated together.

Windows 3.1 is also used in the network as well. Rather than provide a lengthy explanation of these operating systems, contact the following Web address for more information: *www.microsoft.com.*

7.19 Microsoft Windows NT

The network designed and described in the following chapters includes Windows NT operating systems. The NT versions used are Server version 4.0, Workstation version 4.0, Enterprise Edition, Server version 5.0, and Workstation version 5.0.

You can contact Microsoft at the following Web site to obtain more information: *www.microsoft.com.*

7.20 Commercial Desktop Computers (IBM)

IBM personal computers are used in this network. The commercial desktop series used include the PC350 and XL models. Typical general specifications for the base system units (model 350 series) used in this network include

200-MHz Pentium MMX Processor

2.6-GB hard disk (additional 3.0 GB hard drive)

16-MB nonparity EDO (Extended Data Output) memory (additional 48 MB RAM)

3½-in floppy-disk drive

Units used in this network employ a PCI Busmaster controller and SMART (self-monitoring analysis and reporting technology) capabilities. These systems include PCI Enhanced IDE hard drives, Universal Serial Bus (USB) ports, infrared and 64-bit PCI graphics, and Wake-on LAN capability.

Functionality of the USB makes peripheral connectivity easier. The hot-connect ability enables peripheral devices to be connected in seconds. Such devices can be added or removed without reconfiguring or rebooting. Each USB port permits up to 127 USB-capable devices.

Some of the PCs used in this network have the capability for symmetric multiprocessing (SMP) when dual processors are used. An L2 external CPU 256-kB cache and a Pipeline burst L3 cache are also used. The BIOS type is 256-kB flash memory, SurePath. These systems can accommodate up to 192 MB of RAM at a speed of 60 ns deployed by 72-pin SIMMs. Their hard-disk size seek time averages 12 ms with a latency of approximately 5.8 ms. They support RAID and hot-swappable drive bays.

These graphics capabilities of these systems employ an S3 Trio64 V+Graphics chipset. The result is SVGA graphics and data width of 64-bit Video RAM. Graphic resolution (with the standard video RAM) is 1280 × 1024 (pixels) with 16 colors. The maximum resolution (with a maximum video RAM) is 1280 × 1024 with 65,536 colors. The graphics bus interface uses PCI architecture.

The systems have a 200-W power supply for either 110 or 220 V with a universal manual switch. The heat and sound emissions are 48 dB. The typical weight of each cabinet is 28 lb, and dimensions are $h \times w \times d = 6.3 \times 16.5 \times 17.6$ in.

Systems used in this network include the following security features:

Boot sequence control

Boot without keyboard or mouse

Cover key lock

Diskette boot inhibit

Diskette write protect (switch)

Diskette I/O control

Hard-disk I/O control

Parallel I/O control

Power-on password

Secure fixed DASD

Secure removable media

Serial I/O control

Setup utility password (administrator password)

U-Bolt tie-down support

The systems specifications used in this network also include the following product approvals and/or certifications according to IBM: BABT (U.K.); CE; CISPR-22 Class B; CSA C22.2 No. 950 (Canada); DEMKO (EN 60950); EIF (SETI) (EN 60950); Engery Saving Law (refer to N-B 1-9174-001); FCC Class B (U.S.); IECEE CB Certificate and report to IEC-950 Second Edition; ISO 9241-3 Compliant; JATE; NEMKO (EN 60950); NS/G/1234/J/100003

(Telecommunications Safety only: no approval mark); OVE (EN 60950); Power Line Harmonics (refer to N-B 2-4700-017); SEMKO (EN 60950); TUV-GS (EN 60950); TUV-GS—ZH1/618; UL-1950 First Edition; VCCI Class 2 (Japan). In addition, IBM's current warranty is limited warranty period and type 3: 3-year warranty, first year on-site, second, third years carry-in, 3 years parts and labor.

The IBM desktop systems used in this network were supplied with preinstalled software. Some of these systems were reconfigured to meet the needs of the network. However, all legal and ethical respect was given to manufacturers of hardware and software products. Each system used in this network either is covered by a site license or has a dedicated piece of software for each system; and, each system has one user. In the case of servers, workstations, or otherwise, each manufacturer's legal guidelines were followed. I strongly recommend that these matters be factored into the network design of any network. Simply put, using an unpaid-for piece of software, unless it is clear that it is freeware, is stealing. It is no different from someone stealing a tangible item. Consider this when you design your network.

Model 658842U characteristics are as follows. The IBM PC 300XL is designed with the latest 266-MHz technology to handle demanding business Pentium II applications in a networked environment. These are the high-end systems that deliver value, and a 2.5-GB hard drive keeps you ahead of the curve with the performance disks that power users demand. The IBM PC 300XL series includes open-bay models which can be custom-configured via IBM's Authorized Assembler Program (AAP).

Standard features

Processors	Pentium II processors: 233, 266, or 300 MHz with unified 512-kB L2 cache.
Memory	32-MB nonparity EDO Memory (expandable memory to 384 MB) 32 MB, expandable to 384 MB (3 DIMMs), EDO/60 ns.
Hard drives	2.5- or 4.2-GB EIDE (Enhanced IDE) with SMART or 4.3-GB Wide Ultra SCSI with SMART or open-bay PCI Busmaster EIDE controller on planar, SCSI models include an SCSI-2 Fast, and Wide PCI Busmaster adapter.
Graphics and video resolution	S3 Trio64V2; 64-bit; 2-MB standard/maximum video DRAM; 256 colors at 1280×1024 resolution.
Network features	LANClient Control Manager supported, Wake-on LAN, Plug-In and Go, Flash over LAN (BIOS/CMOS), Plug-and-Play, CID.
Network interface	Integrated Intel EtherExpress 10/100 Mbps Ethernet with Wake-on LAN.
CD-ROM	Models available with $16\times$–$8\times$ (variable speed) CD-ROM (variable read rate; actual playback speed will vary and is often less than the maximum possible).

Audio	Models available with Crystal 4236B audio chip, 16-bit, supports Sound Blaster Pro applications.
Diskette drive	One 3.5 in, 1.44 MB standard.
Slots	Three shared PCI/ISA, two ISA.
Bays	Three 3.5 in, two 5.25 in.
BIOS	Flash ROM.
Architecture	PCI local bus, ISA data bus.
Ports	Serial (16550), enhanced parallel (ECP/EPP), two USB ports, SVGA video, EIDE controller, 10/100 Mbps Ethernet RJ-45, IrDA-2-compliant infrared, audio mic-in and line-out minijacks, keyboard, mouse.
Keyboard/mouse	IBM Cameo 104-key (rubber dome) and Enhanced Mouse.
Power supply	200 W.
Security features	IBM AssetCare: serialization and laser etching of memory and processors, third-party registration available through Retainagoup Limited.
IBM AntiVirus and ConfigSafe	Vital Product Data (VPD) support, cover key lock, sliding front door lock, U-bolt anchor support, secure access openings, secure removable media, ⌐ fixed DASD, diskette write protect, power-on password, configuration/administrator password, keyboard/mouse password, Wake-on LAN password prompt, boot sequence control, diskette boot inhibit, boot without keyboard/mouse, mouse-disable, I/O controls.
Software and tools	Windows 95 or Windows NT 4.0 preload available on models with a hard drive, Lotus SmartSuite license, Microsoft NetMeeting (Windows 95 preload models only), LANClient Control Manager (downloadable via Internet), IBM Netfinity Manager software, Intel LANDesk Client Manager, Artisoft CoSession, QAPlus System Support CD (Ready to Configure) with additional software and drivers.
Limited warranty	Three-year parts and one-year labor.

Legal notices

1. The MHz reading measures internal clock speed only, not application performance. Many factors affect application performance.

2. When referring to hard-drive capacity, MB stands for million bytes and GB stands for billion bytes. Total user-accessible capacity may vary depending on operating environments.

3. For terms and conditions or copies of IBM's limited warranty, call 800-772-2227 in the United States. Limited warranty includes International

Warranty Service in those countries where this statement of product is sold by IBM or IBM Business Partners (registration required).

4. Energy Star compliance: The EPA, as a matter of policy, does not endorse any particular company or its products.

5. Battery life (and recharge times) will vary depending on screen brightness, applications, features, power management, battery conditioning, and other references. CD-ROM or hard-disk drive usage may also have a significant impact on battery life.

6. Actual specifications may vary slightly depending on features and components.

7. Unless otherwise indicated, prices shown are estimated reseller prices to end users. Reseller prices may vary. IBM reserves the right to change prices and product specifications and to discontinue marketing products without notice.

For more information on IBM products, contact:

www.ibm.com
International Business Machines Corp.
One Old Orchard Road
Armonk, NY 10504
Phone: 914-765-1900
Fax: 914-288-1147

7.21   Remote Workstations (IBM ThinkPads)

Multiple remote workstation were required to work with this network. After examination of notebook computers available, I selected IBM ThinkPads. The following are typical specifications for those ThinkPads used in this network. The IBM ThinkPad model 765D has the latest power, connectivity, and 166-MHz configuration flexibility available to optimize Pentium with effectiveness and maximize investment return. Multimedia MMX high-performance features may include large technology1 13.3- or 12.1-in high-resolution displays with superb graphics, the latest Pentium processors, 13.3-in TFTs (thin-film transistors) with MMX technology, large hard drives, 65,536-color 1024×768 integrated infrared resolution, and advanced multimedia. The IBM ThinkPad also has a 3-GB hard disk, 2 MB of RAM with 32 MB of nonparity EDO memory (expandable to 104 MB), 8× CD-ROM, MPEG-1, and interface with Microsoft Windows 95.

Standard features

Pointing device type	TrackPoint III
Standard diskette size	3.5 in, 1.44 MB
Optional diskette size	3.5 in, 2.88 MB

Diskette drive configuration	External.
Keyboard type standard	Full-size, 84-key (tilt/palm rest space)
Keyboard type(s) selectable	Numeric keypad, integrated.
Product approvals and certifications	CISPR-22 Class B; CSA approvals/certifications 4: C22.2 No. 950 (Canada); FCC Class B—Part 15; IEC-950; JATE; NOM (Mexico); SASO; UK-PTT; UL-1950; VCCI Class 2 (Japan)
Warranty	Limited warranty, period and type 3: 3-year (system battery: 1 year) customer carry-in repair or provided by ThinkPad EasyServ (North America only).
Weight and dimensions	Weight 7.7 lb; dimensions $h \times w \times d = 2.2 \times 11.7 \times 9.3$ in.

Legal notices

1. The MHz reading measures internal clock speed only, not application performance. Many factors affect application performance.

2. When referring to hard-drive capacity, MB stands for million bytes and GB stands for billion bytes. Total user-accessible capacity may vary depending on operating environments.

3. For terms and conditions or copies of IBM's limited warranty, call 800-772-2227 in the United States. Limited warranty includes International Warranty Service in those countries where this statement of product is sold b by IBM or IBM Business Partners (registration required).

4. Energy Star compliance: The EPA, as a matter of policy, does not endorse any particular company or its products.

5. Battery life (and recharge times) will vary depending on screen brightness, applications, features, power management, battery conditioning, and other references. CD-ROM or hard-disk drive usage may also have a significant impact on battery life.

6. Actual specifications may vary slightly depending on features and components.

7. Unless otherwise indicated, prices shown are estimated reseller prices to end users. Reseller prices may vary. IBM reserves the right to change prices and product specifications and to discontinue marketing products without notice.

7.22   Network Hub (3Com USRobotics)

A 3Com USRobotics Enterprise Network Hub was selected to use in this network. Data-communication equipment is the single most critical link in any network. This is true because it is the central point of attachment between remote users and a backbone network, regardless of the size of the backbone or location. It is also true if all users are in the same physical location. Data-communication equipment is central to networks; as they go (fail), so goes the network. At one time *remote computing* meant having a device in one location and a terminal attached to it by a wire. USRobotics revolutionized that definition by designing the Enterprise Network Hub. This device, explained in greater detail later, is powerful.

Consider Figure 7.20, which illustrates the network designed (here) in Dallas and remote users and a remote network, both located in Chicago. Note that the remote users are connecting directly into the Dallas network via the communications Hub. In this case the remote users use their modem and connect directly to the Hub.

When remote users or remote network(s) are concerned, many issues must be considered during the planning and design phases; these include at least the following issues:

Security   Internal protocol compatibility

Reliability   Expandability

Maintenance   Internal design architecture

Ease of use   Interface standard compatibility

Security has become the single most important topic in networking, regardless of the type of network or location. Networks can have a considerable degree of security built into the design if proper components are used that implement security. Where data communication equipment is concerned, having a device that can provide a security firewall is best. Consider Figure 7.21, which shows a secure firewall implemented in the communications hub. Remote users in this illustration are required to sign on to the hub, which serves as a point of isolation. Other devices on the network require signons and passwords as well.

The USRobotics communication hub used in this network has three possible configurations regarding hub function in the network, referred to collectively as *gateway application cards:*

1. *X.25 card:* According to USRobotics, the X.25 card provides access capability to packet-switched networks. This card uses an EIA-232/v.35 interface connection point.

2. *NETServer Card:* The NETServer card functions as either a router, a terminal server, or both. Ethernet and Token Ring NICs can be used with it. USRobotics also refers to this card as the *EdgeServe card.* This card has Windows NT loaded onto it, and the functionality provided by this card is discussed later.

3. *API card:* The API card is designed to let customers design their own applications using USRobotics software development kits. Figure 7.22

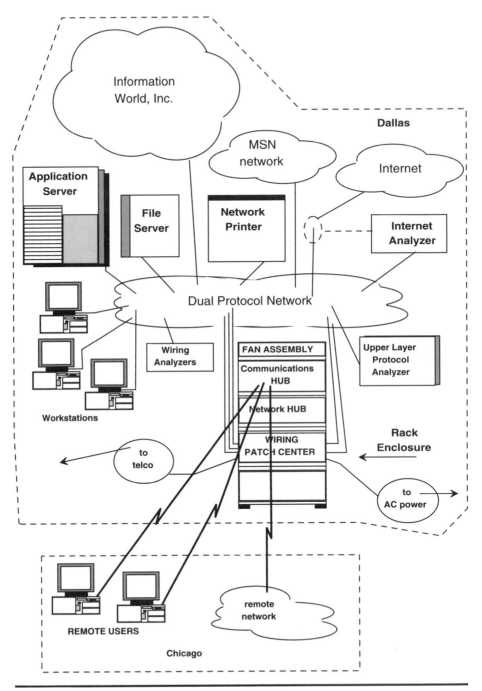

Figure 7.20   Communications Server

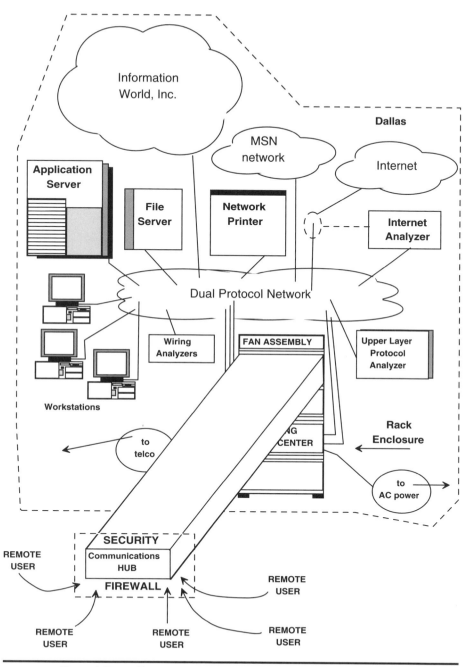

Figure 7.21 Network Firewall

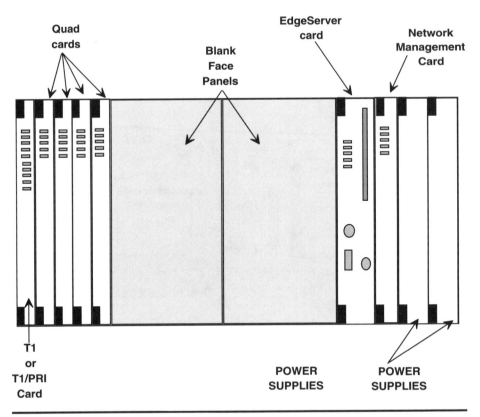

Figure 7.22 Enterprise Network Hub

shows the enterprise hub with blank face panels. These panels can be removed and other cards inserted. There are 17 slots in total. Slot 1 is the T1 card. Beginning with slot 2, analog or digital quad modem cards are located. These cards are loaded with the equivalent of four modems. The EdgeServer card is located on slots 15 and 16; the network management card is located on slot 17. The remaining slots house two power supplies. Although not shown in Figure 7.22, the undercradle portion of the hub houses approximately 16 fans to cool the components.

Reliability is another important factor for all communication equipment. The design of the USRobotics hub has reliability built into it. One example supports this observation—the hub has two power supplies, but only one is required to operate the unit. The hub has built-in redundancy even to the level of the power supply unit.

Maintenance is another part of the equation for communication equipment. The hub used in this network has remote management capability, local management capability, and easy access for those components that may need to be removed.

Operation of any communication device requires skill. Usually a fairly advanced level of skill is required for maximized use. The capability of any communication device has little to do with its ease of use, which is a design issue. Ease of use was designed into the hub used in this network. Ease of use can be measured in communication equipment by documentation provided, how thorough and detailed it is; by accessibility to configure ports, and by the ability to use the equipment in a practically failed state (should that occur). My rule of thumb is: The more complex functions a device offers, the simpler the documentation should be. The simple fact is that data-communication equipment is complex enough without humans adding another layer of complexity to it.

Another factor to analyze with data-communication equipment is protocol compatibility. This includes evaluation of upper- and lower-layer protocols. Because this hub has the EdgeServer card in it, NetBEUI, TCP/IP, and IPX upper-layer protocols are supported. Token Ring and Ethernet lower-layer protocols are supported as well. Regarding the USRobotics hub used in this network, the author notes that the use of Token Ring and Ethernet is more than sufficient because these two protocols are the dominant lower-layer protocols used in networks today.

Expandability is very important with data-communication equipment. The design of this enterprise network hub is such that a network of any size can be built around this technology. This is so because of how the equipment has been architected. It is possible with the 3Com USRobotics equipment to start a network with one or two enterprise hubs and then continue to add them until all the racks are filled.

Internal design architecture is also very important to data-communication equipment. The internal architecture of data-communication gear is the proverbial pivot on which all communication transactions hinge. The internal communications bus and the incoming port architecture constitute the foundation of the device and should be capable of handling a complete load on the device without causing hangups or system slowdown.

Interface standard compatibility is another matter to examine when you are evaluating data-communication equipment. In this network, the hub has flexibility regarding the manner in which certain connections are made. In some instances there are options for making connections. This alone makes for ease of use, installation, and maintenance. It also means that some existing equipment at your site may be usable, which can save money.

For additional information, you can contact 3Com USRobotics at

3Com USRobotics
Network Systems Division
1800 Central Road
Mount Prospect, IL 60056-2293
www.3com.com

7.23   Multimedia Components (Creative Labs)

Creative Labs was chosen as the vendor for multimedia equipment. In the past, buying IBM-compatibles, or clones, was not a problem. However, all things change. In the arena of multimedia, Creative Labs wrote the book on how to do it. Since multimedia is primarily add-on at this point in time, systems do not depend on multimedia as they do on the hard disk or monitor, for example.

However, there are some multimedia clone products. Many of these products attempt to copy what Creative Labs has already designed. In the arena of multimedia, clones are the incorrect way to invest money. The operational nature of some multimedia software is such that multimedia "clone" equipment may not be able to execute all the exploits of multimedia. This may sound strange, but it is true.

Today, systems typically have CD-ROMs, speakers, microphones, line outputs for amplifiers, line inputs for peripheral integration, and software that enables a user to create, play back, and listen to or see various data streams.

All the desktop systems in this network are IBM 350 series. I selected these units because each one could be customized to deliver a robust workload and also because this series is easily upgradable. The same is true with Creative Labs' equipment.

In each system Creative Labs' equipment serves as the multimedia hardware and software. One system has a package of multimedia equipment from Creative Labs, including an interface board, speakers, necessary cabling, microphone, CD-ROM, infrared remote control, software drivers, and various software titles for viewing and listening.

Creative Labs has designed the benchmark for multimedia systems. The significance of this should not be overlooked during the design phase of your network. Windows 95 and NT4.0 acknowledges most, if not all, Creative Labs' hardware and software. It is plug-and-play compatible. Another significant aspect of this equipment is its adaptability. Creative Labs is continually upgrading its equipment to stay competitive with other vendors; however, they support equipment and systems that are not this year's product.

Multimedia are more than a CD-ROM and speakers. Today multimedia typically encompasses a digital videodisk (DVD) and enhanced display support. More than at any other time, displays need powerful drivers and memory to store the screen of information to be presented.

Creative Labs is based in California, but has offices around the world. I recommend contacting the one closest to you for additional information about multimedia. Creative Labs can be reached on the Internet at *www.sound-blaster.com* and at

Creative Labs
1901 McCarthy Blvd.
Milpitas, CA 95035

Creative Technology Ltd.
67 Ayer Rajah Crescent #03-18
Singapore 0513

Creative Labs Technical Support
1523 Cimarron Plaza
Stillwater, OK 74075

Creative Labs Ltd.
Blanchardstown Industrial Park
Blanchardstown, Budlin 15
Ireland

7.24   Ethernet and SCSI Adapters (Adaptec Corp.)

In the initial phase of network design I realized that devices using a Small Computer Serial Interface (SCSI) were going to be part of the network. Consequently, I determined that the Adaptec Corporation would be the best company to use for SCSI adapters. On initial investigation with Adaptec, I discovered that they offer some very powerful Ethernet adapters. Information on the SCSI and Ethernet adapters used in this network is provided here.

The Adaptec AHA-2940 SCSI adapter is used in this network. Some of this product's family highlights include

- 20 MB/s UltraSCSI data transfer rate

- High-performance Busmaster architecture for improved system performance

- Tested for compatibility with more than 200 systems and peripherals from major manufacturers

- Compatible with all major operating systems

- Easy plug-and-play installation

The AHA-2940 Ultra host adapter delivers UltraSCSI speed for demanding professional applications and high-performance peripherals. With its Busmastering architecture and advanced SCSI features, the AHA-2940 Ultra host adapter improves system performance, especially in multitasking environments. In addition, the AHA-2940 Ultra adapter offers unsurpassed system and peripheral compatibility.

By doubling the data transfer speed using UltraSCSI technology, the AHA-2940 Ultra host adapter doubles the maximum data transfer rate on the SCSI bus from 10 to 20 MB/s. By increasing the throughput rate between peripherals and the desktop system, the AHA-2940 Ultra adapter accelerates system performance and user productivity.

In addition to UltraSCSI speed, the AHA-2940 Ultra host adapter features a high-performance Busmastering architecture that regulates data movement directly between peripherals and system memory. The on-board Adaptec PhaseEngine RISC processor takes over I/O processing from the CPU, which frees it for other tasks. The result is lower CPU utilization and noticeably faster response time.

The AHA-2940 Ultra host adapter makes true multitasking possible. SCSI technology offers unique features, including disconnect/reconnect, tagged command queuing, and multithreaded I/O, which allow the system CPU to access data on multiple peripheral devices simultaneously.

All Adaptec host adapters are rigorously tested with hundreds of different SCSI peripherals and systems, which makes them the most compatible and reliable host adapters in the marketplace. The AHA-2940 Ultra adapter is also fully compatible with all popular desktop and network operating systems, including DOS, Windows, Windows NT, Windows 95, OS/2, NetWare, and UNIX.

Installing the AHA-2940 Ultra host adapter is quick and easy. Simply insert the host adapter in the PCI slot, and the system BIOS will assign resources to it. Using the SCSISelect utility, users can then fine-tune the performance of the adapter by making on-screen choices from the utility menu. Software automatically determines what hardware is present, loads the correct drivers, and modifies system configuration files. Completely compatible with Windows 95, the AHA-2940 Ultra host adapter utilizes advanced plug-and-play features that automatically assign IDs and control termination.

The AHA-2940 Ultra kit provides everything necessary for connecting high-performance SCSI peripherals to PCs and workstations. It features the AHA-2940AU host adapter board with an internal cable, complete user documentation, and Adaptec EZ-SCSI software for simple installation. Kit contents include

- AHA-2940AU PCI-to-UltraSCSI host adapter board.

- Adaptec 7800 Family Manager Set software drivers for Windows NT, Windows 95, OS/2 2.x and 3.x, NetWare 3.x and 4.x, SCO Unix 3.2.x, and UnixWare 1.x and 2.x. Adaptec EZ-SCSI software for DOS, Windows, Windows NT, Windows 95, and Windows for Workgroups includes applications such as SCSI Backup (Backup Basics), QuickScan, CD Player, Photo CD Viewer (Magic Lantern), Advanced Power Management, SCSI Interrogator, SCSI Disk Partitioner, SCSITutor, and SCSIBench. It also provides device support for hard disks, removable disks, MO, CD-ROM, CD-Recordable, Photo CD, and tape drives and scanners.

- Standard, three-position internal SCSI ribbon cable.

- Complete user documentation.

The Adaptec AHA-2040 technical specifications are

Computer bus	PCI local bus
Interface protocol	Busmaster DMA

Host bus data transfer rate	Up to 133 MB/s burst rate
Peripheral bus	8-bit Ultra SCSI
SCSI synchronous data transfer rate	20 MB/s
SCSI asynchronous data transfer rate	6 MB/s
Device protocol	SCSI-1, SCSI-2, SCSI-3, UltraSCSI
Advanced SCSI features	Advanced SCSI Programming Interface (ASPI)-compliant, multithreaded I/O (up to 255 tasks simultaneously), scatter/gather, tagged queuing, disconnect/reconnect, synchronous and asynchronous Fast and Wide, Bootable from attached disks
External connector	50-pin high-density
Electrical drivers	Single-ended, active, programmable via SCSISelect
Hard-disk capacity	Extended translation supports drive capacity up to 8 GB per disk
Device support	Supports up to seven (7) disks under DOS 5.0; electrical termination—single-ended, active, software-controlled
I/O operating environment	Windows 95, Windows 3.1, Windows NT, Windows for Workgroups, DOS, IBM OS/2 2.x and 3.x, NetWare 3.12 and 4.x, SCO UNIX 3.2.x, and UnixWare 1.x and 2.x. Mean time between failures (MTBF): 544,264.3 h (Bellcore, TR-NWT-000332, Method I, QL-I)
Physical and environmental specifications	Dimensions: $l \times h$ = 4.75 × 3.5 in (12 × 8.75 cm). Operating temperature 0 to 55°C, storage temperature −55 to 85°C. Humidity (operating) 10–90%, noncondensing

Another Adaptec component used in the network is the AHA-2940 UW (ultrawide). Product highlights for this adapter are

- 40 MB/s Ultra Wide SCSI data transfer rate

- Connection for up to 15 SCSI peripheral devices

- Designed for true multitasking

- Tested for compatibility with hundreds of systems and peripherals from major manufacturers

The AHA-2940 Ultra Wide host adapter is the ideal PCI-to-SCSI host adapter for entry-level servers and workstations. It moves data fast—up to 40 MB/s. And it connects up to 15 SCSI devices for expanded storage capacity. In addition, the AHA-2940 Ultra Wide adapter delivers unrivaled system and peripheral compatibility.

Combining UltraSCSI speed and 16-bit wide SCSI data transfers, the AHA-2940 Ultra Wide host adapter moves data on the SCSI bus at a maximum rate of 40 MB/s. By increasing the throughput rate between peripherals and the system CPU, the AHA-2940 Ultra Wide adapter accelerates system performance and user productivity.

The AHA-2940 Ultra Wide host adapter delivers expanded connectivity to meet the storage capacity requirements of server environments. It supports up to 15 SCSI devices simultaneously. Both 8- and 16-bit devices can be configured in any combination for maximum configuration flexibility.

The AHA-2940 Ultra Wide host adapter makes true multitasking possible. SCSI technology offers unique features, including disconnect/reconnect, tagged command queuing, and multithreaded I/O, which allow the system CPU to move data to and from multiple peripheral devices simultaneously.

All Adaptec host adapters are rigorously tested with hundreds of different SCSI peripherals and systems, which makes them the most compatible and reliable host adapters in the marketplace. The AHA-2940 Ultra Wide adapter is fully compatible with all popular desktop and network operating systems, including Microsoft Windows 3.1, DOS, Windows NT, Windows 95, OS/2, NetWare, and UNIX. Under Windows 95, the AHA-2940 Ultra Wide adapter utilizes advanced plug-and-play features that automatically assign IDs and control termination.

The AHA-2940 Ultra Wide kit provides everything necessary for connecting high-performance SCSI peripherals to workstations and entry-level servers. It features the AHA-2940 UW host adapter board with internal SCSI cables, and complete user documentation. The kit also includes Adaptec EZ-SCSI software for simple installation and the SCSISelect utility for easy on-screen performance tuning.

The complete AHA-2940 Ultra Wide kit includes

- AHA-2940 UW PCI-to-Wide UltraSCSI host adapter board
- Adaptec 7800 Family Manager Set software drivers for Windows NT, Windows 95, OS/2 2.x and 3.x, Netware 3.x and 4.x, SCO Unix 3.2.x, and UnixWare 1.x and 2.x
- Adaptec EZ-SCSI software for Windows NT, Windows 95, Windows for Workgroups, and DOS
- Applications such as SCSI Tape Backup (Backup Basics), QuickScan, CD Player, Photo CD Viewer (Magic Lantern), Advanced Power Management, SCSI Interrogator, SCSI Disk Partitioner, SCSITutor, SCSIBench
- Device support for hard disks, removable disks, MO, CD-ROM, CD-Recordable, Photo CD, and tape drives and scanners
- One 3-position, 68-pin UltraSCSI internal ribbon cable
- One 3-position, 50-pin UltraSCSI internal ribbon cable

- Complete user documentation
- Five-year warranty card

The technical specifications for the AHA-2940 UW are:

Computer bus	PCI local bus
Interface protocol	Busmaster DMA
Host bus burst data (transfer) rate	133 MB/s
Peripheral bus	8- and 16-bit Wide UltraSCSI
SCSI synchronous data rate	40 MB/s
SCSI asynchronous data rate	3.3 MB/s
Device protocol	SCSI-1, SCSI-2, SCSI-3, Wide UltraSCSI
Advanced SCSI features	Multithreaded I/O (up to 255 tasks simultaneously), scatter/gather, disconnect/reconnect, tagged command queuing, synchronous and asynchronous data transfer
External connector	68-pin high-density
Hard-disk capacity	Extended translation supports drive capacity up to 8 GB per disk
Device support	Up to 15 devices under DOS 5.0 and above
Electrical termination	Automatic, active, programmable via SCSISelect
Operating environment	Microsoft Windows 3.x, DOS, Windows NT, Windows 95, OS/2 2.x and 3.x, NetWare 3.12 and 4.x, SCO UNIX 3.2.x, and UnixWare 1.x and 2.x.
Physical and environmental specifications	Dimensions: $l \times h = 6.87 \times 3.87$ in (17.0×9.5 cm). Operating temperature 0 to 55°C, storage temperature -55 to 85°C. Humidity (operating) 10–90% noncondensing. MTBF 494,641 h, per Bellcore TR-NWT-000332, Issue 4, Method 1

Another Adaptec product was used in the network discussed in later chapters; it is the Cogent four-port Ethernet adapter by Adaptec, interface product highlights of which include

- Four connectors support four separate network segments, all at full bandwidth.
- All four channels operate at independent speeds for maximum flexibility (10, 20, 100, 200 Mbps).
- Full-duplex Fast Ethernet on UTP, for up to 800 Mbps throughput on one adapter.
- NWay Autosensing of maximum line speed on 10/100 TX adapters.
- Duralink Failover offers FDDI-like port resiliency for optimum availability.

Adaptec's Cogent Quartet adapters are the ultimate performance solution for PCI servers operating on Fast Ethernet and Ethernet networks. With four channels on a single board and full-duplex support, these adapters have the features today's 32-bit Fast Ethernet and Ethernet servers need to handle users' graphics, multimedia, database, and mission-critical applications.

These innovative adapters provide ample bandwidth for even the most demanding networks. They support up to four network segments on separate channels for a cumulative throughput of up to 800 Mbps (depending on model). The Quartet adapters multiply flexibility, performance, and cabling compatibility by four, and provide easy migration paths from Ethernet to Fast Ethernet network solutions.

The key features and benefits of the four-port Ethernet adapters are as follows.

Scalability

Using the Quartet adapter, information systems organizations can increase the total network bandwidth without the need to buy a new server. Although the PCI bus offers 132 Mbps of bandwidth, typically only a limited number of slots are available, thereby restricting the number of segments that a server can handle. The Quartet adapters solve this problem by providing the power of four Fast Ethernet, or Ethernet, segments on a single adapter. These adapters use an on-board PCI-to-PCI bridge chip to extend the machine's internal bus. Multiple Quartets can be installed on each server for even greater overall bandwidth.

Flexible configuration

The Quartet adapters support all four network channels at full cable bandwidth. Each channel is fully independent and is automatically configured by the system BIOS. Each adapter's four ID nodes can be customized at load time.

The Autosense feature of the 10/100-Mbps models allows the adapters to automatically detect the network's maximum line speed. No adapter configuration is necessary. For maximum flexibility, the Autosense feature is compatible with all 10- and 100-Mbps devices, including those without NWay line speed negotiation.

With the Quartet T4 model, cabling plant upgrades aren't necessary. They run on any UTP cable currently running 10BaseT and can be used in the future to run at 100 Mbps, providing an easy migration path.

Resilient, redundant links

Duralink Failover drivers included with each 10/100 TX adapter, ensure the integrity of mission-critical Ethernet server links. Duralink Failover establishes an FDDI-like port resiliency with both active and hot-standby links. In the event that the active link fails, the standby link is automatically activated to preserve the network link and maintain the server's availability. Duralink Manager, also included, is a data compilation tool that simplifies adapter monitoring and configuration.

Full duplex mode

Full Duplex Fast Ethernet (FDFE) and Full Duplex Ethernet (FDE) capabilities double the cumulative system throughput in Fast Ethernet and Ethernet networks. Servers using the Quartet adapters can handle, receive, and transmit requests simultaneously, over multiple ports, so workstations benefit from much faster service.

Designed for performance

The Quartet adapters' efficient bus master design minimizes CPU utilization for optimum throughput. Independent transmit and receive FIFO buffers (first-in, first-out memory) for each port on board, and a powerful DMA capability mean consistently high performance, even during periods of peak network activity.

The following is a Cogent-to-Adaptec Model Number Conversion Chart:

Cogent PCI Quartet

New model #	Previous model #	Bus speed	Interface Pentium	Pentium Pro
ANA-6944A/TX	N/A	PCI 4 × 10/100 Mbps	RJ-45 (4)	X
ANA-6944/T4	EM440T4-PCI	PCI 10/100 Mbps	RJ-45 (4)	X
ANA-6940/TX	EM400TX-PCI	PCI 4 × 100 Mbps	RJ-45 (4)	X
ANA-6904/BNC	EM964BNC	PCI 4 × 10 Mbps	BNC (4)	X
ANA-6904	EM964TP	PCI 4 × 10 Mbps	RJ-45 (4)	X

The four-port Ethernet adapter technical specifications include the following:

Systems supported	PCI local bus systems based on Intel, DEC Alpha, MIPS, and PowerPC processors
Bus interface	PCI, 32-bit Busmaster (PCI 2.1 for ANA-6944A/TX)
Ethernet controller	DECchip LAN coprocessor chip (4)
FIFO buffer memory	10-Mbps models—256 bytes transmit, 256 bytes receive (per port); 100-Mbps models—24 kB transmit, 4 kB receive per port
Hardware interrupts	PCI interrupt A, supports shared interrupts Base I/O or memory address: assigned by BIOS
PCI configuration space	Supports DWORD, WORD, and BYTE access
Reliability	Calculated MTBF > 100,000 h
Power requirements	5 V at 2 A max (ANA-6904), 5 V at 3.5 A max (all other models)

Environmental operating range	Temperature 0 to 50°C
Relative humidity	5–85% noncondensing
Altitude	3000 m max
Interface connections	10-Mbps models—RJ-45 female (4), or BNC (4); RJ-45 supports Categories 3, 4, and 5 UTP, and Type 1 STP BNC supports RG-58 coax cable; 100-Mbps models—RJ-45 female (4), T4 model supports Categories 3, 4, and 5 UTP and Type 1 STP for 10BaseT and 100BaseT4 operation. TX models support Categories 3, 4, and 5 UTP and Type 1 STP for 10BaseT operation, and Category 5 UTP and Type 1 STP for 100BaseT operation. Full-duplex support on all RJ-45 connectors on all models for 10BaseT operation; additional full-duplex support on TX models for 100BaseTX operation
Dimensions	9.75 × 4 in to conform to PCI Long Card specifications (ANA-6904 models); 12 × 4.2 in to conform to PCI Long Card specifications (ANA-6944 models)
Standards compliance	IEEE 802.3 10Base2, IEEE 802.3 10BaseT, IEEE 802.3u 100Base-TX, IEEE 802.3u 100BaseT4; FCC Class A, CE Class A
Drivers available	3.5-in diskette—Novell NetWare 3.x, 4.x, and SFT III, Windows for Workgroups (NDIS 3.0), Windows 95, Windows NTO for Intel, DEC Alpha, PowerPC, and MIPS platforms, DOS NDIS (NDIS 2.0), OS/2 Warp (NDIS 2.0), MS LAN Manager, Artisoft LANtastic, Banyan Vines DOS client, FTP PC/TCP, DEC PathWorks, Sun Solaris, SCO OpenServer, SCO UnixWare (not all drivers are available for every adapter), Duralink for NetWare and Windows NT servers
Duralink	3.5-in diskette—Duralink Failover and Duralink Manager for ANA-6944A/TX (Cogent EM 440TX PCI) at no charge
Diagnostic LEDs	Link integrity for each channel (4); network activity for each channel (4)
Warranty	Limited lifetime warranty

For additional information about these and other Adaptec products, contact the company at one of the following addresses:

Adaptec Asia
Block 1002
Jalan Bukit Merah, #06-07
Singapore 159456
Phone: 65-273-7300
Fax: 65-273-0163

Adaptec Japan, Ltd.
Kiocho Hills, 4F
3-32 Kiocho
Chiyoda-ku, Tokyo, 102, Japan
Phone: 81-3-5276-9882
Fax: 81-3-5276-9884

Adaptec Europe
Dreve Richelle 161
Building A, 2d Floor
B1410 Waterloo
Belgium
Phone: 32-2-352-34-11
Fax: 32-2-352-34-00

Additional sales offices

France
Phone: 33-1-3452-3434
Fax: 33-1-3452-3432

Germany
Phone: 49-89-4564060
Fax: 49-89-4560615

United Kingdom
Phone: 44-1252-811200
Fax: 44-1252-811212

Latin America (Miami)
Phone: 305-265-1387
Fax: 305-265-0399

Adaptec, Inc.
691 South Milpitas Boulevard
Milpitas, CA 95035
Phone: 408-945-8600
Fax: 408-262-2533

Additional information can be obtained from Adaptec as follows:

Literature	1-800-934-2766 (USA and Canada) or 510-732-3829
Pre-sales support	1-800-442-7274 (USA and Canada) or 408-957-7274
World Wide Web	*http://www.adaptec.com*
Internet ftp server	*ftp.adaptec.com*
Adaptec USA Bulletin Board Service (BBS)	408-945-7727 (up to 28,800 bps, using 8 bits, 1 stop bit, no parity)
Interactive fax	303-684-3400

Adaptec, the Adaptec logo, AHA, SCSISelect, EZ-SCSI, SCSI Interrogator, SCSI Tape Backup, SCSITutor, ThreadMark, and Magic Lantern are trademarks of Adaptec, Inc., which may be registered in some jurisdictions. Microsoft, Windows, the Windows logo, and Windows 95 are registered trademarks, and Windows NT and the Windows NT logo are trademarks of Microsoft Corporation used under license. All other trademarks used are owned by their respective owners. Information supplied by Adaptec, Inc. is believed to be accurate and reliable at the time of printing, but Adaptec, Inc. assumes no responsibility for any errors that may appear in this section. Adaptec, Inc. reserves the right, without notice, to make changes in product design or specifications. Information is subject to change without notice.

7.25   Network Security and Virus Protection Software (McAfee)

Computer and network security is probably the single most important issue today. I predict that it will become 3 to 5 times as important as it is today. Viruses, bots, and all sorts of antidata objects exist within the Internet. Most people have no idea how vulnerable parts of the Internet actually are. Even "service providers" are more vulnerable than they will admit. The sad fact is every company—yes, every company, of any size—that the author knows of has disinformation arsenals to make people feel secure. Management at the higher levels in most corporations operate in ignorance of these matters because this is legally safe for them and prudent they do so; ask and this statement will be denied, but remember where you read it. I point this out because I want you to be aware of this problem. There is no magic program or anything else that can make networks safe. Good programs exist—the ones chosen and implemented in this network are examples; however, no single program can render your network 100 percent immune.

Remember this during the design phase of your network. Networks can have security designed into them from the outset. Security in your network needs to be factored into every area from electricity provision, telephone access, and every other aspect that categorizes your network.

The McAfee software suite was selected to meet the needs of this network. Part of the reason for this is the amount of antivirus programs and information they have—and the fact that these work. The second reason for selecting McAfee was the frequency with which they update their antivirus software. At present McAfee has over 250 highly technical documents available on viruses; likewise, they claim to have information about the 1000 most common viruses. When the security analysis for this network was complete, the following software packages were selected and are used in this network:

VirusScan

Desktop Security Suite

Commuter

QuickBackup

McAfee Service Desk

NetShield

WebScan

PCCrypto

These products have been implemented to varying degrees on each system. Each program's benefits and highlights are presented here.

VirusScan

This program may well be the most popular antivirus software in the marketplace today. It operates with Windows 3.1, 95, Windows NT4.0, DOS, and OS/2. It is software that, once installed, operates automatically on power-up. It can be used at will once a system is operational. This program requires minimal space but does a professional job. This program is NCSAA-certified.

Author's policy. I recommend that you dedicate a system for testing software, initially. Then I recommend installing McAfee VirusScan. Then scan each and every diskette you have. That's right. It does not matter if it takes someone 2 months. Even new diskettes out of the box, every diskette you receive from a manufacturer must be scanned. You say: "But Ed, isn't this going a bit too far?" I'll say this. One year (I won't say which) I bought some software; it was new. It came from the original vendor in shrink-wrapped plastic. The shrink-wrapped diskettes were enclosed in a box with a seal on it. The box with a seal on it was shrink-wrapped. I didn't think anything about it. Within 10 minutes after opening the software, it brought one of my systems to its knees. The diskette had a virus. How do I know? I checked it personally. How do I know the system it went into was "clean"? It was, and is, my benchmark system. Furthermore, those who know me know that nobody, not anyone, puts a disk in my systems except me. It took me 2 days to recover the system. Consider this next time you stick a new program on diskette in your system. You can pay now or gamble, but remember that the odds are against you.

Desktop Security Suite

This program also operates with Windows 3.1, 95, and NT4.0. This suite of programs includes antivirus software, backup abilities, and encryption technology. The virus program is VirusScan. QuickBackup operates with Zip and Jaz drives, the Internet, or rewritable CD-ROMs. The backup program enables hourly backup or on demand, whichever is best for you. The cryptographic part of the suite provides 160-bit encryption, enabling users to encrypt files before they are sent over the Internet and also permitting network traffic to be encrypted between Windows-based computers and those running UNIX.

Commuter

Commuter is more than just a communication software. It also includes virus protection, desktop storage management, electronic mail, personal information organizer, calendar, to-do lists, and a contact manager.

QuickBackup

This backup program works with Windows 95 and NT4.0. It enables transparent backup of files to SCSI, Zip, and Jaz drives. An icon-driven program makes for ease of use. The program installs quickly and works well. It does provide encryption protection and Internet support.

Service desk

The service desk product is powerful. It is actually multiple products in one box. It works with Windows 3.1, 95, and NT4.0. The product lets customer support personnel have access to information about the customer and make a remote connection to a system reported with a problem. The package comes with the ability to distribute software. The package also includes a system diagnostic part for support personnel to use with customers.

NetShield

NetShield uses McAfee's proprietary code, called *Code Trace, Code Matrix,* and *Code Poly.* The product actually operates in an NT environment in native mode. The program takes full advantage of NT's server/client remote task distribution capability. The product supports real-time scanning during operation of other tasks.

WebScan

The WebScan product is designed to detect viruses within a browser. It examines downloads and email attachments, making it a power addition to any desktop or laptop system communicating in networks today. It also provides a cybersitter that blocks out unwanted Web sites and chatgroups. Coverage of the program includes examination of `.doc`, `lzip.` `exe. zrc. arj.`, and other file types.

PCCrypto

PCCrypto is used to secure documents and other data files created by anyone using computers. It can encrypt graphics, spreadsheets, and text documents. It uses a 160-bit blowfish encryption mechanism. The package consumes a minimal amount of space and is one of the most powerful, if not *the* most powerful, tools of its kind on the market today.

Other McAfee products and information

McAfee has other products that may meet your needs. I recommend that you contact them. My experience with them has always been pleasant, and their staff are very informative. They can be reached on the Internet at *www.mcafee.com* or at

McAfee
2710 Walsh Avenue
Santa Clara, CA 95051
Phone: 408-988-3832

McAfee Canada
178 Main Street
Unionville, Ontario
Canada L3R 2G9

McAfee France S.A.
50 rue de Londres
75008 Paris, France

McAfee (UK) Ltd.
Hayley House, London Road
Bracknell, Berkshire GR12 2TH
United Kingdom

McAfee Europe B.V.
Orlypein 81—Busitel 1
1043 DS Amsterdam
The Netherlands

McAfee Deutschland GmbH
Industriestrasse 1
D-82110 Germering
Germany

7.26 Network Tape Drive (SONY)

Early in the design phase for this network I realized the need for a network tape drive. After reviewing literature on tape drives, I selected the SDX-300C, in Sony's new SDX series of tape drives and media. The ability to store large amounts of data and retrieve information quickly is critical in today's applications. Tape storage and retrieval has been revolutionized by Sony's award-winning Memory-in-Cassette (MIC) architecture. The MIC consists of a memory chip built into the data cartridge which holds the system's log and other user-definable information. Applications that benefit from MIC's capabilities include hierarchical storage management, video server, film editing, and real-time data acquisition.

SDX-300C features and specifications include the following:

1. *High-speed data transfer:* With a recording density of 116 kbpi (kilobits per inch), the SDX-300C offers a sustained data transfer rate of 3.0 MB/s (native) to over 6 MB/s (compressed*). The drive uses a fast/wide SCSI with a burst transfer rate of 20 MB/s. It also has a large cartridge capacity; the SDX-300C family can store 25 GB (native) or 50 GB (compressed*) on a single 8-mm data cartridge.

2. *System design convenience:* The SDX-300C family includes a fast/wide SCSI interface with a 68-pin single-ended or differential interface or an 80-pin SCA connector and a self-cooling design.

3. *Exceptional reliability:* Utilizing Sony's extensive technology expertise in 8-mm tape recording, the SDX-300C products are designed to provide 200,000-h MTBF, an average head life of 50,000 h and an average of 30,000 media uses.

4. *Memory-in-Cassette:* Incorporating a flash memory chip within the data cartridge, the SDX-300C provides ultrafast media load and fast file search as well as the ability for applications to read and write to the memory chip.

5. *Media compatibility:* The SDX-300C family is designed exclusively for use with Sony's Advanced Metal Evaporated (AME) media technology incorporating pure cobalt metallization with a superdurable diamondlike carbon coating (DLC). AME tape is available with or without Memory-In-Cassette (MIC). Specifications reflect 2:1 data compression. MTBF, head life, and media use specifications are averages based on normal office environmental conditions. Actual experience may vary.

Other specifications are as follows:

Drive type	3.5-in (8-mm) tape drive
Media	170-m AME tape: SDX-T3N (without MIC), SDX-T3C (with MIC)
Interface	SCSI-2 fast/wide, single-ended or differential
Data compression (SDX-300C)	IBM's Adaptive Lossless Data Compression (ALDC)
Capacity	25 GB (native), 50 GB (compressed*)
Sustained transfer rate	3 MB/s (native), 6 MB/s (compressed*)
Burst transfer rate	Asynchronous 5.0 MB/s, Synchronous 20.0 MB/s
Linear recording density	116,000 bpi
Recording block length	Variable or fixed

---

*Specifications reflect 2:1 data compression.

Average media load time	20 s (without MIC), 10 s (with MIC)
Average access time	55 s (without MIC), 27 s (with MIC)
Search speed	60 in/s (without MIC), 120 in/s (with MIC)
Rewind speed	120 in/s (150 times nominal)
Drum rotational speed	4800 rpm (r/min)
Buffer size	4 MB
Uncorrectable error rate	Less than 10 to 17 bits
MTBF	200,000 power-on hours (POH)
Average R/W (read/write) head life	50,000 tape contact hours
Media uses	30,000 end-to-end passes
Vibration (operating)	0.25 G peak, half sine wave of 50 to 500 Hz (swept)
Shock (operating)	5.0 G peak, half sine wave of 3 ms duration
Altitude	10,000 ft
Maximum wet-bulb temperature	26°C
Operating temperature	5 to 40°C (40 to 104°F)
Storage temperature	-40 to 70°C (-40 to 158°F)
Operating humidity	20–80% (noncondensing)
Power requirement	Dc 5 V $\pm$ 5 percent, dc 12 V $\pm$ 10 percent (internal); ac 100 to 200/220 to 240 V (external)
Power consumption	12 W (average, internal), 21 W (average, external)
Dimensions	$h \times w \times d$ = 1.62 $\times$ 4.0 $\times$ 6.10 in (41.1 $\times$ 101.6 $\times$ 154.9 mm) internal, 2.28 $\times$ 7.44 $\times$ 10.31 in (57.9 $\times$ 189 $\times$ 261.9 mm) external
Weight	1 lb 11 oz (765 g) internal, 4 lb 14 oz (2.2 kg) external
Models	SDX-300C 68-pin single-ended, SDX-302C 80-pin SCA, SDX-310C 68-pin differential, SDX-S300C/NB external single-ended

Specifications reflect 2:1 data compression. MTBF, head life, and media use specifications are averages based on normal office environmental conditions. Actual experience may vary. Nonmetric weights and measurements are approximate.

7.27   Computer Cabling (Belkin)

This network is no different from the rest; for example, there is always a need for special cabling and adapters. For this need I elected to use Belkin. Belkin has a wide variety of peripheral cabling and accessories, and they make the best products on the market.

The following is a brief list of the components I used from Belkin:

DB9 female/female gender bender   DB25 female/female gender bender

DB9 male/male gender bender   IEEE 1284 printer cable, 20 ft

DB15 female/female gender bender   IEEE 1284 printer cable, 35 ft

DB15 male/male gender bender   DB25 serial cable

SCSI-2 interface cable   DB9 serial cable

SCSI DB68 terminator   Super VGA monitor extension cable

DB25 male/male gender bender

All these cables and accessories, and others, were used in this network. I selected Belkin because they make the best computer and printer cables on the market. They also have the best designed and highest-quality gender benders.

I strongly recommend that you consider Belkin when you need gender benders and cables, especially when cables are required to meet specifications such as the IEEE 1284. You can reach them at

www.belkin.com
Belkin Components
501 West Walnut Street
Compton, CA 90220-5030
Phone: 310-604-2000

7.28   Infrared Network Interface [JetEye (Extended Systems)]

For an infrared network interface I selected JetEye, by Extended Systems. This device enables portable workstations to be moved about and perform network printing via their infrared port. To meet the need for printing, it is probably one of the most cost-effective methods of network connection available.

The JetEye features include

- Line-of-site infrared transmission for any infrared portable computer
- Supports Windows NT, Windows 95, Windows 98, TCP/IP, NetWare, LAN Manager, and LAN Server
- Supports operating distances up to three feet away

The JetEye used in this network is dedicated to the ThinkPads which are remote workstations as well as portable. Each has been configured to operate with the JetEye infrared network interface.

For more information, contact:

Extended Systems
5777 North Meeker Avenue
Boise, ID 83713
Phone: 800-235-7576

7.29   Power Protection

Power protection in any computing, network, or peripheral equipment is not optional. I have a standard reply when asked if such-and-such needs to be protected with power protection equipment: "If you can afford to throw away any or all of your equipment, replace it, and not be negatively impacted by downtime, then don't use power protection equipment." With that in mind, let us examine the power protection equipment used in this network.

I determined that the following were needed to adequately protect the network components:

- Data shield parallel dataline surge suppressors
- Data shield 10BaseT surge suppressors
- Data shield dial-up line surge suppressors
- Data shield AUI 802.3 surge suppressors
- Data shield DB9 surge suppressors
- Data shield DB-25 serial surge suppressors

The data shield protectors are used at all points in the network. These inline devices are used with serial, parallel, 10BaseT, AUI, modem cable, and DB9 connections. Additionally, various electrical protection equipment also has telephone line spike/surge protection that is used to protect all incoming phone lines.

Tripp-Lite has other power protection equipment. I recommend that you contact them at

www.tripplite.com
Tripp-Lite
500 North Orleans
Chicago, IL 60610

7.30   Summary

This chapter presented equipment used in this network. It is important to do most of the initial network planning on marker board and/or paper. Once this is done, one can begin to acquire equipment and build the network. I think it is best to design the network, acquire the equipment, and then build the network. This approach makes the installation, operation, and maintenance much easier.

The following chapter go into more detail about the network, the equipment used, how it works, and how to troubleshoot it.

8

Network Troubleshooting Case Study: Part 2 (How to Baseline)

How to baseline a network begins with understanding the network's major functions, where its users are, and the equipment that is used on the network. This chapter presents some of the equipment used in my network, information that I use to maintain my baseline reports, and what you should consider when you begin to baseline your network.

8.1 How to Baseline Your Network

First, make a list of your computer equipment. Depending on your experience or situation, this may vary. For example, the following is a simple list of the major components in this network. This is an example of the high-level list you should have reflecting your equipment. The following list is somewhat similar to the one in the beginning of Chapter 7; however, this list focuses on what is installed and required to make the network function. Operation of these network components is explained later in this chapter.

- Electrical wiring
- Copper-based network infrastructure
- Fiber-optic backbone components
- The author's fiber-optic backbone
- Network analyzer
- Network UPS

- Network computers
- Remote workstations
- Network communication hub

The following steps will help you begin the baseline process:

1. Make an inventory of equipment you have in your network.
2. List the equipment by user, function, and location such as office and floor. (Include any geographic description as appropriate.)
3. If possible, maintain all the original documentation pertinent to each piece of equipment in your network. Organize it in such a way that it makes sense for your company or group and for anyone who might have to come along behind or with you to fix a problem.
4. Maintain these files in a fireproof location, and preferably a maximum-security location.
5. Identify a person or persons who could take your place in case of sickness, accident, or an otherwise unplanned event that could cause your absence.
6. After some time is passed, or depending on your background or experience, list the spare parts needed for your equipment; it never hurts to have a few spare parts available.
7. Have the names, addresses, phone numbers, or whatever information is appropriate for the following people or agencies: electrician, plumber, fire-fighters, police, paramedics and ambulance service, emergency water shutoff service, and HVAC technician.

8.2   Electrical and Environmental Aspects

One important aspect of any network is the electrical wiring throughout the facility. Be sure you have the names, addresses (if appropriate), and telephone numbers of the electricians who did some of the original work if possible.

You should also keep a record of the temperature of the room(s) where equipment is located, and these records should be continuously updated during network implementation.

Electrical

The electrical part of your network should include surge protection as well as distribution of electricity to your equipment. This could seem trivial now, but should you encounter a problem with your network in the future, you will find this level of preparation well-heeded advice!

First, take readings of appropriate network devices. Figure 8.1 is the first example reading, measuring the voltage, frequency, and amperage of a notebook computer and ac adapter.

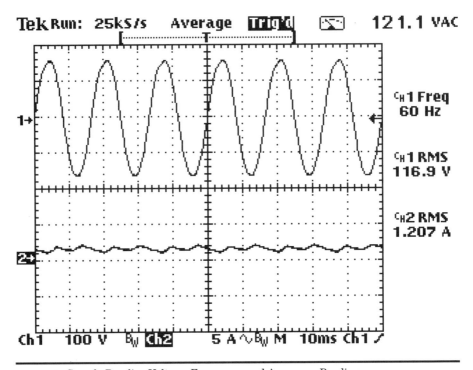

Figure 8.1 Sample Baseline Voltage, Frequency, and Amperage Reading

Figure 8.2 is another sample reading from the same line as shown in Figure 8.1, but at a later time.

Consider now Figure 8.3, which is a baseline voltage, frequency, rms V ac, and amperage reading on initial power-on of the network printer (IBM Network Printer 17).

The reading in Figure 8.4 is similar to that in Figure 8.3, but taken between drum cycles of the printer.

The reading in Figure 8.5 was taken when the network printer drum element cycled on and began heating.

Figures such as these shown here are really important when you need a baseline reference to "normal" conditions. I recommend that you take readings such as these (or have an electrician do it). Then, file these readings for future reference to determine proper operation of the printer with regard to electrical current under normal circumstances.

Figure 8.6 shows the site load center, the load center to data center, the data center, and UPS.

As many details as you can obtain about your site and the electrical aspects of your environment will greatly assist you when you need this level of information for troubleshooting.

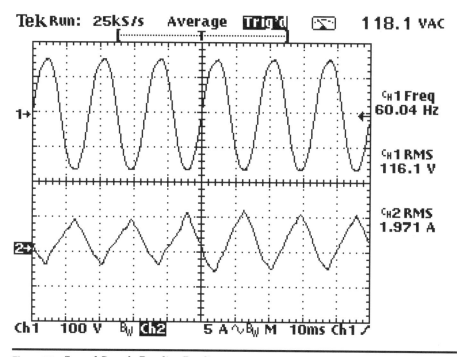

Figure 8.2 Second Sample Baseline Reading

Environmental

Another important aspect that is parallel to the electrical readings is temperature readings. It is also good to maintain records of temperature readings reflecting the environment over a period of time. Once you have the network installed, capture a temperature reading such as shown in Figure 8.7, which is an initial reading at the beginning of a business day in the network data center. Note that the temperature reading is displayed in degrees Fahrenheit.

Consider Figure 8.8, which shows a reading taken with the same instrument, in the same location, about 2 h after all equipment was powered on and operating. Notice the temperature has risen by approximately 4 degrees.

Now consider Figure 8.9, which shows a reading taken with the same instrument, in the same place, only at a later time during the same day. Note that the temperature now has climbed 6 degrees, and is now 82.3°F. Since the initial reading just a short time earlier in the day, the room temperature has risen by almost 10 degrees.

At the time of this reading no cooling fans, blowers, or air circulation equipment was operating. The room was an average room with normal central air conditioning and ventilation.

Now, consider Figure 8.10. Before the middle of the day the room temperature is at a shocking 93.3°F. At this point air blowers and cooling fans were

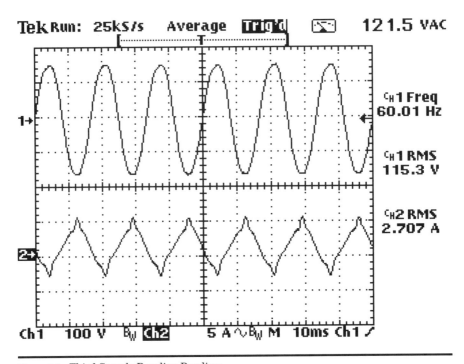

Figure 8.3 Third Sample Baseline Reading

turned on, increasing the airflow to the room where the readings were taken. The temperature shown in Figure 8.10 is far above what should be normal operating temperature.

Normally, the temperature would not reach this level. However, in certain places where equipment is concentrated in a given area, the ambient temperature around such equipment can be much higher than the room temperature, say, 15 or 20 ft away in another location in the same room. The significance of these readings should not be overlooked. It proves a point that airflow, cooling, and various air circulation equipment is important to maintain stable and normal operating temperatures throughout a room in which equipment is concentrated.

This is a good example of why rack-mount cabinets are important. With well-designed rack-mount cabinets, equipment can be placed so that the blowers and fans can create a positive airflow and thus maintain temperatures at a level safe for the equipment and personnel working with it.

Parallel to the idea of monitoring temperature in equipment areas is another important aspect of network design: providing free space around equipment to ensure adequate airflow or ventilation. Many vendors supply free-space recommendations with the specifications accompanying their equipment.

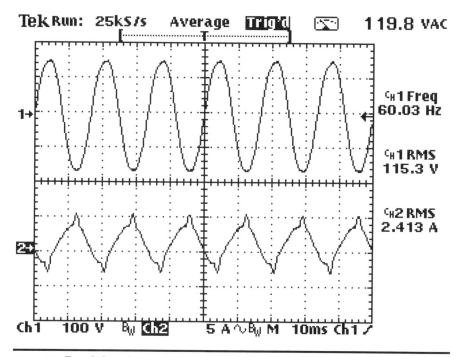

Figure 8.4 Fourth Sample Baseline Reading

8.3 Copper-Based Network Infrastructure

Wiring any network is either planned for, or there is a potential for chaos. Believe me, I speak from experience of having walked through layers of cable behind equipment that was not labeled. With that thought in mind, the design for wiring in this network was examined from multiple angles, including reliability of the cable manufacturer and the actual implementation—whether it would be easy to reconfigure equipment once installed. How would one know which cables go where? With this level of thought and multiple designs on the marker board, this is where I decided to use a rack enclosure, which is actually an inline (or straight-through) pinning. Consider Figure 8.11, which shows an inside view of the enclosure from the rear. The inline panel has RJ-45 female connectors on what is considered the backside.

Figure 8.12 shows front and rear views of the inline panel. The significance of this inline panel will become very clear later.

Many rack-mount panels are available on the market and they have RJ-45 female connectors on the front but a 110 connector on the rear. This is neither good nor bad. Some environments require this type of rear connection point for each connection. However, in this case it is different.

To have a patch panel with all connection points wired straight through makes it easier to troubleshoot and switch cables. Some people think this is no big deal, but with a full rack enclosure, would you like to work inside from

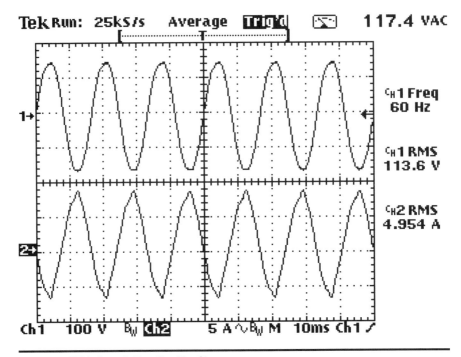

Figure 8.5 Fifth Sample Baseline Reading

the rear or be able to work with all the equipment from the front? That's what I thought.

Now, consider Figure 8.13, which shows a side view of the rack enclosure. Note the XYLAN switch, ALL-LAN patch panel, the inline panel, and connections to network devices. Look closely at the area in the dashed-line rectangular box. This illustrates that any combination of connections can be achieved from the front of the enclosure. How? All equipment is connected into the rear of the inline panel. Actual physical configuration is then made via patch cables from the front. In this network a 48-port inline panel is used; however, Hubble has larger panels as well.

This example of component and wiring design is what I mean by designing ease of use, flexibility, and expandability into the network from the outset. Go one step further, and you will see that troubleshooting or monitoring upper-layer protocols with an Internet Advisor can be easily connected to the inline panel to monitor network traffic and other operating parameters.

During my installation of this equipment, colors, numbers, and labels were assigned to all ports, equipment, and other entry points to the network. There is no reason why a network design should not be documented completely from the very beginning. A well-designed network will be such that anyone who understands the technology would be able to perform any applicable work function.

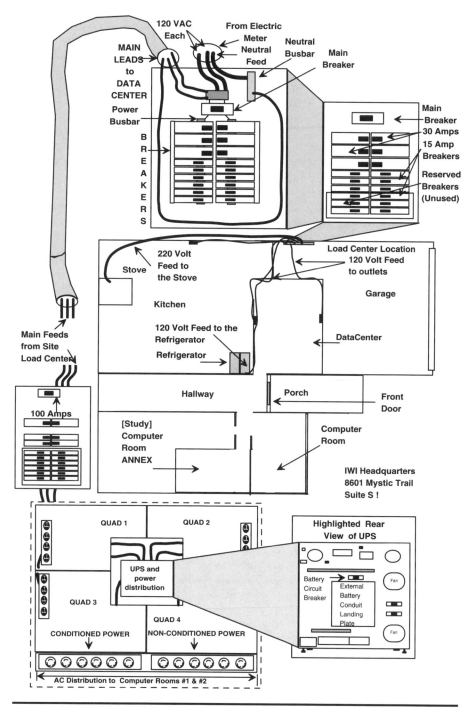

Figure 8.6 View of Wiring and UPS

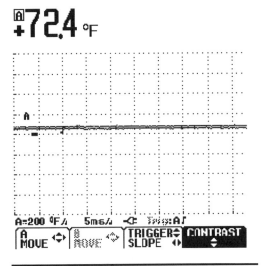

Figure 8.7 Temperature Reading 1

The network also uses copper wiring, but it is not the main backbone of the network. The copper-based components are primarily ALL-LAN wiring, along with other custom cables from Thomas & Betts. My decision to use this wiring was due to its performance potential. Another characteristic of this cable is its high-frequency bandwidth ability. The cable itself is jacketed with PVC (polyvinyl chloride), then aluminum shielding, then four pairs of twisted pair wire wrapped with aluminum shielding. The intense shielding of each pair of cables makes the high bandwidth possible.

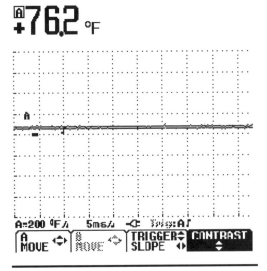

Figure 8.8 Temperature Reading 2

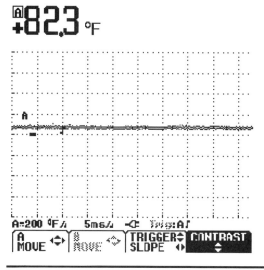

Figure 8.9 Temperature Reading 3

Some of the specifications of the ALL-LAN cable include the following information. Channel and link performance significantly exceeds existing Cat5 (Category 5) specifications, including superior ACR performance at frequencies from 30 to 300 MHz (>16 dB) and is EMC-compliant in all protocols through 300 MHz and beyond without using multilevel encoding non-RJ-45-based connectivity. ALL-LAN has a low profile: 0.650 × 0.695 × 1.525. It is a full 360° connector shielding with a cable jack that has only three components.

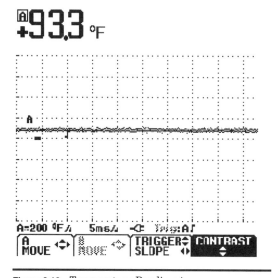

Figure 8.10 Temperature Reading 4

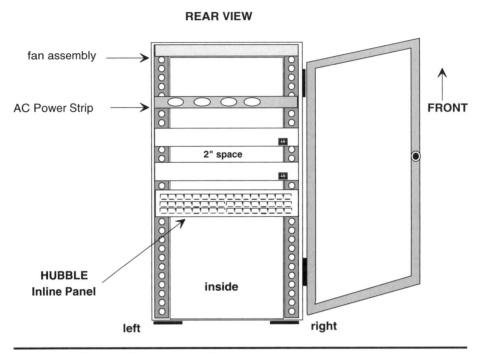

Figure 8.11   Inline Panel Access from the Rear

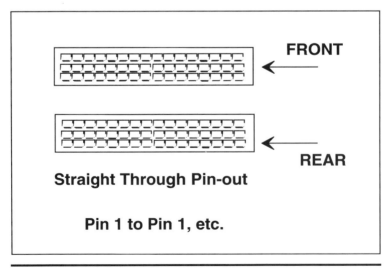

Figure 8.12   Inline Panel

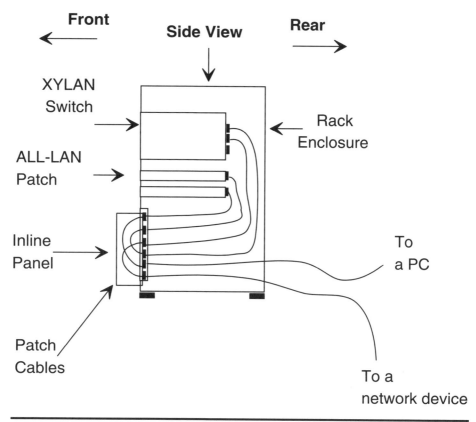

Figure 8.13 Inline Panel Patch (Side View)

It is easy to field-install, and the integral strain relief accommodates cable up to 0.320 IDC, compatible with 23- to 26-AWG wire. It has a unique latch design with damage-free unmating at pullout forces greater than 30 lb and durability exceeding 2500 cycles.

I used ALL-LAN cable to connect PCs, servers, printers, and other devices to the hubs. The main network patch panel is an ALL-LAN panel with ALL-LAN connectors and cabling. The important point here is that you get the idea of how to include this level of detail in your network documentation for troubleshooting purposes.

8.4   Fiber-Optic Backbone Components

My network backbone is fiber-based. I converted all nonfiber to fiber, where possible.

Component examination

For your purposes, I am going to present the fiber components and actual illustrations compliments of Siecor. This is important for you to get a good representation of the actual product. In addition, later in this chapter I use my own illustrations to show you how I integrated this equipment along with the other components in my network.

First, I used a major interface component to assist in the centralizing of the patching ability. The purpose for this was to maximize the ability to patch one system to another with minimal effort once installed. Consider Figure 8.14, which shows Siecor Closet Connector Housing model CCH-04U, which has a capacity for 144 fibers. This unit is the center of my patching center because it can accommodate 144 fibers and can be loaded with SC single-mode, SC multimode, or ST connectors.

Figure 8.15 shows Siecor Closet Connector Housing model CCH-02U. This unit can hold a four 6-pack load (as I call it). A "six pack" is a common industry reference to a module with six fiber connection points mounted on it. I used these units to house one SC six-pack, one ST six-pack, and two MTP modules. Later in this chapter I will clarify this in an illustration of my exact implementation.

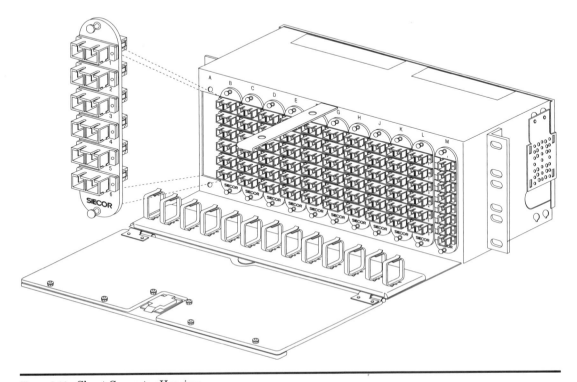

Figure 8.14   Closet Connector Housing

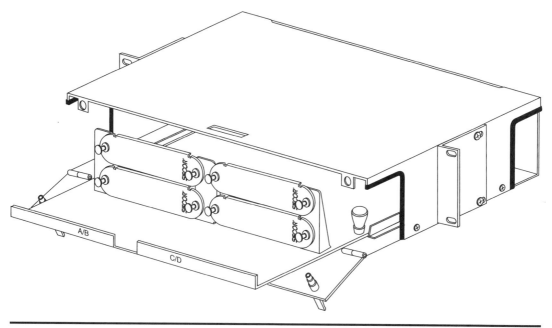

Figure 8.15   Closet Connector Housing

Another major component I used in my network is the MTP module from Siecor. This power module makes fiber installation plug-and-play (PnP). The module I used has 12 SC-duplex fiber connection points on the front side (as viewed from a mounting in a closet connector housing unit) and a MTP connector on the rear. The cable designed to work with this module makes it a very powerful solution to fiber requirements. Its inherent flexibility, its integratability into existing technology, and its very small cable used to extend it to another MTP connecting port create a solution-in-a-box concept. The added beauty to this is the ease of implementation and different cable lengths that can be employed. In the next section I show how I implemented these MTP modules in my network.

Standards to understand

In the implementation and troubleshooting of fiber, it is important to know the standards that apply. Those presented here are intended to provide you with a baseline for understanding some important standards.

Figure 8.16 presents commercial building telecommunications cabling standards. This example of standards covers the backbone and horizontal cabling requirements. Hopefully, lengths

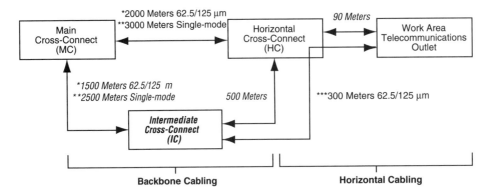

* Backbone distances based on optical fiber cable. When IC to HC distance is less than 500 meters, then the MC
  to IC can be increased accordingly but, the total MC to HC shall not exceed 2000 meters for 62.5/125 µm or
  3000 meters for single-mode.

** Single-mode fiber can support distances up to 60 km (37 mi); however, this is outside the scope of TIA/EIA-568A.

*** Centralized optical fiber cabling (TSB-72).

Figure 8.16 Commercial Building Telecommunications Cabling Standards

and cabling locations will be recorded for your environment. If not, it is time
to check into this in the troubleshooting stage. The need for this is the significance of the lengths as presented here.

Figure 8.17 shows Siecor's recommendation for adapter installation orientation on each end of the link where SC connections are made. Siecor refers to
this as the *crossover cabling* with the 568SC. The crossover cabling shows
installation of the adapter in opposite orientations. This recommendation is
endorsed by Siecor and the TIA/EIA, specifically 568A.

Figure 8.18 shows the Siecor illustration of the 568SC adapter orientation
in the network. This illustration shows the main cross-connect, the horizontal
cross-connect, and the telecommunications outlet. This provides a good picto-
rial understanding of actual implementation.

Fiber-optic measurements

It is important to understand, and see, illustrations of fiber-optic measurements. Your network will undoubtedly produce readings appropriate for your
site. I am including these measurements here with explanations compliments
of Siecor in order to assist you.

First, consider Figure 8.19, which compares a laser and an LED wavelength. This is applicable to transmitters used in fiber-based networks. These
transmitters are characterized by the light they emit. Nominal emission
wavelength is called the *center wavelength* of the transmitter; however, the
transmitted signal is actually a collection of wavelengths around this value.
This center wavelength is primarily a function of the type and configuration

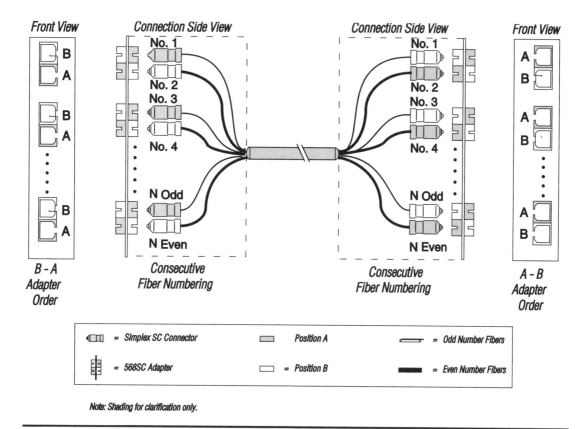

Figure 8.17 Recommendation for Adapter Installation Orientation

of the materials used to fabricate the transmitter. It is usually measured in nanometers.

Figure 8.20 shows the pulse width of a light source showing the *full width, at half-maximum* (FWHM), which represents the total power of the optical transmitter; hence this range of width is called the *spectral width*.

Figure 8.21 shows the relationship between spectral width, response time, and data rate. The spectral width was defined above. The *data rate* is the maximum number of bits per second that can be transmitted and received with a bit error rate below a certain level. According to Siecor documentation, a typical bit error rate is 1 error bit out of a total of 10 bits, usually affecting the 9th through 12th waveform pulses. Figure 8.21 illustrates that the receiver also has rise and fall times that can limit the data rate. Siecor documentation indicates that the longer the response time, the slower the rate of successful data transmittal.

Figure 8.22 shows a network application and the number of fibers required. The SONET (Synchronous Optical Network) and video are listed here because of the system design requirements to incorporate these applications into existing communication networks.

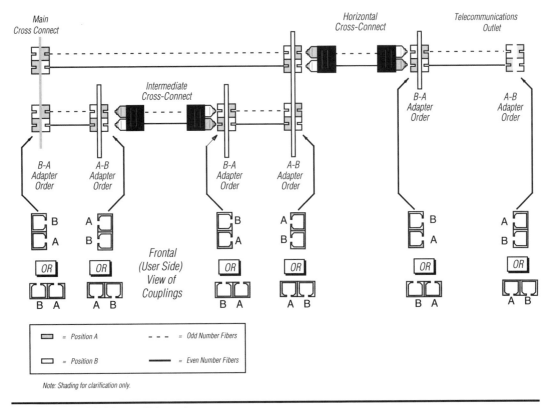

Figure 8.18   568SC Adapter Orientation

Figure 8.23 is a Siecor drawing showing standard and enhanced options in networking. The upper panels in the illustration show a standard, unsophisticated electronics option in which a total of 12 fibers are required. The lower panels show an enhanced sophisticated electronics option in which four fibers are required. This illustration is extremely helpful because of the detail shown and the placement of equipment. At a minimum, it will definitely assist you on any network design you may be involved with.

Siecor Optical Time Domain Reflectometer (OTDR) information

Siecor's information is very good technically, as well as articulate. I am including it here because of its accuracy and integrity.

According to Siecor, an OTDR works like a radar. It sends pulses of laser light out through the fiber and then precisely measures the level and time delay of the reflected pulses as they return. The OTDR presents this as loss and distance information in graphical format providing a detailed overview of the entire cable length at once. Consider Figure 8.24, which shows the distance and relative loss. The top of the illustration shows a correlation

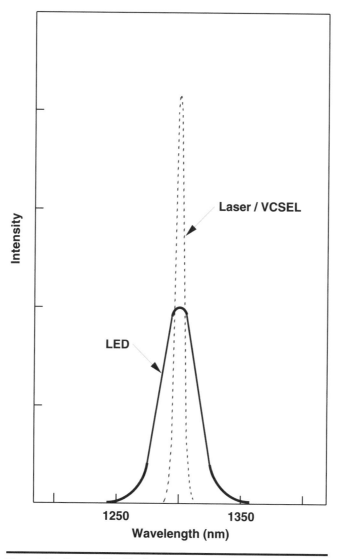

Figure 8.19 Spectral Profile Comparison of Laser and LED

between the significant information: patch panel, fusion splice, mechanical splice, and a patch panel (fiber end).

Further interpretation of Figure 8.24 shows the OTDR distance plot in meters or feet on the horizontal scale (abscissa) and relative loss in decibels on the vertical scale (ordinate). The overall trace decreases from left to right, indicating that the light is being attenuated by the fiber, connectors, and splices as it travels down the length of the cable. The linear sections represent continuous spans of cable; the slopes indicate the distributed loss over a

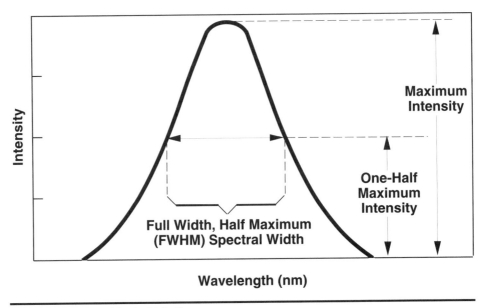

Figure 8.20   Pulse Width of a Light Source

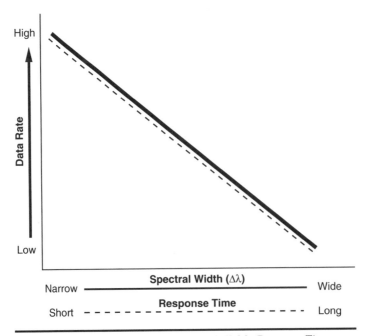

Figure 8.21   Relationship Between Spectral Width, Response Time, and Data Rate

Network System	Fiber Required to Support Network	Fiber Type
ATM	2 Fibers	Single-mode or 62.5/125 μm
10BaseF (Ethernet)	2 Fibers	Multimode, 62.5/125 μm
100BaseF (Ethernet)	2 Fibers	Multimode, 62.5/125 μm
1000BaseF (Ethernet)	2 Fibers	Single-mode or 62.5/125 μm
Token Ring	4 Fibers	Multimode, 62.5/125 μm
FDDI	4 Fibers (DAS), 2 Fibers (SAS)	Multimode, 62.5/125 μm
Fibre Channel	2 Fibers	Multimode, 62.5/125 μm
SONET	4 Fibers	Single-mode
Voice (Two Way)	2 Fibers	Multimode, 62.5/125 μm
Video (Broadcast)	1 or 2 Fibers	Single-mode or 62.5/125 μm
Video (Security)	1 Fiber	Multimode, 62.5/125 μm
Video (Interactive)	2 Fibers	Multimode, 62.5/125 μm
Telemetry	1 or 2 Fibers	Multimode, 62.5/125 μm

* SONET and Video are listed here due to system design requirements to incorporate these applications into existing communication networks.

Note: DAS is an FDDI term for Dual Attachment Station. SAS is an FDDI term for Single Attachment Station.

Figure 8.22 Network Applications and Fibers Required

section of fiber [the steeper slopes indicate higher fiber loss in decibels per kilometer (dB/km)]. The vertical drops represent point losses at connectors (points A and B), splices (points C and D), and faults. The magnitude of the drop represents loss in dB. The spikes or humps indicate reflective events such as connectors or mechanical splices where the continuity of the glass is interrupted. The final spike on the trace indicates the end of the fiber.

The widths associated with the spikes or humps as shown in Figure 8.24 represent an OTDR dead zone—in other words, the blind spots that immediately follow each reflective event as the OTDR recovers from the reflection.

Figure 8.25 shows the results of a sample OTDR automatic analysis. Figure 8.25 is a measurement of the connector loss at the optical patch panel, with a test fiber box used to connect between the OTDR output and the interconnect hardware. The connection loss shown in this figure can be measured as the drop in vertical position before and after the connection.

In the context of Figure 8.25, a user can place markers and cursors on the trace to make measurements easier and more reliable. Not all OTDRs provide the Autotest function that automatically configures the OTDR, performs a signature trace, and measures the position and loss of each event in the cable system. However, the Siecor OTDR used in my network does perform these functions; this is another reason why I selected Siecor as the fiber test tool provider of choice.

Figure 8.26 shows a summary of information obtained via the OTDR. Summary of this information and the previous trace information make working with fiber test results much easier.

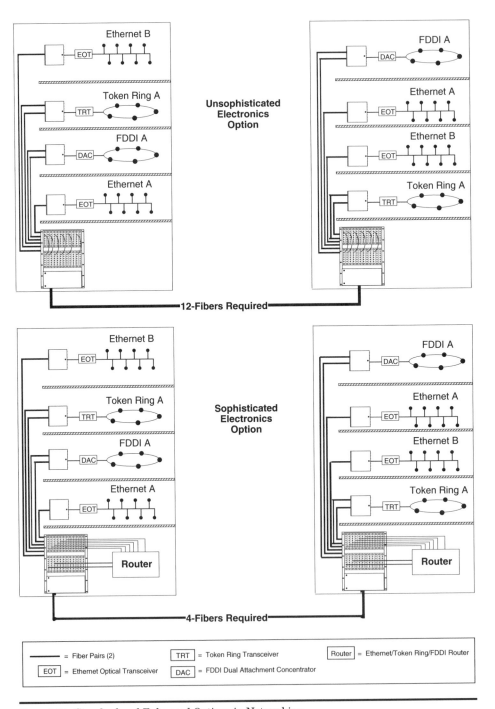

Figure 8.23 Standard and Enhanced Options in Networking

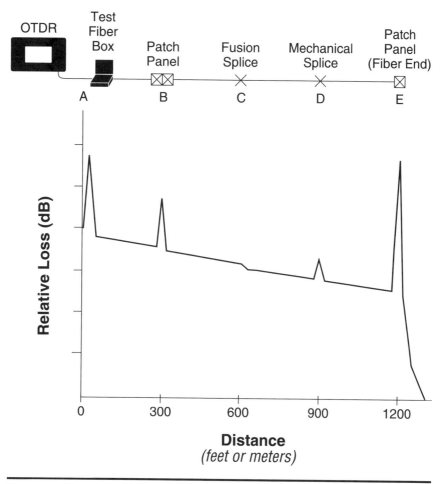

Figure 8.24   Distance and Relative Loss

Figure 8.27 is another very helpful chart of information courtesy of Siecor. This chart is helpful for those relatively new to the fiber arena because of the breakdown of the test tool and related information.

Figure 8.28 is another very helpful piece of information. This troubleshooting chart is really a helpful tool to begin with. You may want to incorporate this in your standard set of procedures for troubleshooting fiber at your location. Another helpful piece of information is presented in Figure 8.29. This selection guide can help you in determining what test instruments to use. The information Siecor has graciously provided is extremely valuable. I included this information here because it is valuable—I wanted you to have it.

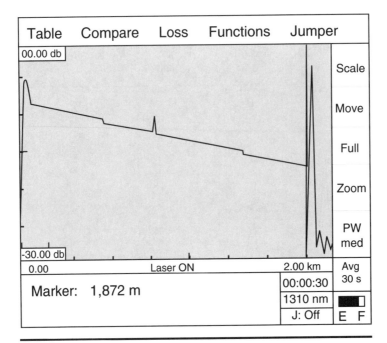

Figure 8.25 Sample OTDR Automatic Analysis

Event Table

#	Type	Position	Loss	Reflectance	
1		412 m	0.09	Non	
2		792 m	0.17	-39	Trace
3		1.341 km	0.11	Non	Page Up
4		1.827 km	END	-17	Page Dn
5					
6					Program

Click on item to see close-up.
Press Start/Stop to run test again.

E F

Figure 8.26 Summary of Information Obtained via the OTDR

Premises Segment			
Test Method	**Backbone Cabling**	**Horizontal Cabling (Multimode)**	**Equipment required**
End-to-End Attenuation	Dual wavelength insertion loss in one direction: • Multimode: 850 and 1300 nm • Single-mode: 1310 and 1550 nm Acceptable loss based on Figures 10.2 and 10.3. Bidirectional testing as required.	850 or 1300 nm (multimode) Acceptable loss ≤ 2.0 dB	• Optical Meter • Optical Source(s) • 2 Test Jumpers • 1 Adapter Bidirectional test: • 2 Optical Testers
OTDR Test	OTDR inspection of each fiber > 300 feet • Multimode: 850 or 1300 nm • Single-mode: 1310 or 1550 nm Signature trace documentation by computer file or printout for each fiber with splices or mid-span interconnection. Dual wavelength or bidirectional testing as required.	Troubleshooting as required for links exceeding the 2.0 dB limit above.	• OTDR • Test Fiber Box
Connector and Splice Loss	OTDR measurement of each field-terminated connector (≤ 0.75 dB) and each splice (≤ 0.3 dB) at one wavelength: • Multimode: 850 or 1300 nm • Single-mode: 1310 or 1550 nm **(Note: Simultaneous testing of a fiber's signature trace (above) and near-end connector loss can save test time and documentation.)**	Troubleshooting as required for links exceeding the 2.0 dB limit.	• OTDR • Test Fiber Box
Bandwidth/ Dispersion	Save manufacturer's specification sheet documenting the specified fiber bandwidth (multimode) and dispersion (single-mode) for the cable used.		• None required

Figure 8.27 Cable System Testing Recommendations

8.5 The Author's Fiber-Optic Backbone Implementation

My network has evolved over a period of time. In the beginning I had a plan, and that plan has grown. Not too long ago I realized that I would be forced to migrate to a complete fiber backbone in order to carry the payload. When one begins to work with multimedia and video, and to incorporate distance, then fiber becomes a requirement. My purpose in this section is to demonstrate how I implemented the Siecor equipment.

The best place to start is give you an overview of my lab and network backbone. Consider Figure 8.30, which shows my lab, the environment in which this network exists. Note that there are three distinct physical areas: locations 1, 2, and 3. The major patch center is housed in location 2. In this room

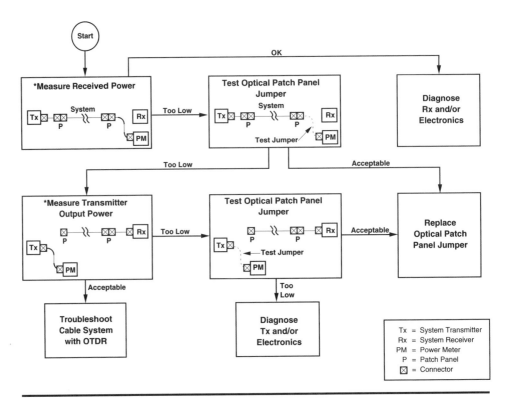

Figure 8.28 Troubleshooting Chart with a Power Meter

the 144-load Siecor fiber patch is rack-mounted. Two additional Siecor patch panels are rack-mounted as well. Note that they have three interfaces each: two MTP interfaces, one ST interface, and one SC interface.

Figure 8.31 is a highlighted view of the two interfaces with varying modules loaded in them. Figure 8.31 shows the different modules installed in the interface housing. The purpose for this is the great flexibility of this module for connecting or for patching with a varying number of connectors and performing troubleshooting tasks, which often requires a specific patch.

Figure 8.32 shows the lab's physical areas—namely, physical locations 1 and 2. Figure 8.32 highlights the distribution of cabling between these two locations. Examine the illustration. With this configuration, I can achieve almost any conceivable patch resulting with a connection between equipment in any given physical area to any other given physical area shown in Figure 8.32.

Figure 8.33 further highlights physical location 1, showing that the workstations there are connected directly into the patch panel interface. This patch is connected to the patch in physical location 2 by MTP cables. These MTP cables provide a slim-line method for integration of sites. These MTP cables are easy to install and are not affected by electrical or magnetic inter-

	Multimode Only	Multimode/Single-Mode

End-to-End Attenuation	• OTS-110/OTS-210 Data: Optical Meter
	• OS-100D/OS-301: Optical Source
	• OTS-300 MD-KIT
	  (850/1300 nm multimode)
	Bidirectional:
	• OTS-111D/OTS-211D Data/
	  OTS-311D Express
	  Optical Testers, 850/1300 nm
	  (pair requiredfor installed links)
		• OTS-110/OTS-210 Data: Optical Meter
		  (multimode/single-mode)
		• OS-301: Optical Source
		  (850/1300 LED/1550 Laser)
		or
		• OTS-3MDSD-KIT
		  (850/1300/1310/1550 nm
		  multimode LED and
		  single-mode Laser)

OTDR Testing and End-to-End Attenuation	• OTDR Plus Multitester fitted with
	  the following options:
	• Multimode OTDR option
	  ⇒ 850 nm minimum **or**
	  ⇒ 850/1300 nm dual wavelength
	• Integral power meter option
	• OS-100D: Optical Source
	  (850/1300 nm multimode)
		• OTDR Plus Multitester fitted with
		  the following options:
		• Multimode OTDR option
		  ⇒ 850 nm minimum **or**
		  ⇒ 850/1300 nm dual wavelength
		• Single-mode OTDR option
		  ⇒ 1310 nm minimum **or**
		  ⇒ 1310/1550 nm dual wavelength
		• Integral power meter option
		• OS-100D: Optical Source
		  (850/1300 nm multimode)
		• OS-210XD: Optical Source
		  (1310/1550 nm single-mode)
		or
		• OS-301: Optical Source
		  (850/1300 LED/1550 Laser)

Troubleshooting	• Fault Isolation: • End Fault Location: • Cable Fault Location: (Note: The OTDR Plus Multitester can combine the functions of all these tools with upgradeable power meter and visual fault locator options, useful for both installation and troubleshooting.)	CPM Compact Power Meter VFL-200 Visual Fault Locator OTDR Plus Multitester

Customized test kits that combine test equipment for specific applications are also available, such as Siecor's Hand-Held Test Kits that meet TIA/EIA-568 testing recommendations.

Figure 8.29 Test Equipment Product Selection Guide

ference. Figure 8.33 also shows one interface in physical location 2 connected to physical location 3. Fiber test equipment is housed in physical location 2, thus making testing of all three locations possible.

Figure 8.34 shows a highlighted view of physical location 3, where servers and workstations are located. The CD silo and main server (Cherokee) are located here. Operationally, any-to-any connectivity is achieved among all physical locations.

Figure 8.35 is an illustration of two distinct FDDI concentrators. This illustration indicates a collective network incorporating all three locations or two distinct locations capable of operating independently of one another. This type of implementation is easy to manage because of the flexibility achievable due to the versatile patching capability.

Figure 8.36 is a variation on physical implementation. This figure shows two copper-based Ethernet switches with multiple devices attached. Note that the switches are converted to fiber and thus patched across the backbone, enabling length extensions beyond that of traditional Ethernet with copper-based wire.

Another powerful implementation I achieved with a fiber backbone is shown in Figure 8.37, where FDDI and Ethernet are integrated over a single-fiber backbone. The beauty of this is that either the FDDI or Ethernet segments can be removed without affecting the other. This again is another pow-

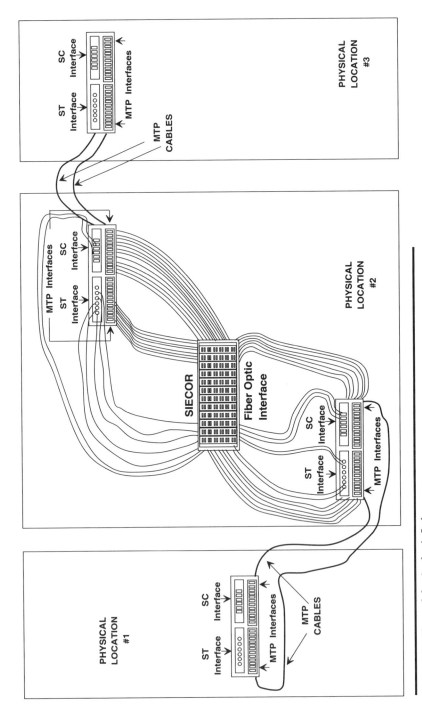

Figure 8.30   View of the Author's Lab

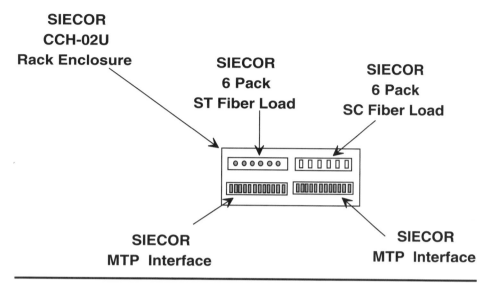

**SIECOR
CCH-02U
Rack Enclosure**

**SIECOR
6 Pack
ST Fiber Load**

**SIECOR
6 Pack
SC Fiber Load**

**SIECOR
MTP Interface**

**SIECOR
MTP Interface**

Figure 8.31 Interface Modules

erful troubleshooting tool if the network is built on a fiber backbone. For my purposes, this type of backbone is the most effective.

Figure 8.38 shows ATM and Ethernet integrated into a single logical network over a fiber backbone. This illustration shows the ATM interfaces in physical locations 1 and 3. In reality, this means that two network segments are superimposed over the fiber backbone that spans three distinct physical locations.

Figure 8.39 shows the network equipment installed in physical location 2. Figure 8.39 shows video, mail, file, CD, FTP archive, and application servers in physical location 2. With these devices located in this portion of the physical facility, I can patch them in any of a number of ways to achieve maximum flexibility and to troubleshoot from different perspectives.

The final example of my lab and fiber network backbone is illustrated in Figure 8.40, which shows the network backbone with workstations and servers. It also shows network test equipment in physical area number 2. Configuration of the fiber backbone in this manner makes troubleshooting the entire network feasible from physical location 2.

8.6   Network Analyzer [Internet Advisor (Hewlett-Packard)]

This network, like others, requires a network analyzer to obtain and properly maintain adequate information. If you are relatively new to networking, you may want to refer back to this section later as it contains information that is considered advanced.

After considering which tools to use with this network, I selected the Internet Advisor because of its strength as a tool. The HP Internet Advisor

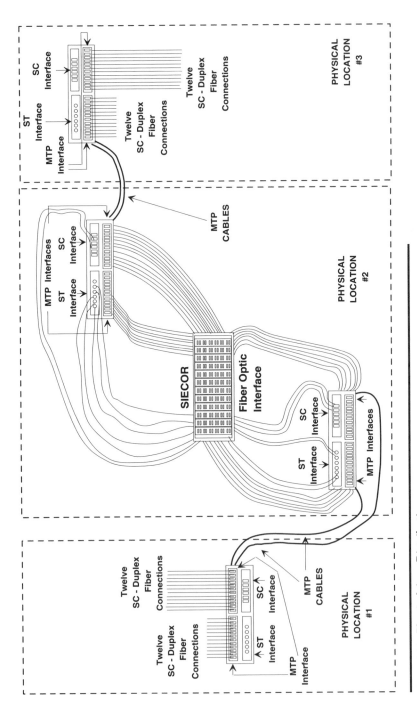

Figure 8.32 Physical Area Distribution

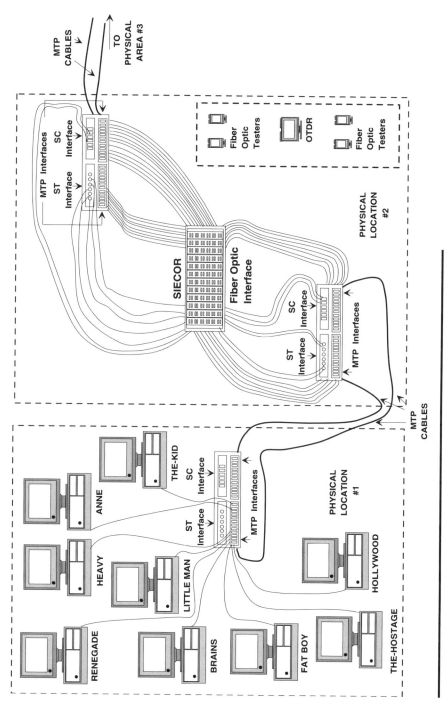

Figure 8.33 Physical Area 1 Highlights

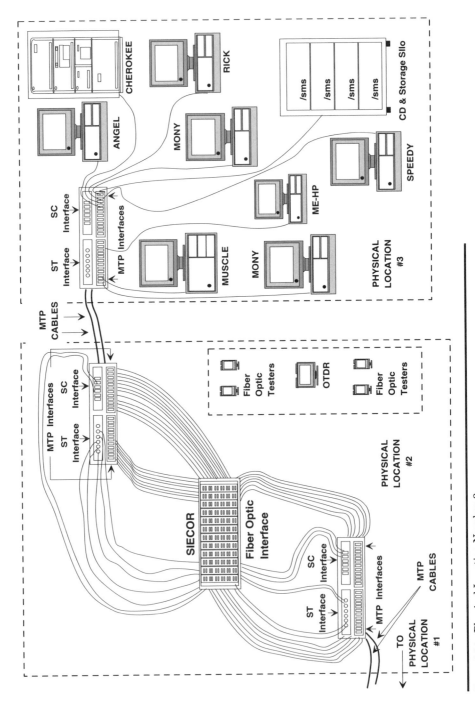

Figure 8.34 Physical Location Number 3

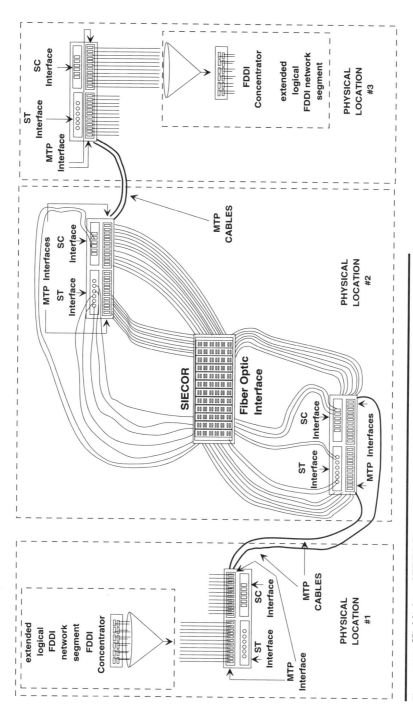

Figure 8.35 Highlights of FDDI Connections

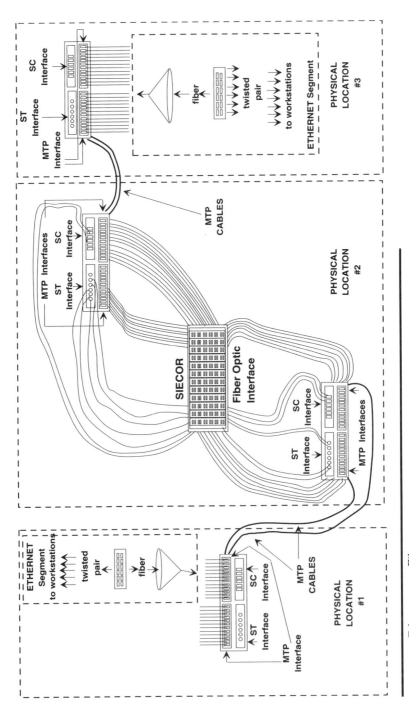

Figure 8.36 Ethernet over Fiber

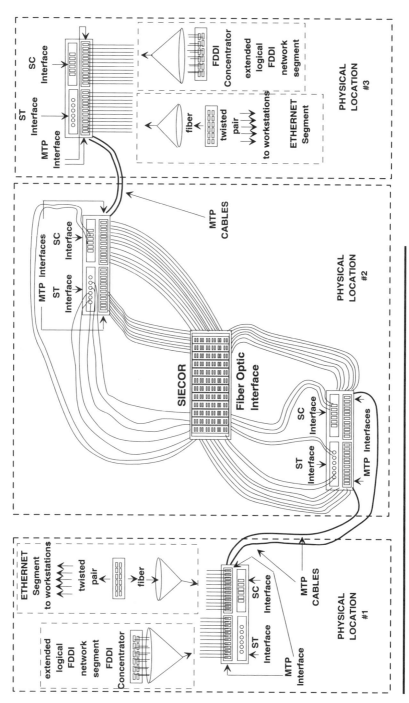

Figure 8.37 FDDI and Ethernet

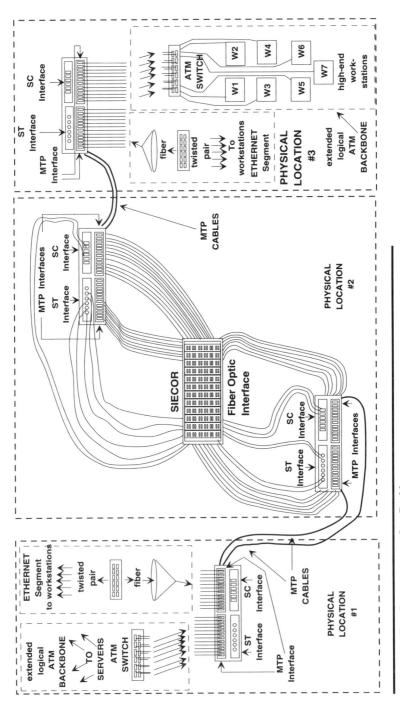

Figure 8.38 Two Segments over One Backbone

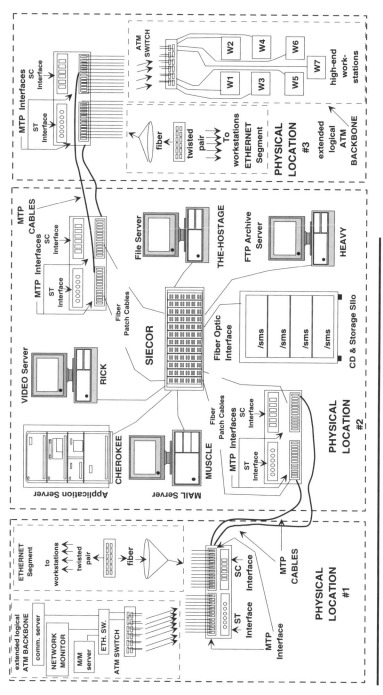

Figure 8.39 Server Implementations

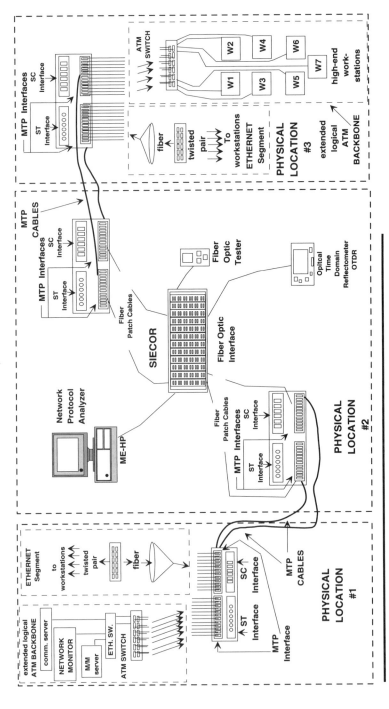

Figure 8.40 Testing the Backbone

(J2522B) provides comprehensive Ethernet testing. It is a portable, full-featured network analysis solution that allows users to install, support, and maintain local area network (LAN), wide area network (WAN), and Asynchronous Transfer Mode (ATM) networks by providing features that facilitate troubleshooting of any network. Some of these features are a portable platform with a rugged built-in Pentium PC, commentators that help solve network problems quickly and effectively, seven-layer decoding of all major protocols, comprehensive network statistics, and traffic generation.

Internet Advisor mainframe characteristics include

Intel Pentium 133-MHz processor

32 MB of PC memory

VGA color display, 26.4-cm (10.4-in) diagonal or active-matrix display (as an optional feature)

814-MB hard drive (as standard) or 1.4-GB hard drive (as an optional feature)

3.5-in flexible disk drive

PCMCIA slot (Type I/II)

Built-in mouse

Serial, parallel, and external VGA monitor ports

Windows 95

Internet Advisor general specifications include a 10 Mbps data rate, two RJ-45 connectors with hub logic that allows for testing in switched environments, and an AUI connector for universal Ethernet testing through external transceivers. Other Internet Advisor specifications are as follows:

Hardware filtering	Hardware time stamp with 100-ns resolution
Physical characteristics	Weight: 6.2 kg (13.7 lb)
	Dimensions: $h \times w \times d$ cm = 8.5 × 30 × 29 cm (3.4 × 12 × 11.5 in)
Display	26.5-cm diagonal (10.4-in) passive DSTNcolor LCD VGA; optional 26.5-cm diagonal (10.4-in) active-matrix TFT color VGA
Operating conditions	Temperature: operating, 5 to 40°C (41 to 104°F); nonoperating, −25 to + 60°C (−13 to 140°F). Humidity: operating, 20–80% relative humidity (RH) to 40°C noncondensing; storage, 10 to 90% RH to 60°C noncondensing
Power requirements	100 to 240 V ac, 50 to 60 Hz, 75 W max
Warranty	3 years
Regulatory compliances	Bears the CE and CSA marks

The particular Internet Advisor and accessories I used were

HP J2522B Internet Advisor LAN—Ethernet

Opt 221 26.4-cm active-matrix color display

HP J2514A Deluxe Carrying Case

HP J2533A Token Ring—Parallel Port Adapter (International)

HP J2531A Internet Reporter—LAN

How to baseline your network

Network baselining is simple. It means that you obtain records in various forms of the original equipment on the network and its operation. When this is done, the information can be used as a solid reference point of known good operation. The examples presented below with the Internet Advisor provide such information.

Consider Figure 8.41, which provides a lot of information. The purpose of this trace is to obtain the systems on the network. The name of the screen is at the top of the figure. Note that it says "Node Discovery measurement." The names of the computers participating in the network I created are as follows:

BRAINS

MUSCLE

SILO

THE-HOSTAGE

CHEROKEE

TAYLOR'S ANALYZER

Note that the IP addresses are also shown that correlate to the systems on the network. Further information about these systems, such as what they are doing (broadcasting, etc.) is also given.

Consider Figure 8.42. Figure 8.42 shows the addition of FAT BOY on the network. The previous hosts are also participating on the network as well. This figure also shows the protocols in use on the network: NetBIOS, Ethernet, and IP.

To put this information into perspective, consider Figure 8.43, which presents an overview of the network nodes representing participants in the network I designed. Note that the ME-HP node is surrounded by a highlighted box. The Internet Advisor is capable of listening to the communication of all nodes on this network. Consider the information presented in Figure 8.44.

Note that a wide variety of information is obtained in Figure 8.44. First, the protocol used is identified; that is, NOV for Novell and TCP for TCP/IP. NetBIOS is also indicated as being in use. IP addresses are shown, including the functions they perform, such as the General Service Query, Close

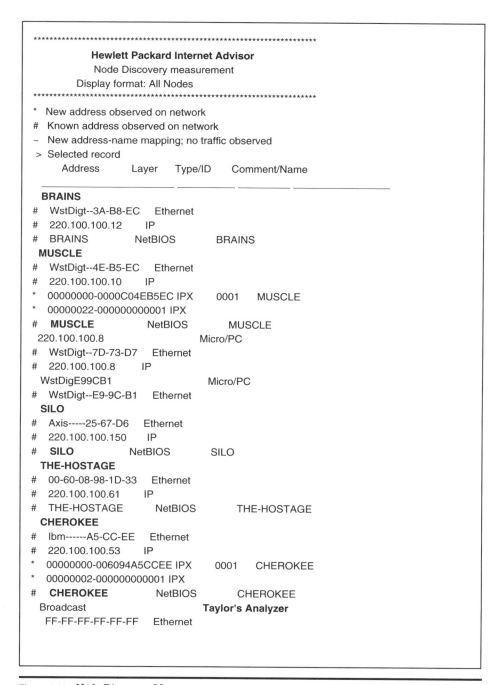

```
****************************************************************
              Hewlett Packard Internet Advisor
                 Node Discovery measurement
                 Display format: All Nodes
****************************************************************
  *  New address observed on network
  #  Known address observed on network
  ~  New address-name mapping; no traffic observed
  >  Selected record
          Address         Layer     Type/ID     Comment/Name

     BRAINS
  #   WstDigt--3A-B8-EC     Ethernet
  #   220.100.100.12        IP
  #   BRAINS              NetBIOS         BRAINS
     MUSCLE
  #   WstDigt--4E-B5-EC     Ethernet
  #   220.100.100.10        IP
  *   00000000-0000C04EB5EC IPX      0001     MUSCLE
  *   00000022-000000000001 IPX
  #   MUSCLE              NetBIOS         MUSCLE
     220.100.100.8                      Micro/PC
  #   WstDigt--7D-73-D7     Ethernet
  #   220.100.100.8         IP
     WstDigE99CB1                       Micro/PC
  #   WstDigt--E9-9C-B1     Ethernet
     SILO
  #   Axis-----25-67-D6     Ethernet
  #   220.100.100.150       IP
  #   SILO               NetBIOS         SILO
     THE-HOSTAGE
  #   00-60-08-98-1D-33     Ethernet
  #   220.100.100.61        IP
  #   THE-HOSTAGE         NetBIOS         THE-HOSTAGE
     CHEROKEE
  #   Ibm------A5-CC-EE     Ethernet
  #   220.100.100.53        IP
  *   00000000-006094A5CCEE IPX      0001     CHEROKEE
  *   00000002-000000000001 IPX
  #   CHEROKEE            NetBIOS         CHEROKEE
     Broadcast                      Taylor's Analyzer
        FF-FF-FF-FF-FF-FF    Ethernet
```

Figure 8.41 Node Discovery Measurement

```
*************************************************************************
                    HEWLETT-PACKARD NETWORK ADVISOR
                    Node Discovery measurement
                    Run on Mar 16, 1998 @ 18:54:43
                         3 nodes observed
*************************************************************************
 *   New address observed on network
 #   Known address observed on network
 ~   New address-name mapping; no traffic observed
 >   Selected record
          Address        Layer     Type/ID      Comment/Name
    _____   _____  _____  _____

    220.100.100.8                            Micro/PC
 #   WstDigt--7D-73-D7    Ethernet
 #   220.100.100.8        IP
 *>  FAT BOY             NetBIOS              FAT BOY
     BRAINS
 #   WstDigt--3A-B8-EC    Ethernet
 #   220.100.100.12       IP
 #>  BRAINS              NetBIOS              BRAINS
     Broadcast                            Taylor's Analyzer
     FF-FF-FF-FF-FF-FF    Ethernet
     CHEROKEE
     Ibm------A5-CC-EE    Ethernet
     220.100.100.53       IP
     CHEROKEE            NetBIOS              CHEROKEE
     MUSCLE
 #   WstDigt--4E-B5-EC    Ethernet
 #>  220.100.100.10       IP             INFO
 *>  00000000-0000C04EB5EC IPX       0001      MUSCLE
 #>  MUSCLE              NetBIOS          MUSCLE
     SILO
     Axis-----25-67-D6    Ethernet
     220.100.100.150      IP
     SILO                NetBIOS          SILO
     THE-HOSTAGE
     00-60-08-98-1D-33    Ethernet
     220.100.100.61       IP
     THE-HOSTAGE         NetBIOS              THE-HOSTAGE
     WstDigE99CB1                         Micro/PC
     WstDigt--E9-9C-B1    Ethernet
```

Figure 8.42 Network Information Take 2

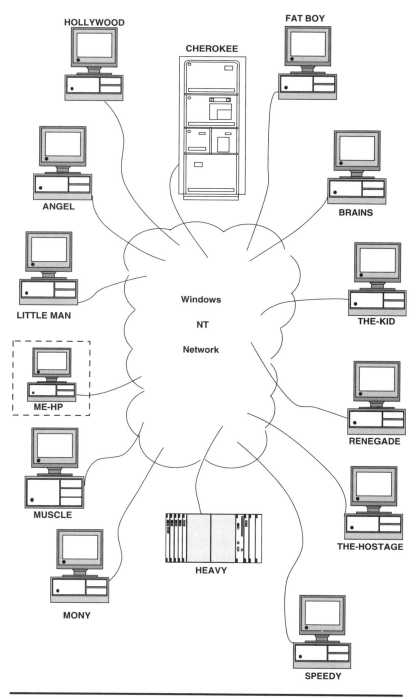

Figure 8.43 Overview of Network Nodes

```
TCP: Close Connection   [Normal] Mar 13@19:45:05.8432606
220.100.100.53     <-> 220.100.100.10
CHEROKEE                MUSCLE
Port: 1144         LOC-SRV 135
Tx Packets: 6          5
Low Window: 0          0
Retrans: 0             0
Connection Duration: 0:00:00.0081942
Frame Number(s): 220

TCP: Close Connection  [Normal] Mar 13@19:45:05.8527809
220.100.100.53     <-> 220.100.100.10
CHEROKEE                MUSCLE
Port: 1145         1034
Tx Packets: 6          5
Low Window: 0          0
Retrans: 0             0
Connection Duration: 0:00:00.0068831
Frame Number(s): 231

NOV: Routing Information Reply [Normal] Mar 13@19:45:10.5468778
To Node: FF-FF-FF-FF-FF-FF, Broadcast
00000000-006094A5CCEE      --> 00000000-FFFFFFFFFFFF
Network number: 00000002
Number of hops: 1 Number of ticks: 2
Frame Number: 235

NOV: General Service Query [Normal] Mar 13@19:45:40.0371709
 From Node: 00-00-C0-E9-9C-B1, WstDigE99CB1
00000000-0000C0E99CB1      --> 00000000-FFFFFFFFFFFF
 Server Type: File Server
 Frame Number: 272

NOV: Nearest Service Query  [Normal] Mar 13@19:46:05.1400663
 From Node: 00-00-C0-4E-B5-EC, MUSCLE
00000000-0000C04EB5EC      --> 00000000-FFFFFFFFFFFF
 Server Type: File Server
 Frame Number: 314

NOV: Nearest Service Query  [Normal] Mar 13@19:46:05.852107
 From Node: 00-00-C0-4E-B5-EC, MUSCLE
00000000-0000C04EB5EC      --> 00000000-FFFFFFFFFFFF
 Server Type: File Server
 Frame Number: 319

NOV: Nearest Service Query  [Normal] Mar 13@19:46:06.57323
 From Node: 00-00-C0-4E-B5-EC, MUSCLE
00000000-0000C04EB5EC      --> 00000000-FFFFFFFFFFFF
 Server Type: File Server
 Frame Number: 321

NOV: Nearest Service Query  [Normal] Mar 13@19:46:07.2943876
 From Node: 00-00-C0-4E-B5-EC, MUSCLE
00000000-0000C04EB5EC      --> 00000000-FFFFFFFFFFFF
 Server Type: File Server
 Frame Number: 322
```

Figure 8.44 Network Commentator for Ethernet

```
NOV: Nearest Service Query  [Normal] Mar 13@19:46:08.0155127
 From Node: 00-00-C0-4E-B5-EC, MUSCLE
 00000000-0000C04EB5EC      --> 00000000-FFFFFFFFFFFF
 Server Type: File Server
 Frame Number: 325


NOV: Nearest Service Query  [Normal] Mar 13@19:46:08.7365608
 From Node: 00-00-C0-4E-B5-EC, MUSCLE
 00000000-0000C04EB5EC      --> 00000000-FFFFFFFFFFFF
 Server Type: File Server
 Frame Number: 326


NOV: Nearest Service Query  [Normal] Mar 13@19:46:09.4577
 From Node: 00-00-C0-4E-B5-EC, MUSCLE
 00000000-0000C04EB5EC      --> 00000000-FFFFFFFFFFFF
 Server Type: File Server
 Frame Number: 327


NOV: Nearest Service Query  [Normal] Mar 13@19:46:10.1788107
 From Node: 00-00-C0-4E-B5-EC, MUSCLE
 00000000-0000C04EB5EC      --> 00000000-FFFFFFFFFFFF
 Server Type: File Server
 Frame Number: 329


NOV: Routing Information Reply [Normal] Mar 13@19:46:10.5455269
 To Node: FF-FF-FF-FF-FF-FF, Broadcast
 00000000-006094A5CCEE      --> 00000000-FFFFFFFFFFFF
 Network number: 00000002
 Number of hops: 1 Number of ticks: 2
 Frame Number: 330


NOV: Nearest Service Query  [Normal] Mar 13@19:46:10.8999035
 From Node: 00-00-C0-4E-B5-EC, MUSCLE
 00000000-0000C04EB5EC      --> 00000000-FFFFFFFFFFFF
 Server Type: File Server
 Frame Number: 331


NOV: Nearest Service Query  [Normal] Mar 13@19:46:11.6210437
 From Node: 00-00-C0-4E-B5-EC, MUSCLE
 00000000-0000C04EB5EC      --> 00000000-FFFFFFFFFFFF
 Server Type: File Server
 Frame Number: 332


NOV: General Service Query  [Normal] Mar 13@19:46:12.3421574
 From Node: 00-00-C0-4E-B5-EC, MUSCLE
 00000000-0000C04EB5EC      --> 00000000-FFFFFFFFFFFF
 Server Type: File Server
 Frame Number: 333


NOV: General Service Query  [Normal] Mar 13@19:46:13.0632036
 From Node: 00-00-C0-4E-B5-EC, MUSCLE
 00000000-0000C04EB5EC      --> 00000000-FFFFFFFFFFFF
 Server Type: File Server
 Frame Number: 334
```

Figure 8.44 (*Continued*)

```
NOV: General Service Query  [Normal] Mar 13@19:46:13.7843639
 From Node: 00-00-C0-4E-B5-EC, MUSCLE
 00000000-0000C04EB5EC      --> 00000000-FFFFFFFFFFFF
 Server Type: File Server
 Frame Number: 335

NOV: General Service Query  [Normal] Mar 13@19:46:14.5054544
 From Node: 00-00-C0-4E-B5-EC, MUSCLE
 00000000-0000C04EB5EC      --> 00000000-FFFFFFFFFFFF
 Server Type: File Server
 Frame Number: 344

TCP: Close Connection   [Normal] Mar 13@19:46:27.4038468
 220.100.100.8      <-> 220.100.100.150
 220.100.100.8     SILO
 Port: 1043     NETBIOS 139
 Tx Packets: 10    8
 Low Window: 0     0
 Retrans: 0     0
 Connection Duration: 0:00:02.0613844
 Frame Number(s): 407

NOV: Nearest Service Query  [Normal] Mar 13@19:46:39.9998894
 From Node: 00-00-C0-E9-9C-B1, WstDigE99CB1
 00000000-0000C0E99CB1      --> 00000000-FFFFFFFFFFFF
 Server Type: File Server
 Frame Number: 472

NOV: Routing Information Reply [Normal] Mar 13@19:47:10.544317
 To Node: FF-FF-FF-FF-FF-FF, Broadcast
 00000000-006094A5CCEE      --> 00000000-FFFFFFFFFFFF
 Network number: 00000002
 Number of hops: 1    Number of ticks: 2
 Frame Number: 488

TCP: Reset Connection   [Warning] Mar 13@19:47:19.720187
 220.100.100.12        --> 220.100.100.53
 BRAINS        CHEROKEE
 Port: NETBIOS 139     1111
 Tx Packets: 1     0
 Low Window: 0      0
 Retrans: 0      0
 Connection Duration: 0:00:00.0
 Frame Number(s): 489

NOV: General Service Query  [Normal] Mar 13@19:47:39.960695
 From Node: 00-00-C0-E9-9C-B1, WstDigE99CB1
 00000000-0000C0E99CB1      --> 00000000-FFFFFFFFFFFF
 Server Type: File Server
 Frame Number: 562

TCP: Reset Connection [Warning] Mar 13@19:47:47.6089335
 220.100.100.41     --> 220.100.100.53
       CHEROKEE
 Port: NETBIOS 139    1136
 Tx Packets: 1    0
```

Figure 8.44 *(Continued)*

```
Low Window: 0    0
Retrans: 0    0
Connection Duration: 0:00:00.0
Frame Number(s): 566


TCP: Close Connection   [Normal] Mar 13@19:48:07.5697698
 220.100.100.19    <-> 220.100.100.150
         SILO
Port: 1029    NETBIOS 139
Tx Packets: 10    8
Low Window: 0    0
Retrans: 0    0
Connection Duration: 0:00:02.0748997
Frame Number(s): 658


NOV: Routing Information Reply [Normal] Mar 13@19:48:10.5430294
 To Node: FF-FF-FF-FF-FF-FF, Broadcast
 00000000-006094A5CCEE    --> 00000000-FFFFFFFFFFFF
 Network number: 00000002
 Number of hops: 1  Number of ticks: 2
 Frame Number: 697


TCP: Reset Connection  [Warning] Mar 13@19:48:31.2433202
 220.100.100.77    --> 220.100.100.53
           CHEROKEE
Port: NETBIOS 139    1143
Tx Packets: 1    0
Low Window: 0    0
Retrans: 0    0
Connection Duration: 0:00:00.0
Frame Number(s): 1545


NOV: Nearest Service Query  [Normal] Mar 13@19:48:39.9249748
 From Node: 00-00-C0-E9-9C-B1, WstDigE99CB1
 00000000-0000C0E99CB1    --> 00000000-FFFFFFFFFFFF
 Server Type: File Server
 Frame Number: 1858


TCP: Reset Connection [Warning] Mar 13@19:48:49.3872264
 220.100.100.61    --> 220.100.100.53
 THE-HOSTAGE    CHEROKEE
Port: NETBIOS 139    1139
Tx Packets: 1    0
Low Window: 0    0
Retrans: 0    0
Connection Duration: 0:00:00.0
Frame Number(s): 1899


NOV: Nearest Service Query  [Normal] Mar 13@19:49:01.7757016
 From Node: 00-00-C0-4E-B5-EC, MUSCLE
 00000000-0000C04EB5EC    --> 00000000-FFFFFFFFFFFF
 Server Type: File Server
 Frame Number: 1920


NOV: Nearest Service Query  [Normal] Mar 13@19:49:02.4938427
 From Node: 00-00-C0-4E-B5-EC, MUSCLE
```

Figure 8.44 *(Continued)*

```
00000000-0000C04EB5EC        --> 00000000-FFFFFFFFFFFF
Server Type: File Server
Frame Number: 1921

NOV: Nearest Service Query  [Normal] Mar 13@19:49:03.2149768
 From Node: 00-00-C0-4E-B5-EC, MUSCLE
 00000000-0000C04EB5EC        --> 00000000-FFFFFFFFFFFF
 Server Type: File Server
 Frame Number: 1922

NOV: Nearest Service Query  [Normal] Mar 13@19:49:03.936104
 From Node: 00-00-C0-4E-B5-EC, MUSCLE
 00000000-0000C04EB5EC        --> 00000000-FFFFFFFFFFFF
 Server Type: File Server
 Frame Number: 1923

NOV: Nearest Service Query  [Normal] Mar 13@19:49:04.6572385
 From Node: 00-00-C0-4E-B5-EC, MUSCLE
 00000000-0000C04EB5EC        --> 00000000-FFFFFFFFFFFF
 Server Type: File Server
 Frame Number: 1924

NOV: Nearest Service Query  [Normal] Mar 13@19:49:05.3783097
 From Node: 00-00-C0-4E-B5-EC, MUSCLE
 00000000-0000C04EB5EC        --> 00000000-FFFFFFFFFFFF
 Server Type: File Server
 Frame Number: 1925

NOV: Nearest Service Query  [Normal] Mar 13@19:49:06.0994503
 From Node: 00-00-C0-4E-B5-EC, MUSCLE
 00000000-0000C04EB5EC        --> 00000000-FFFFFFFFFFFF
 Server Type: File Server
 Frame Number: 1926

NOV: Nearest Service Query  [Normal] Mar 13@19:49:06.8205179
 From Node: 00-00-C0-4E-B5-EC, MUSCLE
 00000000-0000C04EB5EC        --> 00000000-FFFFFFFFFFFF
 Server Type: File Server
 Frame Number: 1927

NOV: Nearest Service Query  [Normal] Mar 13@19:49:07.5416253
 From Node: 00-00-C0-4E-B5-EC, MUSCLE
 00000000-0000C04EB5EC        --> 00000000-FFFFFFFFFFFF
 Server Type: File Server
 Frame Number: 1932

NOV: Nearest Service Query  [Normal] Mar 13@19:49:08.2627509
 From Node: 00-00-C0-4E-B5-EC, MUSCLE
 00000000-0000C04EB5EC        --> 00000000-FFFFFFFFFFFF
 Server Type: File Server
 Frame Number: 1933

NOV: General Service Query  [Normal] Mar 13@19:49:08.9838831
 From Node: 00-00-C0-4E-B5-EC, MUSCLE
 00000000-0000C04EB5EC        --> 00000000-FFFFFFFFFFFF
```

Figure 8.44 *(Continued)*

```
Server Type: File Server
Frame Number: 1934

NOV: General Service Query  [Normal] Mar 13@19:49:09.7049542
  From Node: 00-00-C0-4E-B5-EC, MUSCLE
  00000000-0000C04EB5EC       --> 00000000-FFFFFFFFFFFF
  Server Type: File Server
  Frame Number: 1935

NOV: General Service Query  [Normal] Mar 13@19:49:10.426067
  From Node: 00-00-C0-4E-B5-EC, MUSCLE
  00000000-0000C04EB5EC       --> 00000000-FFFFFFFFFFFF
  Server Type: File Server
  Frame Number: 1937

NOV: Routing Information Reply [Normal] Mar 13@19:49:10.5417939
  To Node: FF-FF-FF-FF-FF-FF, Broadcast
  00000000-006094A5CCEE       --> 00000000-FFFFFFFFFFFF
  Network number: 00000002
  Number of hops: 1 Number of ticks: 2
  Frame Number: 1938

NOV: General Service Query  [Normal] Mar 13@19:49:11.1471537
  From Node: 00-00-C0-4E-B5-EC, MUSCLE
  00000000-0000C04EB5EC       --> 00000000-FFFFFFFFFFFF
  Server Type: File Server
  Frame Number: 1939

NOV: General Service Query  [Normal] Mar 13@19:49:39.8876314
  From Node: 00-00-C0-E9-9C-B1, WstDigE99CB1
  00000000-0000C0E99CB1       --> 00000000-FFFFFFFFFFFF
  Server Type: File Server
  Frame Number: 2002
```

Figure 8.44 *(Continued)*

Connection, and other functions. A time stamp that yields the hour is also indicated. This and other information provided show a wealth of insights into different aspects of the network operation. This level of information is critical to have after the network is designed and installed. What is helpful is to see the information that can be obtained prior to your network design. In the case of my network, the HP Internet Advisor is indispensable.

Another type of information that the Internet Advisor can obtain is the 802.3/Ethernet Decode. The following is a view of detailed information on all frames. Afterward, consider the synthesis of this level of information.

```
*******************************************************************  *****
HEWLETT PACKARD INTERNET ADVISOR  *****
*****    *****
*****   Measurement:  802.3/Ethernet Decode      *****
*****   Print Type: All Frames          *****
*****   Open Views: Detailed          *****
*****   Display Mode: Viewing All Frames      *****
*****   Print Date: 03/13/98          *****
```

```
*****  Print Time: 20:4:31              *****
*****                     *****
********************************************************************

_____
Frame: 1    Time: Mar 13@20:02:56.9192136 Length: 64

Destination address  Broadcast  Broadcast
Source address    220.100.100.8 Individual, global
Type          08-06        ARP
> Data size    46
Frame check sequence    8E-69-77-43
_____
Frame: 2    Time: Mar 13@20:02:58.4297056 Length: 64

Destination address  Broadcast  Broadcast
Source address    220.100.100.8  Individual, global
Type          08-06        ARP
> Data size    46
Frame check sequence    1E-DE-8C-55
_____
Frame: 3    Time: Mar 13@20:02:59.9403448 Length: 64

Destination address  Broadcast  Broadcast
Source address    220.100.100.8   Individual, global
Type          08-06        ARP
> Data size    46
Frame check sequence    8E-69-77-43
_____
Frame: 4    Time: Mar 13@20:03:01.6672512 Length: 65

Destination address  03-00-00-00-00-01 Group, local
Source address     220.100.100.8   Individual, global
Length      47
> Data size    47
Frame check sequence   F4-31-89-29
_____
Frame: 5    Time: Mar 13@20:03:01.6676236 Length: 65

Destination address  220.100.100.8  Individual, global
Source address    CHEROKEE       Individual, global
Length      47
> Data size    47
Frame check sequence   3A-9A-CD-F5
_____
Frame: 6    Time: Mar 13@20:03:01.6679466 Length: 64

Destination address   CHEROKEE     Individual, global
Source address      220.100.100.8 Individual, global
Length     3
> Data size   3
Padding:
 00-06-04-00-01-00-00-C0 7D-73-D7-DC-64-64-08-00
 00-00-00-00-00-DC-64-64 4D-02-53-BF-8B-50-18-15
 38-81-A1-00-00-00-00-00 23-FF-53
Frame check sequence   20-62-02-76
_____
Frame: 7    Time: Mar 13@20:03:01.6681270 Length: 64

Destination address  220.100.100.8  Individual, global
Source address    CHEROKEE       Individual, global
```

```
Length      3
> Data size    3
Padding:
 00-00-00-00-00-00-00-00 00-00-00-00-00-00-00-00
 00-00-00-00-00-00-00-00 00-00-00-00-00-00-00-00
 00-00-00-00-00-00-00-00 00-00-00
Frame check sequence  66-1B-6E-95
```

```
Frame: 8     Time: Mar 13@20:03:01.6683975 Length: 64

Destination address  CHEROKEE      Individual, global
Source address        220.100.100.8 Individual, global
Length      4
> Data size    4
Padding:
 00-FF-EF-0A-17-30-00-00 00-30-00-43-48-45-52-4F
 4B-45-45-20-20-20-20-20 20-20-20-46-41-54-20-42
 4F-59-20-20-20-20-20-20 20-20
Frame check sequence  47-41-9D-7D
```

```
Frame: 9     Time: Mar 13@20:03:01.6685602 Length: 64

Destination address   220.100.100.8 Individual, global
Source address        CHEROKEE      Individual, global
Length      4
> Data size    4
Padding:
 00-00-00-00-00-00-00-00 00-00-00-00-00-00-00-00
 00-00-00-00-00-00-00-00 00-00-00-00-00-00-00-00
 00-00-00-00-00-00-00-00 00-00
Frame check sequence  49-07-D3-43
```

```
Frame: 10    Time: Mar 13@20:03:01.6688476 Length: 64

Destination address  CHEROKEE      Individual, global
Source address        220.100.100.8 Individual, global
Length     18
> Data size   18
Padding:
 00-00-00-00-00-00-DC-64 64-4D-02-53-BF-8B-50-18
 15-38-81-A1-00-00-00-00 00-23-FF-53
Frame check sequence 93-AD-15-BE
```

```
Frame: 11    Time: Mar 13@20:03:01.6690630 Length: 64

Destination address  220.100.100.8 Individual, global
Source address        CHEROKEE      Individual, global
Length      4
> Data size    4
Padding:
 00-00-00-00-00-00-00-00 00-00-00-00-00-00-00-00
 00-00-00-00-00-00-00-00 00-00-00-00-00-00-00-00
 00-00-00-00-00-00-00-00 00-00
Frame check sequence  BF-EA-F4-CD
```

```
Frame: 12    Time: Mar 13@20:03:01.6691318 Length: 64

Destination address  220.100.100.8  Individual, global
Source address        CHEROKEE       Individual, global
Length     18
> Data size   18
```

```
Padding:
 00-00-00-00-00-00-00-00 00-00-00-00-00-00-00-00
 00-00-00-00-00-00-00-00 00-00-00-00
Frame check sequence  A4-37-97-40
```

```
Frame: 13    Time: Mar 13@20:03:01.6694761 Length: 64
```

```
Destination address  CHEROKEE      Individual, global
Source address    220.100.100.8  Individual, global
Length      4
> Data size    4
Padding:
 00-FF-EF-0A-17-30-00-00 00-30-00-43-48-45-52-4F
 4B-45-45-20-20-20-20-20 20-20-20-46-41-54-20-42
 4F-59-20-20-20-20-20-20 20-20
Frame check sequence  FD-84-2C-50
```

```
Frame: 14    Time: Mar 13@20:03:01.6701895 Length: 190
```

```
Destination address  CHEROKEE      Individual, global
Source address    220.100.100.8  Individual, global
Length      172     Partial packet store
> Data size    86
> Sliced data
```

```
Frame: 15    Time: Mar 13@20:03:01.6706443 Length: 123
```

```
Destination address  220.100.100.8 Individual, global
Source address      CHEROKEE      Individual, global
Length      105        Partial packet store
> Data size    86
> Sliced data
```

```
Frame: 16    Time: Mar 13@20:03:01.6710735 Length: 64
```

```
Destination address  CHEROKEE      Individual, global
Source address    220.100.100.8  Individual, global
Length      4
> Data size    4
Padding:
 00-FF-EF-0A-17-30-00-00 00-30-00-43-48-45-52-4F
 4B-45-45-20-20-20-20-20 20-20-20-46-41-54-20-42
 4F-59-20-20-20-20-20-20 20-20
Frame check sequence  5D-42-26-5E
```

```
Frame: 17    Time: Mar 13@20:03:01.6725487 Length: 189
```

```
Destination address  CHEROKEE      Individual, global
Source address    220.100.100.8  Individual, global
Length      171        Partial packet store
> Data size    86
> Sliced data
```

```
Frame: 18    Time: Mar 13@20:03:01.6833829 Length: 130
```

```
Destination address 220.100.100.8 Individual, global
Source address      CHEROKEE      Individual, global
Length      112        Partial packet store
> Data size    86
> Sliced data
```

```
Frame: 19    Time: Mar 13@20:03:01.6838061 Length: 64


Destination address CHEROKEE       Individual, global
Source address    220.100.100.8   Individual, global
Length     4
> Data size    4
Padding:
 00-FF-EF-0A-17-30-00-00 00-30-00-43-48-45-52-4F
 4B-45-45-20-20-20-20-20 20-20-20-46-41-54-20-42
 4F-59-20-20-20-20-20-20 20-20
Frame check sequence AB-AF-01-D0
```

```
Frame: 20    Time: Mar 13@20:03:01.6843194 Length: 145


Destination address  CHEROKEE           Individual, global
Source address       220.100.100.8   Individual, global
Length           127         Partial packet store
> Data size       86
> Sliced data
```

```
Frame: 21    Time: Mar 13@20:03:01.6953938 Length: 568


Destination address  220.100.100.8  Individual, global
Source address       CHEROKEE           Individual, global
Length           550         Partial packet store
> Data size       86
> Sliced data
```

```
Frame: 22    Time: Mar 13@20:03:01.6967575 Length: 64


Destination address  CHEROKEE           Individual, global
Source address       220.100.100.8   Individual, global
Length     4
> Data size    4
Padding:
 00-FF-EF-0A-17-30-00-00 00-30-00-43-48-45-52-4F
 4B-45-45-20-20-20-20-20 20-20-20-46-41-54-20-42
 4F-59-20-20-20-20-20-20 20-20
Frame check sequence  EB-22-14-CC
```

```
Frame: 23    Time: Mar 13@20:03:01.7274710 Length: 64


Destination address  CHEROKEE           Individual, global
Source address       220.100.100.8 Individual, global
Length       18
> Data size    18
Padding:
 FF-53-4D-42-25-00-00-00 00-00-00-80-00-00-00-00
 00-00-00-00-00-00-00-00 01-08-BB-14
Frame check sequence  F9-E9-49-5B
```

```
Frame: 24    Time: Mar 13@20:03:01.7276453 Length: 64


Destination address  220.100.100.8   Individual, global
Source address       CHEROKEE           Individual, global
Length     4
> Data size    4
Padding:
 00-00-00-00-00-00-00-00 00-00-00-00-00-00-00-00
```

```
00-00-00-00-00-00-00-00 00-00-00-00-00-00-00-00
00-00-00-00-00-00-00-00 00-00
Frame check sequence  A4-57-F8-98
```

```
Frame: 25    Time: Mar 13@20:03:03.3579381 Length: 64

Destination address  Broadcast     Broadcast
Source address       220.100.100.8  Individual, global
Type            08-06      ARP
> Data size    46
Frame check sequence   20-1A-22-FA
```

```
Frame: 26    Time: Mar 13@20:03:03.5655960 Length: 65

Destination address 03-00-00-00-00-01 Group, local
Source address     220.100.100.8    Individual, global
Length      47
> Data size     47
Frame check sequence  E5-04-DF-65
```

```
Frame: 27    Time: Mar 13@20:03:03.5668637 Length: 65

Destination address  220.100.100.8   Individual, global
Source address       SILO       Individual, global
Length      47
> Data size     47
Frame check sequence  99-9F-D2-6F
```

```
Frame: 28    Time: Mar 13@20:03:03.5672027 Length: 64

Destination address  SILO       Individual, global
Source address       220.100.100.8  Individual, global
Length     3
> Data size    3
Padding:
 00-06-04-00-01-00-00-C0 7D-73-D7-DC-64-64-08-00
 00-00-00-00-00-DC-64-64 4D-20-20-20-46-41-54-20
 42-4F-59-20-20-20-20-20 20-20-20
Frame check sequence  AD-D6-F0-E6
```

```
Frame: 29    Time: Mar 13@20:03:03.5678517 Length: 64

Destination address  220.100.100.8   Individual, global
Source address       SILO       Individual, global
Length     3
> Data size    3
Padding:
 FF-FF-FF-FF-FF-FF-FF-FF FF-FF-FF-FF-FF-FF-FF-FF
 FF-FF-FF-FF-FF-FF-FF-FF FF-FF-FF-FF-FF-FF-FF-FF
 FF-FF-FF-FF-FF-FF-FF-FF FF-FF-FF
Frame check sequence 56-42-97-30
```

```
Frame: 30    Time: Mar 13@20:03:03.5681241 Length: 64

Destination address  SILO       Individual, global
Source address       220.100.100.8  Individual, global
Length     4
> Data size    4
Padding:
 00-FF-EF-0A-17-31-00-00 00-31-00-53-49-4C-4F-20
```

```
20-20-20-20-20-20-20-20 20-20-20-46-41-54-20-42
4F-59-20-20-20-20-20-20 20-20
Frame check sequence  45-C9-1F-6B
```

```
Frame: 31    Time: Mar 13@20:03:03.5762576 Length: 64

Destination address  220.100.100.8   Individual, global
Source address       SILO         Individual, global
Length     4
> Data size     4
Padding:
 FF-FF-FF-FF-FF-FF-FF-FF FF-FF-FF-FF-FF-FF-FF-FF
 FF-FF-FF-FF-FF-FF-FF-FF FF-FF-FF-FF-FF-FF-FF-FF
 FF-FF-FF-FF-FF-FF-FF-FF FF-FF
Frame check sequence B5-8D-1C-0D
```

```
Frame: 32    Time: Mar 13@20:03:03.5765530 Length: 64

Destination address     SILO        Individual, global
Source address          220.100.100.8  Individual, global
Length    18
> Data size    18
Padding:
 00-00-00-00-00-00-DC-64 64-4D-20-20-20-46-41-54
 20-42-4F-59-20-20-20-20 20-20-20-20
Frame check sequence  34-5F-09-87
```

```
Frame: 33    Time: Mar 13@20:03:03.5768360 Length: 64

Destination address  220.100.100.8   Individual, global
Source address       SILO         Individual, global
Length     4
> Data size     4
Padding:
 10-65-00-00-40-06-E3-53 DC-64-64-96-DC-64-64-0C
 00-8B-04-95-BC-08-EC-B0 02-47-4D-3C-50-10-10-00
 1B-60-00-00-FF-FF-FF-FF FF-FF
Frame check sequence 5E-04-1A-D6
```

```
Frame: 34    Time: Mar 13@20:03:03.5772064 Length: 64

Destination address  220.100.100.8  Individual, global
Source address       SILO         Individual, global
Length    18
> Data size    18
Padding:
 FF-FF-FF-FF-FF-FF-FF-FF FF-FF-FF-FF-FF-FF-FF-FF
 FF-FF-FF-FF-FF-FF-FF-FF FF-FF-FF-FF
Frame check sequence  AD-5B-8C-60
```

```
Frame: 35    Time: Mar 13@20:03:03.5774858 Length: 64

Destination address  SILO        Individual, global
Source address       220.100.100.8  Individual, global
Length     4
> Data size    4
Padding:
 00-FF-EF-0A-17-31-00-00 00-31-00-53-49-4C-4F-20
 20-20-20-20-20-20-20-20 20-20-20-46-41-54-20-42
 4F-59-20-20-20-20-20-20 20-20
```

```
Frame check sequence   04-FA-BD-01
```

```
Frame: 36    Time: Mar 13@20:03:03.8540212 Length: 71

Destination address  CHEROKEE       Individual, global
Source address      220.100.100.8 Individual, global
Length      53
> Data size    53
Frame check sequence   50-18-B5-38
```

```
Frame: 37    Time: Mar 13@20:03:03.8543697 Length: 71

Destination address  220.100.100.8  Individual, global
Source address       CHEROKEE       Individual, global
Length      53
> Data size    53
Frame check sequence   14-F9-A7-A2
```

```
Frame: 38    Time: Mar 13@20:03:03.8547697 Length: 64

Destination address  CHEROKEE       Individual, global
Source address      220.100.100.8  Individual, global
Length      18
> Data size    18
Padding:
 4F-20-20-20-20-20-20-20 20-20-20-20-20-46-41-54
 20-42-4F-59-20-20-20-20 20-20-20-20
Frame check sequence  DE-8D-26-6E
```

```
Frame: 39    Time: Mar 13@20:03:03.8549544 Length: 64

Destination address  220.100.100.8  Individual, global
Source address       CHEROKEE       Individual, global
Length      4
> Data size    4
Padding:
 00-00-00-00-00-00-00-00 00-00-00-00-00-00-00-00
 00-00-00-00-00-00-00-00 00-00-00-00-00-00-00-00
 00-00-00-00-00-00-00-00 00-00
Frame check sequence   09-8A-C6-5F
```

```
Frame: 40    Time: Mar 13@20:03:03.8552476 Length: 64

Destination address  CHEROKEE       Individual, global
Source address      220.100.100.8  Individual, global
Length      18
> Data size    18
Padding:
 FF-53-4D-42-71-00-00-00 00-00-01-80-00-00-00-00
 00-00-00-00-00-00-00-00 01-08-00-00
Frame check sequence  FC-6F-C1-6A
```

```
Frame: 41    Time: Mar 13@20:03:03.8554348 Length: 64

Destination address  220.100.100.8  Individual, global
Source address       CHEROKEE       Individual, global
Length      4
> Data size    4
Padding:
 00-00-00-00-00-00-00-00 00-00-00-00-00-00-00-00
```

```
00-00-00-00-00-00-00-00 00-00-00-00-00-00-00-00
00-00-00-00-00-00-00-00 00-00
Frame check sequence  7F-7D-CA-E9
```

```
Frame: 42    Time: Mar 13@20:03:03.8557614 Length: 64

Destination address  CHEROKEE        Individual, global
Source address       220.100.100.8  Individual, global
Length      3
> Data size    3
Padding:
 0B-0E-00-FF-EF-14-00-00 00-04-00-00-00-05-30-4F
 20-20-20-20-20-20-20-20 20-20-20-20-46-41-54-20
 42-4F-59-20-20-20-20-20 20-20-20
Frame check sequence  3C-F0-22-3F
```

```
Frame: 43    Time: Mar 13@20:03:03.8559136 Length: 64

Destination address  220.100.100.8  Individual, global
Source address       CHEROKEE        Individual, global
Length      3
> Data size    3
Padding:
 00-00-00-00-00-00-00-00 00-00-00-00-00-00-00-00
 00-00-00-00-00-00-00-00 00-00-00-00-00-00-00-00
 00-00-00-00-00-00-00-00 00-00-00
Frame check sequence  66-1B-6E-95
```

```
Frame: 44    Time: Mar 13@20:03:04.8565401 Length: 64

Destination address  Broadcast      Broadcast
Source address       220.100.100.8  Individual, global
Type        08-06  ARP
> Data size    46
Frame check sequence  36-08-6B-61
```

```
Frame: 45    Time: Mar 13@20:03:06.3670765 Length: 64

Destination address  Broadcast      Broadcast
Source address       220.100.100.8  Individual, global
Type        08-06  ARP
> Data size    46
Frame check sequence  20-1A-22-FA
```

```
Frame: 46    Time: Mar 13@20:03:06.7809019 Length: 64

Destination address  Broadcast  Broadcast
Source address       BRAINS     Individual, global
Type        08-06  ARP
> Data size    46
Frame check sequence  CE-8F-B9-E2
```

```
Frame: 47    Time: Mar 13@20:03:06.7812445 Length: 64

Destination address  BRAINS         Individual, global
Source address       220.100.100.8  Individual, global
Type        08-06  ARP
> Data size    46
Frame check sequence  8A-03-34-7C
```

```
Frame: 48     Time: Mar 13@20:03:06.7816335 Length: 126

Destination address   220.100.100.8    Individual, global
Source address        BRAINS           Individual, global
Type        08-00     IP
> Data size     86
> Sliced data
```

```
Frame: 49     Time: Mar 13@20:03:06.7823637 Length: 105

Destination address  BRAINS           Individual, global
Source address       220.100.100.8    Individual, global
Type        08-00    IP
> Data size     86
> Sliced data
```

```
Frame: 50     Time: Mar 13@20:03:06.7834375 Length: 140

Destination address  220.100.100.8    Individual, global
Source address       BRAINS           Individual, global
Type        08-00    IP
> Data size     86
> Sliced data
```

```
Frame: 51     Time: Mar 13@20:03:06.7841119 Length: 97

Destination address  BRAINS           Individual, global
Source address       220.100.100.8    Individual, global
Type        08-00    IP
> Data size     79
Frame check sequence   6B-39-72-1F
```

```
Frame: 52     Time: Mar 13@20:03:06.7974856 Length: 161

Destination address  220.100.100.8   Individual, global
Source address       BRAINS          Individual, global
Type        08-00    IP
> Data size     86
> Sliced data
```

```
Frame: 53     Time: Mar 13@20:03:06.7990992 Length: 687

Destination address  BRAINS          Individual, global
Source address       220.100.100.8   Individual, global
Type        08-00    IP
> Data size     86
> Sliced data
```

```
Frame: 54     Time: Mar 13@20:03:06.8081367 Length: 140

Destination address  220.100.100.8   Individual, global
Source address       BRAINS          Individual, global
Type        08-00     IP
> Data size     86
> Sliced data
```

```
Frame: 55     Time: Mar 13@20:03:06.8088484 Length: 97

Destination address  BRAINS            Individual, global
```

```
Source address       220.100.100.8    Individual, global
Type         08-00    IP
> Data size     79
Frame check sequence    C0-B3-14-66
```

This snapshot from the network reflects 55 frames. The destination and source addresses identify the directional flow of data. This is important because knowing this can help you understand how and what two nodes are communicating on a network. This level of information is informative when you begin to baseline your network. To do this, you need an Internet Advisor. The level of information that can be obtained here can also help you understand the flow of data between hosts. Length and type of data frames also provide information about the hosts communicating on the network, and this information can be used to deduce network traffic loads at given intervals. Having information that can be referenced that includes date and times of the traffic provides a reference point for aspects of network maintenance such as future planning for expanding the network and adding or removing various segments of the network. Later, I will provide additional information that the Internet Advisor obtained for me during the operation and maintenance of my network.

I recommend that you contact HP for additional information. They can be reached at

www.hp.com
Hewlett-Packard
5070 Centennial Blvd.
Colorado Springs, CO 80919

8.7 Network Uninterruptible Power Supplies

A UPS is a device that is prepared to provide interim power. This device should be baselined, and all pertinent information logged and maintained for reference in future troubleshooting scenarios.

UPSs are not a solution to power outages; they are an interim solution to bridge the time when power ceases and is restored. Large UPSs may be able to provide a considerable number of minutes or even hours of uptime. However, UPS use presupposes that power from the electric company will be restored or an alternative power supply will be provided from a source such as a generator.

Because of the amount of equipment in my network, Liebert's reputation, and the quality of their products, I selected a 15-kVA UPS from Liebert. Consider Figure 8.45, which shows the network equipment used. It also shows the Liebert UPS as the power protection device used to accommodate all the equipment in the network. Now consider Figure 8.46, which shows the rear view of the UPS I used in my network. A great advantage of the UPS is the accessibility of components that need to be accessed.

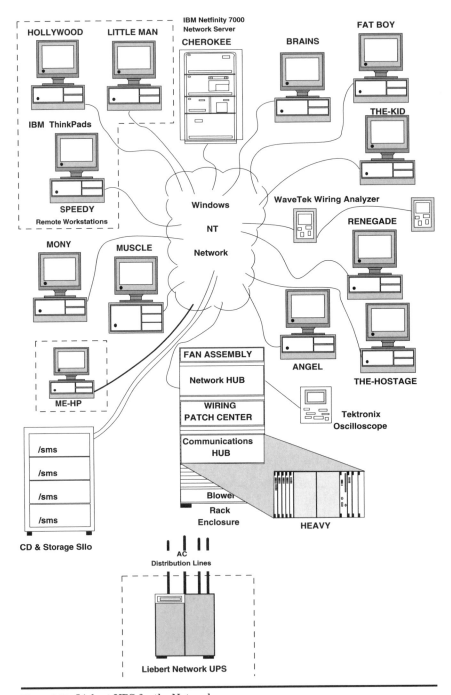

Figure 8.45 Liebert UPS for the Network

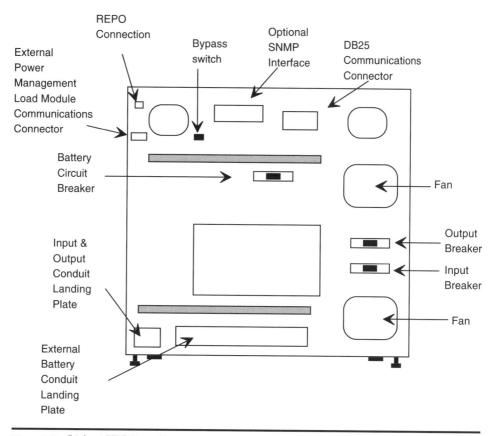

Figure 8.46   Liebert UPS Rear View

After determining the size of UPS I needed, I decided that I needed one with an apparent power of 15 kVA. It arrived weighing in over 800 lb. With the person who made the delivery helping, it took only an hour to get the well-packed UPS in the prepared place I had reserved for it. About 2 weeks before the UPS arrived I decided on the location where I wanted to receive it from the shipper. I marked off the locations to ensure that enough unobstructed space would be available. Doing this level of preplanning saved a lot of time.

As I mentioned, it took only about an hour to get the UPS into the place I had prepared to receive it. It then took approximately an hour to get it unpacked and in its final resting place. Believe me, moving an 800-lb UPS is not something I want to do on a daily basis. Now that you are reading this, take the time to make this level of plans for yourself. If you do, the people who work with you will be all the happier. If you do not, well, you just may have a sizable amount of weight arrive on pallet and have nowhere to put it.

If you are new to the networking industry, take advantage of my experience and plan similarly.

Another function of the Liebert UPS used in my network is its participation in the network via the SNMP interface. Liebert did an excellent job making the UPS functional with existing SNMP protocol standards. It supports standard MIB definitions and interoperates well in the network. The SNMP interface is optional on the UPStation S UPSs from Liebert, and this is advantageous for those purchasing UPSs because not all networks will use an SNMP network management application. The crux of the matter is that it saves the customer money.

The 15-kVA Liebert UPS requires wiring into the load center of the facility in which it is operating. I recommend that you obtain the services of a licensed electrician to assist you in your preplanning, especially during the installation of the UPS (or contact Liebert). Working with equipment like this is no trivial task, and it should not be played with because it can kill you. I don't mean to promote fear; I simply want you to understand that wiring in a UPS as large as the one I have is only for those who have some training in electricity or who plan to implement the UPS under the guidance of a licensed electrician. Consider Figure 8.47, which consists of three parts: the ac load center that feeds alternating current to the facility where the network is located (lower right), a highlighted view of the UPS wired into the load center (upper right), and a conceptual view of how some of the equipment is connected to the UPS (left).

This is the basic overview of how the UPS fits into the network. It is more complex than this because of all the equipment that the UPS protects. Because the UPS is capable of protecting the entire network, approximately four output feeds (lines with outlets) were required to accommodate all components.

This is an overview of the UPS used in this network; many more details could be included, but the significance here is to provide baseline information. Your situation will vary; however, consider how I implemented the UPS here as a reference point for thought.

In order to do the Liebert UPS justice, and provide an example of significant information you should have included in your baselining procedure, I present the Liebert documentation here for the UPS I used. Consider this as a very good example of what you'll need when you baseline your UPS. The information presented here is an adaptation of the actual Liebert documentation for the Liebert UPStation S UPS (copyright © 1995, 1996, 1997, 1998, Liebert Corporation).

This specification defines the electrical and mechanical characteristics and requirements for a continuous-duty, single-phase, solid-state, uninterruptible power supply system. The uninterruptible power supply system, hereafter referred to as the UPS, shall provide high-quality ac power for sensitive electronic equipment loads.

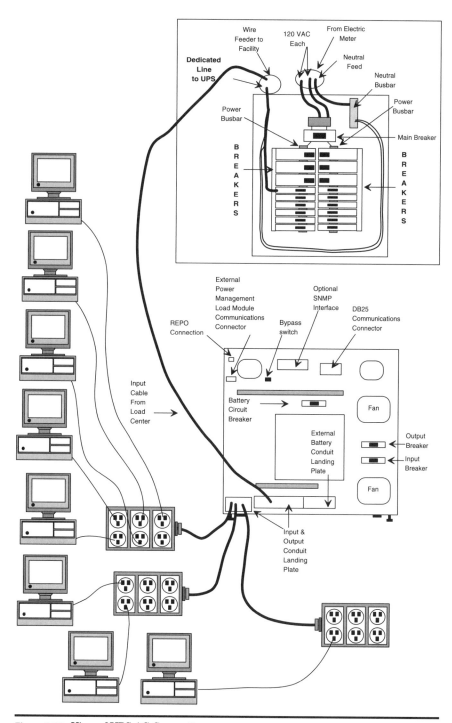

Figure 8.47 View of UPS AC Connection

Standards

The UPS shall be designed in accordance with the applicable sections of the current revision of the following documents. Where a conflict arises between these documents and statements made herein, the statements in this specification shall govern.

- ANSI C62.41-1980 (IEEE 587), Categories A and B
- ASME
- CSA 22.2, No. 107.1
- FCC Part 15, Subpart J, Class A
- National Electrical Code (NFPA 70)
- NEMA PE-l
- OSHA
- UL Standard 1778

The UPS is UL-listed to UL Standard 1778, and is CSA-certified.

System description (modes of operation)

The UPS shall be designed to operate as a true online system in the following modes:

A. Normal: The critical ac load is continuously supplied by the UPS inverter. The input converter derives power from a utility ac source and supplies dc power to the inverter. The battery charger shall maintain a float charge on the battery.

B. Backup: On failure of utility ac power, the critical ac load is supplied by the inverter, which obtains power from the battery. There shall be no interruption in power to the critical load on failure or restoration of the utility ac source.

C. Recharge: On restoration of utility ac power, after a utility ac power outage, the input converter shall automatically restart and resume supplying power to the inverter. Also the battery charger shall recharge the battery.

D. Automatic restart: On restoration of utility ac power, after a utility ac power outage and complete battery discharge, the UPS shall automatically restart and resume supplying power to the critical load. Also the battery charger shall automatically recharge the battery. This feature shall be enabled from the factory and shall be capable of being disabled by the user.

E. Bypass: The factory-installed bypass (optional on 3.5- to 6.0-kVA UPS modules) shall provide an alternate path for power to the critical load that shall be capable of operating in the following manner:

1. Automatic: In the event of an internal failure, or should the inverter overload capacity be exceeded, the UPS shall perform an automatic transfer of the critical ac load from the inverter to the bypass source.
2. Manual: Should the UPS need to be taken out of service for limited maintenance or repair, manual activation of the bypass shall cause an immediate transfer of the critical ac load from the inverter to the bypass source. The input converter, inverter, and battery charging operations shall be inhibited until the switch is moved back to the "UPS" position and the unit restarted.

System performance requirements

A. Upgradability: Select UPS systems shall be field-upgradable to higher power ratings as follows:

3.5-kVA modules shall be field-upgradable to 4.5-kVA modules

3.5-kVA modules shall be field-upgradable to 6.0-kVA modules

4.5-kVA modules shall be field-upgradable to 6.0-kVA modules

8.0-kVA modules shall be field-upgradable to 10.0-kVA modules

8.0-kVA modules shall be field-upgradable to 12.0-kVA modules

10.0-kVA modules shall be field-upgradable to 12.0-kVA modules

15.0-kVA modules shall be field-upgradable to 18.0-kVA modules

B. Isolation: Input-to-output isolation shall be provided when operating in the UPS mode.

C. Remote Emergency Power Off: The UPS shall provide provisions for Remote Emergency Power Off capability.

Ac input to UPS

A. Voltage configuration: 176 to 264 V ac, single-phase, 3-wire-plus-ground. 2-wire-plus-ground can be utilized for 3.5- to 6.0-kVA UPS modules without the optional bypass. The UPS modules (8 to 18 kVA only) shall also be capable of three phase input to the rectifier. The UPS modules shall be capable of dual input to provide a separate power path for the bypass (optional on 8- to 18-kVA UPS modules only).

B. Frequency: 45 to 65 Hz.

C. Input current distortion: 5 percent THD maximum at full load. If three-phase input is utilized (available on 8- to 18-kVA units), maximum THD shall not exceed 30 percent.

D. Input power factor: 0.98 lagging minimum from 50 to 100 percent rated load.

E. Inrush current: 150 percent of full load input current maximum for 3 cycles.

F. Surge protection: Sustains input surges without damage per criteria listed in ANSI C62.41-1980 (IEEE 587), Categories A and B.

Ac output, UPS inverter

A. Voltage configuration: 208/120 V ac, single-phase, 3-wire-plus-ground. Field-programmable to 240/120 V ac, 230/115 V ac, 220/127 V ac, 220/110 V ac, 200/100 V ac. The UPS can also be ordered to supply line to neutral voltages of 240, 230, and 220 V ac.

B. Voltage regulation: ±2 percent steady state.

C. Frequency regulation: Field-selectable 50 or 60 Hz, ±0.01 percent.

D. Frequency slew rate: 1.0 Hz/s maximum. Field-selectable from 0.3, 0.5, 1, 2, or 3 Hz/s from the LCD display.

E. Bypass frequency synchronization range: ±1.0 Hz. Field-selectable from ±0.1 to ±5.0 Hz, in 0.1-Hz increments from the LCD display.

F. Voltage distortion: 3 percent total harmonic distortion (THD) maximum into a 100 percent linear load, 5 percent THD maximum into a 100 percent nonlinear load with crest factor ratio of 3:1.

G. Load power factor range: 0.5 lagging to 0.5 leading.

H. Output power rating: Rated kVA at 0.8 lagging power factor for 3.5- and 4.5-kVA models; 0.67 to 0.77 lagging power factor for 6.0-kVA models depending on output voltage; 0.75 lagging power factor for 8.0- and 10.0-kVA models; 0.7 lagging power factor for 12.0-, 15.0-, and 18.0-kVA models.

I. Inverter overload capability: 105 percent continuously, 125 percent for 10 min, 150 percent for 10 s, 250 percent for 12 cycles. For units with the bypass option installed, the load shall be transferred to bypass when any of the above conditions are exceeded.

J. Inverter output voltage adjustment: ±5 percent manual adjustment from the LCD by qualified service personnel.

K. Voltage transient response: ±5 percent maximum for any load step up to and including 100 percent of the UPS rating.

L. Transient recovery time: To within 1 percent of steady-state output voltage within 50 ms.

Batteries

A. Internal battery: The battery shall consist of sealed, valve-regulated, reduced-maintenance, lead acid cells. Flame-retardant batteries can also be provided, which renders the UPS suitable for installation inside a computer room per requirements of UL Standard 1778.

B. Reserve time (with ambient temperature between 20 and 30°C): The UPS shall contain an internal battery system to provide the following reserve time:

3.5 kVA/ 2.8 kW—18 min at full load
4.5 kVA/ 3.6 kW—12 min at full load
6.0 kVA/ 4.0 kW—11 min at full load
8.0 kVA/ 6.0 kW—17 min at full load
10.0 kVA/ 7.5 kW—11 min at full load
12.0 kVA/ 8.4 kW—10 min at full load
15.0 kVA/ 10.5 kW—14 min at full load
18.0 kVA/ 12.6 kW—10 min at full load

The UPS shall contain provisions to interface with an external matching battery cabinet to extend reserve time capabilities.

C. Battery recharge: To prolong battery life, the UPS shall contain temperature-compensated battery charging. Recharge time shall be 10 times discharge time to 95 percent capacity. (Field selectable to 20 times discharge time to 95 percent capacity from the LCD display.)

Environmental conditions

A. Ambient temperature

Operating: UPS 0 to 40°C; battery 20 to 30°C for optimum performance.
Storage: UPS −30 to +70°C; battery 0 to 32°C for maximum 6 months.

B. Relative humidity

Operating: 0–95% noncondensing.
Storage: 0–95% noncondensing.

C. Altitude

Operating: To 4000 ft. Derating or reduced operating temperature range required for higher altitudes.
Storage: To 50,000 ft.

D. Audible noise: Noise generated by the UPS during normal operation shall not exceed 55 dBA measured at 1 meter from the surface of the UPS.

E. Electrostatic discharge: The UPS shall be able to withstand a minimum 15 kV without damage and shall not affect the critical load.

User documentation

The specified UPS system shall be supplied with one (1) user's manual. Manuals shall include installation drawings and instructions, a functional description of the equipment with block diagrams, safety precautions, illustrations, step-by-step operating procedures, and routine maintenance guidelines.

Warranty

The UPS manufacturer shall warrant the UPS against defects in materials and workmanship for one (1) year. The warranty shall cover all parts for one

(1) year and on-site labor for 90 days. With the optional start-up provided by Customer Service and Support, the warranty shall cover all parts and on-site labor for one (1) year. Extended warranty packages shall also be available.

Quality assurance

A. Manufacturer qualifications: A minimum of 20 years' experience in the design, manufacture, and testing of solid-state UPS systems is required.

B. Factory testing: Before shipment, the manufacturer shall fully and completely test the system to assure compliance with the specification. These tests shall include operational discharge and recharge tests on the internal battery to guarantee rated performance.

Product fabrication

All materials and components making up the UPS shall be new, of current manufacture, and shall not have been in prior service except as required during factory testing. The UPS shall be constructed of replaceable subassemblies. All active electronic devices shall be solid-state.

Product wiring

Wiring practices, materials, and coding shall be in accordance with the requirements of the National Electrical Code (NFPA 70) and other applicable codes and standards.

Product cabinet

The UPS unit, comprising input converter, battery charger, inverter, bypass, and battery consisting of the appropriate number of sealed battery cells, shall be housed in a single freestanding NEMA type 1 enclosure and meets the requirements of IP20. The UPS cabinet shall be cleaned, primed, and painted with the manufacturer's standard color. Casters and leveling feet shall be provided. UPS cabinet dimensions shall not exceed {[select one: 9 in wide, 27 in deep, and 29 in high (for 3.5- to 6.0-kVA units]; [18 in wide, 27 in deep, and 29 in high (for 8.0- to 12.0-kVA units)]; [27 in wide, 27 in deep, and 29 in high (for 15.0- to 18.0-kVA units)]}.

Product cooling

The UPS shall be forced-air-cooled by internally mounted, variable speed fans to reduce audible noise.

Components

A. Input converter (general): Incoming ac power shall be converted to a regulated dc output by the input converter for supplying dc power to the inverter. The input converter shall provide input power factor and input current distortion correction. The input converter shall provide input to output isolation by means of a high-frequency transformer.

B. Ac input current limit: The input converter shall be provided with ac input current limiting whereby the maximum input current shall be limited to 125 percent of the full load input current rating.

C. Input protection: The UPS shall have built-in protection against under-voltage, overcurrent, and overvoltage conditions including low-energy surges, introduced on the primary ac source and the bypass source. The UPS shall sustain input surges without damage per criteria listed in ANSI C62.41-1980 (IEEE 587). The UPS shall contain {[select one: input fuses (3.5- to 6.0-kVA)]—or—[an input circuit breaker (8.0- to 18.0 kVA)]} sized to supply full rated load and to recharge the battery at the same time.

D. Battery recharge: To prolong battery life, the UPS shall contain two bat-tery recharge rates, and charging voltage shall be temperature-compensat-ed. The "turbo" mode of recharge shall be capable of recharging the battery to 95 percent capacity within 10 times the discharge time of the battery. The "slow" mode of recharge shall be capable of recharging the battery to 95 percent capacity within 20 times the discharge time. The factory default shall be "turbo" mode, and the microprocessor shall determine how often the faster recharge rate is employed to optimize battery life.

E. Charger output filter: The battery charger shall have an output filter to minimize ripple current into the battery. Under no conditions shall ripple current into the battery exceed 2 percent rms.

F. Overvoltage protection: There shall be dc overvoltage protection so that if the dc voltage exceeds the preset limit, the UPS shall shut down automati-cally and the critical load shall be transferred to bypass (if optional bypass is installed).

A. Inverter (general): The UPS shall contain two independently controlled inverters and shall be of a pulse-width-modulated (PWM) design capable of providing the specified ac output. The inverters shall convert dc power from the input converter output, or the battery, into precise regulated sine-wave ac power for supporting the critical ac load.

B. Overload: The inverter shall be capable of supplying current and voltage for overloads exceeding 100 percent and up to 150 percent of full load cur-rent. A visual indicator and audible alarm shall indicate overload opera-tion. For greater currents or longer time duration, the inverter shall have electronic current-limiting protection to prevent damage to components. The inverter shall be self-protecting against any magnitude of connected output overload. Inverter control logic shall sense and disconnect the inverter from the critical ac load without the requirement to clear protective fuses. For units supplied with the bypass option, the load shall be transferred to bypass when any of the above conditions are exceeded.

C. Inverter dc protection: The inverter shall be protected by the following dc shutdown levels:

Dc overvoltage shutdown

Dc undervoltage shutdown (end of discharge)

Dc undervoltage warning (low-battery reserve) shall be factory set at 2 min and user-adjustable from 1 to 99 min from the LCD display.

D. Inverter output voltage adjustment: The inverter shall employ a manual control to adjust the output voltage from ±5 percent of the nominal value from the LCD by qualified service personnel.

E. Output frequency: The output frequency of the inverter shall be controlled by an oscillator. The oscillator shall hold the inverter output frequency to ±0.01 percent for steady-state and transient conditions. For units equipped with a bypass, the inverter shall track the bypass continuously, provided the bypass source maintains a frequency within the user-selected synchronization range. If the bypass source fails to remain within the selected range, the inverter shall revert to the internal oscillator.

F. Output protection: The UPS inverter shall employ electronic current limiting and an output circuit breaker. The main output breaker shall be rated for a minimum of 10 kA IC.

G. Battery overdischarge protection: To prevent battery damage from overdischarging, the UPS control logic shall automatically raise the shutdown voltage set point as discharge time increases beyond 15 min.

Display and controls

A. General: The UPS shall be provided with a microprocessor-based unit status display and controls section designed for convenient and reliable user operation. The monitoring functions such as metering, status, and alarms shall be displayed on a 4-line × 16-character alphanumeric LCD display. Additional features of the LCD monitoring system shall include

Menu-driven display with text format

Real-time clock (time and date)

Alarm history with time and date stamp

Battery backed-up memory

B. Metering: The following parameters shall be displayed:

Input ac voltage line-to-line and line-to-neutral for each phase

Input ac current for each phase

Input frequency

Battery voltage

Battery charge/discharge current

Output ac voltage line-to-line and line-to-neutral for each phase

Output ac current for each phase

Output frequency

Percent of rated load being supplied by the UPS

Output kVA and kW for each phase

Battery time remaining during battery operation

Operating temperature of input converter, inverter, and internal battery

C. Status messages: The following UPS status messages shall be displayed:

Normal operation

UPS on battery

System shutdown

Start-up sequence aborted

Battery test enabled/disabled

System time set by operator

Load on bypass

D. Alarm messages: The following alarm messages shall be displayed:

Input power out of tolerance

UPS output not synchronized to input

Output undervoltage

Input power single-phased

Output overvoltage

Incorrect input frequency

Output overcurrent

Input in current-limit-charging batteries

Overcurrent detected in inverter

Charger failure

Control error: software timeout

Battery charger problem

Control error: internal test

Battery failed test

Critical power supply failure

Can't execute battery test: not recharged

External shutdown (remote EPO activated)

Can't execute battery test at this time

Fan failure

Low-battery shutdown

Low-battery warning (adjustable 1 to 99 min)

Dc bus overvoltage

System shutdown due to overload

PFC fault

System shutdown impending due to overtemperature

Inverter fault

Inverter failure

System shutdown: loss of control power

Overtemperature shutdown

System output overloaded

An audible alarm shall be provided and activated by any of these alarm conditions. For units equipped with the bypass option, the following additional alarms shall be displayed:

Bypass frequency out of tolerance

Bypass power out of tolerance

Fault load transferred to bypass

Load transferred to bypass due to overload

Load transferred to bypass due to dc overvoltage

Excessive retransfers attempted

An audible alarm shall be provided and activated by any of these alarm conditions.

E. Controls: UPS start-up and shutdown operations shall be accomplished via the front LCD display panel. An advisory display and menu-driven user prompts shall be provided to guide the operator through system operation without the use of additional manuals. Push buttons shall be provided to display the status of the UPS and to test and reset visual and audible alarms. The UPS shall contain an output circuit breaker and a manual bypass switch (optional on 3.5- to 6.0-kVA units) as additional user controls, which shall be located on the rear of the unit.

Online battery test

The UPS shall be provided with an online battery test feature. The test shall ensure the capability of the battery to supply power to the inverter while the load is supplied power in the normal mode. If the battery fails the test, the UPS shall display a warning message and sound an audible alarm. The battery test feature shall have the following user-selectable options, accessible from the LCD display:

Dc bus voltage threshold (pass/fail value)

Interval between tests (2 to 9 weeks)

Duration of test (30 to 900 s; factory default is 30 s)

Date and time of initial test

Enable/disable test

Remote Emergency Power Off (REPO)

Remote Emergency Power Off (REPO) capabilities shall be provided. A connector shall be provided for connection of a normally open contact supplied by the user. A 50-ft cable with the mating connector and push button shall be available as an option.

Bypass (optional on 3.5- to 6.0-kVA UPS modules)

A. General: A bypass circuit shall be provided as an integral part of the UPS. The bypass shall have an overload rating of 300 percent rated load for 10 cycles and 1000 percent for subcycle fault clearing. The bypass control logic shall contain an automatic transfer control circuit that senses the status of the inverter logic signals, and operating and alarm conditions. This control circuit shall provide a transfer of the load to the bypass source, without exceeding the transient limits specified herein, when an overload or malfunction occurs within the UPS.

B. Automatic transfers: The transfer control logic shall automatically activate the bypass, transferring the critical ac load to the bypass source, after the transfer logic senses one of the following conditions:

Inverter overload capacity exceeded

Critical ac load overvoltage or undervoltage

UPS fault condition

For inverter overload conditions, the transfer control logic shall inhibit an automatic transfer of the critical load to the bypass source if one of the following conditions exists:

Inverter/bypass voltage difference exceeding preset limits (+10 percent, -15 percent of nominal)

Bypass frequency out of preset limits (± 1.0 Hz, field-selectable from ± 0.1 to ± 5.0 Hz, in 0.1-Hz increments)

For UPS fault or output over/undervoltage conditions, the transfer control logic shall not inhibit automatic transfers of the critical load to the bypass source.

C. Automatic retransfers: Retransfer of the critical ac load from the bypass source to the inverter output shall be automatically initiated unless inhibited by manual control. The transfer control logic shall inhibit an automatic retransfer of the critical load to the inverter if one of the following conditions exists:

Bypass out-of-synchronization range with inverter output

Overload condition exists in excess of inverter full load rating

UPS fault condition present

D. Manual transfer: Manual operation of the bypass shall directly connect the critical load to the input ac power source, bypassing the input converter, battery charger, inverter, and battery.

Internal battery

Sealed, valve-regulated, low maintenance, lead acid batteries shall be used as a stored-energy source for the specified UPS system. Flame retardant batteries shall be available for computer room applications. The battery shall be housed internal to the UPS cabinet, and sized to support the inverter at rated load and power factor, in an ambient temperature between 20 and 30°C, for a minimum of 10 min of reserve time. The expected life of the battery shall be 5 years or a minimum 250 complete discharge cycles. For extended battery reserve time, external matching battery cabinets shall be available as an option.

Output load modules

(Required on 3.5- to 6.0-kVA modules. May be used on 8- to 12-kVA units only with configurable distribution module.) Output load modules (maximum of 4 on 3.5- to 12.0-kVA units; maximum of 8 on 8.0- to 12.0-kVA units optional configurable distribution module) shall be provided for field addition to the UPS cabinet. Each load module shall include user-specified receptacle(s), LED indicator lamp, and circuit breaker protection. The following load modules shall be provided:

Receptacle	Voltage (configuration)	Circuit breaker
5-15R2	120 (L-N-G)	15A, 2 pole
L5-15R1	120 (L-N-G)	15A, 1 pole
6-15R1	208 or 240 (L-L-G)	15A, 2 pole
L6-15R1	208 or 240 (L-L-G)	15A, 2 pole
L5-15R2	120 (L-N-G)	15A, 2 pole
5-20R2	120 (L-N-G)	20A, 2 pole
L5-20R1	120 (L-N-G)	20A, 1 pole
L6-20R1	208 or 240 (L-L-G)	20A, 2 pole
L14-20R1	208/120 or 240/120 (L-L-N-G)	30A, 1 pole
L5-30R1	120 (L-N-G)	30A, 1 pole
L6-30R1	208 or 240 (L-L-G)	30A, 2 pole
L-14-30R1	208/120 or 240/120 (L-L-N-G)	30A, 2 pole
Hardwire (15A)	208/120 or 240/120 (L-L-N-G)	15A, 2 pole
Hardwire (20A)	208/120 or 240/120 (L-L-N-G)	20A, 2 pole
Hardwire (30A)	208/120 or 240/120 (L-L-N-G)	Not required

UPS accessories (optional components)

Communication interface boards

A. General: Communication interfaces shall be provided on field-installable, plug-in printed-circuit boards. Installation shall be from the top of the UPS cabinet. Two interface slots shall be provided to allow multiple communication capabilities.

B. RS-232 interface board: The RS-232 interface board shall facilitate communication interfaces for the following:

RS-232 communication

External modem

Computer/LAN interface

AS/400 interface

Customer-configured relay interface

1. RS-232 Interface Port: The RS-232 interface port shall transmit UPS status for display at a remote terminal, computer, or external modem (all by others), via a DB25 connector. The remote display shall mimic the information provided on the LCD monitoring and control panel, including status of all UPS alarms, input voltage, output voltage, percentage load, and battery time remaining.

2. Auto-Dial: The UPS RS-232 interface port shall be capable of interfacing with an external modem to report alarm and status information to a remote location. The modem control system shall have the capability to store one telephone number. The UPS shall automatically dial the remote location in the event of the occurrence of any of the following alarms:

User-initiated UPS shutdown

Battery SCR fault (short or open circuit)

PFC voltage high

Dc bus undervoltage

PFC voltage low

ON battery

PFC shutdown due to overtemperature

Low battery

PFC fault (hardware fault)

Battery failed test

Charger shutdown due to overtemperature

UPS fault

Inverter shutdown due to overcurrent

Excessive retransfer attempts

Inverter shutdown due to overload

Control power supply failure

Inverter shutdown due to under/overvoltage

ROM test failed

Inverter shutdown due to overtemperature

RAM test failed

Bypass shutdown due to overload (UPS shutdown)

Timeout fault (self-test at start-up)

3. Computer/LAN Interface Kits: Computer/LAN interface kits shall consist of a 10-ft communication cable and software. Two separate software kits shall be available to operate in the following manner. Computer/LAN shutdown software shall run as a background task on the computer while monitoring the UPS. The software shall perform an unattended orderly shutdown of the computer operating system, when signaled by the UPS of a power failure or low battery condition. Power Surveillance software shall run as a background task on the computer while monitoring the UPS. The Power Surveillance software shall incorporate the shutdown capabilities of Computer/LAN shutdown software (except DOS) and shall also provide UPS monitoring and control capabilities from a standalone computer.

4. IBM* AS/400* Interface Kits: A shielded cable compliant with NEMA Class 2 for plenum applications, with subminiature 9-pin D-type connector, shall be provided for connection to the IBM* AS/400* signal interface. Contacts rated for 1.0 A at 30 V ac or dc shall be provided to indicate a change of status of each of the following conditions:

ON UPS

ON battery

Low battery

ON bypass

An optional splitter cable shall be available to allow connection to either RS-232, Power Surveillance, or external modem communication *and* Computer/LAN shutdown software or AS/400 interface simultaneously.

5. Customer-configured relay interface: An interface board shall be available that allows the customer to have UPS status/alarm conditions available for remote panel monitoring via relay contact closures. Programming is done via the LCD display.

C. Simple Network Management Protocol (SNMP) interface board: The SNMP interface board (agent) shall be provided to allow communication

---

*IBM and AS/400 are registered trademarks of International Business Machines Corporation.

between the UPS and any Network Management System (NMS). The SNMP agent shall be installed in the UPS cabinet; external "proxy" agent configurations shall not be allowed. The SNMP interface shall be available in Ethernet or Token Ring TCP/IP message format to permit direct connection to the network. Ethernet connection shall be unshielded twisted pair (UTP). Token Ring connection shall be unshielded twisted pair (UTP) and shielded twisted pair (STP). The SNMP agent shall include software that contains the standard library of commands in the Management Information Base (MIB). An extended MIB shall be available to enable the user access to create custom UPS variable interface screens. SNMP snap-in interfaces shall be available for major NOS platforms. The SNMP connection shall allow multiple network managers to both monitor the status and control many operational features of the UPS. Monitoring data supplied by the UPS shall include but not be limited to the input, output, and battery voltages and currents, battery condition, battery reserve time remaining, internal component temperatures, UPS loading, and UPS status and alarm indicators. UPS operational features shall include but not be limited to setting UPS operating parameters, turning the UPS off and on, and manually initiating battery tests.

Power Management load modules (optional on 3.5- to 12.0-kVA units). Power Management load modules (maximum of 4 on 3.5- to 12.0-kVA units, or maximum of 8 on 8.0- to 12.0-kVA units) shall be provided for field addition to the UPS cabinet. Power Management load modules shall provide the ability to individually control power through the output receptacles. The load modules listed (in section 2.2.8 of Liebert specifications) are available as optional Power Management load modules with the exception of the hardwire modules. The output receptacles shall be capable of being turned on and off by either manual initiation or programmed time intervals. Power Management load modules shall enable the user to

A. Extend battery run time, by selectively turning off loads at predetermined time intervals.

B. Conserve energy, by allowing the user to turn off "idle" equipment.

C. Reset or reboot loads, by remotely turning the load off and on, which enables the user to reboot "locked up" equipment.

D. Increase security, by remotely turning off loads to prohibit unauthorized personnel access.

E. Sequence load restarting, by selectively turning on loads at predetermined time intervals to minimize high inrush currents.

Power Management programming shall be password protected and can be accessed via the LCD display. The power management programming shall be user-specified, based on four elements: load module identification, events, action, and delay. Load modules shall be numerically identified and shall be capable of containing a user-defined alphanumeric label of up to 16 characters. An event shall be the triggering occurrence to cause the load module to take action. Events include but shall not be limited to system power-up, utility failure, utility restored, battery time remaining, time and date (day), and ON bypass. Programmable actions include but shall not be limited to output on (turns inverter on), output off (turns entire UPS off), turn on load [turns specified load module(s) on], and turn off load [turns specified load module(s) off]. Each action shall have an associated delay, user-selected from 0 to 99 s or 0 to 99 min, prior to the execution of the action.

External battery cabinet.   An external battery cabinet shall be provided for the UPS. The battery cabinet shall be used in parallel with the internal battery for extended power outage reserve time. The battery cabinet shall contain (one or two) strings of sealed, valve regulated, low-maintenance, lead acid cells, housed in a separate cabinet that matches the UPS cabinet styling. Flame-retardant batteries shall be available for computer room applications. Intercabinet wiring with mating connectors shall be supplied with the external battery cabinet (for 3.5- to 12.0-kVA modules only). The external battery cabinet shall contain two fuses per string, to provide individual string protection and isolation. The external battery cabinet shall increase power outage reserve time to x minutes at full load, when operating in an ambient temperature between 20 and 30°C.

Battery cabinets containing their own ac-dc chargers shall be available for applications requiring run times greater than 4 h.

Dual input (optional on 8.0- to 18.0-kVA UPS modules).   The UPS shall be provided with a separate input terminal block to provide the UPS with dual input capabilities. This separate feed shall be single-phase, 3-wire-plus-ground to match the UPS output configuration. The UPS inverter shall track the bypass source per parameters specified (in section 2.2.2.E of the Liebert specification).

Field quality control

The following inspections and test procedures shall be performed by factory-trained field service personnel during the UPS start-up:

A. Visual inspection
   1. Inspect equipment for signs of shipping or installation damage.
   2. Verify installation per drawings.
   3. Inspect cabinets for foreign objects.
   4. Verify that neutral and ground conductors are properly sized and configured.
   5. Inspect battery cases.

6. Inspect battery for proper polarity.

7. Verify that all printed-circuit boards are configured properly.

B. Mechanical inspection

    1. Check all control wiring connections for tightness.

    2. Check all power wiring connections for tightness.

    3. Check all terminal screws, nuts, and/or spade lugs for tightness.

C. Electrical inspection

    1. Check all fuses for continuity.

    2. Confirm that input voltage and phase rotation are correct.

    3. Verify that control transformer connections are correct for voltages being used.

    4. Assure connection and voltage of the battery string(s).

Unit start-up and site testing

Site testing shall be provided by the manufacturer's field service personnel if requested. Site testing shall consist of a complete test of the UPS system and the associated accessories supplied by the manufacturer. A partial battery discharge test shall be provided as part of the standard start-up procedure. The test results shall be documented, signed, and dated for future reference.

Manufacturer's field service

Service personnel. The UPS manufacturer shall directly employ a nationwide service organization, consisting of factory-trained Liebert customer engineers dedicated to the start-up, maintenance, and repair of UPS and power equipment. The organization shall consist of factory-trained customer engineers working out of Liebert district offices in most major cities. An automated procedure shall be in place to ensure that the manufacturer is dedicating the appropriate technical support resources to match escalating customer needs.

The manufacturer shall provide a fully automated national dispatch center to coordinate field service personnel schedules. One toll-free number shall reach a qualified support person 24 h/day, 7 days/week, 365 days/year. If emergency service is required, callback response time from a local customer engineer shall be 20 min or less.

Replacement parts stocking. Parts shall be available through an extensive network to ensure around-the-clock parts availability throughout the country.

Replacement spare parts shall be stocked by local customer engineers with backup available from Liebert district service offices and the manufacturing location.

Liebert customer support parts coordinators shall be on call 24 h a day, 7 days a week, 365 days a year for immediate parts availability.

UPS maintenance training

Maintenance training courses for customer employees shall be available by the UPS manufacturer. This training is in addition to the basic operator training conducted as a part of the system start-up. The training course shall cover UPS theory, location of subassemblies, safety, battery considerations, and UPS operational procedures. The course shall include ac-to-dc conversion and dc-to-ac inversion techniques as well as control, metering, and feedback circuits to the printed-circuit board (PCB) level. Troubleshooting and fault isolation using alarm information and internal self-diagnostics shall be stressed.

Maintenance contracts

A complete offering of preventive and full service maintenance contracts for both the UPS system and battery system shall be available. An extended warranty and preventive maintenance package shall be available. Warranty and preventive maintenance service shall be performed by factory-trained Liebert customer engineers.

Note: These Guide Specifications comply with the format outlined by the Construction Specifications Institute per CSI MP-2-1 and CSI MP-2-2. In correspondence, refer to Liebert document SL-24860 (R9/93).

Liebert Corporation year 2000 product compliance statement

Liebert Corporation certifies that all Liebert software and firmware accompanying Liebert-manufactured air conditioning, power conditioning and distribution (PCD), and uninterruptible power supply (UPS) products are year 2000–compliant. Attached is a list of products covered by this statement.

These Liebert products will function and operate as warranted in accordance with their performance specifications without regard for calendar year changes. Year 2000–compliant product design features consist of

Device functionality

Date data and century recognition

Calculations that accommodate same century and multicentury formulas and data values

Date data interface values that reflect the century

Liebert product resident monitoring firmware does no sorting or processing by date; their products only store and retrieve alarms. The date generator will work properly irrespective of calendar year changes, so alarm histories will remain intact and correct. Embedded firmware in all Liebert microprocessor applications uses time increments and does not process dates. Therefore, all Liebert products will operate properly, and all alarm dates will be displayed on the customer display correctly.

Liebert product-monitoring front-end software (SiteScan 2000W, SiteScan SS2W, and Alert, version 2.6) is presently not year 2000–compliant. This software will be corrected to be year 2000–compliant with the release of version 3.0. This version is scheduled for release in 1998, and will be available as an upgrade revision for all current SiteScan systems. Liebert Access Control Security Systems are not year 2000–compliant.

Product compliance

Liebert is committed to providing its customers quality state-of-the-art products and timely solutions to current and future needs. The products listed below, when operated by Liebert-embedded firmware, Liebert controls, and/or Liebert software, are year 2000–compliant:

Environmental			
Atlas PEC	Dealermate	Logicool	Process Chiller
Challenger	Deluxe System 2	LS400	Quantum
Climate 3000	Deluxe System 3	Mini Air	Slimcool
CoolGuard	Deluxe System 4	Mini Tower	Small Systems Monitors
Condensers	Drycoolers	MiniMate	Spacemaster-SX
COP-SX	Industrial Cooling Series	MiniMate Plus	
CSU3000	Intelecool	Modular 3000	
Datamate	Leak Detection System	Modular Plus	
Data Pad	Little Glass House	Modupac Chiller	

UPS and Power Products			
Accupower	Powersure Interactive	Series 4000	Sitenet SNMP Manager
AL 300	PPD6300	Series 7200	TVSS/Surge Suppressor
AL 3300	Precision Power Center	Series 7200 1 + 1	Transformers
AP 70X	Resource	Series 7200 HE	UPStation D
AP 200	Select	Series 7200 Single Phase	UPStation G
AP 400	Series AP100 (1xx)	Series 7400	UPStation G RT
AP 4300	Series AP300 (3xx)	Series 8000, 9000	UPStation GX
Data Wave	Series AP500 (5xx)	Static Transfer Switch	UPStation GXT
MicroUPS	Series AP600 (6xx)	SmartSwitch	UPStation S
PowerMate	Series 600T	Sitenet Integrator	UPStation S-3
Powersure	Series AP700 (70x)	Sitenet 1 and 2	

On-Site Access Control software and year 2000 compliance

Liebert's OEM supplier has informed them that the On-Site Access Control software is not year 2000–compliant. This noncompliance includes Liebert On-Site/4, On-Site/10, On-Site/16, On-Site/64, and On-Site/128, the latest DOS version that Liebert has been marketing. There are both external and internal causes of noncompliance:

1. *External to On-Site software:* The On-Site software relies on the system clock controlled by the BIOS of the host PC. Depending on the DOS version, when the year rolls over from 1999 to 2000, the system clock may fail to make

the transition properly (e.g., treating "00" as 1900 instead of 2000). If uncorrected, the On-Site software will receive incorrect time-stamp information. If the date is manually corrected, the system clock should proceed to function properly.

2. *Internal to On-Site software:* The On-Site software records dates using the two-digit format. This outdated strategy means that date comparison operations may not function properly. Functions that perform date comparisons include transaction history reports, which will not be able to span across the new millennium. Two separate reports—one for the twentieth-century dates, another for the twenty-first-century dates—need to be performed. Note that transactions will continue to be logged with the time stamp as supplied by the system BIOS. User access cards have an optional "expiration date" feature, which relies on two-digit date comparisons. This feature can be disabled.

The overall access control system should still accurately maintain its basic functionality, as the distributed IGMs (information-gathering modules—door controllers for determining access) do not perform calculations involving dates.

On November 30, 1997 Liebert Corporation announced their decision to discontinue the sale of the On-Site Access Control product family of software and hardware components. This is in keeping with their ongoing efforts to only provide products that directly tie into their existing environmental and UPS/Power market strategies. Liebert Corporation has evaluated a recommended supplier who can continue to support Access Control products for their customers. This supplier has demonstrated backward compatibility to the existing On-Site systems and full year 2000 compliance for their software and hardware components. Please contact your local Liebert representative to obtain more information and product specifications.

For more information, contact Liebert at *webmaster@liebertweb.com.*

8.8   Network Computers

Each computer in your network should be inventoried and baselined. The easy way to do this is to create a folder for each computer on your network and include as much pertinent information as possible about each one. This really does make troubleshooting these systems easier.

In my network I used IBM PCs. The commercial desktop series used include the PC350 and XL series. The following is a system report for ANNE, one of the servers on the network. This is an example of the information you should obtain about your systems.

```
Baseline for the Workstation ANNE
Diagnostics Report For \\ANNE
```
```
OS Version Report
```

```
Microsoft (R) Windows NT (TM) Server
Version 4.0 (Build 1381: Service Pack 1) x86 Uniprocessor Free
Registered Owner: ANNE, Information World, Inc.
Product Number: 50370-807-5268635-77274
```

System Report

```
System: AT/AT COMPATIBLE
Hardware Abstraction Layer: UP MPS 1.4 - APIC platform
BIOS Date: 09/17/97
BIOS Version: <unavailable>
Processor list:
 0: x86 Family 6 Model 1 Stepping 9 GenuineIntel ˇ7E199 Mhz
```

Video Display Report

```
BIOS Date: 04/01/96
BIOS Version: S3 86C765 Video BIOS. Version 1.01-05A
Adapter:
 Setting: 640 x 480 x 256
       60 Hz
 Type: s3 compatible display adapter
 String: S3 Compatible
 Memory: 1 MB
 Chip Type: S3 765
 DAC Type: S3
Driver:
 Vendor: Microsoft Corporation
 File(s): s3.sys, s3.dll
 Version: 4.00, 4.0.0
Drives Report
```

```
C:\ (Local - FAT) ANNE Total: 2,200,704KB, Free: 1,887,552KB
 Serial Number: FC35 - B832
 Bytes per cluster: 512
 Sectors per cluster: 128
 Filename length: 255
E: (Remote - FAT) \\Muscle\MUSCLE-C MUSCLE Total: 2,096,320KB, Free:
1,197,664KB
 Serial Number: 833 - E695
 Bytes per cluster: 512
 Sectors per cluster: 64
 Filename length: 255
Memory Report
```

```
Handles: 2,363
Threads: 158
Processes: 18
Physical Memory (K)
 Total: 32,180
 Available: 5,112
 File Cache: 6,700
Kernel Memory (K)
 Total: 5,868
 Paged: 4,232
 Nonpaged: 1,636
Commit Charge (K)
 Total: 24,000
 Limit: 74,924
 Peak: 24,004
```

```
Pagefile Space (K)
 Total: 51,200
 Total in use: 128
 Peak: 128
C:\pagefile.sys
 Total: 51,200
 Total in use: 128
 Peak: 128
Services Report
```

```
Alerter               Running (Automatic)
 C:\WINNT\System32\services.exe
 Service Account Name: LocalSystem
 Error Severity: Normal
 Service Flags: Shared Process
 Service Dependencies:
  LanmanWorkstation
Computer Browser      Running (Automatic)
 C:\WINNT\System32\services.exe
 Service Account Name: LocalSystem
 Error Severity: Normal
 Service Flags: Shared Process
 Service Dependencies:
  LanmanWorkstation
  LanmanServer
  LmHosts
ClipBook Server       Stopped (Manual)
 C:\WINNT\system32\clipsrv.exe
 Service Account Name: LocalSystem
 Error Severity: Normal
 Service Flags: Own Process
 Service Dependencies:
  NetDDE
DHCP Client (TDI)     Stopped (Disabled)
 C:\WINNT\System32\services.exe
 Service Account Name: LocalSystem
 Error Severity: Normal
 Service Flags: Shared Process
 Service Dependencies:
  Tcpip
  Afd
  NetBT
EventLog (Event log)     Running (Automatic)
 C:\WINNT\system32\services.exe
Service Account Name: LocalSystem
 Error Severity: Normal
 Service Flags: Shared Process
Gopher Publishing Service Running (Automatic)
 C:\WINNT\System32\inetsrv\inetinfo.exe
 Service Account Name: LocalSystem
 Error Severity: Ignore
 Service Flags: Shared Process
 Service Dependencies:
  RPCSS
  NTLMSSP
 Server               Running (Automatic)
 C:\WINNT\System32\services.exe
 Service Account Name: LocalSystem
 Error Severity: Normal
 Service Flags: Shared Process
```

```
 Group Dependencies:
  TDI
Workstation (NetworkProvider)     Running (Automatic)
 C:\WINNT\System32\services.exe
 Service Account Name: LocalSystem
 Error Severity: Normal
 Service Flags: Shared Process
 Group Dependencies:
  TDI
License Logging Service     Running (Automatic)
 C:\WINNT\System32\llssrv.exe
 Service Account Name: LocalSystem
 Error Severity: Normal
 Service Flags: Own Process
TCP/IP NetBIOS Helper     Running (Automatic)
 C:\WINNT\System32\services.exe
 Service Account Name: LocalSystem
 Error Severity: Normal
 Service Flags: Shared Process
 Group Dependencies:
  NetworkProvider
Messenger     Running (Automatic)
 C:\WINNT\System32\services.exe
 Service Account Name: LocalSystem
 Error Severity: Normal
 Service Flags: Shared Process
 Service Dependencies:
  LanmanWorkstation
  NetBios
FTP Publishing Service     Running (Automatic)
 C:\WINNT\System32\inetsrv\inetinfo.exe
 Service Account Name: LocalSystem
 Error Severity: Ignore
 Service Flags: Shared Process
 Service Dependencies:
  RPCSS
  NTLMSSP
Network DDE (NetDDEGroup)     Stopped (Manual)
 C:\WINNT\system32\netdde.exe
 Service Account Name: LocalSystem
 Error Severity: Normal
 Service Flags: Shared Process
 Service Dependencies:
  NetDDEDSDM
Network DDE DSDM     Stopped (Manual)
 C:\WINNT\system32\netdde.exe
 Service Account Name: LocalSystem
 Error Severity: Normal
 Service Flags: Shared Process
Net Logon (RemoteValidation)     Stopped (Manual)
 C:\WINNT\System32\lsass.exe
 Service Account Name: LocalSystem
 Error Severity: Normal
 Service Flags: Shared Process
 Service Dependencies:
  LanmanWorkstation
  LmHosts
Network Monitor Agent     Stopped (Manual)
 C:\WINNT\System32\nmagent.exe
 Service Account Name: LocalSystem
```

```
                  Error Severity: Normal
                  Service Flags: Own Process
                  Service Dependencies:
                   bh
            NT LM Security Support Provider     Running (Manual)
                  C:\WINNT\System32\SERVICES.EXE
                  Service Account Name: LocalSystem
                  Error Severity: Normal
                  Service Flags: Shared Process
            Plug and Play (PlugPlay)      Running (Automatic)
                  C:\WINNT\system32\services.exe
                  Service Account Name: LocalSystem
                  Error Severity: Normal
                  Service Flags: Shared Process
            Directory Replicator          Stopped (Manual)
                  C:\WINNT\System32\lmrepl.exe
                  Service Account Name: LocalSystem
                  Error Severity: Normal
                  Service Flags: Own Process
                  Service Dependencies:
                   LanmanWorkstation
                   LanmanServer
            Remote Procedure Call (RPC) Locator     Stopped (Manual)
                  C:\WINNT\System32\LOCATOR.EXE
                  Service Account Name: LocalSystem
                  Error Severity: Normal
                  Service Flags: Own Process
            Remote Procedure Call (RPC) Service     Running (Automatic)
                  C:\WINNT\system32\RpcSs.exe
                  Service Account Name: LocalSystem
                  Error Severity: Normal
                  Service Flags: Own Process
            Schedule            Stopped (Manual)
                  C:\WINNT\System32\AtSvc.Exe
                  Service Account Name: LocalSystem
                  Error Severity: Normal
                  Service Flags: Own Process
            Seattle Lab Telnet Server      Running (Automatic)
                  C:\WINNT\SLNET\slnet.exe
                  Service Account Name: LocalSystem
                  Error Severity: Normal
                  Service Flags: Own Process
                  Service Dependencies:
                   tcpip
            Spooler (SpoolerGroup)       Running (Automatic)
                  C:\WINNT\system32\spoolss.exe
                  Service Account Name: LocalSystem
                  Error Severity: Normal
                  Service Flags: Own Process, Interactive
            Telephony Service         Stopped (Manual)
                  C:\WINNT\system32\tapisrv.exe
                  Service Account Name: LocalSystem
                  Error Severity: Normal
                  Service Flags: Own Process
            UPS             Stopped (Manual)
                  C:\WINNT\System32\ups.exe
                  Service Account Name: LocalSystem
                  Error Severity: Normal
                  Service Flags: Own Process
            World Wide Web Publishing Service     Running (Automatic)
                  C:\WINNT\System32\inetsrv\inetinfo.exe
```

```
    Service Account Name: LocalSystem
    Error Severity: Ignore
    Service Flags: Shared Process
    Service Dependencies:
     RPCSS
     NTLMSSP
   Windows Internet Name Service          Running (Automatic)
   C:\WINNT\System32\wins.exe
    Service Account Name: LocalSystem
    Error Severity: Normal
    Service Flags: Own Process
    Service Dependencies:
     RPCSS
     NTLMSSP


   Drivers Report
   ─────────────────────────────────────────

   Abiosdsk (Primary disk)           Stopped (Disabled)
    Error Severity: Ignore
    Service Flags: Kernel Driver, Shared Process
   AFD Networking Support Environment (TDI)     Running (Automatic)
    C:\WINNT\System32\drivers\afd.sys
    Error Severity: Normal
    Service Flags: Kernel Driver, Shared Process
   Aha154x (SCSI miniport)           Stopped (Disabled)
    Error Severity: Normal
    Service Flags: Kernel Driver, Shared Process
   Aha174x (SCSI miniport)           Stopped (Disabled)
    Error Severity: Normal
    Service Flags: Kernel Driver, Shared Process
   aic78xx (SCSI miniport)           Running (Boot)
    C:\WINNT\System32\DRIVERS\aic78xx.sys
    Error Severity: Normal
    Service Flags: Kernel Driver, Shared Process
   Always (SCSI miniport)            Stopped (Disabled)
    Error Severity: Normal
    Service Flags: Kernel Driver, Shared Process
   ami0nt (SCSI miniport)            Stopped (Disabled)
    Error Severity: Normal
    Service Flags: Kernel Driver, Shared Process
   amsint (SCSI miniport)            Stopped (Disabled)
    Error Severity: Normal
    Service Flags: Kernel Driver, Shared Process
   Arrow (SCSI miniport)             Stopped (Disabled)
    Error Severity: Normal
    Service Flags: Kernel Driver, Shared Process
   atapi (SCSI miniport)             Stopped (Disabled)
    Error Severity: Normal
    Service Flags: Kernel Driver, Shared Process
   Atdisk (Primary disk)             Stopped (Disabled)
    Error Severity: Ignore
    Service Flags: Kernel Driver, Shared Process
   ati (Video)            Stopped (Disabled)
    Error Severity: Ignore
    Service Flags: Kernel Driver, Shared Process
   Beep (Base)            Running (System)
    Error Severity: Normal
    Service Flags: Kernel Driver, Shared Process
   Network Monitor Tools and Agent Drivers  Stopped (Manual)
    C:\WINNT\System32\drivers\bhnt.sys
    Error Severity: Normal
```

```
                  Service Flags: Kernel Driver, Shared Process
                  Group Dependencies:
                   NDIS
                  BusLogic (SCSI miniport)        Stopped (Disabled)
                   Error Severity: Normal
                   Service Flags: Kernel Driver, Shared Process
                  Busmouse (Pointer Port)         Stopped (Disabled)
                   Error Severity: Ignore
                   Service Flags: Kernel Driver, Shared Process
                  Cdaudio (Filter)           Stopped (System)
                   Error Severity: Ignore
                   Service Flags: Kernel Driver, Shared Process
                  Cdfs (File system)              Running (Disabled)
                   Error Severity: Normal
                   Service Flags: File System Driver, Shared Process
                   Group Dependencies:
                    SCSI CDROM Class
                  Cdrom (SCSI CDROM Class)           Running (System)
                   Error Severity: Ignore
                   Service Flags: Kernel Driver, Shared Process
                   Group Dependencies:
                    SCSI miniport
                  Changer (Filter)           Stopped (System)
                   Error Severity: Ignore
                   Service Flags: Kernel Driver, Shared Process
                  cirrus (Video)           Stopped (Disabled)
                   Error Severity: Ignore
                   Service Flags: Kernel Driver, Shared Process
                  Cpqarray (SCSI miniport)        Stopped (Disabled)
                   Error Severity: Normal
                   Service Flags: Kernel Driver, Shared Process
                  cpqfws2e (SCSI miniport)        Stopped (Disabled)
                   Error Severity: Normal
                   Service Flags: Kernel Driver, Shared Process
                  dac960nt (SCSI miniport)        Stopped (Disabled)
                   Error Severity: Normal
                   Service Flags: Kernel Driver, Shared Process
                  dce376nt (SCSI miniport)        Stopped (Disabled)
                   Error Severity: Normal
                   Service Flags: Kernel Driver, Shared Process
                  Delldsa (SCSI miniport)         Stopped (Disabled)
                   Error Severity: Normal
                   Service Flags: Kernel Driver, Shared Process
                  Dell_DGX (Video)           Stopped (Disabled)
                   Error Severity: Ignore
                   Service Flags: Kernel Driver, Shared Process
                  Disk (SCSI Class)               Running (Boot)
                   Error Severity: Ignore
                   Service Flags: Kernel Driver, Shared Process
                  Group Dependencies:
                    SSCI miniport
                  Diskperf (Filter)          Stopped (Disabled)
                   Error Severity: Normal
                   Service Flags: Kernel Driver, Shared Process
                  DptScsi (SCSI miniport)         Stopped (Disabled)
                   Error Severity: Normal
                   Service Flags: Kernel Driver, Shared Process
                  dtc329x (SCSI miniport)         Stopped (Disabled)
                   Error Severity: Normal
                   Service Flags: Kernel Driver, Shared Process
```

```
et4000 (Video)              Stopped (Disabled)
 Error Severity: Ignore
 Service Flags: Kernel Driver, Shared Process
Fastfat (Boot file system)     Running (Disabled)
 Error Severity: Normal
 Service Flags: File System Driver, Shared Process
Fd16_700 (SCSI miniport)       Stopped (Disabled)
 Error Severity: Normal
 Service Flags: Kernel Driver, Shared Process
Fd7000ex (SCSI miniport)       Stopped (Disabled)
 Error Severity: Normal
 Service Flags: Kernel Driver, Shared Process
Fd8xx (SCSI miniport)        Stopped (Disabled)
 Error Severity: Normal
 Service Flags: Kernel Driver, Shared Process
flashpnt (SCSI miniport)       Stopped (Disabled)
 Error Severity: Normal
 Service Flags: Kernel Driver, Shared Process
Floppy (Primary disk)        Running (System)
 Error Severity: Ignore
 Service Flags: Kernel Driver, Shared Process
Ftdisk (Filter)          Stopped (Disabled)
 Error Severity: Ignore
 Service Flags: Kernel Driver, Shared Process
i8042 Keyboard and PS/2 Mouse Port Driver (Keyboard Port) Running
(System)
 System32\DRIVERS\i8042prt.sys
 Error Severity: Normal
 Service Flags: Kernel Driver, Shared Process
Inport (Pointer Port)       Stopped (Disabled)
 Error Severity: Ignore
 Service Flags: Kernel Driver, Shared Process
Jazzg300 (Video)          Stopped (Disabled)
 Error Severity: Ignore
 Service Flags: Kernel Driver, Shared Process
Jazzg364 (Video)          Stopped (Disabled)
 Error Severity: Ignore
 Service Flags: Kernel Driver, Shared Process
Jzvxl484 (Video)          Stopped (Disabled)
 Error Severity: Ignore
 Service Flags: Kernel Driver, Shared Process
Keyboard Class Driver (Keyboard Class)     Running (System)
 System32\DRIVERS\kbdclass.sys
 Error Severity: Normal
 Service Flags: Kernel Driver, Shared Process
KSecDD (Base)           Running (System)
 Error Severity: Normal
 Service Flags: Kernel Driver, Shared Process
Kingston PCI Fast Ethernet Adapter Driver (NDIS) Running (Automatic)
 C:\WINNT\System32\drivers\KTC100.sys
 Error Severity: Normal
 Service Flags: Kernel Driver, Shared Process
mga (Video)            Stopped (Disabled)
 Error Severity: Ignore
 Service Flags: Kernel Driver, Shared Process
mga_mil (Video)          Stopped (Disabled)
 Error Severity: Ignore
 Service Flags: Kernel Driver, Shared Process
mitsumi (SCSI miniport)       Stopped (Disabled)
 Error Severity: Normal
```

```
                    Service Flags: Kernel Driver, Shared Process
mkecr5xx (SCSI miniport)        Stopped (Disabled)
 Error Severity: Normal
 Service Flags: Kernel Driver, Shared Process
Modem (Extended base)          Stopped (Manual)
 Error Severity: Ignore
 Service Flags: Kernel Driver, Shared Process
Mouse Class Driver (Pointer Class)    Running (System)
 System32\DRIVERS\mouclass.sys
 Error Severity: Normal
 Service Flags: Kernel Driver, Shared Process
Msfs (File system)        Running (System)
 Error Severity: Normal
 Service Flags: File System Driver, Shared Process
Mup (Network)          Running (Manual)
 C:\WINNT\System32\drivers\mup.sys
 Error Severity: Normal
 Service Flags: File System Driver, Shared Process
NetBEUI Protocol (PNP_TDI)        Running (Automatic)
 C:\WINNT\System32\drivers\nbf.sys
 Error Severity: Normal
 Service Flags: Kernel Driver, Shared Process
Ncr53c9x (SCSI miniport)       Stopped (Disabled)
 Error Severity: Normal
 Service Flags: Kernel Driver, Shared Process
ncr77c22 (Video)          Stopped (Disabled)
 Error Severity: Ignore
 Service Flags: Kernel Driver, Shared Process
Ncrc700 (SCSI miniport)        Stopped (Disabled)
 Error Severity: Normal
 Service Flags: Kernel Driver, Shared Process
Ncrc710 (SCSI miniport)        Stopped (Disabled)
 Error Severity: Normal
 Service Flags: Kernel Driver, Shared Process
Microsoft NDIS System Driver (NDIS)    Running (System)
 Error Severity: Normal
 Service Flags: Kernel Driver, Shared Process
NetBIOS Interface (NetBIOSGroup)    Running (Manual)
 C:\WINNT\System32\drivers\netbios.sys
 Error Severity: Normal
 Service Flags: File System Driver, Shared Process
 Group Dependencies:
  TDI
WINS Client(TCP/IP) (PNP_TDI)      Running (Automatic)
 C:\WINNT\System32\drivers\netbt.sys
 Error Severity: Normal
 Service Flags: Kernel Driver, Shared Process
 Service Dependencies:
  Tcpip
NetDetect          Stopped (Manual)
 C:\WINNT\system32\drivers\netdtect.sys
 Error Severity: Normal
 Service Flags: Kernel Driver, Shared Process
Npfs (File system)        Running (System)
 Error Severity: Normal
 Service Flags: File System Driver, Shared Process
Ntfs (File system)        Stopped (Disabled)
 Error Severity: Normal
 Service Flags: File System Driver, Shared Process
Null (Base)          Running (System)
```

```
 Error Severity: Normal
 Service Flags: Kernel Driver, Shared Process
NWLink IPX/SPX Compatible Transport Protocol (PNP_TDI) Running
(Automatic)
 C:\WINNT\System32\drivers\nwlnkipx.sys
 Error Severity: Normal
 Service Flags: Kernel Driver, Shared Process
NWLink NetBIOS (PNP_TDI)            Running (Automatic)
 C:\WINNT\System32\drivers\nwlnknb.sys
 Error Severity: Normal
 Service Flags: Kernel Driver, Shared Process
 Service Dependencies:
  NwlnkIpx
NWLink SPX/SPXII Protocol           Running (Manual)
 C:\WINNT\System32\drivers\nwlnkspx.sys
 Error Severity: Normal
 Service Flags: Kernel Driver, Shared Process
 Service Dependencies:
  NwlnkIpx
Oliscsi (SCSI miniport)            Stopped (Disabled)
 Error Severity: Normal
 Service Flags: Kernel Driver, Shared Process
Parallel (Extended base)           Running (Automatic)
 Error Severity: Ignore
 Service Flags: Kernel Driver, Shared Process
 Service Dependencies:
  Parport
 Group Dependencies:
  Parallel arbitrator
Parport (Parallel arbitrator)       Running (Automatic)
 Error Severity: Ignore
 Service Flags: Kernel Driver, Shared Process
ParVdm (Extended base)             Running (Automatic)
 Error Severity: Ignore
 Service Flags: Kernel Driver, Shared Process
 Service Dependencies:
  Parport
 Group Dependencies:
  Parallel arbitrator
PCIDump (PCI Configuration)         Stopped (System)
 Error Severity: Ignore
 Service Flags: Kernel Driver, Shared Process
Pcmcia (System Bus Extender)        Stopped (Disabled)
 Error Severity: Normal
 Service Flags: Kernel Driver, Shared Process
PnP ISA Enabler Driver (Base)       Stopped (System)
 Error Severity: Ignore
 Service Flags: Kernel Driver, Shared Process
psidisp (Video)          Stopped (Disabled)
 Error Severity: Ignore
 Service Flags: Kernel Driver, Shared Process
Ql10wnt (SCSI miniport)            Stopped (Disabled)
 Error Severity: Normal
 Service Flags: Kernel Driver, Shared Process
qv (Video)              Stopped (Disabled)
 Error Severity: Ignore
 Service Flags: Kernel Driver, Shared Process
Rdr (Network)               Running (Manual)
 C:\WINNT\System32\drivers\rdr.sys
 Error Severity: Normal
```

```
 Service Flags: File System Driver, Shared Process
s3 (Video)                Running (System)
 Error Severity: Normal
 Service Flags: Kernel Driver, Shared Process
Scsiprnt (Extended base)       Stopped (Automatic)
 Error Severity: Ignore
 Service Flags: Kernel Driver, Shared Process
 Group Dependencies:
  SCSI miniport
Scsiscan (SCSI Class)          Stopped (System)
 Error Severity: Ignore
 Service Flags: Kernel Driver, Shared Process
 Group Dependencies:
  SCSI miniport
Serial (Extended base)         Running (Automatic)
 Error Severity: Ignore
 Service Flags: Kernel Driver, Shared Process
Sermouse (Pointer Port)        Stopped (Disabled)
 Error Severity: Ignore
 Service Flags: Kernel Driver, Shared Process
Sfloppy (Primary disk)         Stopped (System)
 Error Severity: Ignore
 Service Flags: Kernel Driver, Shared Process
 Group Dependencies:
  SCSI miniport
Simbad (Filter)           Stopped (Disabled)
 Error Severity: Normal
 Service Flags: Kernel Driver, Shared Process
slcd32 (SCSI miniport)         Stopped (Disabled)
 Error Severity: Normal
 Service Flags: Kernel Driver, Shared Process
Sparrow (SCSI miniport)        Stopped (Disabled)
 Error Severity: Normal
 Service Flags: Kernel Driver, Shared Process
Spock (SCSI miniport)          Stopped (Disabled)
 Error Severity: Normal
 Service Flags: Kernel Driver, Shared Process
Srv (Network)             Running (Manual)
 C:\WINNT\System32\drivers\srv.sys
 Error Severity: Normal
 Service Flags: File System Driver, Shared Process
symc810 (SCSI miniport)    Stopped (Disabled)
 Error Severity: Normal
 Service Flags: Kernel Driver, Shared Process
T128 (SCSI miniport)           Stopped (Disabled)
 Error Severity: Normal
 Service Flags: Kernel Driver, Shared Process
T13B (SCSI miniport)           Stopped (Disabled)
 Error Severity: Normal
 Service Flags: Kernel Driver, Shared Process
TCP/IP Service (PNP_TDI)       Running (Automatic)
 C:\WINNT\System32\drivers\tcpip.sys
 Error Severity: Normal
 Service Flags: Kernel Driver, Shared Process
tga (Video)               Stopped (Disabled)
 Error Severity: Ignore
 Service Flags: Kernel Driver, Shared Process
tmv1 (SCSI miniport)           Stopped (Disabled)
 Error Severity: Normal
 Service Flags: Kernel Driver, Shared Process
```

```
Ultra124 (SCSI miniport)        Stopped (Disabled)
  Error Severity: Normal
  Service Flags: Kernel Driver, Shared Process
Ultra14f (SCSI miniport)        Stopped (Disabled)
  Error Severity: Normal
  Service Flags: Kernel Driver, Shared Process
Ultra24f (SCSI miniport)        Stopped (Disabled)
  Error Severity: Normal
  Service Flags: Kernel Driver, Shared Process
v7vram (Video)           Stopped (Disabled)
  Error Severity: Ignore
  Service Flags: Kernel Driver, Shared Process
VgaSave (Video Save)         Running (System)
  C:\WINNT\System32\drivers\vga.sys
  Error Severity: Ignore
  Service Flags: Kernel Driver, Shared Process
VgaStart (Video Init)        Stopped (System)
  C:\WINNT\System32\drivers\vga.sys
  Error Severity: Ignore
  Service Flags: Kernel Driver, Shared Process
Wd33c93 (SCSI miniport)        Stopped (Disabled)
  Error Severity: Normal
  Service Flags: Kernel Driver, Shared Process
wd90c24a (Video)           Stopped (Disabled)
  Error Severity: Ignore
  Service Flags: Kernel Driver, Shared Process
wdvga (Video)            Stopped (Disabled)
  Error Severity: Ignore
  Service Flags: Kernel Driver, Shared Process
weitekp9 (Video)           Stopped (Disabled)
  Error Severity: Ignore
  Service Flags: Kernel Driver, Shared Process
Xga (Video)            Stopped (Disabled)
  Error Severity: Ignore
  Service Flags: Kernel Driver, Shared Process


IRQ and Port Report
_____

Devices          Vector Level    Affinity
_____

UP MPS 1.4 - APIC platform   8   8 0x00000001
UP MPS 1.4 - APIC platform   0   0 0x00000001
UP MPS 1.4 - APIC platform   1   1 0x00000001
UP MPS 1.4 - APIC platform   2   2 0x00000001
UP MPS 1.4 - APIC platform   3   3 0x00000001
UP MPS 1.4 - APIC platform   4   4 0x00000001
UP MPS 1.4 - APIC platform   5   5 0x00000001
UP MPS 1.4 - APIC platform   6   6 0x00000001
UP MPS 1.4 - APIC platform   7   7 0x00000001
UP MPS 1.4 - APIC platform   8   8 0x00000001
UP MPS 1.4 - APIC platform   9   9 0x00000001
UP MPS 1.4 - APIC platform  10  10 0x00000001
UP MPS 1.4 - APIC platform  11  11 0x00000001
UP MPS 1.4 - APIC platform  12  12 0x00000001
UP MPS 1.4 - APIC platform  13  13 0x00000001
UP MPS 1.4 - APIC platform  14  14 0x00000001
UP MPS 1.4 - APIC platform  15  15 0x00000001
UP MPS 1.4 - APIC platform  16  16 0x00000001
UP MPS 1.4 - APIC platform  17  17 0x00000001
UP MPS 1.4 - APIC platform  18  18 0x00000001
```

```
UP MPS 1.4 - APIC platform    19   19 0x00000001
UP MPS 1.4 - APIC platform    20   20 0x00000001
UP MPS 1.4 - APIC platform    21   21 0x00000001
UP MPS 1.4 - APIC platform    22   22 0x00000001
UP MPS 1.4 - APIC platform    23   23 0x00000001
UP MPS 1.4 - APIC platform    24   24 0x00000001
UP MPS 1.4 - APIC platform    25   25 0x00000001
UP MPS 1.4 - APIC platform    26   26 0x00000001
UP MPS 1.4 - APIC platform    27   27 0x00000001
UP MPS 1.4 - APIC platform    28   28 0x00000001
UP MPS 1.4 - APIC platform    29   29 0x00000001
UP MPS 1.4 - APIC platform    30   30 0x00000001
UP MPS 1.4 - APIC platform    31   31 0x00000001
UP MPS 1.4 - APIC platform    32   32 0x00000001
UP MPS 1.4 - APIC platform    33   33 0x00000001
UP MPS 1.4 - APIC platform    34   34 0x00000001
UP MPS 1.4 - APIC platform    35   35 0x00000001
UP MPS 1.4 - APIC platform    36   36 0x00000001
UP MPS 1.4 - APIC platform    37   37 0x00000001
UP MPS 1.4 - APIC platform    38   38 0x00000001
UP MPS 1.4 - APIC platform    39   39 0x00000001
UP MPS 1.4 - APIC platform    40   40 0x00000001
UP MPS 1.4 - APIC platform    41   41 0x00000001
UP MPS 1.4 - APIC platform    42   42 0x00000001
UP MPS 1.4 - APIC platform    43   43 0x00000001
UP MPS 1.4 - APIC platform    44   44 0x00000001
UP MPS 1.4 - APIC platform    45   45 0x00000001
UP MPS 1.4 - APIC platform    46   46 0x00000001
UP MPS 1.4 - APIC platform    47   47 0x00000001
UP MPS 1.4 - APIC platform    61   61 0x00000001
UP MPS 1.4 - APIC platform    65   65 0x00000001
UP MPS 1.4 - APIC platform    80   80 0x00000001
UP MPS 1.4 - APIC platform   193  193 0x00000001
UP MPS 1.4 - APIC platform   225  225 0x00000001
UP MPS 1.4 - APIC platform   253  253 0x00000001
UP MPS 1.4 - APIC platform   254  254 0x00000001
UP MPS 1.4 - APIC platform   255  255 0x00000001
i8042prt           1     1 0xffffffff
i8042prt          12    12 0xffffffff
Serial             4     4 0x00000000
Serial             3     3 0x00000000
Floppy             6     6 0x00000000
KTC100            16    16 0x00000000
aic78xx            4     4 0x00000000
```

```
Devices                        Physical Address   Length

UP MPS 1.4 - APIC platform     0x00000000         0x0000000010
UP MPS 1.4 - APIC platform     0x00000020         0x0000000002
UP MPS 1.4 - APIC platform     0x00000040         0x0000000004
UP MPS 1.4 - APIC platform     0x00000048         0x0000000004
UP MPS 1.4 - APIC platform     0x00000061         0x0000000001
UP MPS 1.4 - APIC platform     0x00000070         0x0000000002
UP MPS 1.4 - APIC platform     0x00000080         0x0000000010
UP MPS 1.4 - APIC platform     0x00000092         0x0000000001
UP MPS 1.4 - APIC platform     0x000000a0         0x0000000002
UP MPS 1.4 - APIC platform     0x000000c0         0x0000000010
UP MPS 1.4 - APIC platform     0x000000f0         0x0000000010
i8042prt           0x00000060  0x0000000001
i8042prt           0x00000064  0x0000000001
```

```
Parport        0x000003bc  0x0000000003
Serial         0x000003f8  0x0000000007
Serial         0x000002f8  0x0000000007
Floppy         0x000003f0  0x0000000006
Floppy         0x000003f7  0x0000000001
KTC100         0x00006400  0x0000000080
aic78xx        0x00006000  0x0000000100
s3             0x000003c0  0x0000000010
s3             0x000003d4  0x0000000008
s3             0x000042e8  0x0000000002
s3             0x00004ae8  0x0000000002
s3             0x000082e8  0x0000000004
s3             0x000086e8  0x0000000004
s3             0x00008ae8  0x0000000004
s3             0x00008ee8  0x0000000004
s3             0x000092e8  0x0000000004
s3             0x000096e8  0x0000000004
s3             0x00009ae8  0x0000000004
s3             0x00009ee8  0x0000000004
s3             0x0000a2e8  0x0000000004
s3             0x0000a6e8  0x0000000004
s3             0x0000aae8  0x0000000004
s3             0x0000aee8  0x0000000004
s3             0x0000b6e8  0x0000000004
s3             0x0000bae8  0x0000000004
s3             0x0000bee8  0x0000000004
s3             0x0000e2e8  0x0000000004
s3             0x0000c2e8  0x0000000004
s3             0x0000c6e8  0x0000000004
s3             0x0000cae8  0x0000000004
s3             0x0000cee8  0x0000000004
s3             0x0000d2e8  0x0000000004
s3             0x0000d6e8  0x0000000004
s3             0x0000dae8  0x0000000004
s3             0x0000dee8  0x0000000004
s3             0x0000e6e8  0x0000000004
s3             0x0000eae8  0x0000000004
s3             0x0000eee8  0x0000000004
s3             0x0000f6e8  0x0000000004
s3             0x0000fae8  0x0000000004
s3             0x0000fee8  0x0000000004
VgaSave         0x000003b0  0x000000000c
VgaSave         0x000003c0  0x0000000020
VgaSave         0x000001ce  0x0000000002
```

DMA and Memory Report

Devices	Channel Port
Floppy	2 0

Devices	Physical Address	Length
UP MPS 1.4 - APIC platform	0xfec00000	0x00000400
UP MPS 1.4 - APIC platform	0xfee00000	0x00000400
aic78xx	0x50000000	0x00001000
s3	0x000a0000	0x00010000
s3	0xf8000000	0x04000000
s3	0x000c0000	0x00008000
VgaSave	0x000a0000	0x00020000

```
Environment Report
_____

System Environment Variables
 ComSpec = C:\WINNT\system32\cmd.exe
 NUMBER_OF_PROCESSORS = 1
 OS = Windows_NT
 Os2LibPath = C:\WINNT\system32\os2\dll;
 Path = C:\WINNT\system32;C:\WINNT
 PROCESSOR_ARCHITECTURE = x86
 PROCESSOR_IDENTIFIER = x86 Family 6 Model 1 Stepping 9, GenuineIntel
 PROCESSOR_LEVEL = 6
 PROCESSOR_REVISION = 0109
 windir = C:\WINNT
Environment Variables for Current User
 TEMP = C:\TEMP
 TMP = C:\TEMP


Network Report
_____

Your Access Level: Admin & Local
Workgroup or Domain: INFO.COM
Network Version: 4.0
LanRoot: INFO.COM
Logged On Users: 1
Current User (1): Administrator
Logon Domain: ANNE
Logon Server: ANNE

Transport: NetBT_KTC1001, 00-C0-F0-30-CB-C6, VC's: 2, Wan: Wan
Transport: Nbf_KTC1001, 00-C0-F0-30-CB-C6, VC's: 1, Wan: Wan
Transport: NwlnkNb, 00-C0-F0-30-CB-C6, VC's: 1, Wan: Wan

Character Wait: 3,600
Collection Time: 250
Maximum Collection Count: 16
Keep Connection: 600
Maximum Commands: 5
Session Time Out: 45
Character Buffer Size: 512
Maximum Threads: 17
Lock Quota: 6,144
Lock Increment: 10
Maximum Locks: 500
Pipe Increment: 10
Maximum Pipes: 500
Cache Time Out: 40
Dormant File Limit: 45
Read Ahead Throughput: 4,294,967,295
Mailslot Buffers: 3
Server Announce Buffers: 20
Illegal Datagrams: 5
Datagram Reset Frequency: 60
Log Election Packets: False
Use Opportunistic Locking: True
Use Unlock Behind: True
Use Close Behind: True
Buffer Pipes: True
Use Lock, Read, Unlock: True
Use NT Caching: True
Use Raw Read: True
```

```
Use Raw Write: True
Use Write Raw Data: True
Use Encryption: True
Buffer Deny Write Files: True
Buffer Read Only Files: True
Force Core Creation: True
512 Byte Max Transfer: False
Bytes Received: 2,635
SMB's Received: 21
Paged Read Bytes Requested: 0
Non Paged Read Bytes Requested: 0
Cache Read Bytes Requested: 0
Network Read Bytes Requested: 0
Bytes Transmitted: 2,906
SMB's Transmitted: 21
Paged Read Bytes Requested: 0
Non Paged Read Bytes Requested: 0
Cache Read Bytes Requested: 0
Network Read Bytes Requested: 0
Initally Failed Operations: 0
Failed Completion Operations: 0
Read Operations: 0
Random Read Operations: 0
Read SMB's: 0
Large Read SMB's: 0
Small Read SMB's: 0
Write Operations: 0
Random Write Operations: 0
Write SMB's: 0
Large Write SMB's: 0
Small Write SMB's: 0
Raw Reads Denied: 0
Raw Writes Denied: 0
Network Errors: 0
Sessions: 5
Failed Sessions: 0
Reconnects: 0
Core Connects: 0
LM 2.0 Connects: 0
LM 2.x Connects: 0
Windows NT Connects: 5
Server Disconnects: 0
Hung Sessions: 0
Use Count: 8
Failed Use Count: 0
Current Commands: 0
Server File Opens: 0
Server Device Opens: 0
Server Jobs Queued: 0
Server Session Opens: 0
Server Sessions Timed Out: 0
Server Sessions Errored Out: 0
Server Password Errors: 0
Server Permission Errors: 0
Server System Errors: 0
Server Bytes Sent: 265
Server Bytes Received: 473
Server Average Response Time: 0
Server Request Buffers Needed: 0
Server Big Buffers Needed: 0
```

For more information on IBM products, contact:

www.ibm.com
International Business Machines
One Old Orchard Road
Armonk, New York 10504
Phone: 914-765-1900
Fax: 914-288-1147

8.9 Remote Workstations (IBM ThinkPads)

I used multiple remote workstations in my network. Figure 8.48 illustrates these systems and the network. Remote workstations were used because mobility was required in my network. I chose IBM ThinkPads because of their features, reliability, and value for the money. The following is the baseline report for one of my remote workstations. The following information is what I maintain to baseline my system called *SPEEDY*. I recommend that you obtain similar information for your remote workstations.

```
 Baseline for SPEEDY
******************* SYSTEM SUMMARY *******************
Windows version: 4.00.950
Computer Name: SPEEDY
Processor Type: Pentium
System BUS Type: ISA
BIOS Name: IBM
BIOS Date: 10/23/96
BIOS Version: EPP BIOS Revision31.00
Machine Type: IBM PC/AT
Math Co-processor: Not Present
Registered Owner: Ed Taylor
Registered Company: Information World, Inc.

******************* IRQ SUMMARY *******************

IRQ Usage Summary:
00 - System timer
01 - Standard 101/102-Key or Microsoft Natural Keyboard
02 - Programmable interrupt controller
03 - IBM PCMCIA 28.8+14.4 Data+Fax Modem
*04 - Communications Port
*05 - ESS ES1688 AudioDrive
06 - Standard Floppy Disk Controller
07 - Printer Port (LPT1)
08 - System CMOS/real time clock
12 - Standard PS/2 Port Mouse
13 - Numeric data processor
14 - Standard IDE/ESDI Hard Disk Controller
15 - SMC EtherEZ PC Card (SMC8020)

******************* IO PORT SUMMARY *******************

I/O Port Usage Summary:
0000h-000Fh - Direct memory access controller
```

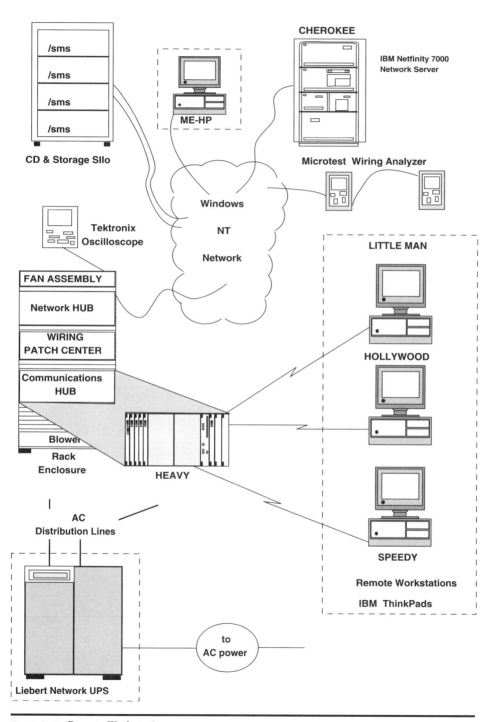

Figure 8.48 Remote Workstations

```
0020h-0021h - Programmable interrupt controller
0040h-0043h - System timer
0060h-0060h - Standard 101/102-Key or Microsoft Natural Keyboard
0061h-0061h - Motherboard resources
0064h-0064h - Standard 101/102-Key or Microsoft Natural Keyboard
0070h-0071h - System CMOS/real time clock
0080h-008Fh - Direct memory access controller
0092h-0092h - Motherboard resources
0094h-0094h - Motherboard resources
00A0h-00A1h - Programmable interrupt controller
00C0h-00DFh - Direct memory access controller
00F0h-00FFh - Numeric data processor
**********************************************************************

System Resource Report

************************
0100h-0107h - Motherboard resources
0110h-011Fh - SMC EtherEZ PC Card (SMC8020)
01F0h-01F7h - Standard IDE/ESDI Hard Disk Controller
0201h-0201h - Gameport Joystick
*0220h-022Fh - ESS ES1688 AudioDrive
026Eh-026Fh - Motherboard resources
02F8h-02FFh - IBM PCMCIA 28.8+14.4 Data+Fax Modem
*0330h-0331h - ESS ES1688 AudioDrive
*0388h-038Bh - ESS ES1688 AudioDrive
03B0h-03BBh - Trident Super VGA
03BCh-03BFh - Printer Port (LPT1)
03C0h-03DFh - Trident Super VGA
03E0h-03E1h - PCIC or compatible PCMCIA controller
*03E8h-03EFh - Communications Port
03F0h-03F5h - Standard Floppy Disk Controller
03F6h-03F6h - Standard IDE/ESDI Hard Disk Controller
03F7h-03F7h - Standard Floppy Disk Controller
0D00h-0D01h - Motherboard resources
15E8h-15EFh - Motherboard resources
FCF0h-FCF7h - Standard IDE/ESDI Hard Disk Controller
**********************************************************************


*******************UPPER MEMORY USAGE SUMMARY *******************

Memory Usage Summary:
000A0000h-000AFFFFh - Trident Super VGA
000B0000h-000BFFFFh - Trident Super VGA
000C0000h-000C7FFFh - Trident Super VGA
08000000h-081FFFFFh - Trident Super VGA
08200000h-0820FFFFh - Trident Super VGA


****************** DMA USAGE SUMMARY ******************

DMA Channel Usage Summary:
*01 - ESS ES1688 AudioDrive
02 - Standard Floppy Disk Controller
04 - Direct memory access controller

****************** MEMORY SUMMARY ******************

640 KB Total Conventional Memory40480 KB Total Extended Memory
```

```
******************** DISK DRIVE INFO ********************

A: Floppy Drive, 3.5" 1.44M
80 Cylinders 2 Heads
512 Bytes/Sector 18 Sectors/Track
System Resource Report
C: Fixed Disk
792032K Total
589344K Free 786 Cylinders 32 Heads
512 Bytes/Sector 63 Sectors/Track
D: CD-ROM Drive

******************** SYSTEM DEVICE INFO ********************

Class: PCMCIA socket
Device: PCIC or compatible PCMCIA controller
Resources:
I/O: 03E0h-03E1h
Device drivers:
C:\WINDOWS\SYSTEM\PCCard.vxd
File size: 0 bytes.
Manufacturer: Microsoft Corporation
File version: 4.00.950
Copyright: Copyright + Microsoft Corp. 1988-1995
C:\WINDOWS\SYSTEM\csmapper.sys
File size: 13390 bytes.
Manufacturer: Microsoft Corporation
File version: 4.00.950
Copyright: Copyright + Microsoft Corp. 1988-1995
C:\WINDOWS\SYSTEM\carddrv.exe
File size: 27296 bytes.
No version information.
C:\WINDOWS\SYSTEM\SRAMMTD.VXD
File size: 3202 bytes.
Manufacturer: Microsoft Corporation
File version: 4.00.950
Copyright: Copyright + Microsoft Corp. 1988-1995
C:\WINDOWS\SYSTEM\FLS1MTD.VXD
File size: 3706 bytes.
Manufacturer: Microsoft Corporation
File version: 4.00.950
Copyright: Copyright + Microsoft Corp. 1988-1995
C:\WINDOWS\SYSTEM\FLS2MTD.VXD
File size: 3810 bytes.
Manufacturer: Microsoft Corporation
File version: 4.00.950
Copyright: Copyright + Microsoft Corp. 1988-1995
C:\WINDOWS\SYSTEM\socketsv.vxd
File size: 9806 bytes.
Manufacturer: Microsoft Corporation
File version: 4.00.950
Copyright: Copyright Microsoft Corp. 1988-1995
********************************

************System Resource Report********************

Class: Network adapters
Device: SMC EtherEZ PC Card (SMC8020)
```

```
Resources:
IRQ: 15
I/O: 0110h-011Fh3F
Class: Network adapters
Device: AOL Adapter
No resources used.
Class: Network adapters
Device: Dial-Up Adapter
No resources used.
*DISABLED DEVICE*
Class: Ports (COM & LPT)
Device: Generic IRDA Compatible Device
No resources used.
*DISABLED DEVICE*
Class: Ports (COM & LPT)
Device: Communications Port
Resources:
IRQ: 04
I/O: 03E8h-03EFh
Device drivers:
C:\WINDOWS\SYSTEM\serial.vxd
File size: 18572 bytes.
Manufacturer: Microsoft Corporation
File version: 4.00.950
Copyright: Copyright Microsoft Corp. 1992-1995
C:\WINDOWS\SYSTEM\serialui.dll
File size: 12032 bytes.
Manufacturer: Microsoft Corporation
File version: 4.00.950
Copyright: Copyright Microsoft Corp. 1993-1995
Class: Ports (COM & LPT)
Device: Printer Port (LPT1)
Resources:
IRQ: 07
I/O: 03BCh-03BFh
Device drivers:
C:\WINDOWS\SYSTEM\lpt.vxd
File size: 35479 bytes.
Manufacturer: Microsoft Corporation

***********System Resource Report**************

File version: 4.00.95
Copyright: Copyright Microsoft Corp. 1992-1995
Class: Mouse
Device: Standard PS/2 Port Mouse
Resources:
IRQ: 12
Device drivers:
C:\WINDOWS\SYSTEM\mouse.drv
File size: 7712 bytes.
Manufacturer: Microsoft Corporation
File version: 9.01.0.000
Copyright: Copyright + Microsoft Corp. 1990-1995
C:\WINDOWS\SYSTEM\msmouse.vxd
File size: 15804 bytes.
Manufacturer: Microsoft Corporation
File version: 4.00.950
Copyright: Copyright Microsoft Corp. 1988-1995
Class: Hard disk controllers
```

```
Device: Standard IDE/ESDI Hard Disk Controller
Resources:
IRQ: 14
I/O: 01F0h-01F7h
I/O: 03F6h-03F6h
I/O: FCF0h-FCF7h
Class: Floppy disk controllers
Device: Standard Floppy Disk Controller
Resources:
IRQ: 06
I/O: 03F0h-03F5h
I/O: 03F7h-03F7h
DMA: 02
Class: Display adapters
Device: Trident Super VGA
Resources:
I/O: 03B0h-03BBh
I/O: 03C0h-03DFh
MEM: 000C0000h-000C7FFFh
MEM: 000A0000h-000AFFFFh
MEM: 000B0000h-000BFFFFh
MEM: 08000000h-081FFFFFh
MEM: 08200000h-0820FFFFh
Device drivers:
C:\WINDOWS\SYSTEM\framebuf.drv


**************System Resource Report******************


File size: 16752 bytes.
Manufacturer: Microsoft Corporation
File version: 4.00.950
Copyright: Copyright Microsoft Corp. 1992-1995
C:\WINDOWS\SYSTEM\supervga.drv
File size: 52320 bytes.
Manufacturer: Microsoft Corporation
File version: 4.00.950
Copyright: Copyright Microsoft Corp. 1991-1995
Class: CDROM Device: TEAC CD-44E
No resources used.Class:
Monitor Device: Laptop Display Panel (1024x768)
No resources used. Class:
Modem Device: IBM PCMCIA 28.8+14.4 Data+Fax Modem
Resources:
IRQ: 03
I/O: 02F8h-02FFhClass: System devices
Device: IO read data port for ISA Plug and Play enumerator
No resources used.Class: System devices
Device: Intel Triton PCI to ISA bridge
No resources used. Class: System devices
Device: PCI standard host CPU bridge
No resources used.Class: System devices
Device: Motherboard resources
Resources:
I/O: 0061h-0061h
I/O: 0092h-0092h
I/O: 0094h-0094h
I/O: 0100h-0107h
I/O: 026Eh-026Fh
I/O: 0D00h-0D01h
```

```
I/O: 15E8h-15EFhSystem Resource ReportClass: System devicesDevice: PCI
bus
No resources used.
Device drivers:
C:\WINDOWS\SYSTEM\pci.vxd
File size: 24535 bytes.
Manufacturer: Microsoft Corporation
File version: 4.00.950
Copyright: Copyright Microsoft Corp. 1988-1995
Class: System devices
Device: Numeric data processor
Resources:
IRQ: 13
I/O: 00F0h-00FFh
Class: System devices
Device: System CMOS/real time clock
Resources:
IRQ: 08
I/O: 0070h-0071h
Class: System devices
Device: System timer
Resources:
IRQ: 00
I/O: 0040h-0043h
Class: System devices
Device: Direct memory access controller
Resources:
I/O: 0000h-000Fh
I/O: 0080h-008Fh
I/O: 00C0h-00DFh
DMA: 04
Class: System devices
Device: Programmable interrupt controller
Resources:
IRQ: 02
I/O: 0020h-0021h
I/O: 00A0h-00A1h
Class: System devices
Device: Advanced Power Management support
No resources used.

********************System Resource Report****************

Class: System devices
Device: Plug and Play BIOS
No resources used.
Device drivers:
C:\WINDOWS\SYSTEM\VMM32\bios.vxd
No version information.
Class: System devices
Device: System board
No resources used.
Class: Keyboard
Device: Standard 101/102-Key or Microsoft Natural Keyboard
Resources:
IRQ: 01
I/O: 0060h-0060h
I/O: 0064h-0064h
Device drivers:
C:\WINDOWS\SYSTEM\keyboard.drv
```

```
File size: 12688 bytes.
Manufacturer: Microsoft Corporation
File version: 4.00.950
Copyright: Copyright Microsoft Corp. 1991-1995
C:\WINDOWS\SYSTEM\VMM32\vkd.vxd
No version information.
*DISABLED DEVICE*
Class: Sound, video and game controllers
Device: ESS ES1688 AudioDrive
Resources:
IRQ: 05
I/O: 0220h-022Fh
I/O: 0388h-038Bh
I/O: 0330h-0331h
DMA: 01
Device drivers:
C:\WINDOWS\SYSTEM\es1688.drv
File size: 50128 bytes.
Manufacturer: Microsoft Corporation
File version: 4.0.950
Copyright: Copyright + Microsoft Corp. 1991-1995
C:\WINDOWS\SYSTEM\es1688.vxd
File size: 22168 bytes.
Manufacturer: Microsoft Corporation
File version: 4.00.950
Copyright: Copyright Microsoft Corp. 1994-1995
C:\WINDOWS\SYSTEM\essfm.drv

*****************System Resource Report******************

File size: 17920 bytes.
Manufacturer: Microsoft Corporation
File version: 4.0.950
Copyright: Copyright Microsoft Corp. 1991-1995
C:\WINDOWS\SYSTEM\essmpu.drv
File size: 8240 bytes.
Manufacturer: Microsoft Corporation
File version: 4.0.950
Copyright: Copyright Microsoft Corp. 1991-1995
Class: Sound, video and game controllers
Device: Gameport Joystick
Resources:
I/O: 0201h-0201h
Device drivers:
C:\WINDOWS\SYSTEM\vjoyd.vxd
File size: 20590 bytes.
Manufacturer: Microsoft Corporation
File version: 4.00.950
Copyright: Copyright Microsoft Corp. 1994-1995
C:\WINDOWS\SYSTEM\msjstick.drv
File size: 7744 bytes.
Manufacturer: Microsoft Corporation
File version: 4.0.950
Copyright: Copyright Microsoft Corp. 1991-1995
Class: Disk drives
Device: GENERIC IDE DISK TYPE<7
No resources used.
Class: Disk drives
Device: GENERIC NEC FLOPPY DISK
No resources used.
```

```
Class: Printer
Device:
No resources used.
Class: Printer
Device: IBM 2390 PS/1
No resources used.
Device drivers:
C:\WINDOWS\SYSTEM\IBM239X.DRV
File size: 30560 bytes.
Manufacturer: Microsoft Corporation
File version: 4.00.950
Copyright: Copyright Microsoft Corp. 1991-1995

*************System Resource Report**************************

*
C:\WINDOWS\SYSTEM\UNIDRV.DLL
File size: 416 bytes.
Manufacturer: Microsoft Corporation
File version: 4.00.950
Copyright: Copyright Microsoft Corp. 1991-1995
C:\WINDOWS\SYSTEM\UNIDRV.HLP
File size: 15343 bytes.
No version information.
C:\WINDOWS\SYSTEM\ICONLIB.DLL
File size: 12176 bytes.
Manufacturer: Microsoft Corporation
File version: 4.00.950
Copyright: Microsoft Corp. 1991-1995

**********************End-of-Report**************************
```

Additional information about remote systems should be obtained. It is important to know the configuration and view this information from the system itself. Consider the following information:

- Background and identification
  Volume SPEEDY created 08-02-1998 11:59 P.M.
  Volume serial number is 2503-0146

- Hard-disk information
  811,057,152 bytes total disk space
  14,286,848 bytes in 144 hidden files
  3,817,472 bytes in 232 directories
  189,497,344 bytes in 3,125 user files
  603,455,488 bytes available on disk

- System memory
  16,384 bytes in each allocation unit
  49,502 total allocation units on disk
  36,831 available allocation units on disk

655,360 total bytes memory

615,184 bytes free

Another view of SPEEDY's memory is as follows:

Memory	Total	Used	Free
Conventional	640K	39K	601K
Upper	0K	0K	0K
Reserved	384K	384K	0K
Extended (XMS)	39,936K	160K	39,776K
Total memory	40,960K	583K	40,377K
Total <1 MB	640K	39K	601K
Total Expanded (EMS)	40 MB (41,451,520 bytes)		
Free Expanded (EMS)	16 MB (16,777,216 bytes)		

Also

- The largest executable program size is 601K (614,960 bytes).

- The largest free upper memory block is 0K (0 bytes).

- MS-DOS is resident in the high-memory area.

Since SPEEDY is connected to the network, having baseline information regarding this server is important as well. Consider the following:

Computer name	`\\SPEEDY`
User name	`SPEEDY`
Workgroup	`INFO.COM`
Workstation root directory	`C:\WINDOWS`
Software version	4.00.950
Redirector version	4.00

The following information on servers available in workgroup `INFO.COM.` is pertinent to understanding the interaction of SPEEDY on the network:

Server name	Remark
`\\ANNE`	`THE-ANNE-MACHINE`
`\\BRAINS`	—
`\\CHEROKEE`	—
`\\FATBOY`	`FATBOY`
`\\MONY`	`MONY`
`\\MUSCLE`	—
`\\SPEEDY`	`SPEEDY`
`\\THE-HOSTAGE`	`THE-HOSTAGE`

Your situation may differ, so you should analyze your environment and determine how much information you should maintain on each remote workstation.

8.10   How to Baseline Your Data Communications Network Hub

I use a USRobotics Enterprise Network communications hub in my network. Data-communication equipment is the single most critical link in any network because it is the central point of attachment between remote users and a backbone network, regardless of the size of the backbone or location. This is also true if all users are in the same physical location. Data-communication equipment is central to networks; if this equipment fails, the network will fail. Before examining some baseline information about the communciaiton hub, it is helpful to understand it in relation to the network. Consider Figure 8.49, which illustrates the network designed (here) in Dallas and remote users and a remote network, both located in Chicago.

Note that remote users are connecting directly into the Dallas network via the communications hub. In this case the remote users use their modems to connect directly to the hub. As you baseline your communications equipment, consider what information is pertinent to have on hand about the remote environment.

When remote users or remote network(s) are concerned, multiple issues must be considered. Some of the functions that the communications server in my network performs are listed here; you should consider this and make appropriate adjustments in understanding your equipment in terms of baselining:

- Security
- Reliability
- Maintenance
- Ease of use
- Internal protocol compatibility
- Expandability
- Internal design architecture
- Interface standard compatibility

Security has become the single most important topic in networking, regardless of the type network or location. Networks can have a considerable degree of security built into the design if proper components are used to implement security. Where data-communication equipment is concerned, having a device that can provide a security firewall is best. Consider Figure 8.50. It is really helpful to know and understand what functions are performed by various pieces of equipment in the network. In this case, Figure

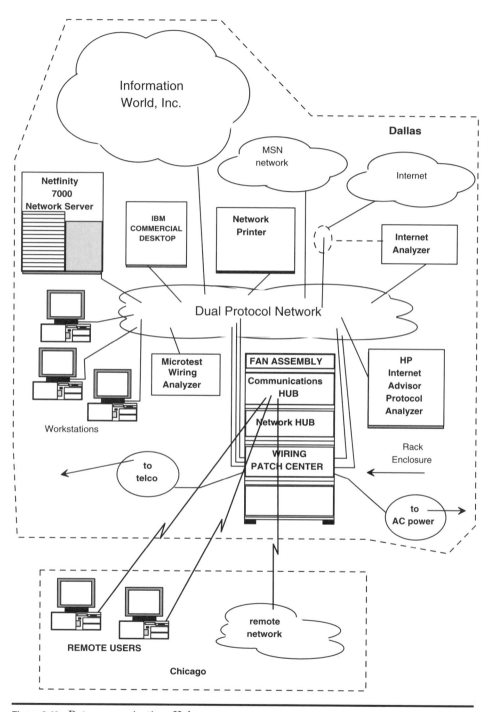

Figure 8.49 Datacommunications Hub

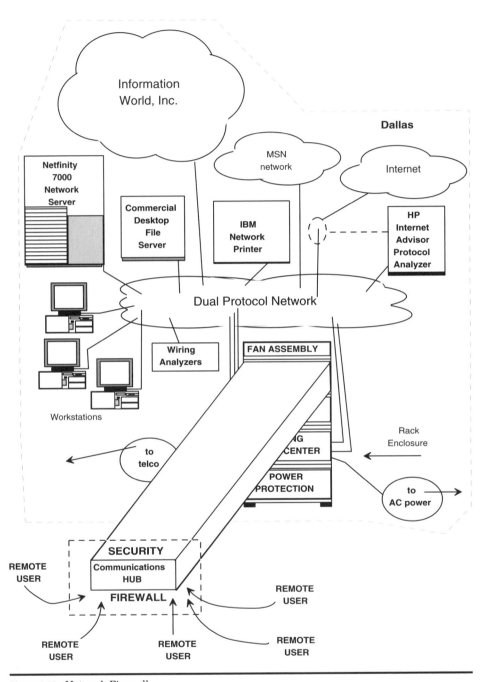

Figure 8.50 Network Firewall

8.50 shows a secure firewall implemented in the communications hub. Remote users shown in this illustration are required to sign on to the hub. It is a point of isolation. Other devices on the network require signons and passwords as well.

The USRobotics communication hub used in this network has three possible configurations regarding function in the network. USRobotics refers to this as gateway application cards. USRobotics uses the following terminology and explanation:

X.25	Provides access capability to packet-switched networks; uses a EIA-232/V.35 interface connection point.
NETServer Card	Functions as either a router, terminal server, or both. Ethernet and Token Ring NICs can be used with this card, which USRobotics also refers to as the *EdgeServer card*. This card has Windows NT loaded onto it; the functionality this card provides is explained later.
API Card	Lets customers design their own applications using USRobotics software development kits. Figure 8.51 illustrates the enterprise hub.

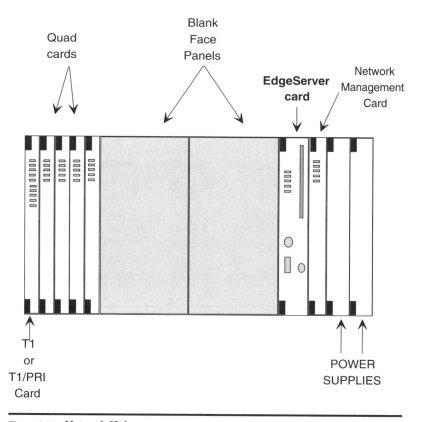

Figure 8.51 Network Hub

It is important to know as much about your equipment as possible. You may want to list the features and functions for your equipment, but consider my explanation of the equipment in the network. Figure 8.51 shows the hub with blank face panels, which can be removed. Other cards can be inserted; there are 17 slots. The T1 card is in slot 1. Beginning with slot 2, one finds analog or digital quad modem cards, which are loaded with the equivalent of four modems. The EdgeServer card is located in slots 15 and 16. The network management card is located in slot 17. The remaining slots house two power supplies. Although not shown in this illustration, the undercradle portion of the hub houses approximately 16 fans to cool the components.

Reliability is another important factor for any communication equipment. The design of the USRobotics hub has reliability built into it. One example supports this observation—the hub has two power supplies, but only one is required to operate the unit. They have built-in redundancy even to the level of power supply unit.

Maintenance is another part of the equation for communication equipment. The hub used in this network has remote management capability, local management capability, and easy access for those components that may need to be removed.

Operation of any communication device requires skill; a fairly advanced level of skill is required for maximum use. The capability of any communication device has little to do with its ease of use, which is a design issue. With the hub used in this network, ease of use is designed into it. Ease of use can be measured in communication equipment by documentation provided, including how thorough and detailed it is; and by accessibility to configure ports and the ability to use the equipment in a practically failed state (should that occur). My rule of thumb is that the more complex functions a device offers, the simpler the documentation should be. Data-communication equipment is complex enough without humans adding another layer of complexity to it.

Another factor to analyze with data-communication equipment is the protocol compatibility, including evaluation of upper- and lower-layer protocols. Because this hub has the EdgeServer card loaded in it, NetBEUI, TCP/IP, and IPX upper-layer protocols are supported. Token Ring and Ethernet lower-layer protocols are supported as well. (Author's note regarding the USRobotics hub used in this network: Use of Token Ring and Ethernet is more than sufficient because these two protocols are dominant lower-layer protocols used in networks today.)

Expandability is very important with data-communication equipment. The design of the USRobotics Enterprise Network Hub is such that a network of any size can be built around this technology. This is true because of how the equipment has been architected. With the USRobotics equipment, it is possible to start a network with one or two enterprise hubs and then continue to add them until all racks are filled with them.

Internal design architecture is also very important to data communication equipment. The internal architecture of data-communication gear is the proverbial pivot on which all communication transactions hinge. The internal communications bus and the incoming port architecture constitute the foundation of the device. These should be capable of handling a complete load on the device without causing hangups or system slowdown.

Interface standard computability is another matter to examine when you are evaluating data-communication equipment. In this network, the hub has flexibility regarding how certain connections are made. In some instance there are options for making a connection. This alone makes for ease of use, installation, and maintenance. It also means that some of the existing equipment at your site may be usable, which can save money.

The 3Com USRobotics Enterprise Network Hub has the EdgeServer card preinstalled. This card has the following:

1.44-in floppy drive	SCSI port
Mouse port	Minimum of 800-MB hard drive
Keyboard port	Minimum 100-MHz processor
Display port	10BaseT capability

My hub has an EdgeServer card with the Windows NT Server 4.0 and the Service Pack 3 option both preinstalled. EdgeServer card functionality appears as shown in Figure 8.52.

In the context of my use, this hub serves a specific purpose. However, analysis of obtaining a typical functional perspective of the EdgeServer card involves many aspects. First, when remote users access the communications hub for information purposes only, they can stop there and not access other systems that are part of the network. Second, remote users who require access to other systems can use the EdgeServer card as a gateway, if you will, to access the network behind it. The EdgeServer card can function as an excellent firewall to protect the assets behind it while permitting access to it.

Still another powerful feature of the EdgeServer card is the SCSI port located on back of it. This feature makes it possible to connect a CD-ROM drive to this card. Documentation is provided with the USRobotics Enterprise Network Hub, but it is also provided via CD, which makes it convenient to access when manuals are not easily accessible.

A network management card is also part of the hub's component configuration. The card supports Ethernet and Token Ring as lower-layer protocols. It is a separate card, and it provides a console port that can be used for:

1. Remote access: It can be dialed into from a remote site.

2. Local access: Management access locally with an RJ-45 and DB25 cable with a null-modem adapter provided with the hub is possible.

3. Software download: This also possible to aid in the management aspect of the hub.

The network management card supports 10BaseT, 10Base5, and 10Base2 connection points for Ethernet cable flexibility. Token Ring cable support

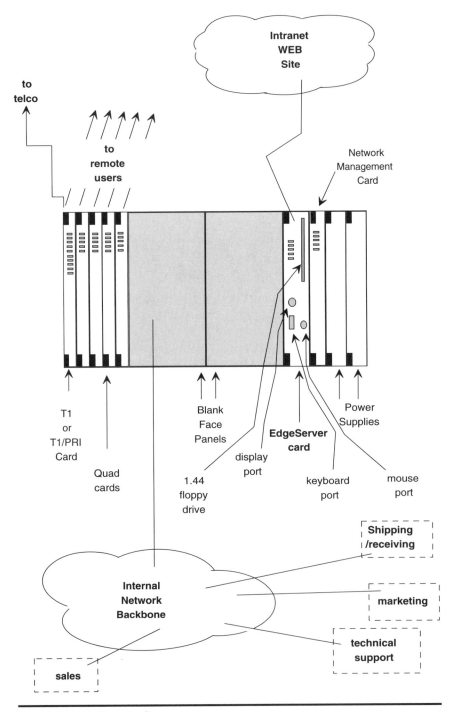

Figure 8.52 Hub Functionality

includes shielded twisted-pair (also known as IBM type 1) and unshielded twisted-pair (also known as IBM type 3) cable.

The network management card does not run SNMP management agents directly on the card; however, the support for SNMP is not compromised. The network management card technically functions as a proxy agent; but the functionality and management ability with SNMP operation features the same support.

The enterprise hub used in this network has a T1 card, which operates as a Primary Rate Interface (PRI). The T1 card is managed by the Total Control Manager (TCM), which is SMP-based and works with MS-Windows. The card itself is easily configurable. Either a dumb terminal, remote PC, LAN PC, or direct connect PC can work with configuration management parameters. Its operands function within the SNMP MIB standards; both GET and SET operations can be issued against the T1 card.

The T1 front panel includes LEDs to indicate the operational status of the card. These LEDs include

ALARM	Activated on existence of either alarm indication signal, frame slip, out-of-frame state, excessive CRC errors, change of frame alignment, line format violation, or frame alignment error
CARRIER	Indicates whether a carrier is present; an unframed signal LED indicates if an out-of-frame condition exists, when a loss-of-signal condition occurs, and if a signal is reported "not present"
LOOPBACK	Indicates whether test is in operation, initiated from the local telephone company
RUN/FAIL	Indicates operational mode of the T1 card; that is, if it is operating normal or in a "critical" mode because of a hardware and/or software fail condition

USRobotics Enterprise Network Hub modems are either analog or digital. Consider Figure 8.53, which shows the Enterprise Network Hub with analog modems (quad cards) connected to analog telephone lines. The gateway interface card in this illustration shows a generic connectivity to a network. The gateway connectivity portion of this hub does not necessarily require the Windows NT Server, but this implementation is popular.

Figure 8.54 shows another hub implementation, with a T1 link to the telephone company. It also shows the digital modems users use after a signal is in the hub. The gateway aspect of the hub indicates that users can have access outbound to a network if such functionality is configured. Technically, the network access that a remote user has is configurable for either analog or digital modem connectivity.

The data-communication hub used in this network provides robust throughput for remote users. Because of its ability to implement security well, a considerable degree of secure access has been obtained. Internal (local) users are also able to access the network because it functions as a node on the network; hence it is seen by other systems as a Windows NT node on the network.

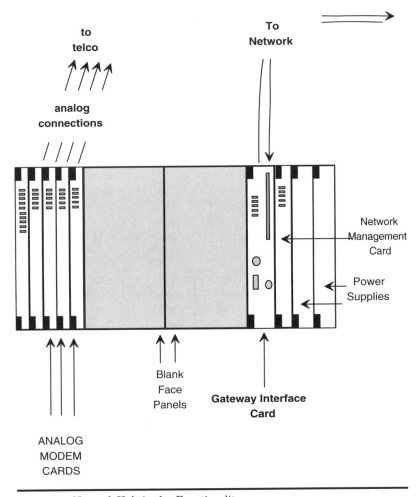

Figure 8.53 Network Hub Analog Functionality

Now that you have an understanding of the operational nature of the hub in my network, here is the baseline information on the specifics of the system I keep on hand. I think you should keep equally detailed statistics. The following is a baseline report for HEAVY generated by the operating system. Consider the detail presented; it includes hardware, network, software, and driver information.

```
Diagnostics Report For \\HEAVY

OS Version Report

Microsoft (R) Windows NT (TM) Server
Version 4.0 (Build 1381: Service Pack 1) x86 Uniprocessor Free
Registered Owner: HEAVY, Information World, Inc.
```

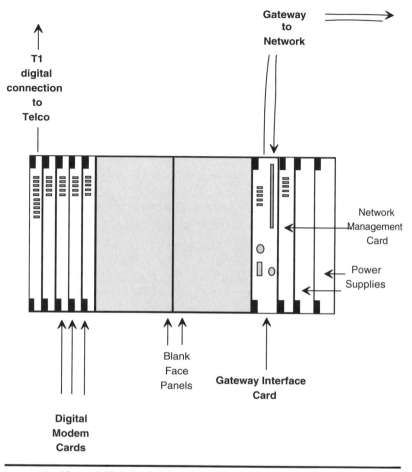

Figure 8.54 Network Hub Digital Functionality

```
Product Number: 50370-807-5268635-67393
─────────────────────────────────────────

System Report
─────────────────────────────────────────

System: AT/COMPATIBLE
Hardware Abstraction Layer: PC Compatible Eisa/Isa HAL
BIOS Date: 05/28/96
BIOS Version: v4.02 Copyright 1992-93 Phoenix
Processor list:
 0: x86 Family 4 Model 8 Stepping 3 GenuineIntel

Video Display Report
─────────────────────────────────────────

BIOS Date: 08/10/94
BIOS Version: CL-GD5429 VGA BIOS Version 1.00
Adapter:
```

```
Setting: 640 x 480 x 256
    60 Hz
Type: cirrus compatible display adapter
String: Cirrus Logic Compatible
Memory: 512 KB
Chip Type: CL 5429
DAC Type: Integrated RAMDAC
Driver:
Vendor: Microsoft Corporation
File(s): cirrus.sys, vga.dll, cirrus.dll, vga256.dll, vga64K.dll
Version: 4.00, 4.0.0
```

Drives Report
_____

```
C:\ (Local - FAT) HEAVY Total: 794,048KB, Free: 606,896KB
 Serial Number: 2E6B - 11D7
 Bytes per cluster: 512
 Sectors per cluster: 32
 Filename length: 255
```

Memory Report
_____

```
Handles: 1,521
Threads: 141
Processes: 18
Physical Memory (K)
 Total: 64,696
 Available: 35,128
 File Cache: 6,020
Kernel Memory (K)
 Total: 8,680
 Paged: 3,684
 Nonpaged: 4,996
Commit Charge (K)
 Total: 22,272
 Limit: 136,424
 Peak: 22,288
Pagefile Space (K)
 Total: 81,920
 Total in use: 0
Peak: 0
C:\pagefile.sys
 Total: 81,920
 Total in use: 0
 Peak: 0
```

Services Report
_____

```
Alerter        Running (Automatic)
 C:\WINNT\System32\services.exe
 Service Account Name: LocalSystem
 Error Severity: Normal
 Service Flags: Shared Process
 Service Dependencies:
  LanmanWorkstation
Computer Browser          Running (Automatic)
 C:\WINNT\System32\services.exe
 Service Account Name: LocalSystem
 Error Severity: Normal
 Service Flags: Shared Process
 Service Dependencies:
```

```
 LanmanWorkstation
 LanmanServer
 LmHosts
ClipBook Server          Stopped (Manual)
 C:\WINNT\system32\clipsrv.exe
 Service Account Name: LocalSystem
 Error Severity: Normal
 Service Flags: Own Process
 Service Dependencies:
  NetDDE
Confserv          Running (Automatic)
 C:\WINNT\System32\confserv.exe
 Service Account Name: LocalSystem
 Error Severity: Normal
 Service Flags: Own Process
DHCP Client (TDI)        Stopped (Disabled)
 C:\WINNT\System32\services.exe
 Service Account Name: LocalSystem
 Error Severity: Normal
 Service Flags: Shared Process
 Service Dependencies:
  Tcpip
  Afd
  NetBT
EventLog (Event log)       Running (Automatic)
 C:\WINNT\system32\services.exe
 Service Account Name: LocalSystem
 Error Severity: Normal
 Service Flags: Shared Process
Server          Running (Automatic)
 C:\WINNT\System32\services.exe
 Service Account Name: LocalSystem
 Error Severity: Normal
 Service Flags: Shared Process
 Group Dependencies: TDI
Workstation (NetworkProvider)       Running (Automatic)
 C:\WINNT\System32\services.exe
 Service Account Name: LocalSystem
 Error Severity: Normal
 Service Flags: Shared Process
 Group Dependencies: TDI
License Logging Service      Running (Automatic)
 C:\WINNT\System32\llssrv.exe
 Service Account Name: LocalSystem
 Error Severity: Normal
 Service Flags: Own Process
TCP/IP NetBIOS Helper       Running (Automatic)
 C:\WINNT\System32\services.exe
 Service Account Name: LocalSystem
 Error Severity: Normal
 Service Flags: Shared Process
 Group Dependencies:
  NetworkProvider
Messenger          Running (Automatic)
 C:\WINNT\System32\services.exe
 Service Account Name: LocalSystem
 Error Severity: Normal
 Service Flags: Shared Process
 Service Dependencies:
  LanmanWorkstation
  NetBios
```

```
Network DDE (NetDDEGroup)    Stopped (Manual)
 C:\WINNT\system32\netdde.exe
 Service Account Name: LocalSystem
 Error Severity: Normal
 Service Flags: Shared Process
 Service Dependencies: NetDDEDSDM
Network DDE DSDM        Stopped (Manual)
 C:\WINNT\system32\netdde.exe
 Service Account Name: LocalSystem
 Error Severity: Normal
 Service Flags: Shared Process
Net Logon (RemoteValidation)    Stopped (Manual)
 C:\WINNT\System32\lsass.exe
 Service Account Name: LocalSystem
 Error Severity: Normal
 Service Flags: Shared Process
 Service Dependencies:
  LanmanWorkstation
  LmHosts
Norton SpeedDisk        Running (Automatic)
 C:\Program Files\Norton Speed Disk Trial\SDSRV.EXE
 Service Account Name: LocalSystem
 Error Severity: Normal
 Service Flags: Own Process
NT LM Security Support Provider    Stopped (Manual)
 C:\WINNT\System32\SERVICES.EXE
 Service Account Name: LocalSystem
 Error Severity: Normal
 Service Flags: Shared Process
SAP Agent          Running (Automatic)
 C:\WINNT\system32\services.exe
 Service Account Name: LocalSystem
 Error Severity: Normal
 Service Flags: Shared Process
 Service Dependencies:
  NWLNKIPX
Plug and Play (PlugPlay)    Running (Automatic)
 C:\WINNT\system32\services.exe
 Service Account Name: LocalSystem
 Error Severity: Normal
 Service Flags: Shared Process
Remote Access Autodial Manager   Stopped (Disabled)
 C:\WINNT\system32\rasman.exe
 Service Account Name: LocalSystem
 Error Severity: Normal
 Service Flags: Shared Process
 Service Dependencies:
  RasMan
Remote Access Connection Manager (Network)    Running (Manual)
 C:\WINNT\system32\rasman.exe
 Service Account Name: LocalSystem
 Error Severity: Normal
 Service Flags: Shared Process, Interactive
 Service Dependencies:
  tapisrv
Virtual Motion RAS Port Manager      Running (Automatic)
 C:\WINNT\system32\raspmsvc.exe
 Service Account Name: LocalSystem
 Error Severity: Normal
 Service Flags: Own Process
```

```
 Service Dependencies:
  RemoteAccess
Remote Access Server (Network)        Running (Automatic)
 C:\WINNT\system32\rassrv.exe
 Service Account Name: LocalSystem
 Error Severity: Normal
 Service Flags: Own Process
 Service Dependencies:
  LanmanServer
  RasMan
  NetBios
  NwlnkRip
  NwSapAgent
  NetBT
  Nbf
  NwlnkIpx
Directory Replicator        Stopped (Manual)
 C:\WINNT\System32\lmrepl.exe
 Service Account Name: LocalSystem
 Error Severity: Normal
 Service Flags: Own Process
 Service Dependencies:
  LanmanWorkstation
  LanmanServer
Remote Procedure Call (RPC) Locator    Stopped (Manual)
 C:\WINNT\System32\LOCATOR.EXE
 Service Account Name: LocalSystem
 Error Severity: Normal
 Service Flags: Own Process
Remote Procedure Call (RPC) Service     Running (Automatic)
 C:\WINNT\system32\RpcSs.exe
 Service Account Name: LocalSystem
 Error Severity: Normal
 Service Flags: Own Process
 Schedule          Stopped (Manual)
  C:\WINNT\System32\AtSvc.Exe
  Service Account Name: LocalSystem
  Error Severity: Normal
  Service Flags: Own Process
Spooler (SpoolerGroup)        Running (Automatic)
 C:\WINNT\system32\spoolss.exe
 Service Account Name: LocalSystem
 Error Severity: Normal
 Service Flags: Own Process, Interactive
Telephony Service         Running (Manual)
 C:\WINNT\system32\tapisrv.exe
 Service Account Name: LocalSystem
 Error Severity: Normal
 Service Flags: Own Process
UPS            Stopped (Manual)
 C:\WINNT\System32\ups.exe
 Service Account Name: LocalSystem
 Error Severity: Normal
 Service Flags: Own Process


Drivers Report
_____

Abiosdsk (Primary disk)        Stopped (Disabled)
 Error Severity: Ignore
 Service Flags: Kernel Driver, Shared Process
```

```
AFD Networking Support Environment (TDI)    Running (Automatic)
 C:\WINNT\System32\drivers\afd.sys
 Error Severity: Normal
 Service Flags: Kernel Driver, Shared Process
Aha154x (SCSI miniport)      Stopped (Disabled)
 Error Severity: Normal
 Service Flags: Kernel Driver, Shared Process
Aha174x (SCSI miniport)      Stopped (Disabled)
 Error Severity: Normal
 Service Flags: Kernel Driver, Shared Process
aic78xx (SCSI miniport)      Stopped (Disabled)
 Error Severity: Normal
 Service Flags: Kernel Driver, Shared Process
Always (SCSI miniport)       Stopped (Disabled)
 Error Severity: Normal
 Service Flags: Kernel Driver, Shared Process
ami0nt (SCSI miniport)       Stopped (Disabled)
 Error Severity: Normal
 Service Flags: Kernel Driver, Shared Process
amsint (SCSI miniport)       Stopped (Disabled)
 Error Severity: Normal
 Service Flags: Kernel Driver, Shared Process
Arrow (SCSI miniport)        Stopped (Disabled)
 Error Severity: Normal
 Service Flags: Kernel Driver, Shared Process
Remote Access Mac (NDIS)        Stopped (Disabled)
 C:\WINNT\system32\drivers\asyncmac.sys
 Error Severity: Normal
 Service Flags: Kernel Driver, Shared Process
atapi (SCSI miniport)        Stopped (Disabled)
 Error Severity: Normal
 Service Flags: Kernel Driver, Shared Process
Atdisk (Primary disk)        Running (Boot)
 Error Severity: Normal
 Service Flags: Kernel Driver, Shared Process
ati (Video)          Stopped (Disabled)
 Error Severity: Ignore
 Service Flags: Kernel Driver, Shared Process
Beep (Base)              Running (System)
 Error Severity: Normal
 Service Flags: Kernel Driver, Shared Process
BusLogic (SCSI miniport)        Stopped (Disabled)
 Error Severity: Normal
 Service Flags: Kernel Driver, Shared Process
Busmouse (Pointer Port)       Stopped (Disabled)
 Error Severity: Ignore
 Service Flags: Kernel Driver, Shared Process
Cdaudio (Filter)         Stopped (System)
 Error Severity: Ignore
 Service Flags: Kernel Driver, Shared Process
Cdfs (File system)         Stopped (Disabled)
 Error Severity: Normal
 Service Flags: File System Driver, Shared Process
 Group Dependencies:
  SCSI CDROM Class
Cdrom (SCSI CDROM Class)        Stopped (System)
 Error Severity: Ignore
 Service Flags: Kernel Driver, Shared Process
 Group Dependencies:
  SCSI miniport
```

```
Changer (Filter)           Stopped (System)
 Error Severity: Ignore
 Service Flags: Kernel Driver, Shared Process
cirrus (Video)             Running (System)
 Error Severity: Normal
 Service Flags: Kernel Driver, Shared Process
Cpqarray (SCSI miniport)       Stopped (Disabled)
 Error Severity: Normal
 Service Flags: Kernel Driver, Shared Process
cpqfws2e (SCSI miniport)       Stopped (Disabled)
 Error Severity: Normal
 Service Flags: Kernel Driver, Shared Process
dac960nt (SCSI miniport)       Stopped (Disabled)
 Error Severity: Normal
 Service Flags: Kernel Driver, Shared Process
dce376nt (SCSI miniport)       Stopped (Disabled)
 Error Severity: Normal
 Service Flags: Kernel Driver, Shared Process
Delldsa (SCSI miniport)        Stopped (Disabled)
 Error Severity: Normal
 Service Flags: Kernel Driver, Shared Process
Dell_DGX (Video)           Stopped (Disabled)
 Error Severity: Ignore
 Service Flags: Kernel Driver, Shared Process
Disk (SCSI Class)          Stopped (Boot)
 Error Severity: Ignore
 Service Flags: Kernel Driver, Shared Process
 Group Dependencies:
  SCSI miniport
Diskperf (Filter)          Stopped (Disabled)
 Error Severity: Normal
 Service Flags: Kernel Driver, Shared Process
DptScsi (SCSI miniport)        Stopped (Disabled)
 Error Severity: Normal
 Service Flags: Kernel Driver, Shared Process
dtc329x (SCSI miniport)        Stopped (Disabled)
 Error Severity: Normal
 Service Flags: Kernel Driver, Shared Process
et4000 (Video)             Stopped (Disabled)
 Error Severity: Ignore
 Service Flags: Kernel Driver, Shared Process
Fastfat (Boot file system)     Running (Disabled)
 Error Severity: Normal
 Service Flags: File System Driver, Shared Process
Fd16_700 (SCSI miniport)       Stopped (Disabled)
 Error Severity: Normal
 Service Flags: Kernel Driver, Shared Process
Fd7000ex (SCSI miniport)       Stopped (Disabled)
 Error Severity: Normal
 Service Flags: Kernel Driver, Shared Process
Fd8xx (SCSI miniport)          Stopped (Disabled)
 Error Severity: Normal
 Service Flags: Kernel Driver, Shared Process
flashpnt (SCSI miniport)       Stopped (Disabled)
 Error Severity: Normal
 Service Flags: Kernel Driver, Shared Process
Floppy (Primary disk)          Running (System)
 Error Severity: Ignore
 Service Flags: Kernel Driver, Shared Process
Ftdisk (Filter)            Stopped (Disabled)
```

```
Error Severity: Ignore
Service Flags: Kernel Driver, Shared Process
i8042 Keyboard and PS/2 Mouse Port Driver (Keyboard Port) Running
(System)
System32\DRIVERS\i8042prt.sys
Error Severity: Normal
Service Flags: Kernel Driver, Shared Process
Inport (Pointer Port)        Stopped (Disabled)
Error Severity: Ignore
Service Flags: Kernel Driver, Shared Process
Jazzg300 (Video)        Stopped (Disabled)
Error Severity: Ignore
Service Flags: Kernel Driver, Shared Process
Jazzg364 (Video)        Stopped (Disabled)
Error Severity: Ignore
Service Flags: Kernel Driver, Shared Process
Jzvxl484 (Video)        Stopped (Disabled)
Error Severity: Ignore
Service Flags: Kernel Driver, Shared Process
Keyboard Class Driver (Keyboard Class)    Running (System)
System32\DRIVERS\kbdclass.sys
Error Severity: Normal
Service Flags: Kernel Driver, Shared Process
KSecDD (Base)        Running (System)
Error Severity: Normal
Service Flags: Kernel Driver, Shared Process
mga (Video)        Stopped (Disabled)
Error Severity: Ignore
Service Flags: Kernel Driver, Shared Process
mga_mil (Video)        Stopped (Disabled)
Error Severity: Ignore
Service Flags: Kernel Driver, Shared Process
mitsumi (SCSI miniport)        Stopped (Disabled)
Error Severity: Normal
Service Flags: Kernel Driver, Shared Process
mkecr5xx (SCSI miniport)        Stopped (Disabled)
Error Severity: Normal
Service Flags: Kernel Driver, Shared Process
Modem (Extended base)        Stopped (Manual)
Error Severity: Ignore
Service Flags: Kernel Driver, Shared Process
Mouse Class Driver (Pointer Class)    Running (System)
System32\DRIVERS\mouclass.sys
Error Severity: Normal
Service Flags: Kernel Driver, Shared Process
Msfs (File system)        Running (System)
Error Severity: Normal
Service Flags: File System Driver, Shared Process
Mup (Network)        Running (Manual)
C:\WINNT\System32\drivers\mup.sys
Error Severity: Normal
Service Flags: File System Driver, Shared Process
NetBEUI Protocol (PNP_TDI)        Running (Automatic)
C:\WINNT\System32\drivers\nbf.sys
Error Severity: Normal
Service Flags: Kernel Driver, Shared Process
Ncr53c9x (SCSI miniport)        Stopped (Disabled)
Error Severity: Normal
Service Flags: Kernel Driver, Shared Process
ncr77c22 (Video)        Stopped (Disabled)
Error Severity: Ignore
```

```
 Service Flags: Kernel Driver, Shared Process
Ncrc700 (SCSI miniport)          Stopped (Disabled)
 Error Severity: Normal
 Service Flags: Kernel Driver, Shared Process
Ncrc710 (SCSI miniport)          Stopped (Disabled)
 Error Severity: Normal
 Service Flags: Kernel Driver, Shared Process
Microsoft NDIS System Driver (NDIS)      Running (System)
 Error Severity: Normal
 Service Flags: Kernel Driver, Shared Process
Microsoft NDIS TAPI driver (NDIS)        Running (System)
 C:\WINNT\system32\drivers\ndistapi.sys
 Error Severity: Normal
 Service Flags: Kernel Driver, Shared Process
Remote Access WAN Wrapper (NDISWAN)          Running (Automatic)
 C:\WINNT\system32\drivers\ndiswan.sys
 Error Severity: Normal
 Service Flags: Kernel Driver, Shared Process
NetBIOS Interface (NetBIOSGroup)       Running (Manual)
 C:\WINNT\System32\drivers\netbios.sys
 Error Severity: Normal
 Service Flags: File System Driver, Shared Process
 Group Dependencies:
  TDI
WINS Client(TCP/IP) (PNP_TDI)          Running (Automatic)
 C:\WINNT\System32\drivers\netbt.sys
 Error Severity: Normal
 Service Flags: Kernel Driver, Shared Process
 Service Dependencies:
  Tcpip
NetDetect                Stopped (Manual)
 C:\WINNT\system32\drivers\netdtect.sys
 Error Severity: Normal
 Service Flags: Kernel Driver, Shared Process
Npfs (File system)          Running (System)
 Error Severity: Normal
 Service Flags: File System Driver, Shared Process
Ntfs (File system)          Stopped (Disabled)
 Error Severity: Normal
 Service Flags: File System Driver, Shared Process
Null (Base)             Running (System)
 Error Severity: Normal
 Service Flags: Kernel Driver, Shared Process
NWLink IPX/SPX Compatible Transport Protocol (PNP_TDI) Running
(Automatic)
 C:\WINNT\System32\drivers\nwlnkipx.sys
 Error Severity: Normal
 Service Flags: Kernel Driver, Shared Process
NWLink NetBIOS (PNP_TDI)             Running (Automatic)
 C:\WINNT\System32\drivers\nwlnknb.sys
 Error Severity: Normal
 Service Flags: Kernel Driver, Shared Process
 Service Dependencies:
  NwlnkIpx
RIP for NWLink IPX          Running (Automatic)
 C:\WINNT\system32\drivers\nwlnkrip.sys
 Error Severity: Normal
 Service Flags: Kernel Driver, Shared Process
 Service Dependencies:
  NWLNKIPX
NWLink SPX/SPXII Protocol             Running (Manual)
```

```
C:\WINNT\System32\drivers\nwlnkspx.sys
 Error Severity: Normal
 Service Flags: Kernel Driver, Shared Process
 Service Dependencies:
  NwlnkIpx
Oliscsi (SCSI miniport)        Stopped (Disabled)
 Error Severity: Normal
 Service Flags: Kernel Driver, Shared Process
Parallel (Extended base)       Running (Automatic)
 Error Severity: Ignore
 Service Flags: Kernel Driver, Shared Process
 Service Dependencies:
  Parport
 Group Dependencies:
  Parallel arbitrator
Parport (Parallel arbitrator)    Running (Automatic)
 Error Severity: Ignore
 Service Flags: Kernel Driver, Shared Process
ParVdm (Extended base)         Running (Automatic)
 Error Severity: Ignore
 Service Flags: Kernel Driver, Shared Process
 Service Dependencies:
  Parport
 Group Dependencies:
  Parallel arbitrator
PCIDump (PCI Configuration)      Stopped (System)
 Error Severity: Ignore
 Service Flags: Kernel Driver, Shared Process
Pcmcia (System Bus Extender)      Stopped (Disabled)
 Error Severity: Normal
 Service Flags: Kernel Driver, Shared Process
PnP ISA Enabler Driver (Base)     Stopped (System)
 Error Severity: Ignore
 Service Flags: Kernel Driver, Shared Process
psidisp (Video)        Stopped (Disabled)
 Error Severity: Ignore
 Service Flags: Kernel Driver, Shared Process
Ql10wnt (SCSI miniport)        Stopped (Disabled)
 Error Severity: Normal
 Service Flags: Kernel Driver, Shared Process
qv (Video)             Stopped (Disabled)
 Error Severity: Ignore
 Service Flags: Kernel Driver, Shared Process
Remote Access Auto Connection Driver (Streams Drivers) Running
(Automatic)
 C:\WINNT\system32\drivers\rasacd.sys
 Error Severity: Normal
 Service Flags: Kernel Driver, Shared Process
Remote Access ARP Service (PNP_TDI) Running (Automatic)
 C:\WINNT\system32\drivers\rasarp.sys
 Error Severity: Normal
 Service Flags: Kernel Driver, Shared Process
 Service Dependencies:
  TCPIP
Rdr (Network)     Running (Manual)
 C:\WINNT\System32\drivers\rdr.sys
 Error Severity: Normal
 Service Flags: File System Driver, Shared Process
s3 (Video)      Stopped (Disabled)
 Error Severity: Ignore
```

```
 Service Flags: Kernel Driver, Shared Process
Scsiprnt (Extended base)  Stopped (Automatic)
 Error Severity: Ignore
 Service Flags: Kernel Driver, Shared Process
 Group Dependencies:
  SCSI miniport
Scsiscan (SCSI Class)    Stopped (System)
 Error Severity: Ignore
 Service Flags: Kernel Driver, Shared Process
 Group Dependencies:
  SCSI miniport
Serial (Extended base)      Running (Automatic)
 Error Severity: Ignore
 Service Flags: Kernel Driver, Shared Process
Sermouse (Pointer Port)  Stopped (Disabled)
 Error Severity: Ignore
 Service Flags: Kernel Driver, Shared Process
Sfloppy (Primary disk) Stopped (System)
 Error Severity: Ignore
 Service Flags: Kernel Driver, Shared Process
 Group Dependencies: SCSI miniport
Simbad (Filter)    Stopped (Disabled)
 Error Severity: Normal
 Service Flags: Kernel Driver, Shared Process
slcd32 (SCSI miniport)  Stopped (Disabled)
 Error Severity: Normal
 Service Flags: Kernel Driver, Shared Process
Sparrow (SCSI miniport)    Running (Boot)
 C:\WINNT\System32\DRIVERS\sparrow.sys
 Error Severity: Normal
 Service Flags: Kernel Driver, Shared Process
Spock (SCSI miniport)        Stopped (Disabled)
 Error Severity: Normal
 Service Flags: Kernel Driver, Shared Process
Srv (Network)        Running (Manual)
 C:\WINNT\System32\drivers\srv.sys
 Error Severity: Normal
 Service Flags: File System Driver, Shared Process
symc810 (SCSI miniport)  Stopped (Disabled)
 Error Severity: Normal
 Service Flags: Kernel Driver, Shared Process
T128 (SCSI miniport)  Stopped (Disabled)
 Error Severity: Normal
 Service Flags: Kernel Driver, Shared Process
T13B (SCSI miniport)   Stopped (Disabled)
 Error Severity: Normal
 Service Flags: Kernel Driver, Shared Process
TCP/IP Service (PNP_TDI)    Running (Automatic)
 C:\WINNT\System32\drivers\tcpip.sys
 Error Severity: Normal
 Service Flags: Kernel Driver, Shared Process
tga (Video)      Stopped (Disabled)
 Error Severity: Ignore
 Service Flags: Kernel Driver, Shared Process
tmv1 (SCSI miniport)      Stopped (Disabled)
 Error Severity: Normal
 Service Flags: Kernel Driver, Shared Process
Ultra124 (SCSI miniport)   Stopped (Disabled)
 Error Severity: Normal
 Service Flags: Kernel Driver, Shared Process
```

```
Ultra14f (SCSI miniport)  Stopped (Disabled)
 Error Severity: Normal
 Service Flags: Kernel Driver, Shared Process
Ultra24f (SCSI miniport)  Stopped (Disabled)
 Error Severity: Normal
 Service Flags: Kernel Driver, Shared Process
U.S. Robotics USRMDM Driver (NDIS)    Running (Automatic)
 C:\WINNT\System32\drivers\USRMdm.sys
 Error Severity: Normal
 Service Flags: Kernel Driver, Shared Process
 Service Dependencies:    USRPBUS
U.S. Robotics USRMGMT Driver (extended base) Running (Automatic)
 C:\WINNT\System32\drivers\USRMGMT.SYS
 Error Severity: Normal
 Service Flags: Kernel Driver, Shared Process
U.S. Robotics USRPBUS Driver (NDIS)    Running (Automatic)
 C:\WINNT\System32\drivers\USRPBUS.SYS
 Error Severity: Normal
 Service Flags: Kernel Driver, Shared Process
USRobotics PCNET Family Ethernet Adapter Driver (NDIS) Running
(Automatic)
 C:\WINNT\System32\drivers\usrpcn.sys
 Error Severity: Normal
 Service Flags: Kernel Driver, Shared Process
U.S. Robotics USRWAN Driver (NDIS)    Running (Automatic)
 C:\WINNT\System32\drivers\USRWAN.sys
 Error Severity: Normal
 Service Flags: Kernel Driver, Shared Process
 Service Dependencies:
  NdisTapi
  USRMdm
v7vram (Video)      Stopped (Disabled)
 Error Severity: Ignore
 Service Flags: Kernel Driver, Shared Process
VgaSave (Video Save)      Stopped (System)
 C:\WINNT\System32\drivers\vga.sys
 Error Severity: Ignore
 Service Flags: Kernel Driver, Shared Process
VgaStart (Video Init)      Stopped (System)
 C:\WINNT\System32\drivers\vga.sys
 Error Severity: Ignore
 Service Flags: Kernel Driver, Shared Process
Wd33c93 (SCSI miniport)      Stopped (Disabled)
 Error Severity: Normal
 Service Flags: Kernel Driver, Shared Process
wd90c24a (Video)      Stopped (Disabled)
 Error Severity: Ignore
 Service Flags: Kernel Driver, Shared Process
wdvga (Video)      Stopped (Disabled)
 Error Severity: Ignore
 Service Flags: Kernel Driver, Shared Process
weitekp9 (Video)      Stopped (Disabled)
 Error Severity: Ignore
 Service Flags: Kernel Driver, Shared Process
Xga (Video)          Stopped (Disabled)
 Error Severity: Ignore
 Service Flags: Kernel Driver, Shared Process

IRQ and Port Report
```

```
Devices        Vector Level Affinity
```

Devices	Vector	Level	Affinity
i8042prt	1	1	0xffffffff
i8042prt	12	12	0xffffffff
Serial	4	4	0x00000000
Atdisk	14	14	0x00000000
Floppy	6	6	0x00000000
USRPCN	5	5	0x00000000
Sparrow	0	10	0x00000000

```
───────────────────────────────────Devices Physical Address Length
                                   ─i8042prt        0x00000060   0x0000000001
```

Devices	Physical Address	Length
i8042prt	0x00000064	0x0000000001
Parport	0x000003bc	0x0000000003
Serial	0x000003e8	0x0000000007
Atdisk	0x000001f0	0x0000000008
Atdisk	0x000003f6	0x0000000001
Floppy	0x000003f0	0x0000000006
Floppy	0x000003f7	0x0000000001
USRMdm	0x00001180	0x0000000001
USRMGMT	0x00001000	0x0000000001
USRPCN	0x00000300	0x0000000020
Sparrow	0x00000340	0x0000000020
cirrus	0x000003b0	0x000000000c
cirrus	0x000003c0	0x0000000020

DMA and Memory Report

Devices	Channel	Port
Floppy	2	0
USRPCN	5	0

Devices	Physical Address	Length
cirrus	0x000a0000	0x00020000

Environment Report

System Environment Variables
 ComSpec 5 C:\WINNT\system32\cmd.exe
 NUMBER_OF_PROCESSORS 5 1
 OS 5 Windows_NT
 Os2LibPath 5 C:\WINNT\system32\os2\dll;
 Path 5 C:\WINNT\system32;C:\WINNT
 PROCESSOR_ARCHITECTURE 5 x86
 PROCESSOR_IDENTIFIER 5 x86 Family 4 Model 8 Stepping 3, GenuineIntel
 PROCESSOR_LEVEL 5 4
 PROCESSOR_REVISION 5 0803
 windir 5 C:\WINNT
Environment Variables for Current User
 TEMP 5 C:\TEMP
 TMP 5 C:\TEMP
Network Report

Your Access Level: Admin & Local
Workgroup or Domain: INFO.COM
Network Version: 4.0
LanRoot: INFO.COM
Logged On Users: 1
Current User (1): Administrator

```
Logon Domain: HEAVY
Logon Server: HEAVY

Transport: NetBT_USRPCN1, 00-C0-49-09-AC-50, VC's: 1, Wan: Wan
Transport: Nbf_USRPCN1, 00-C0-49-09-AC-50, VC's: 0, Wan: Wan
Transport: NwlnkNb, 00-C0-49-09-AC-50, VC's: 0, Wan: Wan

Character Wait: 3,600
Collection Time: 250
Maximum Collection Count: 16
Keep Connection: 600
Maximum Commands: 5
Session Time Out: 45
Character Buffer Size: 512
Maximum Threads: 17
Lock Quota: 6,144
Lock Increment: 10
Maximum Locks: 500
Pipe Increment: 10
Maximum Pipes: 500
Cache Time Out: 40
Dormant File Limit: 45
Read Ahead Throughput: 4,294,967,295
Mailslot Buffers: 3
Server Announce Buffers: 20
Illegal Datagrams: 5
Datagram Reset Frequency: 60
Log Election Packets: False
Use Opportunistic Locking: True
Use Unlock Behind: True
Use Close Behind: True
Buffer Pipes: True
Use Lock, Read, Unlock: True
Use NT Caching: True
Use Raw Read: True
Use Raw Write: True
Use Write Raw Data: True
Use Encryption: True
Buffer Deny Write Files: True
Buffer Read Only Files: True
Force Core Creation: True
512 Byte Max Transfer: False
Bytes Received: 11,930
SMB's Received: 114
Paged Read Bytes Requested: 0
Non Paged Read Bytes Requested: 0
Cache Read Bytes Requested: 0
Network Read Bytes Requested: 0
Bytes Transmitted: 13,647
SMB's Transmitted: 114
Paged Read Bytes Requested: 0
Non Paged Read Bytes Requested: 104
Cache Read Bytes Requested: 0
Network Read Bytes Requested: 0
Initally Failed Operations: 0
Failed Completion Operations: 0
Read Operations: 0
Random Read Operations: 0
Read SMB's: 0
Large Read SMB's: 0
```

```
Small Read SMB's: 0
Write Operations: 2
Random Write Operations: 0
Write SMB's: 0
Large Write SMB's: 0
Small Write SMB's: 0
Raw Reads Denied: 0
Raw Writes Denied: 0
Network Errors: 0
Sessions: 5
Failed Sessions: 0
Reconnects: 0
Core Connects: 0
LM 2.0 Connects: 0
LM 2.x Connects: 0
Windows NT Connects: 5
Server Disconnects: 0
Hung Sessions: 0
Use Count: 2
Failed Use Count: 0
Current Commands: 0
Server File Opens: 0
Server Device Opens: 0
Server Jobs Queued: 0
Server Session Opens: 0
Server Sessions Timed Out: 0
Server Sessions Errored Out: 0
Server Password Errors: 0
Server Permission Errors: 0
Server System Errors: 0
Server Bytes Sent: 265
Server Bytes Received: 477
Server Average Response Time: 0
Server Request Buffers Needed: 0
Server Big Buffers Needed: 0
```

The USRobotics Enterprise Network Hub is but one of many products offered by 3Com USRobotics. For additional information, contact them at

www.usr.com
3Com USRobotics
Corporate Systems Division
8100 North McCormick Blvd.
Skokie, IL 60076

8.11 Summary

This chapter presented part of what should be baselined in your network. The following chapters present additional information to factor into the baselining of your network. This information may vary according to your environment, but I have presented it as a minimum guideline to the type and amount of information I think you should have about each of your systems.

Network Troubleshooting Case Study: Part 3 (How to Baseline)

Baselining a network is no trivial task! It presupposes that you understand the equipment and how it operates in your network. The easiest networks I have worked with are those that have access to information on how the network operated when it worked properly. This includes installation information, configuration files, network protocol traffic, and other such information.

The information presented in this chapter provides you with an example of what the author considers important in baselining a network. Use this information to determine what baseline information you should obtain and keep on hand later.

9.1 Components to be Baselined

Three critical components in my network are a server, a storage silo, and a mail server. The remainder of this chapter presents that information I considered important enough to include in a baseline for my own network. It will help you in determining what you should consider.

9.2 How to Baseline Your Network Server

My network includes an IBM Netfinity 7000, a critical component in the network. To baseline this server, I began by obtaining pertinent information about it, and then I obtained a system report. Next, I performed some additional baseline functions by obtaining some specific network-related data on it.

Server general information

It is important to have access to overall information about each piece of equipment on your network. The Netfinity 7000 general information includes

- Three (3) 200-MHz Pentium processors
- 0.75 GB of RAM (750 MB of RAM)
- 39-MB hard disk (RAID support)
- RAID implementation
- Two 200-W power supplies
- 512-KB of L2 Cache
- Network Management interface board
- Ethernet Network Interface Card
- IBM's standard software bundle

Consider Figure 9.1, which shows the server with respect to the network. Figure 9.1 shows a conceptual view of how the Netfinity 7000 is implemented and some features it provides to users, both local and remote. The network server shows the following applications available to all network users:

- DB2 server
- Lotus Domino
- Lotus SmartSuite
- RAID Manager

These applications are for all users except the RAID Manager; this application is for the user with administrative privileges. Figure 9.1 shows three users accessing the system: ANGEL, LITTLE MAN, and BRAINS. These are names I gave my computers on the network. A great advantage to owning the network is being able to "name" the computers that participate on it! Anyway, all of these systems can access the Netfinity 7000 as well as all other systems shown in the network diagram. In addition, as the illustration shows users can also access the network silo.

Network server baseline report

The Netfinity 7000 baseline report includes the following configuration:

```
Diagnostics Report For \\CHEROKEE

OS Version Report

Microsoft (R) Windows NT (TM) Server
Version 4.0 (Build 1381: Service Pack 3) x86 Multiprocessor Free
Registered Owner: Ed Taylor
```

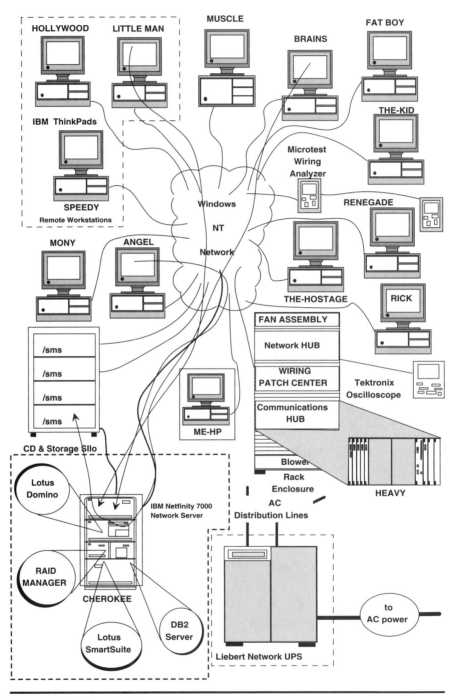

Figure 9.1 Netfinity 7000 Network Server

Product Number: 51222-270-1251174-59767

System Report

System: AT/AT COMPATIBLE
Hardware Abstraction Layer: MPS 1.4 - APIC platform
BIOS Date: 10/20/97
BIOS Version: BIOS Version 1.00.14.CD0
Processor list:
 0: x86 Family 6 Model 1 Stepping 9 GenuineIntel ˇ7E198 Mhz
 1: x86 Family 6 Model 1 Stepping 9 GenuineIntel ˇ7E198 Mhz
 2: x86 Family 6 Model 1 Stepping 9 GenuineIntel ˇ7E198 Mhz

Video Display Report

BIOS Date: 01/07/94
BIOS Version: CL-GD542X VGA BIOS Version 1.41
Adapter:
 Setting: 640 x 480 x 256
       60 Hz
 Type: cirrus compatible display adapter
 String: Cirrus Logic Compatible
 Memory: 512 KB
 Chip Type: CL 5424
 DAC Type: Integrated RAMDAC
Driver:
 Vendor: Microsoft Corporation
 File(s): cirrus.sys, vga.dll, cirrus.dll, vga256.dll, vga64K.dll
 Version: 4.00, 4.0.0

Drives Report

C:\ (Local - NTFS) CHEROKEE Total: 0KB, Free: 0KB
D:\ (Removable - FAT) Total: 1,045,200KB, Free: 1,045,184KB
E:\ (Local - NTFS) CHEROKEE-E Total: 37,556,692KB, Free: 36,256,336KB
G:\ (CDROM - CDFS) IE_DISP_R1_0 Total: 189,020KB, Free: 0KB
H:\ (CDROM - CDFS) PUBS1310 Total: 366,396KB, Free: 0KB
I:\ (CDROM - CDFS) ROCKYSERVICEP Total: 178,218KB, Free: 0KB

Memory Report

Handles: 2,088
Threads: 169
Processes: 28
Physical Memory (K)
 Total: 785,840
 Available: 707,232
 File Cache: 15,748

Services Report

Alerter	Running (Automatic)
Computer Browser	Running (Automatic)
EventLog (Event log)	Running (Automatic)
Server	Running (Automatic)
Workstation (NetworkProvider)	Running (Automatic)
License Logging Service	Running (Automatic)
TCP/IP NetBIOS Helper	Running (Automatic)
Messenger	Running (Automatic)

```
Netfinity Support Program         Running (Automatic)
Net Logon (RemoteValidation)       Running (Automatic)
Norton SpeedDisk                  Running (Automatic)
Plug and Play (PlugPlay)           Running (Automatic)
Remote Access Connection Manager (Network)  Running (Automatic)
Remote Access Server (Network)     Running (Automatic)
Remote Procedure Call (RPC) Locator    Running (Automatic)
Remote Procedure Call (RPC) Service    Running (Automatic)
Spooler (SpoolerGroup)            Running (Automatic)
Telephony Service                Running (Manual)
```
——————————————————————————————

```
Drivers Report
```
——————————————————————————————

```
AFD Networking Support Environment (TDI)  Running (Automatic)
aic78xx (SCSI miniport)           Running (Boot)
Remote Access Mac (NDIS)           Running (Automatic)
atapi (SCSI miniport)             Running (Boot)
Beep (Base)                      Running (System)
Cdfs (File system)               Running (Disabled)
Cdrom (SCSI CDROM Class)            Running (System)
cirrus (Video)                   Running (System)
Disk (SCSI Class)                Running (Boot)
Diskperf (Filter)                Running (Boot)
Intel 82557-based PRO Adapter Driver (NDIS) Running (Automatic)
Fastfat (Boot file system)         Running (Disabled)
Floppy (Primary disk)            Running (System)
i8042 Keyboard and PS/2 Mouse Port Driver (Keyboard Port) Running
(System)
ipsraidn (SCSI miniport)          Running (Boot)
Keyboard Class Driver (Keyboard Class)    Running (System)
KSecDD (Base)                    Running (System)
Modem (Extended base)             Running (Boot)
Mouse Class Driver (Pointer Class)    Running (System)
Msfs (File system)               Running (System)
Mup (Network)                    Running (Manual)
NetBEUI Protocol (PNP_TDI)          Running (Automatic)
Microsoft NDIS System Driver (NDIS)    Running (System)
Microsoft NDIS TAPI driver (NDIS)  Running (System)
Remote Access WAN Wrapper (NDISWAN)      Running (Automatic)
NetBIOS Interface (NetBIOSGroup)   Running (Automatic)
WINS Client(TCP/IP) (PNP_TDI)      Running (Automatic)
NetFin (Extended base)           Running (Automatic)
Npfs (File system)              Running (System)
Ntfs (File system)              Running (Disabled)
Null (Base)                     Running (System)
NWLink IPX/SPX Compatible Transport Protocol (PNP_TDI) Running
(Automatic)
NWLink NetBIOS (PNP_TDI)           Running (Automatic)
NWLink SPX/SPXII Protocol          Running (Manual)
Parallel (Extended base)          Running (Automatic)
Parport (Parallel arbitrator)  Running (Automatic)
ParVdm (Extended base)            Running (Automatic)
Remote Access Auto Connection Driver (Streams Drivers) Running
(Automatic)
Remote Access ARP Service (PNP_TDI)    Running (Automatic)
Rdr (Network)                   Running (Manual)
Scsiscan (SCSI Class)            Running (System)
Serial (Extended base)           Running (Automatic)
Srv (Network)                   Running (Automatic)
TCP/IP Service (PNP_TDI)           Running (Automatic)
```

```
IRQ and Port Report

Devices                    Vector Level Affinity

MPS 1.4 - APIC platform        8    8 0x00000007
MPS 1.4 - APIC platform        0    0 0x00000007
MPS 1.4 - APIC platform        1    1 0x00000007
MPS 1.4 - APIC platform        2    2 0x00000007
MPS 1.4 - APIC platform        3    3 0x00000007
MPS 1.4 - APIC platform        4    4 0x00000007
MPS 1.4 - APIC platform        5    5 0x00000007
MPS 1.4 - APIC platform        6    6 0x00000007
MPS 1.4 - APIC platform        7    7 0x00000007
MPS 1.4 - APIC platform        8    8 0x00000007
MPS 1.4 - APIC platform        9    9 0x00000007
MPS 1.4 - APIC platform       10   10 0x00000007
MPS 1.4 - APIC platform       11   11 0x00000007
MPS 1.4 - APIC platform       12   12 0x00000007
MPS 1.4 - APIC platform       13   13 0x00000007
MPS 1.4 - APIC platform       14   14 0x00000007
MPS 1.4 - APIC platform       15   15 0x00000007
MPS 1.4 - APIC platform       16   16 0x00000007
MPS 1.4 - APIC platform       17   17 0x00000007
MPS 1.4 - APIC platform       18   18 0x00000007
MPS 1.4 - APIC platform       19   19 0x00000007
MPS 1.4 - APIC platform       20   20 0x00000007
MPS 1.4 - APIC platform       21   21 0x00000007
MPS 1.4 - APIC platform       22   22 0x00000007
MPS 1.4 - APIC platform       23   23 0x00000007
MPS 1.4 - APIC platform       24   24 0x00000007
MPS 1.4 - APIC platform       25   25 0x00000007
MPS 1.4 - APIC platform       26   26 0x00000007
MPS 1.4 - APIC platform       27   27 0x00000007
MPS 1.4 - APIC platform       28   28 0x00000007
MPS 1.4 - APIC platform       29   29 0x00000007
MPS 1.4 - APIC platform       30   30 0x00000007
MPS 1.4 - APIC platform       31   31 0x00000007
MPS 1.4 - APIC platform       32   32 0x00000007
MPS 1.4 - APIC platform       33   33 0x00000007
MPS 1.4 - APIC platform       34   34 0x00000007
MPS 1.4 - APIC platform       35   35 0x00000007
MPS 1.4 - APIC platform       36   36 0x00000007
MPS 1.4 - APIC platform       37   37 0x00000007
MPS 1.4 - APIC platform       38   38 0x00000007
MPS 1.4 - APIC platform       39   39 0x00000007
MPS 1.4 - APIC platform       40   40 0x00000007
MPS 1.4 - APIC platform       41   41 0x00000007
MPS 1.4 - APIC platform       42   42 0x00000007
MPS 1.4 - APIC platform       43   43 0x00000007
MPS 1.4 - APIC platform       44   44 0x00000007
MPS 1.4 - APIC platform       45   45 0x00000007
MPS 1.4 - APIC platform       46   46 0x00000007
MPS 1.4 - APIC platform       47   47 0x00000007
MPS 1.4 - APIC platform       61   61 0x00000007
MPS 1.4 - APIC platform       65   65 0x00000007
MPS 1.4 - APIC platform       80   80 0x00000007
MPS 1.4 - APIC platform      193  193 0x00000007
MPS 1.4 - APIC platform      225  225 0x00000007
MPS 1.4 - APIC platform      253  253 0x00000007
```

```
MPS 1.4 - APIC platform      254 254 0x00000007
MPS 1.4 - APIC platform      255 255 0x00000007
i8042prt                   1    1 0xffffffff
i8042prt                  12   12 0xffffffff
Serial                   4    4 0x00000000
Serial                   3    3 0x00000000
E100B                    9    9 0x00000000
Floppy                   6    6 0x00000000
aic78xx                 11   11 0x00000000
aic78xx                 10   10 0x00000000
aic78xx                  5    5 0x00000000
aic78xx                 15   15 0x00000000
atapi              0   14 0x00000000
ipsraidn          11   11 0x00000000
```

```
Devices                 Physical Address Length
```

```
MPS 1.4 - APIC platform       0x00000000 0x0000000010
MPS 1.4 - APIC platform       0x00000020 0x0000000002
MPS 1.4 - APIC platform       0x00000040 0x0000000004
MPS 1.4 - APIC platform       0x00000048 0x0000000004
MPS 1.4 - APIC platform       0x00000061 0x0000000001
MPS 1.4 - APIC platform       0x00000070 0x0000000002
MPS 1.4 - APIC platform       0x00000080 0x0000000010
MPS 1.4 - APIC platform       0x00000092 0x0000000001
MPS 1.4 - APIC platform       0x000000a0 0x0000000002
MPS 1.4 - APIC platform       0x000000c0 0x0000000010
MPS 1.4 - APIC platform       0x000000d0 0x0000000010
MPS 1.4 - APIC platform       0x000000f0 0x0000000010
MPS 1.4 - APIC platform       0x00000400 0x0000000010
MPS 1.4 - APIC platform       0x00000461 0x0000000002
MPS 1.4 - APIC platform       0x00000464 0x0000000002
MPS 1.4 - APIC platform       0x00000480 0x0000000010
MPS 1.4 - APIC platform       0x000004c2 0x000000000e
MPS 1.4 - APIC platform       0x000004d0 0x0000000002
MPS 1.4 - APIC platform       0x000004d4 0x000000002c
MPS 1.4 - APIC platform       0x00000c84 0x0000000001
i8042prt             0x00000060 0x0000000001
i8042prt             0x00000064 0x0000000001
Parport              0x00000378 0x0000000003
Serial               0x000003f8 0x0000000007
Serial               0x000002f8 0x0000000007
E100B                0x0000e4e0 0x0000000014
Floppy               0x000003f0 0x0000000006
Floppy               0x000003f7 0x0000000001
aic78xx              0x0000ec00 0x0000000100
aic78xx              0x0000e800 0x0000000100
aic78xx              0x0000dc00 0x0000000100
aic78xx              0x0000d800 0x0000000100
atapi                0x000001f0 0x0000000008
atapi                0x000003f6 0x0000000001
ipsraidn             0x0000fc00 0x0000000100
cirrus               0x000003b0 0x000000000c
cirrus               0x000003c0 0x0000000020
```

```
DMA and Memory Report
```

```
Devices                 Channel Port
```

```
Floppy                   2    0
```

Devices	Physical Address	Length
MPS 1.4 - APIC platform	0xfec00000	0x00000400
MPS 1.4 - APIC platform	0xfec08000	0x00000400
E100B	0xfe0ff000	0x00000014
E100B	0xfe0ff000	0x00000014
aic78xx	0xfe8ff000	0x00001000
aic78xx	0xfe8fe000	0x00001000
aic78xx	0xfe1ff000	0x00001000
aic78xx	0xfe1fe000	0x00001000
ipsraidn	0xfeafe000	0x00002000
cirrus	0x000a0000	0x00020000

Environment Report
_____

System Environment Variables
 ComSpec = C:\WINNT\system32\cmd.exe
 NUMBER_OF_PROCESSORS = 3
 OS = Windows_NT
 Os2LibPath = C:\WINNT\system32\os2\dll;
 Path = E:\Notes;C:\WINNT\system32;C:\WINNT;C:\WNETFIN
 PROCESSOR_ARCHITECTURE = x86
 PROCESSOR_IDENTIFIER = x86 Family 6 Model 1 Stepping 9, GenuineIntel
 PROCESSOR_LEVEL = 6
 PROCESSOR_REVISION = 0109
 windir = C:\WINNT
Environment Variables for Current User
 TEMP = C:\TEMP
 TMP = C:\TEMP

Network Report
_____

Your Access Level: Admin & Local (total control)
Workgroup or Domain: INFO
Network Version: 4.0
LanRoot: INFO
Logged On Users: 1
Current User (1): Administrator
 Logon Domain: INFO
 Logon Server: CHEROKEE
Transport: NetBT_E100B1, 00-60-94-A5-CC-EE, VC's: 0, Wan: Wan
Transport: Nbf_E100B1, 00-60-94-A5-CC-EE, VC's: 0, Wan: Wan
Transport: NwlnkNb, 00-60-94-A5-CC-EE, VC's: 0, Wan: Wan
Character Wait: 3,600
Collection Time: 250
Maximum Collection Count: 16
Keep Connection: 600
Maximum Commands: 5
Session Time Out: 45
Character Buffer Size: 512
Maximum Threads: 17
Lock Quota: 6,144
Lock Increment: 10
Maximum Locks: 500
Pipe Increment: 10
Maximum Pipes: 500
Cache Time Out: 40
Dormant File Limit: 45
Read Ahead Throughput: 4,294,967,295

```
Mailslot Buffers: 3
Server Announce Buffers: 20
Illegal Datagrams: 5
Datagram Reset Frequency: 60
Bytes Received: 3,395
SMB's Received: 33
```

The CHEROKEE, the network server in my network, is more than capable of not only providing applications to network users but also performing certain file server functions. Implementation of RAID with the server makes it a strong component in the network, and a safe server to use for sensitive data.

Command-line-generated baselining

Additional commands can be entered at a command-line prompt to provide information helpful in a baseline report. One such example of command-line information is provided through the NET SHARE command. Consider the following:

Statistics command

```
Statistics for \\CHEROKEE
─────────────────────────────────
Statistics since 8/21/02 10:03 AM
Sessions accepted               0
Sessions timed-out              0
Sessions errored-out            0
Kilobytes sent                  8
Kilobytes received              8
Mean response time (msec)       0
System errors                   0
Permission violations           0
Password violations             0
Files accessed                  0
Communication devices accessed  0
Print jobs spooled              0
Times buffers exhausted
 Big buffers                    0
 Request buffers                0
```

SHARE command

```
Share name     Resource            Remark
─────────────────────────────────────────────────────────
E$        E:\          Default share   C$    C:\
Default share   ADMIN$   C:\WINNT           Remote Admin   PC$
            Remote IPC     CHEROKEE    I:\         THE—-I
    CHEROKEE- G G:\          THE —-G     CHEROKEE—F F:\
        THE — F      cherokee-c C:\          THE CHEROKEE - C
   CHEROKEE-E E:\             E-DRIVE    CHEROKEE-H H:\
      THE—H       CHEROKEE C:\              C DRIVE    JAZ
BAND ! D:\                  NETLOGON
C:\WINNT\system32\Repl\Import\S Logon server share
   -       Server Statistics Command
Server Statistics for \\CHEROKEE
Sessions accepted             0
```

```
Sessions timed-out              0
Sessions errored-out            0
Server Name                     \\CHEROKEE
Server Comment
Software version                Windows NT 4.0
Server is active on                     NetBT_KTC1006 (00c0f030c29e)
NetBT_KTC1006
(00c0f030c29e)  NwlnkIpx (00c0f030c29e)  NwlnkNb (00c0f030c29e)
Nbf_KTC1006
(00c0f030c29e) Server hidden           No
Maximum Logged On Users         Unlimited
Maximum open files per session  2048
Idle session time (min)     15
```

`Status` command

```
Status     Local        Remote        Network
───────────────────────────────────────────────────
OK             \\MUSCLE\IPC$          Microsoft Windows Network
OK             \\MUSCLE\IPC$          Microsoft Windows Network
```

`CHKDSK` command

```
The type of the file system is NTFS.
Warning! F parameter not specified
Running CHKDSK in read-only mode.
        CHKDSK is verifying files...
        0 percent completed...
        100 percent completed.
        File verification completed.
        CHKDSK is verifying indexes...
        0 percent completed...
        100 percent completed.
        Index verification completed.
        CHKDSK detected minor inconsistencies on the drive.
        CHKDSK is verifying security descriptors...
        0 percent completed...
        100 percent completed.
        Security descriptor verification completed.
        CHKDSK discovered free space marked as allocated in the volume
        bitmap.
        2096230 kilobytes total disk space.
        234990 kilobytes in 3341 user files.
        780 kilobytes in 196 indexes.
        11263 kilobytes in use by the system.
        4096 kilobytes occupied by the logfile.
        1849196 kilobytes available on disk.
        512 bytes in each allocation unit.
        4192460 total allocation units on disk.
        3698393 allocation units available on disk.
```

Active connections

```
Proto   Local Address      Foreign Address      State
TCP     CHEROKEE:1027          0.0.0.0:0         LISTENING
TCP     CHEROKEE:135           0.0.0.0:0         LISTENING
TCP     CHEROKEE:135           0.0.0.0:0         LISTENING
TCP     CHEROKEE:13991         0.0.0.0:0         LISTENING
TCP     CHEROKEE:1025          0.0.0.0:0         LISTENING
```

```
TCP      CHEROKEE:1025           localhost:1027     ESTABLISHED
TCP      CHEROKEE:1027           localhost:1025     ESTABLISHED
TCP      CHEROKEE:137            0.0.0.0:0          LISTENING
TCP      CHEROKEE:138            0.0.0.0:0          LISTENING
TCP      CHEROKEE:nbsession        0.0.0.0:0          LISTENING
TCP      CHEROKEE:nbsession        220.100.100.19:1035 SYN_RECEIVED
TCP      CHEROKEE:nbsession        220.100.100.61:1042 SYN_RECEIVED
TCP      CHEROKEE:nbsession        220.100.100.77:1038 SYN_RECEIVED
UDP      CHEROKEE:135          *:*
UDP      CHEROKEE:13991        *:*
UDP CHEROKEE:nbname          *:*
UDP CHEROKEE:nbdatagram      *:*
```

Interface statistics

	Received	Sent
Bytes	1,502,968	59,034,797
Unicast packets	11,572	41,899
Nonunicast packets	2,144	807
Discards	0	0
Errors	0	0

Unknown protocols: 6060.

CMD command. This command starts a new instance of the Windows/NT command interpreter:

```
CMD [/X | /Y] [/A | /U] [/Q] [[/C | /K] string]
```

/C	Carries out the command specified by string and then terminates
/K	Carries out the command specified by string but remains
/Q	Turns the echo off
/A	Causes the output of internal commands to a pipe or file to be ANSI
/U	Causes the output of internal commands to a pipe or file to be Unicode
/T:fg	Sets the foreground/background colors (see COLOR /? for more info)
/X	Enable extensions to the Windows NT version of CMD.EXE
/Y	Disable extensions to the Windows NT version of CMD.EXE

Multiple commands separated by the command separator '&&' are accepted for string if surrounded by quotes; command extensions are enabled by default. You may also disable extensions for all invocations of the command processor by setting the following value in the registry to 0:

```
HKEY_CURRENT_USER\Software\Microsoft\Command
```

Processor\enable extensions. The command extensions involve changes and/or additions to the following commands:

```
DEL or ERASE    ENDLOCAL
COLOR           IF
```

```
CD or CHDIR    FOR

MD or MKDIR    CALL

PROMPT         SHIFT

PUSHD          GOTO

POPD           START*

SET            ASSOC

SETLOCAL       FTYPE
```

These are only a few commands that can be issued against the command line of the server in my network. The purpose here is to show you how additional information can be obtained and incorporated in your baseline process.

Figure 9.2 highlights the high-speed network connections Netfinity 7000 utilizes. Figure 9.2 shows the Netfinity 7000 using an Adaptec Quad card. This four-port Ethernet adapter is a good match for the server and this network. It enables the server to maximize its potential to the network users requiring its resources.

9.3 Network Storage Silo

In the early phase of network design I concluded that SMS Data Products had the best solution for network storage. The primary driving force behind the decision was ease of use. Consider Figure 9.3, which shows the SMS network server with the following components:

- 28-bay rack
- 25 CD-ROM drives
- 1 Barracuda hard-disk drive
- 1 CD-ROM recorder
- 1 Jaz drive
- 1 AXIS StorPoint module
- 1 NetWare connectivity module

Technically, the 28-bay tower from SMS can be configured any way you want it when ordering. For example, it could have three recordable CDs, four Barracuda hard drives, and multiple Jaz drives. Or, it could have 28 CD-ROM drives. I selected this configuration because of the power of this array for network implementation.

---

*Also includes changes to external command invocation.

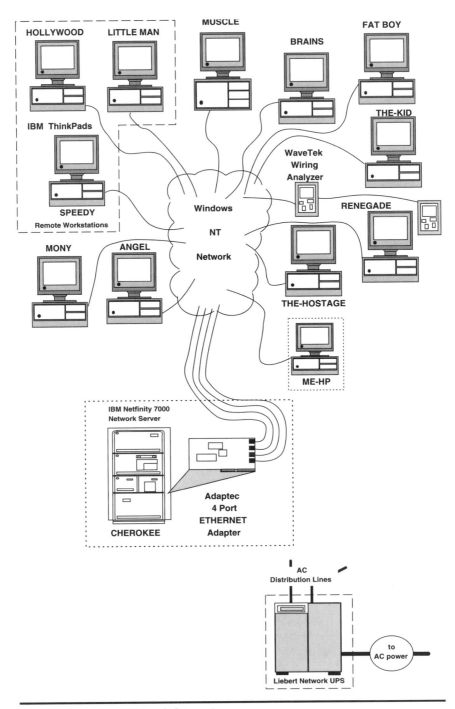

Figure 9.2 High-Speed Network Connection

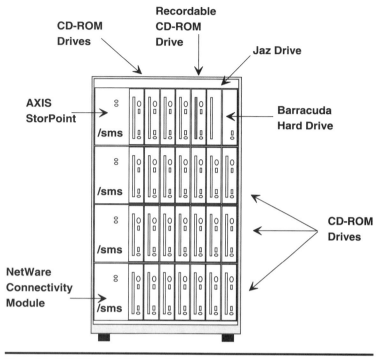

Figure 9.3 SMS Network Storage Silo

I will explain how I configured the SMS tower for my network later, but remember that the simplicity in SMS products is one aspect that makes them powerful assets to a network.

SMS has other products, too many to mention here; however, I have presented the information below which was provided by SMS Data Products Group.

Millennia Series S70028

The Millennia Series S70028 comes with 28 CD-ROM drive cells in a single frame using 4 Series 700 chassis that can be integrated with connectivity modules for Novell, Windows NT, and the Web. The core of the Millennia Series is the Series 700 chassis: a robust, standards-based platform that can be preconfigured as a S70028 with the features listed below. Each seven-drive rack chassis can be separated into four individual towers, and the following characteristics apply:

- Network direct connectivity modules for any network
- Scales up from 28 to 196 drives
- Swappable drives, LAN connectivity modules, and power supplies

- Locking door
- 3-year advanced replacement warranty
- UL-listed and FCC-B-certified

In addition, note the following features:

Standard SCSI (S70028S): A preconfigured SCSI server-attached workgroup enclosure consisting of four Series 700 chassis and 28 standard CD-ROM drive cells.

Network Direct for Novell (S70028NOV): A Novell network direct 28 CD-ROM drive cell enclosure using four Series 700 towers with a Novell Connectivity Module. Comes complete with everything needed to install and access CD-ROMs on your network. Token Ring version part number S70028NOVTR.

Network Direct for Windows NT (S70028NT): A Windows NT network direct 28 CD-ROM drive cell enclosure using four Series 700 towers with a Windows NT Connectivity Module. Comes complete with everything needed to install and access CD-ROMs on your network. Token Ring version part number S70028NTTR.

NETower for Windows NT

NETowers use a built-in AXIS StorPoint Connectivity Module for Windows NT, WFW, Banyan Vines, UNIX, LAN Manager, and OS/2 environments. Features are as follows:

- Plugs directly into network node
- No software required
- Multiple CDs as one drive letter
- No dedicated file server necessary
- Token Ring or Ethernet
- CD-ROM license metering
- No SCSI interface card to install
- Allows unlimited users
- SCSI 12× speed drives
- RJ-45 and AUI connections
- Easy installation

Another feature of NETower is easy sharing of CD-ROMs. The NETower allows several users to access CDs at the same time. No more changing disks, and no need to search for disks around the office. Up to seven CD-ROM drives per NETower. Other features are as follows:

Security and license	User access can be controlled by password; can also restrict the number of users.
Designed for mixed LAN environment	Can be used simultaneously from Windows, OS/2, DOS, and UNIX.
Location-independent	Can be placed anywhere on the network, and does not need a file server.
Quick to install and easy to use	No special drivers or software needed, configuration and management is done via preexisting application tools, and 12× speed CD-ROM drives are supported through use of 32-bit RISC processor technology.
Supported protocols	SMB, NetBIOS/NetBEUI, NFS, TCP, UDP, IP, RARP, BOOTP, SNMP, HTTP, FTP.
Supported file systems	High Sierra (HSF), ISO 9660.
Warranty and listings	NETowers come with a 1-year warranty, universal power supply, and a powerful cooling fan. The FCC-B, UL, and CUL listing labels indicate quality and safety.

SMS AXIS StorPoint connectivity module. A serverless solution for Windows NT and UNIX CD-ROM networking, the AXIS StorPoint CD/T provides a flexible and cost-effective solution for sharing CD-ROM disks over networks, making all CDs easily accessible to all users at all times.

It attaches directly to the network without involving any file server or additional software. The AXIS StorPoint CD/T is a CD-ROM server that enables users to access and share CD-ROMs over the network. No more changing of disks or searching for them around the office. Place the AXIS StorPoint where needed and connect up to seven CD-ROM drives and up to 56 disks to each unit.

The AXIS StorPoint makes the SMS tower easy to use on any network. The CDs appear as shared disks to all users. AXIS StorPoint CD/T can be used with NetWare, UNIX, Windows (including Windows NT and Windows 95), OS/2, and WWW/Intranet simultaneously. It is easily set up using platform-independent Web-based management.

The AXIS Storpoint is file-server-independent. AXIS StorPoint CD/T installs and operates completely independent of any file server. This approach allows peer-to-peer communication between the client and the CD-ROM server, which keeps the network traffic to a minimum, giving users direct, fast, and familiar access to all CDs.

It can also function as an Internet/intranet Web server. A built-in WWW server makes it possible to access the CDs using any WWW browser (e.g., Internet Explorer or Netscape Navigator). Put Web pages on a CD-ROM for a quick WWW site.

The AXIS StorPoint technical specifications include the following:

Network systems	Simultaneous operation in Novell NetWare 3.11, 3.12, and 4.10; Windows 95, NT, and Windows for Workgroups; Microsoft LAN Manager 1.

File systems and protocols	Simultaneous operation of NetWare—NCP over IPX; Windows, OS/2—SMB over NetBIOS and TCP/IP, SMB over NetBIOS and NetBEUI; UNIX—NFS over UDP/IP, TCP, ARP, RARP, B.
CD-ROM standards	ISO 9660, High Sierra (HSF), Multisession, ISO 9660 Rock Ridge.
Installation	NetWare—shows up as a NetWare file server; mount with NetWare tools; all CDs can be mounted under one drive letter. Windows—shows up as an NT server; mount in Explorer or File Manager.
Network management	SNMP MIB-II, and private enterprise. MIB—platform-independent configuration and status monitoring via standard Web browser.
Software updates	Flash memory allows central and remote software updates over the network using FTP over TCP/IP.
Security	The server unit can be user/group-access-controlled by password, and the number of users, specified in unit resident database, can be restricted. NetWare—encrypted passwords. Authorization via file server, including NDS.
Performance	Network throughput up to 900 kB/s.
Logical connection	Ethernet—IEEE802.2, IEEE802.3, SNAP, DIX, and Ethernet II frame types simultaneously; Token Ring—IEEE 802.2, IEEE802.3 (with early token release support for 16 Mbps) frame types simultaneously.
Network attachment	Ethernet—10BaseT (twisted pair) and 10Base2 (thin); Token Ring—STP (media type 1/DB9) and UTP (media type 3/RJ-45).
Hardware	CPU—32-bit RISC processor; 2 MB of flash memory; RAM—2 MB, 32 MB of cache expansion.

RAID: The S700HDA

The S700HDA is the cornerstone of your future data storage architecture. A universal, standards-based storage platform for hard disk, CD-ROM, DVD, and tape storage devices delivered on multiple and redundant SCSI and Fibre Channel Data I/O paths.

1. *High availability:* Beyond hot swap, the S700HDA provides automatic hot-spare failover. RAID levels 1, 0/1, and 5 can be configured on the fly. Superior physical fault tolerance with active/active automatic failover power and cooling is also provided. Logical fault tolerance is further enhanced with real-time predictive failure sensing and reporting for each drive.

2. *High performance:* Utilizing advanced Adaptec parity and calculating and caching technology, data are mobilized more rapidly than in native OS and server manufacturer "RAID-like" solutions. For blazing speed, parity calculations are performed via a coprocessor accelerator on a separate, yet paral-

lel, data I/O path. SCSI channels support data transfer rates of up to 40 MB/s. FC-AL backplane options will support 100 MB/s burst rates and beyond.

3. *High capacity:* The S700HDA chassis meets the cooling and vibration isolation requirements of both current and future drive densities. The S700HDA is always available with the latest drive densities for the maximum storage capacity per array. As storage densities of drives double each year, the capacity of this subsystem will keep pace.

4. *Low cost:* Utilizing the latest storage technologies, the S700HDA is not bound by the cost structures of legacy systems. The S700HDA's fresh and modular approach delivers advanced storage features at prices comparable to those of just the raw drives included with servers and legacy subsystems.

5. *Storage management:* The S700HDA Array Management software is the command center for the network manager. Monitor and command the enterprise's storage subsystem from any workstation.

6. *Reconfigure arrays:* Reconfiguration is merely a point and click away; simply highlight the drives from the graphical interface. Bar graphs instantly show data protection and performance tradeoffs among the RAID levels you select. Multiple arrays, spares, and banks of spares can be configured both within each chassis and across subsystems.

7. *View array and device information:* On a single screen, physical and logical array configurations, individual channels, and PCI host information are provided. Capacities, availability, and predictive failure data are instantly displayed.

8. *Monitor array activity:* Color-coded messages and charts alert the System Administrator of all array activity. Status indicators depict all active fault tolerant and critical states. Real-time predictive failure sensing and analysis allows disks to be replaced before failure.

Features and benefits are as follows:

- Active hot spare
  Enables fast rebuild of a failed disk
  No user intervention required

- Active/active power supplies and cooling fans
  Improve data integrity
  Improve data availability
  Eliminate single point of failure

- Swappable and field-replaceable drives
  Minimal downtime when replacing failed drives
  Easily upgrade to the latest hard disk capacities

- RAID coprocessor
  Offloads parity calculations and controlled tasks
  Free the CPU for other I/O tasks

- Instant rack mounting

  Standard 19-in rack

  Easy data management and expandability

- 3-year advanced replacement warranty

  Replacement products shipped overnight

- Scalable storage capacity

  Expand on initial investment

  Storage capacity grows with network requirements

- Unlimited, toll-free technical support

  Fast response

  Assured of support for the life of the product

- Compatible with Windows NT and Novell

- FCC-B-approved and UL-listed

DiscPort PRO XL

The Microtest DiscPort Pro is a high-performance CD-ROM networking solution that enables NetWare and Windows NT Workgroups to share up to 14 CD-ROM devices simultaneously.

Your CD-ROM sharing solution should keep up with the demands of your growing network. If you're looking for Windows NT and NetWare compatibility, increased speed, and enhanced performance—look no further than DiscPort PRO, the CD-ROM networking solution for workgroups that offers speed and compatibility in one. With DiscPort PRO, you can access CD devices as easily as accessing an application on a file server.

DiscPort PRO and CD Sharing. DiscPort PRO is easy to install and requires no TSRs or client software on your workstations. Attach DiscPort PRO anywhere on your Thin Ethernet or 10BaseT network, and install DiscView PRO management software. Attach up to 14 CD-ROM devices per DiscPort PRO, and load your CD-ROM titles. DiscPort PRO supports 8× CD-ROM drives on your 10-Mbps Ethernet network and works with popular CD-ROM drives, towers, and disk changers. And as your network grows, it's easy to add more DiscPort PROs and other Microtest Workgroup products or Enterprise solutions. All Microtest CD-ROM networking products work together seamlessly.

- One product, DiscPort PRO, supports both NetWare and Windows NT networks.

- Easy to install, DiscPort PRO plugs into any network connection.

- It includes two (2) SCSI ports, providing network users simultaneous access to as many as 14 CD-ROM devices per DiscPort PRO unit.

- It lets you physically place CDs within workgroups, allowing local control of and access to CD-ROM libraries.

- DiscView PRO graphical user interface (GUI) is included, making DiscPort PRO easy to manage and use.

- DiscPort PRO supports multiple protocols including IPX/SPX and TCP/IP.

- DiscPort PRO works seamlessly with additional DiscPort PROs or other Microtest Workgroup and Enterprise solutions.

One device supports NetWare and Windows NT networks. Whether you're running NetWare, Windows NT, or a combination of the two, DiscPort PRO works with both operating systems. Administrators will find sharing CD-ROMs effortless with DiscView PRO software, Microtest's CD-ROM management interface. DiscView PRO includes SmartLaunch, the totally transparent user Interface that allows users to access CD-ROM titles with point-and-click simplicity. DiscView PRO supports ISO 9660, HFS (Macintosh), CD-Bridge and Photo CDs on NetWare, and ISO 9660 on Windows NT. DiscView PRO allows CD-ROM sharing using as little as 6K of RAM per CD, auto mounts and shares CDs instantly, and offers dynamic security and support for volume sets. CD-ROMs can appear as subdirectories under a single volume, so there is no need to map and unmap numerous drive letters.

DiscPort PRO comes complete with DiscView PRO, Windows-based software for easy CD-ROM installation, management, and use. DiscView PRO:

- Allows your networked CD-ROMs to appear as subdirectories of a single drive letter—no need to map and unmap numerous DOS drive letters.

- Integrates NetWare and NT security, caching, and usage statistics for your CD-ROMs.

- Integrates with NetWare Directory Services (NDS) and NT Domains.

- Instantly mounts and shares CD-ROM titles.

- Provides cache control for managing server resources.

- Offers drag-and-drop CD-ROM management.

- Offers dynamic security and dynamic volume sets for easy management.

DiscView PRO's SmartLaunch provides any user easy access to entire libraries of CD-ROMs. SmartLaunch

- Automatically prepares and mounts your CD-ROMs—users can access titles with point-and-click simplicity.

- CD format support includes ISO 9660 (NT) and ISO 9660, HFS (Macintosh), CD-I/Bridge, and Photo CDs.

- Allows easy access by DOS, Windows, Macintosh, UNIX, and OS/2 clients to CD-ROMs attached to DiscPort PRO.

Specifications for DiscView PRO are as follows:

- SCSI PORT
  Two (2) high-density Mini-D connectors
  One (1) MiniD-to-SCSI 50 pin cable included
  SCSI II protocol
- File server requirements
  Novell NetWare 3.11 or higher with 8 MB of RAM
  or Windows NT 3.51 (Intel-based) with 16 MB of RAM
- Ethernet compatibility
  Thin Ethernet RG-58 A/U BNC, and 10BaseT
- Twisted-pair RJ-45 connectors
  IPX: 802.2, 802.3, Ethernet II, or SNAP frame types
  TCP/IP: Ethernet II frame types
- Workstation requirements
  Windows 3.1 or higher recommended
  At least 4 MB recommended for Windows users
  Macintosh users running System 6.0.7 or higher
  Novell NetWare for Macintosh installed

Silo-1 configuration file

The configuration file shown here controls 14 CDs, and the configuration file following it also controls 14 CDs. It is important to have a complete list of the configuration to know the complete `silo` configuration.

```
[Axis Communications AB] Configuration AXIS StorPoint CD100
──────────────────────────────────
AXIS StorPoint CD100 Parameter List
V4.20 Nov 26 1997 S/N:00408c324135
[Server]
HardwareAddress = 00:40:8c:32:41:35;Can be changed to local address
Date       = 95-01-01 ; yy-mm-dd, append '!' to set
Time       = 00:24:51 ; hh:mm:ss, append '!' to set
FactoryDefaults =  no ; yes/no
Restart    =   no ; yes/no
MediaAgentMode  =  no ; yes/no
TimeZone   =   UTC
TimeSyncSource  =  NDS; None/NDS/NTP
──────────────────────────────────
[SCSI]
JukeBoxLockTime      =   0 ; seconds, 0 to disable
Disconnect/Reselect  =  off ; on/off
──────────────────────────────────
[IP]
InternetAddress      =  220.100.100.175
DefaultRouter        =  0.0.0.0
```

```
NetMask             =  0.0.0.0
BOOTPEnable            =  yes ; yes/no
DHCPEnable             =  yes   ; yes/no
RARPEnable             =  yes   ; yes/no
DomainName             =  INFO.COM
PrimaryDNS             =  220.100.100.10
SecondaryDNS            =  0.0.0.0
NTPServer           =
_____

[SMB]
EnableNetBEUI          =  yes   ; yes/no
EnableNBT              =  yes   ; yes/no
EnableWINS             =  no      ; yes/no
PrimaryWINSserver         =  220.100.100.10
SecondaryWINSserver       =  220.100.100.132
NBTscopeID          =
Domain/GroupName          =  INFO.COM
ServerName          =  SILO-1
NetBEUIFrameType       =  auto ; auto/802_2/dix
ShowAllShares          =  yes ; yes/no
SecurityMode        =  userLevel; shareLevel/userLevel
AuthenticationDomain  =  ; Authenticate users against this domain
AdministratorPassword  =  PASS ; Local administrator password
_____

[NFS]
NFSEnable              =  yes   ; yes/no
DefaultUid          =  -2    ; Default uid or 0 to disable
PCNFSDAuthentServer     =  0.0.0.0 ; 0.0.0.0 to disable
_____

[HTTP/FTP]
Password               =  take-a-guess
HTTPEnable             =  yes   ; yes/no
BaseURL                =  www.axis.com
_____

[SNMP]
GetCommunityName       =  public
SetCommunityName       =  pass
TrapDestination        =  0.0.0.0 ; Internet address
TrapCommunityName        =  public
SystemContact          =
SystemName          =
SystemLocation         =
AuthenticationTrap     =  disabled ; disabled/enabled
_____

[NetWare]
NWEnable               =  no  ; yes/no
Frame_802.2            =  auto ; auto/off/XX-XX-XX-XX
Frame_802.3            =  auto ; auto/off/XX-XX-XX-XX
Frame_EthernetII       =  auto ; auto/off/XX-XX-XX-XX
Frame_SNAP             =  auto ; auto/off/XX-XX-XX-XX
NetWareIP_Enable        =  no ; yes/no
NetWareIP_DSS_Server   =      ; Host name or IP address
ServerName          =  AXIS324135_NW
InternalNetAddress  =  8C-32-41-35
BurstMode              =  on ; on/off
ShowAllVolumes         =  yes ; yes/no
BinderyEnable          =  yes ; yes/no
SupervisorPassword     =  PASS
BindAuthentication     =  ; Servername
```

```
NDSEnable              =  yes ; yes/no
NDSTreeName            =
NDSServerContext       =
NDSAdminName           =  ; Distinguished name of supervisor equivalent
user
NDSAdminPassword       =
NDSInstall    =  no ; no/install/forced
NDSRightsStorage   =  NDS ; NDS/File
NDSRightsFile      =    ; SERVER/VOLUME:DIR/FILE.DAT
TimeSyncSources    =  SAP ; SAP or SERVER1,SERVER2,...
```

Silo-2 configuration file

This configuration file controls 14 CDs. It is also important to keep a list of which CDs are in what part of the SILO.

```
[Axis Communications AB] Configuration AXIS StorPoint CD100

AXIS StorPoint CD100 Parameter List
V4.20 Nov 26 1997 S/N:00408c324135
[Server]
HardwareAddress = 00:40:8c:32:41:35;Can be changed to local address
Date       =  98-08-07 ; yy-mm-dd, append '!' to set
Time       =  00:24:51 ; hh:mm:ss, append '!' to set
FactoryDefaults =  no ; yes/no
Restart      =  no ; yes/no
MediaAgentMode   =  no ; yes/no
TimeZone     =  UTC
TimeSyncSource   =  NDS; None/NDS/NTP

[SCSI]
JukeBoxLockTime      =  0 ; seconds, 0 to disable
Disconnect/Reselect  =  off ; on/off

[IP]
InternetAddress      =  220.100.100.180
DefaultRouter        =  0.0.0.0
NetMask        =  0.0.0.0
BOOTPEnable          =  yes  ; yes/no
DHCPEnable           =  yes  ; yes/no
RARPEnable           =  yes  ; yes/no
DomainName           =  INFO.COM
PrimaryDNS           =  220.100.100.10
SecondaryDNS         =  220.100.100.132
NTPServer      =

[SMB]
EnableNetBEUI        =  yes  ; yes/no
EnableNBT            =  yes  ; yes/no
EnableWINS           =  no   ; yes/no
PrimaryWINSserver    =  220.100.100.10
SecondaryWINSserver  =  220.100.100.132
NBTscopeID           =
Domain/GroupName     =  INFO.COM
ServerName           =  SILO-2
NetBEUIFrameType     =  auto ; auto/802_2/dix
ShowAllShares        =  yes ; yes/no
```

```
SecurityMode          =  userLevel; shareLevel/userLevel
AuthenticationDomain  =  ; Authenticate users against this domain
AdministratorPassword =  PASS ; Local administrator password

[NFS]
NFSEnable             =  yes   ; yes/no
DefaultUid            =  -2  ; Default uid or 0 to disable
PCNFSDAuthentServer         =  0.0.0.0 ; 0.0.0.0 to disable

[HTTP/FTP]
Password             =  take-a-guess
HTTPEnable           =  yes ; yes/no
BaseURL              =  www.axis.com

[SNMP]
GetCommunityName     =  public
SetCommunityName     =  pass
TrapDestination      =  0.0.0.0 ; Internet address
TrapCommunityName    =  public
SystemContact        =
SystemName           =
SystemLocation       =
AuthenticationTrap   =  disabled ; disabled/enabled

[NetWare]
NWEnable          =  no ; yes/no
Frame_802.2       =  auto ; auto/off/XX-XX-XX-XX
Frame_802.3       =  auto ; auto/off/XX-XX-XX-XX
Frame_EthernetII  =  auto ; auto/off/XX-XX-XX-XX
Frame_SNAP        =  auto ; auto/off/XX-XX-XX-XX
NetWareIP_Enable     =  no ; yes/no
NetWareIP_DSS_Server =        ; Host name or IP address
ServerName        =  AXIS324135_NW
InternalNetAddress =  8C-32-41-35
BurstMode         =  on ; on/off
ShowAllVolumes   =  yes ; yes/no
BinderyEnable    =  yes ; yes/no
SupervisorPassword  =  PASS
BindAuthentication  =  ; Servername
NDSEnable        =  yes ; yes/no
NDSTreeName      =
NDSServerContext =
NDSAdminName     =  ; Distinguished name of supervisor equivalent user
NDSAdminPassword =
NDSInstall       =  no ; no/install/forced
NDSRightsStorage    =  NDS ; NDS/File
NDSRightsFile    =  ; SERVER/VOLUME:DIR/FILE.DAT
TimeSyncSources  =  SAP ; SAP or SERVER1,SERVER2,...
```

9.4 How to Baseline Your Mail Server

This section includes baseline information for the mail server in my network. This information provides you with some insight as to what you should have on hand to baseline your mail server. From this information, I can ascertain the services running, such as WWW, FTP, and Gopher. It also reveals the services started such as the mail server processes.

Mail server system baseline report

```
Diagnostics Report For \\MUSCLE
─────────────────────────────────
OS Version Report
─────────────────────────────────
Microsoft (R) Windows NT (TM) Server
Version 4.0 (Build 1381: Service Pack 3) x86 Uniprocessor Free
Registered Owner: MUSCLE, Information World, Inc.
Product Number: 50370-807-5268635-98401
─────────────────────────────────
System Report
─────────────────────────────────
System: AT/AT COMPATIBLE
Hardware Abstraction Layer: PC Compatible Eisa/Isa HAL
BIOS Date: 02/27/97
BIOS Version: <unavailable>
Processor list:
0: x86 Family 5 Model 4 Stepping 4 GenuineIntel ˇ7E199 Mhz
─────────────────────────────────
Video Display Report
─────────────────────────────────
BIOS Date: 04/01/96
BIOS Version: S3 86C765 Video BIOS. Version 1.01-05A
Adapter:
 Setting: 640 x 480 x 256
      60 Hz
 Type: s3 compatible display adapter
 String: S3 Compatible
 Memory: 1 MB
 Chip Type: S3 765
 DAC Type: S3
Driver:
 Vendor: Microsoft Corporation
 File(s): s3.sys, s3.dll
 Version: 4.00, 4.0.0
Drives Report
─────────────────────────────────
C:\ (Local - FAT) MUSCLE Total: 2,096,320KB, Free: 1,197,248KB
 Serial Number: 833 - E695
 Bytes per cluster: 512
 Sectors per cluster: 64
 Filename length: 255
D:\ (Local - FAT) MUSCLE2 Total: 402,952KB, Free: 213,184KB
 Serial Number: 3211 - BE2
 Bytes per cluster: 512
 Sectors per cluster: 16
 Filename length: 255
F: (Remote - FAT) \\Brains\MY-BRAIN-C BRAINS Total: 1,584,320KB, Free:
883,744KB
 Serial Number: 142B - 16D3
 Bytes per cluster: 512
 Sectors per cluster: 64
 Filename length: 255
Memory Report
─────────────────────────────────
Handles: 5,893
Threads: 298
Processes: 49
Physical Memory (K)
```

```
 Total: 97,716
 Available: 45,028
 File Cache: 10,264
Kernel Memory (K)
 Total: 9,824
 Paged: 6,280
 Nonpaged: 3,544
Commit Charge (K)
 Total: 68,208
 Limit: 184,444
 Peak: 69,608
Pagefile Space (K)
 Total: 98,304
 Total in use: 12,136
 Peak: 12,172
 C:\pagefile.sys
 Total: 98,304
 Total in use: 12,136
 Peak: 12,172
Services Report
```

```
Netscape Administration Server 3.5 Running (Automatic)
 C:\Netscape\SuiteSpot\bin\admin\ns-admin.exe
 Service Account Name: LocalSystem
 Error Severity: Normal
 Service Flags: Own Process, Interactive
Alerter            Running (Automatic)
 C:\WINNT\System32\services.exe
 Service Account Name: LocalSystem
 Error Severity: Normal
 Service Flags: Shared Process
 Service Dependencies:
  LanmanWorkstation
Computer Browser    Running (Automatic)
 C:\WINNT\System32\services.exe
 Service Account Name: LocalSystem
 Error Severity: Normal
 Service Flags: Shared Process
 Service Dependencies:
  LanmanWorkstation
  LanmanServer
  LmHosts
ClipBook Server             Stopped (Manual)
 C:\WINNT\system32\clipsrv.exe
 Service Account Name: LocalSystem
 Error Severity: Normal
 Service Flags: Own Process
 Service Dependencies:
  NetDDE
DHCP Client (TDI)      Stopped (Disabled)
 C:\WINNT\System32\services.exe
 Service Account Name: LocalSystem
 Error Severity: Normal
 Service Flags: Shared Process
 Service Dependencies:
  Tcpip
  Afd
  NetBT
Microsoft DHCP Server  Running (Automatic)
 C:\WINNT\System32\tcpsvcs.exe
```

```
                  Service Account Name: LocalSystem
                  Error Severity: Normal
                  Service Flags: Shared Process
                  Service Dependencies:
                   Rpcss
                   NTLMSSP
                  Group Dependencies:
                   TDI
                Microsoft DNS Server  Running (Automatic)
                 C:\WINNT\System32\dns.exe
                  Service Account Name: LocalSystem
                  Error Severity: Normal
                  Service Flags: Own Process
                  Service Dependencies:
                   Tcpip
                   Afd
                   NetBT
                   RpcSs
                   NTLmSsp
                EventLog (Event log) Running (Automatic)
                 C:\WINNT\system32\services.exe
                  Service Account Name: LocalSystem
                  Error Severity: Normal
                  Service Flags: Shared Process
                Gopher Publishing Service        Running (Automatic)
                 C:\WINNT\System32\inetsrv\inetinfo.exe
                  Service Account Name: LocalSystem
                  Error Severity: Ignore
                  Service Flags: Shared Process
                  Service Dependencies:
                   RPCSS
                   NTLMSSP
                Server                  Running (Automatic)
                 C:\WINNT\System32\services.exe
                  Service Account Name: LocalSystem
                  Error Severity: Normal
                  Service Flags: Shared Process
                  Group Dependencies:
                   TDI
                Workstation (NetworkProvider)    Running (Automatic)
                 C:\WINNT\System32\services.exe
                  Service Account Name: LocalSystem
                  Error Severity: Normal
                  Service Flags: Shared Process
                  Group Dependencies:
                   TDI
                License Logging Service        Running (Automatic)
                 C:\WINNT\System32\llssrv.exe
                  Service Account Name: LocalSystem
                  Error Severity: Normal
                  Service Flags: Own Process
                TCP/IP NetBIOS Helper        Running (Automatic)
                 C:\WINNT\System32\services.exe
                  Service Account Name: LocalSystem
                  Error Severity: Normal
                  Service Flags: Shared Process
                  Group Dependencies:
                   NetworkProvider
                TCP/IP Print Server        Stopped (Manual)
                 C:\WINNT\System32\tcpsvcs.exe
                  Service Account Name: LocalSystem
```

```
Error Severity: Normal
Service Flags: Shared Process
Messenger                          Running (Automatic)
C:\WINNT\System32\services.exe
Service Account Name: LocalSystem
Error Severity: Normal
Service Flags: Shared Process
Service Dependencies:
 LanmanWorkstation
 NetBios
FTP Publishing Service             Running (Automatic)
C:\WINNT\System32\inetsrv\inetinfo.exe
Service Account Name: LocalSystem
Error Severity: Ignore
Service Flags: Shared Process
Service Dependencies:
 RPCSS
 NTLMSSP
Network DDE (NetDDEGroup)          Stopped (Manual)
C:\WINNT\system32\netdde.exe
Service Account Name: LocalSystem
Error Severity: Normal
Service Flags: Shared Process
Service Dependencies:
 NetDDEDSDM
Network DDE DSDM                   Stopped (Manual)
C:\WINNT\system32\netdde.exe
Service Account Name: LocalSystem
Error Severity: Normal
Service Flags: Shared Process
Net Logon (RemoteValidation)       Running (Automatic)
C:\WINNT\System32\lsass.exe
Service Account Name: LocalSystem
Error Severity: Normal
Service Flags: Shared Process
Service Dependencies:
 LanmanWorkstation
 LanmanServer
 LmHosts
Netscape Directory Synchronization Service Running (Automatic)
C:\Netscape\SuiteSpot\dssynch\ns-dssynch.exe
Service Account Name: LocalSystem
Error Severity: Normal
Service Flags: Own Process
Netscape Messaging Server 3.5  Running (Automatic)
C:\Netscape\SuiteSpot\bin\mail\Server\NetscapeMTA.exe
Service Account Name: info.com\netscapemta
Error Severity: Normal
Service Flags: Own Process
Service Dependencies:
 Tcpip
 Afd
Netscape Collabra Server (news-muscle) Running (Automatic)
C:/Netscape/SuiteSpot/bin/news/bin/innd.exe
Service Account Name: LocalSystem
Error Severity: Normal
Service Flags: Own Process, Interactive
Network Monitor Agent              Stopped (Manual)
C:\WINNT\System32\nmagent.exe
Service Account Name: LocalSystem
Error Severity: Normal
```

```
         Service Flags: Own Process
         Service Dependencies:
          bh
Norton SpeedDisk                    Running (Automatic)
         C:\Program Files\Norton Speed Disk Trial\SDSRV.EXE
         Service Account Name: LocalSystem
         Error Severity: Normal
         Service Flags: Own Process
NT LM Security Support Provider       Running (Manual)
         C:\WINNT\System32\SERVICES.EXE
         Service Account Name: LocalSystem
         Error Severity: Normal
         Service Flags: Shared Process
SAP Agent                          Running (Automatic)
         C:\WINNT\system32\services.exe
         Service Account Name: LocalSystem
         Error Severity: Normal
         Service Flags: Shared Process
         Service Dependencies:
          NWLNKIPX
Plug and Play (PlugPlay)       Running (Automatic)
         C:\WINNT\system32\services.exe
         Service Account Name: LocalSystem
         Error Severity: Normal
         Service Flags: Shared Process
Remote Access Autodial Manager    Stopped (Disabled)
         C:\WINNT\system32\rasman.exe
         Service Account Name: LocalSystem
         Error Severity: Normal
         Service Flags: Shared Process
         Service Dependencies:
          RasMan
Remote Access Connection Manager (Network)   Running (Manual)
         C:\WINNT\system32\rasman.exe
         Service Account Name: LocalSystem
         Error Severity: Normal
         Service Flags: Shared Process, Interactive
         Service Dependencies:
          tapisrv
DHCP Relay Agent                    Stopped (Disabled)
         C:\WINNT\System32\router.exe
         Service Account Name: LocalSystem
         Error Severity: Normal
         Service Flags: Shared Process
         Group Dependencies:
          NDIS
Remote Access Server (Network)       Stopped (Automatic)
         C:\WINNT\system32\rassrv.exe
         Service Account Name: LocalSystem
         Error Severity: Normal
         Service Flags: Own Process
         Service Dependencies:
          LanmanServer
          RasMan
          NetBios
          NwlnkRip
          NwSapAgent
          NetBT
          Nbf
          NwlnkIpx
```

```
Directory Replicator              Stopped (Manual)
 C:\WINNT\System32\lmrepl.exe
 Service Account Name: LocalSystem
 Error Severity: Normal
 Service Flags: Own Process
 Service Dependencies:
  LanmanWorkstation
  LanmanServer
Remote Procedure Call (RPC) Locator   Running (Automatic)
 C:\WINNT\System32\LOCATOR.EXE
 Service Account Name: LocalSystem
 Error Severity: Normal
 Service Flags: Own Process
 Service Dependencies:
  LanmanWorkstation
  Rdr
Remote Procedure Call (RPC) Service    Running (Automatic)
 C:\WINNT\system32\RpcSs.exe
 Service Account Name: LocalSystem
 Error Severity: Normal
 Service Flags: Own Process
Schedule                          Stopped (Manual)
 C:\WINNT\System32\AtSvc.Exe
 Service Account Name: LocalSystem
 Error Severity: Normal
 Service Flags: Own Process
Spooler (SpoolerGroup)      Running (Automatic)
 C:\WINNT\system32\spoolss.exe
 Service Account Name: LocalSystem
 Error Severity: Normal
 Service Flags: Own Process, Interactive
Telephony Service               Running (Manual)
 C:\WINNT\system32\tapisrv.exe
 Service Account Name: LocalSystem
 Error Severity: Normal
 Service Flags: Own Process
UPS                           Stopped (Manual)
 C:\WINNT\System32\ups.exe
 Service Account Name: LocalSystem
 Error Severity: Normal
 Service Flags: Own Process
World Wide Web Publishing Service   Running (Automatic)
 C:\WINNT\System32\inetsrv\inetinfo.exe
 Service Account Name: LocalSystem
 Error Severity: Ignore
 Service Flags: Shared Process
 Service Dependencies:
  RPCSS
  NTLMSSP
Windows Internet Name Service       Running (Automatic)
 C:\WINNT\System32\wins.exe
 Service Account Name: LocalSystem
 Error Severity: Normal
 Service Flags: Own Process
 Service Dependencies:
  RPCSS
  NTLMSSP
Drivers Report
_____

Abiosdsk (Primary disk)           Stopped (Disabled)
```

```
 Error Severity: Ignore
 Service Flags: Kernel Driver, Shared Process
AFD Networking Support Environment (TDI) Running (Automatic)
 C:\WINNT\System32\drivers\afd.sys
 Error Severity: Normal
 Service Flags: Kernel Driver, Shared Process
Aha154x (SCSI miniport)    Stopped (Disabled)
 Error Severity: Normal
 Service Flags: Kernel Driver, Shared Process
Aha174x (SCSI miniport)    Stopped (Disabled)
 Error Severity: Normal
 Service Flags: Kernel Driver, Shared Process
aic78xx (SCSI miniport)    Stopped (Disabled)
 Error Severity: Normal
 Service Flags: Kernel Driver, Shared Process
Always (SCSI miniport)    Stopped (Disabled)
 Error Severity: Normal
 Service Flags: Kernel Driver, Shared Process
ami0nt (SCSI miniport)    Stopped (Disabled)
 Error Severity: Normal
 Service Flags: Kernel Driver, Shared Process
amsint (SCSI miniport)    Stopped (Disabled)
 Error Severity: Normal
 Service Flags: Kernel Driver, Shared Process
Arrow (SCSI miniport)    Stopped (Disabled)
 Error Severity: Normal
 Service Flags: Kernel Driver, Shared Process
Remote Access Mac (NDIS)    Running (Automatic)
 C:\WINNT\system32\drivers\asyncmac.sys
 Error Severity: Normal
 Service Flags: Kernel Driver, Shared Process
atapi (SCSI miniport)       Running (Boot)
 C:\WINNT\System32\DRIVERS\atapi.sys
 Error Severity: Normal
 Service Flags: Kernel Driver, Shared Process
Atdisk (Primary disk)          Stopped (Disabled)
 Error Severity: Ignore
 Service Flags: Kernel Driver, Shared Process
ati (Video)        Stopped (Disabled)
 Error Severity: Ignore
 Service Flags: Kernel Driver, Shared Process
Beep (Base)        Running (System)
 Error Severity: Normal
 Service Flags: Kernel Driver, Shared Process
Network Monitor Agent Driver        Stopped (Manual)
 C:\WINNT\System32\drivers\bhnt.sys
 Error Severity: Normal
 Service Flags: Kernel Driver, Shared Process
 Group Dependencies: NDIS
BusLogic (SCSI miniport)    Stopped (Disabled)
 Error Severity: Normal
 Service Flags: Kernel Driver, Shared Process
Busmouse (Pointer Port)  Stopped (Disabled)
 Error Severity: Ignore
 Service Flags: Kernel Driver, Shared Process
Cdaudio (Filter)        Stopped (System)
 Error Severity: Ignore
 Service Flags: Kernel Driver, Shared Process
Cdfs (File system)     Running (Disabled)
 Error Severity: Normal
 Service Flags: File System Driver, Shared Process
```

```
  Group Dependencies:
   SCSI CDROM Class
Cdrom (SCSI CDROM Class)                Running (System)
 Error Severity: Ignore
 Service Flags: Kernel Driver, Shared Process
 Group Dependencies: SCSI miniport
Changer (Filter)        Stopped (System)
 Error Severity: Ignore
 Service Flags: Kernel Driver, Shared Process
cirrus (Video)        Stopped (Disabled)
 Error Severity: Ignore
 Service Flags: Kernel Driver, Shared Process
Cpqarray (SCSI miniport) Stopped  (Disabled)
 Error Severity: Normal
 Service Flags: Kernel Driver, Shared Process
cpqfws2e (SCSI miniport)             Stopped (Disabled)
 Error Severity: Normal
 Service Flags: Kernel Driver, Shared Process
dac960nt (SCSI miniport)      Stopped (Disabled)
 Error Severity: Normal
 Service Flags: Kernel Driver, Shared Process
dce376nt (SCSI miniport)      Stopped (Disabled)
 Error Severity: Normal
 Service Flags: Kernel Driver, Shared Process
Delldsa (SCSI miniport)   Stopped (Disabled)
 Error Severity: Normal
 Service Flags: Kernel Driver, Shared Process
Dell_DGX (Video)         Stopped (Disabled)
 Error Severity: Ignore
 Service Flags: Kernel Driver, Shared Process
Disk (SCSI Class)            Running (Boot)
 Error Severity: Ignore
 Service Flags: Kernel Driver, Shared Process
 Group Dependencies:
  SCSI miniport
Diskperf (Filter)               Stopped (Disabled)
 Error Severity: Normal
 Service Flags: Kernel Driver, Shared Process
DptScsi (SCSI miniport)  Stopped (Disabled)
 Error Severity: Normal
 Service Flags: Kernel Driver, Shared Process
dtc329x (SCSI miniport)  Stopped (Disabled)
 Error Severity: Normal
 Service Flags: Kernel Driver, Shared Process
et4000 (Video)       Stopped (Disabled)
 Error Severity: Ignore
 Service Flags: Kernel Driver, Shared Process
Fastfat (Boot file system) Running (Disabled)
 Error Severity: Normal
 Service Flags: File System Driver, Shared Process
Fd16_700 (SCSI miniport)      Stopped (Disabled)
 Error Severity: Normal
 Service Flags: Kernel Driver, Shared Process
Fd7000ex (SCSI miniport)      Stopped (Disabled)
 Error Severity: Normal
 Service Flags: Kernel Driver, Shared Process
Fd8xx (SCSI miniport)     Stopped (Disabled)
 Error Severity: Normal
 Service Flags: Kernel Driver, Shared Process
flashpnt (SCSI miniport) Stopped (Disabled)
 Error Severity: Normal
```

```
 Service Flags: Kernel Driver, Shared Process
Floppy (Primary disk)  Running (System)
 Error Severity: Ignore
 Service Flags: Kernel Driver, Shared Process
Ftdisk (Filter)    Stopped (Disabled)
 Error Severity: Ignore
 Service Flags: Kernel Driver, Shared Process
i8042 Keyboard and PS/2 Mouse Port Driver (Keyboard Port) Running
(System)
 System32\DRIVERS\i8042prt.sys
 Error Severity: Normal
 Service Flags: Kernel Driver, Shared Process
Inport (Pointer Port)  Stopped (Disabled)
 Error Severity: Ignore
 Service Flags: Kernel Driver, Shared Process
Jazzg300 (Video)       Stopped (Disabled)
 Error Severity: Ignore
 Service Flags: Kernel Driver, Shared Process
Jazzg364 (Video)       Stopped (Disabled)
 Error Severity: Ignore
 Service Flags: Kernel Driver, Shared Process
Jzvxl484 (Video)     Stopped (Disabled)
 Error Severity: Ignore
 Service Flags: Kernel Driver, Shared Process
Keyboard Class Driver (Keyboard Class) Running (System)
 System32\DRIVERS\kbdclass.sys
 Error Severity: Normal
 Service Flags: Kernel Driver, Shared Process
KSecDD (Base)              Running (System)
 Error Severity: Normal
 Service Flags: Kernel Driver, Shared Process
Kingston PCI Fast Ethernet Adapter Driver (NDIS) Running (Automatic)
 C:\WINNT\System32\drivers\KTC100.sys
 Error Severity: Normal
 Service Flags: Kernel Driver, Shared Process
mga (Video)         Stopped (Disabled)
 Error Severity: Ignore
 Service Flags: Kernel Driver, Shared Process
mga_mil (Video)                Stopped (Disabled)
 Error Severity: Ignore
 Service Flags: Kernel Driver, Shared Process
mitsumi (SCSI miniport)   Stopped (Disabled)
 Error Severity: Normal
 Service Flags: Kernel Driver, Shared Process
mkecr5xx (SCSI miniport)   Stopped (Disabled)
 Error Severity: Normal
 Service Flags: Kernel Driver, Shared Process
Modem (Extended base)                Stopped (Manual)
 Error Severity: Ignore
 Service Flags: Kernel Driver, Shared Process
Mouse Class Driver (Pointer Class)      Running (System)
 System32\DRIVERS\mouclass.sys
 Error Severity: Normal
 Service Flags: Kernel Driver, Shared Process
Msfs (File system)       Running (System)
 Error Severity: Normal
 Service Flags: File System Driver, Shared Process
Mup (Network)          Running (Manual)
 C:\WINNT\System32\drivers\mup.sys
 Error Severity: Normal
 Service Flags: File System Driver, Shared Process
```

```
NetBEUI Protocol (PNP_TDI)    Running (Automatic)
 C:\WINNT\System32\drivers\nbf.sys
 Error Severity: Normal
 Service Flags: Kernel Driver, Shared Process
Ncr53c9x (SCSI miniport)    Stopped (Disabled)
 Error Severity: Normal
 Service Flags: Kernel Driver, Shared Process
ncr77c22 (Video)                Stopped (Disabled)
 Error Severity: Ignore
 Service Flags: Kernel Driver, Shared Process
Ncrc700 (SCSI miniport)         Stopped (Disabled)
 Error Severity: Normal
 Service Flags: Kernel Driver, Shared Process
Ncrc710 (SCSI miniport)         Stopped (Disabled)
 Error Severity: Normal
 Service Flags: Kernel Driver, Shared Process
Microsoft NDIS System Driver (NDIS)       Running (System)
 Error Severity: Normal
 Service Flags: Kernel Driver, Shared Process
Microsoft NDIS TAPI driver (NDIS)       Running (System)
 C:\WINNT\system32\drivers\ndistapi.sys
 Error Severity: Normal
 Service Flags: Kernel Driver, Shared Process
Remote Access WAN Wrapper (NDISWAN) Running (Automatic)
 C:\WINNT\system32\drivers\ndiswan.sys
 Error Severity: Normal
 Service Flags: Kernel Driver, Shared Process
NetBIOS Interface (NetBIOSGroup)       Running (Manual)
 C:\WINNT\System32\drivers\netbios.sys
 Error Severity: Normal
 Service Flags: File System Driver, Shared Process
 Group Dependencies:
  TDI
WINS Client(TCP/IP) (PNP_TDI) Running (Automatic)
 C:\WINNT\System32\drivers\netbt.sys
 Error Severity: Normal
 Service Flags: Kernel Driver, Shared Process
 Service Dependencies: Tcpip
NetDetect        Stopped (Manual)
 C:\WINNT\system32\drivers\netdtect.sys
 Error Severity: Normal
 Service Flags: Kernel Driver, Shared Process
Npfs (File system)                Running (System)
 Error Severity: Normal
 Service Flags: File System Driver, Shared Process
Ntfs (File system)    Stopped (Disabled)
 Error Severity: Normal
 Service Flags: File System Driver, Shared Process
Null (Base)            Running (System)
 Error Severity: Normal
 Service Flags: Kernel Driver, Shared Process
NWLink IPX/SPX Compatible Transport Protocol (PNP_TDI) Running
(Automatic)
 C:\WINNT\System32\drivers\nwlnkipx.sys
 Error Severity: Normal
 Service Flags: Kernel Driver, Shared Process
NWLink NetBIOS (PNP_TDI)        Running (Automatic)
 C:\WINNT\System32\drivers\nwlnknb.sys
 Error Severity: Normal
 Service Flags: Kernel Driver, Shared Process
 Service Dependencies:   NwlnkIpx
```

```
RIP for NWLink IPX    Stopped (Automatic)
 C:\WINNT\system32\drivers\nwlnkrip.sys
 Error Severity: Normal
 Service Flags: Kernel Driver, Shared Process
 Service Dependencies:    NWLNKIPX
NWLink SPX/SPXII Protocol       Running (Manual)
 C:\WINNT\System32\drivers\nwlnkspx.sys
 Error Severity: Normal
 Service Flags: Kernel Driver, Shared Process
 Service Dependencies:    NwlnkIpx
Oliscsi (SCSI miniport)   Stopped (Disabled)
 Error Severity: Normal
 Service Flags: Kernel Driver, Shared Process
Parallel (Extended base)  Running (Automatic)
 Error Severity: Ignore
 Service Flags: Kernel Driver, Shared Process
 Service Dependencies: Parport
 Group Dependencies: Parallel arbitrator
Parport (Parallel arbitrator) Running (Automatic)
 Error Severity: Ignore
 Service Flags: Kernel Driver, Shared Process
ParVdm (Extended base) Running (Automatic)
 Error Severity: Ignore
 Service Flags: Kernel Driver, Shared Process
 Service Dependencies:
  Parport
 Group Dependencies:
  Parallel arbitrator
PCIDump (PCI Configuration)         Stopped (System)
 Error Severity: Ignore
 Service Flags: Kernel Driver, Shared Process
Pcmcia (System Bus Extender)    Stopped (Disabled)
 Error Severity: Normal
 Service Flags: Kernel Driver, Shared Process
PnP ISA Enabler Driver (Base)         Stopped (System)
 Error Severity: Ignore
 Service Flags: Kernel Driver, Shared Process
psidisp (Video)        Stopped (Disabled)
 Error Severity: Ignore
 Service Flags: Kernel Driver, Shared Process
Ql10wnt (SCSI miniport)   Stopped (Disabled)
 Error Severity: Normal
 Service Flags: Kernel Driver, Shared Process
qv (Video)         Stopped (Disabled)
 Error Severity: Ignore
 Service Flags: Kernel Driver, Shared Process
Remote Access Auto Connection Driver (Streams Drivers)  Running
(Automatic)
 C:\WINNT\system32\drivers\rasacd.sys
 Error Severity: Normal
 Service Flags: Kernel Driver, Shared Process
Remote Access ARP Service (PNP_TDI) Running (Automatic)
 C:\WINNT\system32\drivers\rasarp.sys
 Error Severity: Normal
 Service Flags: Kernel Driver, Shared Process
 Service Dependencies:
  TCPIP
Rdr (Network)                Running (Manual)
 C:\WINNT\System32\drivers\rdr.sys
 Error Severity: Normal
 Service Flags: File System Driver, Shared Process
```

```
s3 (Video)                      Running (System)
 Error Severity: Normal
 Service Flags: Kernel Driver, Shared Process
Scsiprnt (Extended base)     Stopped (Automatic)
 Error Severity: Ignore
 Service Flags: Kernel Driver, Shared Process
 Group Dependencies:
  SCSI miniport
Scsiscan (SCSI Class)      Stopped (System)
 Error Severity: Ignore
 Service Flags: Kernel Driver, Shared Process
 Group Dependencies:
  SCSI miniport
Serial (Extended base)     Running (Automatic)
 Error Severity: Ignore
 Service Flags: Kernel Driver, Shared Process
Sermouse (Pointer Port)    Stopped (Disabled)
 Error Severity: Ignore
 Service Flags: Kernel Driver, Shared Process
Sfloppy (Primary disk)     Stopped (System)
 Error Severity: Ignore
 Service Flags: Kernel Driver, Shared Process
 Group Dependencies:      SCSI miniport
Simbad (Filter)       Stopped (Disabled)
 Error Severity: Normal
 Service Flags: Kernel Driver, Shared Process
slcd32 (SCSI miniport)  Stopped (Disabled)
 Error Severity: Normal
 Service Flags: Kernel Driver, Shared Process
Sparrow (SCSI miniport)   Stopped (Disabled)
 Error Severity: Normal
 Service Flags: Kernel Driver, Shared Process
Spock (SCSI miniport)      Stopped (Disabled)
 Error Severity: Normal
 Service Flags: Kernel Driver, Shared Process
Srv (Network)           Running (Manual)
 C:\WINNT\System32\drivers\srv.sys
 Error Severity: Normal
 Service Flags: File System Driver, Shared Process
symc810 (SCSI miniport)     Stopped (Disabled)
 Error Severity: Normal
 Service Flags: Kernel Driver, Shared Process
T128 (SCSI miniport)  Stopped (Disabled)
 Error Severity: Normal
 Service Flags: Kernel Driver, Shared Process
T13B (SCSI miniport)   Stopped (Disabled)
 Error Severity: Normal
 Service Flags: Kernel Driver, Shared Process
TCP/IP Service (PNP_TDI)    Running (Automatic)
 C:\WINNT\System32\drivers\tcpip.sys
 Error Severity: Normal
 Service Flags: Kernel Driver, Shared Process
tga (Video)             Stopped (Disabled)
 Error Severity: Ignore
 Service Flags: Kernel Driver, Shared Process
tmv1 (SCSI miniport)      Stopped (Disabled)
 Error Severity: Normal
 Service Flags: Kernel Driver, Shared Process
Ultra124 (SCSI miniport)  Stopped (Disabled)
 Error Severity: Normal
 Service Flags: Kernel Driver, Shared Process
```

```
Ultra14f (SCSI miniport)  Stopped (Disabled)
 Error Severity: Normal
 Service Flags: Kernel Driver, Shared Process
Ultra24f (SCSI miniport)  Stopped (Disabled)
 Error Severity: Normal
 Service Flags: Kernel Driver, Shared Process
v7vram (Video)            Stopped (Disabled)
 Error Severity: Ignore
 Service Flags: Kernel Driver, Shared Process
VgaSave (Video Save)                 Running (System)
 C:\WINNT\System32\drivers\vga.sys
 Error Severity: Ignore
 Service Flags: Kernel Driver, Shared Process
VgaStart (Video Init)            Stopped (System)
 C:\WINNT\System32\drivers\vga.sys
 Error Severity: Ignore
 Service Flags: Kernel Driver, Shared Process
Wd33c93 (SCSI miniport)   Stopped (Disabled)
 Error Severity: Normal
 Service Flags: Kernel Driver, Shared Process
wd90c24a (Video)     Stopped (Disabled)
 Error Severity: Ignore
 Service Flags: Kernel Driver, Shared Process
wdvga (Video)         Stopped (Disabled)
 Error Severity: Ignore
 Service Flags: Kernel Driver, Shared Process
weitekp9 (Video)      Stopped (Disabled)
 Error Severity: Ignore
 Service Flags: Kernel Driver, Shared Process
Xga (Video)           Stopped (Disabled)
 Error Severity: Ignore
 Service Flags: Kernel Driver, Shared Process
 IRQ and Port Report
```

Devices	Vector	Level	Affinity
i8042prt	1	1	0xffffffff
i8042prt	12	12	0xffffffff
Serial	4	4	0x00000000
Serial	3	3	0x00000000
Floppy	6	6	0x00000000
KTC100	11	11	0x00000000
atapi	0	14	0x00000000

Devices	Physical Address	Length
i8042prt	0x00000060	0x0000000001
i8042prt	0x00000064	0x0000000001
Parport	0x000003bc	0x0000000003
Serial	0x000003f8	0x0000000007
Serial	0x000002f8	0x0000000007
Floppy	0x000003f0	0x0000000006
Floppy	0x000003f7	0x0000000001
KTC100	0x00005000	0x0000000080
atapi	0x000001f0	0x0000000008
atapi	0x000003f6	0x0000000001
s3	0x000003c0	0x0000000010
s3	0x000003d4	0x0000000008
s3	0x000042e8	0x0000000002
s3	0x00004ae8	0x0000000002

```
s3                 0x000082e8 0x0000000004
s3                 0x000086e8 0x0000000004
s3                 0x00008ae8 0x0000000004
s3                 0x00008ee8 0x0000000004
s3                 0x000092e8 0x0000000004
s3                 0x000096e8 0x0000000004
s3                 0x00009ae8 0x0000000004
s3                 0x00009ee8 0x0000000004
s3                 0x0000a2e8 0x0000000004
s3                 0x0000a6e8 0x0000000004
s3                 0x0000aae8 0x0000000004
s3                 0x0000aee8 0x0000000004
s3                 0x0000b6e8 0x0000000004
s3                 0x0000bae8 0x0000000004
s3                 0x0000bee8 0x0000000004
s3                 0x0000e2e8 0x0000000004
s3                 0x0000c2e8 0x0000000004
s3                 0x0000c6e8 0x0000000004
s3                 0x0000cae8 0x0000000004
s3                 0x0000cee8 0x0000000004
s3                 0x0000d2e8 0x0000000004
s3                 0x0000d6e8 0x0000000004
s3                 0x0000dae8 0x0000000004
s3                 0x0000dee8 0x0000000004
s3                 0x0000e6e8 0x0000000004
s3                 0x0000eae8 0x0000000004
s3                 0x0000eee8 0x0000000004
s3                 0x0000f6e8 0x0000000004
s3                 0x0000fae8 0x0000000004
s3                 0x0000fee8 0x0000000004
VgaSave                0x000003b0 0x000000000c
VgaSave                0x000003c0 0x0000000020
VgaSave                0x000001ce 0x0000000002
DMA and Memory Report
```

Devices	Channel Port
Floppy	2 0

Devices	Physical Address Length
s3	0x000a0000 0x00010000
s3	0xf8000000 0x04000000
s3	0x000c0000 0x00008000
VgaSave	0x000a0000 0x00020000

```
Environment Report
```

```
System Environment Variables
 ComSpec = C:\WINNT\system32\cmd.exe
 Os2LibPath = C:\WINNT\system32\os2\dll;
 Path = C:\WINNT\system32;C:\WINNT
 windir = C:\WINNT
 OS = Windows_NT
 PROCESSOR_ARCHITECTURE = x86
 PROCESSOR_LEVEL = 5
 PROCESSOR_IDENTIFIER = x86 Family 5 Model 4 Stepping 4, GenuineIntel
 PROCESSOR_REVISION = 0404
 NUMBER_OF_PROCESSORS = 1
Environment Variables for Current User
 TEMP = C:\TEMP
```

```
 TMP = C:\TEMP
Network Report
────────────────────────────────────

Your Access Level: Admin & Local
Workgroup or Domain: INFO.COM
Network Version: 4.0
LanRoot: INFO.COM
Logged On Users: 2
Current User (1): NetscapeMTA
 Logon Domain: INFO.COM
 Logon Server: MUSCLE
Current User (2): Administrator
 Logon Domain: INFO.COM
 Logon Server: MUSCLE

Transport: NetBT_KTC1001, 00-C0-F0-30-C2-43, VC's: 1, Wan: Wan
Transport: Nbf_KTC1001, 00-C0-F0-30-C2-43, VC's: 0, Wan: Wan
Transport: NwlnkNb, 00-C0-F0-30-C2-43, VC's: 0, Wan: Wan
Character Wait: 3,600
Collection Time: 250
Maximum Collection Count: 16
Keep Connection: 600
Maximum Commands: 5
Session Time Out: 45
Character Buffer Size: 512
Maximum Threads: 17
Lock Quota: 6,144
Lock Increment: 10
Maximum Locks: 500
Pipe Increment: 10
Maximum Pipes: 500
Cache Time Out: 40
Dormant File Limit: 45
Read Ahead Throughput: 4,294,967,295
Mailslot Buffers: 3
Server Announce Buffers: 20
Illegal Datagrams: 5
Datagram Reset Frequency: 60
Log Election Packets: False
Use Opportunistic Locking: True
Use Unlock Behind: True
Use Close Behind: True
Buffer Pipes: True
Use Lock, Read, Unlock: True
Use NT Caching: True
Use Raw Read: True
Use Raw Write: True
Use Write Raw Data: True
Use Encryption: True
Buffer Deny Write Files: True
Buffer Read Only Files: True
Force Core Creation: True
512 Byte Max Transfer: False
Bytes Received: 2,528
SMB's Received: 22
Paged Read Bytes Requested: 0
Non Paged Read Bytes Requested: 0
Cache Read Bytes Requested: 0
Network Read Bytes Requested: 0
Bytes Transmitted: 2,715
```

```
SMB's Transmitted: 22
Paged Read Bytes Requested: 0
Non Paged Read Bytes Requested: 1,104
Cache Read Bytes Requested: 0
Network Read Bytes Requested: 0
Initally Failed Operations: 0
Failed Completion Operations: 0
Read Operations: 0
Random Read Operations: 0
Read SMB's: 0
Large Read SMB's: 0
Small Read SMB's: 0
Write Operations: 12
Random Write Operations: 0
Write SMB's: 0
Large Write SMB's: 0
Small Write SMB's: 0
Raw Reads Denied: 0
Raw Writes Denied: 0
Network Errors: 0
Sessions: 3
Failed Sessions: 0
Reconnects: 0
Core Connects: 0
LM 2.0 Connects: 0
LM 2.x Connects: 0
Windows NT Connects: 3
Server Disconnects: 0
Hung Sessions: 0
Use Count: 1
Failed Use Count: 0
Current Commands: 0
Server File Opens: 185
Server Device Opens: 0
Server Jobs Queued: 0
Server Session Opens: 3
Server Sessions Timed Out: 6
Server Sessions Errored Out: 68
Server Password Errors: 0
Server Permission Errors: 0
Server System Errors: 0
Server Bytes Sent: 544,159
Server Bytes Received: 274,602
Server Average Response Time: 0
Server Request Buffers Needed: 0
Server Big Buffers Needed: 0
```

NET commands for baseline information

Mail server \\MUSCLE

```
Server Name              \\MUSCLE
Server Comment
Software version         Windows NT 4.0
Server is active on      NetBT_KTC1001 (00c0f030c243) NetBT_KTC1001
(00c0f030c243)  NwlnkIpx  (000000000001)  NwlnkNb  (00c0f030c243)
Nbf_KTC1001
(00c0f030c243) Server hidden              No
Maximum Logged On Users        Unlimited
```

```
Maximum open files per session   2048
Idle session time (min)       15
The command completed successfully.
```

Server statistics for \\MUSCLE

```
Statistics since 8/20/98 11:00 PM
Sessions accepted                    3
Sessions timed-out                   6
Sessions errored-out                70
Kilobytes sent                     594
Kilobytes received                 274
Mean response time (msec)            0
System errors                        0
Permission violations                0
Password violations                  0
Files accessed                     194
Communication devices accessed       0
Print jobs spooled                   0
Times buffers exhausted
 Big buffers                         0
 Request buffers                     0
```

User accounts for \\MUSCLE

```
Administrator      ANGEL       ANNE       BRAINS
CHEROKEE           FATBOY   Guest         HOLLYWOOD
IUSR_MUSCLE    Jan          Martha-Stewart     MONY
NetscapeMTA      RENEGADE        taylor       THE-HOSTAGE
THE-KID
```

NET view for the mail server

```
System Name         Remark
\\ANNE                              \\BRAINS
   \\CHEROKEE                           \\FATBOY      FATBOY
         \\MONY            MONY               \\MUSCLE
                          \\RENEGADE
\\SILO-1    AXIS StorPoint CD100, CD-ROM Server, V4.20 \\SILO-2
AXIS StorPoint CD100, CD-ROM Server, V4.20 \\SPEEDY      SPEEDY
         \\THE-HOSTAGE        THE-HOSTAGE
```

NET user command for the mail server \\MUSCLE

```
Administrator      ANGEL       ANNE       BRAINS
CHEROKEE           FATBOY   Guest         HOLLYWOOD
IUSR_MUSCLE    Jan          Martha-Stewart     MONY
NetscapeMTA      RENEGADE        taylor       THE-HOSTAGE
THE-KID          RICK
```

NET USE command for the mail server

```
Status    Local   Remote              Network
Disconnected F:    \\Brains\MY-BRAIN-C     Microsoft
      Windows Network
Unavailable G:     \\The-hostage\THE-HOSTAGE Microsoft
          Windows Network
```

```
Unavailable H:  \\Brains\MY-BRAIN-C    Microsoft
     Windows Network
Unavailable I:  \\Cherokee\cherokee-c  Microsoft
     Windows Network
Unavailable J:  \\Fatboy\THE-FATMAN-C    Microsoft
     Windows Network
```

NET session command for the mail server

```
Computer     User name     Client Type OpensIdle   time ─────────────────
──────────────────
\\ANNE     Administrator   Windows NT 1381 0    03:43:58 \\ANNE
   Windows NT 1381  1  00:14:53 \\BRAINS               Windows NT 1381 0
00:15:31 \\BRAINS     brains        Windows NT 1381       0 00:00:08
\\CHEROKEE
           Windows NT 1381 0    00:07:08 \\CHEROKEE       Windows
NT 1381   2   00:00:53 \\CHEROKEE               Windows NT 1381 0
00:05:44
\\FATBOY  FATBOY          Windows 4.0    3  03:48:59 \\FATBOY
   INFO.COM   0       00:04:20 \\FATBOY            Windows 4.0 0
01:38:12
```

Mail server protocol analysis

Other commands can be helpful to baseline your mail server. However, there is no substitute for performing a protocol analysis with an Internet Advisor. This level of detail provides interesting insight into the users, transactions, and actual communication at various layers in the network. I used the following information to baseline the mail server in my network.

```
*************************************************************
*****                    *****                    *****
*****   HEWLETT PACKARD NETWORK ADVISOR           *****
*****                                             *****
*****                                             *****
***** Measurement:   Brief Network Stack Decode   *****
***** Print Type:  All Frames                     *****
***** Open Views: Summary                         *****
***** Display Mode:   Viewing All Frames          *****
***** Print Date: 08/14/98                        *****
***** Print Time: 17:10:57                        *****
*****                                             *****
*****                                             *****
*************************************************************
1   09:18.418 HP──-21-08-A0 HP──-21-08-A0 ARP R PA = [15.6.72.18]
    HA = 0060B02108A0
2   09:18.456 WellfleetE8-8F-1B 01-80-C2-00-00-00 LLC C S = 42 D = 42 UI
3   09:18.864 Kingston-30-C2-43 Broadcast        ARP C
    PA = [220.100.100.132]
4   09:18.864 Kingston-30-CB-C6 Kingston-30-C2-43 ARP R
    PA = [220.100.100.132] HA = 00C0F030CBC6
5   09:18.864 220.100.100.10 220.100.100.132  SMB C Tree disconnect
6   09:18.865 220.100.100.132 220.100.100.10  SMB R Tree disconnect
7   09:18.865 220.100.100.10 220.100.100.132  SMB C User logoff
8   09:18.866 220.100.100.132 220.100.100.10  SMB R User logoff
9   09:18.866 220.100.100.10 220.100.100.132  TCP S = 1157 D = 139
```

```
        FIN ACK = 1905633 WIN = 8174
10  09:18.866 220.100.100.132 220.100.100.10 TCP S = 139 D = 1157
        FIN ACK = 18778126 WIN = 8129
11  09:18.867 220.100.100.10 220.100.100.132 TCP S = 1157 D = 139
        ACK = 1905634 WIN = 8174
12  09:18.867 Kingston-30-C2-43 Broadcast ARP C PA = [220.100.100.41]
13  09:18.867 Ibm——45-43-F3 Kingston-30-C2-43 ARP R
        PA = [220.100.100.41] HA = 0060944543F3
14  09:18.867 220.100.100.10 220.100.100.41 SMB C Tree disconnect
15  09:18.883 220.100.100.41 220.100.100.10 SMB R Tree disconnect
16  09:18.883 220.100.100.10 220.100.100.41 SMB C User logoff
17  09:18.884 220.100.100.41 220.100.100.10 SMB R User logoff
18  09:18.884 220.100.100.10 220.100.100.41 TCP S = 1159 D = 139
        FIN ACK = 1928322 WIN = 8351
19  09:18.885 220.100.100.41 220.100.100.10 TCP S = 139 D = 1159
        FIN ACK = 18779035 WIN = 8717
20  09:18.885 220.100.100.10 220.100.100.41 TCP S = 1159 D = 139
        ACK = 1928323 WIN = 8351
21  09:19.860 00000000-HP——210 00000000-Broadcast SAP C Find
        general Unkn service
22  09:19.864 00000000-HP——210 00000000-Broadcast SAP C Find
        general Unkn service
23  09:19.865 00000000-Kingst30C 00000000-HP——210 SAP R MUSCLE
24  09:19.868 00000000-HP——210 00000000-Broadcast SAP C Find
        general Unkn service
25  09:19.872 00000000-HP——210 00000000-Broadcast SAP C Find
        general Unkn service
26  09:19.941 WstDigt—3A-B8-EC Kingston-30-C2-43 LLC C S = F0 D = F0
        RR NR = 4 P
27  09:19.941 Kingston-30-C2-43 WstDigt—3A-B8-EC LLC R S = F0 D = F0
        RR NR = 5 F
28  09:20.456 WellfleetE8-8F-1B 01-80-C2-00-00-00 LLC C S = 42 D = 42 UI
29  09:21.331 Kingston-30-C2-9E Kingston-30-C2-43 LLC C S = F0 D = F0
        RR NR = 5 P
30  09:21.332 Kingston-30-C2-43 Kingston-30-C2-9E LLC R S = F0 D = F0
        RR NR = 6 F
31  09:21.558 Kingston-30-C2-43 Kingston-30-C2-9E LLC C S = F0 D = F0
        RR NR = 6 P
32  09:21.558 Kingston-30-C2-43 WstDigt—3A-B8-EC LLC C S = F0 D = F0
        RR NR = 5 P
33  09:21.559 WstDigt—3A-B8-EC Kingston-30-C2-43 LLC R S = F0 D = F0
        RR NR = 4 F
34  09:21.559 Kingston-30-C2-9E Kingston-30-C2-43 LLC R S = F0 D = F0
        RR NR = 5 F
35  09:22.456 WellfleetE8-8F-1B 01-80-C2-00-00-00 LLC C S = 42 D = 42 UI
36  09:24.456 WellfleetE8-8F-1B 01-80-C2-00-00-00 LLC C S = 42 D = 42 UI
37  09:25.332 00000000-Kingst30C 00000001-WstDig3AB NETB Session
        Data S = 4003 D = 200A SEQ = 3 NS = 4
38  09:25.332 00000001-WstDig3AB 00000000-Kingst30C NETB Session
        ACK S = 200A D = 4003 SEQ = 4 NS = 3
39  09:26.456 WellfleetE8-8F-1B 01-80-C2-00-00-00 LLC C S = 42 D = 42 UI
40  09:27.173 00000001-WstDig3AB 00000000-Kingst30C NETB Session
        Data S = 200A D = 4003 SEQ = 4 NS = 3
41  09:27.176 00000000-Kingst30C 00000001-WstDig3AB NETB Session
        ACK S = 4003 D = 200A SEQ = 3 NS = 4
42  09:28.456 WellfleetE8-8F-1B 01-80-C2-00-00-00 LLC C S = 42 D = 42 UI
43  09:28.880 Kingston-30-C2-43 Broadcast      ARP C
        PA = [220.100.100.175]
44  09:28.881 Axis——-32-41-35 Kingston-30-C2-43 ARP R
        PA = [220.100.100.175] HA = 00408C324135
```

```
45  09:28.881 220.100.100.10   220.100.100.175    SMB C Tree disconnect
46  09:28.885 220.100.100.175   220.100.100.10    SMB R Tree disconnect
47  09:28.885 220.100.100.10   220.100.100.175    SMB C User logoff
48  09:28.889 220.100.100.175   220.100.100.10    SMB R User logoff
    Invalid SMB CMD
49  09:28.890 220.100.100.10   220.100.100.175    TCP S = 1161
    D = 139 FIN ACK = 531891121 WIN = 7768
50  09:28.891 220.100.100.175   220.100.100.10    TCP S = 139
    D = 1161
    ACK = 18789997 WIN = 4096
51  09:28.891 220.100.100.175   220.100.100.10    TCP S = 139  D = 1161
    FIN ACK = 18789997 WIN = 4096
52  09:28.892 220.100.100.10   220.100.100.175    TCP S = 1161 D = 139
    ACK = 531891122 WIN = 7768
53  09:30.456 WellfleetE8-8F-1B 01-80-C2-00-00-00 LLC C S = 42 D = 42 UI
54  09:32.456 WellfleetE8-8F-1B 01-80-C2-00-00-00 LLC C S = 42 D = 42 UI
55  09:34.456 WellfleetE8-8F-1B 01-80-C2-00-00-00 LLC C S = 42 D = 42 UI
56  09:35.005 220.100.100.41   220.100.100.10    NETB C ID = 32854
    Refresh Name = INFO.COM
57  09:35.012 220.100.100.10   220.100.100.41    NETB R ID = 32854
    Register Name = INFO.COM
58  09:35.025 220.100.100.41   220.100.100.10    NETB C ID = 32856
    Refresh Name = ANGEL
59  09:35.030 220.100.100.10   220.100.100.41    NETB R ID = 32856
    Register Name = ANGEL
60  09:35.045 220.100.100.41   220.100.100.10    NETB C ID = 32858
    Refresh Name = INFO.COM
61  09:35.050 220.100.100.10   220.100.100.41    NETB R ID = 32858
    Register Name = INFO.COM
62  09:35.065 220.100.100.41   220.100.100.10    NETB C ID = 32860
    Refresh Name = ANGEL
63  09:35.075 220.100.100.10   220.100.100.41    NETB R ID = 32860
    Register Name = ANGEL
64  09:35.086 220.100.100.41   220.100.100.10    NETB C ID = 32862
    Refresh Name = ANGEL
65  09:35.089 220.100.100.10   220.100.100.41    NETB R ID = 32862
    Register Name = ANGEL
66  09:35.223 Kingston-1C-78-4D Broadcast      ARP C
    PA = [220.100.100.10]
67  09:35.224 Kingston-30-C2-43 Kingston-1C-78-4D ARP R
    PA = [220.100.100.10] HA = 00C0F030C243
68  09:35.224 220.100.100.144   220.100.100.10    NETB C ID = 123
    Refresh Name = JAN
69  09:35.228 220.100.100.10   220.100.100.144  NETB R ID = 123
    Register Name = JAN
70  09:36.457 WellfleetE8-8F-1B 01-80-C2-00-00-00 LLC C S = 42 D = 42 UI
71  09:37.837 220.100.100.10 Broadcast   BOOTP Request
72  09:38.457 WellfleetE8-8F-1B 01-80-C2-00-00-00 LLC C S = 42 D = 42 UI
73  09:39.665 Kingston-30-C2-43 Broadcast      ARP C
    PA = [220.100.100.180]
74  09:39.666 Axis—-32-41-3F Kingston-30-C2-43 ARP R
    PA = [220.100.100.180] HA = 00408C32413F
75  09:39.666 220.100.100.10   220.100.100.180   SMB C Transaction2
    Len = 17
76  09:39.695 220.100.100.180   220.100.100.10 SMB R Transaction2
77  09:39.697 220.100.100.10   220.100.100.180  SMB C Transaction2
    Len = 21
78  09:39.703 220.100.100.180   220.100.100.10    SMB R Transaction2
    Len = 7
79  09:39.704 220.100.100.10   220.100.100.180  SMB C Handle = 0002
```

```
      Find close
 80   09:39.708 220.100.100.180    220.100.100.10 SMB R Find close
 81   09:39.755 220.100.100.144    220.100.100.10  NETB C ID = 124
      Refresh Name = INFO.COM
 82   09:39.806 220.100.100.10     220.100.100.144  NETB R ID = 124
      Register Name = INFO.COM
 83   09:39.847 220.100.100.10     220.100.100.180  TCP S = 1162 D = 139
      ACK = 532692546 WIN = 8606
 84   09:40.084 220.100.100.10     220.100.100.180  SMB C Mkdir
      \host-news
 85   09:40.088 220.100.100.180    220.100.100.10   SMB R Mkdir No access
      rights
 86   09:40.090 220.100.100.10     220.100.100.180  SMB C Check path
      \host-news
 87   09:40.097 220.100.100.180    220.100.100.10   SMB R Check
      path Path
      not found
 88   09:40.098 220.100.100.10     220.100.100.180  SMB C Open
      \host-news\hostinfo.dat
 89   09:40.105 220.100.100.180    220.100.100.10   SMB R Open File not
      found
 90   09:40.106 220.100.100.10     220.100.100.180  SMB C Check path
      \host-news
 91   09:40.113 220.100.100.180    220.100.100.10   SMB R Check path Path
      not found
 92   09:40.114 220.100.100.10     220.100.100.180  SMB C Open
      \host-news\hostinfo.dat
 93   09:40.121 220.100.100.180    220.100.100.10   SMB R Open Write
      protected
 94   09:40.248 220.100.100.10     220.100.100.180  TCP S = 1162 D = 139
      ACK = 532692741 WIN = 8411
 95   09:40.523 WellfleetE8-8F-1B 01-80-C2-00-00-00 LLC C S = 42 D = 42 UI
 96   09:42.457 WellfleetE8-8F-1B 01-80-C2-00-00-00  LLC C S = 42 D = 42
      UI
 97   09:44.314 220.100.100.144    220.100.100.10   NETB C ID = 125
      Refresh Name = INFO.COM
 98   09:44.321 220.100.100.10     220.100.100.144  NETB R ID = 125
      Register Name = INFO.COM
 99   09:44.457 WellfleetE8-8F-1B 01-80-C2-00-00-00 LLC C S = 42 D = 42 UI
100   09:44.985 0.0.0.0   Broadcast  BOOTP Request
101   09:45.383 00000000-WstDig4EB 00000000-Broadcast SAP C Find
      nearest file server
102   09:46.457 WellfleetE8-8F-1B 01-80-C2-00-00-00 LLC C S = 42 D = 42 UI
103   09:47.100 Kingston-30-C2-43 03-00-00-00-00-01 NETB Name query
      FATBOY
104   09:47.100 Kingston-30-C2-4A Kingston-30-C2-43 NETB Name
      recognized FATBOY
105   09:47.101 Kingston-30-C2-43 Kingston-30-C2-4A NETB Name query
      FATBOY
106   09:47.101 Kingston-30-C2-4A Kingston-30-C2-43 NETB Name
      recognized FATBOY
107   09:47.101 Kingston-30-C2-43 Kingston-30-C2-4A LLC C S = F0 D = F0
      SABME P
108   09:47.101 Kingston-30-C2-4A Kingston-30-C2-43 LLC R S = F0 D = F0
      UA F
109   09:47.101 Kingston-30-C2-43 Kingston-30-C2-4A LLC C S = F0 D = F0
      RR NR = 0 P
110   09:47.102 Kingston-30-C2-4A Kingston-30-C2-43 LLC R S = F0 D = F0
      RR NR = 0 F
111   09:47.102 Kingston-30-C2-43 Kingston-30-C2-4A NETB S = 38 D = 15
      Session init
```

```
112 09:47.102 Kingston-30-C2-4A Kingston-30-C2-43 NETB S = 15 D = 38
    Session confirm
113 09:47.102 Kingston-30-C2-4A Kingston-30-C2-43 LLC R S = F0 D = F0
    RR NR = 1 F
114 09:47.102 Kingston-30-C2-43 Kingston-30-C2-4A LLC R S = F0 D = F0
    RR NR = 1 F
115 09:47.104 Kingston-30-C2-43 Broadcast     ARP C
    PA = [220.100.100.121]
116 09:47.109 00000001-000000000 00000000-Broadcast NETB Find Name
    FATBOY
117 09:47.110 Kingston-30-C2-4A Kingston-30-C2-43 ARP R
    PA = [220.100.100.121] HA = 00C0F030C24A
118 09:47.110 220.100.100.10 220.100.100.121 TCP S = 1167 D = 139
    SYN WIN = 8192
119 09:47.110 220.100.100.121 220.100.100.10 TCP S = 139 D = 1167
    SYN ACK = 19410874 WIN = 5840
120 09:47.110 220.100.100.10 220.100.100.121 TCP S = 1167 D = 139
    ACK = 18482677 WIN = 8760
121 09:47.110 220.100.100.10 220.100.100.121 NETB Session Req
    MUSCLE -> FATBOY
122 09:47.111 220.100.100.121 220.100.100.10 NETB Session confirm
123 09:47.111 Kingston-30-C2-43 Kingston-30-C2-4A NETB S = 38 D = 15
    Session end
124 09:47.111 Kingston-30-C2-4A Kingston-30-C2-43 LLC R S = F0 D = F0 RR
    NR = 2 F
125 09:47.112 Kingston-30-C2-43 Kingston-30-C2-4A LLC C S = F0 D = F0
    DISC P
126 09:47.112 Kingston-30-C2-4A Kingston-30-C2-43 LLC R S = F0 D = F0
    UA F
127 09:47.112 220.100.100.10  220.100.100.121   SMB C Negotiate
    Protocol PC NETWORK PROGRAM 1.0
128 09:47.112 220.100.100.121  220.100.100.10   SMB R Negotiated
    Protocol 7 Len = 7
129 09:47.114 220.100.100.10  220.100.100.121   SMB C Session setup
    Len = 57
130 09:47.114 220.100.100.121  220.100.100.10   SMB R Session setup
131 09:47.115 220.100.100.10  220.100.100.121   SMB C Open
    \PIPE\srvsvc
132 09:47.116 220.100.100.121  220.100.100.10   SMB R Open No access
    rights
133 09:47.132 220.100.100.10  220.100.100.121   SMB C Transaction
    name \PIPE\LANMAN
134 09:47.132 220.100.100.121  220.100.100.10   SMB R Transaction
    name Len = 121
135 09:47.140 220.100.100.10  220.100.100.121   SMB C Open
    \PIPE\srvsvc
136 09:47.141 220.100.100.121  220.100.100.10   SMB R Open No access
    rights
137 09:47.158 220.100.100.10  220.100.100.121   SMB C Transaction
    name
    \PIPE\LANMAN
138 09:47.158 220.100.100.121  220.100.100.10   SMB R Transaction
    name Len = 39
139 09:47.259 220.100.100.10  220.100.100.121   TCP S = 1167 D = 139
    ACK = 18483176 WIN = 8261
140 09:47.650 00000001-000000000 00000000-Broadcast NETB Find Name
    FATBOY
141 09:48.011 220.100.100.10 Broadcast BOOTP Request
142 09:48.191 00000001-000000000 00000000-Broadcast NETB Find Name
    FATBOY
143 09:48.457 WellfleetE8-8F-1B 01-80-C2-00-00-00 LLC C S = 42 D = 42 UI
```

```
144 09:48.846 220.100.100.144   220.100.100.10  NETB C ID = 126
    Refresh Name = HOLLYWOOD
145 09:48.853 220.100.100.10   220.100.100.144  NETB R ID = 126
    Register Name = HOLLYWOOD
146 09:49.843 00000000-Kingst30C 00000000-Broadcast IPX RIP
    Response: 1 networks
147 09:50.457 WellfleetE8-8F-1B 01-80-C2-00-00-00 LLC C S = 42 D = 42 UI
148 09:51.992 WstDigt—3A-B8-EC Kingston-30-C2-43 LLC C S = F0 D = F0
    RR NR = 4 P
149 09:51.992 Kingston-30-C2-43 WstDigt—3A-B8-EC LLC R S = F0 D = F0
    RR NR = 5 F
150 09:52.457 WellfleetE8-8F-1B 01-80-C2-00-00-00 LLC C S = 42 D = 42 UI
151 09:52.622 00000000-006008981 00000000-Broadcast SAP C Find
    general file server
152 09:53.333 Kingston-30-C2-9E Kingston-30-C2-43 LLC C S = F0 D = F0 RR
    NR = 5 P
153 09:53.333 Kingston-30-C2-43 Kingston-30-C2-9E LLC R S = F0 D = F0 RR
    NR = 6 F
154 09:53.378 220.100.100.144   20.100.100.10   NETB C ID = 127 Refresh
    Name = HOLLYWOOD
155 09:53.384 220.100.100.10 220.100.100.144 NETB R ID = 127
    Register Name = HOLLYWOOD
156 09:53.609 Kingston-30-C2-43 WstDigt—3A-B8-EC LLC C S = F0 D = F0
    RR NR = 5 P
157 09:53.609 Kingston-30-C2-43 Kingston-30-C2-9E LLC C S = F0 D = F0
    RR NR = 6 P
158 09:53.610 WstDigt—3A-B8-EC Kingston-30-C2-43 LLC R S = F0 D = F0
    RR NR = 4 F
159 09:53.610 Kingston-30-C2-9E Kingston-30-C2-43 LLC R S = F0 D = F0
    RR NR = 5 F
160 09:54.457 WellfleetE8-8F-1B 01-80-C2-00-00-00 LLC C S = 42 D = 42 UI
161 09:56.457 WellfleetE8-8F-1B 01-80-C2-00-00-00 LLC C S = 42 D = 42 UI
162 09:57.333 00000000-Kingst30C 00000001-WstDig3AB NETB Session
    Data S = 4003 D = 200A SEQ = 3 NS = 4
163 09:57.333 00000001-WstDig3AB 00000000-Kingst30C NETB Session
    ACK S = 200A D = 4003 SEQ = 4 NS = 3
164 09:57.753 00000000-Kingst30C 00000000-Broadcast SAP C Find
    nearest file server
165 09:57.910 220.100.100.144 220.100.100.10 NETB C ID = 128
    Refresh Name = HOLLYWOOD
166 09:57.914 220.100.100.10 220.100.100.144 NETB R ID = 128
    Register Name = HOLLYWOOD
167 09:58.457 WellfleetE8-8F-1B 01-80-C2-00-00-00 LLC C S = 42 D = 42 UI
168 09:58.615 00000000-WstDig4EB 00000000-Broadcast NETB Find Name
    INFO.COM
169 09:58.615 00000001-000000000 00000000-WstDig4EB NETB Name
    INFO.COM Recognized
170 09:58.888 00000000-Kingst30C 00000001-Broadcast SAP R
    ANNE!!!!!!!!!!!!A5569B20ABE511CE9CA400004C762832
171 09:59.223 00000001-WstDig3AB 00000000-Kingst30C NETB Session
    Data S = 200A D = 4003 SEQ = 4 NS = 3
172 09:59.223 00000000-Kingst30C 00000001-WstDig3AB NETB Session
    ACK S = 4003 D = 200A SEQ = 3 NS = 4
173 10:00.458 WellfleetE8-8F-1B 01-80-C2-00-00-00 LLC C S = 42 D = 42 UI
174 10:01.412 220.100.100.10 Broadcast BOOTP Request
175 10:02.458 WellfleetE8-8F-1B 01-80-C2-00-00-00 LLC C S = 42 D = 42 UI
176 0:04.076 00000000-Kingst30C 00000000-Broadcast SAP R MUSCLE
177 10:04.458 WellfleetE8-8F-1B 01-80-C2-00-00-00 LLC C S = 42 D = 42 UI
178 10:06.458 WellfleetE8-8F-1B 01-80-C2-00-00-00 LLC C S = 42 D = 42 UI
179 10:08.458 WellfleetE8-8F-1B 01-80-C2-00-00-00 LLC C S = 42 D = 42 UI
```

```
180 10:10.524 WellfleetE8-8F-1B 01-80-C2-00-00-00 LLC C S = 42 D = 42 UI
181 10:12.458 WellfleetE8-8F-1B 01-80-C2-00-00-00 LLC C S = 42 D = 42 UI
182 10:13.391 220.100.100.10   224.0.1.24     UDP S = 42 D = 42 LEN = 19
183 10:13.737 220.100.100.10   220.100.100.121  SMB C Session setup
    Len = 50
184 10:13.737 220.100.100.121  220.100.100.10    SMB R Session setup
185 10:13.740 220.100.100.10  220.100.100.121   SMB C Open
    \PIPE\srvsvc
186 10:13.740 220.100.100.121  220.100.100.10   SMB R Open No access
    rights
187 10:13.757 220.100.100.10   220.100.100.121  SMB C Transaction
    name \PIPE\LANMAN
188 10:13.758 220.100.100.121   220.100.100.10   SMB R Transaction
    name Len = 121
189 10:13.761 220.100.100.10   220.100.100.121  SMB C Tree connect
190 10:13.761 220.100.100.121   220.100.100.10  SMB R Tree connect
    Bad password
191 10:13.769 220.100.100.10   220.100.100.121  SMB C Tree connect
192 10:13.769 220.100.100.121   220.100.100.10  SMB R Tree connect
    Bad password
193 10:13.773 220.100.100.10   220.100.100.121  SMB C Open
    \PIPE\srvsvc
194 10:13.780 220.100.100.121   220.100.100.10  SMB R Open No access
    rights
195 10:13.796 220.100.100.10   220.100.100.121 SMB C Transaction
    name \PIPE\LANMAN
196 10:13.797 220.100.100.121   220.100.100.10  SMB R Transaction
    name Len = 121
197 10:13.848 00000000-WstDigCF0 00000000-WstDig4EB SMB C Echo
    Len = 3
198 10:13.850 00000000-WstDig4EB 00000000-WstDigCF0 SMB R Echo
    Len = 3
199 10:13.869 220.100.100.10  220.100.100.121   SMB C Open
    \PIPE\srvsvc
200 10:13.869 220.100.100.121  220.100.100.10   SMB R Open No access
    rights
201 10:13.885 220.100.100.10  220.100.100.121   SMB C Transaction
    name \PIPE\LANMAN
202 10:13.886 220.100.100.121  220.100.100.10   SMB R Transaction
    name Len = 121
203 10:13.888 220.100.100.10   220.100.100.121  SMB C Tree connect
204 10:13.889 220.100.100.121   220.100.100.10  SMB R Tree connect
    Bad password
205 10:13.915 220.100.100.10   220.100.100.121 SMB C Tree connect
206 10:13.916 220.100.100.121   220.100.100.10 SMB R Tree connect
    Bad password
207 10:13.934 220.100.100.10    220.100.100.121 SMB C Tree connect
208 10:13.934 220.100.100.121 220.100.100.10 SMB R Tree connect
    Bad password
209 10:14.102 220.100.100.10 220.100.100.121 TCP S = 1167 D = 139
    ACK = 18484076 WIN = 7361
210 10:14.458 WellfleetE8-8F-1B 01-80-C2-00-00-00 LLC C S = 42 D = 42 UI
211 10:16.196 00000000-Kingst30C 00000000-Broadcast IPX NCP Unkn
    type = 0000
212 10:16.196 220.100.100.121 220.100.100.10 NETB C ID = 267 Query
    Name = CHEROKEE
213 10:16.196 Kingston-30-C2-4A 03-00-00-00-00-01 NETB Name query
    CHEROKEE
214 10:16.197 220.100.100.10  220.100.100.121   NETB R ID = 267 Query
    Name = CHEROKEE
```

```
215 10:16.198 Kingston-30-C2-4A Broadcast        ARP C
    PA = [220.100.100.139]
216 10:16.209 00000001-Kingst30C 00000001-Kingst30C IPX NCP Unknown
    type = 0000
217 10:16.209 Kingston-30-C2-9E Kingston-30-C2-4A NETB Name
    recognized CHEROKEE
218 10:16.209 Kingston-30-C2-9E Kingston-30-C2-4A ARP R
    PA = [220.100.100.139] HA = 00C0F030C29E
219 10:16.209 Kingston-30-C2-4A Kingston-30-C2-9E LLC C S = F0 D = F0
    SABME P
220 10:16.209 220.100.100.121 220.100.100.139 TCP S = 1033 D = 139
    SYN WIN = 5840
221 10:16.224 Kingston-30-C2-9E Kingston-30-C2-4A LLC R S = F0 D = F0
    UA F
222 10:16.224 220.100.100.139  220.100.100.121 TCP S = 139 D = 1033
    SYN ACK = 18511766 WIN = 8760
223 10:16.225 Kingston-30-C2-4A Kingston-30-C2-9E LLC C S = F0 D = F0
    RR NR = 0 P
224 10:16.225 220.100.100.121  220.100.100.139  TCP S = 1033 D = 139
    ACK = 2492926 WIN = 5840
225 10:16.225 220.100.100.121  220.100.100.139  NETB Session data Len =
    0
*******************************************************************
```

Detailed mail server protocol analysis. It is also important to evaluate the protocol frames as they traverse the network. The following is an analysis of the frames I used in the baseline for the mail server in my network. I recommend that you obtain a baseline analysis such as this in your files.

```
*****************************************************************************
         *****  *****                                *****
*****    HEWLETT PACKARD NETWORK ADVISOR *****
*****                                      *****
*****    Measurement:  MS Windows Stack Decode    *****
*****    Print Type: All Frames   *****  *****Open Views: Detailed
         *****
*****    Display Mode:     Viewing All Frames *****
*****    Print Date: 08/14/98             *****
*****    Print Time: 17:6:1               *****
*****                                     *****
****************************************************************
```

```
  Frame: 3     Time: Aug 14@17:04:37.3217379 Length: 70
Novell NetBios (IPX/SPX)
Connection Control Flag C0
                1.......    System Packet
                .1......    Send ACK
                ..0.....    Not Attention
                ...0....    Not End of Message
                ....0...    No Rsend Needed
Operation            6         Session Data
Source Conn ID        4003
Dest Conn ID          200A
Sequence Number        3
Next Expected Seq Number    4
```

```
  Frame: 4     Time: Aug 14@17:04:37.3221132 Length: 70
Novell NetBios (IPX/SPX)
```

```
Connection Control Flag  80
                 1.......        System Packet
                 .0......        Non Send ACK
                 ..0.....        Not Attention
                 ...0....        Not End of Message
                 ....0...        No Rsend Needed
Operation              6         Session ACK
Source Conn ID         200A
Dest Conn ID           4003
Sequence Number            4
Next Expected Seq Number      3
```

```
  Frame: 6      Time: Aug 14@17:04:38.7197886 Length: 70
  Novell NetBios (IPX/SPX)
Connection Control Flag  C0
                 1.......        System Packet
                 .1......        Send ACK
                 ..0.....        Not Attention
                 ...0....        Not End of Message
                 ....0...        No Rsend Needed
Operation              6         Session Data
Source Conn ID         200A
Dest Conn ID           4003
Sequence Number            4
Next Expected Seq Number      3
```

```
  Frame: 7      Time: Aug 14@17:04:38.7281683 Length: 70
  Novell NetBios (IPX/SPX)
Connection Control Flag  80
                 1.......        System Packet
                 .0......        Non Send ACK
                 ..0.....        Not Attention
                 ...0....        Not End of Message
                 ....0...        No Rsend Needed
Operation              6         Session ACK
Source Conn ID         4003
Dest Conn ID           200A
Sequence Number            3
Next Expected Seq Number      4
```

```
  Frame: 10     Time: Aug 14@17:04:39.4543500 Length: 97

  SMB
Identifier        SMB
Command Code           71         Tree Disconnect
Error Class       00           Success
Reserved          00
Error Code        0000           Success
Flags             00011000        OK
 Response Request     0.......       Request
 Client Notification .0......    Flag Not Set
 File Lock         ..0.....    Flag Not Set
 Canonical Form       ...1....  Flag Set
 Case Sensitive       ....1...  Flag Set
 Reserved             .....0..
 Rcv Buffer Posted      ......0.  Flag Not Set
 Subdialect           .......0   Flag Not Set
Flags_2 8003
Reserved (Truncated) 00-00-00-00-00-00-00-00-0
Authenticated Resource ID 0801
```

```
Callers Process ID     CAFE
Unauthenticated User ID  0801
Multiplex ID         0300
Word Count              0
Buffer Count            0
 NetBIOS (TCP/IP)
Service Type :                    Session Service
Packet Type  :                    Session Message
Type             00
Flags            00               See Bit Fields Below
Reserved Bits        0000000.
Length Extension Bit  .......0
Length           35
User Data                         SMB Data
```

Frame: 11   Time: Aug 14@17:04:39.4549445 Length: 97

```
 SMB
Identifier       SMB
Command Code         71              Tree Disconnect
Error Class      00              Success
Reserved         00
Error Code       0000            Success
Flags            10011000        OK
 Response Request    1.......        Response
 Client Notification .0......        Flag Not Set
 File Lock       ..0.....     Flag Not Set
 Canonical Form      ...1....     Flag Set
 Case Sensitive      ....1...     Flag Set
 Reserved        .....0..
 Rcv Buffer Posted       ......0. Flag Not Set
 Subdialect          .......0     Flag Not Set
Flags_2              8003
Reserved (Truncated)     00-00-00-00-00-00-00-00-0
Authenticated Resource ID 0801
Callers Process ID     CAFE
Unauthenticated User ID  0801
Multiplex ID         0300
Word Count              0
Buffer Count            0
 NetBIOS (TCP/IP)
Service Type :                    Session Service
Packet Type  :                    Session Message
Type             00
Flags            00               See Bit Fields Below
 Reserved Bits       0000000.
 Length Extension Bit .......0
Length           35
User Data                         SMB Data
```

Frame: 12   Time: Aug 14@17:04:39.4553662 Length: 101

```
 SMB
 Identifier      SMB
 Command Code        74              User Logoff And X
 Error Class     00              Success
 Reserved        00
 Error Code      0000            Success
 Flags           00011000        OK
 Response Request    0.......        Request
```

```
Client Notification  .0......        Flag Not Set
File Lock            ..0.....      Flag Not Set
Canonical Form          ...1....   Flag Set
Case Sensitive          ....1...   Flag Set
Reserved                .....0..
Rcv Buffer Posted          ......0.  Flag Not Set
Subdialect                 .......0   Flag Not Set
Flags_2              8003
Reserved (Truncated)     00-00-00-00-00-00-00-00-0
Authenticated Resource ID 0801
Callers Process ID    CAFE
Unauthenticated User ID  0801
Multiplex ID         0340
Word Count           2
Parameters           00FF
Parameters           0144
Buffer Count         0
 NetBIOS (TCP/IP)
 Service Type :                      Session Service
 Packet Type  :                      Session Message
 Type            00
 Flags           00                  See Bit Fields Below
  Reserved Bits      0000000.
  Length Extension Bit .......0
Length               39
User Data                            SMB Data Decode
```

```
 Frame: 13        Time: Aug 14@17:04:39.4557111 Length: 101

  SMB
Identifier        SMB
Command Code         74                User Logoff And X
Error Class          00             Success
Reserved             00
Error Code           0000               Success
Flags             10011000            OK
 Response Request      1.......         Response
 Client Notification  .0......       Flag Not Set
 File Lock            ..0.....     Flag Not Set
 Canonical Form          ...1....    Flag Set
 Case Sensitive          ....1...    Flag Set
 Reserved                .....0..
 Rcv Buffer Posted          ......0.   Flag Not Set
 Subdialect                 .......0   Flag Not Set
Flags_2              8003
Reserved (Truncated)     00-00-00-00-00-00-00-00-0
Authenticated Resource ID 0801
Callers Process ID    CAFE
Unauthenticated User ID  0801
Multiplex ID         0340
Word Count           2
Parameters           00FF
Parameters           0027
Buffer Count         0
 NetBIOS (TCP/IP)
Service Type :                       Session Service
Packet Type  :                       Session Message
Type            00
Flags           00                   See Bit Fields Below
 Reserved Bits      0000000.
```

```
 Length Extension Bit  .......0
Length              39
User Data                           SMB Data
```

```
 Frame: 40       Time: Aug 14@17:04:52.8535453 Length: 102
 Novell NetBios (IPX/SPX)
Connection Control Flag  00
               0.......        Non-System Packet
               .0......        Non Send ACK
               ..0.....        Not Attention
               ...0....        Not End of Message
               ....0...        No Rsend Needed
Operation            1             Find Name
Name Type Flag           00
               0.......        Unique Name
               .0......        Name Not Used
               .....0..        Name Not Registered
               ......0.        Name Not Duplicated
               .......0        Name Not Deregistered
Operation            1             Find Name
Name Claim String        JSPNRMPTGSBSSDIR
```

```
 Frame: 41       Time: Aug 14@17:04:53.4162026 Length: 102
 Novell NetBios (IPX/SPX)
Connection Control Flag  00
               0.......        Non-System Packet
               .0......        Non Send ACK
               ..0.....        Not Attention
               ...0....        Not End of Message
               ....0...        No Rsend Needed
Operation            1             Find Name
Name Type Flag           00
               0.......        Unique Name
               .0......        Name Not Used
               .....0..        Name Not Registered
               ......0.        Name Not Duplicated
               .......0        Name Not Deregistered
Operation            1         Find Name
Name Claim String        JSPNRMPTGSBSSDIR
```

```
 Frame: 42       Time: Aug 14@17:04:53.9786014 Length: 102
 Novell NetBios (IPX/SPX)
Connection Control Flag  00
               0.......        Non-System Packet
               .0......        Non Send ACK
               ..0.....        Not Attention
               ...0....        Not End of Message
               ....0...        No Rsend Needed
Operation            1             Find Name
Name Type Flag           00
               0.......        Unique Name
               .0......        Name Not Used
               .....0..        Name Not Registered
               ......0.        Name Not Duplicated
               .......0        Name Not Deregistered
Operation            1             Find Name
Name Claim String        JSPNRMPTGSBSSDIR
```

```
 Frame: 44       Time: Aug 14@17:04:54.5416676 Length: 96
 NetBIOS (TCP/IP)
Service Type :                      Name Service
```

```
Name_Trn_ID              32968
Packet Type :                            Name Query Request
Opcode, NM_Flags, Rcode   01-00          See Bit Fields Below
 Response Flag        0.......      Request Packet
 Opcode              .0000...       Query
 Auth. Answer Flag   .....0..       False
 Truncation Flag     ......0.       False
 Recursion Desired Flag  .......1   True
 Recursion Available Flag 0.......  False
 Reserved            .00.....
 Broadcast Flag          ...0....   False
 Rcode               ....0000
Qdcount              1           No. Of Entries In Question
 Section
Ancount              0           No. Of Entries In Answer
 Section
Nscount              0           No. Of Entries In Authority
 Section
Arcount              0           No. of Entries In
 Additional Records Section
Name Length          32
Question_Name        JSPNRMPTGSBSSDIR        NetBIOS Name
Question_Type        32          General Name Service
 Resource Record
Question_Class       1           Internet Class
```

```
  Frame: 45      Time: Aug 14@17:04:54.5419805 Length: 75
 NetBIOS (NetBEUI)
Header Length         44
Delimiter             EFFF
Command               08          DATAGRAM
Optional Data 1       00          Reserved field
Optional Data 2       0000        Reserved field
Transmit Correlator   0000        Reserved field
Response Correlator   0000        Reserved field
Destination Name      JSPNRMPTGSBSSDIR
Source Name           CHEROKEE
```

```
  Frame: 46      Time: Aug 14@17:04:54.5430143 Length:      102
 NetBIOS (TCP/IP)
Service Type :                    Name Service
Name_Trn_ID           32968
Packet Type :                     Negative Name Query Response
Opcode, NM_Flags, Rcode   85-83   See Bit Fields Below
 Response Flag        1.......     Response Packet
 Opcode              .0000...      Query
 Auth. Answer Flag   .....1..      True
 Truncation Flag     ......0.      False
 Recursion Desired Flag .......1   True
 Recursion Available Flag 1.......  True
 Reserved            .00.....
 Broadcast Flag          ...0....  False
 Rcode               ....0011      Name Error
Qdcount              0           No. Of Entries In Question
 Section
Ancount              0           Error: Invalid Value
Nscount              0           No. Of Entries In Authority
 Section
Arcount              0           No. of Entries In
 Additional Records Section
```

```
   Frame: 52       Time: Aug 14@17:05:00.5414083 Length: 96
NetBIOS (TCP/IP)
Service Type :                          Name Service
Name_Trn_ID             32968
Packet Type :                        Name Query Request
Opcode, NM_Flags, Rcode 01-10              See Bit Fields Below
 Response Flag          0.......      Request Packet
 Opcode                .0000...       Query
 Auth. Answer Flag     .....0..       False
 Truncation Flag       ......0.       False
 Recursion Desired Flag  .......1       True
 Recursion Available Flag 0.......      False
 Reserved               .00.....
 Broadcast Flag         ...1....       True
 Rcode                  ....0000
Qdcount                 1              No. Of Entries In Question
 Section
Ancount                 0              No. Of Entries In Answer
 Section
Nscount                 0              No. Of Entries In Authority
 Section
Arcount                 0              No. of Entries In
 Additional Records Section
Name Length             32
Question_Name           JSPNRMPTGSBSSDIR          NetBIOS Name
Question_Type           32         General Name Service
 Resource Record
Question_Class           1          Internet Class
```

```
   Frame: 53       Time: Aug 14@17:05:01.2913179 Length: 96
NetBIOS (TCP/IP)
Service Type :                       Name Service
Name_Trn_ID             32968
Packet Type :                      Name Query Request
Opcode, NM_Flags, Rcode   01-10      See Bit Fields Below
 Response Flag          0.......      Request Packet
 Opcode                .0000...       Query
 Auth. Answer Flag     .....0..       False
 Truncation Flag       ......0.       False
 Recursion Desired Flag  .......1      True
 Recursion Available Flag 0...... . False
 Reserved               .00.....
 Broadcast Flag         ...1....      True
 Rcode                  ....0000
Qdcount                 1             No. Of Entries In Question
 Section
Ancount                 0             No. Of Entries In Answer
 Section
Nscount                 0             No. Of Entries In Authority
 Section
Arcount                 0             No. of Entries In
 Additional Records Section
Name Length             32
Question_Name           JSPNRMPTGSBSSDIR          NetBIOS Name
Question_Type           32         General Name Service
 Resource Record
Question_Class           1          Internet Class
```

```
   Frame: 54     Time: Aug 14@17:05:02.0416210 Length: 96
NetBIOS (TCP/IP)
Service Type :                       Name Service
```

```
Name_Trn_ID              32968
Packet Type :                        Name Query Request
Opcode, NM_Flags, Rcode  01-10          See Bit Fields Below
 Response Flag           0.......      Request Packet
 Opcode                  .0000...      Query
 Auth. Answer Flag.....0..             False
 Truncation Flag ......0.              False
 Recursion Desired Flag .......1     True
 Recursion Available Flag 0.......   False
 Reserved                .00.....
 Broadcast Flag          ...1....     True
 Rcode                   ....0000
Qdcount                  1            No. Of Entries In Question
 Section
Ancount                  0            No. Of Entries In Answer
 Section
Nscount                  0            No. Of Entries In Authority
 Section
Arcount                  0            No. of Entries In
 Additional Records Section
Name Length              32
Question_Name            JSPNRMPTGSBSSDIR          NetBIOS Name
Question_Type            32           General Name Service
 Resource Record
Question_Class           1            Internet Class
```

```
 Frame: 62     Time: Aug 14@17:05:06.0851577 Length: 92

  SMB
Identifier        SMB
Command Code             2B                Echo
Error Class       00                  Success
Reserved          00
Error Code        0000                Success
Flags             00000000            Good
 Response Request       0.......        Request
 Client Notification .0......        Flag Not Set
 File Lock         ..0.....         Flag Not Set
 Canonical Form         ...0....        Flag Not Set
 Case Sensitive         ....0...        Flag Not Set
 Reserved          .....0..
 Rcv Buffer Posted      ......0.    Flag Not Set
 Subdialect             .......0     Flag Not Set
Flags_2           8001
Reserved (Truncated)    00-00-00-2A-10-02-00-00-0
Authenticated Resource ID 0800
Callers Process ID    0000
Unauthenticated User ID  0800
Multiplex ID      4581
Word Count        1
Parameters        0001
Buffer Count      4
Buffer Type       00                 Not Recognized
ASCII Data
```

```
 Frame: 63     Time: Aug 14@17:05:06.0856426 Length: 92

  SMB
Identifier        SMB
Command Code             2B                Echo
Error Class       00                  Success
```

```
Reserved              00
Error Code            0000              Success
Flags            10000000              OK
 Response Request     1.......         Response
 Client Notification .0......    Flag Not Set
 File Lock           ..0.....    Flag Not Set
 Canonical Form       ...0....  Flag Not Set
 Case Sensitive       ....0...  Flag Not Set
 Reserved             .....0..
 Rcv Buffer Posted     ......0.  Flag Not Set
 Subdialect           .......0   Flag Not Set
Flags_2              8001
Reserved (Truncated)       00-00-00-2A-10-02-00-00-0
Authenticated Resource ID   0800
Callers Process ID    0000
Unauthenticated User ID  0800
Multiplex ID          4581
Word Count             1
Parameters            0001
Buffer Count           4
Buffer Type           00 Not          Recognized
ASCII Data
```

```
 Frame: 66      Time: Aug 14@17:05:08.4657250 Length: 178

 SMB
Identifier      SMB
Command Code          25               Transaction Name
Error Class     00                 Success
Reserved        00
Error Code      0000                   Success
Flags            00000000              Good
 Response Request     0.......         Request
 Client Notification .0......     Flag Not Set
 File Lock           ..0.....     Flag Not Set
 Canonical Form       ...0....   Flag Not Set
 Case Sensitive       ....0...   Flag Not Set
 Reserved             .....0..
 Rcv Buffer Posted ......0.         Flag Not Set
 Subdialect           .......0   Flag Not Set
Flags_2              0000
Reserved (Truncated)     00-00-00-00-00-00-00-00-0
Authenticated Resource ID 0000
Callers Process ID          0000
Unauthenticated User ID 0000
Multiplex ID         0000
Word Count             17
Parameters            0000
Parameters            0007
Parameters            0000
Parameters            0000
Parameters (Truncated)   00-02-00-01-00-01-00-03-0
Buffer Count          24
ASCII Data            \MAILSLOT\BROWSE
Buffer Type           0B               Not Recognized
ASCII Data            ANGEL
 Novell NetBios (IPX/SPX)
Connection Control Flag 00
             0.......      Non-System Packet
             .0......      Non Send ACK
```

```
                    ..0.....        Not Attention
                    ...0....        Not End of Message
                    ....0...        No Rsend Needed
Operation                 11          Directed Datagram
Source Name               MUSCLE
Dest Name                 INFO.COM
```

```
 Frame: 67          Time: Aug 14@17:05:09.3228674 Length: 70
 Novell NetBios (IPX/SPX)
Connection Control Flag  C0
                    1.......        System Packet
                    .1......        Send ACK
                    ..0.....        Not Attention
                    ...0....        Not End of Message
                    ....0...        No Rsend Needed
Operation 6                          Session Data
Source Conn ID            4003
Dest Conn ID              200A
Sequence Number           3
Next Expected Seq Number  4
```

```
 Frame: 68       Time: Aug 14@17:05:09.3232387 Length: 70
 Novell NetBios (IPX/SPX)
Connection Control Flag  80
                    1.......        System Packet
                    .0......        Non Send ACK
                    ..0.....        Not Attention
                    ...0....        Not End of Message
                    ....0...        No Rsend Needed
Operation 6                          Session ACK
Source Conn ID            200A
Dest Conn ID              4003
Sequence Number           4
Next Expected Seq Number  3
```

```
 Frame: 70       Time: Aug 14@17:05:10.7701529 Length: 70
 Novell NetBios (IPX/SPX)
Connection Control Flag  C0
                    1.......        System Packet
                    .1......        Send ACK
                    ..0.....        Not Attention
                    ...0....        Not End of Message
                    ....0...        No Rsend Needed
Operation        6          Session Data
Source Conn ID            200A
Dest Conn ID              4003
Sequence Number           4
Next Expected Seq Number  3
```

```
 Frame: 71       Time: Aug 14@17:05:10.7762108 Length: 70
 Novell NetBios (IPX/SPX)
Connection Control Flag  80
                    1.......        System Packet
                    .0......        Non Send ACK
                    ..0.....        Not Attention
                    ...0....        Not End of Message
                    ....0...        No Rsend Needed
Operation        6          Session ACK
Source Conn ID            4003
Dest Conn ID              200A
```

```
Sequence Number           3
Next Expected Seq Number    4
```

```
 Frame: 72      Time: Aug 14@17:05:11.5956237 Length: 64
 NetBIOS (NetBEUI)
Header Length            14
Delimiter                EFFF
Command                  1F          SESSION_ALIVE
Optional Data 1          00          Reserved field
Optional Data 2          0000         Reserved field
Transmit Correlator      0000          Reserved field
Response Correlator      0000           Reserved field
```

```
 Frame: 77      Time: Aug 14@17:05:13.4735985 Length: 97

 SMB
Identifier         SMB
Command Code              71              Tree Disconnect
Error Class       00               Success
Reserved          00
Error Code        0000                Success
Flags        00011000             OK
 Response Request    0.......      Request
 Client Notification .0......    Flag Not Set
 File Lock         ..0.....     Flag Not Set
 Canonical Form      ...1....  Flag Set
 Case Sensitive      ....1...  Flag Set
 Reserved          .....0..
 Rcv Buffer Posted    ......0 . Flag Not Set
 Subdialect         .......0    Flag Not Set
Flags_2           8003
Reserved (Truncated)    00-00-00-00-00-00-00-00-0
Authenticated Resource ID 0801
Callers Process ID     CAFE
Unauthenticated User ID 0800
Multiplex ID       1B40
Word Count         0
Buffer Count       0
 NetBIOS (TCP/IP)
Service Type :                Session Service
Packet Type  :                Session Message
Type         00
Flags        00             See Bit Fields Below
 Reserved Bits      0000000.
 Length Extension Bit .......0
Length            35
User Data                     SMB Data
```

```
 Frame: 78      Time: Aug 14@17:05:13.4967227 Length: 97

 SMB
Identifier         SMB
Command Code              71              Tree Disconnect
Error Class       00               Success
Reserved          00
Error Code        0000                Success
Flags        10011000             OK
 Response Request     1.......      Response
 Client Notification  .0......   Flag Not Set
 File Lock            .0.....   Flag Not Set
```

```
Canonical Form             ...1....    Flag Set
Case Sensitive             ....1...    Flag Set
Reserved                   .....0..
Rcv Buffer Posted          ......0.  Flag Not Set
Subdialect                 .......0    Flag Not Set
Flags_2              8003
Reserved (Truncated)     00-00-00-00-00-00-00-00-0
Authenticated Resource ID  0801
Callers Process ID     CAFE
Unauthenticated User ID  0800
Multiplex ID         1B40
Word Count              0
Buffer Count            0
 NetBIOS (TCP/IP)
Service Type :                  Session Service
Packet Type  :                  Session Message
Type            00
Flags           00              See Bit Fields Below
 Reserved Bits        0000000.
 Length Extension Bit .......0
Length          35
User Data                       SMB Data
```

```
Frame: 79      Time: Aug 14@17:05:13.4971788 Length: 101

 SMB
Identifier       SMB
Command Code        74              User Logoff And X
Error Class      00              Success
Reserved         00
Error Code       0000              Success
Flags          00011000          OK
 Response Request    0.......      Request
 Client Notification .0......    Flag Not Set
 File Lock      ..0.....    Flag Not Set
 Canonical Form     ...1....      Flag Set
 Case Sensitive     ....1...      Flag Set
 Reserved       .....0..
 Rcv Buffer Posted      ......0.   Flag Not Set
 Subdialect         .......0    Flag Not Set
Flags_2          8003
Reserved (Truncated)    00-00-00-00-00-00-00-00-0
Authenticated Resource ID   0801
Callers Process ID     CAFE
Unauthenticated User ID  0800
Multiplex ID         1B80
Word Count              2
Parameters           00FF
Parameters           FFFF
Buffer Count            0
 NetBIOS (TCP/IP)
Service Type :                  Session Service
Packet Type  :                  Session Message
Type            00
Flags           00              See Bit Fields Below
 Reserved Bits        0000000.
 Length Extension Bit .......0
Length          39
User Data                       SMB Data
```

Frame: 80   Time: Aug 14@17:05:13.4977581 Length: 101

```
SMB
Identifier           SMB
Command Code              74                User Logoff And X
Error Class          00                 Success
Reserved             00
Error Code           0000                   Success
Flags                10011000            OK
 Response Request        1.......        Response
 Client Notification  .0......      Flag Not Set
 File Lock            ..0.....      Flag Not Set
 Canonical Form          ...1....   Flag Set
 Case Sensitive          ....1...   Flag Set
 Reserved                .....0..
 Rcv Buffer Posted          ......0.  Flag Not Set
 Subdialect                 .......0  Flag Not Set
Flags_2              8003
Reserved (Truncated)      00-00-00-00-00-00-00-00-0
Authenticated Resource ID    0801
Callers Process ID     CAFE
Unauthenticated User ID  0800
Multiplex ID           1B80
Word Count              2
Parameters             00FF
Parameters             0027
Buffer Count           0
 NetBIOS (TCP/IP)
Service Type :                    Session Service
Packet Type  :                    Session Message
Type                 00
Flags                00             See Bit Fields Below
 Reserved Bits          0000000.
 Length Extension Bit .......0
Length               39
User Data                           SMB Data
```

Frame: 81   Time: Aug 14@17:05:13.4981454 Length: 101

```
SMB
Identifier           SMB
Command Code              74                User Logoff And X
Error Class          00                 Success
Reserved             00
Error Code           0000                   Success
Flags                00011000            OK
 Response Request     0.......        Request
 Client Notification .0......      Flag Not Set
 File Lock            ..0.....      Flag Not Set
 Canonical Form          ...1....   Flag Set
 Case Sensitive          ....1...   Flag Set
 Reserved                .....0..
 Rcv Buffer Posted          ......0.  Flag Not Set
 Subdialect                 .......0  Flag Not Set
Flags_2              8003
Reserved (Truncated)      00-00-00-00-00-00-00-00-0
Authenticated Resource ID  0801
Callers Process ID     CAFE
Unauthenticated User ID  0801
Multiplex ID           1BC0
```

```
Word Count              2
Parameters              00FF
Parameters              FFFF
Buffer Count            0
 NetBIOS (TCP/IP)
Service Type :                      Session Service
Packet Type  :                      Session Message
Type            00
Flags           00                  See Bit Fields Below
 Reserved Bits          0000000.
 Length Extension Bit .......0
Length          39
User Data                           SMB Data
```

```
 Frame: 82       Time: Aug 14@17:05:13.4984095 Length: 101

 SMB
Identifier      SMB
Command Code            74                  User Logoff And X
Error Class     00                  Success
Reserved        00
Error Code      0000                    Success
Flags           10011000                OK
 Response Request       1.......        Response
 Client Notification  .0......    Flag Not Set
 File Lock          ..0.....    Flag Not Set
 Canonical Form       ...1....    Flag Set
 Case Sensitive       ....1...  Flag Set
 Reserved           .....0..
 Rcv Buffer Posted      ......0. Flag Not Set
 Subdialect           .......0    Flag Not Set
Flags_2         8003
Reserved (Truncated)    00-00-00-00-00-00-00-00-0
Authenticated Resource ID 0801
Callers Process ID    CAFE
Unauthenticated User ID  0801
Multiplex ID    1BC0
Word Count      2
Parameters      00FF
Parameters      0027
Buffer Count    0
 NetBIOS (TCP/IP)
Service Type :                      Session Service
Packet Type  :                      Session Message
Type            00
Flags           00                  See Bit Fields Below
 Reserved Bits          0000000.
 Length Extension Bit  .......0
Length          39
User Data                           SMB Data
```

```
 Frame: 89       Time: Aug 14@17:05:18.4815128 Length: 97

 SMB
Identifier      SMB
Command Code            71                  Tree Disconnect
Error Class     00                  Success
Reserved        00
Error Code      0000                    Success
Flags           00011000                OK
```

```
Response Request       0.......           Request
Client Notification .0......        Flag Not Set
File Lock            ..0.....      Flag Not Set
Canonical Form         ...1....    Flag Set
Case Sensitive         ....1...   Flag Set
Reserved               .....0..
Rcv Buffer Posted      ......0.  Flag Not Set
Subdialect             .......0  Flag Not Set
Flags_2              8003
Reserved (Truncated)     00-00-00-00-00-00-00-00-0
Authenticated Resource ID  0803
Callers Process ID     CAFE
Unauthenticated User ID 0800
Multiplex ID         4340
Word Count            0
Buffer Count          0
 NetBIOS (TCP/IP)
Service Type :                    Session Service
Packet Type  :                    Session Message
Type                 00
Flags                00           See Bit Fields Below
 Reserved Bits         0000000.
 Length Extension Bit .......0
Length               35
User Data                         SMB Data
```

Frame: 90   Time: Aug 14@17:05:18.4821778 Length: 97

```
 SMB
Identifier          SMB
Command Code            71               Tree Disconnect
Error Class         00            Success
Reserved            00
Error Code          0000             Success
Flags               10011000         OK
 Response Request      1.......         Response
 Client Notification .0......      Flag Not Set
 File Lock           ..0.....     Flag Not Set
 Canonical Form        ...1....     Flag Set
 Case Sensitive        ....1...    Flag Set
 Reserved              .....0..
 Rcv Buffer Posted     ......0.   Flag Not Set
 Subdialect            .......0   Flag Not Set
Flags_2             8003
Reserved (Truncated)     00-00-00-00-00-00-00-00-0
Authenticated Resource ID  0803
Callers Process ID     CAFE
Unauthenticated User ID  0800
Multiplex ID         4340
Word Count            0
Buffer Count          0
 NetBIOS (TCP/IP)
Service Type :                    Session Service
Packet Type  :                    Session Message
Type                 00
Flags                00           See Bit Fields Below
 Reserved Bits         0000000.
 Length Extension Bit .......0
Length               35
User Data                         SMB Data
```

```
Frame: 96         Time: Aug 14@17:05:27.3899747 Length: 245

SMB
Identifier          SMB
Command Code             25              Transaction Name
Error Class         00              Success
Reserved            00
Error Code          0000            Success
Flags               00000000        Good
 Response Request      0.......        Request
 Client Notification .0......     Flag Not Set
 File Lock           ..0.....      Flag Not Set
 Canonical Form      ...0....       Flag Not Set
 Case Sensitive      ....0...       Flag Not Set
 Reserved            .....0..
 Rcv Buffer Posted      ......0. Flag Not Set
 Subdialect          .......0  Flag Not Set
Flags_2             0000
Reserved (Truncated)    00-00-00-00-00-00-00-00-0
Authenticated Resource ID  0000
Callers Process ID     0000
Unauthenticated User ID  0000
Multiplex ID        0000
Word Count          17
Parameters          0000
Parameters          001F
Parameters          0000
Parameters          0000
Parameters (Truncated)    00-02-00-01-00-01-00-03-0
Buffer Count        47
ASCII Data          \MAILSLOT\LANMAN
Buffer Type         01              Server Data Block
ASCII Data          C August 21, 1998 L'LITTLE MAN ED T
ASCII Data          AYLOR
 NetBIOS (TCP/IP)
Service Type :                  Datagram Service
Packet Type  :                  Direct_Group Datagram
Msg_Type            11
Flags           1A              See Bit Fields Below
 Reserved Bits       0001....            Warning: Reserved Bit Not
 Zero
 Source End-Node Type    ....10..        Mixed (M) node
 FIRST Flag          ......1.    First Fragment
 MORE Flag           .......0    Last Fragment
DGM ID              50
Source IP           220.100.100.32    Source IP Address
Source Port         138             Source Port Number
DGM Length          185
Packet Offset       0
Name Length         32
Source Name         LITTLE MAN       NetBIOS Name
Name Length         32
Destination Name    INFO            NetBIOS Name
User Data                       SMB Data - See SMB Decode
```

```
Frame: 101       Time: Aug 14@17:05:33.3457937 Length: 101
 Novell NetBios (IPX/SPX)
Connection Control Flag    10
                0.......         Non-System Packet
                .0......         Non Send ACK
                ..0.....         Not Attention
```

```
            ...1....              End of Message
            ....0...              No Rsend Needed
Operation          1               Find Name
Name Type Flag          00
            0.......              Unique Name
            .0......              Name Not Used
            .....0..              Name Not Registered
            ......0.              Name Not Duplicated
            .......0              Name Not Deregistered
Operation          1               Find Name
Name Claim String       INFO.COM
```

```
 Frame: 102    Time: Aug 14@17:05:33.3460866 Length: 102
 Novell NetBios (IPX/SPX)
Connection Control Flag  00
            0.......              Non-System Packet
            .0......              Non Send ACK
            ..0.....              Not Attention
            ...0....              Not End of Message
            ....0...              No Rsend Needed
Operation          2               Name Recognized
Name Type Flag          44
            0.......              Unique Name
            .1......              Name Used
            .....1..              Name Registered
            ......0.              Name Not Duplicated
            .......0              Name Not Deregistered
Operation          2               Name Recognized
Name Claim String       INFO.COM
```

```
 Frame: 103     Time: Aug 14@17:05:33.3473004 Length: 208

   SMB
Identifier        SMB
Command Code          25              Transaction Name
Error Class       00              Success
Reserved          00
Error Code        0000              Success
Flags         00000000          Good
 Response Request      0.......          Request
 Client Notification .0......       Flag Not Set
 File Lock        ..0.....      Flag Not Set
 Canonical Form      ...0....       Flag Not Set
 Case Sensitive      ....0...      Flag Not Set
 Reserved        .....0..
 Rcv Buffer Posted     ......0.      Flag Not Set
 Subdialect       .......0      Flag Not Set
Flags_2          0000
Reserved (Truncated)  00-00-00-00-00-00-00-00-0
Authenticated Resource ID 0000
Callers Process ID    0000
Unauthenticated User ID  0000
Multiplex ID      0000
Word Count        17
Parameters        0000
Parameters        0025
Parameters        0000
Parameters        0000
Parameters (Truncated)  00-02-00-01-00-01-00-03-0
Buffer Count      54
```

```
ASCII Data              \MAILSLOT\BROWSE
Buffer Type             01              Server Data Block
ASCII Data              9L' MONY
ASCII Data              "@ August 21, 1998U_MONY
 Novell NetBios (IPX/SPX)
Connection Control Flag 10
                  0.......          Non-System Packet
                  .0......          Non Send ACK
                  ..0.....          Not Attention
                  ...1....          End of Message
                  ....0...          No Rsend Needed
Operation               11              Directed Datagram
Source Name             MONY
Dest Name               INFO.COM
```

```
 Frame: 104         Time: Aug 14@17:05:33.5055198 Length: 97

 SMB
Identifier              SMB
Command Code            71              Tree Disconnect
Error Class             00              Success
Reserved                00
Error Code              0000            Success
Flags                   00011000        OK
 Response Request       0.......        Request
 Client Notification .0......           Flag Not Set
 File Lock          ..0.....         Flag Not Set
 Canonical Form        ...1....      Flag Set
 Case Sensitive        ....1...   Flag Set
 Reserved              .....0..
 Rcv Buffer Posted     ......0. Flag Not Set
 Subdialect            .......0 Flag Not Set
Flags_2                 8003
Reserved (Truncated)    00-00-00-00-00-00-00-00-0
Authenticated Resource ID 0801
Callers Process ID      CAFE
Unauthenticated User ID  0800
Multiplex ID            4380
Word Count              0
Buffer Count            0
 NetBIOS (TCP/IP)
Service Type :                  Session Service
Packet Type  :                  Session Message
Type            00
Flags           00              See Bit Fields Below
 Reserved Bits          0000000.
 Length Extension Bit .......0
Length          35
User Data                       SMB Data -
```

```
 Frame: 105         Time: Aug 14@17:05:33.5063735 Length: 97

 SMB
Identifier              SMB
Command Code            71              Tree Disconnect
Error Class             00              Success
Reserved                00
Error Code              0000            Success
Flags                   10011000        OK
 Response Request       1.......        Response
```

```
Client Notification .0......      Flag Not Set
File Lock        ..0.....     Flag Not Set
Canonical Form      ...1....      Flag Set
Case Sensitive      ....1...      Flag Set
Reserved        .....0..
Rcv Buffer Posted      ......0.    Flag Not Set
Subdialect       .......0     Flag Not Set
Flags_2        8003
Reserved (Truncated)   00-00-00-00-00-00-00-00-0
Authenticated Resource ID  0801
Callers Process ID     CAFE
Unauthenticated User ID  0800
Multiplex ID       4380
Word Count          0
Buffer Count         0
 NetBIOS (TCP/IP)
Service Type :            Session Service
Packet Type  :            Session Message
Type          00
Flags         00        See Bit Fields Below
 Reserved Bits        0000000.
 Length Extension Bit  .......0
Length           35
User Data             SMB Data -
```

9.5 Summary

This chapter presented some baseline information for components in my network. This information was intended as a sample of the information you should consider keeping on hand in your network. Your network may vary and require additional details far beyond those presented here. Determine what information would be helpful for troubleshooting your network should problems occur, then obtain this information, record it, and keep it readily accessible.

ADSL Technology

The information presented in this chapter is provided by the ADSL Forum. With the exception of Section 10.13 (Summary), each section of this chapter contains, and is identical in content to, a complete ADSL Forum technical report. The presentation of this material has been changed to fit the format and style of this book. The permission and copyright information related to this information is given at the end of this chapter, in Section 10.13.

As you read this chapter, consider each section as a standalone document. The information presented in this chapter is among the best and most comprehensive I have encountered in the marketplace about ADSL.

10.1 Overall Network and ADSL

The ADSL Forum develops technical guidelines for architectures, interfaces, and protocols for telecommunications networks incorporating ADSL transceivers. The overall network diagram shown in Figure 10.1 describes the network elements incorporated in multimedia communications, shows the scope of the Forum's work, and suggests a group of transport configurations that ADSL will encounter as networks migrate from Synchronous Transfer Mode (STM) to Asynchronous Transfer Mode (ATM). Acronyms used in Figure 10.1 are as follows:

ADSL	Asymmetric digital subscriber line
ATM	Asynchronous Transfer Mode
OS	Operations System
PDN	Premises distribution network reference point definitions
SM	Service module
STM	Synchronous Transfer Mode
TE	Terminal equipment

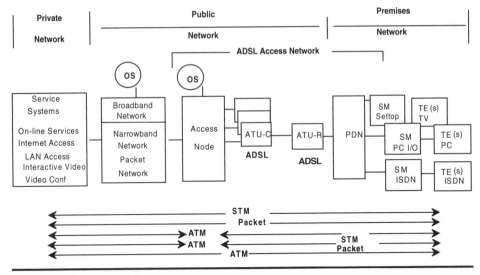

Figure 10.1 Transport Modes

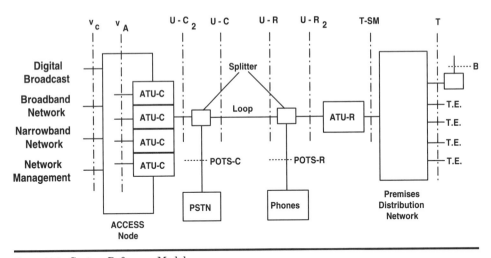

Figure 10.2 System Reference Model

10.2   System Reference Model and Terminology

Figure 10.2 presents an ADSL system reference model. The following terms should be used for interpretation of Figure 10.2.

ATU-C ADSL transmission unit at the network end. The ATU-C may be integrated within an Access Node.

ATU-R ADSL transmission unit at the customer premises end. The ATU-R may be integrated within a SM.

access node Concentration point for broadband and narrowband data. The Access Node may be located at a central office or a remote site. Also, a remote Access Node may subtend from a central access node.

B Auxiliary data input (such as a satellite feed) to a service module (such as a set top box).

broadcast Broadband data input in simplex mode (typically broadcast video).

broadband network Switching system for data rates above 1.5/2.0 Mbps.

loop Twisted-pair copper telephone line. Loops may differ in distance, diameter, age, and transmission characteristics depending on network.

narrowband network Switching system for data rates at or below 1.5/2.0 Mbps.

PDN Premises distribution network: system for connecting ATU-R to service modules. May be point-to-point or multipoint; may be passive wiring or an active network. Multipoint may be a bus or a star.

POTS Plain Old Telephone Service.

POTS-C Interface between PSTN and POTS splitter at network end.

POTS-R Interface between phones and POTS splitter at premises end.

PSTN Public Switched Telephone Network.

SM Service module; performs terminal adaptation functions. Examples are set top boxes, PC interfaces, or LAN router.

splitter Filters which separate high-frequency (ADSL) and low-frequency (POTS) signals at network end and premises end. The splitter may be integrated into the ATU, physically separated from the ATU, or divided between high-pass and low-pass, with the low-pass function physically separated from the ATU. The provision of POTS splitters and POTS-related function is optional.

T Interface between premises distribution network and service modules. May be same as T-SM when network is point-to-point passive wiring. Note that T interface may disappear at the physical level when ATU-R is integrated within a service module.

T-SM Interface between ATU-R and premises distribution network. May be same as T when network is point-to-point passive wiring. An ATU-R may have more than one type of T-SM interface implemented (e.g., a T1/E1 connection and an Ethernet connection). The T-SM interface may be integrated within a service module.

U-C Interface between loop and POTS splitter on the network side. Defining both ends of the loop interface separately arises because of the asymmetry of the signals on the line.

U-C$_2$ Interface between POTS splitter and ATU-C. Note that at present ANSI T1.413 does not define such an interface and separating the POTS splitter from the ATU-C presents some technical difficulties in standardizing this interface.

U-R Interface between loop and POTS splitter on the premises side.

U-R$_2$ Interface between POTS splitter and ATU-R. Note that at present ANSI T1.413

does not define such an interface and separating the POTS splitter from the ATU-R presents some technical difficulties in standardizing the interface.

V$_A$ Logical interface between ATU-C and access node. As this interface will often be within circuits on a common board, the ADSL Forum does not consider physical V$_A$ interfaces. The V interface may contain STM, ATM, or both transfer modes. In the primitive case of point-to-point connection between a switch port and an ATU-C (that is, a case without concentration or multiplexing), then the V$_A$ and V$_C$ interfaces become identical (alternatively, the V$_A$ interface disappears).

V$_C$ Interface between access node and network. May have multiple physical connections (as shown in Figure 10.2) although may also carry all signals across a single physical connection. A digital carrier facility (e.g., a SONET or SDH extension) may be interposed at the V$_C$ interface when the access node and ATU-Cs are located at a remote site. Interface to the PSTN may be a universal tip-ring interface or a multiplexed telephony interface such as specified in Bellcore TR-08 or TR-303, ITU-T G.964, or ETSI 300 324. The broadband segment of the V$_C$ interface may be STM switching, ATM switching, or private-line-type connections.

10.3   ATM over ADSL Recommendation

This section presents the technical report that addresses implementation aspects specific to the transport of ATM over access networks based on asymmetric digital subscriber line (ADSL) technology. Later in this section (under the heading "References related to ATM over ADSL recommendations") a list of reference material is included that correlates to the reference numbers throughout the text in this section. The scope for the first issue of the report is to provide a specification for the transport of ATM over ADSL that is consistent with the ANSI T1.413 standard 1995 [2]. Future issues of this technical report will seek to preserve backward compatibility with this document. The report aims to provide comprehensive guidelines for the selection of bearer channels for the transport of ATM and to provide clear interpretations of the pertinent sections of the ANSI T1.413 standard [2]. Future issues of this specification will address the generic (line-code-independent) requirements on the ATM-TC to ATM layer interface. As the ADSL Forum is line-code-neutral, TC variations required for other specific line codes will be addressed in future versions of this document.

This specification provides a detailed transmission convergence (TC) sublayer specification that can be used with the ANSI T1.413 standard 1995 [2], and provides outline descriptions of the access node and network-termination (NT) functions. In later issues, effort will be made to provide more detailed functional descriptions. This report concentrates on ATM network layer protocols up to the ATM layer; higher layers are considered to be transported transparently by the ADSL-based access network. Interfaces toward both the local exchange and the premises distribution network are covered. All configurable parameters and a means for managing their configuration are defined.

This report intends to describe the functional blocks of the ADSL-based

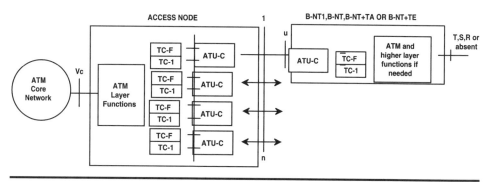

Figure 10.3 Reference Model of ATM Mode

access network from the V_C interface to the T (or other) interface, and not to specify the physical level of the interfaces. Figure 10.3 should be used as a reference to that end. Figure 10.3 is a specific reference model for ATM mode. Although Figure 10.3 shows two paths (fast and interleaved), it is mandatory to implement only a single path. Dual latency is strictly optional. The functional groups broadband NT1, B-NT, B-NT + TA, and B-NT + TE and the reference points T, S, and R are defined in ITU-T recommendation I.413, B-ISDN, *User-Network Interface* [9].

Functional block definitions

ACCESS NODE: An *access node* performs the adaptation between the ATM core network and the access network. In the downstream direction it may perform routing/demultiplexing, while in the upstream direction it may perform multiplexing and/or concentration.

B-NT1, B-NT, B-NT + TA OR B-NT + TE: This functional block performs the functions of terminating the ADSL signal entering the users premises via the twisted pair cable and providing either the T, S, or R interface toward the terminal equipment. Such an interface may be absent in the case of integration of the functional block with the terminal equipment. Its functions are terminating/originating the transmission line, handling the transmission interfacing, and OAM functions (operations, administration, and maintenance). In addition, it may optionally include routing/multiplexing of the fast and interleaved flows.

ATM layer functions

In the access node this function performs in the downstream direction routing/demultiplexing on a VPI (virtual path identifier) and/or VCI (virtual channel identifier) basis, while in the upstream direction multiplexing/concentration, again on a VPI and/or VCI basis. If implemented in the B-NT1, B-NT, B-NT + TA, or B-NT + TE, this function performs cell routing/(de)multiplexing to the fast or interleaved channel in the upstream direction and routing/(de)multiplexing of the two flows into a single ATM stream per T interface instantiation in the downstream direction.

ATU-C   ADSL transceiver unit at the central office end.

ATU-R   ADSL transceiver unit at the remote terminal end.

TC   ATM transmission convergence sublayer functional block.

Transport of ATM over ADSL

Transport classes and bearer channel rates based on multiples of 1.536 Mbps are considered to be inappropriate for the transport of ATM. Reference to the ANSI T1.413 standard [2] is superseded by the information in this section. For the transport of ATM on modems compliant with ANSI T1.413 standard, channels shall be independently set to any bit rate that is an integer multiple of 32 kbps, up to a maximum aggregate capacity determined by the start-up process. In addition, for each channel the bit rates for the upstream and downstream directions may be set independently from each other.

Channelization

For ATM systems the channelization of different payloads is embedded within the ATM data stream using different virtual paths and/or virtual channels. Hence, the basic requirements for ATM are for at least one ADSL channel downstream and at least one ADSL upstream channel.

The ANSI T1.413 standard [2] gives the possibility to use both the Interleaved and Fast paths for services with requirements for either high error performance or low latency, respectively. The real need for this dual nature for ATM services depends on the service/application profile, and is yet to be confirmed. Consequently, different configurations of the ADSL access could be considered. More specifically, possibly three latency classes could be envisaged:

1. Single latency, not necessarily the same for each direction of transmission

2. Dual latency downstream, single latency upstream

3. Dual latency both upstream and downstream

For the transport of only ATM over ADSL, all modems shall use the AS0 channel downstream and the LS0 channel upstream for the single latency class. Channels AS1 and LS1 are reserved for dual latency.

A hybrid implementation of one or more bit synchronous (plesiochronous) channels together with the ATM channels is not precluded by the above. The bandwidth occupied by the bit synchronous channel must first be reserved before allocating the remaining bandwidth to the ATM channel.

In accordance with the channel allocation above, it is mandatory for compliance with these recommendations to implement at least one single path, either via the fast buffer or the interleaved buffer.

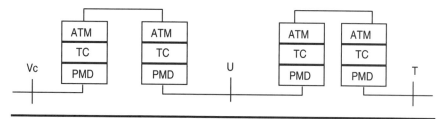

Figure 10.4   Protocol Layers

Protocols

With respect to the protocol reference model for B-ISDN [5], only the physical-medium-dependent (PMD) and transmission convergence (TC) sublayers of the physical layer and the ATM layer are relevant to this report. Figure 10.4 shows the protocol layers for the specific reference model given in Figure 10.3. In Figure 10.4, T interface supports ATM. Non-ATM interfaces are also possible, but not discussed in this report.

Quality of service (QOS)

Data rates.   Modems compliant with ANSI T1.413 standard can be programmed to provide bearer channel data rates which are multiples of 32 kbps. This facility may be exploited for the transport of ATM. Channel data rates can be set on a semipermanent basis depending on the loop characteristics for the particular user. Complete flexibility is therefore given to the network operator.

Bit error rate (BER).   ANSI T1.413 standard [2] specifies a BER of 10:7 with a 6-dB margin. The network operator may decide on a BER/latency/range combination that meets the required service quality for the network. The effect of ADSL performance impairments on ATM performance is for further study.

System issues.   For a future issue of the document.

Description of functional blocks: access node ATM layer functions.   In the downstream direction this block performs cell routing on a VPI and/or VCI basis to the appropriate ADSL modem and optionally to the fast or interleaved TC sublayer of that modem. In the upstream direction the cell streams are combined and/or concentrated to form a single ATM cell stream.

Transmission convergence (TC): access node TC.   The ATM transmission convergence sublayer is based on ITU-T recommendation I.432 [3]. There is no specific relationship between the beginning of an ATM cell and the ADSL frame. The transmitter can transmit the cell octets aligned to any bit in the ADSL octets. The receiver shall assume no alignment between ATM cell octets and the ADSL octets. The functions are described in the following subsections. The transmission order of the bits is as shown in I.432 [3] for SDH; that is, the most significant bit (MSB) of each byte is sent first.

Header error control

Header error control functions. The *header error control* (HEC) covers the entire cell header. The code used for this function is capable of either (1) single bit error correction or (2) multiple bit error detection.

Error detection shall be implemented as defined in ITU-T recommendation I.432 [3] with the exception that any HEC error may be considered as a multiple bit error, and therefore HEC error correction shall not be performed.

Header error control sequence generation. The HEC byte shall be generated as described in ITU-T recommendation I.432 [3] including the recommended modulo 2 addition [exclusive OR (XOR)] of the pattern 01010101 to the HEC bits.

The generator polynomial coefficient set used and the HEC sequence generation procedure shall be in accordance with recommendation I.432 [3].

Idle cells. Idle cells shall be inserted and discarded for cell rate decoupling. Idle cells are identified by the standardized pattern for the cell header given in recommendation I.432 [3].

The ATM layer may also perform cell rate decoupling by inserting and discarding unassigned cells. All implementations shall therefore be capable of receiving and discarding both idle cells (in the physical layer) and unassigned cells (in the ATM layer).

Cell delineation. The cell delineation function permits the identification of cell boundaries in the payload. It uses the HEC field in the cell header.

Cell delineation shall be performed using the HEC-based algorithm described in ITU-T recommendation I.432 [3].

With reference to I.432 [3], the ADSL Forum makes no recommendation for the values of a and d as the choice of these values is not considered to affect interoperability. However, it should be noted that the use of the values suggested in I.432 could be inappropriate due to the particular transmission characteristics of ADSL.

Cell payload scrambling. Scrambling of the cell payload field shall be used to improve the security and robustness of the HEC cell delineation mechanism. In addition, it randomizes the data in the information field, for possible improvement of the transmission performance. The self-synchronizing scrambler polynomial $X43 + 1$ and procedures defined in ITU-T recommendation I.432 [3] shall be implemented.

[B-NT1, B-NT, B-NT + TA or B-NT + TE] TC. The functions of the TC block will be as those described in the valuable information about access nodes.

ATM and higher-layer functions block [B-NT1, B-NT + TA or B-NT + TE]. If implemented, in the downstream direction this block combines the cell streams from the fast and interleaved buffers into a single ATM cell stream. In the upstream direction cell routing is performed on a VPI and/or VCI basis to the fast or interleaved TC sublayers.

Management.   Non-ATM-specific OAM issues are for further study.

Network management across the V interface.   For further study.

Operation, administration, and maintenance (OAM)

Physical Layer OAM functions.   Modems compliant with ANSI T1.413 standard shall perform all OAM functions described in that standard. Further OAM functions specific to ATM (described in ITU-T recommendations I.432 [3] and I.610 [4]) will be performed. LCD indication is derived from a HEC-based cell delineation function. In particular, at the ATU-R the downstream LCD (loss of cell delineation) defect (for the interleaved and fast path separately) shall be detected and backward reported to the ATU-C, via the indicator bits 14 and 15 in modems compliant to ANSI T1.413 standard, as listed in Figure 10.5. The LCD-i (interleaved path) and LCD-ni (fast path) defects are mapped into the reserved indicator bits according to the information as presented in Figure 10.5.

References related to ATM over ADSL recommendations

[1] ADSL Forum reference model, Figure 10.1.

[2] ANS, *Network and Customer Installation Interfaces—Asymmetric Digital Subscriber Line* (ADSL) *Metallic Interface,* T1.413-1995.

[3] ITU-T Recommendation I.432—B-ISDN, *UNI Physical Layer Specification.*

[4] ITU-T Recommendation I.610—B-ISDN, *Operation and Maintenance Principles and Functions.*

[5] ITU-T Recommendation I.321—B-ISDN, *Protocol Reference Model and Its Application.*

[6] ITU-T Recommendation I.361—B-ISDN, *ATM Layer Specification.*

Bit 14	Bit 15	Interpretation
1	1	notLCD-i and notLCD-ni
1	0	notLCD-i and LCD-ni
0	1	LCD-i and notLCD-ni
0	0	LCD-i and LCD-ni

Figure 10.5   Interleaved and Fast Paths Mapped into the Reserved Indicator Bits

[7] ETSI Technical Report, ETR 328, *Transmission and Multiplexing—ADSL Requirements and Performance.*

[8] ITU-T Recommendation I.432.5—B-ISDN, *User-Network Interface Physical Layer for 25600 KBIT/S.*

[9] ITU-T Recommendation I.413—B-ISDN, *User-Network Interface.*

Terms used in ATM over ADSL recommendation

access node   Performs adaptation between the core network and the access network.

ADSL   Asymmetric digital subscriber line.

ANSI   American National Standards Institute.

AS0–3   Downstream simplex subchannel designators.

ATM   Asynchronous Transfer Mode.

ATU-C   ADSL transceiver unit, central office end.

ATU-R   ADSL transceiver unit, remote terminal end.

BER   Bit error rate.

B-ISDN   Broadband ISDN (Broadband Integrated Services Digital Network).

DAVIC   Digital Audio-Visual Council.

ETSI   European Telecommunications Standards Institute.

FTTC   Fiber to the curb.

FTTH   Fiber to the home.

HAN   Home ATM network.

HEC   ATM cell header error control.

HFC   Hybrid fiber coaxial.

ISDN   Integrated Services Digital Network.

ITU-T   International Telecommunications Union—Telecommunications.

LCD   Loss of cell delineation.

LS0–3   Duplex subchannel designators.

NT   Network termination.

B-NT1   B-ISDN network termination type 1.

OAM   Operation, administration, and maintenance.

PC   Personal computer.

PDN   Premises distribution network. System for connecting the B-NT1 to the service modules.

PHY   ATM physical-layer function.

PMD   ATM physical-medium-dependent sublayer.

QoS Quality of service.

RBB (ATM Forum) Residential Broadband (Working Group).

SM Service module; performs terminal adaptation functions.

STB Set top box.

TA Terminal adapter.

TC ATM transmission convergence sublayer.

TE Terminal equipment.

UNI User-network interface.

V_A Logical interface between ATU-C and access node.

V_C Interface between access node and network.

VDSL Very high speed Digital Subscriber Line.

VCI Virtual channel identifier. Identification number for the (logical) connection hierarchy channel (virtual channel) in B-ISDN networks.

VPI Virtual path identifier. Identification number for the (logical) connection hierarchy path (virtual path) in B-ISDN networks.

ATM/ADSL recommendation in relation to reference models

ATM Forum. The ATM Forum Residential Broadband (RBB) Group is defining a complete end-to-end ATM system both to and from the home and within the home, to a variety of devices, for example, STB, PC, and other home devices. The ATM Forum RBB group has produced a baseline text.

ADSL, together with other technologies such as HFC, FTTC, FTTH, and VDSL, has been accepted as one of the methods to connect an ATM access network to the Home ATM Network (HAN).

DAVIC. The pertinent parts of the DAVIC 1.0 specification [7] are as follows:

Part 2: System reference models and scenarios

Part 4: Delivery system architectures and APIs

Part 8: Lower-layer protocols and physical interfaces

Part 4 of the DAVIC 1.0 specification [7] gives two options for the placement of the ADSL modem at the customer premises; inside the NT, resulting in an access network architecture with an active NT; or located in the set top box, resulting in an access network architecture with a passive NT. These two architectures are shown in Figures 10.6 and 10.7.

Figure 10.6 illustrates a DAVIC ADSL access network with active NT. Figure 10.7 is a different example of DAVIC ADSL. Note the difference between Figures 10.6 and 10.7. Figure 10.7 shows the DAVIC ADSL access network with passive NT.

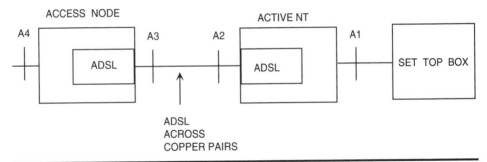

Figure 10.6 DAVIC ADSL Access Network with Active NT

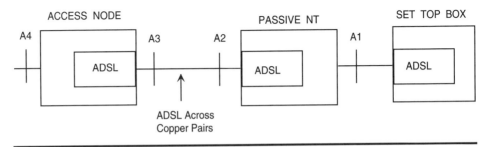

Figure 10.7 DAVIC ADSL Access Network with Passive NT

DAVIC is not concerned with the specification of the A2 and A3 interfaces; therefore, for the case of an access network with active NT, the ADSL signals are not specified. However, in the case of a passive NT, the medium and the protocols at reference points A1, A2, and A3 are equal. In this scenario ADSL signals are specified as they cross the A1 reference point.

Relevant standards and known work in other standards groups or forums
ANSI T1.413 1995

ETSI TM6: The ETSI Technical Report ETR 328, *Transmission and Multiplexing—ADSL Requirements and Performance,* covers primarily performance issues related to particular European specific reference loops, noise models, and transport rate options. This document supersedes sections of ETR 328 with regard to transport rates and bearer channel allocations.

ATM Forum: Most of the work of ATM Forum concerning ADSL is done by the RBB group. In the ATM Forum ADSL is seen as one of the possible physical interfaces between the ATM access network and HAN. System aspects of ATM over ADSL are being addressed.

DAVIC: It is DAVIC's belief that "it would be very beneficial to both DAVIC and ADSL Forum to exchange information and views about matters of common interest, to seek consensus and possibly to co-ordinate respective actions" (quoted from a recent letter from DAVIC's president to ADSL Forum's president). DAVIC's present status related to ADSL is as follows: DAVIC 1.2 Part 8 contains a section on "long range baseband asymmetric PHY [physical layer] on copper," pointing to the ADSL Forum WT-006-R7. This pointer was included after finalizing the Cell-Specific TC Sublayer specification through an intense liaison with the ADSL Forum. DAVIC requested to be informed of further releases and/or updates of the ATM over ADSL Working text.

10.4   ADSL Framing and Encapsulation Standards: Packet Mode

This section presents the technical report describing the framing and encapsulation standards for variable length frames transported over ADSL technology. Herein is a method for transferring variable-length layer 2 frames and/or layer 3 packets over an ADSL link. This section describes the framing mechanisms and protocol encapsulation capabilities required to provide a transmission facility over ADSL links regardless of transmission layer line code. This is one document in a series of ADSL Forum technical reports that address transferring variable-length frames over an ADSL link. Future documents in this specification series will describe implementation specifics for different physical layers signaling management requirements or other features required to ensure multivendor interoperability for these ADSL links. This specification makes no recommendations or requirements for the wide area network interface between the ATU-C and the Network Service Provider.

The specification here relies heavily on existing standards, defined by the ISO, ITU-T, ATM Forum, and IETF standards bodies, applying them with only minimal modification to the transport of data-link layer frames over ADSL links. In particular, it defines two allowable operating modes:

- PPP in HDLC-like frames (RFC 1662 mode)
- ATM Frame UNI (FUNI) frames (FUNI mode)

For this specification, the ADSL physical layer is viewed as simply a point-to-point bit stream provider. The ADSL Forum reference model, a reference diagram for this specification, and some critical terminology are presented below (see Figure 10.8).

ADSL Forum Reference Model

Several topics presented later in this section describe features of this specification by referring to the ADSL Forum's reference model, shown in Figure 10.8.

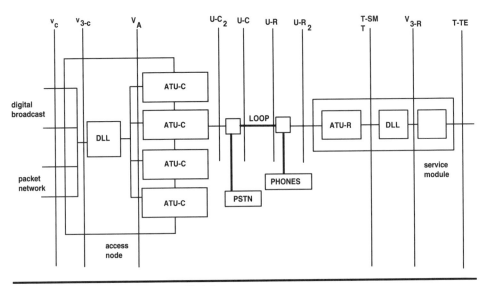

Figure 10.8   ADSL Forum Reference Model

Packet-mode reference diagram

This document uses some additional terms to describe the service points and administrative domains that play a role in this specification. In particular, the document separates the concept of network access from network service. A network access provider (NAP) is the administrative entity that terminates the central office end of an ADSL line. The network service provider (NSP) is the administrative entity that provides access to higher-level network services. Examples of network service providers are Internet service providers or corporate offices providing network services to a remote office or telecommuter. Note that the NAP and NSP might be in the same administrative domain, but need not be. For example, an operator could provide both ADSL service and Internet Access. The NAP and NSP are defined separately in this document to clarify the roles that each play in an end-to-end service scenario. Figure 10.9 shows these entities. Figure 10.9 shows the ADSL packet-mode reference diagram used in this section and in the recommendation.

Terminology of requirements

In this document, several terms are used to signify the requirements of the specification. These words are often capitalized. (They appear in lowercase italics in other chapters of this book, i.e., *Network Troubleshooting Handbook: must, must not, should,* and *may.*)

MUST: This word, or the adjective required, means that the definition is an absolute requirement of the specification.

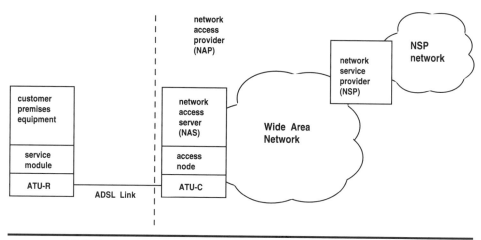

Figure 10.9 ADSL Packet-Mode Reference Diagram

MUST NOT: This phrase means that the definition is an absolute prohibition of the specification.

SHOULD: This word, or the adjective recommended, means that there may exist valid reasons in particular circumstances to ignore this item, but that the full implications must be understood and carefully weighed before choosing a different course.

MAY: This word, or the adjective optional, means that this item is one of an allowed set of alternatives. An implementation that does not include this option MUST be prepared to interoperate with another implementation that does include the option.

ATM adaptation layer 5 terms and acronyms

access node   Concentration point for broadband and narrowband data

ADSL   Asymmetric digital subscriber line

ANSI   American National Standards Institute

ATM   Asynchronous Transfer Mode

ATU-C   ADSL terminal unit—central office

ATU-R   ADSL terminal unit—remote location

CLP   Cell loss priority

CN   Congestion notification

CPE   Customer premise equipment

CRC   Cyclical redundancy check

FCS   Frame-check sequence

frames   Layer 2 (data-link layer) information bundles

FUNI   Frame User Network Interface (ATM Forum specification)

HDLC   High-level data-link control

IETF   Internet Engineering Task Force

ILMI   Integrated Local Management Interface

IPCP   Internet Protocol Control Protocol

ISO   International Organization for Standardization

ITU-T   International Telecommunications Union—Telecommunications Standardization Section (formerly CCITT)

LAN   Local area network

LAPD   Link Access Protocol D (HDLC derivative for ISDN)

LLC   Logical link control

NAP   Network access provider (administrative entity for ATU-C equipment)

NSP   Network service provider (not necessarily the Internet; could be other protocols or other IP-based networks)

OAM   Operation, administration, and maintenance

OUI/PID   Organizationally unique identifier/protocol identifier packets—layer 3 (network layer) information bundles

PDU   Protocol data unit

POP   Point of presence

PPP   Point-to-Point Protocol

PSTN   Public Switched Telephone Network

PTT   Postal Telephone and Telegraph

PUC   Public Utilities Commission

PVC   Permanent virtual circuit

RBOC   Regional Bell Operating Company (Baby Bell)

RFC   Request for Comments (or Change)

SDU   Service data unit

SNAP   Subnetwork access point

SVC   Switched virtual circuit

UNI   User-to-network interface

VPI/VCI   Virtual path identifier/virtual connection identifier

RFC 1662 mode

The information here describes one of two operating modes allowed under this standard for transporting variable-length frames between an ATU-R and

ATU-C over the ADSL link (across the U interface in the ADSL Forum reference diagram, i.e., Figure 10.9). This operating mode leverages existing implementations of the Point-to-Point Protocol (PPP) by following, exactly, the Internet Engineering Task Force Request for Comments (IETF RFC) document RFC 1662 PPP in HDLC-like framing.

PPP in HDLC-like framing

Implementations operating in this mode MUST conform to RFC 1662, specifically following the recommendations for bit-synchronous links and ignoring specifications for asynchronous and octet-synchronous links. There are several references in RFC 1662 to ISO 3309, the standard for HDLC frame structure; implementers may refer to that ISO document for clarification, but where there are differences, implementations over the ADSL facility MUST follow RFC 1662. Figure 10.10 shows the format of packets transported using this operating mode.

PPP encapsulation. Data encapsulation within RFC 1662 framing is described in many other RFCs that provide a rich system for transporting

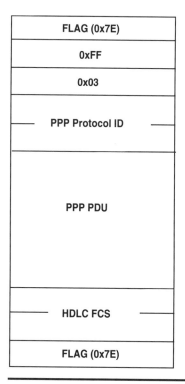

Figure 10.10   FRC 1662 Frame PPP Format

multiprotocol data over point-to-point links. In particular, implementers are referred to the following RFCs as examples of the supporting IETF standards documents:

RFC 1661   *The Point-to-Point Protocol*

RFC 1332   *The PPP Internet Protocol Control Protocol (IPCP)*

Additional RFCs extend PPP for other protocols, bridging, encryption, compression, and authentication. All such implementations that are valid over RFC 1662 are valid over an ADSL facility implementing this PPP operating mode with the following exception. Later in this section a compliant implementation is explained that enables a switch between operation in RFC 1662 mode and FUNI mode operation.

Frame User Network Interface (FUNI) mode

The second allowed operating mode for standard-compliant implementations is based on the FUNI specifications from the ATM Forum. In particular, ADSL end points transmitting variable-length frames or packets across the U interface MUST implement the FUNI variant described in this specification when operating in this FUNI mode. Currently, the only FUNI features specified by this document are basic frame structure and encapsulation methods. Other features such as ILMI and OAM support are under study for future technical reports in this series.

FUNI Framing ATM Frame UNI (currently under revision to version 2, defined in ATM Forum document `strsaa-funi_01.01`, is a derivative of ATM Data Exchange Interface (ATM DXI, ATM Forum `af-dxi-0014_000.doc`). Like the PPP operating mode, the framing is a member of the HDLC family of data link control protocols and, in this implementation, uses the same number of header bytes. It uses standard HDLC start and stop flag bytes to guarantee flag recognition and bit stuffing to achieve data transparency. The ATM FUNI frame header contains address and control fields. The address field encodes the service data units (SDU) virtual connection virtual path identifier (VPI) and virtual connection identifier (VCI). The multiplexing of multiple network layer protocols on a single FUNI virtual connection using RFC 1483 LLC or PPP is discussed below under the heading "Address assignment," paragraph entitled *protocol encapsulation*.

Consider Figure 10.11, which shows ATM FUNI format frame structure.

Implementations of this specification operating in FUNI mode MUST frame data using the ATM FUNI derivative of HDLC framing as described in ATM Forum `str-saa-funi-01.01` with specific restrictions as outlined below. This framing MUST include a 2-byte frame header and 4-byte CRC. Implementations SHOULD support the congestion notification (CN) and cell loss priority (CLP) bits as described in ATM Forum `str-saa-funi-01.01`. At initialization, the default maximum size of the data framed between the FUNI header and the CRC MUST be 1600 bytes to allow interoperation with

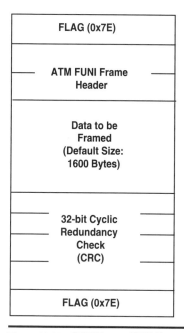

Figure 10.11 ATM Frame UNI Format

most foreseeable encapsulations of 1500-byte Ethernet frames. Implementations MAY negotiate other maximum-size frames through mechanisms that are outside the scope of this document.

Address assignment

Specific VPI/VCI addresses for ADSL physical layer management, vendor-specific channel and default user data channel will be defined in future technical reports in this series.

Protocol encapsulation: A conforming FUNI-mode implementation at the ADSL U interface MUST support the protocol multiplexing techniques defined in RFC 1483, *Multi-Protocol Encapsulation over ATM AAL5.* The specifics of applying RFC 1483 to FUNI mode implementations are described in this section. RFC 1483 describes two multiplexing techniques: LLC encapsulation and virtual-circuit-based multiplexing. If an implementation supports this FUNI mode, it MUST support one of these RFC 1483 multiplexing modes over the Frame UNI and SHOULD support the PPP over FUNI virtual-circuit-based encapsulation.

LLC encapsulation: One encapsulation technique specified in RFC 1483 uses a multiprotocol IEEE 802.1 LAN Logical Link Control (LLC) header to encapsulate the payload. FUNI mode implementations may use this technique for all FUNI payloads, with one important exception for PPP.

PPP PDUs over ADSL FUNI circuits MUST be transported using virtual-circuit-based multiplexing.

Virtual-circuit-based multiplexing. RFC 1483 also allows alternate encapsulations by using virtual-circuit-based multiplexing. Any payload may be transported in a FUNI frame without any additional encapsulation; there is no in-band LLC-based protocol-type discriminator at the beginning of the frame's information field. In this scenario, the end systems create a distinct parallel virtual circuit connection for each payload protocol type. The lack of any protocol type discriminator means that there MUST be some other (out-of-band) method for the endpoints to agree on the interpretation of the payload that immediately follows the FUNI header. See RFC 1483 for further explanation of this multiplexing mode. This ADSL Forum standard defines a special case for PPP payloads inside FUNI frames. A compliant implementation that chooses to carry Point-to-Point Protocol (PPP) PDUs inside a FUNI frame (PPP over FUNI) MUST carry the PPP PDUs directly over FUNI using Virtual circuit based multiplexing. PPP MUST NOT be encapsulated within an LLC header when framed by a FUNI header across the ADSL U interface.

Implementation requirements

RFC 1662 mode and FUNI mode define two methods for framing and encapsulating packet data over the U interface specified in Figure 10.8, which is the ADSL Reference Model. Consider the following three procedural aspects as they pertain to the ATU-R and the ATU-C.

1. *ATU-C attributes:* The ATU-C MUST support the following:

    (*a*) RFC 1662 mode

    (*b*) FUNI mode

2. *ATU-R attributes:* The ATU-R MUST support *at least one* of the following:

    (*a*) RFC 1662 mode

    (*b*) FUNI mode

3. *General attributes:* Both the ATU-C and the ATU-R MAY support the following: vendor-specific channel for FUNI framing that is an *optional* vendor-specific channel defined only for FUNI mode. This standard assigns a dedicated PVC channel for this connection. A well-known (TBD) VPI/VCI pair identifies the vendor-specific channel. For payloads that are outside the scope described in section 3.2 (of ADSL Forum document) above, the vendor-specific virtual connection MUST be implemented and used. Examples of such uses might include negotiation of or indication of private extension, flash ROM updates proprietary debugging, and other vendor-specific actions.

All packets exchanged over the vendor specific channel MUST use RFC 1483 LLC encapsulation. Those packets containing vendor-specific information MUST use a SNAP header having the IEEE-assigned organizationally unique identifier (OUI) value of the implementing vendor. Packets containing unrecognized OUI values MUST be silently discarded. Compliant devices MUST be able to interoperate without using this vendor-specific channel.

The vendor-specific channel may be used to negotiate extensions outside the standard. If both peers indicate agreement to such extensions (in some vendor-specific manner), then those extensions are not restricted in any way by this standard, including use of non-vendor-specific VPI/VCI pairs.

Packet formats

RFC 1662 mode packets are as presented here for PPP-based framing: Figure 10.12 shows an HDLC-like-framed PPP PDU.

FUNI-mode packets. For FUNI implementations, packets (and frames) in the data plane are multiplexed and encapsulated per RFC 1483, using either LLC encapsulation or VC-based multiplexing. PPP frames, if transmitted,

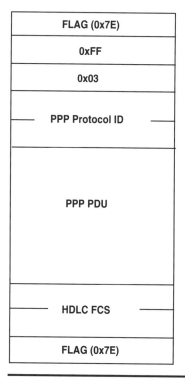

Figure 10.12   HDLC-Like-Framed PPP PDU

MUST be VC-multiplexed. Since, with VC multiplexing, the carried network interconnect protocol is identified implicitly by the corresponding virtual connection, there is no need to include explicit multiplexing information. Therefore, the LLC multiplexing field is not included, and the PPP frame starts at the first byte of the FUNI service data unit field.

The vendor-specific channel, if implemented, MUST be LLC-encapsulated. The packet formats for FUNI-based framing are

1. Figure 10.13: FUNI-based LLC-encapsulated non-ISO PDU

2. Figure 10.14: FUNI-based LLC-encapsulated ISO PDU

3. Figure 10.15: FUNI-based LLC-encapsulated MAC PDU

4. Figure 10.16: FUNI-based, VC-multiplexed PPP PDU

5. Figure 10.17: FUNI-based VC-multiplexed PDU (requires pairwise agreement of ADSL endpoints)

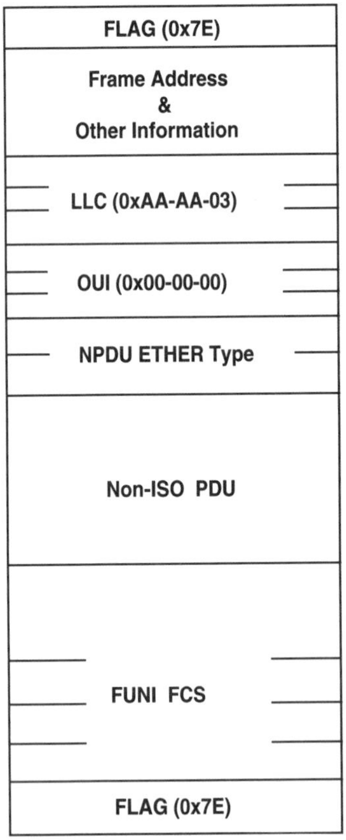

Figure 10.13 FUNI-Based LLC-Encapsulated Non-ISO PDU

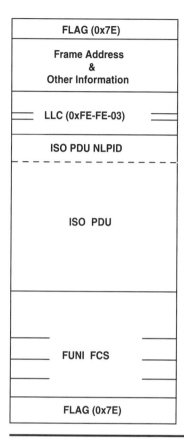

Figure 10.14   FUNI-Based LLC-Encapsulated ISO PDU

References

RFC 1483   *Multiprotocol Encapsulation over ATM Adaptation Layer 5*

RFC 1661   *The Point-to-Point Protocol (PPP)*

RFC 1662   *PPP in HDLC-like Framing*

RFC 1663   *PPP Reliable Transmission*

ISO/IEC 3309   *Information Technology—Telecommunications and Information Exchange between Systems—High-Level Data-Link Control (HDLC) Procedures—Frame Structure*

ISO/IEC 8022-2 *Information Technology—Telecommunications and Information Exchange between Systems—Local and Metropolitan Area Networks—Specific requirements—Part 2: Logical Link Control*

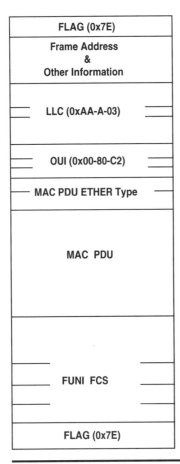

Figure 10.15 FUNI-Based LLC-Encapsulated
MAC PDU

STR-SAA-FUNI-01.01   *ATM Forum: Frame-Based User-to-Network Interface*
                      (FUNI) Specification v2

AF-DXI-0014.000   *ATM Forum: ATM Data eXchange Interface (DXI)*
                      Specification

10.5 Network Migration

This section presents the project described by the network migration ADSL
technical report which presents options for telco access networks incorporating ADSL. Different telcos will have different legacy systems, regulatory and
competitive environments, broadband strategies, and deployment timescales.
Hence it is not feasible to make all encompassing recommendations for network migration options.

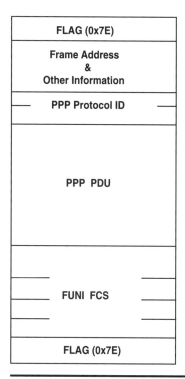

Figure 10.16   FUNI-Based, VC-Multiplexed
PPP PDU

This project seeks to capture the drivers that may lead a telco (telephone company) to consider a particular migration path. It then presents the various technical options together with the salient features, advantages, and disadvantages to assist telcos in forming evolution plans for an access network that will incorporate ADSL. It is hoped that this working text will serve as a useful reference text for both the technical and marketing professionals in the ADSL Forum.

Statement of project

The objective of this project is to capture ADSL network migration options for a set of defined initial and target network scenarios, identifying the key issues associated with each option. It will also describe related technical issues that may impact the deployment of an ADSL access network. The scope of the project is any access network migration scenarios that would involve use of ADSL or VDSL on a customers line in either the initial or target network scenarios, that is, evolution to or from ADSL/VDSL.

The primary focus is ADSL and VDSL technologies and architectures.

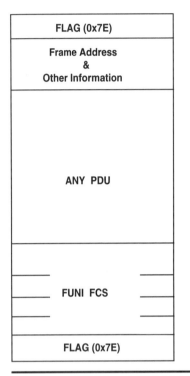

Figure 10.17   FUNI-Based, VC-Multiplexed PDU

However, to complete the picture of evolution scenarios, other xDSL technologies are not specifically excluded.

The approach taken is that for each evolution situation, define it as follows:

1. Starting network scenario

2. Target network scenario

3. Drivers (factors that will initiate and influence the migration)

4. Options (including advantages and disadvantages)

Each evolution situation forms an individual subsection within this Network Migration Working Text. In addition, generic factors influencing migration to ADSL are also described.

Factors influencing migration to ADSL

Some of the major factors influencing the willingness, ability, and speed of a telco or other service provider to migrate their access network to one that embraces the deployment and use of ADSL technology are presented here.

The influencing factors are categorized as being related to either network or architecture issues, equipment issues, or business or service issues. Some of these may be regarded as critical success factors for ADSL.

1. Network–architecture–related factors

    (a) The presence of loading coils in some telco networks. This may have to be dealt with in the same way as they are for ISDN.

    (b) The degree to which digital loop carrier (DLC) technology has been deployed to provision narrowband services, especially the older SLC96 and SLC5 systems. How is ADSL to be jumpered onto the final distribution copper? How will POTS from the SLC be "merged" with the ADSL signal via the splitter? Is the ADSL housed in an adjacent remote housing?

    (c) How will ADSL be housed and provided in next-generation DLCs (NGDLC)?

    (d) The remainder of the broadband network needs to be installed to exploit ADSL, including ATM switches and backbone network or other broadband data overlay network, VoD servers, and so forth.

    (e) There is no plug-and-play standard network solution available in a turnkey form yet. It requires extensive network design, integration, and performance analysis skills.

    (f) Solutions to the problem of dynamic IP address assignment and binding to physical network hardware addresses, particularly over ATM networks, need to be solved, standardized (with one approach, not many), and widely supported.

    (g) Security concerns, especially with some of the earlier proposed router/Ethernet architectures, need to be mitigated and the solutions disseminated.

    (h) The integration of ADSL into the existing copper access network. Changes required to operational processes, test equipment and line-test procedures, network management systems, and their databases. In addition, field personnel need to be trained to understand, install, operate, and maintain this technology. Data equipment such as ATM or Ethernet/router interfaces will be new to many of them.

    (i) Quantifying the impact on existing services (POTS band equipment on the same pair and spectral compatibility with other services on adjacent pairs) and removing any concerns.

    (j) Concern on how to navigate through all the existing transmission technology "barriers" to ADSL that are in today's network, such as ISDN, pair-gain systems, and fiber systems. Also, concern about what

barrier ADSL may be to future technologies such as FTTN or FTTK*
with VDSL, particularly if the telco has made a public commitment to
VDSL or entered into a longer-term contract. Will they have to forklift
any ADSL deployed today to make way for the VDSL deployment committed to for tomorrow?

(*k*) Satisfactory solutions to the home-wiring topology and installation
and process. Can the customer self-install the ADSL remote unit? If
so, under what circumstances? What POTS splitter locations are convenient, work well, facilitate fault demarcation, and look OK from the
customer's perspective? Is an active or passive NT approach best?

(*l*) Satisfactory solutions (equipment and process) to identifying the bit
rate that can be supplied (if at all) to an individual customer. What is
the process from the point of sale (e.g., can a customer have 2 Mbps
VoD service?) to service provisioning with a high degree of confidence
and minimal failures.

(*m*) The ability of DSL products to "fit" existing ISP network architectures
in terms of existing router interfaces, impact on firewall, multicast,
authentication capabilities, tools and methodology for RADIUS
(remote access dialup user service) database updates, and so forth.

2. Equipment-related factors

(*a*) Cost of equipment: When will it reach its floor, and what will this be?
Questions over port density (number of customers per line card, related to power consumption) and rack density and overbooking levels.
The common equipment costs at start-up represent exposed capital
expenditure until there is a high service takeup and hence equipment
utilization.

(*b*) Spectral compatibility of ADSL equipment with other DSL technologies, especially in the unbundled dark-copper regulatory regimes
affecting some networks.

(*c*) Physical space, power, and cooling requirements in the central office
(CO). Linked to rack density issues in (*a*). A particular concern for
ISPs/CLECs seeking collocation in ILEC Cos. These factors will also
be very important to externally sited ADSL electronics for example
when embedded in a next-generation DLC.

(*d*) Physical size and design aesthetics of the remote ADSL customer unit
including the POTS splitter.

---

*Fiber to the kerb; U.K. variant of fiber to the curb (FTTC).

(e) The best choice of physical interface on the remote ADSL customer unit, such as Ethernet, ATM25, two ATM25, one ATM25 plus one Ethernet, Universal Serial Bus (USB), and RS-422, and so forth.

(f) The capability and current status of operational support systems for ADSL (element managers, etc.).

(g) The availability, cost-effectiveness, and ease of use of appropriate test equipment for commissioning ADSL installations (e.g., line qualification testing, field-deployable ATM testers for DSLAM commissioning).

(h) The status of equipment standards (approved and de facto) for ADSL (line code, ATM via dual latency), ATM signaling, and IP over ATM (LANE, MPOA, etc.) and subsequent impact on interoperability. Availability of equipment implementing these standards such as software application-driven SVC setup.

(i) Lack of turnkey end-to-end network equipment from ATM switch to CPE with inherent protocol stacks and plug-and-play software applications.

3. Business/service-related factors

(a) Need for a well-defined strategy and service proposition backed by a viable business case with acceptable levels of risk (to both technology and market).

(b) Forced to deploy ADSL in response to competition (by, e.g., cable modems) when the telco business proposition isn't fully ready yet.

(c) Lack of confidence in the broadband market and concern over maturity of broadband technology inhibits some telcos from committing to large volume procurements in the near term. This holds equipment prices high, which doesn't help the telco business case unless a supplier is prepared to drop margins and carry all the risk with a loss-leader.

(d) The process for identifying customers in range of constant-bit-rate (CBR) services such as VoD to be delivered over ADSL isn't accurate or cost-effective enough. This impacts on the marketing method for such services and the process for deciding on when/where the point of sale occurs.

(e) The impact of regulations on service packaging, unbundling, cross-subsidization, and accounting separation limit the degrees of freedom of some telcos; for example, are they allowed to deliver broadcast services over ADSL, as has been trialled in France and Australia? Do they have to ensure spectral compatibility with other service providers exploiting dark copper, or does the incumbent telco have full control over all ADSL installed on their network?

(*f*) Concern over the impact of ADSL on existing product lines such as ISDN and T1 or E1 private circuits. When is the broadband ADSL market mature enough to risk eating into these revenue streams?

4. Active and passive NT issues: The regulatory view of who owns the remote ADSL unit together with the exact physical manifestation of the endpoint of the telco network can affect the preferred ADSL remote unit form factor. This, in turn, can have a profound impact on migration to and beyond ADSL-based networks. In some telco networks (such as in the United States) the regulatory regime dictates that the remote ADSL unit at the customer end of the line is customer premises equipment (CPE) owned by the customer. Hence the network termination (NT) presented to the customer is a "wires-only" interface and is sometimes termed "passive." In other networks such as in many European countries, the ADSL remote unit is itself considered part of the access network. Hence the NT interface presented to the customer is the ADSL customer interface connection (e.g., 10BaseT Ethernet, ATM 25). In this latter scenario, the NT contains the ADSL electronics and is hence termed "active." Hybrid architectures where the POTS splitter is separated from the ADSL remote unit are possible, and some of these splitters may themselves be active, requiring back-powering from the ADSL remote unit. However, the basic definitions of active/passive NT and the relative merits are broadly the same. ADSL vendors have responded to the different markets and regulatory environments for the ADSL remote unit by developing two basic types of ADSL remote unit. The first was a standalone ADSL box (typically wall-mounted) appropriate for both types of regulatory environment (i.e., wires-only and active NT). In a wires-only passive NT regime, this would constitute CPE (owned or leased by the customer), in an active NT regime it would represent the end of the network (owned by the telco). The second type of ADSL remote unit takes the form of a plug-in PC card [sometimes called an *ADSL NIC* (network interface card)]. This has a lot of synergy with CPE (e.g., the PC it resides in) and so is more aimed at the passive NT environments. In future it may spawn further variants such as ADSL transceivers integrated into set-top boxes or digital TVs. This section presents a list of the advantages often cited for each approach. To keep it simple it compares a standalone active NT ADSL remote unit with a passive NT where the ADSL is embedded in CPE such as on a PC card.

5. Advantages of a standalone active NT ADSL remote unit

(*a*) Facilitates evolution of the access network without impact on the customers CPE or home wiring. ADSL, VDSL, FTTH, and wireless delivery systems could all have the same customer interface (e.g., ATM 25) so that the access network can be provisioned and evolved or upgraded with minimal impact on the customer or their investment in CPE.

(b) The independence of the customer interface from the access delivery mechanism makes it easier for customers to move between different operators and service providers while protecting their investment in CPE and home wiring.

(c) Allows interactive multimedia services in the home to gracefully evolve to multiple CPE connections via a separate home bus having started from a single PC or set-top box. No MAC protocol is needed within the ADSL equipment as for a multiuser passive bus approach.

(d) The access network equipment and CPE are not inextricably locked into each other enabling each to evolve independently at the fastest rate the market drives them to. It removes dependencies such as the latest flavor of PC bus to build ADSL cards for. Also, keeping the network and CPE distinctly separate helps to manage some of the problems of limited line card/remote unit interoperability in the early years. ISDN took several years to get interoperability without performance loss. ADSL is more complex.

(e) Allows asymmetric access (e.g., via ADSL or asymmetric VDSL) with a symmetric home bus.

(f) Simplifies ADSL (and VDSL) provisioning and service penetration. No additional margins or loop length needs to be factored into deployment rules to account for losses in home wiring.

(g) Easier to guarantee a quality of service (QoS) since the DSL system doesn't have to operate over uncontrolled customer wiring.

(h) Facilitates fault demarcation by using loopbacks and the like to determine if a fault is with the access network and ADSL or in the CPE and home wiring (which may be the customer's responsibility). This enables the telco to outsource technical support and troubleshooting more easily. It doesn't require PC experts to understand ADSL or vice versa. This could reduce the whole-life cost of ownership of ADSL for the telco.

(i) Reduces the risk to the telco of the ADSL system damaging the customers PC. Copper lines can be struck by lightning; also, PC hardware faults may damage a PC-based ADSL card. The mutual telco customer liability is reduced with a standalone ADSL customer unit. This may be particularly important to the telco if they lease the ADSL remote unit to the customer.

6. Advantages of a passive NT with ADSL remote unit embedded in CPE

(a) Less boxes on the customer premises; therefore more aesthetically pleasing.

(*b*) Lower capital cost per customer due to less boxes. More functionality put on the PC card, so connector, PCB costs, etc. shared across more functionality; hence lower market entry costs.

(*c*) Simpler powering arrangements (e.g., from the PC).

Classification of migration options

The Network Migration Project team has produced the following list of evolution scenarios for study. These scenarios have been classified as low-, medium-, or high-priority and whether they are relevant to the shorter or longer term decisions of telcos. The initial focus of work has been on those scenarios considered high- or medium-priority as indicated in the final column. Consider Figure 10.18, which presents the classification and prioritization of identified migration paths.

Overview of migration options relationship

Figure 10.19 shows options of ADSL migration paths. Only high and medium priorities shown; low-priority migration options. Each migration option listed in Figure 10.18 is defined in terms of the starting network scenario and the target network scenario. The drivers that will initiate and influence the migration toward the target network scenario are discussed, and the technical options to facilitate the network migration are then presented, including their advantages and disadvantages.

Internet access via voiceband modem to ADSL modem

A customer is provided with Internet access via a POTS analog connection. This is shown in Figure 10.20. Through the use of voiceband analog modems, a maximum bandwidth of 33 kbps exists (or possibly 56 kbps with the latest generation of asymmetric voiceband modems), thereby limiting the Internet services that can be provided.

Internet access via ADSL

Another way a customer can be provided Internet access is by way of an ADSL modem connection. Through the use of ADSL modems it is possible to provide a wide range of both asymmetric and symmetric (SDSL) bandwidths that can deliver today's Internet services, plus provide an evolutionary path to future, bandwidth-intensive services. Consider Figure 10.21. The ADSL central office card could be connected to the Internet backbone and ISP via either a DSLAM or Ethernet switch and router.

Drivers. The majority of mass-market residential access to the Internet is provided by analog voiceband modems operating with a maximum data rate

Starting Network Scenarios	Target Network Scenarios	Timeframe of Scenario	Priority
1. Internet access via voiceband modem	Internet access via ADSL	NOW	high
2. 2nd line OPTS via DAML	ADSL delivered service	NOW	medium
3. ADSL from CO	ADSL from DLC	future	high
4. ISDN for internet access	ADSL for internet access	NOW	high
5. Internet only via ATM ADSL (DSLAM with 10BT presented to customer)	"Full service" set via ATM ADSL (DSLAM with ATM presented to customer)	future	high
6. Internet only via "IP" ADSL (Router plus ETHERNET switch)	"Full service" set via ATM ADSL (DSLAM with ATM approach)	future	high
7. Internet only via "IP" ADSL (Router plus ETHERNET switch)	"Full service" via "IP-Only" ADSL (10BT presented to customer)	future	high
8. ADSL service delivery	VDSL service delivery	future	high
9. Next generation DLC with ADSL (RAM)	ONU with VDSL or ADSL (FTTK)	future	medium
10. VDSL for residential access	VDSL for business services	future	low
11. ADSL for business services	ADSL for residential services	future	low
12. ADSL & POTS	ADSL & 2nd line (2xPOTS)	future	low
13. FTT Node & long range VDSL	FTTK & short range VDSL	future	low
14. FTT Node & VDSL	FTTH	future	low
15. HDSL for Internet access	ADSL for Internet Acccess	NOW	medium
16. IDSL for Internet access	ADSL for Internet Acccess	NOW	medium

Figure 10.18 Classification and Prioritization of Identified Migration Paths

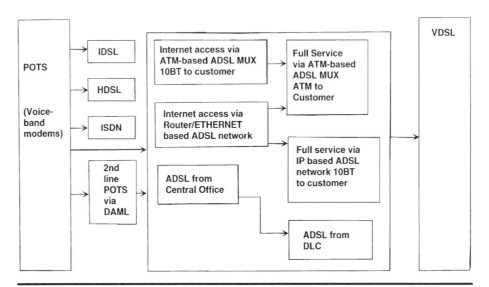

Figure 10.19 Relationship between Migration Options

of 33 kbps. With the advent of the World Wide Web (WWW), a graphics-rich Internet service, bandwidth speed at both access points (client and server) have become a bottleneck. Now, the World Wide Web is often called the "worldwide wait." The principal driver for the telco is to satisfy the need for high-speed Internet access, which should eliminate the largest frustration associated with Internet access, the slow downstream transfer of graphical images from the server to the client (PC host).

A second driver for the telco is to move the Internet traffic, characterized by long holding times, off of the voice network, which usually has short holding times. Many of the switches now carrying Internet traffic to the Internet service providers (ISPs) have been engineering with relatively high-ratio concentration stages and must be modified to reduce the concentration ratio to serve the increasing percentage of Internet traffic. ADSL deployment effectively moves this traffic from the voice network and places it on the more efficient packet or ATM network.

A third driver associated with going directly from analog voiceband modems to ADSL modems is that an expensive ISDN upgrade is not required of the voiceband switch. ISDN is a network concept with a full multilayer protocol stack of its own to support. This requires expensive hardware and software upgrades to the existing voiceband network elements. ADSL, on the other hand, is only a very high-speed modem and uses essentially the protocol stack of today's existing data network, whether packet- or cell-based. This can dramatically reduce the complexity required to implement high-speed Internet access when the previous economics did not justify upgrading to ISDN capability.

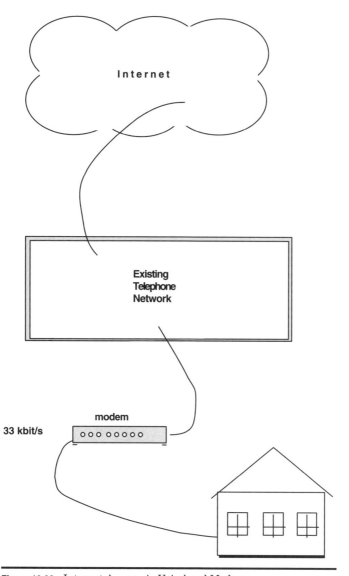

Figure 10.20   Internet Access via Voiceband Modem

A fourth driver is that from the telco subscriber's view it makes more sense to go directly from an analog voiceband modem to an ADSL modem. With a maximum speed of 128 kbps, ISDN does not provide the bandwidth improvement to necessarily warrant the acquisition and wiring inconvenience. Both the telco and the ISP increase their charges to the subscriber, which may be too high to absorb for only a fourfold increase in bandwidth. ADSL modems will be the telco's answer to cable modems, so there should be substantial competitive pressure to kept the monthly service tariffs of ADSL low.

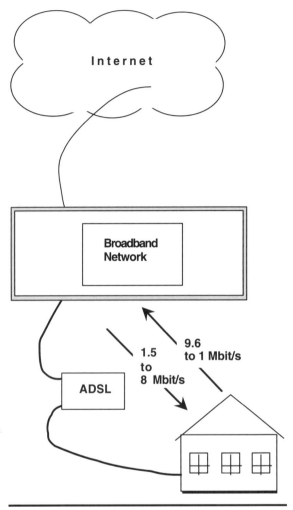

Figure 10.21 Internet Access via ADSL

A fifth driver appears when the telco also decides to become an ISP, which is beginning to happen at a rapid rate in the United States, thanks to the passage of the recent Telecom bill. As more and more government-owned monopolies become privatized, these telcos would also look at providing many nontraditional ways of generating revenue.

Becoming an ISP is one such avenue. There are many ISPs competing for the business. ADSL provides the telco with the ability to differentiate its offering by providing high-speed access along with local content and the mirroring of popular WWW sites for superfast response.

Internet access options with ADSL. The first option is PC-based ATU-R. If the principal driver to ADSL deployment is high-speed Internet access, then an expedient method of providing this service to the telco subscriber is by providing an ADSL modem card that sits on the PC bus just as the majority of today's analog modems do. This reduces the complexity and wiring issues associated with multiple boxes at the subscriber premises. ADSL interoperability trials are important to this approach because this option would lead toward the subscriber owning the ADSL modem. The telco would usually not want to lease an ADSL modem to a subscriber when it is an internal PC card because they do not want to be liable for damaging the PC. One issue here is that the subscriber's initial voiceband access may be via a PCMCIA voiceband modem for ADSL is not a plug-in replacement. If this is the case then the approach below of an external ADSL modem is more suitable.

The second option is an external ADSL modem implementation. The other option is to provide an external ADSL modem that connects to the PC via a 10BaseT Ethernet connection or direct computer serial link such as the Universal Serial Bus (USB). This option may be more complex because the modem must be packaged in a housing and provides its own power supply. This option allows the option of being purchased by the telco subscriber and being leased, which is more similar to the cable modem deployment. In addition to the equipment being more expensive, the monthly fee may also be higher because a portion of the fee could include the leasing fee.

The third option is a remote access router implementation. There is a trend to have more than one computer in a home or small business. In this case, having an external remote access router providing multiple 10BaseT ports served by a single ADSL line would serve homes and small offices who want to share the cost of an ADSL line. The router would be connected between the ADSL remote unit ant the CPE.

Reference

Internet Access—Voiceband Modem to ADSL Modem, ADSL Forum 96-079, Tom Miller, Siemens, Sept. 19, 1996 (London meeting).

Pair-gain-provided POTS to ADSL

The starting network scenario of pair-gain or pair-multiplier systems is used in many countries to provide a second POTS line over a single copper pair. These are called DAML systems in the United States and DACS in the United Kingdom. Many earlier systems were termed *data over voice* or 1+1 systems and used FDM (frequency division multiplexing) to carry either an analog or a 64-kbps digital telephony channel above the normal 4-kHz baseband voice channel. Recent versions of these systems use ISDN transmission devices in conjunction with additional analog POTS interfaces to present two analog POTS interfaces to the customer. Alternatively, the remote end of the

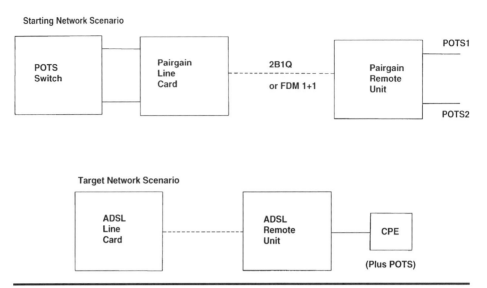

Figure 10.22 Pair-Gain-Served Customers to ADSL

system can be located at a pole top or in a footway box to provide two separate dwellings with digitally derived telephony where both customers share the same physical copper connection from this remote unit back to the central office.

The customer whose telephony is provided by a pair-gain system now wants an ADSL delivered service (in addition to telephony). Consider Figure 10.22.

Drivers. Many telcos have deployed pair-gain systems in order to save the cost of installing new copper cables. This is particularly prevalent in areas where duct space or cable capacity are full and only a small increase in capacity is required to meet new telephony demand but the forecasted growth in that area doesn't justify laying new ducts or cables. In addition, when some single-occupancy buildings are converted into apartments or business, pair-gain systems have proved an expedient way of meeting the demand for additional POTS lines. Now, some of these customers may want a service such as fast Internet access or VoD, which could potentially be delivered using ADSL.

Options related to pair-gain-served customers

1. *ADSL with a 64 kbps-derived POTS channel:* It would be possible to extract a 64 kbps channel from the digital payload of the ADSL (in both directions) in order to derive the capacity necessary to provide a second POTS channel (the first being delivered as normal analog POTS in the voiceband below the frequencies used by ADSL). This would have to use the noninter-

leaved path through the ADSL transceivers to minimize latency. Even then the residual latency in some implementations may be too large for the required latency allocation to the access segment of an end-to-end voice connection. There are several problematic issues associated with this approach of a digitally derived POTS channel. The first is that in some countries there is an obligation on the telco to provide a lifeline POTS service in the event of a power failure. Since ADSL is not line-powered, this presents a problem. It is likely that any attempt to line-power ADSL (using currently permissible voltage levels) would reduce the range of ADSL to that of HDSL (12,000 ft, 3.7 km). Another issue is that many telcos are examining the use of ADSL to deliver ATM cells all the way to the customer. There appears to be a growing consensus that it is not desirable to try to mix ATM and STM channels on the same ADSL bearer. Hence to use such ATM based ADSL systems to derive a second POTS channel would necessitate the transport of POTS over ATM. This results in a 6-ms delay due to the buffering involved in encapsulating the POTS data stream into ATM cells. This can be overcome using proprietary composite cell techniques. Of course, if the original second POTS channel from the pair-gain system was delivered into the same customer's house for use with their voiceband modem, they may not need a second POTS channel once they have ADSL.

2. *Move pair-gain unit:* When pair-gain systems are used externally to deliver POTS to two different tenancies using the same central office line, they can be mounted at pole tops or in footway boxes. There is a physical limit on how many such systems can be collocated at these distribution points, and many telcos will have guidelines for this working practice. For example, in some networks this final distribution point can feed 10 to 20 customers and the maximum number of pole-top pair-gain systems that can be collocated is, say, 4. We need to consider the scenario where a customer whose single POTS line is provided by one of the channels of the pair-gain system wishes to procure a service that could be delivered via ADSL. In such circumstances, the pair-gain systems could be effectively moved to supply a different (non-ADSL) customer from the distribution point simply be rejumpering the connection at the pair-gain system (distribution point and central office ends). The number of copper pairs between the distribution point and the central office remains unchanged. The ratio of total customers fed from a distribution point to those connected via pair-gain systems is usually sufficient to allow the degree of freedom to implement the aforementioned process workaround.

3. *Employ similar techniques as for simultaneous delivery of ISDN and ADSL:* Since many modern pair-gain systems use the same 2B1Q transmission systems as Basic Rate ISDN, some of the (i.e., the ISDN Basic Rate Access channel) techniques for delivering concurrent ISDN and ADSL to the same customer may be applicable in this network migration scenario. The issues related to delivering ISDN "under" ADSL are described in the section covering ISDN-to-ADSL evolution.

4. *Use an additional copper pair:* The obvious solution to the problem is to simply provide a second copper pair to the customer who has one or two POTS lines provided via a pair-gain system and now wants an ADSL-delivered service. At first sight this may seem a costly option; however, two drivers may make this a sensible solution in certain areas. The first is that many telcos (particularly in the United States) are increasing their use of digital loop carrier (DLC) systems. Their deployment may make some additional copper pairs available in some areas. Second, as telcos face more and more competition from operators using alternative technologies (e.g., radio, HFC) then the inevitable loss of some customers to the competition will create some spare pairs in the telco's network.

Central office (CO) ADSL-to-NGDLC-based ADSL

ADSL service(s) is (are) provided from CO-based equipment; that is, the ATU-C is located within the central office. Consider Figure 10.23.

ADSL service is provided from NGDLC-based equipment; that is, the ATU-C is located at the carrier serving area site of a next-generation digital loop carrier. Figure 10.24 shows ADSL access being provided by a digital subscriber line access multiplexer (DSLAM) collocated with a next-generation digital loop carrier (NGDLC).

Future products may combine the DSLAM. NGDLC and SDH/SONET add/drop multiplexer (ADM) into one unit. In addition to using SDH/SONET rings, the fiber feed may also use point-to-point or PON topologies.

Drivers.   There are two principal drivers that will stimulate the migration of ADSL from being CO-based to NGDLC-based:

1. The performance improvement associated with the shorter loop length.

2. The high percentage of present subscribers being served by digital loop carriers.

The adoption of RADSL may mitigate driver 1 for high-speed Internet access and remote LAN access services by allowing an ADSL connection at a reduced performance level over long loop lengths, but future switched digital video services will want to enjoy the high-performance ADSL capability associated with loop lengths of 12,000 ft (3.7 km) or less. Also, if ADSL is to truly compete with cable modems, then ADSL must be capable of competing head to head with the effective bandwidth of cable modem. In the United States, it is forecast that 45 percent of all access lines will be served by DLC systems by the year 2000. Some areas, for example, already have over 50 percent of access lines being served by DLCs. The previous migration to DLCs was motivated by the cost benefits provided by both pair-gain (24/30 2-wire loops to one 4-wire T1/E1 connection) and a first stage of concentration (usually 2:1). These figures provide a great incentive to develop NGDLC capable of deliver-

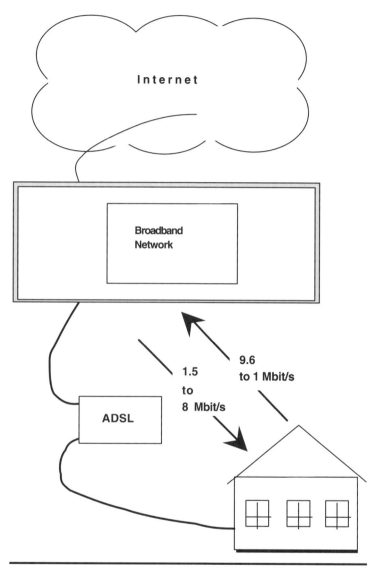

Figure 10.23   Central Office/Exchange-Based ADSL

ing ADSL services to subscribers and aggregating the higher bandwidth through statistical multiplexing and connecting with the network via SONET/SDH.

Options.   There are two physical options and two functional options associated with the migration of ADSL to the DLC site:

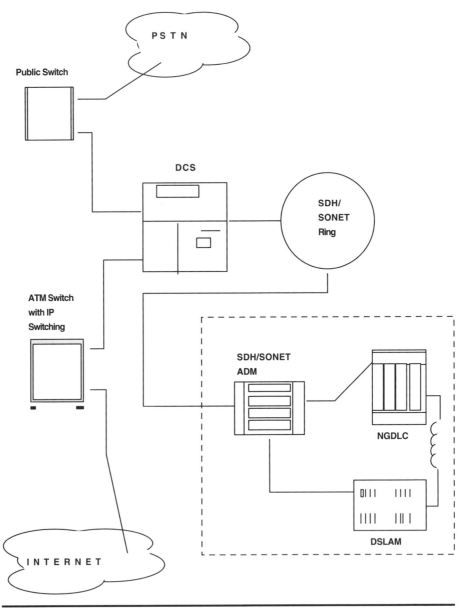

Figure 10.24 ADSL Served from the RDT Site

1. The two physical options would be for the ADSL-capable remote access multiplexer (RAM) to either be collocated with a DLC or integrated into a NGDLC product. By moving the ADSL from the CO to the DLC location, the high transmission rate of the latest ADSL systems (8 to 12 Mbps) will be available to a higher percentage of customers. It will be important to

understand the spectral compatibility issues in this scenario since some implementations of higher speed ADSL use greater bandwidth, which could pose greater problems for compatibility with future VDSL systems. Power backoff may need to be implemented by the DLC-based ADSL transmitter. For pedestal-type locations the resulting use of the feeding fiber's bandwidth will be less efficient or economic. Also it should be noted that many remote terminals (RTs) are copper fed and not fiber and hence have less spare capacity compared to CEVs.

2. The two functional options refer to the RAM being either packet-mode-based or ATM-based. The latter can be further divided into two suboptions: ATM terminating at the RAM or ATM at the desktop. A recent RFP for such a device would indicate that providing ATM to the desktop (or set-top box) seems to be of interest to several operators.

References

RFP-96-07-MJM, *Personal Computer/Data Network Access (PC/DNA)*, issued July 8, 1996 by the Joint Procurement Consortium of Ameritech, BellSouth Telecommunications, Pacific Bell, and SBC Communications.

CO-Based ADSL to NGDLC-Based ADSL, ADSL Forum 96-080, Tom Miller, (Siemens), Sept. 19, 1996 (London meeting).

ISDN to ADSL for Internet access

Figure 10.25 shows a customer is provided with Internet access via a Basic Rate ISDN connection.

However, the target scenario is for the customer to be given higher-speed access to the Internet by use of an ADSL transmission system. Consider Figure 10.26.

Drivers. The majority of mass market residential access to the Internet is provided today by voiceband modems with a maximum data rate of around 28.8 kbps. Many telcos are increasingly selling Internet access based on Basic Rate ISDN. This can provide the customer with a data rate of around 128 kbps (with B-channel bonding). The driver for the customer is the frustration many are feeling with the speed of downloading WWW pages that are rich in graphics. Many customers are switching off graphics display options just to make the Internet usable. The driver for the telco to initially satisfy this thirst for bandwidth using ISDN is that ISDN is a mature, established technology. It has been proved in the network that there are many vendors offering interoperable equipment (if carefully selected), which has driven prices down. There are also a variety of other applications (e.g., PC-based videoconferencing) that are available to exploit ISDN technology. Many telcos have both the transmission and switching infrastructure in place that enables them to offer this speed of digital access over their existing narrowband network. However, it should be noted that this is not true of all telcos. Some who

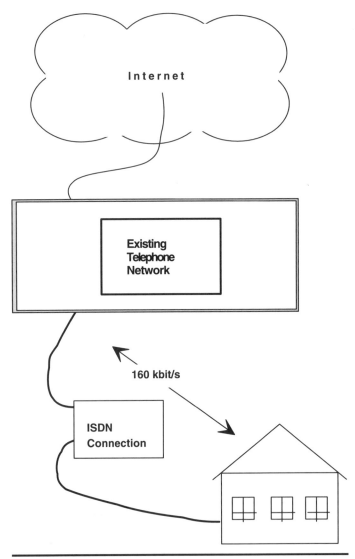

Figure 10.25 ISDN-Based Internet Traffic

would have to provide an ISDN service using an overlay switch fabric may consider going straight to ADSL. The desire for a telco to offer an ADSL-based Internet access upgrade to a customer is mainly driven by the fear of competition from cable modems. Many cable modem vendors are pitching their products as being faster than ISDN. The expectation is that a telco could equal or better this competition by exploiting the higher data rates possible with ADSL. However, for most telcos this will require a new backbone network and switch infrastructure, which is why ISDN is an easier first step.

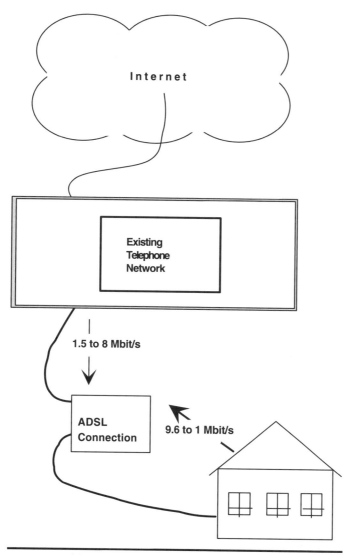

Figure 10.26   ADSL-Based Internet Traffic

The driver for the customer to have even faster Internet access than ISDN is enhanced usability. Developments such as JAVA and software MPEG decoders will lead to increasingly video-rich content on servers. This will be further facilitated by real-time protocol developments. There is also an increasing trend for intranetworking and teleworking. This is leading telcos to consider technologies that allow a combination of Internet access and remote LAN access. The rationale for first fulfilling such a business require-ment is that these early adopters have the deeper pockets necessary to kick-start the ADSL market. This will help increase volumes to drive down costs to a level appropriate for the mass consumer market. This has been the case for ISDN, where tariffs vary considerably around the world. In some countries, initial adoption of Basic Rate ISDN is almost exclusively by business customers. Packaged offerings based on ISDN (as with the Ameritech Home Professional Package). Consider the following World Wide Web address:

http://www.ameritech.com/products/data/ahpp/

These are available, but for increased competitiveness they could potentially be evolved to ADSL transport. Some applications (including email packages with a high degree of client/server interaction) become usable only away from the office LAN at ADSL speeds. The issue for the telco is how to evolve a customer from ISDN- to ADSL-based Internet access with minimal cost and inconvenience to both telco and customer. One factor that helps smooth this transition is the fact that if a line has been conditioned already for ISDN (e.g., loading coils removed), then this aspect of deployment effort doesn't need to be repeated for ADSL. A particular issue of concern is what degree of backward compatibility is possible if the customer has already invested in ISDN-specific CPE and other applications software (e.g., for videoconferencing or telephony) and wishes to continue to run such applications.

Options

1. *Provide the same customer interface on ISDN and ADSL:* This would enable a simple upgrade by replacing the ISDN NT1 with a remote ADSL unit that could physically plug into the existing CPE. The most obvious choice for a common interface is 10BaseT. Hence this option may only really viable if the telco is already providing ISDN with this interface or the customer is using an ISDN terminal adapter that provides this interface to the CPE. Many telcos provide the standard S interface or an RS-232 interface for onward connection to the CPE (PC or terminal adapter) This option would solve only the physical connection issue, which may be sufficient for an Internet only service upgrade However, since ISDN is a dial-up service, the impact on ADSL of signaling issues for other CPE/applications backward compatibility would have to be examined. Consider Figure 10.27, which shows the idea of providing the same customer interface on ISDN and ADSL.

2. *ISDN or POTS under ADSL:* This would enable both a legacy ISDN or POTS service and an ADSL service to be delivered over the same line. This requires the ADSL spectrum to be moved up from its current starting frequency to a higher starting frequency above the ISDN spectrum. In addition, the complexity of the splitter and the effect of reach on the ISDN service must also be taken into account, and these factors could further increase the starting frequency of the ADSL system.

This would reduce capacity left for the ADSL signal unless the entire ADSL signal is shifted to higher frequencies. Even then the ADSL signal would be

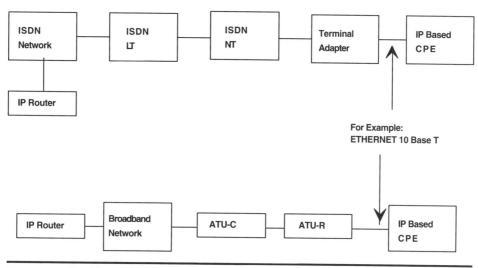

Figure 10.27   Provide the Same Customer Interface on ISDN and ADSL

more attenuated at the higher frequencies; hence some significant ADSL range reduction could occur.

This option would result in wiring complexity at the central office end because the customer's line would need to be capable of onward connection to an ADSL and ISDN or POTS line card. Although this approach along with option 3 (below) are not currently catered for by the ADSL standard (unlike option 4), contributions to ETSI [1–3] propose further work in the standards bodies to develop such an option.

The universal splitter [7] described above (i.e., one capable of passing POTS or ISDN with a fixed spectral allocation for the ADSL signal) results in ADSL operation on POTS-only lines that is nonoptimum. It is possible to conceive of an ADSL customer wiring configuration that has a separate splitter. In such a scenario it would be possible for some forms of ADSL modem to automatically adjust the spectral location of the ADSL data transmission in order to adapt to either a POTS-only or POTS or ISDN splitter (the latter having a wider low-pass filter bandwidth, effectively blocking some of the lower-frequency channel capacity available for ADSL transmission). This would give additional range for the POTS-only customers. However, as mentioned below, there are pilot tone issues to be resolved that would currently prevent standards-compliant DMT modems from being used in this manner. In addition, mixing both POTS-only and ISDN-capable ADSL in the same network will lead to spectral compatibility, customer perception, provisioning and logistics issues [7]. The spectral compatibility problems arise due to a near-end crosstalk (NEXT) problem. POTS-only ADSL systems could start the ADSL signal at round 20 to 40 kHz, whereas ISDN-capable splitters may start the

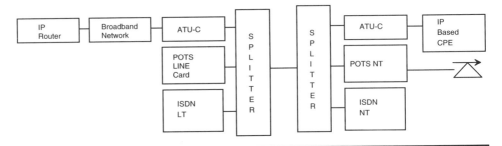

Figure 10.28 ISDN and POTS under ADSL

ADSL signal at 170 kHz [7]. Hence the downstream band of the POTS-only modem will generate NEXT into the upstream band of the ISDN-capable modem. This problem of mixing POTS-only and ISDN-capable ADSL in the same network also applies to the third option presented below. Consider Figure 10.28, which shows ISDN and POTS under ADSL.

3. *ISDN only under ADSL:* A splitter designed only to pass ISDN and not POTS as well can be simpler since there are no ringing transients to cope with. However, this would then require the customer to have their telephony delivered digitally as part of the ISDN payload. This would already be the case if they were subscribing to ISDN Internet access and only had one copper pair entering their tenancy (i.e., ISDN wasn't on a second line, the other which carried POTS). This is a true ISDN/ADSL hybrid. Exclusive use of this variant of ADSL equipment in a telco's network would require that any customer wanting only ADSL Internet access must also be given ISDN in order to have telephony since they couldn't use existing analog POTS simultaneously. Such a splitter design has been built [6], and this type of ADSL system could be of great interest to those countries with a high level of ISDN deployment (Germany, Holland, Switzerland, etc.), especially where ISDN is used to provide telephony. Range performance implication. ADSL spectra must be moved up from a 20- to 40-kHz lower-band edge to start at over 140 kHz [7]. It is possible to design such a splitter that could locate the ADSL signal from 140 kHz and above, this is sufficient to allow both 2B1Q and 4B3T ISDN to pass through it. The subsequent impact on ADSL range may be in the range of 10 to 15 percent or a few hundred meters of range reduction. Splitter design is simpler than option 2 since only ISDN impedances need to be matched, not POTS impedances, which are complex in some operators' networks. There could be a problem in that standardized DMT ADSL relies on a pilot tone at 76 kHz for timing synchronization. Hence some silicon may not work in this configuration. It is likely that both ANSI compliant DMT designs and existing CAP designs would require some modification to accommodate the baseband ISDN. The proposals to ETSI [1–4] for future work on ADSL to examine the ideas presented in options 2 and 3 need to assess these issues.

Pair-gain systems are used in many countries to provide a second POTS line over a single copper pair. These are called *DAML* systems in the United States and *DACS* in the United Kingdom. Many of these systems use ISDN transmission devices in conjunction with additional analog POTS interfaces to present two analog POTS interfaces to the customer. An advantage of the aforementioned approach to operation of ADSL over ISDN is that it would be equally applicable to operating ADSL over such pair-gain systems. Consider Figure 10.29, which shows ISDN only under ADSL.

4. *ISDN embedded in ADSL:* No lifeline powering of ISDN transmission pipe and attached CPE as is normal for some telcos ISDN service (especially in Europe). But, lifeline telephony available from normal analog POTS in baseband. Need to switch off ADSL interleaver for acceptable delay. Latency reduces from around 20 to 2 ms for DMT and <1 ms for CAP. The 2-ms residual delay is acceptable in terms of avoiding voice echo cancellation and may accord with some telco philosophies on end-to-end delay apportionment for overall voice network design. However, some ISDN specific standards, say, 1.25 ms. Switching off interleaving to minimize delay will reduce impulsive noise immunity (on/off hook transients, ringing, access network and in-home impulse pickup, etc.). The resulting impact on range is very difficult to determine since impulse noise occurrence and magnitude varies considerably from line to line. However, some reduction in ADSL range and planning rule guidelines would almost certainly be required for acceptable BER performance of the ISDN portion of the ADSL payload. Note, the rest of the ADSL payload (used for VoD, etc.) could still be routed through the interleaver independently. The ADSL standard accommodates programmability of tradeoff between BER performance and latency for different data streams (e.g., ISDN and VoD) transported over the same ADSL line. Embedding enough payload capacity for ISDN (160 kbps) won't impact the range of an echo-canceling ADSL system since upstream and downstream can overlap and hence both will have a lower-band edge of around 10 to 40 kHz (depending on splitter). It will have an impact on an FDM implementation since compared to say a VoD-type 16-kbps return channel we now need an additional 160 kbps. Hence

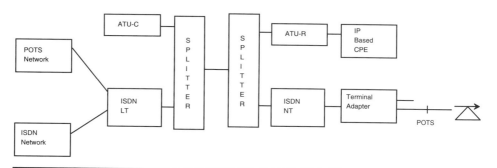

Figure 10.29 ISDN Only under ADSL

to make room for the fatter upstream channel, the downstream channel must be moved up from around 50 kHz lower-band edge to 85 to 100 kHz. This reduces performance margin by around 2 to 3 dB (<300 m on 0.5-mm cable). For Internet access, we'd want more than a 16 kbps VoD-type upstream rate anyway in order to get maximum throughput on a 1.5- to 2-Mbps downstream channel (given the way TCP/IP works, a 14:1 asymmetry ratio is believed to be adequate). Hence the additional return channel payload capacity needed for ISDN would not be much different from that required in a good Internet access 1.5- to 2-Mbps ADSL design. Thus the range loss due to incremental capacity requirement will not even be significant in an FDM implementation if the upstream capacity is shared for Internet access and ISDN. However, if ISDN and fast Internet access are required to operate simultaneously, dedicated upstream capacity is needed for the ISDN, and so the capacity for upstream Internet communications is additional. This could have a significant impact on reach in an FDM implementation but won't affect an echo-canceling implementation. This scenario offers both an analog POTS baseband voice path and potentially a digital ISDN derived voice channel (i.e., a second POTS line). If a second voice channel is not required, then potentially the analog baseband POTS channel could be relinquished to yield additional capacity-rich spectra for ADSL transmission. The customer's telephony would be provided by a digitally derived 64-kbit/s channel within the ISDN portion of the ADSL transmission payload. Some ADSL implementations may then enable the ADSL spectra to be downshifted into the baseband nearer to dc, where there is less signal attenuation. This would enable the ADSL transmission system to recover some or all of the range loss incurred in carrying the additional ISDN payload. This would also avoid the need for a POTS splitter. However, doing this would lose any lifeline POTS capability. Additional interfaces will be required at the customer end. In Europe this would require an S-interface chip (plus glue logic, PCB rework, connector costs, and subsequent impact on production costs). To do the equivalent in the United States would require a more expensive U-interface chip due to the wires-only interface. Appropriate interfaces will be required at the central office end. One option is to extract the ISDN data from the ADSL payload, then put the data through an ISDN U interface chip so that it can then talk to an ISDN line card embedded in the narrowband switch. This could be messy and costly. The alternative is to extract the ISDN payload from several ADSL linecards and multiplex them into a 1.5- or 2-Mbit/s stream for a multiplexed interface (e.g., V5.1) into the telephony switch. The above scenarios have discussed ADSL as a step beyond ISDN. ADSL could also be envisaged as a step towards VDSL. In this scenario the ADSL is more likely to be an ATM to the home solution in order to provide a smooth migration and complimentary deployment capability. ISDN couldn't then be embedded in the ADSL due to ATM buffering/packetization delays. The alternative is to channelize the ADSL to have ATM and non-ATM paths. This could be very complex and expensive. Consider Figure 10.30, which shows ISDN embedded in ADSL.

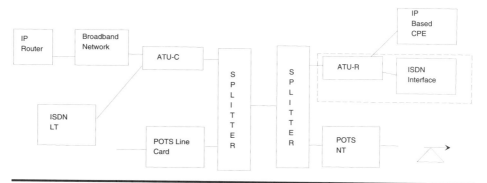

Figure 10.30   ISDN Embedded in ADSL

5. *Don't try to deliver ISDN and ADSL on the same pair:* This option avoids a special hybrid ISDN/ADSL solution by using a second copper pair if joint ISDN and ADSL takeup is expected to be minimal. Why load the costs of the ADSL solution for all ADSL Internet customers if, say, <5 percent want both ADSL and ISDN capability? A second pair, provision of a terminal adapter or offering the customer a CPE swap/upgrade deal, may be cheaper overall to satisfy those few customers wanting simultaneous ISDN and ADSL. This latter idea assumes they were using ISDN CPE only for Internet access. If the customer was also using it for switched access (using ISDN signaling) to their work LAN for teleworking, how does ADSL replace this capability ? So that the telco may need to provide a second pair for such customers. Will there be many? Provision of a second pair, while costly, may be required only for a few customers. In addition, it should be noted that in countries where the incumbent telco faces increasing competition from other network providers using non-copper-based media (such as radio or fiber-coax), any loss of customers to the competition will increase the availability of spare pairs. Apart from avoiding any impact on ADSL equipment designs, this option would also not require the complex central office wiring necessary to connect a customer's ADSL line to ISDN line cards, POTS line cards, *and* a broadband connection to an Internet service provider. It would also avoid the problem of fault handling on a copper line potentially carrying three services (via POTS, ISDN, and ADSL) with associated impact on test equipment and telco operational processes. Do we really need this technology evolution step when in many countries ISDN deployment levels are low or to business customers only? In such territories it may be sensible to skip the ISDN Internet access step for mass market/residential fast Internet access. The option of skipping the ISDN step would depend on the ready availability of a broadband switching and backbone network that could be used in conjunction with ADSL. The issue is how much future ISDN revenue is a telco already relying on to happen and how much of this is expected from the residential sector. Could this

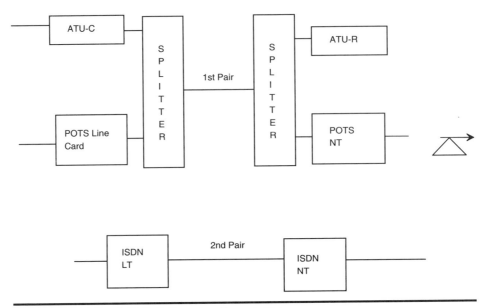

Figure 10.31   ISDN and ADSL Delivered on Separate Pairs

be replaced by ADSL revenue, and what are the business/residential cross-product line dependencies for ISDN? Consider Figure 10.31, which shows ISDN and ADSL delivered on separate pairs.

References

ETSI Contribution 96/2/T04, *ADSL* issue 2, Deutsche Telekom AG, Stephan Heuser.
ETSI Contribution 96/2T/10, *ADSL Future Work,* Motorola, Bernard Dugerdil.
ETSI Contribution 96/2/T15, *ADSL over ISDN BRA,* Ericsson Austria AG, Franz Haberl.
ETSI Contribution, 96/2/T16, *ADSL ISDN Filter,* Ericsson Austria AG, Mr. Etlinger.
ISDN to ADSL for Internet Access, ADSLForum 96-083, Gavin Young, BT, Sept. 19, 1998 (London Meeting).
ETSI Contribution, 97, Tel Aviv meeting, Orckit.
ADSL-Forum/97-139, *On the Migration Path from ISDN to ADSL,* Boaz Rippin, Orckit, Brussels meeting, Sept. 16, 1997.

ADSL in an ATM network: From Internet only to full service

In a starting network scenario, a customer is provided with an ADSL transmission system that connects into an ATM backbone network via an access multiplexer with an ATM network interface [known as a *digital subscriber loop access multiplexer* (DSLAM)]. However, the ADSL remote unit presents an Ethernet 10BaseT interface to the CPE. The system is aimed mainly at use for Internet access and remote teleworking/LAN access. The ADSL remote unit may include integrated bridge/router functionality. Somewhere in this access connection there is functionality to perform protocol conversion between that used at the Ethernet 10BaseT interface and that used in the ATM. The ADSL central office equipment connects to the ATM switched network via an SDH/SONET interface carrying ATM traffic for multiple users. This interface point could conform to VB5.1 or VB5.2 once it is standardized. In some implementations, the multiplexer may perform statistical multiplexing and ATM peak cell rate (PCR) policing to ensure that some customers cannot violate their traffic contract at the expense of other customers. This would add to the complexity of the multiplexer and could require additional buffering. Management of this traffic issue is even more important if rate-adaptive ADSL is used since there is potential for short-range customers to use higher data rates over the ADSL than other customers. At the remote end, the data is presented on a standard fixed rate 10BaseT Ethernet interface.

Consider Figure 10.32, which shows ATM over ADSL for Internet access. The attractions of this scenario are that the CPE does not have to perform ATM adaptation and the ADSL remote unit could be directly connected to the Ethernet card in a PC. The disadvantages are that the ADSL or multiplexer equipment has to perform AAL and perhaps signaling protocol conversion functionality, which adds complexity. It also reduces the flexibility of this ADSL access equipment since it now contains a service-specific element in the access equipment. Another potential disadvantage to the telco is that it puts the same AAL and protocol conversion functionality requirements on any fiber and radio access equipment that the telco may wish to use interchangeably to more economically or conveniently deliver the same service. The protocol conversion will undoubtedly complicate system integration and testing. It is worth noting that while Ethernet cards for PCs are readily available, these reside mostly in business PCs connected to corporate LANs. Most residential users would still have to buy this card for their machine since the dominant communications connection is via a voiceband modem or for a minority, ISDN.

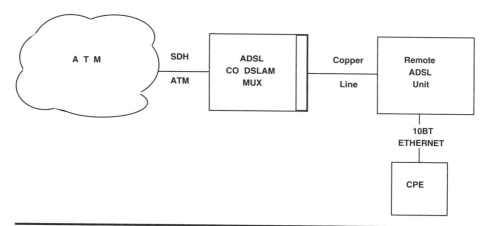

Figure 10.32 ATM over ADSL for Internet Access

In the target network scenario the customer is provided with an ADSL transmission system that presents an ATM interface to their CPE, thus transporting ATM cells end to end over the access link. A wide variety of services are provided over this network.

In this scenario ADSL is acting purely as a transparent pipe, with some cell routing in the access multiplexer to direct traffic to the appropriate line card. The access multiplexer acts as a PVC cross-connect and with the implementation of suitable signaling to an ATM switch higher up in the network, this approach would present a B-ISDN connection to the customer [1]. The ADSL exchange equipment connects to the ATM switched network via an SDH or SONET interface carrying ATM traffic for many users. Cell routing is performed on the traffic to direct it to the appropriate line card, that is, cell delineation, demultiplexing, and rate decoupling from the network to the ADSL line. The individual customer's cell stream is presented on an ATM physical layer interface (such as a 25-Mbps 4-bit/5-bit encoded NRZI ATM Forum interface) at the ADSL remote unit.

Consider Figure 10.33, which shows ATM over ADSL for a multiservice access network. The attractions of this network scenario are that it is relatively simple as far as the ADSL is concerned and would result in an ADSL system that is compatible with and complementary to a longer-term ATM access delivery technology such as FTTN/VDSL. No signaling protocol conversion is required in the access equipment, and there are no service specific elements in the access equipment. It could present a simple open standard interface to the CPE with signaling presented on the same wires and interface separated out by cell headers. It could also facilitate simple integrated end-to-end management all the way to the CPE including alarm surveillance and connectivity verification via ATM OAM cell flows. Several vendors are already developing

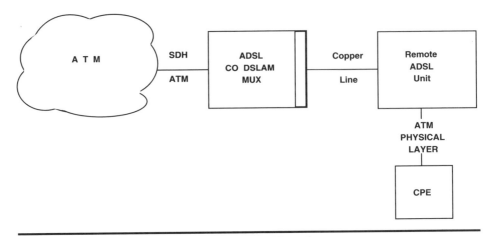

Figure 10.33 ATM over ADSL for Multiservice Access Network

PC cards and set-top boxes that would constitute the CPE that could be connected to this network. The disadvantages are that the CPE must perform the ATM AAL function, and implement Q.2931 call control (i.e., the B-ISDN terminal adapter function). This could, for example, drain some of a PC's available processing power. Until ATM switches implementing Q.2931 are widely deployed, nailed-up or permanent VCs (PVCs) are necessary in early manifestations of this architecture until switched VCs (SVCs) are implemented. In this latter scenario the access multiplexer could be purely an ATM cross-connect with signaling dialog occurring between the CPE and ATM switch. Hence SVCs would be supported by "tunneling" signaling messages through to a UNI at the ATM switch. Alternatively, the DSLAM could evolve to an ATM edge switch presenting a NNI to the ATM switch. Another issue to resolve in this pure ATM architecture is flow control and the dimensioning (and location) of suitable buffers for traffic shaping. Some of today's ATM NIC cards that would reside in a PC may just burst out the data.

Drivers.   The descriptions here explain commercial and technical influences that could cause a telco to deploy the access network for Internet access described as the starting network scenario described above and then want to migrate it toward the end-to-end ATM network described as the target network scenario. Initial trials of ADSL were focused very much on interactive services aimed at the mass residential market (VoD, home shopping, home banking, etc.). However, none of these particular services is widely regarded as a killer application in its own right. It is generally considered that ultimately a package of such services will be needed to be competitive. However, in the short term, high-speed Internet access has become thought of by many as the most likely single service that may make a viable business on its own. Much of the telco interest in using ADSL for such a service is to counter the threat of cable modems. Cable modems will enable cable companies to offer a high-speed Internet access service over HFC networks. ADSL is seen by many as the most straightforward telco response to offer an equivalent or better service over the twisted copper-pair telephony network.

The development of cable modems is progressing rapidly and so there is great interest from telcos in making a high-speed Internet access data service the first focus of any ADSL deployment. Many PCs are (or can be) equipped with an Ethernet card with a 10BaseT interface for "network connection." Such cards are mature products and are widely and economically available. Hence adding this sort of interface to the remote ADSL equipment will enable many customers to directly plug in their PCs [or perhaps network computers, (NCs) in the near future] without additional expense. This is more true of the business PC environment since far fewer home PCs today contain an Ethernet card. Another point to note is the huge growth in laptop and notebook PCs. PCMCIA Ethernet cards are available for these as a neat plug-in option. The equivalent developments for an ATM 25 interface are not as mature. A benefit of focusing on Internet access for initial ADSL deployment is that it targets a customer base more likely to be early adopters of such new technology and encompasses business applications such as teleworking, remote LAN access, and intranetworking. This sector of the market is more likely to pay a little extra for what will be a premium service in the early days until equipment prices have reached a mature base level. This is unlike a mass residential service such as VoD, which will be benchmarked against the local video store from day 1.

The data WANs that make up a large proportion of today's Internet backbone use technologies such as Frame Relay (FR) (IBM) and switched multimegabit data service (SMDS). However, increasingly telcos are looking to deploy high-speed ATM networks to transport Internet traffic simultaneously with many other kinds of services. This has resulted in a lot of interest in ADSL or xDSL access multiplexers (DSLAMs) that can connect to such an ATM network. Hence the combination of several drivers result in the starting network scenario described earlier. These drivers are as follows: growth of ATM backbone networks and subsequent acceptance of ATM interconnection by Internet service providers (ISPs), perceived need for high-speed Internet access, threat of competition from cable modems, and availability of cost-effective Ethernet cards for PCs. From the above it is clear why the current focus for high-speed access networks is Internet access. However, most telcos aspire to evolve to a "full-service" network at some time in the future. Some believe that such full-service capabilities may evolve from the Internet itself with the development of real-time protocols, bandwidth reservation (RSVP) for improved QoS, and so on. Others believe that the ultimate flexible, multiservice network must be based on ATM. The migration scenario considered in this document assumes the latter vision and hence part of the migration strategy must consider how Internet access (using TCP/IP) is supported over an ATM network. ATM cards already exist for PCs and set-top boxes and cable modem vendors are also addressing the same development and migration issues involving Ethernet and ATM customer interfaces. An ADSL system that transports ATM cells into some form of home network to deliver a mixture of services such as Internet access, VoD, or broadcast TV is technically feasible today. A combination of maturing equipment, declining prices, increasing availability, and installed volume of ATM equipment will determine how rapidly this "pure ATM" network vision is reached. The next section describes some of the options available in evolving toward this vision.

Options.   In order to facilitate the aforementioned evolution, the starting network scenario needs to include ATM adaptation at some point in the access network. There are three possibilities for where this functionality could be located:

1. At the customer premises (in the remote ADSL unit or a terminal adapter).

2. In a processor within the access multiplexer supporting multiple lines.

3. On each ADSL line-card within the multiplexer. Consider additional information presented here in detail.

ATM adaptation at the customer-end equipment. ATM cells from the backbone network are routed to the appropriate multiplexer line card and on to the ADSL remote unit. The ATM AAL and protocol conversion are carried out by a converter circuit which may be integrated into the ADSL remote unit or could even be housed in a separate collocated box or plug-on module in the manner of a terminal adapter. Generally, additional boxes are not desirable. This converter functionality can be thought of as a B-ISDN terminal adapter. The data are presented to the customer on a standard fixed rate Ethernet 10BaseT interface. Consider Figure 10.34, which shows ATM to 10BaseT Conversion in the remote ADSL Unit. An advantage of this scenario is that the (in-built) terminal adapter functionality could be common to copper, radio, and fiber delivery mechanisms. Although this results in a service-specific (Ethernet) element in the access equipment, it is only at the network periphery, and so an upgrade to full ATM delivery could be as simple as changing the remote unit. If the ATM protocol conversion is placed in a separate terminal adapter box, upgrade could simply involve removing this box. However, in some countries this may raise regulatory complications with respect to the boundary between network and customer-owned equipment.

ATM adaptation by a shared processor in the access multiplexer. This option has the advantage over option 1 that the costs of the processor, SAR function and buffering needed for ATM conversion can be shared among several customers. Unlike option 1, where migration simply required swapping a remote

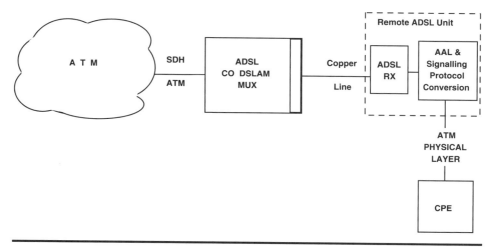

Figure 10.34 ATM-to-10BaseT Conversion in Remote ADSL Unit

unit, upgrade from this scenario could require a significant upgrade to the multiplexer in addition to changing the remote ADSL unit. Hence, it may not be simple to migrate this option to the target network scenario unless a significant amount of this functionality is implemented in software.

ATM adaptation on each multiplexer ADSL line card. This approach has the per line ATM adaptation functionality (and hence complexity) similar to that of option 1. However, like option 2, the problem is with migration to the target ATM all the way to the CPE scenario. Such an upgrade could now involve changing out both the multiplexer ADSL line card and the ADSL remote unit.

For any of the above network migration strategies to be successful, the target network scenario of ATM all the way to the CPE must still be capable of delivering TCP/IP Internet access since in the above scenario this is the legacy service that initiated the deployment of ADSL and will probably still be a significant service in the portfolio to be delivered by the ATM ADSL "full-service" network. There are several options for supporting TCP/IP in an ATM network, and these will now be discussed in more detail.

IP over ATM (IPOA). Classic IP over ATM, as defined by the RFC 1577, predates LANE (LAN emulation), and already has a significant installed base. Strictly this will not provide a general Ethernet service to the user, but a useful set of network services including the World Wide Web, for example, can be delivered using IP. This is a layer 3 routing protocol, unlike LANE which provides layer 2 bridging only.

Thus IP can be implemented directly over ATM [2], in which case ATM is used to connect local LAN segments and IP end stations and routers instead of ethernet. This approach is applicable only to a single IP subnet with no multicasting. The ATM network will in general consist of a number of logical IP subnets (LISs), and each Ethernet segment will also be a separate LIS. The various LISs are interconnected by routers, hence in this scenario the ATU-R would be a small router, providing IP routing between its ATM (ADSL) and Ethernet ports. In summary, each ATM LIS has a server for ATM Address Resolution Protocol (ATMARP, explained below), which provides translation between IP addresses and ATM E164 addresses. Ethernet segments operate Address Resolution Protocol (ARP) in a distributed manner using broadcasts to translate IP to Ethernet MAC addresses. If the ATU-R receives a packet from the Ethernet, it will consult a table to determine the IP address of the next hop router to forward the packet to, and which of its ports to use. Assuming the next hop is via the ATM interface, the ATU-R then needs to know the ATM address of the next hop router. It gets this information by consulting the ATMARP server of the ATM LIS to which it is connected using protocols defined by RFC 1577. The ATU-R would then use UNI signaling to establish a connection to the next hop router. If the ATU-R had a preexisting VPI/VCI to the next hop router, this could be determined at the first stage, in which case the ATMARP request and VC setup would not be needed. The ATU-R needs to hold a table of the MAC and IP addresses of all the stations on the home Ethernet which require IP service. It must register the IP addresses it provides access to with the ATMARP server of its logical IP subnet (LIS). Hosts from different IP subnets must communicate via an intermediate IP router even when a direct VC connection over the ATM network between the two is possible. Hence this approach has limitations. Each separate network administration unit configures its hosts and routers within a closed logical IP subnetwork (LIS), which is effectively the equivalent of a LAN. Each LIS operates and communicates independently of other LISs on the same ATM network. All members of the LIS have the same IP network/subnetwork number and address mask.

Communication to hosts outside the local LIS must go via the IP router, which is configured as a member of one or more LISs. This may have implications for the partitioning of the LIS and location of the router within the target ADSL architecture. For example, would it be practical to have all customers within a central office area form part of a single LIS? Alternatively, a business or advanced residential user with multiple CPEs connected to the ADSL remote unit via a hub could form a LIS. IP addresses are often chosen by the customer, whereas the physical addresses (data equivalent of the telephone number) are often assigned by the telco. ATM assigns each end terminal an address which must be used when establishing a virtual circuit. An ATM physical address is larger than an IP address and thus cannot be encoded within the IP address to give static address "binding" (linking an IP address to an ATM hardware address). Given that the target ADSL architecture is aimed at deployment in large telco networks and not smaller private networks, static address binding is not viable because of the amount of IP addresses that would be required for a large service rollout (say, several tens or hundreds of thousands of IP addresses). Creating and maintaining the address tables would be unmanageable.

Traditional LANs such as Ethernet use ARP (the Address Resolution Protocol) for dynamic address resolution to find the hardware address of another machine [9]. It does this by broadcasting on the LAN an ARP request containing the IP address of the machine for which the hardware address is required. All machines on the LAN receive this and the one which matches the IP address sends back its hardware address so that data communication can commence. For dynamic address allocation where an IP address is not permanently hard-wired to a hardware address, at start-up a host needs to contact a server to be given its IP address. RARP (Reverse ARP) is used for this purpose. On bootup the computer would broadcast a RARP request which contains its hardware address. The server on the LAN would then look to its mapping table and send back an IP address to correspond to the hardware address.

From the descriptions above it is clear that both ARP and RARP rely on broadcasting onto the LAN. ATM however does not support hardware broadcast in this sense, and so the ARP and RARP methods cannot be used to bind IP addresses on ATM networks. ATM PVCs complicate address binding. Since the PVCs are configured manually, a host knows only the VCI/VPI pair. Software on the host may not know the IP address or ATM hardware address of the remote endpoint. Hence any IP to ATM hardware address binding protocol must provide for the identification of a remote computer connected over a PVC as well as the dynamic creation of SVCs to known destinations. SVCs further complicate address binding because when setting up the VC, the destination IP address needs to be mapped to an ATM hardware endpoint. Also, the destination IP address needs to be mapped to the VPI/VCI pair for the circuit to be used each time data are sent over the ATM network. ATMARP is the address discovery protocol to resolve between IP addresses and ATM addresses. ATMARP is the same as classic ARP in a LAN environment, but modified to exist in an ATM LIS. There is no protocol to associate the CPE with the default gateway, and so each host is equipped at setup with the address of the ATMARP server, rather than broadcast a request as in shared medium LANs. Hence this approach requires ARP server functionality at the ATM switch, which is not widely implemented yet. When hosts apply to an ATMARP server for the ATM address of the destination host, the ATMARP server consults its tables and returns a ATMARP reply containing the ATM address required. Each host in the LIS must register with the server by supplying its IP address and ATM address to the server. The ATMARP server uses ATMARP requests to update its tables. Each client in the LIS is also responsible for refreshing its ATMARP information with the server at regular intervals since the address binding is aged and after a timeout must be revalidated (done by opening a VC to the server and exchanging the ATMARP setup packets) or discarded. For PVCs, Inverse ATMARP is used to discover the ATM and IP address of remote computers.

ATMARP packets and IP datagrams are encoded using AAL5 and encapsulated using LLC/SNAP encapsulation. Multiprotocol encapsulation over ATM adaptation layer 5 is described in detail in RFC 1483. It provides for an alternative method of encapsulation which is more suitable for ATM switched virtual circuits and uses the signaling protocols of B-ISDN. The IP over ATM working group of the IETF issued RFC 1755 ATM signaling support for IP over ATM to act as an implementation guide intended to foster interoperability among RFC 1577, RFC 1483, and UNI ATM signaling.

In current IP implementations, communications between nodes on different LISs, even if these are on the same ATM network, must pass through a router every time a LIS boundary is crossed . This is inefficient because there can be a chain of routers, each of which is a potential bottleneck, and it is not possible to have a single ATM connection between source and destination with a specified QOS. Other concerns are whether IP alone can support a sufficiently rich set of services, and the cost and complexity of the router function required in the ATU-R. Also, the address space of the current version, IPv4, is running out.

A new version, IPv6, has been developed which expands the address space. There are also new techniques such as Next Hop Resolution Protocol (NHRP) which enable cut-through routing, avoiding the need for traffic to go through multiple IP routers within the ATM network with consequent throughput and latency limitations. Also under development is the Real Time Protocol (RTP) for transfer of real-time data such as audio or video over IP networks. The IETF is working on a new protocol called *Next Hop Resolution Protocol* (NHRP). The goal is to enable a host to bypass some or all of the routers between source and destination hosts by establishing a direct connection through the ATM switches. NHRP makes routing databases within the ATM network accessible for virtual circuit call setup. An ATM address resolution request is passed from NHRP server to NHRP server until the ATM address for the destination IP address, or that of the router at the exit of the ATM network is discovered. There may be multiple LISs within the ATM network, each with an NHRP server, in which case this process will cross LIS boundaries using multiple hops in much the same way as the classic approach, except that only routing information is transported. Once the ATM address is determined, it is passed back to the requester, along the same route, allowing the intermediate servers to learn the route. When the requester receives the ATM address of the destination, it can establish a direct ATM circuit to the destination using ATM signaling. This is a cut-through route which bypasses any LIS boundaries within the ATM network; hence it avoids router bottlenecks and can have a defined ATM QOS. In some circumstances, traffic may still have to pass through routers, however, for example, when crossing administrative boundaries or firewalls, or if the destination is not on the ATM network.

The main problem with the IP-over-ATM approach is the lack of an inherent protocol to dynamically allocate IP addresses. It has been described above how impractical it is for each customer in the ADSL access architecture to have a static IP address preallocated. Anyone wishing to sell such a service is unlikely to be able to get more than a thousand or so addresses from the IPV4 administrators. Hence this presents a serious scaling issue. It may be possible to device a proxy architecture that employs a PVC from the CPE or ADSL remote unit to a DHCP or BOOTP server which then allocates the IP addresses dynamically. The problem of the remote ADSL/CPE sending out broadcasts to address allocation servers could potentially be overcome by using a router (in the central office or higher up the network) to cache the broadcast and the VC it came in on and then send out a directed request to a preconfigured DHCP server. The returning response can then be tied back to the correct customer VC and passed to the ADSL remote unit and CPE.

Classic IP over ATM is tailored to the transport of just IP traffic and hence is simpler than LAN emulation and generates less overhead. ATM is not hidden from the higher layers as in LAN emulation, and so IP over ATM can take advantage of ATM's features such as ability to specify quality of service, cell delay, and maximum PDU size (which can exceed 9000 bytes). However, this does mean that to access a device with a legacy LAN, one must go through a bridge or router.

The following is an overview of the functions required at the ATU-R, in the network, and at the service provider.

In the ATU-R:

Ethernet PHY

Ethernet MAC

IP ARP: provides IP address resolution to the Ethernet (returns the ATU-Rs MAC address for access to network services, which it recognizes by the requested subnet address being different from that of the local LAN)

Routing function: provides routing of IP packets to Ethernet MAC frames (i.e., the ATU-R is a small router, it needs a table of the MAC and IP addresses of connected CPE)

Logical IP subnet client: operates IP-over-ATM protocols on the network interface ATM network interface (includes UNI signaling)

In the network:

ATMARP servers: provide address translation between IP and ATM E164 addresses

IP routers: handle communications between logical IP subnets

At the service provider:

IP-based service

Logical IP subnet client

ATM network interface

LAN emulation (LANE)

The starting network scenario described earlier effectively requires some form of bridging functionality to connect the customer end "LAN segments" to the ATM network. These bridges can also perform routing functions at the network layer. LAN emulation (LANE) was developed by the ATM Forum to support physical LAN interconnection. The aim of LANE is to make the ATM network invisible to legacy LANs making it possible to benefit from the performance enhancements of ATM without the expense of hardware or software changes to the end devices. This protocol provides an encapsulation mechanism for transporting IEEE 802.3 Ethernet (or Token Ring) frames across the ATM network using AAL5. It also specifies a set of service protocols that make the ATM network (which is point-to-point connection-oriented using switches) emulate a traditional LAN (which is broadcast or point-to-multipoint connectionless-oriented using bridges and routers). LANE is a general solution that allows any protocol defined to run over Ethernet or Token Ring to work transparently in an ATM environment. There are major differences between LAN technology and ATM. In a LAN data packets are broadcast to every station and the LAN protocols such as Ethernet are designed to take advantage of this shared media characteristic.

In a point-to-point ATM network, data packets must in effect be duplicated and sent down multiple wires. Additionally, Ethernet is connectionless whereas ATM is connection oriented (either "nailed up" by PVCs or established via SVC call setup). The LANE protocol provides an ATM network with the ability to behave like a shared-media, connectionless LAN by creating an emulated LAN. It defines a service interface for higher-layer network protocols including IP. This requires a new ATM MAC layer beneath the logical link control (LLC) sublayer to give the appearance of a shared medium such as an IEEE 802.x LAN. This is implemented in a software driver that provides a common interface to upper-layer LAN software as existing LAN drivers do. Many CPE vendors are implementing the protocol in adapter cards, routers, and small switches. The LANE software architecture uses a client/server model. There are four components to the LANE system:

1. The LAN emulation client (LEC) whose main function is to communicate with the remote LAN emulation components (LES, BUS, and LECS).

2. The LAN emulation server (LES), which provides a facility for registration and resolving a MAC address into an ATM address.

3. The broadcast and unknown server (BUS), which forwards broadcast/multicast frames and delivers unicast frames for an unregistered or address-unresolvable LAN host.

4. The LAN emulation configuration server (LECS), which locates the LES and obtains configuration information for each ATM segment. Collectively the three servers are called the *LAN emulation service*. LANE provides only layer 2 bridging; therefore the service must be provided to the telco network as Ethernet frames via a LAN emulation client (LEC), although in practice this could run on a direct-attached ATM server. If the service is not native to Ethernet, then a routing function must exist prior to the service provider LEC interface.

Consider Figure 10.35, which shows an overview of LANE.

Ethernet uses a 6-byte media access control (MAC) address to uniquely identify each end station (e.g., PC). ATM end stations are identified by a 20-byte ATM address. So, to send an Ethernet LAN packet to a particular MAC address requires the LANE protocol to provide an address resolution or mapping service to identify the ATM address associated with the destination MAC address. This happens by the LEC software intercepting the MAC address and signaling to the LES, which then provides the corresponding ATM address to the LEC. In a mature ATM network, the LEC could then use Q.2931 signalling to set up an SVC to the destination over which the data frames are subsequently sent. The database that maps corresponding MAC and ATM addresses is set up by the LES. If the LES doesn't have the destina-

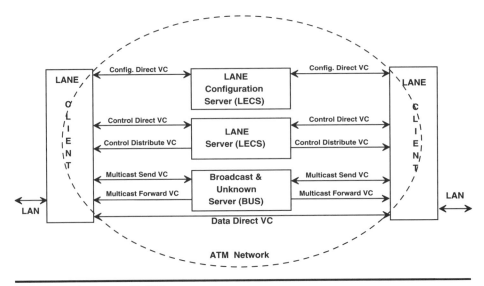

Figure 10.35 Overview of LANE

tion address in its address table, then the source LEC sends the data frame to the BUS, which broadcasts to all stations on the ATM network. When the Ethernet LAN station is turned on, its LEC software sends a request (LE-ARP) to the LES asking to join an emulated LAN by requesting the ATM address of the destination. In a multiple-step process, the LAN client joins the emulated LAN and sends its ATM and MAC addresses to the LES, which builds it into an address table. This process is very SVC-intensive, with the LANE software setting up and tearing down connections continually. Large amounts of control information flow between each client and the servers for initialization, registration, address resolution, and so on. There are scaling issues to be resolved with this option, particularly in the area of server resilience and distribution (i.e., where to locate the server functionality). Before SVCs are widely available, it would be possible to transport the information using four PVCs over the ADSL link: three for the control information (LES, BUS, and LECS) and one for the routed data. There are concerns that this PVC approach could make LANE totally unmanageable for a large-scale ADSL deployment until SVCs are available. However, a more appropriate way forward in the ADSL fast Internet access scenario would be to use a radically stripped-down version of LANE to enable only one PVC to be needed (shared for BUS and data). LANE was developed to emulate the broadcast media used in LANs. However, in the target application of using ADSL for fast Internet access, the main aim is to establish a point-to-point IP link between the customers ADSL unit and the ISP. Note that multiple CPEs may be connected to the ADSL remote unit. Full LANE software features are not required in this ADSL Internet access scenario. Specifically, the broadcast capabilities (via BUS) are not required, and the LES software could have reduced functionality. The client version of the LANE software could reside in the ADSL remote unit or a terminal adapter such as an interworking unit for the starting network scenario described earlier. The amount of processing power and memory required to implement this could therefore have a direct impact on ADSL complexity. As the network evolves to delivering ATM to the CPE as in the target scenario, any client software could reside on the CPE, but the aim would be to use existing standard commercially available protocol stacks on the CPE as far as possible. The server functionality of LANE (which may potentially be a reduced functionality version) could reside in the ATM ADSL access multiplexer, the ISP server/access point router, or an ATM switch (perhaps an edge switch/adjunct). Another issue for this option is where to locate the routing functionality that will allow communication between different emulated LANs.

An advantage of LANE over legacy LANs (particularly when ADSL access is employed) is that congestion is much less since most traffic is carried over dedicated connections per end user. The major advantage of LANE compared to IP over ATM is that it can support multiple protocols (IPX, AppleTalk, DECnet, etc.) and not just IP. This is because it is a layer 2 service bridging LAN and ATM addresses at the MAC layer. It is independent of any higher-layer services, protocols, and applications and effectively hides ATM from them. The vast majority of networks today are mixed-protocol environments, and so an IP-only solution such as IP over ATM poses limitations.

Recent work on MPOA is described below. The disadvantages of LANE are scalability (particularly of the BUS), router bottlenecks and cost, the need to provide an Ethernet-based service or routing at the service provider, high amounts of broadcast traffic, and lack of ATM QOS due to use of unspecified bit rate and the fact that it is limited to the Ethernet maximum frame size of 1500 bytes. The following is a simplified view of the functions required at the ATU-R, in the network, and at the service provider:

In the ATU-R:

Ethernet PHY

Ethernet MAC

LAN emulation client: provides MAC level bridging

ATM network interface (includes UNI signaling)

In the network:

LAN emulation server (LES): provides address translation between MAC and ATM addresses.

LAN emulation configuration server (LECS): provides LEC with addresses of the other servers.

Broadcast and unknown server (BUS): emulates LAN broadcast features which ATM does not normally provide. Used for essential purposes such as LAN address resolution (e.g., for IP). This is the most likely bottleneck in LANE, and its implementation will need very careful consideration for a large network.

ATM routers: interconnecting emulated LANs. The size of an emulated LAN is limited by its ability to support broadcasts; hence there will typically be many small emulated LANs.

At the service provider:

Ethernet-based service

LAN emulation client

ATM network interface

Consider Figure 10.36, which shows the LAN emulation protocol stacks and possible location of functionality.

1. *Multiprotocol over ATM (MPOA):* MPOA, developed by the ATM forum, aims to provide network layer routing for multiple protocols, although initial work concentrates on TCP/IP. It combines and builds on the features of LANE and IP over ATM, providing a way to route IP, and in principle other protocols, with high performance and low latency. It allows traffic to be transported to its destination via a single-hop virtual circuit. It also provides access to ATM quality of service features and supports network-layer virtual subnets and virtual routing. MPOA is a recent development that is still evolving within the ATM Forum and hence is not yet widely supported by any commercial equipment. MPOA will provide end-to-end layer 3 connectivity across the ATM network, including hosts attached directly to the ATM layer and others to legacy LAN technologies. It will enable higher-layer protocols to take advantage of ATM quality of service features and initially used the LANE specification as a baseline text. The Resource Reservation Protocol (known as RSVP) being developed in the IETF would be used for QoS guarantees for connections between systems over an ATM network. However, this is not MPOA-specific. MPOA may use a variant of Next Hop Resolution Protocol (NHRP) of option 4 for route determination. This would use SVCs for data connections with holdtimes more like a stream of related data information as opposed to intermittent bursts. SVCs would also be used when the data service needs a QoS guarantee from the ATM network. MPOA essentially defines a distributed router. MPOA clients within edge devices at the periphery of the ATM network (e.g., the ATU-R) are responsible for forwarding packets while the expensive processing and intelligence of the router resides on servers within the networks which build and maintain routing tables and supply routes to the edge devices on request. Traffic does not pass through the route servers, but is routed directly between edge devices over the ATM network. MPOA clients first attempt address resolution via LANE services,

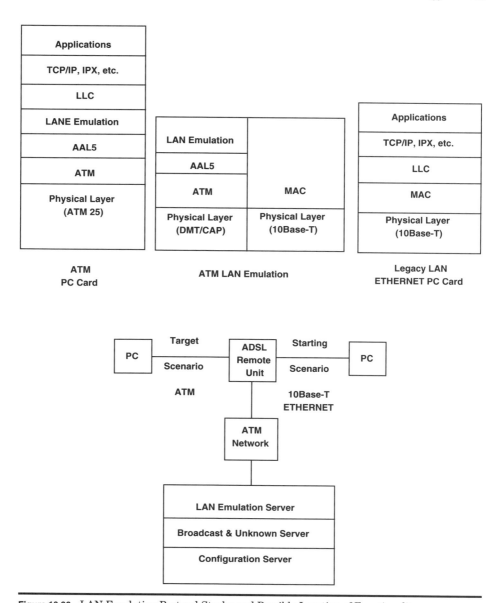

Figure 10.36 LAN Emulation Protocol Stacks and Possible Location of Functionality

and if this fails, they then use the MPOA service. MPOA will use IPv6 addresses to route IP datagrams. However, IP can be carried without MPOA as discussed in the previous section. In a sense MPOA is in competition with IP over ATM in that it offers similar routing functionality, although it potentially supports other protocols. It is not clear whether MPOA will be widely adopted because it may turn out that there is little use of protocols other than

IP. As the LANE specification predates the MPOA draft document, it is viewed that LANE devices will be the first that are stable enough to offer a service. However, ultimately MPOA may provide a more easily scaled solution. The following is an overview of the functions required at the ATU-R, in the network, and at the service provider.

In the ATU-R:
   Ethernet PHY
   Ethernet MAC
   LAN emulation client: provides MAC level bridging for the local subnet
   MPOA client
   ATM network interface (includes UNI signaling)

In the network:
   LANE servers: LECS, LES, BUS
   MPOA servers: configuration, route, multicast/MARS, and forwarding servers

At the service provider:
   Service based on IP or other protocol
   ATM host with MPOA client(s)
   ATM network interface

2. *ATM Gateway:* Either the ATU-R or other CPE (e.g., a set-top box) could act as a gateway to the ATM-delivered network services. In this scenario, the gateway would have functionality necessary to request and control network services, and would provide some form of high-level interface to the user on the Ethernet side, effectively acting as a server providing network services to the end user. Such a system could be implemented in a number of ways, but in general has the disadvantage of putting most of the complexity into the gateway, which is undesirable if this is the ATU-R. Hybrid approaches may also be possible where the functionality is shared between the ATU-R and end station, but these are likely to be messy because both parties have to be aware of what the other is doing.

3. *Cells in frames:* Cells in frames (CIF), specified by the *cells in frames alliance,* is designed to extend ATM protocols directly to legacy (typically Ethernet) end stations, without requiring any hardware changes at the end station. In effect, it uses Ethernet as an ATM bearer. It achieves this by inserting a software "shim" immediately above the Ethernet card driver to package/unpackage cells into frames and manage multiple queues. The end station operates with ATM signaling and ATM ABR flow control. If ABR flow control is not available end-to-end on a particular path, then TCP can be used as a fallback (to allow this switching, modified TCP software is needed on the end station). The end station also needs an ATM protocol stack, including UNI signaling, and this is used directly by ATM-aware applications. If

required, non-ATM legacy applications can be supported using LANE, MPOA, or IP over ATM, but this requires the appropriate client on the end station and the corresponding services within the network. In this scenario, the ATU-R becomes a CIF attachment device (CIF-AD) which packages/unpackages cells to/from Ethernet frames and operates the CIF protocols. This makes it transparent to ATM; hence it does not need extra functionality for LANE, MPOA, or IP over ATM—bridging or routing in the ATU-R is avoided, and the required client functions for these services can be carried out by the end stations as necessary. To make best use of the legacy protocol, up to 31 ATM cell payloads are packed into a frame, with a CIF header which includes the ATM cell header for the group of cells (there is also an option to carry cells from multiple VCs within a frame). Multiple queues are used with different priority based on the required QOS. The CIF-AD would normally have ATM switching capability, but could be a multiplexer or physical layer converter, and this may be an attractive option since it may then be possible to avoid having ATM signaling in the ATU-R.

The CIF attachment device (e.g., the ATU-R) will appear to the user as a switched Ethernet hub; i.e., if multiple ports are provided, each should be a separate collision domain, ideally dedicated to one end station, largely avoiding collisions. It is optional for a CIF-AD to support multiple CIF end systems on a segment, but this is undesirable because it allows Ethernet collisions, making it impossible to guarantee QOS. The CIF-AD may or may not support mixing with non-CIF (legacy) LAN traffic. Users may need this if a LAN is already used, but sharing results in collisions, which compromise ATM QOS. Also, the CIF-AD must then provide bridging or switching between ports for the legacy traffic. In such cases, use of switched Ethernet may be essential. The expected configuration is a single CIF end system sharing a half-duplex LAN segment with a single CIF-AD port. This allows proper ATM QOS agreements to be made for ABR service (subject to preventing the capture effect discussed below). Sharing a segment with multiple CIF end stations or legacy LAN stations means that there can be no QOS guarantees, so this is discouraged. This can still provide a valid ATM service, however (i.e., unspecified bit rate, UBR, or ABR with minimum cell rate = 0). For ABR, the CIF-AD should act as a virtual source/destination for the resource management (RM) cells, reducing their rate to approximately 3 percent of the packet rate (from 3 percent of cell rate on the ATM side). This is to allow software ABR flow control to operate on end stations at an acceptable processing load and interrupt rate. The CIF-AD also needs a mechanism to avoid the capture effect which can occur when Ethernet utilization rises above 50 to 60 percent. This occurs if one station transmits a number of frames in rapid succession, without allowing the other station to gain control of the medium. The following is an overview of the functions required at various locations in this scenario.

In the end station:

    ATM protocol stack.

ATM UNI signaling.

CIF shim for cell packaging, queue management, and ATM flow control.

Modified TCP for fallback flow control.

Existing driver.

Existing Ethernet MAC and PHY.

In the ATU-R (CIF-AD):

Ethernet PHY(s).

Ethernet MAC(s) (for each port).

CIF protocol with multiple queues to ensure QOS.

Virtual source/destination reduces RM cell rate and hence processing load on end station.

ATM network interface (includes signaling if ATU-R is a switch—possibly this can be avoided).

In the network:

If services are pure ATM, nothing special is required.

If services are not pure ATM, may require LANE, MPOA, or IP over ATM capability.

At the service provider:

Pure ATM-based service, or Service based on LANE, MPOA, or IP.

4. *Alternative remote bridging methods:* There are alternative methods for enabling the customers PC to communicate with, say, an Internet service provider (ISP) over an ATM network incorporating ADSL access. An appropriate protocol stack built into the ADSL remote unit and a corresponding stack at the ISP entry point can enable Ethernet MAC layer frames to be remotely bridged over an ATM PVC between the customer's ADSL unit and the ISP. Remote bridging is a simpler alternative to LANE. This does not try to emulate a fully functional LAN but instead provides point-to-point transport of LAN frames over the ADSL link and through the ATM network. In this scenario, the ATU-R contains a half-bridge, which encapsulates Ethernet frames and communicates over an ATM channel with a corresponding half-bridge within the network or at the service provider (e.g., ISP), at which point the encapsulation process is reversed. Possible encapsulation protocols that can be used between the AAL5 layer and Ethernet MAC layer in the ADSL remote unit are IEEE 802.2 Logical Link Control with Sub-Network Attachment Point header (LLC/SNAP) and Point-to-Point Protocol (PPP). Remote Bridging is simpler than LANE, but it shares the disadvantages associated with operation at layer 2. Broadcast traffic which passes through the bridges will be concentrated at the service provider; hence there is a scalability issue in determining how much traffic concentration should be used. Packet filtering by the ATU-R may be appropriate to ensure that only essential traffic is forwarded and also to provide protection against accidental or deliberate flooding of the remote bridge.

Pure ATM	Remote Building	LANE	IP	MPOA	Gateway	CIF-AD	CIF-MUX
VC routing ATM layer Home ATM PHY	Filtering Encapsulation 802.3 MAC 802.3 PHY	ATM UNI LANE Client 802.3 MAC 802.3 PHY	ATM UNI LIS Client IP Routing IP ARP 802.3 MAC 802.3 PHY	ATM UNI MPOA Client LANE Client 802.3 MAC 802.3 PHY	ATM UNI Service control User Interface Routing 802.3 MAC 802.3 PHY	ATM UNI RM handling CIF queuing CIF packing 802.3 MAC 802.3 PHY	RM handling CIF queuing CIF packing 802.3 MAC 802.3 PHY

Figure 10.37 Functionality Required at the Home/Access Network Interface

Summary. Figure 10.37 summarizes the key functions required in the interface between the home and the access network for each migration approach considered [11]. The obvious place to carry out these functions is in the ATU-R, but it may be more economic to locate some or all of them further back in the access network, such as in a street multiplexer or at the local exchange. For comparison, the pure ATM case is included in which the ATU-R only needs to provide physical layer translation between different home and access network ATM physical layers, plus limited VC-based routing to differentiate between home and external traffic. There remain several issues to resolve for ATM over ADSL, and some of these are described herein. Consider Figure 10.37, which shows functionality required at the home/access network interface. An low-level ATM interface to the access network is assumed in all cases. Where ATM UNI is shown, this implies that a full ATM UNI including signaling is required.

All the solutions considered involve increased complexity and reduced performance compared with a pure ATM solution the target network scenario. If Ethernet congestion occurs, it is hard to see how QOS can be guaranteed. Congestion may be controlled using switched Ethernet, but this is a higher cost option which would not normally be installed in the home.

References

"Interactive video on demand," Daniel Deloddere, Willem Verbiest, and Henri Verhille (Alcatel Bell), *IEEE Commun.*, May 1994, **32**(5).

Classical IP and ARP over ATM, M. Laubach, IETF RFC 1577, April 1994. (*Note:* RFCs 1483, 1626, and 1755 are also of relevance.)

"Data communications in ATM Networks," N. Kavak, *IEEE Network,* May/June 1995, pp. 28–37.

"Overview of implementing ATM-based enterprise local area network for desktop multimedia computing," Y. T. Hou, L. Tassiulas, and H. J. Chao, *IEEE Commun. Mag.,* April 1996, p. 75.

ATM Forum, LAN Emulation SWG Drafting Group, *LAN Emulation over ATM Specification version 1.0,* Jan. 1995.

"LAN Emulation bridges LEGACY LAN and ATM Networks," *Time to Market,* (Hewlett-Packard), no. 2, summer 1996.

"ATM LAN Emulation," N. Finn and T. Mason, *IEEE Commun. Mag.,* June 1996, pp. 96–100.

"LAN emulation on an ATM network," H. L. Truong, W. W. Ellington, J. Y. Le Boudec, A. X. Meier, and J. W. Pace, *IEEE Commun. Mag.,* May 1995.

Interworking with TCP/IP, Vol. 1., D. E. Cromer, Prentice-Hall, Englewood Cliffs, N.J., 1995.

ADSL in an ATM Network : From Internet only to Full Service, ADSL Forum 96-082, Gavin Young, BT, Sept. 19, 1996 (London meeting).

ATM/Ethernet Interworking for Home Networks, ADSL Forum 97-010, Robert Dearnaley, BT, March 19, 1997 (Amsterdam meeting).

Comments on Unresolved ATM over ADSL Issues, ADSL Forum 97-142, Alan Weissberger, NEC, Sept. 16, 1997 (Brussels meeting).

Internet only via IP ADSL to full-service set via ATM ADSL

In the starting network scenario a customer is provided with IP-based ser-vices over ADSL from a router plus Ethernet switch data-centric architec-ture. Consider Figure 10.38, which shows Internet access via IP-based ADSL architecture.

In the target network scenario the customer is provided with a wide variety of services (e.g., VoD and LAN access) that may necessitate the use of multi-ple protocols via a DSLAM type of network architecture that transports ATM over the ADSL link to the customers CPE. Consider Figure 10.39, which shows multiservice delivery via ATM-based ADSL architecture.

Drivers. One driver is the desire to sell a new service such as VoD over the same copper pair that was previously used only to deliver data-centric ser-vices such as remote LAN access and fast Internet access. Another driver is the desire to have a future proofed access network capable of transporting many new services with different QoS requirements simultaneously over the same ADSL line.

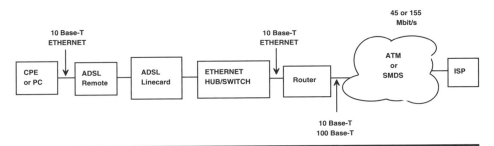

Figure 10.38   Internet Access via IP-Based ADSL Architecture

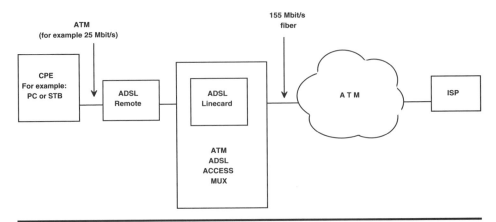

Figure 10.39   Multiservice Delivery via ATM-Based ADSL Architecture

Options. The obvious but undesirable option is to "forklift" the initial ADSL access network and replace it with ADSL equipment that transports ATM to the customer's premises. If the router provides an ATM interface, then it may be possible to employ a network configuration that does not require removal of this subsystem. An alternative is to use a form of access multiplexer that contains layer 2 and layer 3 internetworking functionality. This could enable it to connect to either an Ethernet switch/router or an ATM network depending on the core network interface card. The internetworking capability could enable it to initially terminate ATM in the access mux and forward Ethernet frames carrying IP packets to the customer. Later it could be reconfigured to convey ATM cells all the way to the customer's premises. The remote unit would probably then require upgrading.

It should be noted that in some countries the use of either layer 3 protocol conversion or routing functionality (if deemed analogous to switching) can have a regulatory implication on the classification of the offered service (e.g., perhaps as some form of enhanced service). This may have an impact on the ability of a telco to undertake certain network migration steps described in this working text such as the scenario described in this section.

Internet only via IP ADSL to full-service set via IP only ADSL

In the starting network scenario a customer is provided with IP-based services over ADSL from a router plus Ethernet switch data-centric architecture. The general structure of the IP-over-ADSL access networks is an extension of the traditional enterprise branch access routing model. All subscribers of any given service provider are assigned IP addresses out of that subscriber's domain, either statically or dynamically. Either IP static routing or boundary routing is used between the subscriber premise modems and the ISP POP router. This basic network structure enables IP access from the subscriber premise to the Internet at large.

In the target network scenario a customer is provided with a wide variety of services (e.g., VoD and fast Internet access) which are IP-based over ADSL from a router plus Ethernet switch data-centric architecture.

Drivers. Without a doubt, Internet access is one of the driving applications behind early deployment plans for ADSL. Given the frame-based nature of this killer application, it is not surprising that many service providers have based the design of early ADSL networks on the IP-over-ADSL paradigm. While the sheer speed of this basic Internet access over ADSL may be enough of a service differentiator for some ISPs, long-term competitive issues as well as requirements for value-added revenue on the part of many ISPs will likely drive the need for more exotic applications. There may be a desire to sell a new service such as VoD over the same copper pair that was previously used only to deliver data-centric services such as IP-based remote LAN access and fast Internet access. There may also be a desire to upgrade the service capability of the router and Ethernet switch-based network with minimal change out of network equipment. Two very attractive value-added services that may be desirable enhancements are virtual private networking (VPN) and reserved bandwidth services (RBS).

Options.   The primary option would appear to be overlaying VPNs on top of IP over ADSL. VPNs require the establishment of a peer relationship between the subscriber PC and a foreign network domain over the public Internet. The foreign domain is most commonly a central corporate network that the subscriber wishes to connect with. VPN service enables the subscriber to access corporate resources behind the corporate firewall utilizing an IP address outside the domain of the subscriber's ISP. VPNs also enable the subscriber to utilize protocols other than IP such as Novell IPX when accessing corporate resources.

The ability to connect a subscriber's PC communication stack with a foreign domain over the ISP's network is most easily accomplished using the Layer 2 Tunnelling Protocol (L2TP). Currently defined as an *Internet draft* in the Internet Engineering Task Forces (IETF) PPP working group, L2TP is designed to allow secure access from a workstation's protocol stack to a distant networking domain over an intermediate networking domain such as the Internet.

L2TP-enabled subscriber PCs can utilize an ISPs Internet access service to connect to their corporate central site's L2TP access concentrator (LAC). The L2TP protocol uses an ISP-supplied IP address to tunnel a PPP session through the Internet, where it is terminated in the LAC. The LAC uses the PPP tunnel to authenticate and authorize the subscriber's PC. Once authorized, the subscriber PC can utilize both IP and non-IP protocols across the PPP tunnel as though the PC were directly connected to the LAC via a PPP leased line. This allows the subscriber PC to use corporate-specific IP addresses as well as protocols such as IPX over an ISP's existing backbone without the ISP having to upgrade to multiprotocol routing or change the IP routing tables in its router network.

Reserved Bandwidth Services.   The IETF Resource Reservation Protocol (RSVP) enables subscriber PCs to reserve end-to-end network bandwidth. Functionally, the RSVP protocol is used by a subscriber's PC-based application, presumably through API hooks, to request a specific quality of service for a specific IP stream through all routers between the subscriber's PC and the destination node. This ability to reserve and enforce QoS renders feasible reserved bandwidth applications such as videoconferencing and high-quality Internet telephony.

Applications considerations.   Both VPNs via L2TP as well as Reserved Bandwidth Services via RSVP presuppose extensions to the subscriber's operating environment that are not yet widely available. As an example, L2TP is currently available for Windows NT 4.0 platforms but not Windows 95 platforms. Further, service gateways that implement the LAC functionality are not widely available.

Even more significantly, RSVP, inherently requires end-to-end deployment in order for bandwidth contracts to be well guaranteed. Given the extremely early stages of RSVP deployment, it may be some time before it is useful across the Internet. Also required in order for practical RSVP deployment are well implemented APIs as well as billing/authorization mechanisms that ensure the protection of the ISP business case vis-à-vis bandwidth reservation. The initial Internet-focused IP-over-ADSL deployment can be migrated to more of a full-service network given the adoption of some leading-edge IP-based technologies. As examples, both VPN and Reserved Bandwidth Services are feasible in this migrated network but are greatly dependent on the pace of implementation in the subscriber PC operating systems environment.

ADSL Service Delivery to VDSL Service Delivery

In the starting network scenario a customer is provided with a high-speed ADSL link. The services that could be delivered over the ADSL link range from Internet access to VoD. However, in the short term it is thought by many that the most likely single service that may be a viable business on its own is Internet access. Therefore, the starting network scenario is Internet access using ATM or TCP/IP over an ADSL transmission system. Consider Figure 10.40, which shows Internet access via ADSL.

In the target network scenario a customer is provided with a high-speed VDSL link. It is generally agreed that for xDSL to ultimately be competitive, it must provide a mixture of telephony, video, and data services. This so-called full-service network (FSN) will require higher bit rates and more flexible operation than that which is required for a single service, such as Internet access. Therefore, the target network scenario is a FSN using ATM over a VDSL (or ADSL) transmission system, as shown in Figure 10.41.

Drivers. ADSL can support a variety of services, ranging from VoD to Internet access. Initial trials of ADSL focused on delivering services aimed at the mass residential market, such as VoD, home shopping, and home banking. However, recently there has been a flurry of activity espousing the virtues of supporting high-speed Internet access using ADSL. It seems likely that the telcos will initially employ ADSL to provide high-speed Internet access over the existing copper wires of the distribution area. Data will be transferred using ATM or TCP/IP from an access multiplexer, located primarily in the CO (central office), to a single CPE within the home. This is an adequate network architecture for supporting a single service, but will not suffice when a FSN is required. In the near future consumers will desire sophisticated and bandwidth-intensive services that will far outstrip the capacity of

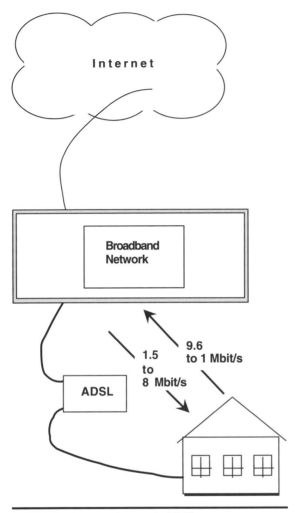

Figure 10.40   Internet Access via ADSL

ADSL transmission systems. An FSN can provide multiple telephone channels, HDTV, VoD, and high-speed data services to the subscriber. One method that can be employed to carry this mixture of services is to use ATM over VDSL, from an access multiplexer to multiple CPEs within the home. Once again the existing copper wires of the distribution area are reused, but in this instance the multiplexer will be sited at a flexibility point in the network, such as at a feeder-to-distribution interface (FDI) or serving area cross-connect (SAC). Alternatively, the multiplexer could be located in the basement of a multiple-dwelling unit or high-rise apartment block, where the broadband signal is transmitted over the existing copper wire riser cables. In

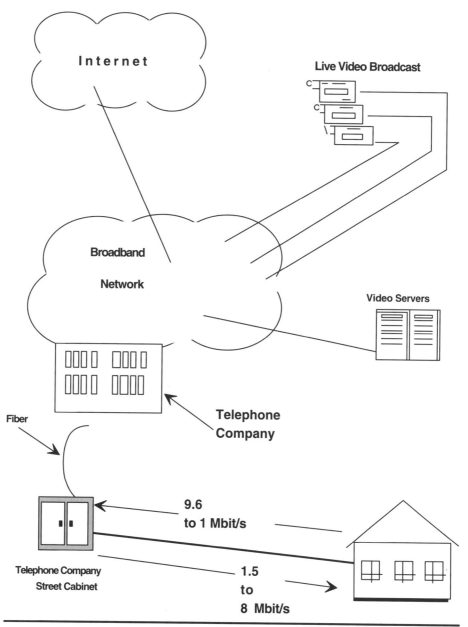

Figure 10.41   VDSL-Based Full-Service Network

either eventuality ADSL systems will probably already be employed in the telco's region, and thus a clear migration path is required to facilitate a smooth transition to VDSL. The next section details some of the options available in evolving toward that goal.

Options. Three major elements impact the migration path from an ADSL service to a VDSL service: the type of signaling used over the xDSL link, the location of the access multiplexer, and the interfaces defined for the access multiplexer.

ATM ADSL to ATM VDSL

Internet access can be provided using ATM over ADSL, where the TCP/IP data are packetized into an ATM cell. When the xDSL transmission system is upgraded to VDSL, a smooth transition can be facilitated. The access multiplexer and CPEs will have the same ATM interface to the xDSL modems. Additionally, if the interface chips and multiplexer backplane are flexible enough to support higher-speed transmission, then it would be necessary to change the xDSL modems only when migrating from ADSL to VDSL. This is illustrated in Figure 10.42, which shows ATM delivered to the customer using ADSL or VDSL. Other issues to consider that will influence the ease of this migration are (1) the fact that many DSLAM ATM ADSL multiplexers are being developed with 155-Mbps interfaces where as a VDSL optical network unit (ONU) will probably require at least a 622-Mbps fiber feed and (2) the work on fast and slow paths through ADSL and VDSL transceivers will have an impact since standardized ADSL has both paths, but some VDSL implementations may end up having only one latency path.

TCP/IP ADSL to ATM VDSL

If high-speed Internet access is provided using TCP/IP over ADSL, then the access equipment will now contain a service specific element, thus reducing its flexibility. Moreover, migrating a TCP/IP data-centric platform to one which supports a FSN via ATM would not be a simple process. The backplane, including its interfaces and functionality, together with the CPE, would all have to be changed to support ATM over VDSL. Indeed, the complete access equipment would probably have to be changed out right from the router interface at the CO to the CPE, as illustrated in Figure 10.43, which shows TCP/IP delivered to the customer via ADSL.

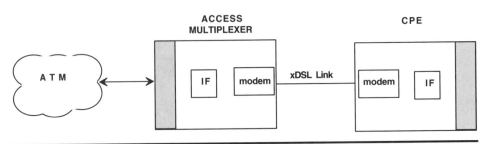

Figure 10.42 ATM Delivered to the Customer Using ADSL or VDSL

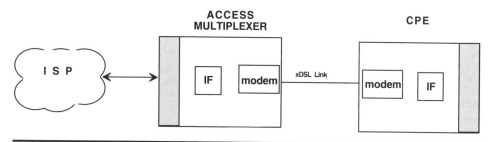

Figure 10.43   Only TCP/IP Dedicated to the Customer via ADSL

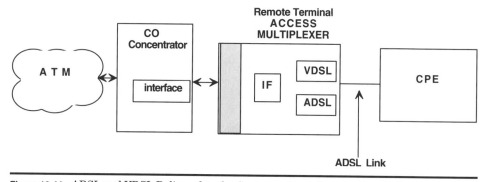

Figure 10.44   ADSL and VDSL Delivered to the Customer from a Remote Terminal

Location of the access multiplexer: central office.   ADSL is currently defined to transport 6 Mbps up to 9000 ft from the access multiplexer. Initially, access multiplexers which support ADSL will reside in the CO. VDSL, on the other hand, is currently defined to transport up to 52 Mbps up to 4000 ft from the access multiplexer. For VDSL, the access multiplexer will now reside at a flexibility point in the network, such as at a FDI/SAC, or in the basement of a multiple-dwelling unit. Therefore, in this instance, it is not possible to migrate CO-based ADSL to VDSL.

Location of the access multiplexer: remote terminal.   In some wiring topologies it will be necessary to locate the ADSL-based access multiplexer in the outside plant as a remote terminal (RT). The RT could be located at a FDI/SAC, collocated with a DLC, or located in the basement of multidwelling unit. The RT may have to be hardened to withstand the physical and environmental requirements as defined in telco specifications. Additionally, it is now necessary to provide some sort of concentration functionality back at the CO to terminate multiple RTs. This architecture is illustrated in Figure 10.44, which shows ADSL and VDSL delivered from a remote terminal. If the copper wire loop or riser length is short enough, then the same RT could support ADSL line cards today and VDSL line cards in the future. However, this does assume that the access multiplexer's backplane can support VDSL bit rates. Nonetheless, this would provide easy migration to higher-rate services when VDSL transceivers become available.

Access multiplexer interfaces. In order to truly migrate an ADSL-based system to a VDSL-based one, the access multiplexer must be able to accept input from both narrowband and broadband sources. The backplane of an xDSL access multiplexer should be able to accommodate input from the following sources:

1. Broadband data over ATM from an Internet edge switch and other data sources

2. Narrowband telephony from a Class 5 switch

3. Broadcast video over ATM from content providers

4. VoD over ATM from content providers

Reference

ADSL to VDSL, ADSL Forum 96-077, Lawrence Ebringer, Next Level Communications, Sept. 19, 1996 (London meeting).

GDLC-based ADSL to ONU-based ADSL/VDSL

The starting scenario is ADSL service(s) is (are) provided from NGDLC-based equipment; that is, the ATU-C is located at the remote site of the NGDLC (next-generation digital loop carrier). Consider Figure 10.45, which shows a digital subscriber line access multiplexer (DSLAM) that provides the wideband/broadband multiplexing function at the remote digital terminal (RDT) site. The NGDLC carrier provides the narrowband services, and the DSLAM provides the wideband and broadband services, including ADSL access. Both are managed by a common SNMP platform and connect to the central office via an SDH/SONET ring.

The SDH/SONET ring terminates into a digital cross-connect system (DCS), with the narrowband traffic connected to the public switch and the ADSL traffic connected to an ATM switch (or router). Figure 10.45 shows a loose integration of the DSLAM and NGDLC products. Eventually, the DSLAM functions would be incorporated into the NGDLC product.

In the target network scenario ADSL service(s) is (are) provided from the ONU equipment; that is, the ATU-C (VDSL or ADSL) is located at the remote site of the ONU (optical network unit) of a fiber-to-the-curb (FTTC) deployment. Figure 10.46 shows migration of fiber closer to the home (or small business) by adding the ONU, which terminates the fiber and provides broadband, wideband, and narrowband services to the home via VDSL or ADSL. Consider Figure 10.46. In addition to an SDH/SONET ring, the fiber feed may use point-to-point or PON topologies.

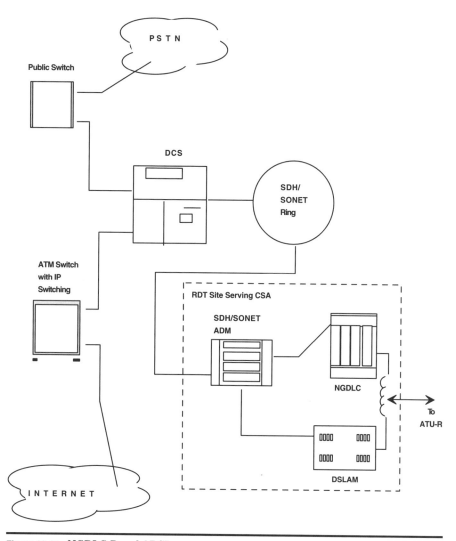

Figure 10.45 NGDLC-Based ADSL

Both VDSL (up to 52 Mbps) and ADSL (up to 13 Mbps) would serve homes and small businesses from small ONUs available in several sizes: from small ONUs (four to eight homes) for residential areas to large ONUs (serving an apartment or condominium building). ADSL connections at the ONU would serve wideband or broadband services to homes falling out of the limited range of VDSL (e.g., rural locations).

The interface between the ONU and remote optical line termination (R-OLT) could be point-to-point optical fiber or a passive optical network with a 1:*n* split (*n* = 16 to 32, e.g.). The R-OLT-to-ONU connection may be proprietary in nature.

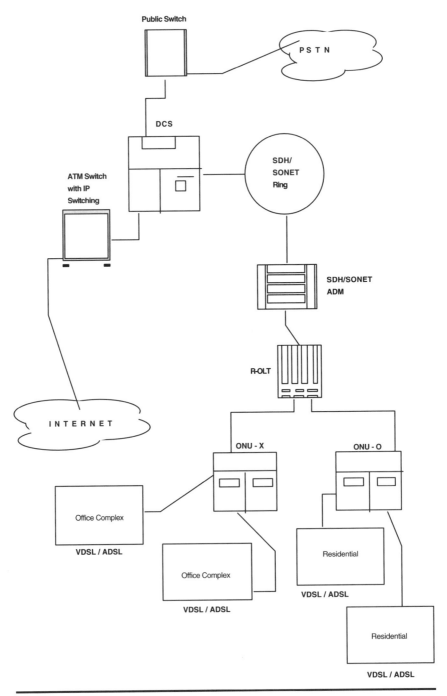

Figure 10.46 ONU-Based ADSL/VDSL

Drivers. While high-speed Internet access is the killer application for the deployment of ADSL, whether CO-based or carrier-serving-area-based, the deployment of an FTTC infrastructure with VDSL deployment must depend on new services to pay for the FTTC deployment. Like ADSL being in competition with cable modems, VDSL deployment (via FTTC) will be competing with the hybrid-fiber-coax (HFC) structure.

The first driver concerns a new market for telephone operating companies. Now that regulation and monopolies are rapidly disappearing, intense competition is beginning between cable television and the traditionally regulated telecommunication companies. FTTC deployment will bring enough bandwidth to the home so that services previously economical only via cable systems can also be provided by FTTC systems. For example, a switched digital broadcast service could compete with an analog broadcast service from an HFC network. In other words, FTTC deployment will take place in many areas as competition to HFC deployment. The second driver may be service quality standards. Both FTTC and HFC infrastructures can support future broadband multimedia services. Cable companies will deploy HFC networks, but telecommunications companies have the option to deploy either FTTC and HFC, depending on the economics and competition in the area. Although cable companies have tried to improve their network quality customer service, the public generally has a very poor opinion of the service quality of cable companies. As an example, many of today's cable modem trials and initial deployments are from companies with names different from those of their sponsoring companies. The name change is occurring to deter customers from regarding this service as a cable television service with the history of poor quality and customer service often associated with CATV. As cable companies begin offering telephony services, the same strategy will likely be employed. If FTTC costs can compare with HFC costs, then the telephone operating companies will have clear advantages in the quality and customer service areas that they can exploit and give FTTC a competitive advantage. It will be interesting to see if cable operators can make enough improvements in these areas to attract customers for lifeline services such as telephony.

A third driver is the array of new services that can be provided with FTTC. ADSL can provide the high-speed Internet access and limited video on demand (VOD), but VDSL-capable optical network units (ONUs) within 300 m of homes and small businesses will add services such as digital broadcast with hundreds of channels and VOD with large libraries of videos to choose from. FTTC pushes fiber very close to the home or small business site, making it the final step before an eventual all-fiber network. Small ONUs (four to eight homes) will serve lower-density residential areas, and larger ONUs (up to about 50 homes) will serve higher-density areas, apartment complexes, and small business parks.

FTTC installations will first be justified for new-build situations, but the demand for the services provided by FTTC will make it a viable alternative to HFC networks. The success to FTTC deployment (and VDSL) will depend on the cost optimizing of the ONUs since most of the initial cost comes from the ONUs. Besides VDSL, ADSL can also be deployed from the ONUs for low-density and rural applications when the VDSL distance limit is exceeded.

A fourth driver will be in the area of remote LAN extensions (RLEs) for high-performance telecommuting and ATM. Moving the ONU close to the home or small business will allow other symmetric interfaces (ATM Forum, IBM, etc.) to provide services were the asymmetric aspects of ADSL and VDSL are inappropriate. While there has been no killer application for FTTC deployment discovered as yet, the variety of services possible will make FTTC economical to deploy. In fact, that point of FTTC is that it is a service-independent network, which can carry all types of services, whether asymmetric or symmetric in nature.

A fifth driver will be the added security provided by a switched architecture as opposed to the broadcast nature of HFC networks. A data or video stream never leaves the host digital terminal (HDT) if the home is not authorized to see it. Also, the star topology of FTTC ensures that programs or data going to one home are not available to another home.

Options. One option to FTTC is to deliver only digital services (requiring set-top boxes and/or PC cards), or, using a relatively new option provided by vendors, also provide an analog video signal, eliminating the need for set-top boxes when only broadcast video services are needed. This option feeds the analog signal to the ONU via a coax cable that also powers the ONU. This analog network is much simpler than the HFC network because it uses only a 450-MHz spectrum and has only a one-way system since the digital portion of the FTTC provides the two-way infrastructure.

Another option that telephone operating companies have is to deploy an HFC network that can evolve to a FTTC network once the demand for interactive and switched services expands. An operating company can initially provide only narrowband telephony services via the HFC network (with its quality and customer service reputation advantage over cable operator's telephony service), then add the broadcast video services and digital services as the market develops.

Reference

NGDLC-Based ADSL to ONU-Based ADSL/VDSL (FTTC), ADSL Forum 96-081, Tom Miller, Siemens, Sept. 19, 1996 (London meeting).

VDSL for residential services to VDSL for business services

In the starting network scenario the telco has begun its initial deployment of VDSL to serve the residential market. In the target network scenario the telco now wishes to use the same basic hybrid fiber/copper architecture to serve business customers.

Drivers. The drivers that may cause a telco to consider moving from use of VDSL for residential customers to also using it for business customers include the fact that it may be quicker and cheaper to deploy a hybrid fiber/copper access connection with VDSL rather than deploy fiber all the way to the business. Also, in some areas, business and residential buildings may be mixed or even collocated, making a homogeneous access solution desirable from an operations perspective. The VDSL link may be needed to satisfy the businesses' growing thirst for bandwidth driven by applications such as CAD/CAM (computer-aided design/manufacturing) or other increasing needs to access centralized company databases. Also, the VDSL connection may be used to replace multiple ADSL or T1 connections.

Options and issues. The relative density of business customers in some locations will have an impact on the economic viability of this evolution strategy because of the need to share the costs of the fiber and ONU electronics across a sufficiently large customer base. The characteristics of the business communications to be carried over the VDSL access system will be different to residential customers in a number of ways. The business VDSL connection may require new and different customer interfaces than will the residential connection (G.703, T1, etc.). A business may well use more CPE with several staff members acting as "points of consumption" for information from a broadband wide area network. This could require greater channelization of the VDSL link. The addressing and numbering issues associated with multiple channels will be greater than for residential users. There may well be a different tariffing regime for the business customers (e.g., per cell/packet or megabyte as opposed to, say, flat rate). This could impact the system management and operations architecture. The business customer who is hosting a Web site, for example, may require more upstream bandwidth. Also, the business customer may require more than one POTS line. The residential VDSL connection may be quite asymmetric, but the business VDSL connection with a greater requirement for upstream bandwidth may be symmetric. Mixing of these two types of VDSL in the same area and hence cables will raise crosstalk compatibility issues between the residential (asymmetric) and business (symmetric) VDSL systems. The spectral compatibility with ADSL also needs to be considered. These issues will impact the performance of the various systems in the cable, and so planning/deployment rules must be devised with care. Symmetric VDSL systems won't have as much range as asymmetric systems.

A business connection is likely to have more exacting performance requirements than a residential connection. Aspects to consider are quality of service (QoS), security, availability, and resilience. The degree of acceptable overbooking on the fiber feeder connection is likely to be less for business customers. To meet some business targets, multiple copper drop VDSL feeds may be needed together with fault-tolerant/redundant ONU electronics and diverse routing of the ONU fiber feeds. VDSL has the potential (although extremely difficult) for data wire taps compared to FTTH. Hence some business applications running over this infrastructure may require the use of encryption for peace of mind of the customer. The vulnerability of the street electronics in the ONU to vandalism may also be a concern to some customers. Many cable companies have suffered from the theft of backup batteries from street cabinets. Modern ONU enclosure technology with alarms will help mitigate this problem.

ADSL for business services to ADSL for residential services

In the starting network scenario the telco has initially deployed ADSL to deliver business services such as remote LAN access and high-speed Internet/intranet access. The initial customer base comprise large corporate early adopters wishing to provide connectivity to teleworkers and branch offices. The services are also sold to small and medium enterprises and SOHO (small office–home office) business customers.

In the target network scenario the telco now wishes to use the same basic network architecture with its ADSL access network to deliver mass market services to residential customers.

Drivers. The drivers for this network migration step include the desire to start off by targeting early adopters of technology who will pay more for a premium service, specifically, to target the top end of the market initially. This is then followed by the desire to not only drive up volume and customer penetration to increase marketshare or profit but also help reduce per unit costs, enabling the service offering to be priced so that it is attractive to a wider customer base. The advent of more user-friendly applications may also make the targeting of residential customers viable when previously only business customers with communications specialists could fully exploit the technology. The trend toward telecommuting may also help drive this migration step. If a customer has remote LAN access via ADSL from home for business purposes, packaging in a VoD service over the same line may be an incremental revenue source for the telco without significant additional infrastructure costs in the access network.

Options and issues. An obvious issue is whether the initial systems architecture deployed for a small number of early adopter business customers (e.g., router and/or Ethernet architecture) is scalable for the mass residential market and can support residential applications such as VoD. Also, does the initial deployment for business customers fit with the telcos' long-term strategic vision for a residential broadband platform (which is possibly ATM-based)? Will the initial business customer offering be a standalone legacy network requiring its own processes and support staff, or can it be evolved economically (including management systems) to the strategic mass residential solution? The initial business offering over ADSL could well be very IP/data-centric, for example, providing LAN and Internet access only. However, a mass residential offering may require greater packaging of a wide range of services to be successful (e.g., including VoD, broadcast TV, games, and home shopping). This may necessitate more of a multiservice delivery platform.

There may well be a different tariffing regime for the business customers (e.g., per cell/packet or megabyte as opposed to, say, flat rate). This could impact the system management and operations architecture. The regulations pertaining to cross-subsidy of different telco product lines will have to be carefully considered. The new residential ADSL customers may accept a lower QoS for some of their applications (e.g., VoD) than, say, profit-critical business applications. However, it is unlikely that the telco would want to have two distinct levels of planning/deployment rules. They may chose to be more rigorous in their implementation for the high-paying business customer but financial transactions in residential applications (e.g., home shopping) is likely to make them just as reliant on network integrity thus reducing scope for shortcuts. The QoS differentiation is more likely to manifest itself in terms of the use of test systems for rapid response to faults. Also, inherent network QoS differentiators such as ATM cell loss priority and degree of traffic overbooking (statistical multiplexing) can be exploited to justify higher business tariffs. The level of support from the service provider (as opposed to the network provider) may also be different. The telco may (although unlikely) consider zoning of the different customer bases (e.g., business parks) as a means of having a different tariff structure. The availability of low-priced mass market services, customer awareness, and true plug-and-play user-friendly applications will have a profound impact on the timing of this migration step for telcos. For instance, can customers now connect to an ATM-based ADSL connection without needing to configure their PC for the appropriate VPI/VCI? Other differences to consider in moving the use of ADSL from business to residential include the aesthetics of the remote unit and the number of boxes. Residential customers will have more onerous requirements. This could impact the preferred location of the POTS splitter and its accessibility, the degrees of freedom for locating the ADSL remote unit may be more constrained by the internal broadband and residential POTS extension wiring which is often less designed to be regularly changed or moved than in a business environment.

ADSL plus POTS to ADSL plus second-line POTS

In the starting network scenario a customer has an ADSL-delivered service over their existing phone line and have a single POTS channel provided over the same line in the baseband frequencies below ADSL.

In the target network scenario the customer wants a second POTS line.

Drivers. A driver that could force a telco to consider this migration step is if their customer has a need for a separate line for the children, the "teenager line." Another driver would be if the customer started to work from home (telecommuting) and wanted a separate line for a fax machine. The need for a second line could also arise if the customer is now running a home-based business and wants a second number for business purposes to avoid tying up the home number and also for billing separation.

Options and issues. The first and most obvious option is for the telco to install a second copper pair to the customer's premises. An alternative to this is to derive a 64-kbps duplex channel from the ADSL payload and add the necessary ringer and analog interface circuitry to provide a digitally derived second line over the existing copper pair. Some of the techniques described in the section of this report covering DAML system migration issues may also be applicable here.

An impact of providing a second POTS line could be the need to rewire some customer inside wiring, especially if the existing ADSL POTS splitter is in the NID, as the NID may not be able to support some configurations.

There will be an impact on the telco's records and test processes for the customer, particularly if one of the POTS channels is normal analog baseband POTS and the other is digitally derived. This will also make it more complicated for the telco's field staff to maintain the line. There could be training and tooling consequences. The additional ringing crosstalk that could result from a second line needs to be considered to develop a configuration that does not bypass the splitter and compromise ADSL performance.

FTTN and long-range VDSL to FTTK and short-range VDSL

In the starting network scenario the telco has an access network based on the hybrid fiber/copper architecture of fiber to the node (FTTN) with long-range VDSL capable of operating over the last 1 km/3000 ft of the customer connection.

In the target network scenario the telco deploys fiber deeper into the network to the curbside, resulting in use of shorter-range VDSL operating over the last 100 to 300 m of the customer connection.

Drivers. The drivers that may encourage a telco to consider taking fiber closer to the customer and hence deploying shorter-range, higher-rate VDSL could include an increase in demand for more bandwidth-intensive services and applications such as HDTV or a high takeup of broadband services to the point where the FTTN ONU is fully utilized and there is no street space to place a second ONU (this is analogous to how cable companies have subdivided their networks and moved HFC street units from 2000 customer serving areas to 500 customer serving areas). The telco may also see such a move as a stepping stone to FTTH. The use of shorter-range VDSL may also be attractive to the telco where new developments occur and they need to extend the fiber and provide additional new ONUs to reach the new customer base.

Options and issues. There are many key issues associated with such a migration step. An obvious one is the increase in operational costs due to the fact that there will be much more street electronics to install, operate, and maintain. An evolution to a network with significantly more street electronics units will take a very long time, and so the shift from FTTN to FTTK is probably only going to occur in isolated and localized areas where the additional bandwidth is really needed. There will be a time and cost impact of taking the additional fiber to the curb (FTTC), especially where duct space has been exhausted. The increased number of street units means more elements for the management systems to cope with and an increase in the size of associated network management databases. The smaller potential customer base sharing the costs of the ONU (e.g., 32 or 16 for FTTK as compared to, say, 300 for FTTN) will give the telco greater exposure to customer churn. The network for power feeding (and degree of maintenance on backup batteries) will increase as the network now has more ONU nodes to power. This may impact the ability to integrate critical narrowband services (i.e., "lifeline" POTS) on the broadband network.

The initial location and hence subsequent accessibility of the FTTK ONUs needs to be considered. They may be pole-top or underground footway box units. These are not as accessible as FTTN street ONUs, and the environment is harsher. Underground units need to be sealed against moisture, and power dissipation is more problematic. Pole-top units also increase the "visual pollution" of the broadband network, which may be unacceptable to some local authorities. In the liberalized dark-copper regulatory environment that now exists in some countries (e.g., the United States), there will be an issue of which service provider installs there FTTK ONU on the customer's copper drop wire first. Can other service providers have access? Are multiple units feasible given limited "real estate" at pole tops and in manholes and footway boxes?

The customer interface on the remote VDSL unit may change in this evolution (e.g., from 12 Mbps or 25 Mbps to, say, 51 Mbps). This will have an impact or the customer's ability to use their existing broadband CPE and broadband home wiring topology.

There could be major spectral compatibility issues for the telco to consider if long- and short-range VDSL must coexist in the same network. A degree of zoning would be possible, and certain modulation and duplexing schemes could minimize the impact, but it would require careful analysis and prudent use of planning and deployment rules. The telco must decide on the transmit PSD levels and bandwidth allocation of upstream and downstream and hence the overall duplexing scheme (e.g., FDD or TDD) that it will use for VDSL and police this from the start. Some compromises (in terms of achievable bit rate) may have to be made in the initial FTTN/VDSL deployment if FTTK is an anticipated next step.

FTTN/FTTK and VDSL to FTTH

In the starting network scenario the telco has an access network based on the hybrid fiber/copper architecture of fiber to the node (FTTN) with long-range VDSL capable of operating over the last 1 km/3000 ft of the customer connection or fiber to the kerb (curb) (FTTK) with shorter-range VDSL operating over the last 100 to 300 m.

In the target network scenario the telco deploys fiber deeper into the access network all the way to the customer's home or business.

Drivers. The factors that may drive a telco to consider migrating from hybrid fiber/copper to FTTH include high takeup of very bandwidth-hungry services such as HDTV or multiple broadcast channels. FTTN/FTTK ONU is fully utilized with no space for modular expansion or a second ONU. A building may have been converted from a residential location to a business premise that has significantly greater bandwidth requirements and justifies FTTH/FTTB. A new development of a business park adjacent to, say, a residential area served by FTTN/FTTK and VDSL may also cause the telco to deploy FTTH to increase the range to reach the new customers. Alternatively, the new business customers may wish the additional security of FTTH, which cannot be wire-tapped. The telco may have deployed FTTN/VDSL and considers FTTH as a cheaper next step than FTTK/VDSL, due to the problems of increased numbers of street electronics. The telco may chose to deploy FTTH in certain locations to avoid RFI problems that some VDSL implementations may suffer from or cause. The telco may have experienced other technical or environmental problems in some areas where it has deployed FTTN or FTTK with VDSL (e.g., power dissipation/equipment heating, moisture ingress, vandalism of the ONU, complaints about the ONU size or location), and FTTH could be a means of solving them.

In some parts of the world, the incumbent telco may wish to race ahead and spend capital on a FTTH deployment before they are subject to the commercial pressures of a fully liberalized telecommunications market, and all capital spend will have to be more fully justified. This may involve making the most of any state subsidies or product line cross-subsidization while this is still possible.

Options and issues. Among the many issues to consider in this network migration step are the impact on customer interfaces (and hence existing CPE and home wiring). What will be the impact on the customer of a new network termination box? Can the same interface be used on the VDSL remote unit and the FTTH delivery system (e.g., a 25- or 51 Mbps ATM interface)?. Where will the FTTH system be terminated? Is it inside or outside the house? Is the

FTTH remote unit integrated with CPE, and if so, what are the standards and certification requirements? The skills, tools, and time to install fiber in the home will have an impact on telco costs. It isn't yet as slick as terminating and routing copper wires around the home. There will be a time and cost impact of taking the additional fiber all the way to the home, especially where duct space has been exhausted. A decision is required on how many fibers should be installed (for future proofing and/or resilience). Installation of a *fiber drop wire,* the final connection into the home, needs to be robust and cost-effective. Blown-fiber techniques may find application here. A telco anticipating a move to FTTH sometime in the future can make the transition easier by using copper drop wires today that include an integral small-tube bore.

The final stage of the FTTH installation at some future date could then effectively blow the fiber into the home. The blown-fiber technique has been successfully used already in Britain. There will be less powering problems with the FTTH approach. However, with VDSL, the broadband network can be deployed as an overlay on top of an existing narrowband network with the narrowband services carried over copper at frequencies below VDSL. Moving to a FTTH network may force the telco to carry all services on the new broadband network. This has a major impact on operational systems and processes. For example, the location of faults in a FTTH network may require more extensive use of time domain reflectometry (TDR) equipment and skilled personnel to operate it. The choice of point-to-point fiber or a passive optical network (PON) will have an impact on the economics of the network and its fault-impact characteristics. In the liberalized dark-copper regulatory environment that now exists in some countries (e.g., the United States), there will be an issue of how to unbundle and resell capacity on the fiber to multiple service providers.

HDSL for Internet access to ADSL for Internet access

In the starting network scenario the telco or ISP deploys HDSL (typically at 384 or 784 kbps) over a single copper pair to provide high-speed Internet access.

In the target network scenario the telco or ISP deploys ADSL for faster Internet access.

Drivers and issues. The telco or ISP may have originally deployed HDSL because of a perceived maturity in the technology and its price. Also, because of the high volumes of HDSL deployment in some areas, it would be considered a proven technology with proven deployment processes, operational procedures, test equipment, and known longer-term performance and reliability. Where an ISP is initially deploying DSL over "dry copper," HDSL may be considered a safer option since if the local telco has previously deployed lots of HDSL lines themselves as part of their business as usual, there can be no dispute over spectral compatibility issues.

The drivers that may lead to a migration to ADSL include the greater downstream bandwidth available over a single pair. To deliver beyond 784 kbps or 1 Mbps using HDSL would require two pairs (or three, with some E1 2-Mbps HDSL implementations). In addition, the use of ADSL allows POTS to be delivered over the same pair. If HDSL was used originally for Internet access, then there must have been a second line into the home providing the telephony. Hence the migration to ADSL would permit the telco to sell a second POTS line to the customer. If the service was provided by a new service provider leasing dry copper, then they could bundle POTS and Internet access over a single leased pair using ADSL. ADSL would permit greater reach for a given downstream bit rate. However, it should be noted that for really long lines HDSL can be repeatered (line powered from the CO). A repeatering option for ADSL does not exist.

There may be an issue in that in some networks, since HDSL has been deployed as part of a leased circuit (T1 or E1) or primary rate ISDN provision, the remote unit may be regarded as network equipment. However, ADSL remote units (particularly PC card implementations) may be considered as CPE. This may be a driver to migrate toward ADSL provisioning in that the equipment could be perceived as more mass market than HDSL with a greater variety of distribution outlets for purchase of the equipment.

Another issue in moving from HDSL to ADSL is that some implementations of ADSL will have a lower upstream data rate than is possible with HDSL. This could be important for customers who have been hosting their own Web sites and using the DSL system to send WWW pages upstream. However, since the HDSL system would typically not be running much faster than 784 kbps and standardized and rate-adaptive ADSL systems are capable of delivering 640 kbps upstream, this may not be a major issue.

IDSL for Internet access to ADSL for Internet access

In the starting network scenario the telco or ISP deploys IDSL over a single copper pair to provide Internet access. IDSL (or ISDN DSL) uses the same 2B1Q transceiver technology as ISDN to transport data over approximately 18,000 ft of copper pair. However, unlike ISDN, it does not get switched through the PSTN. Instead, the central office end (equivalent to a modem bank) would interconnect to the Internet via a router. Hence this technology is used only to carry data and cannot deliver PSTN voice services.

In the target network scenario the telco deploys ADSL for faster Internet access.

Drivers and issues. The telco or ISP may choose to initially deploy IDSL since it is based on a mature and proven transceiver technology that may be perceived as having reached its silicon cost floor. Also, since many operators are familiar with deploying Basic Rate ISDN, many of the planning processes and operational processes for IDSL will have been proved. In addition, much of the technology developed to support ISDN would also be applicable to support IDSL. This could include repeaters, test and commissioning equipment, terminal adapters, PC cards, or routers and bridges with ISDN interfaces. In some countries the customer experience of getting ISDN installed has a reputation for being complex with customers needing to know or find out details of the voice switch they are connected to. IDSL can be a simpler installation experience for customers since technical knowledge of their PSTN switch connection is not required.

The telco or ISP may choose to initially deploy IDSL rather than ISDN for Internet access to move Internet traffic of the PSTN voice switches to avoid traffic congestion problems. This may be particularly important where flat-rate billing for Internet access (as opposed to time-based billing) is to be used.

A driver to migrate from IDSL to ADSL would be the increased downstream bandwidth. ADSL should be able to deliver around 1.5 Mbps downstream over the longest of unrepeatered IDSL connections. There would, however, be a problem if the customer were on a repeatered line. In order for the customer to reap the benefits of the new ADSL access delivery system, other parts of the telco/ISP network may also have to be upgraded to ensure that there are no bandwidth bottlenecks further up the network. If IDSL was used originally for Internet access, then there must have been a second line into the home providing the telephony. Hence the migration to ADSL would permit the telco to sell a second POTS line to the customer. If the service was provided by a new service provider leasing dry copper, then they could bundle POTS and Internet access over a single leased pair using ADSL. IDSL is targeted mainly at Internet access, and so migrating to ADSL would likely involve a substitution by replacing the customer's IDSL with ADSL. It should be noted that this may be in contrast to some situations where customers had been using ISDN instead of IDSL. If they have CPE or applications that have been taking advantage of the ISDN's switched PSTN (e.g., videoconferencing), then a different migration strategy may be needed. Some implementations of IDSL embed the IDSL line card in a form of access multiplexer that enables simple upgrade of customers to ADSL (or HDSL) via replacement of the IDSL line card with an ADSL line card. However, there are other implementations that embed the IDSL line card in a standard D4 channel bank. In order to upgrade a customer from IDSL to ADSL, it would be necessary to move them to a different access platform.

Contributing members of the Working Group

Acknowledgment is made to all the attendees of the Network Migration Working Group meetings for their valuable contribution to discussions and brainstorming sessions that resulted in the content of this working text. The following individuals authored and/or significantly reviewed the sections contained in the working text.

Gavin Young	BT
Tom Miller	Siemens
Harry Mildonian	Lucent Technologies
Robert Dearnaley	BT
Greg McAdoo	Sourcecom
Lawrence Ebringer	MMC
Piotr Korolkiewicz	Ericsson

10.6   ADSL Network Elements

This part of the chapter describes parameters or elements of ADSL modem operation that are subject to network management. It does not describe the protocol(s) by which they are managed or the protocol(s) by which control and management message signals pass from an ATU-C to an ATU-R.

Introduction

This document (section) describes various network management elements required for proper management of ADSL physical layer resources where elements refer to parameters or functions within an ADSL modem pair, either collectively or at an individual end. These elements have been defined without reference to a specific ADSL line code or means of communication between ATU-C and ATU-R.

Reference model

Figure 10.47 shows the system reference model adopted by the ADSL Forum. The network management elements covered by this project exist within ATU-C and ATU-R, and provide access across the V interfaces. By intention, no network management element shall be accessible via the T interface (that is, by the customer).

Network management framework

A network management framework consists of at least four components:

1. One or more managed nodes, each containing an agent. The managed node could be a router, bridge, switch, ADSL modem, or other device.

2. At least one NMS (network management system), which is often called the *manager*. The manager monitors and controls managed nodes and is usually based on a popular computer.

3. A network management protocol, which is used by the manager and agents to exchange management information.

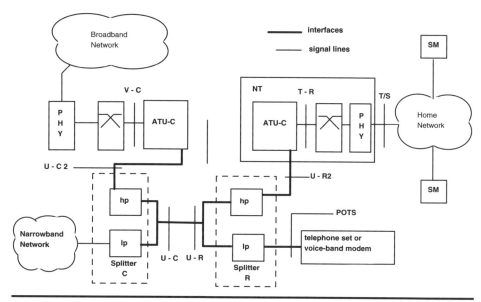

Figure 10.47   ADSL Forum System Reference Model

4. Management information. The unit of management information is an object. A collection of related objects is defined as a *management information base* (MIB).

The MIB definition assumes that the agent is located at the ATU-C and acts as a proxy for the ATU-R. To allow for potential expansion, the MIB will be defined to accommodate the aggregation, so an agent can be located in either a single ATU-C or common equipment to handle multiple ATU-Cs. An indexing scheme is used to accommodate this. The profile concept for configuration parameters will be used as an option to facilitate parameter management by the NMS. In case the use of the individual parameters is preferred, a profile can be created for each ATU-C. Line code (DMT/CAP)-specific objects will be defined in separate MIBs.

Network management elements

Network management refers to parameter, operations, and protocols for the following functions:

1. *Configuration management:* configuring an ADSL modem pair and maintaining inventory information
2. *Fault management:* discovering and correcting faults.
3. *Performance management:* reporting operating conditions and history management includes five elements within the ADSL reference model:

(a) Management communications protocol across the Network Management subinterface of the V interface.

(b) Management communications protocol across the U interface (i.e., between modems).

(c) Parameters and operations within the ATU-C.

(d) Parameters and operations within the ATU-R.

(e) ATU-R side of the T interface.

Issues presented here do not address management of POTS or metallic line testing, the T interface beyond the ATU-R (i.e., the premises distribution network or any interconnected CPE), or protocols above the physical layer. This working text does not cover protocols on the U interface. Standards groups ANSI T1E1.4 and ETSI TM6 are responsible for any standardized protocols at the U interface.

The term *network management system* as used in this document will refer specifically to any information or procedure that can be controlled or instituted via the V interface operations port, without prejudice to the nature of this port (which can be separated and embedded).

Management of all ATU-R parameters specified in this document may be performed only by an NMS via the V (virtual) interface.

Element list.   Figures 10.48 and 10.49 list the required set of elements for an ADSL system, divided into three categories: (1) configuration, (2) fault, and (3) performance management.

The "ATU-C/ATU-R/ADSL Line" column indicates for each element whether it should be managed at the ATU-C-only, ATU-C and ATU-R, or ADSL line. The "Physical/Fast/Interleave" column indicates for each element whether it is a physical layer element or a channelized element. The "Read/Write" column indicates for each element whether it is read-only or read/write. N/A means not applicable. The location of the elements is not specified here.

The following terms used in Figures 10.48 and 10.49 are described a little more for clarification.

ADSL line   ADSL transmission facility, including the two ADSL transmission units

ATU-C   Central office ADSL modem

ATU-C/R   Central office/remote modem

ATU-R   Remote ADSL modem

Fast   The ADSL fast transmission channel as per ANSI T1.413

Interleaved   The ADSL interleaved channel as per ANSI T1.413

Physical   The ADSL facility physical transmission medium

Figures 10.48 and 10.49 show the network management elements.

Category	Element	ATU-C/ATU-R/ ADSL Line	Read/Write	Physical/Fast Interface
Configuration				
	ADSL Line Type	ADSL Line	N/A	Read Only
	ADSL Line Coding	ADSL Line	N/A	Read Only
	Target Noise Margin	ATU-C & ATU-R	Physical	Read/Write
	Minimum Noise Margin	ATU-C & ATU-R	Physical	Read/Write
	Rate Adaption Mode	ATU-C & ATU-R	Physical	Read/Write
	Upshift Noise Margin	ATU-C & ATU-R	Physical	Read/Write
	Minimum Time Interval for Upshift Rate Adaption	ATU-C & ATU-R	Physical	Read/Write
	Downshift Noise Margin	ATU-C & ATU-R	Physical	Read/Write
	Minimum Time Interval for Downshift Rate Adaption	ATU-C & ATU-R	Physical	Read/Write
	Desired Maximum Rate	ATU-C & ATU-R	Fast/Interleave	Read/Write
	Desired Minimum Rate	ATU-C & ATU-R	Fast/Interleave	Read/Write
	Rate Adaption Ratio	ATU-C & ATU-R	Physical	Read/Write
	Maximum Interleave Delay	ATU-C & ATU-R	Interleave	Read/Write
	Alarm event Thresholds:			
	15 minute count threshold on			
	loss of signal	ATU-C & ATU-R	Physical	Read/Write
	loss of frame	ATU-C & ATU-R	Physical	Read/Write
	loss of power	ATU-C & ATU-R	Physical	Read/Write
	loss of link	ATU-C & ATU-R	Physical	Read/Write
	errored seconds	ATU-C only	Physical	Read/Write
	Rate Up Threshold	ATU-C & ATU-R	Fast/Interleave	Read/Write
	Rate Down Threshold	ATU-C & ATU-R	Fast/Interleave	Read/Write
	Vendor ID	ATU-C & ATU-R	Physical	Read Only
	Version Number	ATU-C & ATU-R	Physical	Read Only
	Serial Number	ATU-C & ATU-R	Physical	Read Only

Figure 10.48 Network Management Elements (Part 1)

Configuration management. The following paragraphs describe each element for configuration management. All elements can be used for fast channel and/or interleaved channel except physical layer elements. Interleaving adds delay but provides greater immunity to impulse noise.

ADSL line type. This parameter defines the type of ADSL physical line. Five (5) ADSL line types are defined as follows:

1. No channels exist.

2. Only fast channel exists.

3. Only interleaved channel exists.

4. Either fast or interleaved channels can exist, but only one at any time.

5. Both fast and interleaved channels exist.

Category	Element	ATU-C/ATU-R/ ADSL Line	Read/Write	Physical/Fast Interface
Fault - Indication	ADSL Line Status	ATU-C & ATU-R	Physical	Read Only
	Exceed 15 Minute Count			
	threshold of			
	Loss of Signal	ATU-C & ATU-R	Physical	N/A
	Loss of Frame	ATU-C & ATU-R	Physical	N/A
	Loss of Power	ATU-C & ATU-R	Physical	N/A
	Loss of Link	ATU-C only	Physical	N/A
	Errored seconds	ATU-C & ATU-R	Physical	N/A
	Unable to Initialize ATU-R	ATU-C only	Physical	
	Rate Change	ATU-C & ATU-R	Fast/Interleave	
Fault - Diagnostics				
	Self Test	ATU-C & ATU-R	N/A	N/A
Performance				
	Line Attenuation	ATU-C & ATU-R	Physical	Read Only
	Noise Margin (current)	ATU-C & ATU-R	Physical	Read Only
	Total Output Power	ATU-C & ATU-R	Physical	Read Only
	Maximum Attainable Rate	ATU-C & ATU-R	Physical	Read Only
	Current Rate	ATU-C & ATU-R	Fast/Interleave	Read Only
	Previous Rate	ATU-C & ATU-R	Fast/Interleave	Read Only
	Channel Data Block Length	ATU-C & ATU-R	Fast/Interleave	Read Only
	Interleave Delay	ATU-C & ATU-R	Interleave	Read Only
	15 minute/1 day counters			
	of current & previous			
	values on:			
	Loss of Signal	ATU-C & ATU-R	Physical	Read Only
	Loss of Frame	ATU-C & ATU-R	Physical	Read Only
	Loss of Power	ATU-C & ATU-R	Physical	Read Only
	Loss of Link	ATU-C Only	Physical	Read Only
	Errored seconds	ATU-C & ATU-R	Fast/Interleave	Read Only
	Transmit Blocks	ATU-C & ATU-R	Fast/Interleave	Read Only
	Corrected Blocks	ATU-C & ATU-R	Fast/Interleave	Read Only
	Uncorrectable Blocks	ATU-C & ATU-R	Fast/Interleave	Read Only

Figure 10.49 Network Management Elements (Part 2)

ADSL line coding. This parameter defines the ADSL coding type used on this line.

Noise margin parameters. The following parameters are defined to control the noise margin in the transmit direction in the ATU-C and ATU-R. Note that the noise margin should be controlled to ensure a BER (bit error rate of 1×10^{-7} or better). The following shows the relationship between these parameters of noise margins.

Reduce power

Maximum noise
margin ─────────────────────────────

Increase rate if noise margin > upshift
Noise margin for upshift interval

Upshift noise
margin ──────────────────────────────────────
Steady-state operation

Target noise
margin ──────────────────────────────────────
Steady-state operation

Downshift noise
margin ─────────────────────────────────────

Decrease rate if noise margin < downshift noise margin for downshift
interval

Minimum noise
margin ──────────────────────────────────

Increase Power
If not possible reinitialize

`Upshift noise margin` and `downshift noise margin` **are supported
only for** `rate-adaptive mode. Minimum noise margin < = downshift
noise margin < = target noise margin < = upshift noise margin
< = maximum noise margin.`

Target noise margin. This is the noise margin that the modem (transmit
from ATU-C and ATU-R) must achieve with a BER of 1×10^{-7} or better to
successfully complete initialization.

Maximum noise margin. This is the maximum noise margin a modem
that (transmit from ATU-C and ATU-R) should try to sustain. If the noise
margin is above this, the modem should attempt to reduce its power output to
optimize its operation.

Minimum noise margin. This is the minimum noise margin that the
modem (transmit from ATU-C and ATU-R) should tolerate. If the noise margin falls below this level, the modem should attempt to increase its power
output. If that is not possible, the modem will attempt to reinitialize.

Dynamic rate adaptation parameters. The following parameters are defined to
manage the rate-adaptive behavior in the transmit direction for both ATU-C
and ATU-R.

Rate adaptation mode. This parameter specifies the mode of operation of
a rate-adaptive modem (transmit from ATU-C and ATU-R) (if this functionality is supported).

Mode 1 *Manual:* Rate is changed manually.

At start-up: The desired minimum rate parameter specifies the bit rate the modem
must support, with a noise margin which is at least as large as the specified target
noise margin (TNM) and a BER of better than 1×10^{-7}. If it fails to achieve the bit
rate, the modem will fail, and NMS will be notified. Although the modem might be
able to support a higher bit rate, it will not provide more than what is requested.
When the noise margin for the selected transport configuration is higher than the
maximum noise margin, the modem shall reduce its power to get a noise margin
below this limit (if this functionality is supported).

At showtime: The modem shall maintain the specified desired minimum rate. When the current noise margin falls below the minimum noise margin, the modem will fail, and NMS will be notified. When the current noise margin rises above maximum noise margin, then the power shall be reduced to get the noise margin below this limit. (If this functionality is supported).

Mode 2 `AT_INIT`: rate is automatically selected at start-up only and does not change after that.

At start-up: The desired minimum rate parameter specifies the minimum bit rate that the modem must support, with a noise margin which is at least as large as the specified TNM, and a BER of better than 1×10^{-7}. If it fails to achieve the bit rate, the modem will fail, and NMS will be notified. If the modem is able to support a higher bit rate for that direction at initialization, the excess bit rate will be distributed among the fast and interleaved latency path according to the ratio (0 to 100 percent) specified by the rate adaptation ratio (RAR) parameter. The ratio is defined as fast/(fast+interleave) bit rate $\times$ 100 percent. A ratio of 30 percent means that 30 percent of the excess bit rate should be assigned to the fast latency path, and 70 percent to the interleaved latency path. When the DMR is achieved in one of the latency paths, the remaining excess bit rate is assigned to the other latency path until it also reaches its desired maximum rate. A ratio of 100 percent will assign all excess bit rate first to the fast latency path, and only when the desired maximum rate of fast channel is obtained, the remaining excess bit rate will be assigned to the interleaved latency path, and a ratio of 0 percent will give priority to the interleaved latency path. When the noise margin for the selected transport configuration is higher than the maximum noise margin, then the modem shall reduce its power to get a noise margin below this limit. Note that this can happen only when desired maximum rates are reached for both latencies, since bit-rate increase has priority over power reduction (if this functionality is supported).

At showtime: During showtime, no rate adaptation is allowed. The bit rate which has been settled during initialization shall be maintained. When the current noise margin falls below the minimum noise margin, the modem will fail, and NMS will be notified. When the current noise margin rises above maximum noise margin, the power shall be reduced to get the noise margin below this limit (if this functionality is supported).

Mode 3 *Dynamic:* Rate automatically selected at start-up and is continuously adapted during operation (showtime).

At start-up: In mode 3, the modem shall start up as in mode 2. *At showtime:* During showtime, rate adaptation is allowed with respect to the RAR for distributing the excess bit rate among the interleaved and fast latency paths (see mode 2), and assuring that the desired minimum rate remains available at a BER of 1×10^{-7} or better. The bit rate can vary between the desired minimum rate and the desired maximum rate. Rate adaptation is performed when the conditions specified for upshift noise margin and upshift interval—or for downshift noise margin and downshift interval—are satisfied.

This (mode 3, at showtime) means:

For an upshift action: allowed when the current noise margin is above upshift noise margin during minimum time interval for upshift rate adaptation.

For a downshift action: allowed when the current noise margin is below downshift noise margin during minimum time interval for downshift rate adaptation.

When the current noise margin falls below the minimum noise margin, the modem will fail, and NMS will be notified. When desired maximum rates have been reached in both latency paths, and when the current noise margin rises above maximum noise margin, the power shall be reduced to get the noise margin below this limit.

Upshift noise margin. If the noise margin is above the upshift noise margin and remains above it for more than the time specified by the minimum upshift rate adaptation interval, the modem should increase its data rate (transmit from ATU-C and ATU-R). The *minimum time interval* for *upshift rate* parameter defines the interval of time the noise margin should stay above the upshift noise margin before the modem will attempt to increase data rate (transmit from ATU-C and ATU-R).

Downshift noise margin. If the noise margin is below the downshift noise margin and stays below it for more than the time specified by the minimum downshift rate adaptation interval, the modem should decrease its data rate (transmit from ATU-C and ATU-R). The *minimum time interval for downshift rate adaptation* parameter defines the interval of time the noise margin should stay below the downshift noise margin before the modem will attempt to decrease data rate (transmit from ATU-C and ATU-R).

Bit-rate parameters. These bit-rate parameters refer to the transmit direction for both ATU-C and ATU-R. The two desired bit-rate parameters define the desired bit rate as specified by the operator of the system (the operator of the ATU-C). It is assumed that ATU-C and ATU-R will interpret the value set by the operator as appropriate for the specific implementation of ADSL between the ATU-C and ATU-R in setting the line rates. This model defined in this interface makes no assumptions about the possible range of these attributes. The management system used by the operator to manage the ATU-R and ATU-C may implement its own limits on the allowed values for the desired bit-rate parameters, based on the particulars of the system managed. The definition of such a system is outside the scope of this model.

Desired maximum rate. These parameters specify the desired maximum rates (transmit from the ATU-R and ATU-C) as desired by the operator of the system.

Desired minimum rate. These parameters specify the desired minimum rates (transmit from the ATU-R and ATU-C) as desired by the operator of the system.

Rate adaptation ratio. These parameters (expressed in percentage) specify the ratio that should be taken into account for distributing the bit rate considered for rate adaptation amongst the fast and interleaved channels in case of excess bit rate. The ratio is defined as [fast/(fast+interleaved)] $\times$ 100. Following this rule, a ratio of 20 percent means that 20 percent of the additional bit rate (in excess of the Fast minimum plus the interleaved minimum bit rate) will be assigned to the fast channel and 80 percent, to the Interleaved channel.

Maximum interleave delay. The transmission delay is introduced by the interleaving process. The delay is defined as per ANSI T1.413, and is $(S \times d)/4$ ms, where S is the S factor, and d is the interleaving depth.

Alarm (event) thresholds. Each ATU maintains current 15-min interval counts. Each count may trigger an alarm (event) if it reaches or exceeds a preset threshold. Those thresholds shown in Figures 10.48 and 10.49 will be set individually.

Rate threshold. These parameters provide rate up and down thresholds which trigger a rate change alarm (event) when they are reached or crossed.

Inventory information. Each ATU-R and ATU-C shall make accessible through the NMS port the following information: vendor ID, version number, and serial number. The hardware, software, and firmware version are vendor-specific fields and should be placed in an enterprise-specific equipment MIB for SNMP implementation.

Vendor ID. The vendor ID is assigned by T1E1.4 according to T1.413, which contains a procedure for applying for numbers. The numbers are consecutively assigned, starting with 002.

Version number. The version number is for version control and is vendor-specific information.

Serial number. The serial number is vendor-specific and should be no longer than 32 bytes. Note that the combination of vendor ID and serial number creates a unique number for each ADSL unit.

Fault management

Fault management applies to the process of the identifying the existence of a fault condition, determining its cause, and taking corrective action. For purposes here, faults will be notified by alarms (events) presented over the NMS port from the ATU-C. Network management systems may also determine faults, such as line deterioration, by examining performance reports. However, current telephone company practices favor alarm (event)-driven fault management. For this reason the number of alarm (event) conditions, and range of configurability, is rather large. Note that some alarms (events) may not represent faults as such, but require operations notice because they interrupt service or represent sources for service calls. Unpowered ATU-Rs and unpowered connected CPE are examples.

ADSL line status. ADSL line status shows the current state of the line. The possible states are defined as follows:

- Operational
- Loss of frame

- Loss of signal
- Loss of power
- Loss of link (ATU-C only)

A loss of link condition is declared at the ATU-C if a loss of signal is not proceeded by a "dying-gasp" message from the ATU-R:

- Loss of signal quality
- Initialization failure due to data error (ATU-C only)
- Initialization failure due to configuration error (ATU-C only)
- Initialization failure due to protocol error (ATU-C only)
- Initialization failure due to no peer ATU present (ATU-C only)

Alarms (events). There is no distinction between major and minor alarms (events). To generate alarm (event) on loss of signal/loss of frame, loss of power, loss of link, or error seconds depends on the value of the counter reaching or exceeding the threshold value in a single 15-min interval. The threshold value is configurable. When those alarms (events) clear, it will not report a trap to show the status change. The reason is that if the alarm (event) condition persists for the next 15 min, it will generate another alarm. If no alarm (event) is generated in the next 15 min, the NMS knows that the alarm (event) clears.

Inability to initialize ATU-R from ATU-C will generate an alarm (event). When ATU-C is able to initialize the ATU-R, a clear alarm (event) will be generated.

Rate change will generate an alarm (event) consisting of configurable rate up and down thresholds on upstream and downstream rates, respectively.

All alarms (events) can be enabled or disabled. The default is disabled. Please refer to ANSI T1.413 for more detailed definitions of alarms (events).

Loss of signal at ATU-R	Error seconds at ATU-R
Loss of signal at ATU-C	Error seconds at ATU-C
Loss of frame at ATU-R	Unable to initialize with ATU-R
Loss of frame at ATU-C	(implies knowledge that power is on at ATU-R)
Loss of power at ATU-R	Rate change at ATU-R
Loss of power at ATU-C	Rate change at ATU-C
Loss of link at ATU-R for ATU-C	

Fault isolation. Fault isolation falls more to operations strategy and practices than anything necessarily inherent in the modems and may need to be coordinated with other forms of testing, such as MLT. However, modem tests and test sequences can be helpful in isolating faults to a particular element in a link, comprising an ATU-C, its POTS splitter, the line, the ATU-R POTS splitter, the ATU-R, and equipment attached at the T interface.

To assist fault isolation, the modem systems shall provide the following diagnostics under control of commands transmitted across an NMS port: ATU-C self-test (see T1.413 for details).

Performance management. Each ATU-R and ATU-C shall make accessible through the NMS port the following performance/status-related information:

Status

Line attenuation	The measured difference in the total power transmitted by the peer ATU and the total power received by this ATU in decibels.
Noise margin	The noise margin as seen by this ATU with respect to its received signal in decibels.
Total output power	To show total output power from the modem.
Maximum attainable rate	To indicate the maximum currently attainable data rate by the modem.
Current rate	Parameters that report the current rate (transmit from the ATU-R and ATU-C) to which the ATU-C or ATU-R is adapted. It can be read by the operator of the system.
Previous rate	Parameters that report the rate (transmit from the ATU-R and ATU-C) to which the previous "rate change" event occurred.
Channel data block length	A per channel parameter indicating the size of the data block subject to CRC check. This includes the number of redundant check bytes and the number of message bytes over which these check bytes provide protection. This value may be different for Fast and Interleaved channels as the number of check bytes for each channel is individually negotiated and the number of bytes per symbol depends on the rate of each channel. It will be read-only information.
Interleave delay	The transmission delay is introduced by the interleaving process. The delay is defined as per ANSI T1.413, and is $(S \times d)/4$ ms, where S is the S factor, and d is the interleaving depth.

Performance monitoring. The following raw counters (counters that begin at 0 when the device is started and continue forever wrapping at the maximum count) shall be kept for both the ATU-C and ATU-R:

Loss of signal failure

Loss of frame failure

Loss of power failure

Loss of link failure

Errored seconds

This is a count of one-second (1-s) intervals containing one or more severely errored frame uncorrectable block errors in either the fast or interleaved channel, or one or more `Los` (loss of signal) or `Sef` (severely errored frame) defects. Additional block parameters are as follows:

Transmitted blocks	This counter is available per channel and indicates the number of blocks that have been transmitted by this ATU; should be incremented only when there is a reasonable expectation of end-to-end communication (e.g., showtime).
Receive blocks	This per channel counter indicating the number of blocks received by this ATU; should be incremented only when valid framing is detected.
Corrected blocks	The count of received blocks which were errored when received but corrected by the built-in forward error correction.
Uncorrectable blocks	The count of received blocks which were unable to be corrected by the forward error correction mechanism. Since the counting of corrected and uncorrected errors is based on the forward error correction block, this definition also applies for counting transmitted and received blocks.

The following seconds counters should be available for the current and previous day and current and from 1 to 96 previous 15-min intervals. A seconds counter is incremented when one or more of the relevant events occurred or the condition persisted throughout that second. The counts should be kept for each of the following items with respect to both the ATU-C and ATU-R:

Loss of signal seconds

Loss of frame seconds

Loss of power seconds

Loss of link seconds

Errored second seconds

Block variables are:

Transmit blocks

Receive blocks

Corrected blocks

Uncorrectable blocks

Features for future consideration

Here are some features that have been identified for future consideration.

Single-tone echo test (transmission of a single tone that is echoed back from the ATU-R after frequency translation, assuming FDM; the most robust implementation of this would use analog circuits independent of DSPs)

Measure line attenuation by frequency

CPE synchronization

T-interface cable test

Average S/N ratio on each of the 256 tones

When bit swaps (from one tone to another) are made, and number of bit swaps per 15 min and per day

Transmit power and change in transmit power

Test-related features to support reset, loopback (or other out-of-service performance testing TBD), and out-of-service testing

Management functions in the access node (AN), for example, ATU-C ports, channel cross-connect, broadband channel allocation

DMT/CAP specific elements

ADSL network element terminology

Access node   Concentration point for broadband and narrowband data. The access node may be located at a central office or a remote site. Also, a remote access node may subtend from a central access node.

ATU-C   ADSL transmission unit at the central office end; the ATU-C may be integrated within an access node.

ATU-R   ADSL transmission unit at the customer premises end.

broadband network   Switching system for data rates above 1.5/2.0 Mbps.

broadcast   Broadband data input in simplex mode (typically broadcast video).

hp   High-pass.

loop   Twisted-pair copper telephone line.

lp   Low-pass.

narrowband network   Switching system for data rates at or below 1.5/2.0 Mbps.

NT   Network termination.

POTS   Plain Old Telephone Service.

PSTN   Public Switched Telephone Network.

Service Module (SM)   Performs terminal adaptation functions. Examples are set-top boxes, PC interfaces, or LAN routers.

Splitter   Filters which separate high-frequency (ADSL) and low-frequency (POTS) signals at CO end and premises end. The splitter may be integrated into the ATU, physically separated from the ATU, or divided between high-pass and low-pass, with the low-pass function physically separated from the ATU. The provision of POTS splitters and POTS-related functions is optional.

T-R   Interface(s) between ATU-R and switching layers (e.g., ATM and STM).

T/S   Interface(s) between ANT (ADSL network termination) and CI (customer installation) or home network.

U-C   Interface between loop and ATU-C (analog). Definition of both ends of the loop interface separately arises because of the asymmetry of the signals on the line.

U-C$_2$ Interface between POTS splitter and ATU-C.

U-R   Interface between loop and ATU-R (analog).

U-R$_2$ Interface between POTS splitter and ATU-R.

V-C   Logical interface between ATU-C and a digital network element such as one or more switching systems. A digital carrier facility (e.g., SONET extension) may be interposed at the V-C interface when the ATU-C is located at a remote site.

ADSL network element reference material

ADSL Forum 96-034	*Telecommunications Management Network (an overview of TMN)*
ADSL Forum 96-040	*SNMP Management for ADSL*
ADSL Forum 96-045	*ADSL Data Service Network Management*
ADSL Forum 96-047	*Variable Bit Rate ADSL Using Carrierless AM / PM (CAP)*
ADSL Forum 96-061	*Recommended Values of* `ifType` *Object for ADSL Management with SNMP*
ADSL Forum 96-064	*Rate Adaptive Packet (RAP) Mode ADSL*
ADSL Forum 96-068	*More Facilities for Configuration Management*
ADSL Forum 96-069	*SNMP and ADSL*
ADSL Forum 96-105	*Network Management Group—Status Report (9/19/96)*
ADSL Forum 96-134	*ADSL MIB Definition* (from Alcatel)
ADSL Forum 96-143	*ADSL MIB* draft version (from ADSL Forum Network Management group)
ADSL Forum 97-008	*ADSL Line MIB* (from John Burgess, ed.)
ADSL Forum 97-009	*Updates on the ADSL MIB Definition*
ADSL Forum 97-019	*Defining the Need for a Very Simple Network management Protocol for End-to-End Management of the ATU-C and ATU-R*
ADSL Forum 97-030	*A Network Management Approach to Dealing with Dynamic Bandwidth*
ADSL Forum 97-053	*A Common OAM Interface for UNI and FUNI*
ADSL Forum 97-054	*An Interface to Support SNMP over and ADSL OAM Flow*
ADSL Forum 97-056	*GDMO Representation ADSL Function Model and Information Model*
ADSL Forum 97-057	*ADSL* Issue 2 *Measurements and Counter*
ADSL Forum 97-059	*ATM Layer Management for the ATM UNI and FUNI*
ADSL Forum 97-067	*ADSL MIB Performance Monitoring*
ADSL Forum 97-073	*Proposal for ADSL LINE MIB Conformance Statements*

ADSL Forum 97-074	*Comments on the ADSL Forum Network Management Text*
ADSL Forum 97-082	*A Structure Framework for ADSL Operational Design*
ADSL Forum 97-121	*A "Container" MIB for End-to-End Management of ADSL Networks*
ADSL Forum TR-005	Draft

10.7 SNMP-Based ADSL LINE MIB

This section defines a standard SNMP MIB for ADSL lines based on the ADSL Forum standard data model. The model assumed by this MIB is that the SNMP agent's perspective is from the ATU-C side which acts as a proxy for the ATU-R. Each MIB instance includes information for both parts of a single line, that is, both the ATU-C and ATU-R.

Introduction

This section relates to the previous section (Section 10.6, subsection on ADSL network management element, in which the former, which defined the conceptual ADSL data, needed to be managed). It describes an SNMP implementation of the ADSL LINE MIB which is intended to work with both SNMP (v1) and SNMPv2. The MIB, however, is based on SNMPv2 structure of management information and textual conventions. This does not, however, mean that either the agent or manager must be fully SNMPv2 protocol–compliant. All MIB definitions are backward-compatible for SNMPv1 implementation.

The actual MIB in standard ASN.1 format is attached. The MIB will eventually be located in the MIB tree under MIB-II transmission, as shown later with MIB-II integration (RFCs 1213 and 1573). Until approved by the IETF, however, it is temporarily located under the ADSL Forum Enterprise Identifier. Vendors may also choose to support it under their own enterprise IDs.

```
adslLineMIB MODULE-IDENTITY
...
:: = { adslForum 1 }
where
adslForum :: = { enterprises XXX } — pending assignment
or
adslLineMIB :: = { VendorEnterpriseID nnn}
```

Figure 10.50 shows the overall structure and organization of the MIB.

Relationship between the ADSL LINE MIB and other standard MIBs

The information presented here provides insight to the relationship of this MIB with other MIBs described in RFCs and in various degrees of "standardization." Specifically, MIB-2 (RFCs 1213 and 1573) and the Entity MIB (RFC 2037) are discussed.

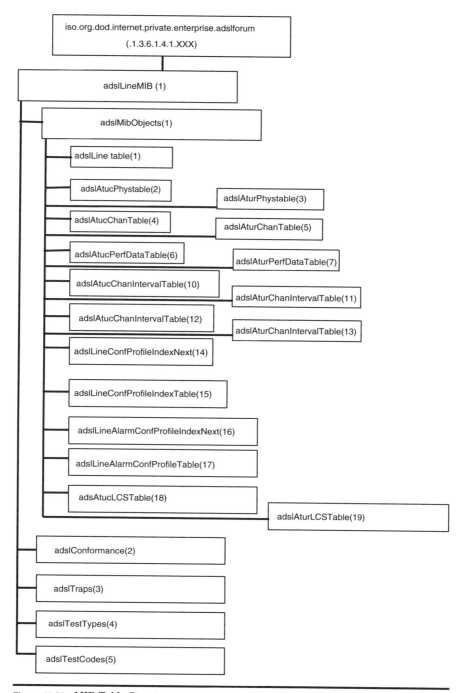

Figure 10.50 MIB Table Structure

MIB-II integration (RFCs 1213 and 1573)   The ADSL LINE MIB specifies the detailed attributes of a data interface. As such, it needs to integrate as neatly as possible with MIB-2 [1, 2, 4–6]. The Internet Assigned Numbers Authority (IANA) has assigned the following `ifTypes` to ADSL:

```
IANAifType ::= TEXTUAL-CONVENTION
        . . .
SYNTAX INTEGER {
        . . .
adsl(94),     — Asymmetric Digital Subscriber Loop
radsl(95),    — Rate-Adapt. Digital Subscriber Loop
sdsl(96),     — Symmetric Digital Subscriber Loop
vdsl(97),     — Very H-Speed Digital Subscrib. Loop
. . .
adslInterleave(124),  — ADSL Interleaved Channel
adslFast(125),  — ADSL Fast Channel
}
```

Of these, only `adsl`, `adslFast`, and `adslInterleave` are intended to be used with this MIB. Use of `radsl`, `sdsl`, and `vdsl` is for further study (or they may have their own MIBs).

Therefore, pending approval of the IETF, RFC 1573 mandates that this MIB will be accessed through `mib-2.transmission.ifType` as shown:

```
adslPhysIf ::= { transmission 94 }    — for the physical  interface tables
adslFastIf ::= { transmission 124}    — Fast Channel tables
adslInterIf ::= { transmission 125 }— Interleaved Channel  tables
```

Each MIB branch contains the appropriate tables for that interface type, as discussed below. Most such tables "augment" the `ifEntry` table, and are indexed by `ifIndex`. In addition, there are two "profile" tables which may be accessed by `ifIndex`, or may be accessed with a profile index.

The previous MIB-II objects are proposed only, and should not be used. Only the `adslForum.adslLineMib` structure or other `enterprise.vendorID.adslLineMib` structure should be used at present, no matter what value is present for `ifType`. In other words, implementations of this issue of the MIB should always use `enterprises.xxx.adslLineMib`.

MIB-II table use (RFC 1573)   The following attributes are part of the mandatory `ifGeneral` group in RFC 1573 [5, p. 51], and are not duplicated in the ADSL MIB. Remember that these apply to the line, not either end in particular.

- `ifDescr` (manufacturer's name, model number, version number).
- `ifType` = 94, 124, or 125, as above.
- `ifSpeed` (should be the same as the "downstream" or ATU-C transmit rate).
- `ifPhysAddress` (not applicable for ADSL, must be `0-length` string).

- ifAdminStatus, ifOperStatus (normal use, supplemented by adslAtu*CurrStatus).

- ifLastChange [Time (sysUpTime) of the last state change for this interface].

- ifLinkUpDownTrapEnable [default to Enable (1) for physical layer entries, and to Disable (2)e otherwise].

- ifConnectorPresent [set to True (1) for physical layer entries, and to False (2) otherwise].

- ifHighSpeed. Since ADSL could operate at a maximum rate of about 8 Mbps circa 1997, ifHighSpeed is irrelevant, it should be set to NULL.

- ifName ("textual name of the interface"). See also adslLineSpecific. A network manager needs to be able to associate an ifEntry with a specific node/shelf/slot/port. IfName provides a text mechanism, but there is no generic standard MIB linkage. The following attributes are from the ifFixedLengthGroup which is optional, but is the closest set to ADSL. They may optionally be implemented when appropriate:

ifInOctets, ifOutOctets (from the perspective of the ATU-C)
ifInUnknownProtos, ifInErrors, ifOutErrors

Figure 10.51 presents this information in a more concise format. "Normal" means that the variable is used normally as specified by MIB-II. The designations *i*, *j*, and *k* indicate three arbitrary ifIndex values, corresponding to the Physical, Interleaved, and Fast entries for a single ADSL line. These designations are used throughout this document.

Use the ifTest table for diagnostic tests, which augments ifEntry. The adslLineMib defines ADSL-specific values for ifTestTypes and ifTestCodes. Specific test codes are not defined in this version or the MIB. Use the ifStackTable to associate the entries for Physical, Fast, Interleaved channels, and higher layers (e.g., ATM) as shown in Figure 10.52.

MIB Variable	Physical Line(i)	Interleaved Channel(j)	Fast Channel (k)
ifDescr	Normal	Normal	Normal
ifType (IANA)	94	124	125
IfSpeed	ATU-C Line Tx Rate	ATU-C Channel Tx Rate	ATU-C Channel Tx Rate
ifPhysAddress	NULL	NULL	NULL
ifAdminStatus	Normal	Normal	Normal
ifOperStatus	Normal	Normal	Normal
ifLastChange	Normal	Normal	Normal
ifLinkUpDownTrapEnable	Normal (default: Enable)	Normal (default: Disable)	Normal (default: Disable)
ifConnectorPresent	True	False	False
ifHighSpeed	Null	Null	Null

Figure 10.51 Use of ifTable Objects

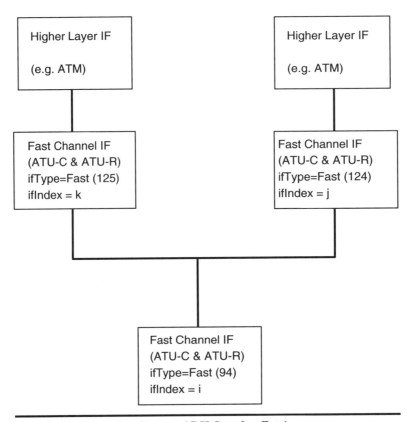

Figure 10.52   Relationship Between ADSL Interface Entries

Use of `ifStackTable` is mandatory, because configuration information is stored in profile tables associated with the physical layer `ifEntry` only. The channels `ifEntrys` need the `ifStackTable` to find their associated physical layer entry and thus their configuration parameters.

Relationship with the Entity MIB (RFC 2037).   Implementation of the Entity MIB (RFC 2037) is optional. It in no way alters the information required in the `adslLineMib`, nor does it alter the relationship with MIB-2, `ifIndex`, and `ifStackTable`. The Entity MIB introduces a standardized way of presenting the components of complex systems, such as a digital subscriber line access multiplexer (DSLAM), that may contain multiple racks, shelves, line cards, and/or ports. The Entity MIB's main goal is to present these system components, their containment relationship, and mapping information with other MIBs such as the Interface MIB and the `adslLineMib`. If implemented, the Entity MIB should include entities for the ATU-C and ATU-R in the `entPhysicalTable`. The MIB's `entAliasMappingTable` would contain mapping information identifying the `ifIndex` object associated with each ATU-C and ATU-R. Also associating the relationship between the `ifTable` and Entity MIB, the `entPhysicalTable` contains an `entPhysicalName` object, which approximates the semantics of the `ifName` object from the Interface MIB.

Conventions used in the MIB

Naming conventions

(a) `Atuc/Atur` are used for the ATU-C and ATU-R. These are sometimes referred to as the *near end* (Ne) and *far end* (Fe), respectively, but not in this document.

(b) Similarly, "transmit" and "receive" are from the perspective of the corresponding table's end of the line. For example, `adslAtucChanConf MaxTxRate` defines the "downstream" rate, while `adslAturChanConf MaxTxRate` defines the "upstream" rate for a particular channel.

(c) There are two possible channels: fast and interleaved. Either one or both may be implemented on a particular ADSL line. The MIB structure supports all three configurations.

(d) `Lof, Lol, Los, Lpr` mean *loss of framing, link, signal, and power,* respectively. `Lpr` is used by T1E1, so it is used for consistency (rather than `Lop`). A loss-of-link condition is declared at the ATU-C if a loss of signal is not preceded by a "dying gasp" message from the ATU-R. Note that loss of link is supported only by the ATU-C.

(e) `ES` means errored second. An *errored second* is any second containing one or more CRC anomaly, or one or more `Los` or severely errored frame (Sef) defect(s).

(f) A "block" is a physical layer "data buffer" (in ANSI T1.413 terms) over which a CRC is calculated. This is to avoid confusion with link layer frames.

(g) `Atn` means *attenuation,* `Psd` is *power spectral density,* and `Snr` is *signal-to-noise ratio.*

(h) `LCS` means *line-code-specific.* There are tables (defined elsewhere) for

DMT = discrete `MultiTone`

CAP = carrierless amplitude and phase modulation

QAM = quadrature amplitude modulation

(i) Vendor (in the Inventory variables) refers to the manufacturer or the ATU-C or ATU-R assembly, not the modem chip vendor. When in doubt, use the manufacturer of the smallest field-replaceable unit (e.g., stand-alone modem box, plug-in board).

Structure. The MIB has multiple parallel tables for different purposes. There are tables for

- `line`: common attributes
- `atuc` and `atur` status
- `atuc` and `atur` performance: current and up to 96 buckets of 15-min performance history data
- Current and previous 1-day bucket performance history data
- `profiles`: configuration parameters and alarm parameters

Also, there are separate tables for physical and channel layers. Only one "channel" object is defined, which is used for both fast and interleaved channels, since the attributes are the same. The corresponding `ifType` gives the proper interpretation for that `ifEntry`. Finally, there are separate LCS tables, also for each end. These are currently stubs. These will each be separate MIB modules.

There could have been fewer tables by combining the ATU-C and ATU-R information into shared tables. However, the tables are more easily read when there are two identical sets of data. The following `adslLineType` options are supported:

No Channels (1)	Only interface (i) is supported.
Fast channel only (2)	Interfaces (i) and (k) are supported.
Interleaved channel only (3)	Interfaces (i) and (j) are supported.
Either Fast or Interleaved channel (4)	Interfaces (i), and one of (j) or (k) are supported.
Both Fast and Interleaved channels (5)	Interfaces (i), and both of (j) and (k) are supported.

In (4) the manager may select the channel to be used. Individual tables are used either with a physical layer entry or with channel entries, as shown in Figure 10.53.

Counters, interval buckets, and thresholds

For physical-level ES, Los, Lof, Lol, and Lpr, there are free-running event counters, current 15-min and up to ninety-six 15-min history buckets of "interval-counters," as well as current and previous 1-day interval counters.

There is no requirement for an agent to ensure a fixed relationship between the start of a 15-min interval and any wall clock; however, some implementations may align the 15-min intervals with quarter-hours. Likewise, an implementation may choose to align one day intervals with start of a day. In all cases, the sum of the corresponding 15-min interval timers for the current day should equal the current 1-day timers. However, in most cases, this will not be the sum of all 96 intervals, as they represent a rolling set of data.

Table	ifIndexUsed
adslLineTable	i
adslAtucPhysTable	i
adslAturPhysTable	i
adslAtucChanTable	j and k
adslAturChanTable	j and k
adslAtucPhysPerfDataTable	i
adslAturPhysPerfDataTable	i
adslAtucChanPerfTable	j and k
adslAturChanPerfTable	j and k
adslAtucIntervalTable	i
adslAturIntervalTable	i
adslAtucChanPerfDataTable	j and k
adslAturChanPerfDataTable	j and k
adslAtucChanIntervalTable	j and k
adslAturChanIntervalTable	j and k
adslAtucLCSTable	not yet defined
adslAturLCSTable	not yet defined
adslLineCofProfileTable	
adslLineAlarmConfProfileTable	

Figure 10.53 Use of ADSL MIB Tables with Various `ifIndex` Values

At the channel level there are counters for total received blocks, received-and-corrected blocks, received-but-uncorrectable blocks, and transmitted blocks. Blocks are counted here because octets are counted by `ifInOctets`, `ifOutOctets`. A *block* is the minimum error-correction unit. There are the same set of 15-min and 1-day buckets as at the physical layer.

Separate tables are provided for the 96 interval counters. They are indexed by {`ifIndex, AdslAtu*IntervalNumber`}. Every variable with a 15-min current bucket also has a 15-min threshold trap. Counters are not reset when an ATU-C is reinitialized, only when the agent is reset or reinitialized (or under specific request outside the scope of this MIB).

Profiles

As a managed node can handle a large number of ATU-Cs (e.g., hundreds or perhaps thousands of ADSL lines), provisioning every parameter on every ATU-C may become burdensome. In response, two MIB tables have been created to define ADSL equipment configuration data profiles, as well as a mechanism to associate the equipment to these profiles. This concept is similar to the one used in ATM MIB (RFC 1695) to define ATM traffic descriptor sets.

Profile tables may be implemented in one of two modes:

MODE-I   Dynamic profiles that may be shared by multiple ADSL lines.
MODE-II   Static profiles that are unique to each ADSL line.

MODE-I: dynamic profiles that may be shared by multiple ADSL lines. Implementations using MODE-I will enable the manager to dynamically create and delete profiles as needed. The index of the profile is an arbitrary integer in the range $1, \ldots, N$, where N is the maximum number of profiles supported by the equipment and is implementation-specific.

One or more ADSL lines may be configured to share parameters in Profile-n (adslLineConfProfileIndex = n) by setting their adslLineConfProfile variable to n. If a change is made to Profile-n, all lines that refer to it will be reconfigured to the changed parameters.

Figure 10.54 shows an example of MODE-I. In the example, ADSL lines 1 and x share the configuration in Profile-n, while line 2 uses Profile-1.

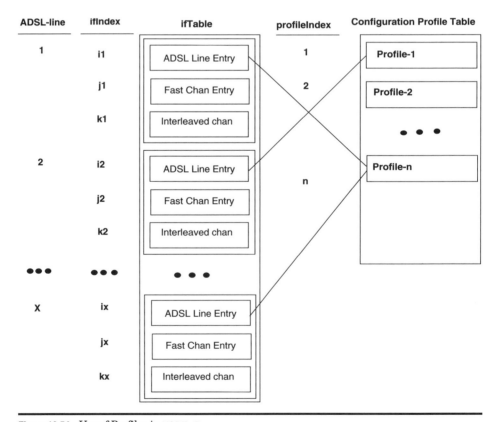

Figure 10.54 Use of Profiles in MODE-I

The three entries for the physical layer, the fast channel, and the interleaved channel for each ADSL line are represented by i, j, and k as before. However, only the physical layer entry i contains an adslLineTable entry, so only those entries contain pointers to the adslConfProfileEntry. The ifStackTable (see RFC 1573) is used to link between the channel entries and the corresponding physical layer entry to get the channel configuration parameters.

The same is true for the alarm profile (not shown), although there is no requirement that its index (call it m) be the same as the configuration profile. In this mode, profiles are allocated and deleted dynamically, and six objects—adslLineConfProfile, adslLineConfProfileIndexNext, adslLineConfProfileRowStatus, adlsLineAlarmProfile, adslLine AlarmConfProfileIndexNext, and adslLineAlarmConf ProfileRow Status—are all used to control the use of profiles.

MODE-II: **static profiles that are unique to each ADSL line.** Implementations with MODE-II will automatically create a profile one-for-one with each ADSL line physical entry with the profileIndex being the same as the ifIndex of the corresponding ADSL line entry (ix).

The agent will not allow a manager to create/delete profiles in MODE-II. The adslLineConfProfile, adslLineConfProfileIndexNext, adslLineConfProfileRowStatus, adlsLineAlarmProfile, adslLine AlarmConfProfileIndexNext, and adslLineAlarmConf ProfileRow Status variables are not used in this mode, as each line has a unique, fixed profile that is not shared with other lines. Figure 10.55 shows an example of MODE-II. In this example, ADSL lines 1, 2, and x each have their own profiles.

Traps

These MIB-2 traps are required: coldStart/warmStart (per [6])—which are per agent (e.g., per DSLAM in such a device), and linkUp/linkDown. The RFC 1573 recommends that linkUp/linkDown only be used at a physical layer ifEntry, as discussed above. A linkDown trap should be generated whenever any of Lof, Los, LoL, or Lpr occurs. At this operational point, a manager can use adslAtu*CurrStatus for additional detailed information. The corresponding linkUp trap is sent when all link failure conditions are cleared. Note that linkUp/linkDown traps are not sent following a management action (e.g., rebooting the agent, setting ifAdminStatus).

The only traps defined in this MIB are for initialization failure, rate change (if RADSL), and the various thresholds: Lofs, Lols, Loss, Lprs, and ESs. Each threshold has its own enable/threshold value. When that value is 0, the trap is disabled. Thus a separate trapEnable bitmask variable is unnecessary.

The variables adslAtu*CurrStatus indicate, through a bitmask, all outstanding error conditions or that the line is operational. Note that each vari-

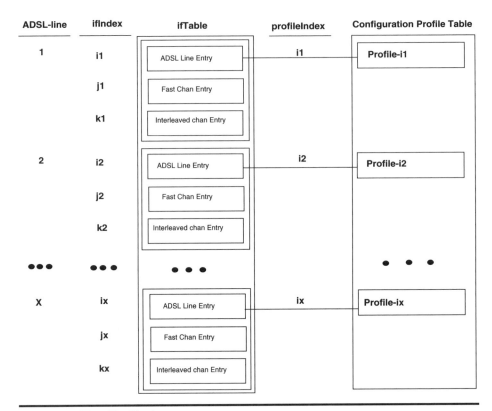

Figure 10.55   Use of Profiles in `MODE-II`

able claims to represent the status of the modem at that end of the line. However, since the SNMP agent coresides with the ATU-C, `adslAturCurrStatus` may be incomplete. For example, when there are errors on the line, the ATU-R may not be able to correctly report this condition. Therefore, not all conditions are included in `adslAturCurrStatus`.

A threshold trap occurs whenever the corresponding current 15-min interval error counter becomes equal to the threshold value. Since the current 15-min counter are reset to 0 every 15 min, if the condition persists, the trap may recur as often as every 15 min but not more frequently than that (on average). For example, to get a trap whenever a "loss of" event occurs (but at most once every 15 min), set the corresponding `Thresh15Min` to 1. The agent will generate a trap when the event originally occurs. Note that the NMS will get a `linkDown` trap, as well, if enabled. At the beginning of the next 15-min interval, the counter is reset. When the first second goes by, the current interval bucket will be 1, which equals the threshold, and the trap will be sent again.

The rate change trap is invoked in RADSL mode when the transmit rate on a channel either increases by `adsl(x)Thresh(y)RateDown` or decreases by

adsl(x)Thresh(y)RateDown. **The trap is per** direction:(x) = = **Atuc**
or Atur, **and per channel:** (y) = = **Fast or** Interleave. **In other words,**
the trap is sent whenever the rate changes in either direction on either channel and CurrTxRate (PrevTxRate plus ThreshRateUp or CurrTxRate
(PrevTxRate minus ThreshRateDown. **No trap is sent on initialization.**
It can be disabled by setting the Up (and/or) Down threshold rates to 0. The
PrevTxRate variable is set to the current value at initialization and when a
trap is sent. Thus rate changes are cumulative until the total change exceeds
the threshold. Conformance and compliance information will be presented at
a later date and available via the adsl Web site.

References

RFC 1902, *Structure of Management Information for Version 2 of the Simple Network Management*
Protocol (*SNMPv2*), Jan. 1996. <ftp://ds.internic.net/rfc/rfc1902.txt>.
RFC 1903, *Textual Conventions for Version 2 of the Simple Network Management Protocol*
(*SNMPv2*), Jan. 1996. <ftp://ds.internic.net/rfc/rfc1903.txt>.
ADSL Forum TR-005, *Network Management Element Management,* March 1998.
<ftp://???.adsl.com/???>
RFC 1213, *Management Information Base for Network Management of TCP/IP-Based Internets:*
MIB-II, March 1991. <ftp://ds.internic.net/rfc/rfc1213.txt>.
RFC 1573, *Evolution of the Interfaces Group of MIB-II,* Jan. 1994. <ftp://ds.internic.net/
rfc/rfc1573.txt>.
RFC 1907, *Management Information Base for Version 2 of the Simple Network Management*
Protocol (*SNMPv2*), Jan. 1996. <ftp://ds.internic.net/rfc/rfc1907.txt>.

The ASN.1 MIB

```
ADSL-LINE-MIB DEFINITIONS ::= BEGIN
    IMPORTS
        MODULE-IDENTITY, OBJECT-TYPE, Counter32, Gauge32,
        NOTIFICATION-TYPE, Integer32, enterprises FROM SNMPv2-SMI
        DisplayString, RowStatus, TruthValue FROM SNMPv2-TC
        ifIndex FROM RFC1213-MIB
        ;
AdslLineProfileType ::=INTEGER
adslMIB MODULE-IDENTITY
    LAST-UPDATED "9801121700Z"
    ORGANIZATION "ADSL Forum"
    DESCRIPTION
        The MIB module defining objects for the management of a pair of
ADSL modems at each end of the ADSL line. Each such
Line is
indexed by ifIndex and appears as an interface on a central
DSLAM (Digital Subscriber Line Access Mux.) Attributes on the
ATUR are proxied by the DSLAM. ADSL lines may support optional Fast or
Interleaved channels.
        If these are supported, additional entries corresponding to the
supported channels must be created in the ifTable. Thus an ADSL
line that supports both channels will have three entries in the
ifTable, one for each physical, fast, and interleaved, whose
ifType values are equal to adsl(94), fast(125), and
interleaved(124), respectively. The ifStackTable is used to
link the entries together.
```

```
Naming Conventions:
        Atuc — (ATUC) modem at near (Central) end of line
        Atur — (ATUR) modem at Remote end of line
        Curr — Current
        Prev — Previous
        Atn — Attenuation
        ES — Errored Second.
        LCS — Line Code Specific
        Lof — Loss of Frame
        Lol — Loss of Link
        Los — Loss of Signal
        Lpr — Loss of Power
        xxxs— interval of Seconds in which xxx occurs
                    (e.g., xxx=Lof, Los, Lpr)
        Max — Maximum
        Mgn — Margin
        Min — Minimum
        Psd — Power Spectral Density
        Snr — Signal to Noise Ratio
        Tx — Transmit
        Blks— Blocks, a data unit, see
                    adslAtuXChanCrcBlockLength
::={ enterprises 99999 }
— temporary assignment clause used for compilation
— reasons only. Upon assignment by the IETF, this
— value will be changed. During this interim
— period, it is recommended that implementors of
— this MIB assign this to a point under their
— private enterprise assignment tree.

adslLineMib      OBJECT IDENTIFIER ::= { adslMIB 1 }
adslMibObjects   OBJECT IDENTIFIER ::= { adslLineMib 1 }
    adslLineTable OBJECT-TYPE
        SYNTAX      SEQUENCE OF AdslLineEntry
        MAX-ACCESS  not-accessible
        STATUS      current
        DESCRIPTION
This table includes common attributes describing both ends of the line.
It is required for all ADSL physical interfaces. ADSL physical inter-
faces are those ifEntries where ifType is equal to adsl(94).
    ::={ adslMibObjects 1 }
    adslLineEntry   OBJECT-TYPE
        SYNTAX      AdslLineEntry
        MAX-ACCESS      not-accessible
        STATUS      current
        DESCRIPTION     "An entry in adslLineTable."
        INDEX    { ifIndex }
    ::={ adslLineTable 1 }
     AdslLineEntry ::=
        SEQUENCE {
        adslLineCoding      INTEGER,
        adslLineType        INTEGER,
        adslLineSpecific    OBJECT IDENTIFIER,
        adslLineConfProfile AdslLineProfileType,
        adslLineAlarmConfProfile AdslLineProfileType
        }
        adslLineCoding OBJECT-TYPE
         SYNTAX      INTEGER {
                        other (1),
                        dmt (2), — Discrete MultiTone
```

```
                              cap(3), - Carrierless Amplitude & Phase modulation
                              qam (4) - Quadrature Amplitude Modulation
            }
         MAX-ACCESS read-only
          STATUS   current
          DESCRIPTION
         "Specifies the ADSL coding type used on this line. Other types may
be added in the future."
         ::={ adslLineEntry 1 }
         adslLineType OBJECT-TYPE
           SYNTAX      INTEGER {
   noChannel (1),      - no channels exist
    fastOnly (2),      - fast channel exists only
interleavedOnly (3),   - interleaved channel exists
               - only
  fastOrInterleaved (4),- either fast or interleaved
            - channels can exist, but
         - only one at any time
  fastAndInterleaved (5)- both fast or interleaved
    - channnels exist
         }
         MAX-ACCESS read-only
         STATUS    current
         DESCRIPTION
"Defines the type of ADSL physical line entity that exists, by defining
whether and how the line is channelized. If the line is channelized, a
value other than noChannel(1), this object defines which channel type(s)
are suppored. In the case that the line is channelized, the manager can
use the ifStackTable to determine the ifIndex for the associated chan-
nel(s)."
         ::={ adslLineEntry 2 }
         adslLineSpecific OBJECT-TYPE
           SYNTAX        OBJECT IDENTIFIER
           MAX-ACCESS read-only
           STATUS   current
           DESCRIPTION
"OID instance in vendor-specific MIB. The Instance may
be used to determine shelf/slot/port of the ATUC
interface in a DSLAM."
         ::={ adslLineEntry 3 }
         adslLineConfProfile OBJECT-TYPE
           SYNTAX        AdslLineProfileType
           MAX-ACCESS    read-write
           STATUS   current
           DESCRIPTION
           "The value of this object identifies the row in the ADSL Line
Configuration Profile Table, (adslLineConfProfileTable), which applies
for this ADSL line, and channels if applicable. In the case which the
configuration profile has not been set, the
value will be set to '0'.
         If the implementator of this MIB has choosen not
to implement 'dynamic assignment' of profiles, this
object is not useful and should return noSuchName
upon SNMP request."  ::={ adslLineEntry 4 }
                    adslLineAlarmConfProfile OBJECT-TYPE
             SYNTAX    AdslLineProfileType
             MAX-ACCESS    read-write
             STATUS   current
             DESCRIPTION
```

"The value of this object identifies the row
in the ADSL Line Alarm Configuration Profile Table,
(adslLineAlarmConfProfileTable), which applies to this
ADSL line, and channels if applicable. In the case
which the configuration profile has not been set, the
value will be set to '0'.

If the implementator of this MIB has choosen not
to implement 'dynamic assignment' of profiles, this
object is not useful and should return noSuchName
upon SNMP request."
```
        ::={ adslLineEntry 5 }
        adslAtucPhysTable        OBJECT-TYPE
   SYNTAX        SEQUENCE OF AdslAtucPhysEntry
   MAX-ACCESS       not-accessible
   STATUS        current
   DESCRIPTION
```
"This table provides one row for each ATUC.
Each row contains the Physical Layer Parameters
table for that ATUC. ADSL physical interfaces are
those ifEntries where ifType is equal to adsl(94)."
```
     ::= { adslMibObjects 2 }
     adslAtucPhysEntry        OBJECT-TYPE
     SYNTAX          AdslAtucPhysEntry
     MAX-ACCESS          not-accessible
     STATUS    current
     DESCRIPTION  "An entry in the adslAtucPhysTable."
       INDEX    { ifIndex }
     ::= { adslAtucPhysTable 1 }
     AdslAtucPhysEntry ::=
        SEQUENCE {
      adslAtucInvSerialNumber   DisplayString,
      adslAtucInvVendorID       Integer32,
      adslAtucInvVersionNumber      Integer32,
     adslAtucCurrSnrMgn            INTEGER,
      adslAtucCurrAtn              INTEGER,
      adslAtucCurrStatus          INTEGER,
     adslAtucCurrOutputPwr        INTEGER,
     adslAtucCurrAttainableRate    Integer32
        }
 — inventory group —
— These items should describe the lowest level identifiable
— component, be it a stand-alone modem, a card in a rack,
— a child-board, etc. —
 adslAtucInvSerialNumber OBJECT-TYPE
        SYNTAX          DisplayString (SIZE(1..32))
        MAX-ACCESS        read-only
        STATUS    current
        DESCRIPTION
```
"Vendor specific string that identifies the vendor equipment."
```
     ::= { adslAtucPhysEntry 1 }
        adslAtucInvVendorID OBJECT-TYPE
        SYNTAX  Integer32
        MAX-ACCESS read-only
        STATUS    current
        DESCRIPTION
```
"The vendor ID assigned by T1E1.413 according to its Annex D."
```
     ::= { adslAtucPhysEntry 2 }
        adslAtucInvVersionNumber OBJECT-TYPE
          SYNTAX   Integer32
```

```
          MAX-ACCESS read-only
          STATUS    current
          DESCRIPTION
"Vendor specific Version number sent by this ATU as
part of the initialization messages."
          ::= { adslAtucPhysEntry 3 }
    — current status group —
          adslAtucCurrSnrMgn OBJECT-TYPE
          SYNTAX       INTEGER(0..310)
          UNITS     "tenth dB"
          MAX-ACCESS read-only
          STATUS    current
          DESCRIPTION
"Noise Margin as seen by this ATU with respect to its received signal in
tenth dB."
          ::= { adslAtucPhysEntry 4 }
          adslAtucCurrAtn OBJECT-TYPE
          SYNTAX       INTEGER(0..630)
          UNITS     "tenth dB"
          MAX-ACCESS       read-only
          STATUS    current
          DESCRIPTION
"Measured difference in the total power transmitted by
the peer ATU and the total power received by this ATU.
This is measured in in tenth dB."
          ::= { adslAtucPhysEntry 5 }
          adslAtucCurrStatus OBJECT-TYPE
          SYNTAX       INTEGER(1..1023)
          MAX-ACCESS       read-only
          STATUS    current
          DESCRIPTION
"Status indicates current state ATUC line. This is a bit-map of possible
conditions. The various bit positions are:
1      noDefect There no defects on the line
2      lossOfFraming     ATUC failure due to not receiving valid frame.
4 lossOfSignal    ATUC failure due to not receiving signal.
8 lossOfPower     ATUC failure due to loss of power. The Agent may still
                  function.
16 lossOfLink     ATUC failure due to inability to link with ATUR.
32 lossOfSignalQuality     Loss of Signal Quality is declared when the
                           Noise Margin falls below
                           the Minimum Noise Margin, or the bit-error-
                           rate exceeds 10^-7.


64 dataInitFailure  ATUC failure during initialization due to bit errors
corrupting startup exchange data.
128 configInitFailure
          ATUC failure during initialization due to peer ATU not able to
support requested configuration
256 protocolInitFailure
          ATUC failure during initialization due to
incompatible protocol used by the peer ATU.
512   noPeerAtuPresent
ATUC failure during initialization due to no
activation sequence detected from peer ATU.
This is intended to supplement ifOperStatus.

          ::= { adslAtucPhysEntry 6 }
          adslAtucCurrOutputPwr OBJECT-TYPE
          SYNTAX       INTEGER(0..310)
```

```
                          UNITS    "tenth dBm"
                          MAX-ACCESS   read-only
                          STATUS    current
                          DESCRIPTION
"Measured total output power transmitted by this ATU."
            ::= { adslAtucPhysEntry 7 }
                 adslAtucCurrAttainableRate OBJECT-TYPE
                     SYNTAX    Integer32
                     UNITS    "bps"
                     MAX-ACCESS read-only
                     STATUS    current
                     DESCRIPTION
"Indicates the maximum currently attainable data rate
by the ATU. This value will be equal or greater than
the current line rate."
              ::= { adslAtucPhysEntry 8 }
         adslAturPhysTable     OBJECT-TYPE
                 SYNTAX           SEQUENCE OF AdslAturPhysEntry
                 MAX-ACCESS        not-accessible
                 STATUS         current
                 DESCRIPTION
This table provides one row for each ATUR
Each row contains the Physical Layer Parameters
table for that ATUR. ADSL physical interfaces are
those ifEntries where ifType is equal to adsl(94).

         ::= { adslMibObjects 3 }
         adslAturPhysEntry     OBJECT-TYPE
             SYNTAX         AdslAturPhysEntry
             MAX-ACCESS        not-accessible
             STATUS         current
             DESCRIPTION
"An entry in the adslAturPhysTable."
             INDEX          { ifIndex }
          ::= { adslAturPhysTable 1 }
         AdslAturPhysEntry ::=
             SEQUENCE {
             adslAturInvSerialNumber     DisplayString,
             adslAturInvVendorID      Integer32,
             adslAturInvVersionNumber      Integer32,
             adslAturCurrSnrMgn          INTEGER,
             adslAturCurrAtn             INTEGER,
             adslAturCurrStatus        INTEGER,
             adslAturCurrOutputPwr        INTEGER,
             adslAturCurrAttainableRate Integer32
             }
             — inventory group—
             adslAturInvSerialNumber OBJECT-TYPE
                 SYNTAX     DisplayString (SIZE(1..32))
                 MAX-ACCESS read-only
                 STATUS     current
                 DESCRIPTION
"Vendor specific string that identifies the vendor
equipment."
             ::= { adslAturPhysEntry 1 }
             adslAturInvVendorID OBJECT-TYPE
                 SYNTAX     Integer32
                 MAX-ACCESS    read-only
                 STATUS    current
                 DESCRIPTION
```

The vendor ID assigned by T1E1.413 according to its
Annex D.
```
        ::= { adslAturPhysEntry 2 }
        adslAturInvVersionNumber OBJECT-TYPE
          SYNTAX        Integer32
          MAX-ACCESS        read-only
          STATUS    current
          DESCRIPTION
```
"Vendor specific Version number sent by this ATU as
part of the initialization messages."
```
        ::= { adslAturPhysEntry 3 }
        — current status group —
        adslAturCurrSnrMgn OBJECT-TYPE
          SYNTAX        INTEGER(0..310)
          UNITS     "tenth dB"
          MAX-ACCESS        read-only
          STATUS    current
          DESCRIPTION
```
Noise Margin as seen by this ATU with respect to its
received signal.
```
        ::= { adslAturPhysEntry 4 }
        adslAturCurrAtn OBJECT-TYPE
          SYNTAX        INTEGER(0..630)
          UNITS     "tenth dB"
          MAX-ACCESS        read-only
          STATUS    current
          DESCRIPTION
```
Measured difference in the total power transmitted by
the peer ATU and the total power received by this ATU.
```
        ::= { adslAturPhysEntry 5 }
        adslAturCurrStatus OBJECT-TYPE
          SYNTAX        INTEGER(1..7)
          MAX-ACCESS        read-only
          STATUS    current
          DESCRIPTION
```
        "Status indicates current state ATUR line. This is a bit-map of
possible conditions. Due to the isolation of the ATUR when line problems
occur, many state conditions like loss of power, loss of quality signal,
and initialization errors, can not be determined.
While trouble shooting ATUR, also use object, adslAtucCurrStatus. The various bit positions are:
 1   noDefect There no defects on the line
2   lossOfFraming
        ATUR failure due to not receiving valid frame
4 lossOfSignal ATUR failure due to not receiving signal
 8 lossOfPower ATUR failure due to loss of power
 32 lossOfSignalQuality
 Loss of Signal Quality is declared when the Noise Margin falls below
the Minimum Noise Margin, or the bit-error-rate exceeds 10^{-7}. This is
intended to supplement ifOperStatus."

```
        ::= { adslAturPhysEntry 6 }
        adslAturCurrOutputPwr OBJECT-TYPE
          SYNTAX        INTEGER(0..310)
          UNITS     "tenth dBm"
          MAX-ACCESS        read-only
          STATUS    current
          DESCRIPTION
```
*Measured total output power transmitted by this ATU."
```
        ::= { adslAturPhysEntry 7 }
```

```
            adslAturCurrAttainableRate OBJECT-TYPE
                SYNTAX        Integer32
                UNITS         "bps"
                MAX-ACCESS        read-only
                STATUS    current
                DESCRIPTION
"Indicates the maximum currently attainable data rate
by the ATU. This value will be equal or greater than
the current line rate."
                ::= { adslAturPhysEntry 8 }
            adslAtucChanTable  OBJECT-TYPE
                SYNTAX          SEQUENCE OF AdslAtucChanEntry
                MAX-ACCESS        not-accessible
                STATUS    current
                DESCRIPTION
"This table provides one row for each ATUC channel.
ADSL channel interfaces are those ifEntries where ifType is equal to
adslInterleave(124) or adslFast(125)."
                ::= { adslMibObjects 4 }
            adslAtucChanEntry  OBJECT-TYPE
                SYNTAX      AdslAtucChanEntry
                MAX-ACCESS  not-accessible
                STATUS      current
                DESCRIPTION    "An entry in the adslAtucChanTable."
                INDEX     { ifIndex }
            ::= { adslAtucChanTable 1 }
            AdslAtucChanEntry ::=
                SEQUENCE {
                adslAtucChanInterleaveDelay  Gauge32,
                adslAtucChanCurrTxRate       Gauge32,
                adslAtucChanPrevTxRate       Gauge32,
                adslAtucChanCrcBlockLength   Gauge32
                }
                — current group—
                adslAtucChanInterleaveDelay OBJECT-TYPE
                    SYNTAX      Gauge32
                    MAX-ACCESS      read-only
                    STATUS      current
                    DESCRIPTION
"Interleave Delay for this channel per ANSI T1.413, ==
                        (S-factor x d)
                        ————---
                        4 milli-seconds,
where 'd' is the Interleaving Depth. Interleave delay applies only to
the interleave channel and defines the mapping (relative spacing)
between subsequent input bytes at the interleaver input and their place-
ment in the bit stream at the interleaver output.
Larger numbers provide greater separation between consecutive input
bytes in the output bit stream allowing for improved impulse noise immu-
nity at the expense of payload latency.

In the case where the ifType is Fast(125), use noSuchName.
                ::= { adslAtucChanEntry 1 }
                adslAtucChanCurrTxRate OBJECT-TYPE
                SYNTAX      Gauge32
                UNITS       "bps"
                MAX-ACCESS      read-only
                STATUS    current
                DESCRIPTION
 "Actual transmit rate on this channel."
```

```
        ::= { adslAtucChanEntry 2 }
   adslAtucChanPrevTxRate OBJECT-TYPE
        SYNTAX      Gauge32
        UNITS     "bps"
        MAX-ACCESS    accessible-for-notify
        STATUS   current
        DESCRIPTION
"The rate at the time of the last adslAtucRateChangeTrap event. It is
also set at initialization to prevent a trap being sent.
Rate changes less than adslAtucThresh(*)RateDown or less than
adslAtucThresh(*)RateUp will not cause a trap or cause this object to
change.
 (*) == Fast or Interleave.
 See AdslLineAlarmConfProfileEntry."
 ::= { adslAtucChanEntry 3 }
      adslAtucChanCrcBlockLength OBJECT-TYPE
        SYNTAX      Gauge32
        UNITS     "byte"
        MAX-ACCESS    read-only
        STATUS   current
        DESCRIPTION
"Indicates the length of the channel data-block on which the CRC oper-
ates."
        ::= { adslAtucChanEntry 4 }
   adslAturChanTable     OBJECT-TYPE
        SYNTAX         SEQUENCE OF AdslAturChanEntry
        MAX-ACCESS      not-accessible
        STATUS         current
        DESCRIPTION
This table provides one row for each ATUR channel. ADSL channel inter-
faces are those ifEntries where ifType is equal to adslInterleave(124)
or adslFast(125).
        ::= { adslMibObjects 5 }
        adslAturChanEntry  OBJECT-TYPE
        SYNTAX         AdslAturChanEntry
        MAX-ACCESS      not-accessible
        STATUS         current
        DESCRIPTION   "An entry in the adslAturChanTable."
        INDEX   { ifIndex }
    ::= { adslAturChanTable 1 }
    AdslAturChanEntry ::=
        SEQUENCE {
        adslAturChanInterleaveDelay  Gauge32,
        adslAturChanCurrTxRate     Gauge32,
        adslAturChanPrevTxRate     Gauge32,
        adslAturChanCrcBlockLength   Gauge32
        }
        — current group—
        adslAturChanInterleaveDelay OBJECT-TYPE
           SYNTAX      Gauge32
           MAX-ACCESS    read-only
           STATUS   current
           DESCRIPTION
Interleave Delay for this channel per ANSI T1.413, ==
     (S-factor x d)
     ----------
     4 milli-seconds,
where 'd' is the Interleaving Depth. Interleave delay applies only to
the interleave channel and defines the mapping (relative spacing)
between subsequent input bytes at the interleaver input and their place-
```

ment in the bit stream at the interleaver
output. Larger numbers provide greater separation
between consecutive input bytes in the output bit
stream allowing for improved impulse noise immunity at
the expense of payload latency. In the case where the ifType is
Fast(125), use noSuchName.
    ::= { adslAturChanEntry 1 }
    adslAturChanCurrTxRate OBJECT-TYPE
      SYNTAX   Gauge32
      UNITS   "bps"
      MAX-ACCESS   read-only
      STATUS   current
      DESCRIPTION
"Actual transmit rate on this channel."
    ::= { adslAturChanEntry 2 }
    adslAturChanPrevTxRate OBJECT-TYPE
      SYNTAX   Gauge32
      UNITS   "bps"
      MAX-ACCESS   accessible-for-notify
      STATUS   current
      DESCRIPTION
"The rate at the time of the last adslAturRateChangeTrap event. It is
also set at initialization to prevent a trap being sent.
Rate changes less than adslAturThresh(*)RateDown or less than
adslAturThresh(*)RateUp will not cause a trap or cause this object to
change.
  (*) == Fast or Interleave.
  See AdslLineAlarmConfProfileEntry."
    ::= { adslAturChanEntry 3 }
    adslAturChanCrcBlockLength OBJECT-TYPE
      SYNTAX   Gauge32
      MAX-ACCESS   read-only
      STATUS   current
      DESCRIPTION
"Indicates the length of the channel data-block on which the CRC operates."
    ::= { adslAturChanEntry 4 }
  adslAtucPhysPerfDataTable OBJECT-TYPE
      SYNTAX   SEQUENCE OF AdslAtucPerfDataEntry
      MAX-ACCESS   not-accessible
      STATUS   current
      DESCRIPTION
This table provides one row for each ATUC. ADSL physical interfaces are
those ifEntries where ifType is equal to adsl(94).
    ::= { adslMibObjects 6 }
  adslAtucPerfDataEntry OBJECT-TYPE
      SYNTAX   AdslAtucPerfDataEntry
      MAX-ACCESS   not-accessible
      STATUS   current
      DESCRIPTION
"An entry in adslAtucPhysPerfDataTable."
      INDEX   { ifIndex }
    ::= { adslAtucPhysPerfDataTable 1 }
    AdslAtucPerfDataEntry ::=
      SEQUENCE {
      adslAtucPerfLof   Counter32,
      adslAtucPerfLos   Counter32,
      adslAtucPerfLol   Counter32,
      adslAtucPerfLpr   Counter32,
      adslAtucPerfES   Counter32,

```
        adslAtucPerfValidIntervals   INTEGER,
        adslAtucPerfInvalidIntervals INTEGER,
        adslAtucPerfCurr15MinTimeElapsed  INTEGER,
        adslAtucPerfCurr15MinLofs    Gauge32,
        adslAtucPerfCurr15MinLoss     Gauge32,
        adslAtucPerfCurr15MinLols     Gauge32,
        adslAtucPerfCurr15MinLprs     Gauge32,
        adslAtucPerfCurr15MinESs      Gauge32,
        adslAtucPerfCurr1DayTimeElapsed INTEGER,
        adslAtucPerfCurr1DayLofs     Gauge32,
        adslAtucPerfCurr1DayLoss      Gauge32,
        adslAtucPerfCurr1DayLols      Gauge32,
        adslAtucPerfCurr1DayLprs      Gauge32,
        adslAtucPerfCurr1DayESs       Gauge32,
        adslAtucPerfPrev1DayMoniSecs   INTEGER,
        adslAtucPerfPrev1DayLofs     Gauge32,
        adslAtucPerfPrev1DayLoss      Gauge32,
        adslAtucPerfPrev1DayLols      Gauge32,
        adslAtucPerfPrev1DayLprs      Gauge32,
        adslAtucPerfPrev1DayESs       Gauge32
        }
        — Event Counters—
    — Also see adslAtucIntervalTable for 15 minute interval
        — elapsed counters —
        adslAtucPerfLof OBJECT-TYPE
          SYNTAX       Counter32
          MAX-ACCESS       read-only
          STATUS    current
          DESCRIPTION
"Count of the number of Loss of Framing failures since
agent reset."
        ::= { adslAtucPerfDataEntry 1 }
        adslAtucPerfLos OBJECT-TYPE
          SYNTAX       Counter32
          MAX-ACCESS       read-only
          STATUS    current
          DESCRIPTION
"Count of the number of Loss of Signal failures since
agent reset."
        ::= { adslAtucPerfDataEntry 2 }
        adslAtucPerfLol OBJECT-TYPE
          SYNTAX       Counter32
          MAX-ACCESS       read-only
          STATUS    current
          DESCRIPTION
"Count of the number of Loss of Link failures since
agent reset."
        ::= { adslAtucPerfDataEntry 3 }
        adslAtucPerfLpr OBJECT-TYPE
          SYNTAX       Counter32
          MAX-ACCESS       read-only
          STATUS    current
          DESCRIPTION
Count of the number of Loss of Power failures since
agent reset.
        ::= { adslAtucPerfDataEntry 4 }
        adslAtucPerfES OBJECT-TYPE
          SYNTAX       Counter32
          MAX-ACCESS       read-only
          STATUS     current
```

```
                    DESCRIPTION
Count of the number of Errored Seconds since agent reset. The errored
second parameter is a count of one-second intervals containing one or
more crc anomolies, or one or more los or sef defects.
            ::= { adslAtucPerfDataEntry 5 }
            — general 15 min interval information—
            adslAtucPerfValidIntervals OBJECT-TYPE
            SYNTAX      INTEGER(0..96)
            MAX-ACCESS    read-only
            STATUS      current
            DESCRIPTION
Number of previous 15-minute intervals in the adslAtucInterval table for
which valid data has been stored. This value will be equal to the maximum
number of intervals that are kept (n) unless the device was brought online
within the last (nx15) minutes. In
the case where the agent is a proxy, it is possible that some intervals
are unavailable. In this case, this interval is the maximum interval for
which valid
                    data is available."
        ::= { adslAtucPerfDataEntry 6 }
        adslAtucPerfInvalidIntervals OBJECT-TYPE
            SYNTAX      INTEGER(0..96)
            MAX-ACCESS    read-only
            STATUS      current
            DESCRIPTION
The number of 15 minute intervals which no valid data
is available."
        ::= { adslAtucPerfDataEntry 7 }
        — 15 min current performance group —
        adslAtucPerfCurr15MinTimeElapsed OBJECT-TYPE
            SYNTAX      INTEGER(0..899)
            UNITS      "seconds"
            MAX-ACCESS    read-only
            STATUS      current
            DESCRIPTION
Total elapsed seconds in this interval. A full interval is 900 seconds."
        ::= { adslAtucPerfDataEntry 8 }
            adslAtucPerfCurr15MinLofs OBJECT-TYPE
            SYNTAX      Gauge32
            MAX-ACCESS    read-only
            STATUS      current
            DESCRIPTION
Count of seconds in the current 15 minute interval
when there was Loss of Framing.
        ::= { adslAtucPerfDataEntry 9 }
        adslAtucPerfCurr15MinLoss OBJECT-TYPE
            SYNTAX      Gauge32
            MAX-ACCESS    read-only
            STATUS      current
            DESCRIPTION
Count of seconds in the current 15 minute interval when there was Loss of
Signal.
        ::= { adslAtucPerfDataEntry 10 }
        adslAtucPerfCurr15MinLols OBJECT-TYPE
            SYNTAX      Gauge32
            MAX-ACCESS    read-only
            STATUS      current
            DESCRIPTION
Count of seconds in the current 15 minute interval when
there was Loss of Link.
```

```
            ::= { adslAtucPerfDataEntry 11 }
            adslAtucPerfCurr15MinLprs OBJECT-TYPE
                SYNTAX        Gauge32
                MAX-ACCESS        read-only
                STATUS        current
                DESCRIPTION
Count of seconds in the current 15 minute interval when
there was Loss of Power.
            ::= { adslAtucPerfDataEntry 12 }
            adslAtucPerfCurr15MinESs OBJECT-TYPE
                SYNTAX        Gauge32
                MAX-ACCESS        read-only
                STATUS        current
                DESCRIPTION
Count of Errored Seconds in the current 15 minute
interval. The errored second parameter is a count of
one-second intervals containing one or more crc
anomolies, or one or more los or sef defects.
            ::= { adslAtucPerfDataEntry 13 }


            — 1 Day current and previous performance group—
            adslAtucPerfCurr1DayTimeElapsed OBJECT-TYPE
                SYNTAX        INTEGER(0..86399)
                UNITS      "seconds"
                MAX-ACCESS        read-only
                STATUS        current
                DESCRIPTION
Number of seconds that have elapsed since the beginning
of the current 1Day interval.
            ::= { adslAtucPerfDataEntry 14 }
            adslAtucPerfCurr1DayLofs OBJECT-TYPE
                SYNTAX        Gauge32
                MAX-ACCESS        read-only
                STATUS        current
                DESCRIPTION
Count of the number of seconds when there was Loss of Framing during the
current day as measured by adslAtucPerfCurr1DayTimeElapsed.
     ::= { adslAtucPerfDataEntry 15 }
                adslAtucPerfCurr1DayLoss OBJECT-TYPE
                    SYNTAX        Gauge32
                    MAX-ACCESS        read-only
                    STATUS        current
                    DESCRIPTION
Count of the number of seconds when there was Loss of
Signal during the current day as measured by
adslAtucPerfCurr1DayTimeElapsed.
            ::= { adslAtucPerfDataEntry 16 }
            adslAtucPerfCurr1DayLols OBJECT-TYPE
                SYNTAX        Gauge32
                MAX-ACCESS        read-only
                STATUS        current
                DESCRIPTION
Count of the number of seconds when there was Loss of
Link during the current day as measured by
adslAtucPerfCurr1DayTimeElapsed.
            ::= { adslAtucPerfDataEntry 17 }
            adslAtucPerfCurr1DayLprs OBJECT-TYPE
                SYNTAX          Gauge32
                MAX-ACCESS          read-only
                STATUS    current
```

```
            DESCRIPTION
Count of the number of seconds when there was Loss of
Power during the current day as measured by
adslAtucPerfCurr1DayTimeElapsed.
            ::= { adslAtucPerfDataEntry 18 }
            adslAtucPerfCurr1DayESs OBJECT-TYPE
            SYNTAX        Gauge32
            MAX-ACCESS        read-only
            STATUS    current
            DESCRIPTION
Count of  Errored  Seconds  during  the  current  day  as  measured  by
adslAtucPerfCurr1DayTimeElapsed. The errored second parameter is a count
of one-second intervals containing one or more crc
anomolies, or one or more los or sef defects.
            ::= { adslAtucPerfDataEntry 19 }
            adslAtucPerfPrev1DayMoniSecs OBJECT-TYPE
            SYNTAX        INTEGER(0..899)
            UNITS     "seconds"
            MAX-ACCESS        read-only
            STATUS    current
            DESCRIPTION
The time in the previous 1-day interval over which the performance moni-
toring information is actually counted. This value will normally be the
same as the total interval duration except in a situation where perfor-
mance monitoring dara can  not  be  collected  for  any  reason.  Typically
Elapsed 1-day Time will be
copied into Monitored Seconds when the 1-day roll-over occurs.
            ::= { adslAtucPerfDataEntry 20 }
            adslAtucPerfPrev1DayLofs OBJECT-TYPE
            SYNTAX        Gauge32
            MAX-ACCESS        read-only
            STATUS      current
            DESCRIPTION
Count of seconds in the interval when there was Loss of
Framing within the most recent previous 1 day period.
            ::= { adslAtucPerfDataEntry 21 }
            adslAtucPerfPrev1DayLoss OBJECT-TYPE
            SYNTAX        Gauge32
            MAX-ACCESS        read-only
            STATUS    current
            DESCRIPTION
Count of seconds in the interval when there was Loss of
Signal within the most recent previous 1 day period.
            ::= { adslAtucPerfDataEntry 22 }
            adslAtucPerfPrev1DayLols OBJECT-TYPE
            SYNTAX        Gauge32
            MAX-ACCESS        read-only
            STATUS      current
            DESCRIPTION
Count of seconds in the interval when there was Loss of
Link within the most recent previous 1 day period.
            ::= { adslAtucPerfDataEntry 23 }
            adslAtucPerfPrev1DayLprs OBJECT-TYPE
            SYNTAX        Gauge32
            MAX-ACCESS        read-only
            STATUS      current
            DESCRIPTION
Count of seconds in the interval when there was Loss of
Power within the most recent previous 1 day period.
            ::= { adslAtucPerfDataEntry 24 }
```

```
        adslAtucPerfPrev1DayESs OBJECT-TYPE
          SYNTAX        Gauge32
          MAX-ACCESS      read-only
          STATUS    current
          DESCRIPTION
Count of Errored Seconds within the most recent previous 1 day period.
The errored second parameter is a count of one-second intervals contain-
ing one or more crc anomolies, or one or more los or sef defects.
        ::= { adslAtucPerfDataEntry 25 }
     adslAturPhysPerfDataTable OBJECT-TYPE
          SYNTAX        SEQUENCE OF AdslAturPerfDataEntry
          MAX-ACCESS      not-accessible
          STATUS    current
          DESCRIPTION
This table provides one row for each ATUR. ADSL physical interfaces are
those ifEntries where ifType is equal to adsl(94).
     ::= { adslMibObjects 7 }
     adslAturPerfDataEntry  OBJECT-TYPE
       SYNTAX          AdslAturPerfDataEntry
       MAX-ACCESS      not-accessible
       STATUS    current
       DESCRIPTION
     "An entry in adslAturPhysPerfDataTable."
          INDEX   { ifIndex }
     ::= { adslAturPhysPerfDataTable 1 }
     AdslAturPerfDataEntry ::=
          SEQUENCE {
          adslAturPerfLof          Counter32,
          adslAturPerfLos           Counter32,
          adslAturPerfLpr          Counter32,
          adslAturPerfES            Counter32,
          adslAturPerfValidIntervals   INTEGER,
          adslAturPerfInvalidIntervals INTEGER,
          adslAturPerfCurr15MinTimeElapsed  INTEGER,
          adslAturPerfCurr15MinLofs   Gauge32,
          adslAturPerfCurr15MinLoss   Gauge32,
          adslAturPerfCurr15MinLprs   Gauge32,
          adslAturPerfCurr15MinESs    Gauge32,
          adslAturPerfCurr1DayTimeElapsed INTEGER,
          adslAturPerfCurr1DayLofs    Gauge32,
          adslAturPerfCurr1DayLoss    Gauge32,
          adslAturPerfCurr1DayLprs    Gauge32,
          adslAturPerfCurr1DayESs     Gauge32,
          adslAturPerfPrev1DayMoniSecs   INTEGER,
          adslAturPerfPrev1DayLofs    Gauge32,
          adslAturPerfPrev1DayLoss    Gauge32,
          adslAturPerfPrev1DayLprs    Gauge32,
          adslAturPerfPrev1DayESs     Gauge32
          }
          — Event (Raw) Counters —
     — Also see adslAturIntervalTable for 15 minute interval
          — elapsed counters —
          adslAturPerfLof OBJECT-TYPE
          SYNTAX        Counter32
          MAX-ACCESS      read-only
          STATUS    current
          DESCRIPTION
Count of the number of Loss of Framing failures since
agent reset.
     ::= { adslAturPerfDataEntry 1 }
```

```
    adslAturPerfLos OBJECT-TYPE
      SYNTAX        Counter32
      MAX-ACCESS        read-only
      STATUS    current
      DESCRIPTION
Count of the number of Loss of Signal failures since
agent reset.
      ::= { adslAturPerfDataEntry 2 }
    adslAturPerfLpr OBJECT-TYPE
      SYNTAX        Counter32
      MAX-ACCESS        read-only
      STATUS    current
      DESCRIPTION
Count of the number of Loss of Power failures since
agent reset.
      ::= { adslAturPerfDataEntry 3 }
    adslAturPerfES OBJECT-TYPE
      SYNTAX        Counter32
      MAX-ACCESS        read-only
      STATUS    current
      DESCRIPTION
Count of the number of Errored Seconds since agent
reset. The errored second parameter is a count of
one-second intervals containing one or more crc
anomolies, or one or more los or sef defects.
      ::= { adslAturPerfDataEntry 4 }
   general 15 min interval information—
      adslAturPerfValidIntervals OBJECT-TYPE
      SYNTAX        INTEGER(0..96)
      MAX-ACCESS        read-only
      STATUS    current
      DESCRIPTION
Number of previous 15-minute intervals in the
adslAturInterval Table for which valid data
has been stored. This value will be equal to the maximum
number of intervals that are kept (n) unless the device
was brought online within the last (nx15) minutes. In
the case where the agent is a proxy, it is possible
that some intervals are unavailable. In this case, this
interval is the maximum interval for which valid data
is available.
      ::= { adslAturPerfDataEntry 5 }
    adslAturPerfInvalidIntervals OBJECT-TYPE
      SYNTAX        INTEGER(0..96)
      MAX-ACCESS        read-only
      STATUS    current
      DESCRIPTION
The number of 15 minute intervals which no valid data
is available.
      ::= { adslAturPerfDataEntry 6 }
      — 15 min current performance group—
    adslAturPerfCurr15MinTimeElapsed OBJECT-TYPE
      SYNTAX        INTEGER(0..899)
      UNITS        "seconds"
      MAX-ACCESS        read-only
      STATUS    current
      DESCRIPTION
Total elapsed seconds in this interval. A full interval is 900 seconds.
      ::= { adslAturPerfDataEntry 7 }
    adslAturPerfCurr15MinLofs OBJECT-TYPE
```

```
          SYNTAX        Gauge32
          MAX-ACCESS        read-only
          STATUS      current
          DESCRIPTION
Count of seconds in the current 15 minute interval
when there was Loss of Framing.
          ::= { adslAturPerfDataEntry 8 }
          adslAturPerfCurr15MinLoss OBJECT-TYPE
          SYNTAX        Gauge32
          MAX-ACCESS      read-only
          STATUS      current
          DESCRIPTION
Count of seconds in the current 15 minute interval when
there was Loss of Signal.
          ::= { adslAturPerfDataEntry 9 }
          adslAturPerfCurr15MinLprs OBJECT-TYPE
          SYNTAX        Gauge32
          MAX-ACCESS        read-only
          STATUS      current
          DESCRIPTION
Count of seconds in the current 15 minute interval when
there was Loss of Power.
          ::= { adslAturPerfDataEntry 10 }
          adslAturPerfCurr15MinESs OBJECT-TYPE
           SYNTAX        Gauge32
          MAX-ACCESS        read-only
          STATUS      current
          DESCRIPTION
Count of Errored Seconds in the current 15 minute interval. The errored
second parameter is a count of one-second intervals containing one or
more crc anomolies, or one or more los or sef defects.
          ::= { adslAturPerfDataEntry 11 }
          — 1 Day current and previous performance group—
            adslAturPerfCurr1DayTimeElapsed OBJECT-TYPE
            SYNTAX        INTEGER(0..86399)
            UNITS      "seconds"
            MAX-ACCESS        read-only
            STATUS      current
            DESCRIPTION
Number of seconds that have elapsed since the beginning
of the current 1Day interval.
          ::= { adslAturPerfDataEntry 12 }
          adslAturPerfCurr1DayLofs OBJECT-TYPE
           SYNTAX        Gauge32
           MAX-ACCESS        read-only
          STATUS      current
          DESCRIPTION
Count of the number of seconds when there was Loss of
Framing during the current day as measured by
adslAturPerfCurr1DayTimeElapsed.
          ::= { adslAturPerfDataEntry 13 }
          adslAturPerfCurr1DayLoss OBJECT-TYPE
            SYNTAX        Gauge32
            MAX-ACCESS        read-only
            STATUS      current
            DESCRIPTION
"Count of the number of seconds when there was Loss of Signal during the
current day as measured by
adslAturPerfCurr1DayTimeElapsed.
          ::= { adslAturPerfDataEntry 14 }
```

```
                    adslAturPerfCurr1DayLprs OBJECT-TYPE
                    SYNTAX        Gauge32
                    MAX-ACCESS        read-only
                    STATUS        current
                    DESCRIPTION
Count of the number of seconds when there was Loss of
Power during the current day as measured by
adslAturPerfCurr1DayTimeElapsed.
                    ::= { adslAturPerfDataEntry 15 }
                    adslAturPerfCurr1DayESs OBJECT-TYPE
                    SYNTAX        Gauge32
                    MAX-ACCESS        read-only
                    STATUS        current
                    DESCRIPTION
Count of Errored Seconds during the current day as measured by
adslAturPerfCurr1DayTimeElapsed. The errored second parameter is a count
of one-second intervals containing one or more crc
anomolies, or one or more los or sef defects.
                    ::= { adslAturPerfDataEntry 16 }
                    adslAturPerfPrev1DayMoniSecs OBJECT-TYPE
                    SYNTAX        INTEGER(0..899)
                    UNITS        "seconds"
                    MAX-ACCESS        read-only
                    STATUS        current
                    DESCRIPTION
The time in the previous 1-day interval over which
the performance monitoring information is actually counted. This value
will normally be the same as the
total interval duration except in a situation where
performance monitoring data can not be collected
for any reason. Typically Elapsed 1-day Time will be
copied into Monitored Seconds when the 1-day roll-over
occurs.
                    ::= { adslAturPerfDataEntry 17 }
                    adslAturPerfPrev1DayLofs OBJECT-TYPE
                    SYNTAX        Gauge32
                    MAX-ACCESS        read-only
                    STATUS        current
                    DESCRIPTION
Count of seconds in the interval when there was Loss of
Framing within the most recent previous 1 day period.
                    ::= { adslAturPerfDataEntry 18 }
                    adslAturPerfPrev1DayLoss OBJECT-TYPE
                    SYNTAX        Gauge32
                    MAX-ACCESS        read-only
                    STATUS        current
                    DESCRIPTION
Count of seconds in the interval when there was Loss of
Signal within the most recent previous 1 day period.
                    ::= { adslAturPerfDataEntry 19 }
                    adslAturPerfPrev1DayLprs OBJECT-TYPE
                    SYNTAX        Gauge32
                    MAX-ACCESS        read-only
                    STATUS        current
                    DESCRIPTION
Count of seconds in the interval when there was Loss of
Power within the most recent previous 1 day period.
                    ::= { adslAturPerfDataEntry 20 }
                    adslAturPerfPrev1DayESs OBJECT-TYPE
                    SYNTAX        Gauge32
```

```
            MAX-ACCESS       read-only
            STATUS    current
            DESCRIPTION
Count of Errored Seconds within the most recent previous 1 day period.
The errored second parameter is a count of one-second intervals contain-
ing one or more crc anomolies, or one or more los or sef defects.
            ::= { adslAturPerfDataEntry 21 }
        adslAtucIntervalTable OBJECT-TYPE
            SYNTAX          SEQUENCE OF AdslAtucIntervalEntry
            MAX-ACCESS      not-accessible
            STATUS    current
            DESCRIPTION
This table provides one row for each ATUC
performance data collection interval. ADSL physical interfaces are those
ifEntries where ifType is equal to adsl(94).
        ::= { adslMibObjects 8 }
        adslAtucIntervalEntry OBJECT-TYPE
            SYNTAX          AdslAtucIntervalEntry
            MAX-ACCESS      not-accessible
            STATUS    current
            DESCRIPTION
      An entry in the adslAtucintervalTable.
          INDEX   { ifIndex, adslAtucIntervalNumber }
      ::= { adslAtucIntervalTable 1 }
      AdslAtucIntervalEntry ::=
          SEQUENCE {
          adslAtucIntervalNumber      INTEGER,
          adslAtucIntervalLofs        Gauge32,
          adslAtucIntervalLoss        Gauge32,
          adslAtucIntervalLols        Gauge32,
          adslAtucIntervalLprs        Gauge32,
          adslAtucIntervalESs         Gauge32,
          adslAtucIntervalValidData   TruthValue
          }
          adslAtucIntervalNumber OBJECT-TYPE
            SYNTAX        INTEGER(1..96)
            MAX-ACCESS      not-accessible
            STATUS    current
            DESCRIPTION
Performance Data Interval number. 1 is he most recent interval; interval
96 is 24 hours ago. Interval 2..96 are optional.
            ::= { adslAtucIntervalEntry 1 }
          adslAtucIntervalLofs OBJECT-TYPE
            SYNTAX        Gauge32
            MAX-ACCESS      read-only
            STATUS    current
            DESCRIPTION
Count of seconds in the interval when there was Loss of
Framing.
            :: = { adslAtucIntervalEntry 2 }
          adslAtucIntervalLoss OBJECT-TYPE
            SYNTAX        Gauge32
            MAX-ACCESS      read-only
            STATUS    current
            DESCRIPTION
Count of seconds in the interval when there was Loss of
Signal.
            :: = { adslAtucIntervalEntry 3 }
          adslAtucIntervalLols OBJECT-TYPE
            SYNTAX        Gauge32
```

```
                     MAX-ACCESS      read-only
                     STATUS    current
                     DESCRIPTION
Count of seconds in the interval when there was Loss of Link.
             :: = { adslAtucIntervalEntry 4 }
             adslAtucIntervalLprs OBJECT-TYPE
                SYNTAX        Gauge32
                MAX-ACCESS      read-only
                STATUS     current
                DESCRIPTION
Count of seconds in the interval when there was Loss
of Power.


             :: = { adslAtucIntervalEntry 5 }
             adslAtucIntervalESs OBJECT-TYPE
                SYNTAX        Gauge32
                MAX-ACCESS      read-only
                STATUS     current
                DESCRIPTION
Count of Errored Seconds in the interval. The errored second paramter is
a count of one-second intervals containing one or more crc anomolies, or
one or more los or sef defects.
             :: = { adslAtucIntervalEntry 6 }
             adslAtucIntervalValidData OBJECT-TYPE
                SYNTAX TruthValue
                MAX-ACCESS read-only
                STATUS current
                DESCRIPTION
This variable indicates if there is valid data
for this interval.
                :: = { adslAtucIntervalEntry 7 }
        adslAturIntervalTable OBJECT-TYPE
             SYNTAX          SEQUENCE OF AdslAturIntervalEntry
             MAX-ACCESS       not-accessible
             STATUS     current
             DESCRIPTION
This table provides one row for each ATUR performance data collection
interval. ADSL physical interfaces are those ifEntries where ifType is
equal to adsl(94).
        :: = { adslMibObjects 9 }
        adslAturIntervalEntry OBJECT-TYPE
             SYNTAX          AdslAturIntervalEntry
             MAX-ACCESS       not-accessible
             STATUS     current
             DESCRIPTION
An entry in the adslAturIntervalTable.
             INDEX        { ifIndex, adslAturIntervalNumber }
        :: = { adslAturIntervalTable 1 }
        AdslAturIntervalEntry :: =
             SEQUENCE {
             adslAturIntervalNumber           INTEGER,
             adslAturIntervalLofs             Gauge32,
             adslAturIntervalLoss             Gauge32,
             adslAturIntervalLprs             Gauge32,
             adslAturIntervalESs              Gauge32,
             adslAturIntervalValidData         TruthValue
             }
             adslAturIntervalNumber OBJECT-TYPE
                SYNTAX        INTEGER(1..96)
                MAX-ACCESS not-accessible
```

```
                    STATUS     current
                    DESCRIPTION
Performance Data Interval number. 1 is the most recent interval; inter-
val 96 is 24 hours ago. Interval 2..96 are optional.
            :: = { adslAturIntervalEntry 1 }
            adslAturIntervalLofs   OBJECT-TYPE
              SYNTAX          Gauge32
              MAX-ACCESS        read-only
              STATUS      current
              DESCRIPTION
Count of seconds in the interval when there was Loss of
Framing.
            :: = { adslAturIntervalEntry 2 }
            adslAturIntervalLoss   OBJECT-TYPE
              SYNTAX          Gauge32
              MAX-ACCESS          read-only
              STATUS      current
              DESCRIPTION
Count of seconds in the interval when there was Loss of Signal.
            :: = { adslAturIntervalEntry 3 }
            adslAturIntervalLprs   OBJECT-TYPE
              SYNTAX          Gauge32
              MAX-ACCESS          read-only
              STATUS    current
              DESCRIPTION
Count of seconds in the interval when there was Loss of Power.
            :: = { adslAturIntervalEntry 4 }
            adslAturIntervalESs    OBJECT-TYPE
              SYNTAX          Gauge32
              MAX-ACCESS          read-only
              STATUS    current
              DESCRIPTION
Count of Errored Seconds in the interval. The errored second paramter is
a count of one-second intervals containing one or more crc anomolies, or
one or more los or sef defects.
            :: = { adslAturIntervalEntry 5 }
            adslAturIntervalValidData OBJECT-TYPE
              SYNTAX      TruthValue
              MAX-ACCESS read-only
              STATUS current
              DESCRIPTION
This variable indicates if there is valid data
for this interval.
              :: = { adslAturIntervalEntry 6 }
    adslAtucChanPerfDataTable        OBJECT-TYPE
          SYNTAX        SEQUENCE OF AdslAtucChanPerfDataEntry
          MAX-ACCESS        not-accessible
          STATUS        current
          DESCRIPTION
This table provides one row for each ATUC channel. ADSL channel inter-
faces are those ifEntries where ifType is equal to adslInterleave(124)
or adslFast(125).
      :: = { adslMibObjects 10 }
    adslAtucChanPerfDataEntry  OBJECT-TYPE
          SYNTAX          AdslAtucChanPerfDataEntry
          MAX-ACCESS        not-accessible
          STATUS      current
          DESCRIPTION
An entry in adslAtucChanPerfDataTable.
          INDEX    { ifIndex }
```

```
                ::={ adslAtucChanPerfDataTable 1 }
                AdslAtucChanPerfDataEntry ::=
                    SEQUENCE {
                    adslAtucChanReceivedBlks            Counter32,
                    adslAtucChanTransmittedBlks         Counter32,
                    adslAtucChanCorrectedBlks           Counter32,
                    adslAtucChanUncorrectBlks           Counter32,
                    adslAtucChanPerfValidIntervals      INTEGER,
                    adslAtucChanPerfInvalidIntervals    INTEGER,
                    adslAtucChanPerfCurr15MinTimeElapsed    INTEGER,
                    adslAtucChanPerfCurr15MinReceivedBlks   Gauge32,
                    adslAtucChanPerfCurr15MinTransmittedBlks Gauge32,
                    adslAtucChanPerfCurr15MinCorrectedBlks  Gauge32,
                    adslAtucChanPerfCurr15MinUncorrectBlks  Gauge32,
                    adslAtucChanPerfCurr1DayTimeElapsed     INTEGER,
                    adslAtucChanPerfCurr1DayReceivedBlks    Gauge32,
                    adslAtucChanPerfCurr1DayTransmittedBlks   Gauge32,
                    adslAtucChanPerfCurr1DayCorrectedBlks   Gauge32,
                    adslAtucChanPerfCurr1DayUncorrectBlks   Gauge32,
                    adslAtucChanPerfPrev1DayMoniSecs        INTEGER,
                    adslAtucChanPerfPrev1DayReceivedBlks    Gauge32,
                    adslAtucChanPerfPrev1DayTransmittedBlks   Gauge32,
                    adslAtucChanPerfPrev1DayCorrectedBlks   Gauge32,
                    adslAtucChanPerfPrev1DayUncorrectBlks   Gauge32
                    }
                    — performance group—
            — Note: block is intended to be the length of the channel
            —   data-block on which the CRC operates. See
            —   adslAtucChanCrcBlockLength for more information—
                    adslAtucChanReceivedBlks OBJECT-TYPE
                    SYNTAX      Counter32
                    MAX-ACCESS      read-only
                    STATUS      current
                    DESCRIPTION
Count of all encoded blocks received on this channel
since agent reset.
                    ::={ adslAtucChanPerfDataEntry 1 }
                    adslAtucChanTransmittedBlks    OBJECT-TYPE
                    SYNTAX      Counter32
                    MAX-ACCESS      read-only
                    STATUS  current
                    DESCRIPTION
Count of all encoded blocks transmitted on this
channel since agent reset.
                    ::={ adslAtucChanPerfDataEntry 2 }
                    adslAtucChanCorrectedBlks    OBJECT-TYPE
                    SYNTAX      Counter32
                    MAX-ACCESS      read-only
                    STATUS      current
                    DESCRIPTION
Count of all blocks received with errors that were
corrected since agent reset. These blocks are passed on
as good data.
                    ::={ adslAtucChanPerfDataEntry 3 }
                    adslAtucChanUncorrectBlks    OBJECT-TYPE
                    SYNTAX      Counter32
                    MAX-ACCESS      read-only
                    STATUS      current
                    DESCRIPTION
Count of  all  blocks  received  with  uncorrectable  errors  since  agent
reset.
```

```
            ::= { adslAtucChanPerfDataEntry 4 }
            — general 15 min interval information—
            adslAtucChanPerfValidIntervals OBJECT-TYPE
               SYNTAX      INTEGER(0..96)
               MAX-ACCESS      read-only
               STATUS      current
               DESCRIPTION
Number of previous 15-minute intervals in the adslAtucChanIntervalTable
Table for which valid data has been stored. This value will be equal to
the maximum number of intervals that are kept (n) unless the device was
brought online within the last (nx15) minutes. In the case where the agent
is a proxy, it is possible that some intervals are unavailable. In this
case, this interval is the maximum interval for which valid
data is available.
            ::= { adslAtucChanPerfDataEntry 5 }
            adslAtucChanPerfInvalidIntervals OBJECT-TYPE
               SYNTAX      INTEGER(0..96)
               MAX-ACCESS      read-only
               STATUS    current
               DESCRIPTION
The number of 15 minute intervals which no valid data
is available.
            ::= { adslAtucChanPerfDataEntry 6 }
            — 15 min current performance group—
         adslAtucChanPerfCurr15MinTimeElapsed OBJECT-TYPE
               SYNTAX      INTEGER(0..899)
               UNITS   "seconds"
               MAX-ACCESS    read-only
               STATUS    current
               DESCRIPTION
Total elapsed seconds in this interval. A full interval is 900 seconds.
            ::= { adslAtucChanPerfDataEntry 7 }
            adslAtucChanPerfCurr15MinReceivedBlks OBJECT-TYPE
               SYNTAX      Gauge32
               MAX-ACCESS      read-only
               STATUS    current
               DESCRIPTION
Count of all encoded blocks received on this channel
within the current 15 minute interval.
            ::= { adslAtucChanPerfDataEntry 8 }
            adslAtucChanPerfCurr15MinTransmittedBlks OBJECT-TYPE
               SYNTAX      Gauge32
               MAX-ACCESS    read-only
               STATUS    current
               DESCRIPTION
Count of all encoded blocks transmitted on this channel
within the current 15 minute interval.
            ::= { adslAtucChanPerfDataEntry 9 }
            adslAtucChanPerfCurr15MinCorrectedBlks OBJECT-TYPE
               SYNTAX      Gauge32
               MAX-ACCESS      read-only
               STATUS    current
               DESCRIPTION
Count of all blocks received with errors that were
corrected on this channel within the current 15 minute
interval.
            ::= { adslAtucChanPerfDataEntry 10 }
            adslAtucChanPerfCurr15MinUncorrectBlks OBJECT-TYPE
               SYNTAX      Gauge32
               MAX-ACCESS      read-only
               STATUS      current
```

```
                          DESCRIPTION
Count of all blocks received with uncorrectable
errors on this channel within the current 15 minute
interval.
                 :: = { adslAtucChanPerfDataEntry 11 }
        — 1 Day current and previous performance group—
              adslAtucChanPerfCurr1DayTimeElapsed OBJECT-TYPE
              SYNTAX      INTEGER(0..86399)
              UNITS    "seconds"
              MAX-ACCESS    read-only
              STATUS    current
              DESCRIPTION
Number of seconds that have elapsed since the beginning of the current
1Day interval.
                 :: = { adslAtucChanPerfDataEntry 12 }
              adslAtucChanPerfCurr1DayReceivedBlks OBJECT-TYPE
              SYNTAX     Gauge32
              MAX-ACCESS     read-only
              STATUS    current
              DESCRIPTION
Count of all encoded blocks received on this channel
during the current day as measured by
adslAtucChanPerfCurr1DayTimeElapsed.
                 :: = { adslAtucChanPerfDataEntry 13 }
              adslAtucChanPerfCurr1DayTransmittedBlks OBJECT-TYPE
              SYNTAX     Gauge32
              MAX-ACCESS     read-only
              STATUS    current
              DESCRIPTION
Count of all encoded blocks transmitted on this channel during the cur-
rent day as measured by      adslAtucChanPerfCurr1DayTimeElapsed.
                 :: = { adslAtucChanPerfDataEntry 14 }
              adslAtucChanPerfCurr1DayCorrectedBlks OBJECT-TYPE
              SYNTAX     Gauge32
              MAX-ACCESS     read-only
              STATUS    current
              DESCRIPTION
Count of all blocks received with errors that were
corrected on this channel during the current day as
measured by adslAtucChanPerfCurr1DayTimeElapsed.
              :: = { adslAtucChanPerfDataEntry 15 }
adslAtucChanPerfCurr1DayUncorrectBlks OBJECT-TYPE
          SYNTAX     Gauge32
          MAX-ACCESS     read-only
          STATUS    current
          DESCRIPTION
Count of all blocks received with uncorrectable
errors on this channel during the current day as measured
by adslAtucChanPerfCurr1DayTimeElapsed.
                 :: = { adslAtucChanPerfDataEntry 16 }
              adslAtucChanPerfPrev1DayMoniSecs OBJECT-TYPE
              SYNTAX      INTEGER(0..86399)
              UNITS    "seconds"
              MAX-ACCESS    read-only
              STATUS    current
              DESCRIPTION
The time in the previous 1-day interval over which the performance moni-
toring information is actually counted. This value will normally be the
same as the total interval duration except in a situation where perfor-
mance monitoring information can not be collected for any reason.
Typically Elapsed 1-day Time will be
```

copied into Monitored Seconds when the 1-day roll-over occurs.
```
        : : = { adslAtucChanPerfDataEntry 17 }
        adslAtucChanPerfPrev1DayReceivedBlks OBJECT-TYPE
          SYNTAX       Gauge32
          MAX-ACCESS    read-only
          STATUS       current
          DESCRIPTION
```
Count of all encoded blocks received on this channel
within the most recent previous 1 day period.
```
        : : = { adslAtucChanPerfDataEntry 18 }


        adslAtucChanPerfPrev1DayTransmittedBlks OBJECT-TYPE
          SYNTAX       Gauge32
          MAX-ACCESS    read-only
          STATUS       current
          DESCRIPTION
```
Count of all encoded blocks transmitted on this channel
within the most recent previous 1 day period.
```
        : : = { adslAtucChanPerfDataEntry 19 }
        adslAtucChanPerfPrev1DayCorrectedBlks OBJECT-TYPE
          SYNTAX       Gauge32
          MAX-ACCESS    read-only
          STATUS       current
          DESCRIPTION
```
Count of all blocks received with errors that were
corrected on this channel within the most recent
previous 1 day period.
```
        : : = { adslAtucChanPerfDataEntry 20 }
        adslAtucChanPerfPrev1DayUncorrectBlks OBJECT-TYPE
          SYNTAX       Gauge32
          MAX-ACCESS    read-only
          STATUS       current
          DESCRIPTION
```
Count of all blocks received with uncorrectable
errors on this channel within the most recent previous
1 day period.
```
        : : = { adslAtucChanPerfDataEntry 21 }
    adslAturChanPerfDataTable  OBJECT-TYPE     SYNTAX         SEQUENCE
OF      AdslAturChanPerfDataEntry
        MAX-ACCESS         not-accessible
        STATUS     current
        DESCRIPTION
```
This table provides one row for each ATUR channel. ADSL channel interfaces
are those ifEntries where ifType is equal to adslInterleave(124) or
adslFast(125).
```
    : : = { adslMibObjects 11 }
    adslAturChanPerfDataEntry      OBJECT-TYPE
        SYNTAX        AdslAturChanPerfDataEntry
        MAX-ACCESS       not-accessible
        STATUS      current
    DESCRIPTION  An entry in adslAturChanPerfDataTable.
        INDEX   { ifIndex }
    : : = { adslAturChanPerfDataTable 1 }
    AdslAturChanPerfDataEntry : : =
        SEQUENCE {
        adslAturChanReceivedBlks            Counter32,
        adslAturChanTransmittedBlks          Counter32,
        adslAturChanCorrectedBlks            Counter32,
        adslAturChanUncorrectBlks            Counter32,
        adslAturChanPerfValidIntervals       INTEGER,
        adslAturChanPerfInvalidIntervals     INTEGER,
```

```
                  adslAturChanPerfCurr15MinTimeElapsed    INTEGER,
                  adslAturChanPerfCurr15MinReceivedBlks    Gauge32,
                  adslAturChanPerfCurr15MinTransmittedBlks Gauge32,
                  adslAturChanPerfCurr15MinCorrectedBlks   Gauge32,
                  adslAturChanPerfCurr15MinUncorrectBlks   Gauge32,
                  adslAturChanPerfCurr1DayTimeElapsed     INTEGER,
                  adslAturChanPerfCurr1DayReceivedBlks     Gauge32,
                  adslAturChanPerfCurr1DayTransmittedBlks  Gauge32,
                  adslAturChanPerfCurr1DayCorrectedBlks    Gauge32,
                  adslAturChanPerfCurr1DayUncorrectBlks    Gauge32,
                  adslAturChanPerfPrev1DayMoniSecs        INTEGER,
                  adslAturChanPerfPrev1DayReceivedBlks     Gauge32,
                  adslAturChanPerfPrev1DayTransmittedBlks  Gauge32,
                  adslAturChanPerfPrev1DayCorrectedBlks    Gauge32,
                  adslAturChanPerfPrev1DayUncorrectBlks    Gauge32
                  }
              - performance group-
       - Note: block is intended to be the length of the channel
       -    data-block on which the CRC operates. See
       -    adslAturChanCrcBlockLength for more information.
       -

       adslAturChanReceivedBlks OBJECT-TYPE
              SYNTAX       Counter32
              MAX-ACCESS     read-only
              STATUS       current
              DESCRIPTION
Count of all encoded blocks received on this channel
since agent reset.
              ::= { adslAturChanPerfDataEntry 1 }
           adslAturChanTransmittedBlks OBJECT-TYPE
              SYNTAX       Counter32
              MAX-ACCESS     read-only
              STATUS       current
              DESCRIPTION
Count of all encoded blocks transmitted on this
channel since agent reset.
              ::= { adslAturChanPerfDataEntry 2 }
           adslAturChanCorrectedBlks OBJECT-TYPE
              SYNTAX       Counter32
              MAX-ACCESS     read-only
              STATUS   current
              DESCRIPTION
Count of all blocks received with errors that were
corrected since agent reset. These blocks are passed on
as good data.
           ::= { adslAturChanPerfDataEntry 3 }
           adslAturChanUncorrectBlks OBJECT-TYPE
              SYNTAX       Counter32
              MAX-ACCESS     read-only
              STATUS   current
              DESCRIPTION
Count of all blocks received with uncorrectable
errors since agent reset.
           ::= { adslAturChanPerfDataEntry 4 }
        - general 15 min interval information-
           adslAturChanPerfValidIntervals OBJECT-TYPE
              SYNTAX       INTEGER(0..96)
              MAX-ACCESS     read-only
              STATUS   current
              DESCRIPTION
```

Number of previous 15-minute intervals in the
adslAturChanIntervalTable Table for which valid data
has been stored. This value will be equal to the maximum
number of intervals that are kept (n) unless the device
was brought online within the last (nx15) minutes. In
the case where the agent is a proxy, it is possible
that some intervals are unavailable. In this case,
this interval is the maximum interval for which valid
data is available.

```
        ::= { adslAturChanPerfDataEntry 5 }
        adslAturChanPerfInvalidIntervals OBJECT-TYPE
          SYNTAX        INTEGER(0..96)
          MAX-ACCESS      read-only
          STATUS      current
          DESCRIPTION
```
The number of 15 minute intervals which no valid data is available.
```
        ::= { adslAturChanPerfDataEntry 6 }
        — 15 min current performance group—
     adslAturChanPerfCurr15MinTimeElapsed OBJECT-TYPE
          SYNTAX        INTEGER(0..899)
          UNITS      "seconds"
          MAX-ACCESS      read-only
          STATUS    current
          DESCRIPTION
```
Total elapsed seconds in this interval. A full interval is 900 seconds.
```
        ::= { adslAturChanPerfDataEntry 7 }


        adslAturChanPerfCurr15MinReceivedBlks OBJECT-TYPE
          SYNTAX      Gauge32
          MAX-ACCESS      read-only
          STATUS    current
          DESCRIPTION
```
Count of all encoded blocks received on this channel
within the current 15 minute interval.
```
        ::= { adslAturChanPerfDataEntry 8 }
        adslAturChanPerfCurr15MinTransmittedBlks OBJECT-TYPE
          SYNTAX      Gauge32
          MAX-ACCESS      read-only
          STATUS    current
          DESCRIPTION
```
Count of all encoded blocks transmitted on this channel
within the current 15 minute interval.
```
        ::= { adslAturChanPerfDataEntry 9 }
        adslAturChanPerfCurr15MinCorrectedBlks OBJECT-TYPE
          SYNTAX      Gauge32
          MAX-ACCESS      read-only
          STATUS    current
          DESCRIPTION
```
Count of all blocks received with errors that were
corrected on this channel within the current 15 minute
interval.
```
        ::= { adslAturChanPerfDataEntry 10 }
        adslAturChanPerfCurr15MinUncorrectBlks OBJECT-TYPE
          SYNTAX      Gauge32
          MAX-ACCESS      read-only
          STATUS    current
          DESCRIPTION
```
Count of all blocks received with uncorrectable
errors on this channel within the current 15 minute
interval.

```
            ::= { adslAturChanPerfDataEntry 11 }
          — 1 Day current and previous performance group—
          adslAturChanPerfCurr1DayTimeElapsed OBJECT-TYPE
              SYNTAX        INTEGER(0..86399)
              UNITS         "seconds"
              MAX-ACCESS        read-only
              STATUS        current
              DESCRIPTION
```
Number of seconds that have elapsed since the beginning
of the current 1Day interval.
```
              ::= { adslAturChanPerfDataEntry 12 }
          adslAturChanPerfCurr1DayReceivedBlks OBJECT-TYPE
              SYNTAX        Gauge32
              MAX-ACCESS        read-only
              STATUS        current
              DESCRIPTION
```
Count of all encoded blocks received on this channel
during the current day as measured by
adslAturChanPerfCurr1DayTimeElapsed."
```
  ::= { adslAturChanPerfDataEntry 13 }


          adslAturChanPerfCurr1DayTransmittedBlks
           OBJECT-TYPE
           SYNTAX      Gauge32
           MAX-ACCESS    read-only
           STATUS      current
           DESCRIPTION
```
Count of all encoded blocks transmitted on this channel
during the current day as measured by
adslAturChanPerfCurr1DayTimeElapsed.
```
              ::= { adslAturChanPerfDataEntry 14 }
          adslAturChanPerfCurr1DayCorrectedBlks OBJECT-TYPE
              SYNTAX        Gauge32
              MAX-ACCESS        read-only
              STATUS        current
              DESCRIPTION
```
Count of all blocks received with errors that were
corrected on this channel during the current day as
measured by adslAturChanPerfCurr1DayTimeElapsed.
```
              ::= { adslAturChanPerfDataEntry 15 }
          adslAturChanPerfCurr1DayUncorrectBlks OBJECT-TYPE
              SYNTAX        Gauge32
              MAX-ACCESS        read-only
              STATUS        current
              DESCRIPTION
```
Count of all blocks received with uncorrectable
errors on this channel during the current day as measured
by adslAturChanPerfCurr1DayTimeElapsed.
```
              ::= { adslAturChanPerfDataEntry 16 }
          adslAturChanPerfPrev1DayMoniSecs OBJECT-TYPE
              SYNTAX        INTEGER(0..86399)
              UNITS         "seconds"
              MAX-ACCESS        read-only
              STATUS        current
              DESCRIPTION
```
The time in the previous 1-day interval over which
the performance monitoring information is actually
counted. This value will normally be the same as the
total interval duration except in a situation where
performance monitoring information can not be collected

for any reason. Typically Elapsed 1-day Time will be
copied into Monitored Seconds when the 1-day roll-over
occurs.
                  :: = { adslAturChanPerfDataEntry 17 }
                  adslAturChanPerfPrev1DayReceivedBlks OBJECT-TYPE
                    SYNTAX   Gauge32
                    MAX-ACCESS   read-only
                    STATUS   current
                    DESCRIPTION
Count of all encoded blocks received on this channel
within the most recent previous 1 day period.
                  :: = { adslAturChanPerfDataEntry 18 }
                  adslAturChanPerfPrev1DayTransmittedBlks OBJECT-TYPE
                    SYNTAX   Gauge32
                    MAX-ACCESS   read-only
                    STATUS   current
                    DESCRIPTION
Count of all encoded blocks transmitted on this channel
within the most recent previous 1 day period.
                  :: = { adslAturChanPerfDataEntry 19 }
                  adslAturChanPerfPrev1DayCorrectedBlks OBJECT-TYPE
                    SYNTAX   Gauge32
                    MAX-ACCESS   read-only
                    STATUS   current
                    DESCRIPTION
Count of all blocks received with errors that were corrected on this
channel within the most recent
previous 1 day period.
                  :: = { adslAturChanPerfDataEntry 20 }
                  adslAturChanPerfPrev1DayUncorrectBlks
                    OBJECT-TYPE
                    SYNTAX   Gauge32
                    MAX-ACCESS   read-only
                    STATUS   current
                    DESCRIPTION
Count of all blocks received with uncorrectable errors on this channel
within the most recent previous 1 day period."
                  :: = { adslAturChanPerfDataEntry 21 }
                  adslAtucChanIntervalTable OBJECT-TYPE
                    SYNTAX   SEQUENCE OF AdslAtucChanIntervalEntry
                    MAX-ACCESS   not-accessible
                    STATUS   current
                    DESCRIPTION
This table provides one row for each ATUC channel's
performance data collection interval. ADSL channel interfaces are those
ifEntries where ifType is equal to adslInterleave(124)
or adslFast(125).
      :: = { adslMibObjects 12 }
      adslAtucChanIntervalEntry OBJECT-TYPE
          SYNTAX   AdslAtucChanIntervalEntry
          MAX-ACCESS   not-accessible
          STATUS   current
          DESCRIPTION
An entry in the adslAtucIntervalTable."   INDEX   {
ifIndex,   adslAtucChanIntervalNumber }
          :: = { adslAtucChanIntervalTable 1 }
      AdslAtucChanIntervalEntry :: =
          SEQUENCE {
          adslAtucChanIntervalNumber   INTEGER,
          adslAtucChanIntervalReceivedBlks   Gauge32,

```
                    adslAtucChanIntervalTransmittedBlks Gauge32,
                    adslAtucChanIntervalCorrectedBlks    Gauge32,
                    adslAtucChanIntervalUncorrectBlks    Gauge32,
                    adslAtucChanIntervalValidData    TruthValue
                    }
                    adslAtucChanIntervalNumber  OBJECT-TYPE
                      SYNTAX      INTEGER(1..96)
                      MAX-ACCESS      not-accessible
                      STATUS    current
                      DESCRIPTION
Performance Data Interval number. 1 is the most recent interval; inter-
val 96 is 24 hours ago. Interval 2..96 are optional.
                      :: = { adslAtucChanIntervalEntry 1 }
                    adslAtucChanIntervalReceivedBlks OBJECT-TYPE
                      SYNTAX      Gauge32
                      MAX-ACCESS      read-only
                      STATUS      current
                      DESCRIPTION
Count of all encoded blocks received on this channel
during this interval.
                      :: = { adslAtucChanIntervalEntry 2 }
                    adslAtucChanIntervalTransmittedBlks OBJECT-TYPE
                      SYNTAX      Gauge32
                      MAX-ACCESS      read-only
                      STATUS    current
                      DESCRIPTION
Count of all encoded blocks transmitted on this channel
during this interval.
                      :: = { adslAtucChanIntervalEntry 3 }
                    adslAtucChanIntervalCorrectedBlks OBJECT-TYPE
                      SYNTAX      Gauge32
                      MAX-ACCESS      read-only
                      STATUS    current
                      DESCRIPTION
Count of all blocks received with errors that were
corrected on this channel during this interval.
                      :: = { adslAtucChanIntervalEntry 4 }

                    adslAtucChanIntervalUncorrectBlks OBJECT-TYPE
                      SYNTAX      Gauge32
                      MAX-ACCESS      read-only
                      STATUS    current
                      DESCRIPTION
Count of all blocks received with uncorrectable
errors on this channel during this interval.
                      :: = { adslAtucChanIntervalEntry 5 }
                    adslAtucChanIntervalValidData OBJECT-TYPE
                      SYNTAX    TruthValue
                      MAX-ACCESS      read-only
                      STATUS current
                      DESCRIPTION
This variable indicates if there is valid data
for this interval.
                      :: = { adslAtucChanIntervalEntry 6 }
                adslAturChanIntervalTable OBJECT-TYPE
                      SYNTAX          SEQUENCE OF AdslAturChanIntervalEntry
                      MAX-ACCESS      not-accessible
                      STATUS      current
                      DESCRIPTION
This table provides one row for each ATUR channel's
```

performance data collection interval. ADSL channel interfaces are those
ifEntries where ifType is equal to adslInterleave(124)
or adslFast(125).
```
      ::={ adslMibObjects 13 }
      adslAturChanIntervalEntry OBJECT-TYPE
          SYNTAX          AdslAturChanIntervalEntry
          MAX-ACCESS      not-accessible
          STATUS     current
          DESCRIPTION
An entry in the adslAturIntervalTable.
          INDEX
          { ifIndex, adslAturChanIntervalNumber }
      ::={ adslAturChanIntervalTable 1 }
      AdslAturChanIntervalEntry ::=
          SEQUENCE {
        adslAturChanIntervalNumber        INTEGER,
        adslAturChanIntervalReceivedBlks   Gauge32,
       adslAturChanIntervalTransmittedBlks Gauge32,
       adslAturChanIntervalCorrectedBlks   Gauge32,
       adslAturChanIntervalUncorrectBlks   Gauge32,
       adslAturChanIntervalValidData       TruthValue
          }
      adslAturChanIntervalNumber OBJECT-TYPE
          SYNTAX        INTEGER(1..96)
          MAX-ACCESS      not-accessible
          STATUS     current
          DESCRIPTION
```
Performance Data Interval number. 1 is the most recent interval; inter-
val 96 is 24 hours ago. Interval 2..96 are optional.
```
        ::={ adslAturChanIntervalEntry 1 }
        adslAturChanIntervalReceivedBlks OBJECT-TYPE
          SYNTAX        Gauge32
          MAX-ACCESS      read-only
          STATUS     current
          DESCRIPTION
```
Count of all encoded blocks received on this channel
during this interval.
```
        ::={ adslAturChanIntervalEntry 2 }
        adslAturChanIntervalTransmittedBlks OBJECT-TYPE
          SYNTAX        Gauge32
          MAX-ACCESS      read-only
          STATUS     current
          DESCRIPTION
```
Count of all encoded blocks transmitted on this channel
during this interval.
```
        ::={ adslAturChanIntervalEntry 3 }
        adslAturChanIntervalCorrectedBlks OBJECT-TYPE
          SYNTAX        Gauge32
          MAX-ACCESS      read-only
          STATUS     current
          DESCRIPTION
```
Count of all blocks received with errors that were
corrected on this channel during this interval.
```
        ::={ adslAturChanIntervalEntry 4 }
  adslAturChanIntervalUncorrectBlks OBJECT-TYPE
          SYNTAX        Gauge32
          MAX-ACCESS      read-only
          STATUS     current
          DESCRIPTION
```
Count of all blocks received with uncorrectable

errors on this channel during this interval.
```
        :: = { adslAturChanIntervalEntry 5 }
  adslAturChanIntervalValidData OBJECT-TYPE
       SYNTAX    TruthValue
       MAX-ACCESS    read-only
     STATUS    current
         DESCRIPTION
```
This variable indicates if there is valid data for this interval.
```
        :: = { adslAturChanIntervalEntry 6 }
     — Profile Group—
     adslLineConfProfileIndexNext OBJECT-TYPE
         SYNTAX        INTEGER
         MAX-ACCESS        read-only
         STATUS    current
         DESCRIPTION
```
This object contains an appropriate value to be used for adslLineConfProfileIndex when creating entries in the adslLineConfProfileTable. The value '0' indicates that no unassigned entries are available. To obtain the adslLineConfProfileIndexNext value for a new entry, the manager issues a management protocol retrieval operation to obtain the current value of this object. After each retrieval, the agent should modify the value to the next unassigned index. If the implementator of this MIB has choosen not to implement 'dynamic assignment' of profiles, this object is not useful and should return noSuchName upon SNMP request.
```
     :: = { adslMibObjects 14}
     adslLineConfProfileTable OBJECT-TYPE
         SYNTAX        SEQUENCE OF AdslLineConfProfileEntry
         MAX-ACCESS        not-accessible
         STATUS    current
         DESCRIPTION
```
This table contains information on the ADSL line configuration. One entry in this table reflects a profile defined by a manager which can be used to configure the ADSL line.
```
     :: = { adslMibObjects 15}
     adslLineConfProfileEntry OBJECT-TYPE
         SYNTAX        AdslLineConfProfileEntry
         MAX-ACCESS        not-accessible
         STATUS    current
         DESCRIPTION
```
Each entry consists of a list of parameters that represents the configuration of an ADSL modem. A profile is created in one step with all necessary parameter values and adslLineProfileRowStatus set to createAndGo. This RowStatus object is also used to delete destroy profiles.
```
         INDEX { adslLineConfProfileIndex}
     :: = { adslLineConfProfileTable 1}
     AdslLineConfProfileEntry :: =
         SEQUENCE {
         adslLineConfProfileIndex      AdslLineProfileType,
         adslAtucConfRateMode          INTEGER,
         adslAtucConfRateChanRatio      INTEGER,
         adslAtucConfTargetSnrMgn       INTEGER,
         adslAtucConfMaxSnrMgn          INTEGER,
         adslAtucConfMinSnrMgn         INTEGER,
         adslAtucConfDownshiftSnrMgn     INTEGER,
         adslAtucConfUpshiftSnrMgn       INTEGER,
         adslAtucConfMinUpshiftTime      INTEGER,
         adslAtucConfMinDownshiftTime      INTEGER,
```

```
          adslAtucChanConfFastMinTxRate        INTEGER,
          adslAtucChanConfInterleaveMinTxRate  INTEGER,
          adslAtucChanConfFastMaxTxRate        INTEGER,
          adslAtucChanConfInterleaveMaxTxRate  INTEGER,
          adslAtucChanConfMaxInterleaveDelay   INTEGER,
          adslAturConfRateMode                 INTEGER,
          adslAturConfRateChanRatio            INTEGER,
          adslAturConfTargetSnrMgn             INTEGER,
          adslAturConfMaxSnrMgn                INTEGER,
          adslAturConfMinSnrMgn                INTEGER,
          adslAturConfDownshiftSnrMgn          INTEGER,
          adslAturConfUpshiftSnrMgn            INTEGER,
          adslAturConfMinUpshiftTime           INTEGER,
          adslAturConfMinDownshiftTime         INTEGER,
          adslAturChanConfFastMinTxRate        INTEGER,
          adslAturChanConfInterleaveMinTxRate  INTEGER,
          adslAturChanConfFastMaxTxRate        INTEGER,
          adslAturChanConfInterleaveMaxTxRate INTEGER,
          adslAturChanConfMaxInterleaveDelay INTEGER,
          adslLineConfProfileRowStatus    RowStatus
          }
          adslLineConfProfileIndex OBJECT-TYPE
              SYNTAX          AdslLineProfileType
              MAX-ACCESS      not-accessible
              STATUS     current
              DESCRIPTION
This object is used by the line configuration table in order to identify
a row of this table
              ::= { adslLineConfProfileEntry 1 }
          adslAtucConfRateMode OBJECT-TYPE
              SYNTAX     INTEGER {
  fixed (1),      — no rate adaption
  adaptAtStartup (2),  — perform rate adaptation
                 — only at initialization
 adaptAtRuntime (3)     — perform rate adaptation at
            — any time (i.e., RADSL)
          }
    MAX-ACCESS read-write
          STATUS     current
          DESCRIPTION
Defines what form of transmit rate adaptation is
configured on this modem. See WT008 for more information.
          ::= { adslLineConfProfileEntry 2 }
          adslAtucConfRateChanRatio OBJECT-TYPE
              SYNTAX     INTEGER(1..100)
              UNITS      "%"
              MAX-ACCESS     read-write
              STATUS current
              DESCRIPTION
Configured allocation ratio of excess transmit bandwidth between fast
and interleaved channels. Only applies when two channel mode and RADSL
are supported. Distribute bandwidth on each channel in excess of the
corresponding ChanConfMinTxRate so that:
   adslAtucConfRateChanRatio =
 [Fast / (Fast + Interleaved)] * 100
 In other words this value is the fast channel percentage.
          ::= { adslLineConfProfileEntry 3 }
          adslAtucConfTargetSnrMgn OBJECT-TYPE
              SYNTAX          INTEGER(0..310)
              UNITS       "tenth dB"
```

```
                MAX-ACCESS      read-write
                STATUS    current
                DESCRIPTION
Configured Target Signal/Noise Margin. This is the Noise Margin the
modem must achieve with a BER of 10-7 or better to successfully complete
initialization.
            ::= { adslLineConfProfileEntry 4 }
            adslAtucConfMaxSnrMgn OBJECT-TYPE
            SYNTAX      INTEGER(0..310)
            UNITS    "tenth dB"
            MAX-ACCESS      read-write
            STATUS    current
            DESCRIPTION
Configured Maximum acceptable Signal/Noise Margin. If the Noise Margin is
above this the modem should attempt to reduce its power output to optimize
its operation.
            ::= { adslLineConfProfileEntry 5 }
            adslAtucConfMinSnrMgn OBJECT-TYPE
            SYNTAX      INTEGER(0..310)
            UNITS    "tenth dB"
            MAX-ACCESS      read-write
            STATUS    current
            DESCRIPTION
Configured Minimum acceptable Signal/Noise Margin. If the noise margin
falls below this level, the modem should attempt to increase its power
output. If that is not possible the modem will attempt to re-initialize or
shut down.
            ::= { adslLineConfProfileEntry 6 }
            adslAtucConfDownshiftSnrMgn OBJECT-TYPE
            SYNTAX      INTEGER(0..310)
            UNITS    "tenth dB"
            MAX-ACCESS      read-write
            STATUS    current
            DESCRIPTION
Configured Signal/Noise Margin for rate downshift. If the noise margin
falls below this level, the modem should attempt to decrease its transmit
rate. In the case that RADSL is not present, the value will be '0'."
            ::= { adslLineConfProfileEntry 7 }
            adslAtucConfUpshiftSnrMgn OBJECT-TYPE
            SYNTAX      INTEGER(0..310)
            UNITS    "tenth dB"
            MAX-ACCESS      read-write
            STATUS    current
            DESCRIPTION
Configured Signal/Noise Margin for rate upshift. If the noise margin
rises above this level, the modem should attempt to increase its trans-
mit rate. In the case that RADSL is not present, the value will be '0'.
            ::= { adslLineConfProfileEntry 8 }
            adslAtucConfMinUpshiftTime OBJECT-TYPE
            SYNTAX      INTEGER(0..16383)
            UNITS    "seconds"
            MAX-ACCESS      read-write
            STATUS    current
            DESCRIPTION
Minimum time that the current margin is above UpshiftSnrMgn before an
upshift occurs. In the case that RADSL is not present, the value will be
'0'.
            ::= { adslLineConfProfileEntry 9 }
            adslAtucConfMinDownshiftTime OBJECT-TYPE
            SYNTAX      INTEGER(0..16383)
```

```
              UNITS      "seconds"
              MAX-ACCESS      read-write
              STATUS   current
              DESCRIPTION
Minimum time that the current margin is below DownshiftSnrMgn before a
downshift occurs.In the case that RADSL is not present, the value will
be '0'.
              ::= { adslLineConfProfileEntry 10 }
              adslAtucChanConfFastMinTxRate OBJECT-TYPE
              SYNTAX      INTEGER(1..32000)
              UNITS      "bps"
              MAX-ACCESS      read-write
              STATUS   current
              DESCRIPTION
Configured Minimum Transmit rate for 'Fast' channels, in bps. See
adslAtucConfRateChanRatio for information regarding RADSL mode and ATUR
transmit rate for ATUC receive rates."
              ::= { adslLineConfProfileEntry 11 }
              adslAtucChanConfInterleaveMinTxRate OBJECT-TYPE
              SYNTAX      INTEGER(1..32000)
              UNITS      "bps"
              MAX-ACCESS      read-write
              STATUS   current
              DESCRIPTION
Configured Minimum Transmit rate for 'Interleave'channels, in bps. See
adslAtucConfRateChanRatio for information regarding RADSL mode and see
ATUR transmit rate for receive rates.
              ::= { adslLineConfProfileEntry 12 }
         adslAtucChanConfFastMaxTxRate OBJECT-TYPE
              SYNTAX      INTEGER(1..32000)
              UNITS      "bps"
              MAX-ACCESS      read-write
              STATUS   current
              DESCRIPTION
Configured Maximum Transmit rate for 'Fast' channels, in bps. See
adslAtucConfRateChanRatio for information regarding RADSL mode and see
ATUR transmit rate for ATUC receive rates."
              ::= { adslLineConfProfileEntry 13 }
              adslAtucChanConfInterleaveMaxTxRate OBJECT-TYPE
              SYNTAX      INTEGER(1..32000)
              UNITS      "bps"
              MAX-ACCESS      read-write
              STATUS   current
              DESCRIPTION
Configured Maximum Transmit rate for 'Interleave' channels, in bps. See
adslAtucConfRateChanRatio for information regarding RADSL mode and ATUR
transmit rate for ATUC receive rates.
              ::= { adslLineConfProfileEntry 14 }
              adslAtucChanConfMaxInterleaveDelay OBJECT-TYPE
              SYNTAX      INTEGER(0..255)
              UNITS    "milli-seconds"
              MAX-ACCESS      read-write
              STATUS   current
              DESCRIPTION
Configured maximum Interleave Delay for this channel
per ANSI T1.413, = =
         (S-factor x d)
         ———————
         4 milli-seconds,
where 'd' is the Interleaving Depth. Interleave delay applies only to the
```

interleave channel and defines the mapping (relative spacing) between subsequent input bytes at the interleaver input and their placement in the bit stream at the interleaver output.
Larger numbers provide greater separation between
consecutive input bytes in the output bit stream allowing
for improved impulse noise immunity at the expense of
payload latency.
        :: = { adslLineConfProfileEntry 15 }
        adslAturConfRateMode OBJECT-TYPE
          SYNTAX   INTEGER {
fixed (1),   – no rate adaption
adaptAtStartup (2),   – perform rate adaptation
        – only at initialization
adaptAtRuntime (3)   – perform rate adaptation at
       – any time (i.e., RADSL)
       }
        MAX-ACCESS   read-write
        STATUS   current
        DESCRIPTION
Defines what form of transmit rate adaptation is configured on this modem.
        :: = { adslLineConfProfileEntry 16 }
        adslAturConfRateChanRatio OBJECT-TYPE
          SYNTAX   INTEGER(1..100)
          UNITS   "%"
        MAX-ACCESS   read-write
        STATUS   current
        DESCRIPTION
Configured allocation ratio of excess transmit bandwidth between fast and interleaved channels. Only applies when two channel mode and RADSL are supported. Distribute bandwidth on each channel in excess of the corresponding ChanConfMinTxRate so that:
adslAturConfRateChanRatio =
   [Fast / (Fast + Interleaved)] * 100
In other words this value is the fast channel percentage.
        :: = { adslLineConfProfileEntry 17 }
        adslAturConfTargetSnrMgn OBJECT-TYPE
          SYNTAX   INTEGER(0..310)
          UNITS   "tenth dB"
        MAX-ACCESS   read-write
        STATUS   current
        DESCRIPTION
Configured Target Signal/Noise Margin. This is the Noise Margin the modem must achieve with a BER of 10-7 or better to successfully complete initialization.
        :: = { adslLineConfProfileEntry 18 }
        adslAturConfMaxSnrMgn OBJECT-TYPE
          SYNTAX   INTEGER(0..310)
          UNITS   "tenth dB"
        MAX-ACCESS   read-write
        STATUS   current
        DESCRIPTION
Configured Maximum acceptable Signal/Noise Margin. If the Noise Margin is above this the modem should attempt to reduce its power output to optimize its operation.
        :: = { adslLineConfProfileEntry 19 }
        adslAturConfMinSnrMgn OBJECT-TYPE
          SYNTAX   INTEGER(0..310)
          UNITS   "tenth dB"
        MAX-ACCESS   read-write

```
                    STATUS    current
                    DESCRIPTION
Configured Minimum acceptable Signal/Noise Margin. If the noise margin
falls below this level, the modem should attempt to increase its power
output. If that is not possible the modem will attempt to re-initialize
or shut down.
                    ::={ adslLineConfProfileEntry 20 }
                adslAturConfDownshiftSnrMgn OBJECT-TYPE
                    SYNTAX      INTEGER(0..310)
                    UNITS     "tenth dB"
                    MAX-ACCESS      read-write
                    STATUS    current
                    DESCRIPTION
Configured Signal/Noise Margin for rate downshift. If the noise margin
falls below this level, the modem should attempt to decrease its trans-
mit rate. In the case that RADSL is not present, the value will be '0'."
                    ::={ adslLineConfProfileEntry 21 }
                adslAturConfUpshiftSnrMgn OBJECT-TYPE
                    SYNTAX      INTEGER(0..310)
                    UNITS     "tenth dB"
                    MAX-ACCESS      read-write
                    STATUS    current
                    DESCRIPTION
Configured Signal/Noise Margin for rate upshift. If the noise margin
rises above this level, the modem should attempt to increase its trans-
mit rate. In the case that RADSL is not present, the value will be '0'."
                    ::={ adslLineConfProfileEntry 22 }
                adslAturConfMinUpshiftTime OBJECT-TYPE
                    SYNTAX      INTEGER(0..16383)
                    UNITS    "seconds"
                    MAX-ACCESS      read-write
                    STATUS    current
                    DESCRIPTION
Minimum time that the current margin is above UpshiftSnrMgn before an
upshift occurs. In the case that RADSL is not present, the value will be
'0'.
                    ::={ adslLineConfProfileEntry 23 }
                adslAturConfMinDownshiftTime OBJECT-TYPE
                    SYNTAX      INTEGER(0..16383)
                    UNITS    "seconds"
                    MAX-ACCESS      read-write
                    STATUS    current
                    DESCRIPTION
Minimum time that the current margin is below DownshiftSnrMgn before a
downshift occurs. In the case that RADSL is not present, the value will be
'0'.
                    ::={ adslLineConfProfileEntry 24 }
                adslAturChanConfFastMinTxRate OBJECT-TYPE
                    SYNTAX      INTEGER(1..32000)
                    UNITS    "bps"
                    MAX-ACCESS      read-write
                    STATUS    current
                    DESCRIPTION
Configured Minimum Transmit rate for 'Fast' channels, in bps. See
adslAturConfRateChanRatio for information regarding RADSL mode and ATUC
transmit rate for ATUR receive rates.
                    ::={ adslLineConfProfileEntry 25 }
                adslAturChanConfInterleaveMinTxRate OBJECT-TYPE
                    SYNTAX      INTEGER(1..32000)
                    UNITS    "bps"
```

```
                        MAX-ACCESS      read-write
                        STATUS    current
                        DESCRIPTION
Configured Minimum Transmit rate for 'Interleave' channels, in bps. See
adslAturConfRateChanRatio for information regarding RADSL mode and ATUC
transmit rate for ATUR receive rates.
                    :: = { adslLineConfProfileEntry 26 }
                    adslAturChanConfFastMaxTxRate OBJECT-TYPE
                        SYNTAX      INTEGER(1..32000)
                        UNITS     "bps"
                        MAX-ACCESS      read-write
                        STATUS    current
                        DESCRIPTION
Configured Maximum Transmit rate for 'Fast' channels, in bps. See
adslAturConfRateChanRatio for information regarding RADSL mode and ATUC
transmit rate for ATUR receive rates.
                    :: = { adslLineConfProfileEntry 27 }
                    adslAturChanConfInterleaveMaxTxRate OBJECT-TYPE
                        SYNTAX      INTEGER(1..32000)
                        UNITS     "bps"
                        MAX-ACCESS      read-write
                        STATUS    current
                        DESCRIPTION
Configured Maximum Transmit rate for 'Interleave' channels, in bps. See
adslAturConfRateChanRatio for information regarding RADSL mode and see
ATUC transmit rate for ATUR receive rates.
                    :: = { adslLineConfProfileEntry 28 }
                    adslAturChanConfMaxInterleaveDelay OBJECT-TYPE
                        SYNTAX      INTEGER(0..255)
                        UNITS     "milli-seconds"
                        MAX-ACCESS       read-write
                        STATUS    current
                        DESCRIPTION
Configured maximum Interleave Delay for this channel per
ANSI T1.413, = =
     (S-factor x d)
     ─────────
     4 milli-seconds,
where 'd' is the Interleaving Depth. Interleave delay applies only to
the interleave channel and defines the mapping (relative spacing)
between subsequent input bytes at the interleaver input and their place-
ment in the bit stream at the interleaver output.
Larger numbers provide greater separation between consecutive input
bytes in the output bit stream allowing for improved impulse noise immu-
nity at the expense of payload latency.
                    :: = { adslLineConfProfileEntry 29 }
                    adslLineConfProfileRowStatus OBJECT-TYPE
                        SYNTAX      RowStatus
                        MAX-ACCESS      read-create
                        STATUS     current
                        DESCRIPTION
This object is used to create a new row or modify or delete an existing
row in this table. If the implementator of this MIB has choosen not to
implement 'dynamic assignment' of profiles, this
object is not useful and should return noSuchName upon SNMP request.
                    :: = { adslLineConfProfileEntry 30 }
                    adslLineAlarmConfProfileIndexNext OBJECT-TYPE
                        SYNTAX      INTEGER
                        MAX-ACCESS      read-only
                        STATUS     current
```

DESCRIPTION
This object contains an appropriate value to be used for
adslLineAlarmConfProfileIndex when creating entries in the
adslLineAlarmConfTable. The value '0' indicates that no unassigned
entries are available. To obtain the adslLineAlarmConfProfileIndexNext
value for a new entry, the manager issues a management protocol
retrieval operation to obtain the current value of this object. After
each retrieval, the agent should modify the value to the next unassigned
index. If the implementator of this MIB has choosen not to implement
'dynamic assignment' of profiles, this object is not useful and should
return noSuchName upon SNMP request."
    :: = { adslMibObjects 16}
    adslLineAlarmConfProfileTable OBJECT-TYPE
        SYNTAX   SEQUENCE OF   AdslLineAlarmConfProfileEntry
        MAX-ACCESS   not-accessible
        STATUS   current
        DESCRIPTION
This table contains information on the ADSL line configuration. One
entry in this table reflects a profile defined by a manager which can be
used to configure the modem for a physical line
    :: = { adslMibObjects 17}
    adslLineAlarmConfProfileEntry OBJECT-TYPE
        SYNTAX   AdslLineAlarmConfProfileEntry
        MAX-ACCESS   not-accessible
        STATUS   current
        DESCRIPTION
Each entry consists of a list of parameters that represents the configuration of an ADSL modem. A profile is created in one step with all necessary parameter values and adslLineAlarmConfProfileRowStatus set to
createAndGo. This RowStatus object is also used to delete destroy profiles.
        INDEX { adslLineAlarmConfProfileIndex}
    :: = { adslLineAlarmConfProfileTable 1}
    AdslLineAlarmConfProfileEntry :: =
        SEQUENCE {
        adslLineAlarmConfProfileIndex   AdslLineProfileType,
        adslAtucThresh15MinLofs   INTEGER,
        adslAtucThresh15MinLoss   INTEGER,
        adslAtucThresh15MinLprs   INTEGER,
        adslAtucThresh15MinESs   INTEGER,
        adslAtucThreshFastRateUp   Integer32,
        adslAtucThreshInterleaveRateUp   Integer32,
        adslAtucThreshFastRateDown   Integer32,
        adslAtucThreshInterleaveRateDown   Integer32,
        adslAtucInitFailureTrapEnable   INTEGER,
        adslAturThresh15MinLofs   INTEGER,
        adslAturThresh15MinLoss   INTEGER,
        adslAturThresh15MinLprs   INTEGER,
        adslAturThresh15MinESs   INTEGER,
        adslAturThreshFastRateUp   Integer32,
        adslAturThreshInterleaveRateUp   Integer32,
        adslAturThreshFastRateDown   Integer32,
        adslAturThreshInterleaveRateDown   Integer32,
        adslLineAlarmConfProfileRowStatus   RowStatus
        }
        adslLineAlarmConfProfileIndex OBJECT-TYPE
            SYNTAX   AdslLineProfileType
            MAX-ACCESS   not-accessible
            STATUS   current
            DESCRIPTION

This object is used by the line alarm configuration table in order to identify a row of this table

```
              :: = { adslLineAlarmConfProfileEntry 1}
              adslAtucThresh15MinLofs OBJECT-TYPE
                SYNTAX      INTEGER(0..900)
                MAX-ACCESS      read-write
                STATUS    current
                DESCRIPTION
```

The number of Loss of Frame Seconds, encountered by an ADSL interface within any given 15 minutes performance data collection period, which causes the SNMP agent to send an adslAtucPerfLofsThreshTrap. Limit of one trap will be sent for any one interval. A value of '0' will disable the trap."

```
              :: = { adslLineAlarmConfProfileEntry 2}
              adslAtucThresh15MinLoss OBJECT-TYPE
                SYNTAX      INTEGER(0..900)
                MAX-ACCESS      read-write
                STATUS    current
                DESCRIPTION
```

The number of Loss of Signal Seconds, encountered by an ADSL interface within any given 15 minutes performance data collection period, which causes the SNMP agent to send an adslAtucPerfLossThreshTrap. Limit of one trap will be sent for any one interval. A value of '0' will disable the trap.

```
              :: = { adslLineAlarmConfProfileEntry 3}
              adslAtucThresh15MinLols OBJECT-TYPE
                SYNTAX      INTEGER(0..900)
                MAX-ACCESS      read-write
                STATUS    current
                DESCRIPTION
```

The number of Loss of Link Seconds, encountered by an ADSL interface within any given 15 minutes performance data collection period, which causes the SNMP agent to send an adslAtucPerfLolsThreshTrap. Limit of one trap will be sent for any one interval. A value of '0' will disable the trap.

```
              :: = { adslLineAlarmConfProfileEntry 4}
              adslAtucThresh15MinLprs OBJECT-TYPE
                SYNTAX      INTEGER(0..900)
                MAX-ACCESS      read-write
                STATUS    current
                DESCRIPTION
```

The number of Loss of Power Seconds, encountered by an ADSL interface within any given 15 minutes performance data collection period, which causes the SNMP agent to send an adslAtucPerfLprsThreshTrap. Limit of one trap will be sent for any one interval. A value of '0' will disable the trap.

```
              :: = { adslLineAlarmConfProfileEntry 5}
              adslAtucThresh15MinESs OBJECT-TYPE
                SYNTAX      INTEGER(0..900)
                MAX-ACCESS      read-write
                STATUS    current
                DESCRIPTION
```

The number of Errored Seconds, encountered by an ADSL interface within any given 15 minutes performance data collection period, which causes the SNMP agent to send an adslAtucPerfESsThreshTrap.
Limit of one trap will be sent for any one interval. A value of '0' will disable the trap.

```
              :: = { adslLineAlarmConfProfileEntry 6}
              adslAtucThreshFastRateUp OBJECT-TYPE
                SYNTAX      Integer32
```

```
                UNITS     "bps"
                MAX-ACCESS      read-write
                STATUS    current
                DESCRIPTION
Applies to 'Fast' channels only. Configured change in rate causing an
adslAtucRateChangeTrap. A trap is produced when: ChanCurrTxRate >
ChanPrevTxRate plus the value of this object. Set to '0' to disable.
                :: = { adslLineAlarmConfProfileEntry 7}
                adslAtucThreshInterleaveRateUp OBJECT-TYPE
                SYNTAX      Integer32
                UNITS     "bps"
                MAX-ACCESS      read-write
                STATUS    current
                DESCRIPTION
Applies to 'Interleave' channels only. Configured change in rate causing
an adslAtucRateChangeTrap. A trap is produced when:
ChanCurrTxRate > ChanPrevTxRate plus the value of this object. Set to
'0' to disable.
                :: = { adslLineAlarmConfProfileEntry 8}
                adslAtucThreshFastRateDown OBJECT-TYPE
                SYNTAX      Integer32
                UNITS     "bps"
                MAX-ACCESS      read-write
                STATUS    current
                DESCRIPTION
Applies to 'Fast' channels only. Configured change in rate causing an
adslAtucRateChangeTrap. A trap is produced when: ChanCurrTxRate <
ChanPrevTxRate minus the value of this object. Set to '0' to disable.
   :: = { adslLineAlarmConfProfileEntry 9 }
                adslAtucThreshInterleaveRateDown OBJECT-TYPE
                SYNTAX  Integer32
                UNITS     "bps"
                MAX-ACCESS  read-write
                STATUS    current
                DESCRIPTION
Applies to 'Interleave' channels only. Configured change in rate causing
an adslAtucRateChangeTrap. A trap is produced when:
ChanCurrTxRate < ChanPrevTxRate minus the value of this object. Set to
'0' to disable.
                :: = { adslLineAlarmConfProfileEntry 10 }
                adslAtucInitFailureTrapEnable OBJECT-TYPE
                SYNTAX      INTEGER {
                  enable (1),
                  disable (2)
                }
                MAX-ACCESS      read-write
                STATUS    current
                DESCRIPTION
Enables and disables the InitFailureTrap. This object is defaulted dis-
able(2).
                DEFVAL { disable }
                :: = { adslLineAlarmConfProfileEntry 11 }
                adslAturThresh15MinLofs OBJECT-TYPE
                SYNTAX      INTEGER(0..900)
                MAX-ACCESS      read-write
                STATUS    current
                DESCRIPTION
The number of Loss of Frame Seconds, encountered by an ADSL interface
within any given 15 minutes performance data collection period, which
causes the SNMP agent to send an adslAtucPerfLofsThreshTrap. Limit of
```

one trap will be sent for any one interval. A value of '0' will disable the trap.
   :: = { adslLineAlarmConfProfileEntry 12 }
  adslAturThresh15MinLoss OBJECT-TYPE
   SYNTAX   INTEGER(0..900)
   MAX-ACCESS read-write
   STATUS current
   DESCRIPTION
The number of Loss of Signal Seconds, encountered by an ADSL interface within any given 15 minutes performance data collection period, which causes the SNMP agent to send an adslAtucPerfLossThreshTrap. Limit of one trap will be sent for any one interval. A value of '0' will disable the trap.
   :: = { adslLineAlarmConfProfileEntry 13 }
  adslAturThresh15MinLprs OBJECT-TYPE
   SYNTAX   INTEGER(0..900)
   MAX-ACCESS read-write
   STATUS current
   DESCRIPTION
The number of Loss of Power Seconds, encountered by an ADSL interface within any given 15 minutes performance data collection period, which causes the SNMP agent to send an adslAtucPerfLprsThreshTrap. Limit of one trap will be sent for any one interval. A value of '0' will disable the trap.
   :: = { adslLineAlarmConfProfileEntry 14 }
  adslAturThresh15MinESs OBJECT-TYPE
   SYNTAX   INTEGER(0..900)
   MAX-ACCESS read-write
   STATUS current
   DESCRIPTION
The number of Errored Seconds, encountered by an ADSL interface within any given 15 minutes performance data collection period, which causes the SNMP agent to send an adslAtucPerfESsThreshTrap.
Limit of one trap will be sent for any one interval. A value of '0' will disable the trap.
   :: = { adslLineAlarmConfProfileEntry 15 }
  adslAturThreshFastRateUp OBJECT-TYPE
   SYNTAX Integer32
   UNITS "bps"
   MAX-ACCESS   read-write
   STATUS current
   DESCRIPTION
Applies to 'Fast' channels only. Configured change in rate causing an adslAtucRateChangeTrap. A trap is produced when: ChanCurrTxRate > ChanPrevTxRate plus the value of this object. Set to '0' to disable.
   :: = { adslLineAlarmConfProfileEntry 16 }
  adslAturThreshInterleaveRateUp OBJECT-TYPE
   SYNTAX Integer32
   UNITS "bps"
   MAX-ACCESS   read-write
   STATUS current
   DESCRIPTION
Applies to 'Interleave' channels only. Configured change in rate causing an adslAtucRateChangeTrap. A trap is produced when:
ChanCurrTxRate < ChanPrevTxRate plus the value of this object. Set to '0' to disable.
   :: = { adslLineAlarmConfProfileEntry 17 }
  adslAturThreshFastRateDown OBJECT-TYPE
   SYNTAX Integer32
   UNITS "bps"

```
            MAX-ACCESS       read-write
            STATUS   current
            DESCRIPTION
Applies to 'Fast' channels only. Configured change in rate causing an
adslAtucRateChangeTrap. A trap is produced when:
ChanCurrTxRate < ChanPrevTxRate minus the value of this object. Set to
'0' to disable.
            :: = { adslLineAlarmConfProfileEntry 18 }
           adslAturThreshInterleaveRateDown OBJECT-TYPE
            SYNTAX      Integer32
            UNITS    "bps"
            MAX-ACCESS       read-write
            STATUS   current
            DESCRIPTION
Applies to 'Interleave' channels only. Configured change in rate causing
an adslAtucRateChangeTrap. A trap is produced when:
ChanCurrTxRate < ChanPrevTxRate minus the value of this object. Set to
'0' to disable.
            :: = { adslLineAlarmConfProfileEntry 19 }
           adslLineAlarmConfProfileRowStatus OBJECT-TYPE
            SYNTAX      RowStatus
            MAX-ACCESS       read-create
            STATUS   current
            DESCRIPTION
This object is used to create a new row or modify or delete an existing
row in this table. If the implementor of this MIB has chosen not to
implement 'dynamic assignment' of profiles, this
```
object is not useful and should return noSuchName upon SNMP request.
```
            :: = { adslLineAlarmConfProfileEntry 20 }
        — Line Code Specific Tables
        adslAtucLCSTable       OBJECT IDENTIFIER :: =
            { adslMibObjects 18 }
        — These are place holders for the Line Code Specific MIBs
        — once they become available.
        adslAturLCSTable  OBJECT IDENTIFIER :: =
            { adslMibObjects 19 }
        — These are place holders for the Line Code Specific MIBs
        — once they become available.
adslConformance OBJECT IDENTIFIER :: = { adslLineMib 2 }
adslGroups    OBJECT IDENTIFIER :: = { adslConformance 1 }
adslCompliances OBJECT IDENTIFIER :: = { adslConformance 2 }
adslTraps     OBJECT IDENTIFIER :: = { adslLineMib 3 }
adslAtucTraps  OBJECT IDENTIFIER :: = { adslTraps 1 }
    adslAtucPerfLofsThreshTrap NOTIFICATION-TYPE
        OBJECTS { ifIndex, adslAtucThresh15MinLofs }
        STATUS current
        DESCRIPTION
Loss of Framing 15-minute interval threshold exceeded
    :: = { adslAtucTraps 0 1 }
    adslAtucPerfLossThreshTrap       NOTIFICATION-TYPE
        OBJECTS { ifIndex, adslAtucThresh15MinLoss }
        STATUS current
        DESCRIPTION
Loss of Signal 15-minute interval threshold exceeded
    :: = { adslAtucTraps 0 2 }
    adslAtucPerfLprsThreshTrap       NOTIFICATION-TYPE
        OBJECTS { ifIndex, adslAtucThresh15MinLprs }
        STATUS current
        DESCRIPTION
Loss of Power 15-minute interval threshold exceeded
```

```
        ::={ adslAtucTraps 0 3 }
        adslAtucPerfESsThreshTrap        NOTIFICATION-TYPE
            OBJECTS { ifIndex, adslAtucThresh15MinESs }
            STATUS current
            DESCRIPTION
Errored Second 15-minute interval threshold exceeded
        ::={ adslAtucTraps 0 4 }
        adslAtucRateChangeTrap NOTIFICATION-TYPE
            OBJECTS {ifIndex, adslAtucChanCurrTxRate,
            adslAtucChanPrevTxRate }
            STATUS current
            DESCRIPTION
The ATUCs transmit rate has changed (RADSL mode only)
        ::={ adslAtucTraps 0 5 }
        adslAtucPerfLolsThreshTrap   NOTIFICATION-TYPE
            OBJECTS { ifIndex, adslAtucThresh15MinLols }
            STATUS current
            DESCRIPTION
Loss of Link 15-minute interval threshold exceeded
        ::={ adslAtucTraps 0 6 }
        adslAtucInitFailureTrap NOTIFICATION-TYPE
            OBJECTS { ifIndex, adslAtucCurrStatus }
            STATUS current
            DESCRIPTION
ATUC initialization failed. See adslAtucCurrStatus
for potential reasons.
        ::={ adslAtucTraps 0 7 }
adslAturTraps OBJECT IDENTIFIER ::={ adslTraps 2 }
        adslAturPerfLofsThreshTrap  NOTIFICATION-TYPE
            OBJECTS { ifIndex, adslAturThresh15MinLofs }
            STATUS current
            DESCRIPTION
Loss of Framing 15-minute interval threshold exceeded
        ::={ adslAturTraps 0 1 }
        adslAturPerfLossThreshTrap  NOTIFICATION-TYPE
            OBJECTS { ifIndex, adslAturThresh15MinLoss }
            STATUS current
            DESCRIPTION
Loss of Signal 15-minute interval threshold exceeded
        ::={ adslAturTraps 0 2 }
        adslAturPerfLprsThreshTrap  NOTIFICATION-TYPE
            OBJECTS { ifIndex, adslAturThresh15MinLprs }
            STATUS current
            DESCRIPTION
Loss of Power 15-minute interval threshold exceeded
         ::={ adslAturTraps 0 3 }
         adslAturPerfESsThreshTrap  NOTIFICATION-TYPE
             OBJECTS { ifIndex, adslAturThresh15MinESs }
             STATUS current       .
             DESCRIPTION
Errored Second 15-minute interval threshold exceeded
         ::={ adslAturTraps 0 4 }
         adslAturRateChangeTrap NOTIFICATION-TYPE
             OBJECTS {ifIndex, adslAturChanCurrTxRate,
             adslAturChanPrevTxRate }
             STATUS current
             DESCRIPTION
The ATURs transmit rate has changed (RADSL mode only)
     ::={ adslAturTraps 0 5 }
     — no adslAturPerfLolsThreshTrap possible { 6 }
```

```
            - no adslAturInitFailureTrap possible { 7 }
            - these are defined for use as ifTestTypes (see RFC1573)
            - additional vendor-specific tests are easily supported
            - (just define in vendor MIB)-
            adslTestTypes OBJECT-TYPE
              SYNTAX  INTEGER {
                    atucSelfTest (1),
                    aturSelfTest (2)
                    }
                MAX-ACCESS read-only
                  STATUS   current
                  DESCRIPTION "values as above"
                :: = { adslLineMib 4 }
      adslTestCodes OBJECT IDENTIFIER :: = { adslLineMib 5 }
      END
```

Remember, this is the ADSL Forum DRAFT SNMP-based ADSL Line MIB.

10.8   Interfaces and System Configurations for ADSL: Customer Premises

This section covers interfaces and system configurations for the ADSL customer premises. It covers electrical interfaces, connectorization, and wiring topologies with emphasis on POTS splitter issues, customer interfaces, and premises distribution networks. Where possible, technical information will be obtained by reference to existing specifications, and by liaison to technical standards groups.

Introduction

Covering of the topic in this section includes efforts to define electrical interfaces, connectorization, and wiring topology for ADSL customer premises installations. Where possible, technical information will be obtained by reference to existing specifications, and by liaison to technical standards groups. The work on this project is limited to addressing the interfaces necessary to support existing single-user connections methods as well as multiuser connection methods utilizing premises distribution networks (passive and active) for bit synchronous data, ATM data, and packet data. Future work may be undertaken that addresses the use of emerging premises distribution networks and the interfaces required to support them.

Acronyms and standards related to ADSL customer premises

ac	Alternating current
ADSL	Asymmetric digital subscriber line
AMI	Alternate mark inversion
ANSI	American National Standards Institute
ATM	Asynchronous transfer mode

ATU-C	ADSL transmission unit at the central office end
ATU-R	ADSL transmission unit at the CPE end
CD	Compact disk
CPE	Customer premises equipment
CEBus	Consumer electronics bus
CSMA/CD	Carrier Sense Multiple Access with Collision Detection
DVCR	Digital videocassette recorder
ETSI	European Telecommunications Standards Institute
HP	High-pass filter
HDB3	High-density bipolar three
IEEE	Institute of Electrical and Electronics Engineers
I/O	Input/output
ISA	Industry Standard Architecture (a PC bus standard)
ISDN	Integrated Services Digital Network
ITU	International Telecommunications Union
ITU G.703	*Physical/Electrical Characteristics of Hierarchical Digital Interfaces*
ITU G.704	*Synchronous Frame Structures Used at Primary and Secondary Hierarchy Levels*
LPF	Low-pass filter
MDSL	Moderate-speed digital subscriber line
NID	Network interface device
P1394	An IEEE serial bus standard
PC	Personal computer
PCI	Peripheral component interconnect
PCMCIA	Personal Computer Memory Card International Association
POTS	Plain Old Telephone Service
PSTN	Public Switched Telephone Network
RJ-45	10BaseT connector standard for connecting UTP cabling
TIA422	A medium-range (typically ≥300 m) serial data transmission standard
SONET	Synchronous Optical Network (a standard)
T1	A Telecommunications Standard Committee
T1.403	*Carrier to Customer Installation DS1 Metallic Interface*
T1.413-1995	*ANSI Standard for ADSL Modems*
T1E1.4	An ANSI committee for Interfaces, Network Power, and Protection Digital Subscriber Loop Access
TBD	To be determined
TE	Terminal equipment
TPA	P1394 signal link

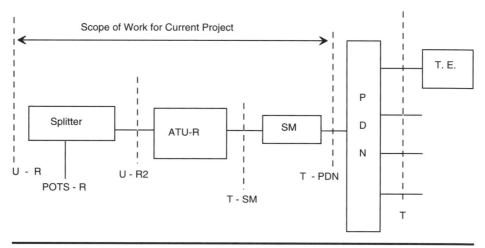

Figure 10.56 Customer-Premises-Specific Reference Model

TPB	P1394 signal link
TR41	User Premises Telecom Requirements Committee
TV	Television
UTP	Unshielded twisted pair (cable)
WT	Working text
WT-003	*Bit synchronous mode working text*

Consider Figure 10.56, which is a view of customer-premises-specific reference model, which is utilized in this project. The interfaces identified in this reference model are logical interfaces and not necessarily physical implementations. Physical topology and implementation are covered in later sections.

The premises end of a DSL link starts with the access line (twisted-pair telephone line) delineated in Figure 10.56 by the U-R interface, and ends with one or more pieces of terminal equipment (TE) (including but not limited to a personal computer or a television set) delineated (in Figure 10.56) by the T interface. The telephone line may or may not be used for Plain Old Telephone Service (POTS) as well as ADSL. If it is used for POTS, then the customer premises installation must include a POTS splitter that provides the POTS-R interface as well as the U-R_2 interface.

The ATU-R terminates the access line and provides digital signals at the T-SM interface. A service module (SM) may be installed to convert the received digital signals into signals suitable for a particular premises distribution network or TE at the T-PDN interface. The ATU-R and SM functionality may be integrated in a common device, obviating the need for the T-SM interface.

The U-R, POTS-R, U-R_2, T-SM, and T-PDN interfaces will be specified in this document.

Relevant work in other standards groups or forums

T1E1.4. ANSI committee T1E1.4 has approved, and ANSI has published, T1.413-1995, an Issue+1 standard for ADSL. T1.413-1995 does address POTS splitters (although not completely) but does not address premises wiring. Applicable work is incorporated by reference herein.

TR41. TR41 may be pursuing work related to a reference architecture, residential wiring, and a residential gateway. No specific information is available for the current issue of this document.

ATM Forum. The ATM Forum Residential Broadband (RBB) Group is working on a specification which includes a definition of an ATM-based customer premises distribution network.

Target applications and system implications

The primary applications supported by ADSL will be POTS and data communications and video on demand. These applications require the transport of packet data, ATM data, or bit synchronous data. The T-SM interface will depend on the application being supported.

In some cases, POTS may not be used, in which case the POTS splitter and POTS-R interface may not be needed. Serving these applications will likely involve connecting more than one TE within a premises, with the second, third, or more terminal connected at some time after the installation of the ADSL modem itself. Furthermore, the installation and use of the ADSL modem should be as simple as possible, with the most reuse of existing wiring as possible, and with the least amount of trouble in migrating from one TE to another as possible.

ATU-R/splitter installation

Conceptually, in the most common case to be considered, the installation of an ADSL modem requires breaking an existing telephone line with active POTS service and attached telephones, inserting a POTS splitter, and then reattaching the premises side POTS wiring back to the POTS splitter (see Figure 10.2, which depicts both logical and physical attributes). In the United States, a network interface device (NID, usually comprising surge protectors) establishes the physical demarcation between network and customer premises. The ability to install the POTS splitter prior to the ATU-R has particular appeal when the ATU-R is owned and installed by the user and not the network provider.

This project will only consider examples of installing the POTS splitter on the CPE side of the primary protection. Country-specific installations of POTS splitters may need to address additional safety regulations.

Consider Figure 10.57, which is a conceptual view of an ADSL ATU-R/splitter installation.

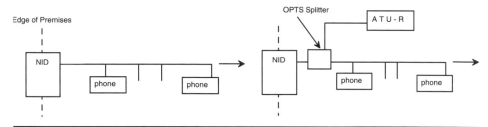

Figure 10.57 Conceptual ADSL ATU-R/Splitter Installation

POTS splitter

The *POTS splitter,* for the purposes of this project, is considered to be the device that splits the POTS signals from the ADSL signals, thus preventing the ADSL signals from reaching the telephone devices.

The POTS splitter may be

- Active or passive, representing the LPF and HPF sections or the LPF section only
- Adjacent to the NID or housed within the NID
- Adjacent to each telephone device, adjacent to the ATU-R, or integrated within the ATU-R

The low-pass filter (LPF) section contains circuitry that passes POTS frequencies (approximately 0 to 4 kHz) to and from the telephone equipment and blocks the ADSL signal. The POTS splitter (LPF-only variation) may allow for the complete spectrum, including the ADSL signals (above ~20 kHz) to pass to the ATU-R.

If a high-pass filter (HPF) section is needed to prevent low-frequency, high-level POTS signals from entering the ATU-R front-end components, the circuitry may be included in and be considered part of the ATU-R or the circuitry may be included as part of POTS splitter (along with the LPF).

ATU-R manufacturers should not assume that the HPF has been implemented external to their equipment. It is recommended that all manufacturers of ATU-R equipment plan on explicitly implementing the appropriate HPF.

POTS splitter characteristics. POTS splitter characteristics will not be specified in this text. Instead, the POTS splitter is used as an existing system component and is shown along with the other system components such as ATU-R and wiring to represent the configurations detailed in sections to follow.

The ANSI standard T1.413-1995 specifies the loop conditions under which the splitter and ADSL must be able to operate without causing significant degradation to the POTS signal, and these characteristics will be incorporated in this document by reference. Work applicable to the POTS splitters that is completed in other groups, such as ETSI or ITU, will be addressed when specifics are available.

ATU-R/splitter configurations.   Various ATU-R/splitter configurations are discussed here:

- ATU-R adjacent to TE with separate POTS splitter
- ATU-R adjacent to TE and split POTS splitter
- ATU-R adjacent to TE and distributed POTS splitter
- ATU-R with integral POTS splitter adjacent to NID
- ATU-R with integral POTS splitter adjacent to TE

A brief introduction for each configuration is presented along with a figure depicting both logical and physical attributes (topology and implementation). This is followed by a list of advantages and disadvantages for each configuration. These advantages and disadvantages can be utilized in order to choose the configuration that best suits the needs of any particular deployment.

A suggested list of criteria is provided below that, when used in conjunction with specific priorities or importance values (as determined by the provider), would allow a selection of the best configuration to be made for any particular ADSL system deployment.

Type of splitter: active or passive

Equipment ownership: customer- or network-owned splitter, ATU-R network demarcation point

Failure effects of splitter, ATU-R

Installation complexity

Testing and maintenance: splitter, ATU-R

ATU-R adjacent to TE with separate POTS splitter.   Figure 10.58 shows a configuration with the POTS splitter separate from the ATU-R. The POTS splitter mounts near the NID while the ATU-R is located at a more convenient installation location, perhaps next to the TE Wiring to the ATU-R may be existing or new, depending on the quality of the existing wire and the desired location of the ATU-R.

Figure 10.58 shows an ATU-R adjacent to TE and separate POTS splitter (LPF & HPF). Some of the following advantages are achieved as shown in Figure 10.58.

- Putting the ATU-R adjacent to or within TE ensures proximity to power.
- T-SM interface cabling will be short or nonexistent (integral to the TE).
- Accessibility: additional TE may be connected easily to the ATU-R.

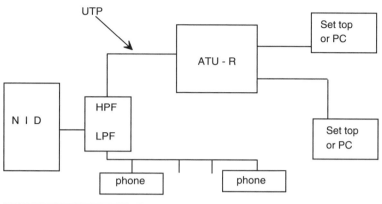

Figure 10.58 ATU-R Adjacent to Terminal Equipment and Separate POTS Splitter (LPF and HPF)

- The POTS splitter can be installed at some time before the ATU-R.

- This arrangement isolates the ADSL signal path wiring from the CP POTS wiring imperfections (bridged lines, nonstandard wiring gauges, etc.) and allows for the reduction of cross-coupled noise.

Disadvantages are

- In countries that require an active POTS splitter, the ATU-R may have to power the splitter over the line or another supply provided.

- Currently, a POTS splitter from one manufacturer won't necessarily work with the ADSL modem of another manufacturer. This is due primarily to the required characteristics of the HPF located in the ADSL signal path.

A variant on the POTS splitter is a system where the low-pass filter portion of the splitter is physically separate from the high-pass filter portion. Two logical configurations are shown in Figures 10.59 and 10.60. Figure 10.59 shows the configuration with the LPF located at the physical split in signal paths. This configuration is as efficient in isolating the premises POTS wiring from the ADSL signal path as the explicit integrated splitter shown in Figure 10.58; however, it offers an advantage because now each manufacture of ATU-R equipment has control of the HPF characteristics. (It is assumed that the LPF requirements are basically the same regardless of a manufacturer's ADSL implementation.)

This split POTS splitter configuration is the most prevalent configuration currently planned to be deployed.

Advantages of configuration shown in Figure 10.59 include

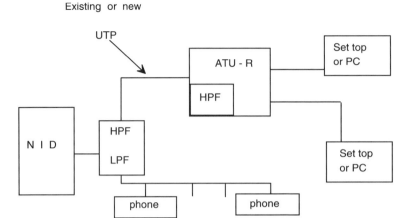

Figure 10.59 ATU-R (w/HPF) Adjacent to TE and Split POTS Splitter
(LPF and LPF-only)

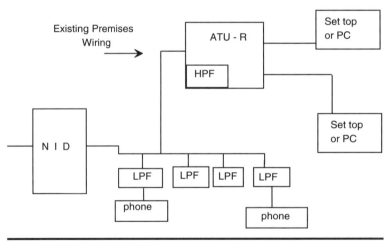

Figure 10.60 ATU-R (w/HPF) Adjacent to TE and Distributed (Split)
POTS Splitter (LPF-only)

- Putting the ATU-R adjacent to or within terminal equipment ensures proximity to power.
- T-SM interface cabling will be short or nonexistent (integral to the TE).
- Accessibility: additional TE may be connected easily to the ATU-R.
- The POTS splitter can be installed at some time before the ATU-R.
- This arrangement isolates the ADSL signal path wiring from the premises POTS wiring imperfections (bridged lines, nonstandard wiring gauges, etc.) and allows for the reduction of cross-coupled noise.

- It increases the probability of compatibility between different manufacturers of ATU-R equipment and LPF hardware.

Disadvantages of configuration shown in Figure 10.59 are

- In countries that require an active POTS splitter, the ATU-R may have to power the splitter over the line or another supply be provided.

Figure 10.60 shows a variant in which the high-pass filter is implemented within the ATU-R and low pass filters are installed in front of each telephone (distributed).

Advantages of configuration shown in Figure 10.60 are

- Putting the ATU-R adjacent to or within TE ensures proximity to power.
- T-SM interface cabling will be short or nonexistent (integral to the TE).
- Accessibility: additional TE may be connected easily to the ATU-R.
- The POTS splitter(s) can be installed at some time before the ATU-R.
- This arrangement increases the probability of compatibility between different manufacturers of ATU-R equipment and LPF hardware.
- It obviates reconfiguration of customer premises wiring entirely.

Disadvantages of configuration shown in Figure 10.60 are

- In countries that require an active POTS splitters, the ATU-R may have to power the splitter over the line or another supply be provided.
- Customer premises wiring becomes a potential bridging network that can cause frequency response discontinuities and is a factor in determining ATU-R performance. The exact nature of the network frequency response is dependent on the installation wiring each individual CP.
- Improper installation of the LPF at each phone, or the omission of the LPF, can cause significant termination problems on the network, which, in turn, can have an impact on ATU-R performance.
- Use of unbalanced line within the CP POTS wiring network can result in additional noise ingress into the ATU-R signal spectrum.
- Increased mechanical installation complexities are involved (i.e., wall phones).

Figure 10.61 shows the installation with the ATU-R adjacent to or close to (within 5 m) the NID. Except for short stubs to connector blocks, this configuration requires no new telephone wiring at the U interface, but will usually require some longer cabling for the T-SM interface.

Advantages of arrangement shown in Figure 10.61 are

- ADSL signals pass over virtually no preexisting premises telephone wiring, thus minimizing potential premises wiring related problems.

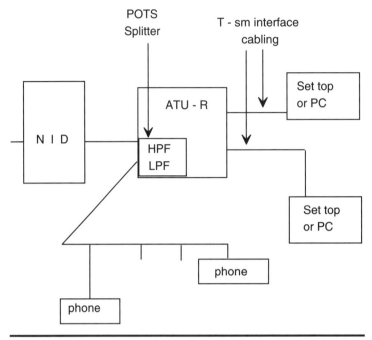

Figure 10.61 ATU-R with Integral POTS Splitter (LPF and HPF) Adjacent to NID

Disadvantages are

- NIDs and entrance telephone wiring are usually not favorably located for access to power.

- ATU-Rs placed in attics, basements, garages, or outside premises may be subject to environmental extremes.

- The installation complexity and length of the T-SM interface wiring to the TE (which potentially limits the use of some of the premises distribution networks currently in use).

Figure 10.62 shows a configuration with the ATU-R adjacent to one TE and therefore likely removed from the NID by as much as 100 ft. This installation requires cutting the telephone line just after the NID, connecting it to the ATU-R over new or existing premises telephone wiring, and then reconnecting the POTS output to the premises telephone system originally serviced by the wire from the NID. In addition, any telephone connected at the ATU-R location must be reconnected on the POTS side.

Advantages of arrangement shown in Figure 10.62 are

- Putting the ATU-R adjacent to or within TE ensures proximity to power.

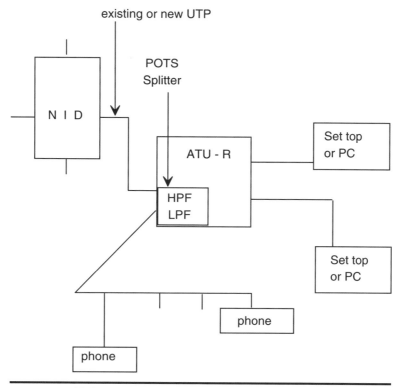

Figure 10.62   ATU-R with Integral POTS Splitter (LPF and HPF) Adjacent to TE

- T-SM interface cabling will be short or non-existent (integral to the TE).

- Accessibility: additional TE may be connected easily to the ATU-R.

- This configuration enables a self-contained ADSL NIC for PCs or set-top boxes (POTS is supported via integral POTS splitter).

- This provides good topology for customer-owned (and -powered) POTS splitter (active).

Disadvantages are

- The premises telephone service now connects through the ATU-R, which could accidentally be disconnected from the line, severing POTS service.

- This configuration may require diverse routing of two wire pairs in order to reduce crosstalk.

- This does not provide good topology for network owned (and powered) POTS splitter (active).

ATU-R deployed without POTS service

In cases where there is no requirement to support existing or new POTS service in addition to deployment of ADSL, installation becomes less complex. Following the example of the preferred configuration, the ATU-R should be located as close as practical to the CPE. In some cases new wiring may need to be installed from the telephone line at the NID or other demarcation to the location where the ATU-R is to be connected.

U-R, POTS-R, and U-R$_2$ interfaces

Wiring. Recent telephone company experience suggests that the quality of in-home wiring varies so much, and that so much of it falls below a level suitable for ADSL transmission, that new wiring of some form or another will be the rule rather than the exception. However, some of the configurations shown (in Section 3.3 of this ADSL Forum document) may have reused existing premises wiring.

New wiring. If new wiring is pulled, it should be UTP Category 5 as specified in EIA/TIA 570. A wall plate shall be installed to terminate the new wiring for DSL.

Interference and the use of existing wiring. The running of ADSL signals and POTS signals together through a single two-pair cable, cross-couples POTS noises generated by ringing, trip ringing, pulse dialing, and hook switch signaling into the low level ADSL receive signals. Studies have shown that just a few feet of adjacent wiring causes cross-coupling of sufficient magnitude to cause errors in received data. This problem could be reduced by the high-pass filtering in the ATU-R. This liability is also mitigated by error control protocols and by interleaving (the noise appears as impulses), but must be recognized as having potential effects on quality of service. However, there is also concern that there may be detrimental effects (unacceptable noise in the telephone user's ear) from cross-coupling of ADSL signals into the post splitter POTS lines. This potential for crosstalk may affect voiceband usage that extends near 4000 Hz such as with V_{pcm} or other high-speed voiceband modems.

U-R. Screw terminals or RJ-11 jack/plug as required by specific configuration wired to center pair (pins 3 and 4).

POTS-R. Screw terminals or RJ-11 jack/plug as required by specific configuration wired to center pair (pins 3 and 4).

Connections for the ATU-R

External POTS splitter. The U-R2 connector at the wall jack shall be RJ-14 (sometimes known as *RJ-11, 4-wire*) with ADSL wired to pins 2 and 5. POTS (optional) will be wired to pins 3 and 4. This wiring precludes the use of a POTS second line on a wire pair connected to pins 2 and 5 for this particular wall jack.

In cases where wiring other than UTP Category 5 is being used, the ADSL signal path from the POTS splitter to the U-R$_2$ connector at the wall jack must be isolated in a separate sheath. This may require a new cable run.

Internal POTS splitter. The U-R$_2$ connector at the wall jack shall be as specified in the physical characteristics section of ANSI T1.413-1995.

T-SM interface

If the ATU-R is merely implementing the basic functions of a bit pump, an external T-SM interface will be necessary to interconnect the ATU-R to a separate service module. This interface will have to carry those data, timing and control signals necessary to permit operation of a variety of services which may be carried on the ADSL link.

The minimum signal set will be one downstream data circuit plus its clock and one upstream data circuit plus its clock. A number of optional signals may be supported for particular applications:

1. *Secondary data channels:* These may be simplex or duplex channels and will always have an associated clock. Some duplex channels may have a common clock.

2. *Auxiliary data timing signals:* Some channels may require an out-of-band frame or byte start signal which is extracted from the ADSL framing structure.

3. *Network timing reference:* Some service modules may require the 8-kHz timing reference when this is carried by the ADSL link.

4. *Control and status circuits:* The ATU-R and service module may each be required to control the other and/or to receive status indications. These may be global signals or be channel-associated.

A basic interface providing the minimum signal set on an RJ-45 connector is specified here where this is sufficient. It is recommended that interfaces which provide additional signals use one of the existing ISO data communications interfaces. The data rate of ADSL equipment requires that only those interfaces using balanced circuits should be used. Suitable interfaces are ISO.4903 (X.21), ISO.2110-Amd1 (TIA.530), and ISO.2593 (V.35). The use of such interfaces will allow existing data communications equipment to connect to an ATU-R without modification. Guidelines are given below as to the mapping of the T-SM signals onto these interfaces.

Signal specifications

Each simplex data channel consists of one data circuit (DD or DU) and one clock circuit (CD or CU). The clocks are normally generated by the ATU-R, but in some instances the upstream clock (CU) may be generated by the SM. These clocks should have a nominal 50 percent duty cycle at the maximum data rate. Extended OFF periods may be inserted when burst clocking is being used. The downstream data are generated by the ATU-R and the upstream data by the SM. The data are NRZ (non-return-to-zero)-encoded with the OFF and ON states representing logic 1 and 0, respectively. Data changes state at OFF-to-ON clock transitions, with the receiver strobing the data at ON-to-OFF clock transitions.

In addition to the clock and data signals, each channel or group of channels may have other signals associated with them. ATU-R and SM equipment not generating these signals shall leave these circuits unconnected, and equipment receiving these signals shall provide pullups/pulldowns so as to force an ON state in the event of an undriven input.

The channel-associated signals may include

1. *Data qualifier (QD or QU)*: A signal driven by the data source to indicate valid data on its transmitter. This signal may be used in place of, or in addition to, burst clocking.

2. *Channel control (CC)*: A signal generated by the SM to enable channel(s).

3. *Channel indication (CI)*: A signal generated by the ATU-R to indicate that channel(s) are in a data-forwarding state.

4. *Byte sync (BS)*: A signal generated by the ATU-R to provide a data alignment signal for byte-structured channels such as G.711 PCM. This signal shall transition from OFF to ON on the byte boundary and may transition from ON to OFF at any other bit boundary.

5. *Frame sync (FS)*: A signal generated by the ATU-R to provide data alignment for frame-structured channels which do not have an embedded frame delimiter. This signal shall transition from OFF to ON at the frame boundary and may transition from ON to OFF at any other bit boundary.

6. *Network timing reference (NR)*: This is a signal with a frequency of 8 kHz, which may be carried by some ADSL links.

Global control and indication signals may be used which relate to the entire ADSL link:

1. *Equipment status (SD or SU)*: A signal generated by either equipment to indicate that it is operational and to qualify all other signals.

2. *Link control (LC)*: A signal generated by the SM to enable the ADSL link.

3. *Link indication (LI)*: A signal generated by the ATU-R to indicate that the ADSL link is operational.

These notes are applicable to the previous items:

1. In both the above lists, item 1 is an alternative to 2 plus 3. This equates to the alternative definitions of circuit 108 in ITU-T V.24 as either *data terminal ready* or *connect data set to line*.

2. Where only one pair of channels is supported, *channel control/indication* and *link control/indication* are essentially the same signals.

3. No signals related to flow control or SM-sourced clocks are specified. It cannot be assumed that an ATU-R is capable of either flow control or speed buffering, and therefore all data flow must be slaved to the ATU-R clocks. Where SM equipment needs such facilities, they should be provided internally by the SM.

ISO interfaces and connectors

All these interfaces provide one downstream and one upstream channel plus clocks and control signals. The ISO.4903 (X.21) interface uses a 15-pole D connector and supports two control circuits and two timing circuits. The ISO.2110-Amd1 (TIA.530) interface uses either a 25-pole D connector or a 26-pole miniature connector and supports more control circuits. The ISO.2593 (V.35) is an obsolete interface but which is still commonly used. It uses a 34-pole connector and supports the same signal set as ISO.2110.

Where ATU-R and SM have different interfaces, interworking by means of an adapter cable will be possible on circuits where both transmitter and receiver are balanced (which is true for data and clocks on all these interfaces) or where a satisfactory unbalanced to balanced conversion can be made. The ISO and ITU-T standards documents address this issue in more detail.

In the ADSL context, the ATU-R is the DCE and will have female connectors, and the SM is the DTE with male connectors. Mapping of T-SM signals to V.24 and X.24 signals is suggested as follows:

T-SM	V.24	X.24	Notes
DD	104 (RXD)	R	
DU	103 (TXD)	T	
CD	115 (RXC)	S	
CU	113 or 114 (TXC)	X	3
QD	109 (DCD)	C	
QU	105 (RTS)	I	
CC	109 (DCD)	C	
CI	105 (RTS)	I	
SD	107 (DSR)	C	
SU	108/2 (DTR)	I	
LC	108/1 (DTR)	C	
LI	107 (DSR)	I	
BS	106 (CTS)	B	2
FS	106 (CTS)	F	2
NR	106 (CTS)	X	1,2

RELATED NOTES:

1. For this application, the X signal is driven by the DCE toward the DTE.

2. The CTS circuit does not have its usual function as these are timing signals. It was chosen because it is a balanced signal on the ISO.2110-Amd1 interface. When the B, F, or X circuit is used to carry these signals, it can only be on either a simplex channel or a full-duplex channel pair with identical data rate as circuit S will need to be a common clock.

3. Where CU is generated by the ATU-R, the X signal is driven by the DCE toward the DTE.

Basic RJ-45 interface. A data-and-clocks-only interface, providing one down-stream channel plus one upstream channel, can be implemented using an RJ-45 plug. The drivers and receivers should conform to ITU-T V.11 (TIA-422) and be connected as shown:

CDa   Pin #1

CDb   Pin #2

DUa   Pin #3

CUa   Pin #4

CUb   Pin #5

DUb   Pin #6

DDa   Pin #7

DDb   Pin #8

The previous correlates the RJ-45 plug for the T-SM Interface. It may be necessary to use screened RJ-45 jacks, plugs, and cables to meet radiated emissions requirements.

T-PDN interfaces: existing premises distribution networks. With the addition of a service module, the T-SM interface may be converted to a more commonly available interface. When the ATU-R and SM functions are integrated into one device, the T-SM interface will disappear at the physical level and the applicable interface then becomes the T-PDN.

The premises distribution networks (PDNs) included in the body of this issue will be some of the commonly available PDNs in use for bit synchronous (serial interface data communications) mode, packet mode, and ATM mode of operation. Evolving PDNs are presented in Annex B (of ADSL Forum document) for reference only.

Bit synchronous interfaces. Terminal equipment such as routers or set-top boxes may support some of the more common serial interface data communications connections (DTE interfaces) at the T-PDN interface. The terminal equipment "expects" the device attached at the T-PDN interface to act as data-communications equipment (DCE).

The following specifications are incorporated in this document by reference and will not be further discussed here:

- TIA-530 or V.35 (ISO 2593): for high-speed serial DTE interface

- T1: 1.544 Mbps ANSI T1.403

- E1: 2.048 Mbps ITU G.703/G.704

Ethernet 10BaseT interface. The following specifications are incorporated in this document by reference and will not be discussed further here:

- 10BaseT on a RJ-45 connector

- Ethernet version 2.0: a *CSMA/CD Local Area Network Specification*

- ANSI/IEEE 802.3, *CSMA/CD Access Method and Physical Layer Specifications*

ATM25 interface. The following specification is incorporated in this document by reference and will not be discussed further here:

- The ATM Forum Technical Committee, *Physical Interface Specification for 25.6 Mbps over Twisted Pair Cable af-phy-0040.000,* Nov. 1995 on a Media Interface Connector specified in ISO/IEC 603-7 (commonly referred to as RJ-45)

Reference model. Consider Figure 10.63, which presents the ADSL Forum system reference model for ADSL network systems. The following terms are used in Figure 10.63.

access node Concentration point for broadband and narrowband data. The access node may be located at a central office or a remote site. Also, a remote access node may subtend from a central access node.

ATU-C ADSL transmission unit at the central office end. The ATU-C may be integrated within an access node.

ATU-R ADSL transmission unit at the customer premises end.

B Auxiliary data input (such as a satellite feed) to service module (such as a set-top box).

broadcast Broadband data input in simplex mode (typically broadcast video).

broadband network Switching system for data rates above 1.5/2.0 Mbps.

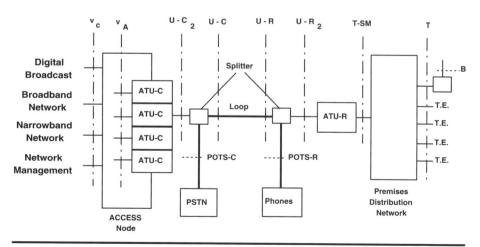

Figure 10.63 System Reference Model

loop   Twisted-pair copper telephone line.

narrowband network   Switching system for data rates at or below 1.5/2.0 Mbps.

POTS   Plain Old Telephone Service.

POTS-C   Interface between PSTN and POTS splitter at network end.

POTS-R   Interface between phones and POTS splitter at premises end.

premises distribution network (PDN)   System for connecting ATU-R to service modules. May be point-to-point or multipoint; may be passive wiring or an active network. Multipoint may be a bus or star.

PSTN   Public Switched Telephone Network.

service module (SM)   Performs terminal adaptation functions. Examples are set-top boxes, PC interfaces, or LAN routers.

splitter   Filters which separate high-frequency (ADSL) and low-frequency (POTS) signals at CO end and premises end. The splitter may be integrated into the ATU, physically separated from the ATU, or divided between high-pass and low-pass, with the low-pass function physically separated from the ATU. The provision of POTS splitters and POTS-related functions is optional.

T   Interface between PDN and SMs. May be same as T-SM when network is point-to-point passive wiring. Note that T interface may disappear at the physical level when ATU-R is integrated within an SM.

T-SM   Interface between ATU-R and PDN. May be same as T when network is point-to-point passive wiring. An ATU-R may have more than one type of T-SM interface implemented (e.g., a T1/E1 connection and an Ethernet connection).

U-C   Interface between loop and ATU-C (analog). Defining both ends of the loop interface separately arises because of the asymmetry of the signals on the line.

U-C$_2$ Interface between POTS splitter and ATU-C. Note that at present ANSI T1.413 does not define such an interface and separating the POTS splitter from the ATU-C presents some technical difficulties in standardizing this interface.

U-R   Interface between loop and ATU-R (analog).

U-R$_2$ Interface between POTS splitter and ATU-R. Note that at present ANSI T1.413 does not define such an interface and separating the POTS splitter from the ATU-R presents some technical difficulties in standardizing the interface.

V$_A$ Logical interface between ATU-C and access node. As this interface will often be within circuits on a common board, the ADSL Forum does not consider physical V$_A$ interfaces. The V interface may contain STM, ATM, or both transfer modes. In the primitive case of point-point connection between a switch port and an ATU-C (i.e., a case without concentration or multiplexing), then the V$_A$ and V$_C$ interfaces become identical (alternatively, the V$_A$ interface disappears).

V$_C$ Interface between access node and network. May have multiple physical connections (as shown) although may also carry all signals across a single physical connection. A digital carrier facility (e.g., a SONET or SDH extension) may be interposed at the V$_C$ interface when the access node and ATU-Cs are located at a remote site.

Interface to the PSTN may be a universal tip-ring interface or a multiplexed telephony interface such as specified in Bellcore TR-08 or TR-303. The broadband segment of the V_C interface may be STM switching, ATM switching, or private-line-type connections.

Evolving premises distribution networks

The information presented here is informative and is included to provide insight into the possible use of emerging PDNs for use with ADSL systems. It is not exclusive of other possible PDNs, but provides guidance as to how these emerging PDNs may be used in conjunction with ADSL access at the customer premises.

A high-speed digital home network serving the needs of ADSL signal distribution and digital information distribution from other local or network resources can be implemented on a high-quality unshielded twisted-pair wiring system. This type of infrastructure has been proposed by the CEBus (consumer electronics bus) committee which recommends the installation of Category 5 unshielded twisted-pair cable in a star topology for both voice and data transmission purposes. Category 5 unshielded twisted-pair cable is also the transmission media for 100BaseTX Ethernet and several other systems. Such an infrastructure would be suitable for the ATM-based system being proposed by the ATM Forum. Two other possible systems which use different media are described.

IEEE 1394 (Firewire).   The IEEE 1394 is an IEEE serial bus standard originally designed for the interconnection of computer peripheral devices. The 1394 standard defines a serial interface which can be used to replace traditional PC parallel, serial, or SCSI bus. The 1394 could be very effective at interconnecting the new generation high-capacity and high-speed storage and I/O devices. The 1394 standard is designed to handle both isochronous and asynchronous data transmission. A 1394-based PDN can be used to distribute ADSL traffic for both data access and video-on-demand applications, subject to the limitations described below.

The current 1394 standard requires the use of a special-purpose shielded twisted-pair cable. The twisted pair cable consists of two data pairs and one power pair. Each data pair is individually shielded and three pairs are then all shielded together. Hence, there are two signal links (TPA, TPB) on a physical connection. A typical 1394 twisted-pair cable is only about 4.5 m long. That cable length may be just long enough for connecting a local cluster of equipment together, but may be insufficient to provide interconnection between rooms. There is activity aimed at producing a longer-reach version of IEEE 1394, a subworking group has produced a draft document.

This PDN should have a star topology with a 1394 root device at the center of the star, but daisy chaining of 1394 devices is also permitted. Other data traffic from in-house or other access networks can also be shared on this

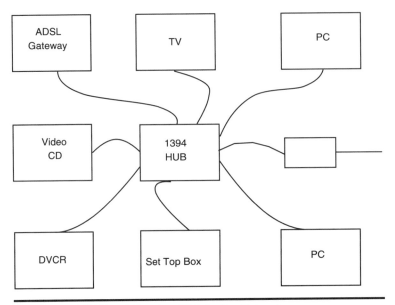

Figure 10.64 1394-Based Premises Distribution Network

PDN. A gateway/router is used to connect the ADSL to this PDN, but may require a longer reach technology. Consider Figure 10.64.

The Universal Serial Bus (USB) standard was originally designed around the PC architecture for the connection of telephony devices such as telephone/fax/modem adapters, answering machines, scanners as well as PDAs (personal digital assistants), keyboards, and mice. The standard was specified and the standard document is available through the USB Forum. Additional assistance is also available through the membership of the Forum. The USB can be used to handle isochronous data transmission. A USB-based PDN might be used to distribute ADSL traffic for both data access and video on demand applications.

The current USB standard requires the use of a 28-AWG shielded twisted-pair cable with a nontwisted power distribution pair of a variable gauge ranging from 20 to 28 AWG. The shielding covers both signal and power distribution pairs. The maximum transmission throughput is 12 Mbps for a maximum cable length of 5 m. A nonshielded cable can also be used for sub-channel (where the transmission rate is 1.5 Mbps) applications.

Data are carried over a USB in packets. The USB employs NRZI data encoding when transmitting packets.

USB topology. A USB is configured around a host, normally a PC, with devices attached directly or through hubs. A hub can connect a host to multiple devices. All devices are logically connected to the host. There are three layers of communication links between a host and its devices. Figure 10.65

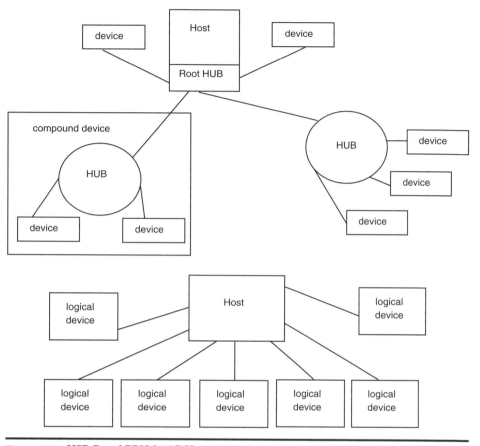

Figure 10.65 USB-Based PDN for ADSL

illustrates the USB (a dedicated ADSL USB host). USB physical topology is shown in the upper portion of the diagram; logical topology, in the lower portion.

TR41 residential gateway. No specific information is available at this time.

1. Out-of-band signaling tones may need to be passed in some applications (this is outside the scope of this document).

2. Cross-coupled noise would again become a factor if a telephone at the set top or PC uses the same cable for connection back to house telephone wiring.

3. Cross-coupled noise would again become a factor if a telephone at the set top or PC uses the same cable for connection back to house telephone wiring.

4. The frequency response discontinuities manifest themselves as increased insertion loss notches and lower than expected ATU-R line termination impedances. The latter can upset the ATU-R hybrid networks by introducing driving impedances that can be 50 percent or more lower than expected.

10.9   Default VPI/VCI Addresses for FUNI Mode Transport: Packet Mode

This section reflects the information contained in the ADSL Forum reports that specifies the default values for VPI/VCI pairs when used in the ADSL Forum FUNI mode transport for frames over an ADSL Link.

Introduction

This information defines the default values for VPI/VCI pairs to be used in the absence of any other FUNI address selection mechanism when transporting frames over an ADSL link using FUNI mode [1]. It is intended to complete the required portion in the third report from the ADSL Forum on address assignment. This is section reflects just one piece of information in the series topics related by way of the ADSL Forum.

Existing documents include *Framing and Encapsulations Standards for ADSL: Packet Mode.* Future documents cited in the information presented here constitute a specification series and will describe

- Packet-mode reference model
- Packet-mode service model examples
- Address management for FUNI mode transport (this document)
- Channelization for DMT and CAP ADSL line codes (WT-017)
- Signaling for SVC setup
- Management requirements

This series of ADSL documents is required to insure multivendor interoperability for ADSL links.

VPI/VCI assignments

The values defined below should be used for transporting FUNI frames across an ADSL link. Other addresses for end-to-end ATM transport should follow existing ATM Forum standards that reserve and specify certain VPI/VCI values.

Data transport

In the absence of any data channel address mechanism and for implementations supporting a single data session, an ADSL endpoint operating in FUNI mode MUST transfer user data using the default $VPI = 1$ and $VCI = 32$ values in the FUNI address field. Provisioning may be used to select one or more alternative VPI/VCI values for any user data transport.

Specific channel

The vendor-specific channel defined in Section 4.4 of [1] MUST be carried in FUNI frames with $VPI = 1$, VCI = 33 values in the FUNI address fields. This VPI/VCI pair is reserved and MUST NOT be used for any other purpose when operating in FUNI mode.

Frame layer management channel

Information related to the performance and configuration of the framing (FUNI) layer MUST be carried in FUNI frames with $VP = 0$ as required for OAM cells.

Reference

ADSL Forum: *Framing and Encapsulations Standards for ADSL: Packet Mode.*

10.10   Channelization for DMT and CAP ADSL Line Codes: Packet Mode

This section specifies the use of physical media dependent–channelization required to implement packet-mode data transport over discrete multitone and carrierless AM/PM ADSL systems.

Introduction

Specific uses of the channelization capabilities for two common ADSL physical layer implementations as required for transport of frames across an ADSL link are discussed here. This report describes such channelization for the user data paths only; management and other channels are defined in the relevant PMD standards. This specification refers directly to existing and developing standards defined by the ANSI T1E1 subcommittee. Specifically, it defines channelization standards for systems implemented using the T1.413 DMT standard [1] and systems designed around the CAP line code and being defined by the CAP/QAM RADSL ad hoc group.

This information reflects that which is a series of ADSL Forum technical reports that address transferring variable length frames over an ADSL link. Existing documents include *Framing and Encapsulations Standards for ADSL: Packet Mode.* Future documents in this specification series will describe the following:

- Packet-mode reference model
- Packet-mode service model examples
- Address management for FUNI mode transport (WT-016)

- Channelization for DMT and CAP ADSL line codes (this document)
- Signaling for SVC setup
- Management requirements

The purpose for the documents available from the ADSL Forum is to ensure multivendor interoperability for ADSL links.

Discrete multitone (DMT) PMD specifics

This information proposes a channelization scheme for use in packet mode ADSL equipment using the ANSI T1.413 DMT PMD layer. For packet-mode systems, the channelization of different payload formats is handled using the ANSI T1.413 standards simplex and duplex channels. The following channels are defined for packet-mode operation:

- One required data channel using AS0 downstream and LS0 upstream
- One optional data channel using AS1 downstream and LS1 upstream

For the transport of frames over DMT-PMD ADSL, all modems MUST use the AS0 channel downstream and the LS0 channel upstream. Channel AS1 may be used to provide an additional downstream channel, and LS1 may be used to provide an additional upstream channel. Any channel may operate over the fast or interleaved paths.

A "hybrid" implementation of one or more bit synchronous (plesiochronous) channels together with the packet-mode channels is not precluded by the above. The bandwidth occupied by the bit synchronous channel must first be reserved before allocating the remaining bandwidth to the packet channel. Simultaneous hybrid operation of packet mode and ATM mode over an ADSL line is precluded by this specification.

Carrierless AM/PM (CAP) PMD specifics

The CAP-PMD defines a single downstream data channel and a single upstream data channel. All higher-layer RFC 1662 and FUNI data frames should be mapped to these interfaces. For the transport of data link frames in RFC 1662 or FUNI mode, all frames MUST be sent over the asymmetric downstream and upstream channels as currently specified.

References

ANSI T1.413-1995, Issue 1, *Telecommunications: Network and Customer Installation Interfaces and Asymmetric Digital Subscriber Line (ADSL) Metallic Interface.*
ANSI T1E1/97-228, *Interface Specification Recommendation for Carrierless AM/PM (CAP) Based Rate Adaptive Digital Subscriber Line (RADSL) Circuits—Baseline Text Proposal.*

10.11   Requirements and Reference Models for
ADSL Access Networks

This section outlines architectural requirements and reference models for ADSL services and service providers. Specifically, it defines target applications, various domain ownership, and requirements of different architectures.

Introduction

The Service Network Architecture Group (SNAG) was formed at the Orlando (Fla.) meeting on June 18, 1996. The objectives of this group were to compile architecture options, requirements, and reference models for several key ADSL applications, and identify various issues associated with each architecture.

It was not expected that this group could identify the optimal architecture, for it was recognized that no architecture would be universally optimal for all carriers. Carriers choose architectures based on not only technical issues but also such considerations as business strategy, economics, and regulatory concerns that are outside the expertise of SNAG membership and outside the scope of this document.

In addition, it became increasingly clear as the work of the ADSL Forum continued that there was significant overlap between what the SNAG was attempting to do and the work of the packet and ATM groups. The board of directors thus made a decision to merge the packet- and cell-based work of the SNAG into the packet and ATM groups, respectively. The requirements and model work which the SNAG team had developed are presented in this section.

SNAG terminology

In this document several terms are used to signify requirements which are often capitalized.

MUST: This word, or the adjective required, means that the definition is an absolute requirement of the specification.

MUST NOT: This phrase means that the definition is an absolute prohibition of the specification.

SHOULD: This word, or the adjective recommended, means that there may exist valid reasons in particular circumstances to ignore this item, but that the full implications must be understood and carefully weighted before choosing a different course.

MAY: This word, or the adjective optional, means that this item is one of an allowed set of alternatives. An implementation that does not include this option, MUST be prepared to interoperate with another implementation, which does include the option.

Revision history

First skeleton draft	9/1/96; 0.2
Extended options and limited discussion on issues	10/1/96; 0.3
Added text from London meeting	2/1/97; 0.4
Very minor edits after the Seattle meeting	4/21/97; 0.5
Several rewrites agreed to in Amsterdam	6/17/97; 0.6
Agreements from Boston meeting	9/17/97; 0.7
Final agreements from Brussels meeting	1/26/98; 0.8

Target applications

SNAG chose to consider the most likely applications for ADSL services as Internet access and remote LAN access. However, it was decided not to preclude a richer set. Internet access can be for either business customers with multiple PCs or residential customers with one or two PCs. Typically one Internet service provider (ISP) that is selected at the service subscription time services an ADSL subscriber. Dynamic connections to multiple destinations are supported with the regular Internet technology through the ISP. Similar to the Internet access case, remote LAN access may be required by residential subscribers for telecommuting or by a business LAN for corporate private network. Multiple concurrent connection is a requirement for remote LAN access. For instance, three branch offices need to be connected in a mesh topology. Both Internet and remote LAN access may be required simultaneously by ADSL subscribers. The scenarios described above, where multiple connections are simultaneously open from one user access point, present a potential security issue. This is due to the fact that traffic from one service provider access point can be funneled to the other either knowingly or unknowingly by the user's end system. See the section on security for further notes on this potential. To provide a reference perspective within which to specify a set of requirements and describe interactions, a SNAG logical reference model was developed by the members of the SNAG group. Consider Figure 10.66, which shows several views of an architecture based on the domain ownership, such as who owns the components of the architecture outside the user perspective. In this reference model, the ATU-R is located in the premises domain and the ATU-C is located in the access domain. Following is a list of the acronyms used above:

ANI	Access network interface
NAP	Network access provider
NSP	Network service provider
NTP	Network transport provider
POP	Point of presence

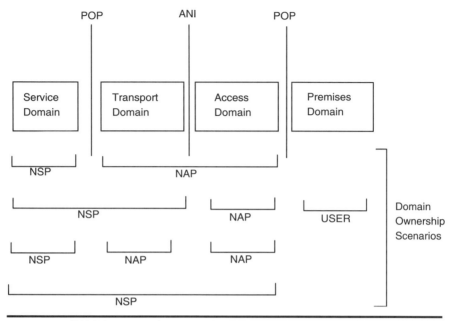

Figure 10.66 SNAG Domain Reference Model

Requirements for ADSL architectures

This section lists the generic requirements of an end-to-end ADSL network. Each requirements is described and then further broken down in terms of how the requirement specifically affects the user, NAP, NTP, and NSP.

- *Privacy:* Privacy needs to be a key attribute of the access and backbone domains. The existing narrowband world typically defines privacy as that provided by the PSTN via circuit switching and a unique physical connection between the central office and the home.

- *User specifics:* Traffic directed to one user premise network MUST NOT be present on another user premise network.

- *NAP specifics:* A NAP MUST provide a unique and private connection between a user and an NSP but otherwise be uninvolved in implementing privacy policy. A NAP MUST NOT be prohibited from offering value added services such as private user groups.

- *NSP specifics:* The NSP needs flexibility in its ability to specify and implement a privacy policy. At a minimum, this encompasses interconnect, premise to premise, and NSP to NSP.

- *Ability to support private address plans:* A user may have business relationships with multiple NSPs. Each NSP may have its own address plan and the user network may also have a private address plan.

User specifics: Users with private local address plans MUST NOT be prohibited from connecting to an NSP with a separately administered address plan. In addition, switching service sessions between separately administered NSP domains MUST be seamless to the user.

NAP specifics: A NAP MUST seamlessly and transparently support sessions between separately administered user and NSP domains.

NSP specifics: An NSP MUST have the ability to serve users with private address plans. Previous sessions of users with separately administered NSPs MUST NOT affect a session with a new NSP.

- *Service selection:* Service selection deals with the user's ability to seamlessly access an NSP.

User specifics: A user MUST have the ability to seemlessly select and connect to multiple NSPs. It should be noted that multiple simultaneous connections to NSPs can expose a potential security risk.

- *Regulatory compliance:* Access frequently, but not always, occurs across a regulated domain. In this scenario, a mechanism whereby a user can choose a destination must be provided. There is an expectation that the network interface at the ATU-R, including all communication to realize a connection to a service providers point-of-presence must be able to be disclosed.

User specifics: A user MUST be able to connect to an NSP in a standard way.

NAP specifics: A regulated NAP MUST comply with local regulatory requirements. These are outside the scope of this document.

- *Session control:* Given that a session between a user and an NSP access may involve the consumption of scarce resources on the NSP's part, and business and billing models may reflect this, the user should have a mechanism to signal intent to the NSP to initiate and terminate a session.

User specifics: A user MUST have a method of explicitly setting up and tearing down a session. The user SHOULD be notified when a session is terminated by a NAP or NSP. This notification may be generated by mechanisms local to the premise.

NAP specifics: A NAP MUST be able to detect if a contracted session service between a user and an NSP is being delivered and where appropriate perform resource recovery.

NSP specifics: An NSP MUST know when a user is attempting access and have the ability to accept or reject the connection.

- *Session negotiation and configuration:* An end-to-end connection between a user and an NSP may require negotiation and configuration. For example, temporary network addresses and server information may have to be exchanged. Such negotiation and configuration should be supported.

User specifics: A user MUST have the ability to negotiate and configure session parameters with an NSP. This capability MUST be available on a session-by-session basis.

NSP specifics: An NSP MUST be able to negotiate and configure session parameters with a user. This capability MUST be available on a session-by-session basis.

- *Simultaneous access to multiple NSPs:* In some situations, it is expected that multiple users on a premise network will share a single ADSL link. An ADSL network should allow for multiple sessions over the ADSL link to the same or different NSP.

User specifics: A user on a premise network MUST be able to access an NSP destination via the ADSL link regardless of whether one or more users on the same premise network are simultaneously accessing the same or another NSP destination. A single user MAY be able to access more than one NSP at a time. This is commonly known as *multihoming.*

NAP specifics: The NAP MUST be able to provide multiple connections to the same user domain.

NSP specifics: The NSP MUST be able to terminate more than one connection from the same user.

- *Minimal interworking:* Maximizing throughput of intermediate systems requires that a minimum of massaging of the data and a minimum of frame/packet hops occurs between the home domain and the service domain.

NAP specifics: It is desirable that the service offered by the NAP be as transparent as possible in order to not be an impediment to services offered by the NSP.

- *Service independence:* The premise to POP protocol may vary over the different sessions carried by a NAP.

NAP specifics: The NAP MUST be transparent to the actual network protocol supported by the user and the NSP.

- *Service tiering:* The NAP, NTP, and NSP require the ability to differentiate between the transport and access services that they provide to the user. This would be in the form of bandwidth and transit guarantees within the backbone and access domains. Ideally, this could be dynamically administered to provide different grades of service on a per-service or flow basis.

User specifics: The user SHOULD be able to administer their service quality.

NAP specifics: The NAP SHOULD be able to provide differentiated services.

NSP specifics: The NSP SHOULD be able to provide differentiated services.

- *Authentication:* The mechanisms must be provided to ensure that the user, NAP, and NSP can have a high degree of confidence with whom they are dealing. The existing narrowband world supports mutual authentication as follows. The users access an NSP via a well-known network identifier (telephone number) which uniquely identifies the service accessed.

User specifics: A user SHOULD connect to an NSP via a well-known, unique network identifier.

NAP specifics: A NAP may or may not want to do authentication. Authentication in the NAP MUST NOT be artificially prohibited.

NSP specifics: An NSP MUST be provided with a mechanism to identify and authenticate a user. For session-oriented access, this is typically done through a username and user password for always on authentication the authentication is coupled to the physical or logical connectivity (e.g., PVC vs. copper).

- *NAP and NSP accounting needs:* Flexible billing options are necessary at both the NAP and NSP. Both parties should be able to extract appropriate information to authoritatively bill their end users with a minimum of customer service issues.

NAP specifics: A NAP MUST have the ability to bill a user or NSP for usage. The type of billing should be flexible (time billing, throughput billing, etc.).

NSP specifics: An NSP MUST have the ability to bill a user for usage. The type of billing should be flexible (time billing, throughput billing, etc.). An NSP SHOULD be able to reconcile billing from a NAP with the billing of the NSP's subscribers.

- *Scalability:* A public ADSL network MUST have the ability to scale to a large number of end users and MAY be required to scale to a suitably large number of service providers.

NAP specifics: A public ADSL network NAP MUST be able to support a large number of users and MAY need support a large number of NSPs with possibly multiple POPs.

NSP specifics: An public ADSL NSP point of presence MUST have the ability to logically or physically scale to support a large number of users.

- *Operational simplicity:* Provisioning at both initial service offering and also over the course of the network's lifetime should be minimal. In addition, an ADSL network should be simple to user. End-to-end connections should be able to be made in a straightforward manner. This serves the needs of both users and NSPs.

User specifics: A user MUST NOT need special training and MUST NOT have to specially configure the end-user system, such as the local PC. An end-user system MUST NOT have to be rebooted to connect to an NSP. The user should not have to be aware what the ADSL link protocol is (layer 2).

NAP specifics: The churn of users from one NSP to another MUST NOT require provisioning on the part of the NAP. The addition of new NSPs MUST require minimal provisioning on the part of the NAP.

NSP specifics: The addition of users or deletion of users from an NSP's service MUST NOT require significant provisioning on the part of the NSP or significant coordination with the NAP.

- *Compatibility with existing resources.* Many resources that will use and ADSL network already exist. The ADSL network should coexist and interoperate with these resources.

  User specifics: Any proposed architecture MUST coexist gracefully with existing PC protocol stacks, and no special configurations should be necessary.

  NAP specifics: Any proposed architecture MUST be capable of utilizing existing backbone structures. An example an existing backbone structure is an ATM PVC network.

  NSP specifics: Any proposed architecture MUST coexist gracefully with existing NSP infrastructures, including the authorization, provisioning, network address assignment and billing methods.

- *Evolution path:* The service set offering should not be constrained such that the first deployment maxes out capability. (The Network Migration group is producing standards documents that apply here.)

Security

The infrastructure of all domains must be secured against the subversion of its function and unauthorized access to privileged information. Security is affected if the end user system provides multiple simultaneous connections between NSPs. For example, if a user has an IP connection to an ISP and also an IP connection to a corporate network simultaneously, irrespective of the underlying transport protocol being used, there is a potential security breach. This is due to the fact that two different IP links are simultaneously established to the user's end system and there is no failsafe way to prevent the end system from be subverted into routing traffic from one open connection to the other. Although there are situations where multiple simultaneous connections are desirable, these must be weighed against the potential security risks they impose.

Related references

Many of the following references are examples of various ADSL architectures and concepts as presented at the ADSL Forum, which served as the inspiration for this information.

ADSL IP Concentration, GTE Labs Contribution ADSL Forum 96-046, June 1996.
ATM Forum, *Packet Mode Report Working Text.*
Business Data Services Platform, 1996 DSL Technologies Summit, March 27–28, 1996.
ITU-T Telecommunication Recommendation I.432, B-ISDN *User-Network Interface Physical Layer Specification.*
Minutes of the ADSL Forum—Services Network Architecture Group (SNAG), Seattle, Dec. 1996.

10.12   An End-to-End Packet Mode Architecture with Tunneling and Service Selection

This section presents information from the ADSL Forum specifying tunneling-based end-to-end architecture using packets between the ATU-R and the NAP and L2TP tunneling between the NAP and NSP. In addition, a method of service selection is specified that allows simultaneous, independent connectivity between multiple users at a premise and multiple NSPs.

Introduction

This technical report specifies a tunneling-based end-to-end architecture using packets between the ATU-R and the NAP and L2TP tunneling between the NAP and NSP. In addition, a method of service selection is specified which allows simultaneous, independent connectivity between multiple users at a premise and multiple NSPs.

The purpose of the specified architecture is to provide PPP sessions between a customer premise and one or more NSPs. The connection between the customer premise and the NAP uses packet-based access as specified. The NAP then forwards PPP sessions through L2TP tunnels to the appropriate NSPs. Tunneling provides:

1. A method of forwarding a PPP termination point to an NSP providing an end-to-end PPP connection

2. Reduced provisioning of a WAN as compared to an end-to-end PVC environment

3. The ability to use PPP negotiation parameters to dynamically select an NSP destination

The method of handling issues in the premise network is not addressed in this technical report.

Reference diagram

The reference diagram of a network capable of supporting the service selection described here is shown in Figure 10.67.

A specific requirement of this architecture is L2TP tunneling between the NAP and the NSP domains.

Requirements

The following sections list the requirements for both FUNI mode and RFC 1662 mode ADSL implementations.

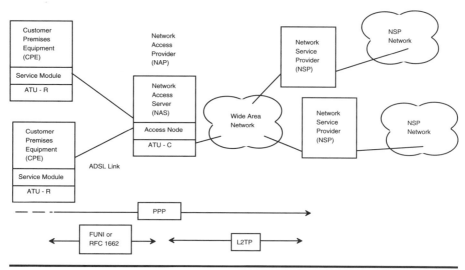

Figure 10.67   Network Reference Diagram

FUNI mode implementations

ATU-R

1. The ATU-R shall support PPP over FUNI over the ADSL link.

2. To initiate a PPP session, the ATU-R shall select a locally unused FUNI frame address and begin PPP negotiation using that selected address.

3. During the authentication stage of negotiation, the user name shall be provided using the format `Error! Bookmark` not defined.

NAP

1. The NAS shall support PPP over FUNI over the ADSL link.

2. The NAS shall use detection of a new locally unused FUNI frame address as the `Link Up` event for the PPP state machine.

3. The NAS shall support L2TP tunneling between the NAS and the NSP.

4. If the domain name specified in the received authentication information identifies a supported NSP, the NAS shall initiate a call on behalf of the subscriber through the L2TP tunnel to that NSP.

5. If the domain name specified in the received authentication information is not supported or a call cannot be established for any other reason, the NAS must terminate the PPP session.

6. Once a PPP session is terminated, the NAS shall consider the corresponding FUNI address as unused.

RF 1662 mode operation. The service selection method described in this document may be implemented using RFC 1662 mode instead of PPP over FUNI with the limitation that only one NSP may be accessed at a given time by a premise network. Requirement changes for RFC 1662 mode support are as follows:

1. The ATU-R shall support RFC 1662 mode over the ADSL link.

2. The NAS shall support RFC 1662 mode over the ADSL link.

References

ADSL Forum, *Framing and Encapsulation Standards for ADSL: Packet Mode,* 1997.
IETF RFC Draft, *Layer Two Tunneling Protocol (L2TP),* Oct. 1996.
RFC 821, *Simple Mail Transport Protocol,* Aug. 1982.
RFC 1661, *The Point-to-Point Protocol (PPP),* July 1994.

10.13 Summary

The ADSL Forum is one of the most credible resources available on ADSL technology. After much research on the topic, I realized that the information provided freely through this Forum was very valuable; so much so that I thought it appropriate to relay it to you, the reader. The following is applicable to all information provided in this chapter:

11

Baselining a Communication Server and an xDSL Router

My network has the need for inbound and outbound access. Most networks have these needs. Beyond this, there is the need to manage my network remotely.

Previously, I introduced you to a communication server in my network. However, it does not have the capability and power of the communication server that I present in this chapter.

Because of the needs of my network, I selected a product from Chase Research. I selected a 16-port rack-mount communication server. With this I was able to meet all the needs I had in my network. In fact, this server is so powerful that I firmly believe, solely on the basis of experience in the marketplace and personal use of this Chase Research communication server, that every network needs one.

Consider the information presented later in this chapter to assist you in interpreting the functionality of both the communication server and the xDSL router technology.

11.1 Logical Perspective

In order to understand some topics presented here, it helps to understand the logical layout of my network. Consider Figure 11.1, which shows the logical view of the network. Servers, workstations, and a CD and hard-drive storage silo are shown. This is a basic view of the network; however, it does not show the incredible number of pieces of equipment that exist to make the network possible.

Figure 11.2, which is a more detailed look at the network, shows additional equipment such as network UPS, communications hub, wiring assembly, and other assorted equipment. The significance of this is that later in the chapter

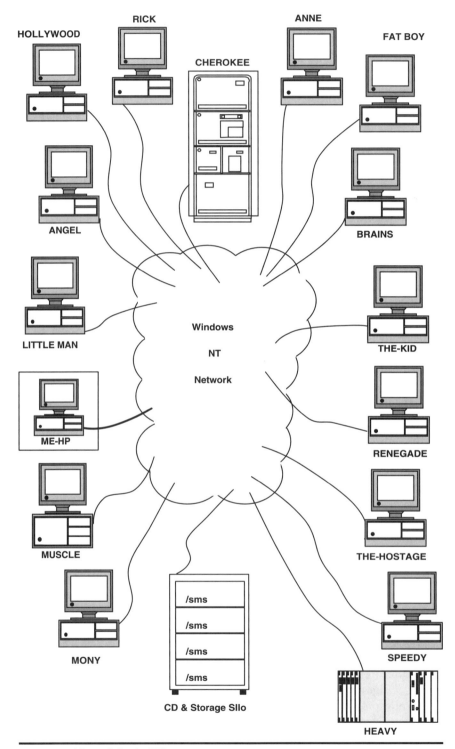

Figure 11.1 Network Logical View

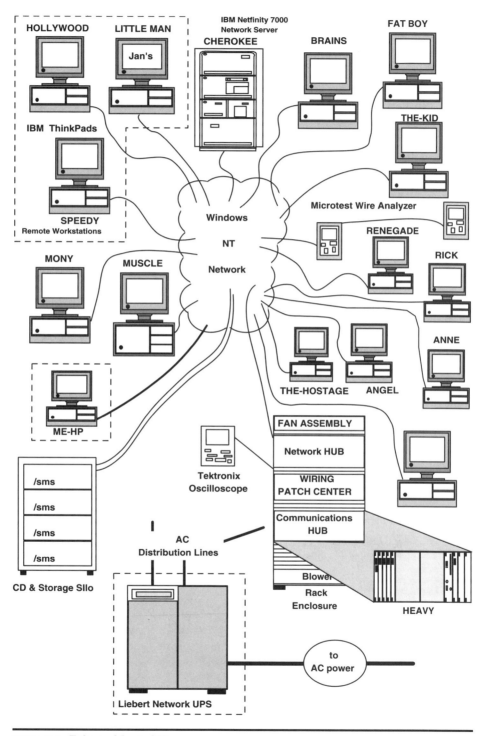

Figure 11.2 Enhanced Logical View

you may want to reference this illustration because the communication server and routers interoperate with all this network equipment. In fact, they are the core of remote networking.

Figure 11.3 shows three remote workstations connected to the network via the Chase communication server. Although not all nodes are shown as in Figure 11.1, they are accessible by the remote workstations.

11.2   Network Functionality

In the context of this chapter it is helpful to review an illustration presented earlier in the book. Consider Figure 11.4, which shows the fiber-based back-bone as discussed previously. It also shows the router and communication server connected to the backbone switch. This is fairly detailed and sufficient for explanation purposes here.

The functionality of the communication server provides the following features for remote users:

- Inbound access
- File transfer capability
- Remote network management
- Primary network backbone access with secondary access through DSL (digital subscriber line) routers

Other functions are available, such as

- Video server access
- WWW access for the private Internet
- FTP access for the private Internet
- Email access for the private Internet

In my network implementation I can also move files from one system to another within the corporate location while being located remotely, dialing in through a network access with the communication server and router access via the DSL routers.

11.3   Chase Server Functionality

IOLAN+ is a feature-rich Ethernet TCP/IP communications server which enables serial devices to be connected directly to LANs. The serial devices can be terminals, printers, modems, bar-code readers, or any other RS-232 device.

IOLAN+ features

TCP/IP protocols, including TELNET, Rlogin, PPP, SLIP Supports terminals, printers, modems, and any other RS-232 device with Fast 115.2-kbps port speeds. Other features include

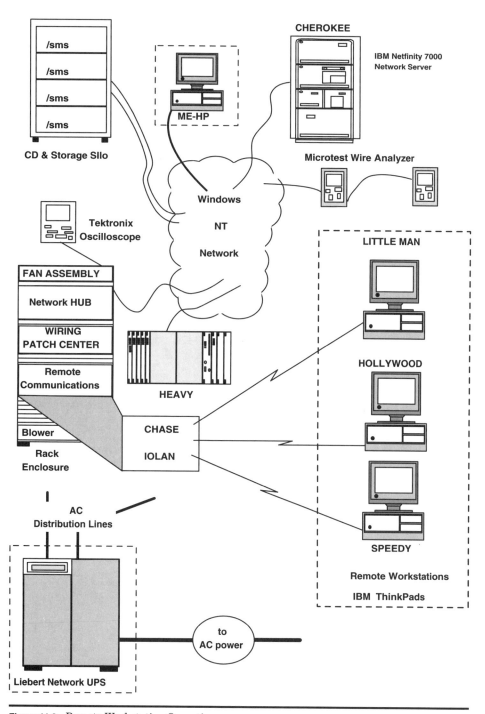

Figure 11.3   Remote Workstation Operation

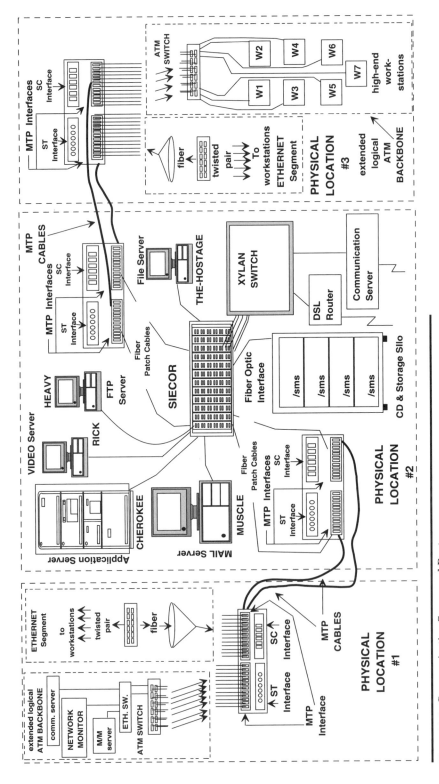

Figure 11.4 Communication Server and Router

Dial-in remote access to Internet and intranet

UNIX and Windows NT/95 dial-out modem pooling for UNIX and Windows NT/95

Autosense Ethernet with RJ-45, BNC, and AUI

19-in rack-mount or desktop drive

Dial-on-demand IP routing

Flash memory for simple upgrade

Universal power supply 90 to 250 V for worldwide use

48-V power supply option for telecommunications operation

Surge protection on all signals on all ports

Easy-to-use menus

Multiple (4, 8, or 16) ports

Lifetime warranty

Applications. IOLAN+ is used wherever serial devices need to be connected to LANs. IOLAN+'s architecture features the flexibility to address a wide variety of applications, from workgroup computing to remote access. Typical areas of application include

POS (point-of-sale) and warehousing systems

Internet service providers

Banking and other financial front-desk systems

Corporate remote access server for home or mobile workers

UNIX terminal and printer workgroups

Modem pools for dial-in and dial-out

Reverse TELNET access for nonnetworked computer systems

Multiplexing RS-232 data over Ethernet and TCP/IP WANs

Console server for remote management of any hardware with console ports

Dial-out features (Chase DialOut/IP) are available for Windows NT systems

Architecture. Our industry-standard connectivity is built around TCP/IP protocols to ensure open systems compatibility. IOLAN+ operates on standard Ethernet networks with autosense (automatic sensing) between BNC, RJ-45, and AUI physical connectors.

Flash memory is used for storing the operating firmware and configuration information. The latest versions of firmware are easily downloaded. Setup information can be saved to a local host for backup purposes.

The built-in power supply will operate in most countries by sensing between 50 and 60 Hz and voltage ranges between 90 and 250 V ac. A 48-V-dc power supply for rack mounting is optional and is used in telecommunications environments.

Performance. IOLAN+ has the performance you need to handle a diverse range of high-speed devices. IOLAN+ can transmit and receive data at speeds of up to 115.2 kbps. This allows high-performance devices to function at their full speed.

To achieve this high speed and maintain a high throughput, IOLAN+ utilizes the performance of RISC-based CD1865 intelligent UARTs in combination with highly tuned firmware.

Easy installation. IOLAN+ setup can be performed in a matter of minutes using a simple menu interface. A quick start requires only the IP address to be set. Initial setup can be done on a directly connected console. IOLAN+ also supports BOOTP and Reverse ARP for setup across the LAN.

IOLAN+ will assist you in stepping through the additional configuration options including port profiles, remote sites, security, and PPP configuration.

Reliability. All serial ports have surge protection devices to protect the unit from electrical damage. ISO 9001 standards adherence results in superior quality and IOLAN+ comes with a lifetime warranty (as does every Chase product).

Terminals and printers. Terminal services include powerful multisessions and a user menu. Ports can be configured individually for dedicated connections to a predefined host, enhancing security and simplicity. Alternatively, a preconfigured host table or DNS support can be used.

Printers can be configured as local (fixed TTYs) on a UNIX host with Chase-supplied utilities. Alternatively, RCP or LPD protocols can be used, enabling IOLAN+ to act as a remote print queue for UNIX and NT hosts. Printer hunt groups can also be configured.

Remote access. IOLAN+ provides remote access to a LAN for terminal or PC connections. Dial-in access can be from a terminal or a terminal emulator such as Hyperterminal, with IOLAN+ providing TELNET and Rlogin services that allow host system access. PPP access (such as from Windows 95 Dial-up adapter) is autodetectable on all ports and Dial-in PCs can use Internet services such as a browser, FTP, or TELNET. Windows file and print sharing is also supported via WINS server setup on the IOLAN+. Windows NT domain services show up in the "network neighborhood" of the client PC. User authentication allows users to be restricted to specific services (TELNET/PPP) or hosts (TELNET), and also provides user-based IP address assignment. User profiles are maintained on a central host, which can be a RADIUS server. IOLAN+ logging records calls for billing.

Modem pooling. All ports provide simultaneous dial-in and dial-out and modems can be shared by UNIX and Windows NT/95 systems on the LAN. UNIX TTY ports and Windows COM ports can be redirected to the IOLAN+ using a combination of Chase utilities and reverse TELNET settings. Modems can be dedicated to certain users, or shared, reducing the total number of phone lines.

Network routing. IP routing connections between LANs can be configured on any port. Dedicated connections, or dial-on-demand PPP connections, can be used. The IOLAN+ can route to any vendor's PPP service (including an ISP) or another IOLAN+. The modems can be shared with dial-in/dial-out users.

Security. A dual-password system for remote access security can be used. Password protection levels can be set per port. Login scripts and automatic PAP negotiations are supported. First-level passwords are validated by the IOLAN+, while user passwords are authenticated against a central host (which can be a RADIUS server). One host can support multiple IOLAN+ servers. Administration is protected by a third password level.

Management. While providing local console or TELNET access from anywhere on the LAN, this important facility allows easy remote configuration and diagnostics. IOLAN+ supports SNMP (Simple Network Management Protocol) with MIB-II, Character MIB, Sessions MIB, and Chase specific enterprise variables. An extensive statistics system allows monitoring of the IOLAN+, providing information such as network activity by protocol, port connect time, idle time, throughput average, and total per port.

IOLAN+ dial-out feature for Windows NT

With an IOLAN+, Windows NT, or Windows 95 system, you can do the following:

Branch connections	Enable the main office of a retail or food chain to call into its branch locations nightly to collect accounting data.
Private networks	Dial-out to private networks not on the Internet, especially to financial institutions and for credit checks.
Internet connections	Allow ISP connections by enabling all networked users access to modems, especially in small offices.

Chase DialOut/IP lets Windows workstations on your network make outbound dialup connections using modems attached to an IOLAN+. With DialOut/IP, your dial-in remote access server can now dial out to branch locations, ISPs, and other network-based services. This allows better use of resources since all modems can be banked onto a central IOLAN+, and all workstations can access the modems as if they were attached locally.

DialOut/IP is a Windows COM port redirector for TCP/IP networks providing transparent access to networked modems for most Windows applications. DialOut/IP creates new "virtual COM ports" in Windows that appear to have directly connected modems. Windows client programs (including Windows Dial-up Networking), that assume the presence of a local modem, can now share pooled modems on your TCP/IP network.

Why dial out through modem pools? The main reason for implementing shared dial-out solutions with DialOut/IP is economics. By using a modem pool to share modems for dial-out purposes, it is possible to achieve significant savings when individual desktop phone lines and modems are eliminated. Another widespread reason for dial-out with shared modems is that central equipment is easier to configure and maintain.

IOLAN technical specifications

RS-232 ports	4, 8, or 16; DB25 or RJ-45 (RS-422 optional)
Network	Ethernet DIX and 802.3
Protocols	TCP/IP, TELNET, Rlogin, raw TELNET, Reverse TELNET, PPP, SLIP, CSLIP, LPD, RCP, DNS, WINS
Management	SNMP, MIB-II, Character and Chase Enterprise variables, TELNET, console port
Menu languages	English, French, German, Italian, and Spanish
Speed range	Serial: 50 bps to 115.2 kbps
Modem support	Full bidirectional
Serial port signals	CTS, RTS, DSR, DTR, DCD, Rx, Tx
Network connector	AUI, BNC, and RJ-45 Autosense
Processor	80C186 25 MHz
Memory	1 MB DRAM, 512K flash
UARTs	CD1865 intelligent
Power Supply	50/60 Hz 90 to 250 V ac, optional 48-V-dc rack
Warranty	Lifetime

For more information about the Chase product I used in my network, or other networking devices, contact them at

Chase Research PLC
7 Cedarwood, Chineham Business Park,
Basingstoke RG24 8WD, United Kingdom
Phone: +44 (0)1256 352260
Fax: +44 (0)1256 810159
http://www.chaser.co.uk
email: *info@chaser.co.uk*

Chase Research GmbH
Zettachring 6
D-70567 Stuttgart
Germany
Phone: +49 (0)711 7287 155
Fax: +49 (0)711 7287 156
email: *info@chaser.de*

Chase Research Inc.
Suite 100, 545 Marriott Drive
Nashville, TN 37214
Phone: 1-615-872-0770
Fax: 1-615-872-0771
email: *info@chaser.com*
http://www.chaser.com

Chase Research China
Room 329, Hua Tong Bldg.
19A Che Gong Zhuang Xi Road
Haidian District, Beijing 100044
People's Republic of China
Phone/Fax: +86 10 6848 3355
email: *infochina@chaser.co.uk*

11.4 How to Baseline a Communication Server

As I did with other equipment that I described in this book, with regard to the communication server, I obtained information that is pertinent to my purposes in troubleshooting my own network. This is a good baseline for you to parallel in preparation for troubleshooting your network.

All network environments are different. Some similarities exist; however, even the closest mirrored environments differ. You may read the information presented here to augment your knowledge of your own network's environment.

First, I took some snapshots of Ethernet statistics while performing some network operational maintenance. It did not take long, and it is helpful.

```
                    SERVER STATISTICS
                    = == ETHERNET ===

Tx:   Pkts:        48    Errors:        0    Collisions: 0
      Retries :     0    Resets:        0    Busy:       0
Rx:   Pkts:     1,862    Bufs:    172/300    No Bufs:    0
      Prot:       790    Miss:          0    Busy:       0

                    === SERIAL LINES ===

Tx:   chars:     10,516    psec:      3
Rx:   chars:          0    psec:      0
```

```
Malformed:              0    Lost:        0    OverRuns:       0
Buffer failures:        0
```

=== ROUTING STATISTICS ===

```
bad redirects: 0    dynamic: 0 new gateway:  0
unreachable:   0    wild card: 0
Uptime:  1 days 00:48:03 hours  Memory free: 113280
```

Here is another view of Ethernet statistics taken from the same server, but revealing different statistical information.

SERVER STATISTICS
=== ETHERNET ===

```
Tx:  Pkts:      1,871    Errors:      0    Collisions:    0
     Retries :      0    Resets:      0    Busy:          0
Rx:  Pkts:      3,967    Bufs:  174/300    No Bufs:       0
     Prot:        929    Miss:        0    Busy:          0
```

=== SERIAL LINES ===

```
Tx:  chars:       83,470    psec:     22
Rx:  chars:      539,439    psec:    143
     Malformed:        0    Lost:      0    OverRuns:    1
     Buffer failures:  0
```

=== ROUTING STATISTICS ===

```
bad redirects:  0    dynamic:  0 new gateway:     0
unreachable: 0       wild card:    0
Uptime:   1 days 01:02:30 hours    Memory free: 106176
```

```
      IOLAN+RACK v4.0      a CDi        MY-CHASER
```

I also collected a copy of the gateway statistics. Note the information it provides, including details such as the IP address. In this case the address is the Chase communication server (which I call MY-CHASER). The host with the IP address of 79 is BRAINS.

Gateway Tables

Destination	Gateway	Flags	Refcnt	Use	Interface
localhost	localhost	UH	0	0	lo0
220.100.100.79	MY-CHASER	UG	0	0	dial
220.100.100.178	MY-CHASER	U	2	2085	lance

IOLAN+RACK v4.0 a CDi MY-CHASER

The following snapshot is extremely helpful because it shows the statistics according to the user.

```
                    SERVER STATISTICS
   USER NAME        CURRENT STATUS        HOW LONG         IDLE TIME
   = = = = = = = = = = = = = = = = = = = = = = = = = = = = = = = = = = = = =
1.  <unknown>       login menu            0000:00:56 0001:00:50
2.  <unknown>       waiting for DSR or DCD    0001:00:47 0001:00:50
3.  <unknown>       login menu            0000:00:54 0001:00:50
4.  <unknown>       waiting for DSR or DCD    0001:00:45 0001:00:50
5.  <unknown>       login menu            0000:00:52 0001:00:50
6.  <unknown>       login menu            0000:00:52 0001:00:50
7.  <TAYLOR>        Talking to host 220.100.100.172.1026
                                              0000:03:22 0000:00:13
8.  <unknown>       login menu            0000:00:53 0001:00:53
9.  <unknown>       login menu            0000:00:53 0001:00:53
10. <unknown>       login menu            0000:00:53 0001:00:53
11. <unknown>       login menu            0000:00:53 0001:00:53
12. <unknown>       waiting for DSR or DCD    0001:00:44 0001:00:53
13. <unknown>       login menu            0000:00:51 0001:00:53
14. <unknown>       login menu            0000:00:51 0001:00:53
15. <unknown>       login menu            0000:00:51 0001:00:53
16. <unknown>       login menu            0000:00:51 0001:00:53
```

IOLAN+RACK v4.0 a CDiMY-CHASER

```
                    SERVER STATISTICS
                    = = = = = = = = = = = =
1.  <unknown>              login menu                    >DTR+RTS
2.  <unknown>              waiting for DSR or DCD         >DTR+RTS
3.  <unknown>              login menu                    >DTR+RTS
4.  <unknown>              waiting for DSR or DCD         >DTR+RTS
5.  <unknown>              login menu                    >DTR+RTS
6.  <unknown>              login menu                    >DTR+RTS
7.  <JAN>                  waiting for DSR or DCD         >DTR+RTS
8.  <unknown>              login menu                    >DTR+RTS
9.  <unknown>              login menu                    >DTR+RTS
10. <unknown>              login menu                    >DTR+RTS
11. <unknown>              login menu                    >DTR+RTS
12. <unknown>              waiting for DSR or DCD         >DTR+RTS
13. <unknown>              login menu                    >DTR+RTS
14. <unknown>              login menu                    >DTR+RTS
15. <unknown>              login menu                    >DTR+RTS
16. <unknown>              login menu                    >DTR+RTS
REM <unknown>              SERVER STATISTICS
LOG                        logger not enabled
```

IOLAN+RACK v4.0 a CDi MY-CHASER

The next table shows the received/transmitted status on the communication server.

```
                SERVER STATISTICS
        ====RECEIVED====      ===========TRANSMITTED===========
PORT      PER SEC       TOTAL    XON    XOFF    PER SEC      TOTAL
  1           0            0      16     0          0         1102
  2           0            0      16     0          0           13
  3           0            0      16     0          0         1102
  4           0            0      16     0          0            0
```

5	0	0	16	0	0	1083
6	0	0	16	0	0	1083
7	93	334980	16	0	13	49648
8	0	0	16	0	0	1083
9	0	0	16	0	0	1083
10	0	0	16	0	0	1083
11	0	0	16	0	0	1083
12	0	0	16	0	0	0
13	0	0	16	0	0	1083
14	0	0	16	0	0	1083
15	0	0	16	0	0	1083
16	0	0	16	0	0	1083

```
IOLAN+RACK v4.0 a CDi MY-CHASER MY-CHASER
```

Still another powerful tool available from Chase Research shows TCP information such as presented here.

```
                    SERVER STATISTICS
                    === TCP PROTOCOL ===

connattempt: 0 accepts: 3      connects: 3      dropped: 0
conndrops: 0   closed: 4  segstimed: 1496      rttupdated: 1496
delayed ack: 504    tmo drop:  0    rexmt tmo:  0  persist tmo: 0
Keep timeo: 0       probes: 0      dropped: 0
Linger: 0      aborted: 0      expired: 0    cancelled: 0
Drop frag: 0   user: 0    merge prev: 0  merge user: 0
Tx: total: 2040    data  pkt: 1688 byte:  718592    rexmitpkt: 0
ctrl: 1    ack-only: 338   win probe: 0    rexmitbyte: 0  urgent: 0
Rx: total:    2130 data pkt: 1282 bytes: 72868    checksum: 0
short:    0    dup pkt:  4     dup byte: 8     partduppkt:  0
badoff: 0     oo pkt: 0 oo byte:   0    partdupbyte:   0
dupack:   0    afterclose: 0 win probe:  0   pktafterwin: 0
ackpack: 1502  ackbyte: 718596    win upd: 0       byteafterwin: 0
acktoomuch: 0
```

```
IOLAN+RACK v4.0      a CDi      MY-CHASER
```

Modem trace. In troubleshooting an actual problem I had on my network, I captured the following trace. If you look at the commands and responses carefully, you can correlate the function to the time. The significance of this is important because you can check matters as they relate to timing as well as actual configuration as opposed to what is sent across the link through the modem. I recommend that you obtain a trace of your modem(s) to establish a baseline.

```
07-07-1998 05:05:23.81 - Modem type: Sportster 14400 V.42bis
07-07-1998 05:05:23.81 - Modem inf path: MDMUSRSP.INF
07-07-1998 05:05:23.81 - Modem inf section: Modem4
07-07-1998 05:05:23.84 - 38400,N,8,1
07-07-1998 05:05:24.03 - 38400,N,8,1
07-07-1998 05:05:24.05 - Initializing modem.
07-07-1998 05:05:24.05 - Send: AT<cr>
07-07-1998 05:05:26.08 - Recv: <no response>
```

```
07-07-1998 05:05:26.08 - WARNING: Unrecognized response. Retrying...
07-07-1998 05:05:26.08 - Send: AT<cr>
07-07-1998 05:05:26.08 - Recv: <cr><lf>OK<cr><lf>
07-07-1998 05:05:26.08 - Interpreted response: Ok
07-07-1998 05:05:26.08 - Send: AT&FE0V1&A3&B1&D2&S0<cr>
07-07-1998 05:05:26.31 - Recv: <cr><lf>OK<cr><lf>
07-07-1998 05:05:26.31 - Interpreted response: Ok
07-07-1998 05:05:26.31 - Send: ATS7=60S19=0L3M1&M4&K1&H1&R2&I0B0X4<cr>
07-07-1998 05:05:26.48 - Recv: <cr><lf>OK<cr><lf>
07-07-1998 05:05:26.48 - Interpreted response: Ok
07-07-1998 05:05:26.48 - Dialing.
07-07-1998 05:05:26.48 - Send: ATDT;<cr>
07-07-1998 05:05:28.71 - Recv: <cr><lf>OK<cr><lf>
07-07-1998 05:05:28.71 - Interpreted response: Ok
07-07-1998 05:05:28.71 - Dialing.
07-07-1998 05:05:28.71 - Send: ATDT#######<cr>
07-07-1998 05:06:02.45 - Hanging up the modem.
07-07-1998 05:06:02.45 - Send: <cr>
07-07-1998 05:06:02.80 - Recv: <cr><lf>NO CARRIER<cr><lf>
07-07-1998 05:06:02.80 - Interpreted response: No Carrier
07-07-1998 05:06:02.80 - Send: ATH<cr>
07-07-1998 05:06:03.03 - Recv: <cr><lf>OK<cr><lf>
07-07-1998 05:06:03.03 - Interpreted response: Ok
07-07-1998 05:06:04.14 - Session Statistics:
07-07-1998 05:06:04.14 -                   Reads : 44 bytes
07-07-1998 05:06:04.14 -                   Writes: 86 bytes
07-07-1998 05:06:04.14 - Sportster 14400 V.42bis closed.
07-07-1998 05:07:53.70 - Sportster 14400 V.42bis in use.
07-07-1998 05:07:53.73 - Modem type: Sportster 14400 V.42bis
07-07-1998 05:07:53.73 - Modem inf path: MDMUSRSP.INF
07-07-1998 05:07:53.73 - Modem inf section: Modem4
07-07-1998 05:07:53.76 - 38400,N,8,1
07-07-1998 05:07:53.95 - 38400,N,8,1
07-07-1998 05:07:53.96 - Initializing modem.
07-07-1998 05:07:53.96 - Send: AT<cr>
07-07-1998 05:07:55.98 - Recv: <no response>
07-07-1998 05:07:55.98 - WARNING: Unrecognized response. Retrying...
07-07-1998 05:07:55.98 - Send: AT<cr>
07-07-1998 05:07:55.98 - Recv: <cr><lf>OK<cr><lf>
07-07-1998 05:07:55.98 - Interpreted response: Ok
07-07-1998 05:07:55.98 - Send: AT&FE0V1&A3&B1&D2&S0<cr>
07-07-1998 05:07:56.19 - Recv: <cr><lf>OK<cr><lf>
07-07-1998 05:07:56.19 - Interpreted response: Ok
07-07-1998 05:07:56.19 - Send: ATS7=60S19=0L3M1&M4&K1&H1&R2&I0B0X4<cr>
07-07-1998 05:07:56.44 - Recv: <cr><lf>OK<cr><lf>
07-07-1998 05:07:56.44 - Interpreted response: Ok
07-07-1998 05:07:56.44 - Dialing.
07-07-1998 05:07:56.44 - Send: ATDT;<cr>
07-07-1998 05:07:58.28 - Recv: <cr><lf>OK<cr><lf>
07-07-1998 05:07:58.28 - Interpreted response: Ok
07-07-1998 05:07:58.28 - Dialing.
07-07-1998 05:07:58.28 - Send: ATDT#######<cr>
07-07-1998 05:08:15.56 - Recv: <cr><lf>CONNECT 14400/ARQ/V32/LAPM/V42BIS
                                 <cr><lf>
07-07-1998 05:08:15.56 - Interpreted response: Connect
07-07-1998 05:08:15.56 - Connection established at 14400bps.
07-07-1998 05:08:15.56 - Error-control on.
07-07-1998 05:08:15.56 - Data compression on.
07-07-1998 05:08:15.87 - 38400,N,8,1
```

```
07-07-1998 05:09:12.07 - Remote modem hung up.
07-07-1998 05:09:14.07 - Recv: <no response>
07-07-1998 05:09:14.07 - WARNING: Unrecognized response. Retrying...
07-07-1998 05:09:15.19 - Session Statistics:
07-07-1998 05:09:15.19 -                    Reads : 604 bytes
07-07-1998 05:09:15.19 -                    Writes: 7608 bytes
07-07-1998 05:09:15.19 - Sportster 14400 V.42bis closed.
07-07-1998 05:09:24.47 - Sportster 14400 V.42bis in use.
07-07-1998 05:09:24.51 - Modem type: Sportster 14400 V.42bis
07-07-1998 05:09:24.51 - Modem inf path: MDMUSRSP.INF
07-07-1998 05:09:24.51 - Modem inf section: Modem4
07-07-1998 05:09:24.52 - 38400,N,8,1
07-07-1998 05:09:24.72 - 38400,N,8,1
07-07-1998 05:09:24.73 - Initializing modem.
07-07-1998 05:09:24.73 - Send: AT<cr>
07-07-1998 05:09:26.73 - ERROR: Unable to send command to the device.
07-07-1998 05:09:27.83 - Session Statistics:
07-07-1998 05:09:27.83 -                    Reads : 0 bytes
07-07-1998 05:09:27.83 -                    Writes: 3 bytes
07-07-1998 05:09:27.83 - Sportster 14400 V.42bis closed.
07-07-1998 05:20:02.74 - Sportster 14400 V.42bis in use.
07-07-1998 05:20:02.77 - Modem type: Sportster 14400 V.42bis
07-07-1998 05:20:02.77 - Modem inf path: MDMUSRSP.INF
07-07-1998 05:20:02.77 - Modem inf section: Modem4
07-07-1998 05:20:02.83 - 38400,N,8,1
07-07-1998 05:20:03.02 - 38400,N,8,1
07-07-1998 05:20:03.03 - Initializing modem.
07-07-1998 05:20:03.03 - Send: AT<cr>
07-07-1998 05:20:05.11 - Recv: <no response>
07-07-1998 05:20:05.11 - WARNING: Unrecognized response. Retrying...
07-07-1998 05:20:05.11 - Send: AT<cr>
07-07-1998 05:20:05.11 - Recv: <cr><lf>OK<cr><lf>
07-07-1998 05:20:05.11 - Interpreted response: Ok
07-07-1998 05:20:05.11 - Send: AT&FE0V1&A3&B1&D2&S0<cr>
07-07-1998 05:20:05.33 - Recv: <cr><lf>OK<cr><lf>
07-07-1998 05:20:05.33 - Interpreted response: Ok
07-07-1998 05:20:05.33 - Send: ATS7=60S19=0L3M1&M4&K1&H1&R2&I0B0X4<cr>
07-07-1998 05:20:05.57 - Recv: <cr><lf>OK<cr><lf>
07-07-1998 05:20:05.57 - Interpreted response: Ok
07-07-1998 05:20:05.57 - Dialing.
07-07-1998 05:20:05.57 - Send: ATDT;<cr>
07-07-1998 05:20:07.49 - Recv: <cr><lf>OK<cr><lf>
07-07-1998 05:20:07.49 - Interpreted response: Ok
07-07-1998 05:20:07.49 - Dialing.
07-07-1998 05:20:07.49 - Send: ATDT#######<cr>
07-07-1998 05:20:24.22 - Recv: <cr><lf>CONNECT    14400/ARQ/V32/LAPM/
                               V42BIS<cr><lf>
07-07-1998 05:20:24.22 - Interpreted response: Connect
07-07-1998 05:20:24.22 - Connection established at 14400bps.
07-07-1998 05:20:24.22 - Error-control on.
07-07-1998 05:20:24.22 - Data compression on.
07-07-1998 05:20:24.51 - 38400,N,8,1
07-07-1998 05:20:45.08 - Remote modem hung up.
07-07-1998 05:20:47.08 - Recv: <no response>
07-07-1998 05:20:47.08 - WARNING: Unrecognized response. Retrying...
07-07-1998 05:20:48.19 - Session Statistics:
07-07-1998 05:20:48.19 -                    Reads : 842 bytes
07-07-1998 05:20:48.19 -                    Writes: 2568 bytes
07-07-1998 05:20:48.19 - Sportster 14400 V.42bis closed.
```

```
07-07-1998 05:24:50.55 - Sportster 14400 V.42bis in use.
07-07-1998 05:24:50.59 - Modem type: Sportster 14400 V.42bis
07-07-1998 05:24:50.59 - Modem inf path: MDMUSRSP.INF
07-07-1998 05:24:50.59 - Modem inf section: Modem4
07-07-1998 05:24:50.61 - 38400,N,8,1
07-07-1998 05:24:50.81 - 38400,N,8,1
07-07-1998 05:24:50.81 - Initializing modem.
07-07-1998 05:24:50.81 - Send: AT<cr>
07-07-1998 05:24:52.82 - ERROR: Unable to send command to the device.
07-07-1998 05:24:53.92 - Session Statistics:
07-07-1998 05:24:53.92 -                  Reads : 0 bytes
07-07-1998 05:24:53.92 -                  Writes: 3 bytes
07-07-1998 05:24:53.92 - Sportster 14400 V.42bis closed.
07-07-1998 05:25:12.30 - Sportster 14400 V.42bis in use.
07-07-1998 05:25:12.33 - Modem type: Sportster 14400 V.42bis
07-07-1998 05:25:12.33 - Modem inf path: MDMUSRSP.INF
07-07-1998 05:25:12.33 - Modem inf section: Modem4
07-07-1998 05:25:12.36 - 38400,N,8,1
07-07-1998 05:25:12.52 - 38400,N,8,1
07-07-1998 05:25:12.54 - Initializing modem.
07-07-1998 05:25:12.54 - Send: AT<cr>
07-07-1998 05:25:14.54 - ERROR: Unable to send command to the device.
07-07-1998 05:25:15.64 - Session Statistics:
07-07-1998 05:25:15.64 -                  Reads : 0 bytes
07-07-1998 05:25:15.64 -                  Writes: 3 bytes
07-07-1998 05:25:15.64 - Sportster 14400 V.42bis closed.
07-07-1998 05:25:42.73 - Sportster 14400 V.42bis in use.
07-07-1998 05:25:42.77 - Modem type: Sportster 14400 V.42bis
07-07-1998 05:25:42.77 - Modem inf path: MDMUSRSP.INF
07-07-1998 05:25:42.77 - Modem inf section: Modem4
07-07-1998 05:25:42.79 - 38400,N,8,1
07-07-1998 05:25:42.97 - 38400,N,8,1
07-07-1998 05:25:42.98 - Initializing modem.
07-07-1998 05:25:42.98 - Send: AT<cr>
07-07-1998 05:25:42.99 - Recv: <cr>
07-07-1998 05:25:42.99 - Interpreted response: Informative
07-07-1998 05:25:42.99 - Recv: <lf>
07-07-1998 05:25:42.99 - Interpreted response: Informative
07-07-1998 05:25:44.00 - Recv: WINSOCK ERROR: network error<cr><lf>
07-07-1998 05:25:44.00 - WARNING: Unrecognized response. Retrying...
07-07-1998 05:25:44.00 - Send: AT<cr>
07-07-1998 05:25:46.00 - Recv: <no response>
07-07-1998 05:25:46.00 - WARNING: Unrecognized response. Retrying...
07-07-1998 05:25:46.00 - Send: AT<cr>
07-07-1998 05:25:48.01 - Recv: <no response>
07-07-1998 05:25:48.01 - WARNING: Unrecognized response. Retrying...
07-07-1998 05:25:48.01 - Send: AT<cr>
07-07-1998 05:25:50.01 - Recv: <no response>
07-07-1998 05:25:50.01 - WARNING: Unrecognized response. Retrying...
07-07-1998 05:25:50.01 - Send: AT<cr>
07-07-1998 05:25:51.00 - Hanging up the modem.
07-07-1998 05:25:51.00 - Send: <cr>
07-07-1998 05:25:53.02 - Send: ATH<cr>
07-07-1998 05:25:55.04 - Recv: <no response>
07-07-1998 05:25:55.04 - WARNING: Unrecognized response. Retrying...
07-07-1998 05:25:55.04 - Send: ATH<cr>
07-07-1998 05:25:57.04 - Recv: <no response>
07-07-1998 05:25:57.04 - WARNING: Unrecognized response. Retrying...
07-07-1998 05:25:57.04 - Send: ATH<cr>
```

```
07-07-1998 05:25:59.05 - Recv: <no response>
07-07-1998 05:25:59.05 - WARNING: Unrecognized response. Retrying...
07-07-1998 05:25:59.05 - Send: ATH<cr>
07-07-1998 05:26:01.05 - Recv: <no response>
07-07-1998 05:26:01.05 - WARNING: Unrecognized response. Retrying...
07-07-1998 05:26:01.05 - Send: ATH<cr>
07-07-1998 05:26:03.06 - Recv: <no response>
07-07-1998 05:26:03.06 - ERROR: Unable to recover from unrecognized
                                  response.
07-07-1998 05:26:03.06 - Hardware hangup by lowering DTR.
07-07-1998 05:32:02.45 - Sportster 14400 V.42bis in use.
07-07-1998 05:32:02.47 - Modem type: Sportster 14400 V.42bis
07-07-1998 05:32:02.47 - Modem inf path: MDMUSRSP.INF
07-07-1998 05:32:02.47 - Modem inf section: Modem4
07-07-1998 05:32:02.51 - 38400,N,8,1
07-07-1998 05:32:02.71 - 38400,N,8,1
07-07-1998 05:32:02.71 - Initializing modem.
07-07-1998 05:32:02.71 - Send: AT<cr>
07-07-1998 05:32:04.81 - Recv: <no response>
07-07-1998 05:32:04.81 - WARNING: Unrecognized response. Retrying...
07-07-1998 05:32:04.81 - Send: AT<cr>
07-07-1998 05:32:04.81 - Recv: <cr><lf>OK<cr><lf>
07-07-1998 05:32:04.81 - Interpreted response: Ok
07-07-1998 05:32:04.81 - Send: AT&FE0V1&A3&B1&D2&S0<cr>
07-07-1998 05:32:05.01 - Recv: <cr><lf>OK<cr><lf>
07-07-1998 05:32:05.01 - Interpreted response: Ok
07-07-1998 05:32:05.01 - Send: ATS7=60S19=0L3M1&M4&K1&H1&R2&I0B0X4<cr>
07-07-1998 05:32:05.37 - Recv: <cr><lf>OK<cr><lf>
07-07-1998 05:32:05.37 - Interpreted response: Ok
07-07-1998 05:32:05.37 - Dialing.
07-07-1998 05:32:05.37 - Send: ATDT;<cr>
07-07-1998 05:32:07.64 - Recv: <cr><lf>OK<cr><lf>
07-07-1998 05:32:07.64 - Interpreted response: Ok
07-07-1998 05:32:07.64 - Dialing.
07-07-1998 05:32:07.64 - Send: ATDT#######<cr>
07-07-1998 05:32:24.81 - Recv: <cr><lf>CONNECT 14400/ARQ/V32/LAPM/V42BIS
                                  <cr><lf>
07-07-1998 05:32:24.81 - Interpreted response: Connect
07-07-1998 05:32:24.81 - Connection established at 14400bps.
07-07-1998 05:32:24.81 - Error-control on.
07-07-1998 05:32:24.81 - Data compression on.
07-07-1998 05:32:27.63 - 38400,N,8,1
07-07-1998 05:33:38.91 - Remote modem hung up.
07-07-1998 05:33:40.91 - Recv: <no response>
07-07-1998 05:33:40.91 - WARNING: Unrecognized response. Retrying...
07-07-1998 05:33:42.03 - Session Statistics:
07-07-1998 05:33:42.03 -                   Reads : 593 bytes
07-07-1998 05:33:42.03 -                   Writes: 8012 bytes
07-07-1998 05:33:42.03 - Sportster 14400 V.42bis closed.
07-07-1998 05:37:23.79 - Sportster 14400 V.42bis in use.
07-07-1998 05:37:23.82 - Modem type: Sportster 14400 V.42bis
07-07-1998 05:37:23.82 - Modem inf path: MDMUSRSP.INF
07-07-1998 05:37:23.82 - Modem inf section: Modem4
07-07-1998 05:37:23.84 - 38400,N,8,1
07-07-1998 05:37:24.04 - 38400,N,8,1
07-07-1998 05:37:24.05 - Initializing modem.
07-07-1998 05:37:24.05 - Send: AT<cr>
07-07-1998 05:37:26.05 - ERROR: Unable to send command to the device.
07-07-1998 05:37:27.15 - Session Statistics:
```

```
07-07-1998 05:37:27.15 -            Reads : 0 bytes
07-07-1998 05:37:27.15 -            Writes: 3 bytes
07-07-1998 05:37:27.15 - Sportster 14400 V.42bis closed.
07-08-1998 03:27:11.27 - Courier V.Everything #2 in use.
07-08-1998 03:27:11.31 - Modem type: Courier V.Everything
07-08-1998 03:27:11.31 - Modem inf path: MDMUSRCR.INF
07-08-1998 03:27:11.31 - Modem inf section: Modem29
07-08-1998 03:27:11.35 - 57600,N,8,1
07-08-1998 03:27:11.53 - 57600,N,8,1
07-08-1998 03:27:11.54 - Initializing modem.
07-08-1998 03:27:11.54 - Send: AT<cr>
07-08-1998 03:27:13.74 - Recv: <no response>
07-08-1998 03:27:13.74 - WARNING: Unrecognized response. Retrying...
07-08-1998 03:27:13.74 - Send: AT<cr>
07-08-1998 03:27:13.77 - Recv: <cr><lf>OK<cr><lf>
07-08-1998 03:27:13.77 - Interpreted response: Ok
07-08-1998 03:27:13.77 - Send: AT&F1&B1&C1&D2E0Q0V1&A3S0=<cr>
07-08-1998 03:27:13.99 - Recv: <cr><lf>OK<cr><lf>
07-08-1998 03:27:13.99 - Interpreted response: Ok
07-08-1998 03:27:13.99 - Send: ATS7=60S19=0M1&M4&K1&H1&R2&I0B0X4<cr>
07-08-1998 03:27:14.22 - Recv: <cr><lf>OK<cr><lf>
07-08-1998 03:27:14.22 - Interpreted response: Ok
07-08-1998 03:27:14.22 - Dialing.
07-08-1998 03:27:14.22 - Send: ATDT#######<cr>
07-08-1998 03:27:19.74 - Recv: <cr><lf>BUSY<cr><lf>
07-08-1998 03:27:19.74 - Interpreted response: Busy
07-08-1998 03:27:21.47 - Session Statistics:
07-08-1998 03:27:21.47 -            Reads : 26 bytes
07-08-1998 03:27:21.47 -            Writes: 78 bytes
07-08-1998 03:27:21.47 - Courier V.Everything #2 closed.
07-08-1998 03:27:23.27 - Courier V.Everything #2 in use.
07-08-1998 03:27:23.30 - Modem type: Courier V.Everything
07-08-1998 03:27:23.30 - Modem inf path: MDMUSRCR.INF
07-08-1998 03:27:23.30 - Modem inf section: Modem29
07-08-1998 03:27:23.32 - 57600,N,8,1
07-08-1998 03:27:23.50 - 57600,N,8,1
07-08-1998 03:27:23.52 - Initializing modem.
07-08-1998 03:27:23.52 - Send: AT<cr>
07-08-1998 03:27:23.75 - Recv: <cr><lf>OK<cr><lf>
07-08-1998 03:27:23.75 - Interpreted response: Ok
07-08-1998 03:27:23.75 - Send: AT&F1&B1&C1&D2E0Q0V1&A3S0=<cr>
07-08-1998 03:27:23.98 - Recv: <cr><lf>OK<cr><lf>
07-08-1998 03:27:23.98 - Interpreted response: Ok
07-08-1998 03:27:23.98 - Send: ATS7=60S19=0M1&M4&K1&H1&R2&I0B0X4<cr>
07-08-1998 03:27:24.22 - Recv: <cr><lf>OK<cr><lf>
07-08-1998 03:27:24.22 - Interpreted response: Ok
07-08-1998 03:27:24.22 - Dialing.
07-08-1998 03:27:24.22 - Send: ATDT#######<cr>
07-08-1998 03:27:29.75 - Recv: <cr><lf>BUSY<cr><lf>
07-08-1998 03:27:29.75 - Interpreted response: Busy
07-08-1998 03:27:31.33 - Session Statistics:
07-08-1998 03:27:31.33 -            Reads : 26 bytes
07-08-1998 03:27:31.33 -            Writes: 75 bytes
07-08-1998 03:27:31.33 - Courier V.Everything #2 closed.
07-08-1998 03:27:32.02 - Courier V.Everything #2 in use.
07-08-1998 03:27:32.04 - Modem type: Courier V.Everything
07-08-1998 03:27:32.04 - Modem inf path: MDMUSRCR.INF
07-08-1998 03:27:32.04 - Modem inf.section: Modem29
07-08-1998 03:27:32.07 - 57600,N,8,1
```

```
07-08-1998 03:27:32.25 - 57600,N,8,1
07-08-1998 03:27:32.26 - Initializing modem.
07-08-1998 03:27:32.26 - Send: AT<cr>
07-08-1998 03:27:32.46 - Recv: <cr><lf>OK<cr><lf>
07-08-1998 03:27:32.46 - Interpreted response: Ok
07-08-1998 03:27:32.46 - Send: AT&F1&B1&C1&D2E0Q0V1&A3S0=<cr>
07-08-1998 03:27:32.70 - Recv: <cr><lf>OK<cr><lf>
07-08-1998 03:27:32.70 - Interpreted response: Ok
07-08-1998 03:27:32.70 - Send: ATS7=60S19=0M1&M4&K1&H1&R2&I0B0X4<cr>
07-08-1998 03:27:32.94 - Recv: <cr><lf>OK<cr><lf>
07-08-1998 03:27:32.94 - Interpreted response: Ok
07-08-1998 03:27:32.94 - Dialing.
07-08-1998 03:27:32.94 - Send: ATDT#######<cr>
07-08-1998 03:27:38.79 - Recv: <cr><lf>BUSY<cr><lf>
07-08-1998 03:27:38.79 - Interpreted response: Busy
07-08-1998 03:27:52.57 - Session Statistics:
07-08-1998 03:27:52.57 -                    Reads : 26 bytes
07-08-1998 03:27:52.57 -                    Writes: 75 bytes
07-08-1998 03:27:52.57 - Courier V.Everything #2 closed.
07-11-1998 03:12:52.44 - Courier V.Everything #2 in use.
07-11-1998 03:12:52.48 - Modem type: Courier V.Everything
07-11-1998 03:12:52.48 - Modem inf path: MDMUSRCR.INF
07-11-1998 03:12:52.48 - Modem inf section: Modem29
07-11-1998 03:12:52.54 - 57600,N,8,1
07-11-1998 03:12:52.71 - 57600,N,8,1
07-11-1998 03:12:52.73 - Initializing modem.
07-11-1998 03:12:52.73 - Send: AT<cr>
07-11-1998 03:12:54.79 - Recv: <no response>
07-11-1998 03:12:54.79 - WARNING: Unrecognized response. Retrying...
07-11-1998 03:12:54.79 - Send: AT<cr>
07-11-1998 03:12:54.81 - Recv: <cr><lf>OK<cr><lf>
07-11-1998 03:12:54.81 - Interpreted response: Ok
07-11-1998 03:12:54.81 - Send: AT&F1&B1&C1&D2E0Q0V1&A3S0=<cr>
07-11-1998 03:12:55.01 - Recv: <cr><lf>OK<cr><lf>
07-11-1998 03:12:55.01 - Interpreted response: Ok
07-11-1998 03:12:55.01 - Send: ATS7=60S19=0M1&M4&K1&H1&R2&I0B0X4<cr>
07-11-1998 03:12:55.25 - Recv: <cr><lf>OK<cr><lf>
07-11-1998 03:12:55.25 - Interpreted response: Ok
07-11-1998 03:12:55.25 - Dialing.
07-11-1998 03:12:55.25 - Send: ATDT#######<cr>
07-11-1998 03:13:00.69 - Recv: <cr><lf>BUSY<cr><lf>
07-11-1998 03:13:00.69 - Interpreted response: Busy
07-11-1998 03:13:02.70 - Session Statistics:
07-11-1998 03:13:02.70 -                    Reads : 26 bytes
07-11-1998 03:13:02.70 -                    Writes: 78 bytes
07-11-1998 03:13:02.70 - Courier V.Everything #2 closed.
07-11-1998 03:13:06.23 - Courier V.Everything #2 in use.
07-11-1998 03:13:06.25 - Modem type: Courier V.Everything
07-11-1998 03:13:06.25 - Modem inf path: MDMUSRCR.INF
07-11-1998 03:13:06.25 - Modem inf section: Modem29
07-11-1998 03:13:06.28 - 57600,N,8,1
07-11-1998 03:13:06.47 - 57600,N,8,1
07-11-1998 03:13:06.49 - Initializing modem.
07-11-1998 03:13:06.49 - Send: AT<cr>
07-11-1998 03:13:09.55 - Recv: <no response>
07-11-1998 03:13:09.55 - WARNING: Unrecognized response. Retrying...
07-11-1998 03:13:09.55 - Send: AT<cr>
07-11-1998 03:13:09.56 - Recv: <cr><lf>OK<cr><lf>
07-11-1998 03:13:09.56 - Interpreted response: Ok
```

```
07-11-1998 03:13:09.56 - Send: AT&F1&B1&C1&D2E0Q0V1&A3S0=<cr>
07-11-1998 03:13:09.73 - Recv: <cr><lf>OK<cr><lf>
07-11-1998 03:13:09.73 - Interpreted response: Ok
07-11-1998 03:13:09.73 - Send: ATS7=60S19=0M1&M4&K1&H1&R2&I0B0X4<cr>
07-11-1998 03:13:09.97 - Recv: <cr><lf>OK<cr><lf>
07-11-1998 03:13:09.97 - Interpreted response: Ok
07-11-1998 03:13:09.97 - Dialing.
07-11-1998 03:13:09.97 - Send: ATDT#######<cr>
07-11-1998 03:13:15.73 - Recv: <cr><lf>BUSY<cr><lf>
07-11-1998 03:13:15.73 - Interpreted response: Busy
07-11-1998 03:13:17.28 - Session Statistics:
07-11-1998 03:13:17.28 -                  Reads : 26 bytes
07-11-1998 03:13:17.28 -                  Writes: 78 bytes
07-11-1998 03:13:17.28 - Courier V.Everything #2 closed.
07-11-1998 03:13:17.65 - Courier V.Everything #2 in use.
07-11-1998 03:13:17.69 - Modem type: Courier V.Everything
07-11-1998 03:13:17.69 - Modem inf path: MDMUSRCR.INF
07-11-1998 03:13:17.69 - Modem inf section: Modem29
07-11-1998 03:13:17.71 - 57600,N,8,1
07-11-1998 03:13:17.88 - 57600,N,8,1
07-11-1998 03:13:17.90 - Initializing modem.
07-11-1998 03:13:17.90 - Send: AT<cr>
07-11-1998 03:13:18.13 - Recv: <cr><lf>OK<cr><lf>
07-11-1998 03:13:18.13 - Interpreted response: Ok
07-11-1998 03:13:18.13 - Send: AT&F1&B1&C1&D2E0Q0V1&A3S0=<cr>
07-11-1998 03:13:18.38 - Recv: <cr><lf>OK<cr><lf>
07-11-1998 03:13:18.38 - Interpreted response: Ok
07-11-1998 03:13:18.38 - Send: ATS7=60S19=0M1&M4&K1&H1&R2&I0B0X4<cr>
07-11-1998 03:13:18.61 - Recv: <cr><lf>OK<cr><lf>
07-11-1998 03:13:18.61 - Interpreted response: Ok
07-11-1998 03:13:18.61 - Dialing.
07-11-1998 03:13:18.61 - Send: ATDT#######<cr>
07-11-1998 03:13:24.69 - Recv: <cr><lf>BUSY<cr><lf>
07-11-1998 03:13:24.69 - Interpreted response: Busy
07-11-1998 03:13:52.57 - Session Statistics:
07-11-1998 03:13:52.57 -                  Reads : 26 bytes
07-11-1998 03:13:52.57 -                  Writes: 75 bytes
07-11-1998 03:13:52.57 - Courier V.Everything #2 closed.
07-11-1998 03:13:52.93 - Courier V.Everything #2 in use.
07-11-1998 03:13:52.97 - Modem type: Courier V.Everything
07-11-1998 03:13:52.97 - Modem inf path: MDMUSRCR.INF
07-11-1998 03:13:52.97 - Modem inf section: Modem29
07-11-1998 03:13:52.98 - 57600,N,8,1
07-11-1998 03:13:53.17 - 57600,N,8,1
07-11-1998 03:13:53.17 - Initializing modem.
07-11-1998 03:13:53.17 - Send: AT<cr>
07-11-1998 03:13:53.41 - Recv: <cr><lf>OK<cr><lf>
07-11-1998 03:13:53.41 - Interpreted response: Ok
07-11-1998 03:13:53.41 - Send: AT&F1&B1&C1&D2E0Q0V1&A3S0=<cr>
07-11-1998 03:13:53.65 - Recv: <cr><lf>OK<cr><lf>
07-11-1998 03:13:53.65 - Interpreted response: Ok
07-11-1998 03:13:53.65 - Send: ATS7=60S19=0M1&M4&K1&H1&R2&I0B0X4<cr>
07-11-1998 03:13:53.89 - Recv: <cr><lf>OK<cr><lf>
07-11-1998 03:13:53.89 - Interpreted response: Ok
07-11-1998 03:13:53.89 - Dialing.
07-11-1998 03:13:53.89 - Send: ATDT#######<cr>
07-11-1998 03:13:59.72 - Recv: <cr><lf>BUSY<cr><lf>
07-11-1998 03:13:59.72 - Interpreted response: Busy
07-11-1998 03:14:01.27 - Session Statistics:
```

```
07-11-1998 03:14:01.27 - Reads : 26 bytes
07-11-1998 03:14:01.27 - Writes: 75 bytes
07-11-1998 03:14:01.27 - Courier V.Everything #2 closed.
07-11-1998 03:14:02.85 - Courier V.Everything #2 in use.
07-11-1998 03:14:02.88 - Modem type: Courier V.Everything
07-11-1998 03:14:02.88 - Modem inf path: MDMUSRCR.INF
07-11-1998 03:14:02.88 - Modem inf section: Modem29
07-11-1998 03:14:02.91 - 57600,N,8,1
07-11-1998 03:14:03.09 - 57600,N,8,1
07-11-1998 03:14:03.10 - Initializing modem.
07-11-1998 03:14:03.10 - Send: AT<cr>
07-11-1998 03:14:03.32 - Recv: <cr><lf>OK<cr><lf>
07-11-1998 03:14:03.32 - Interpreted response: Ok
07-11-1998 03:14:03.32 - Send: AT&F1&B1&C1&D2E0Q0V1&A3S0=<cr>
07-11-1998 03:14:03.57 - Recv: <cr><lf>OK<cr><lf>
07-11-1998 03:14:03.57 - Interpreted response: Ok
07-11-1998 03:14:03.57 - Send: ATS7=60S19=0M1&M4&K1&H1&R2&I0B0X4<cr>
07-11-1998 03:14:03.80 - Recv: <cr><lf>OK<cr><lf>
07-11-1998 03:14:03.80 - Interpreted response: Ok
07-11-1998 03:14:03.80 - Dialing.
07-11-1998 03:14:03.80 - Send: ATDT#######<cr>
07-11-1998 03:14:09.80 - Recv: <cr><lf>BUSY<cr><lf>
07-11-1998 03:14:09.80 - Interpreted response: Busy
07-11-1998 03:14:11.35 - Session Statistics:
07-11-1998 03:14:11.35 -                 Reads : 26 bytes
07-11-1998 03:14:11.35 -                 Writes: 75 bytes
07-11-1998 03:14:11.35 - Courier V.Everything #2 closed.
07-11-1998 03:14:14.13 - Courier V.Everything #2 in use.
07-11-1998 03:14:14.17 - Modem type: Courier V.Everything
07-11-1998 03:14:14.17 - Modem inf path: MDMUSRCR.INF
07-11-1998 03:14:14.17 - Modem inf section: Modem29
07-11-1998 03:14:14.18 - 57600,N,8,1
07-11-1998 03:14:14.39 - 57600,N,8,1
07-11-1998 03:14:14.39 - Initializing modem.
07-11-1998 03:14:14.39 - Send: AT<cr>
07-11-1998 03:14:18.03 - Recv: <no response>
07-11-1998 03:14:18.03 - WARNING: Unrecognized response. Retrying...
07-11-1998 03:14:18.03 - Send: AT<cr>
07-11-1998 03:14:18.03 - Recv: <cr><lf>OK<cr><lf>
07-11-1998 03:14:18.03 - Interpreted response: Ok
07-11-1998 03:14:18.03 - Send: AT&F1&B1&C1&D2E0Q0V1&A3S0=<cr>
07-11-1998 03:14:18.21 - Recv: <cr><lf>OK<cr><lf>
07-11-1998 03:14:18.21 - Interpreted response: Ok
07-11-1998 03:14:18.21 - Send: ATS7=60S19=0M1&M4&K1&H1&R2&I0B0X4<cr>
07-11-1998 03:14:18.44 - Recv: <cr><lf>OK<cr><lf>
07-11-1998 03:14:18.44 - Interpreted response: Ok
07-11-1998 03:14:18.45 - Dialing.
07-11-1998 03:14:18.45 - Send: ATDT#######<cr>
07-11-1998 03:14:24.77 - Recv: <cr><lf>BUSY<cr><lf>
07-11-1998 03:14:24.77 - Interpreted response: Busy
07-11-1998 03:18:46.78 - Session Statistics:
07-11-1998 03:18:46.78 -                 Reads : 26 bytes
07-11-1998 03:18:46.78 -                 Writes: 78 bytes
07-11-1998 03:18:46.78 - Courier V.Everything #2 closed.
07-11-1998 03:18:47.24 - Courier V.Everything #2 in use.
07-11-1998 03:18:47.29 - Modem type: Courier V.Everything
07-11-1998 03:18:47.29 - Modem inf path: MDMUSRCR.INF
07-11-1998 03:18:47.29 - Modem inf section: Modem29
07-11-1998 03:18:47.30 - 57600,N,8,1
```

```
07-11-1998 03:18:47.49 - 57600,N,8,1
07-11-1998 03:18:47.51 - Initializing modem.
07-11-1998 03:18:47.51 - Send: AT<cr>
07-11-1998 03:18:49.51 - Recv: <no response>
07-11-1998 03:18:49.51 - WARNING: Unrecognized response. Retrying...
07-11-1998 03:18:49.51 - Send: AT<cr>
07-11-1998 03:18:51.51 - Recv: <no response>
07-11-1998 03:18:51.51 - WARNING: Unrecognized response. Retrying...
07-11-1998 03:18:51.51 - Send: AT<cr>
07-11-1998 03:18:53.52 - Recv: <no response>
07-11-1998 03:18:53.52 - WARNING: Unrecognized response. Retrying...
07-11-1998 03:18:53.52 - Send: AT<cr>
07-11-1998 03:18:55.52 - Recv: <no response>
07-11-1998 03:18:55.52 - WARNING: Unrecognized response. Retrying...
07-11-1998 03:18:55.52 - Send: AT<cr>
07-11-1998 03:18:57.53 - Recv: <no response>
07-11-1998 03:18:57.53 - ERROR: Unable to recover from unrecognized
                          response.
07-11-1998 03:18:58.63 - Session Statistics:
07-11-1998 03:18:58.63 -                 Reads : 0 bytes
07-11-1998 03:18:58.63 -                 Writes: 15 bytes
07-11-1998 03:18:58.63 - Courier V.Everything #2 closed.
07-11-1998 03:20:07.23 - Courier V.Everything #2 in use.
07-11-1998 03:20:07.27 - Modem type: Courier V.Everything
07-11-1998 03:20:07.27 - Modem inf path: MDMUSRCR.INF
07-11-1998 03:20:07.27 - Modem inf section: Modem29
07-11-1998 03:20:07.28 - 57600,N,8,1
07-11-1998 03:20:07.48 - 57600,N,8,1
07-11-1998 03:20:07.49 - Initializing modem.
07-11-1998 03:20:07.49 - Send: AT<cr>
07-11-1998 03:20:09.52 - Recv: <no response>
07-11-1998 03:20:09.52 - WARNING: Unrecognized response. Retrying...
07-11-1998 03:20:09.52 - Send: AT<cr>
07-11-1998 03:20:09.52 - Recv: <cr><lf>OK<cr><lf>
07-11-1998 03:20:09.52 - Interpreted response: Ok
07-11-1998 03:20:09.52 - Send: AT&F1&B1&C1&D2E0Q0V1&A3S0=<cr>
07-11-1998 03:20:09.70 - Recv: <cr><lf>OK<cr><lf>
07-11-1998 03:20:09.70 - Interpreted response: Ok
07-11-1998 03:20:09.70 - Send: ATS7=60S19=0M1&M4&K1&H1&R2&I0B0X4<cr>
07-11-1998 03:20:09.95 - Recv: <cr><lf>OK<cr><lf>
07-11-1998 03:20:09.95 - Interpreted response: Ok
07-11-1998 03:20:09.95 - Dialing.
07-11-1998 03:20:09.95 - Send: ATDT#######<cr>
07-11-1998 03:20:16.10 - Recv: <cr><lf>BUSY<cr><lf>
07-11-1998 03:20:16.10 - Interpreted response: Busy
07-11-1998 03:20:17.67 - Session Statistics:
07-11-1998 03:20:17.67 -                 Reads : 26 bytes
07-11-1998 03:20:17.67 -                 Writes: 78 bytes
07-11-1998 03:20:17.67 - Courier V.Everything #2 closed.
07-11-1998 03:20:21.50 - Courier V.Everything #2 in use.
07-11-1998 03:20:21.54 - Modem type: Courier V.Everything
07-11-1998 03:20:21.54 - Modem inf path: MDMUSRCR.INF
07-11-1998 03:20:21.54 - Modem inf section: Modem29
07-11-1998 03:20:21.55 - 57600,N,8,1
07-11-1998 03:20:21.74 - 57600,N,8,1
07-11-1998 03:20:21.76 - Initializing modem.
07-11-1998 03:20:21.76 - Send: AT<cr>
07-11-1998 03:20:24.28 - Recv: <no response>
07-11-1998 03:20:24.28 - WARNING: Unrecognized response. Retrying...
```

```
07-11-1998 03:20:24.28 - Send: AT<cr>
07-11-1998 03:20:24.28 - Recv: <cr><lf>OK<cr><lf>
07-11-1998 03:20:24.28 - Interpreted response: Ok
07-11-1998 03:20:24.28 - Send: AT&F1&B1&C1&D2E0Q0V1&A3S0=<cr>
07-11-1998 03:20:24.50 - Recv: <cr><lf>OK<cr><lf>
07-11-1998 03:20:24.50 - Interpreted response: Ok
07-11-1998 03:20:24.50 - Send: ATS7=60S19=0M1&M4&K1&H1&R2&I0B0X4<cr>
07-11-1998 03:20:24.74 - Recv: <cr><lf>OK<cr><lf>
07-11-1998 03:20:24.74 - Interpreted response: Ok
07-11-1998 03:20:24.75 - Dialing.
07-11-1998 03:20:24.75 - Send: ATDT#######<cr>
07-11-1998 03:20:31.15 - Recv: <cr><lf>BUSY<cr><lf>
07-11-1998 03:20:31.15 - Interpreted response: Busy
07-11-1998 03:20:33.00 - Session Statistics:
07-11-1998 03:20:33.00 -                    Reads : 26 bytes
07-11-1998 03:20:33.00 -                    Writes: 78 bytes
07-11-1998 03:20:33.00 - Courier V.Everything #2 closed.
07-11-1998 03:20:36.26 - Courier V.Everything #2 in use.
07-11-1998 03:20:36.30 - Modem type: Courier V.Everything
07-11-1998 03:20:36.30 - Modem inf path: MDMUSRCR.INF
07-11-1998 03:20:36.30 - Modem inf section: Modem29
07-11-1998 03:20:36.31 - 57600,N,8,1
07-11-1998 03:20:36.52 - 57600,N,8,1
07-11-1998 03:20:36.52 - Initializing modem.
07-11-1998 03:20:36.52 - Send: AT<cr>
07-11-1998 03:20:39.59 - Recv: <no response>
07-11-1998 03:20:39.59 - WARNING: Unrecognized response. Retrying...
07-11-1998 03:20:39.59 - Send: AT<cr>
07-11-1998 03:20:39.61 - Recv: <cr><lf>OK<cr><lf>
07-11-1998 03:20:39.61 - Interpreted response: Ok
07-11-1998 03:20:39.61 - Send: AT&F1&B1&C1&D2E0Q0V1&A3S0=<cr>
07-11-1998 03:20:39.79 - Recv: <cr><lf>OK<cr><lf>
07-11-1998 03:20:39.79 - Interpreted response: Ok
07-11-1998 03:20:39.79 - Send: ATS7=60S19=0M1&M4&K1&H1&R2&I0B0X4<cr>
07-11-1998 03:20:40.02 - Recv: <cr><lf>OK<cr><lf>
07-11-1998 03:20:40.02 - Interpreted response: Ok
07-11-1998 03:20:40.02 - Dialing.
07-11-1998 03:20:40.02 - Send: ATDT#######<cr>
07-11-1998 03:20:45.95 - Hanging up the modem.
07-11-1998 03:20:45.95 - Send: <cr>
07-11-1998 03:20:46.27 - Recv: <cr><lf>NO CARRIER<cr><lf>
07-11-1998 03:20:46.27 - Interpreted response: No Carrier
07-11-1998 03:20:46.27 - Send: ATH<cr>
07-11-1998 03:20:46.50 - Recv: <cr><lf>OK<cr><lf>
07-11-1998 03:20:46.50 - Interpreted response: Ok
07-11-1998 03:20:47.61 - Session Statistics:
07-11-1998 03:20:47.61 -                    Reads : 38 bytes
07-11-1998 03:20:47.61 -                    Writes: 83 bytes
07-11-1998 03:20:47.61 - Courier V.Everything #2 closed.
07-11-1998 03:21:00.82 - Courier V.Everything #3 in use.
07-11-1998 03:21:00.86 - Modem type: Courier V.Everything
07-11-1998 03:21:00.86 - Modem inf path: MDMUSRCR.INF
07-11-1998 03:21:00.86 - Modem inf section: Modem29
07-11-1998 03:21:00.88 - 57600,N,8,1
07-11-1998 03:21:01.08 - 57600,N,8,1
07-11-1998 03:21:01.09 - Initializing modem.
07-11-1998 03:21:01.09 - Send: AT<cr>
07-11-1998 03:21:03.11 - Recv: <no response>
07-11-1998 03:21:03.11 - WARNING: Unrecognized response. Retrying...
```

```
07-11-1998 03:21:03.11 - Send: AT<cr>
07-11-1998 03:21:03.12 - Recv: <cr><lf>OK<cr><lf>
07-11-1998 03:21:03.12 - Interpreted response: Ok
07-11-1998 03:21:03.12 - Send: AT&F1&B1&C1&D2E0Q0V1&A3S0=<cr>
07-11-1998 03:21:03.30 - Recv: <cr><lf>OK<cr><lf>
07-11-1998 03:21:03.30 - Interpreted response: Ok
07-11-1998 03:21:03.30 - Send: ATS7=55S19=0M1&M4&K1&H1&R2&I0B0X4<cr>
07-11-1998 03:21:03.55 - Recv: <cr><lf>OK<cr><lf>
07-11-1998 03:21:03.55 - Interpreted response: Ok
07-11-1998 03:21:03.55 - Dialing.
07-11-1998 03:21:03.55 - Send: ATDT#######<cr>
07-11-1998 03:21:23.95 - Recv: <cr>
07-11-1998 03:21:23.95 - Interpreted response: Informative
07-11-1998 03:21:23.95 - Recv: <lf>
07-11-1998 03:21:23.95 - Interpreted response: Informative
07-11-1998 03:21:24.95 - Recv: CONNECT 31200/ARQ/V34/LAPM/V42BIS<cr><lf>
07-11-1998 03:21:24.95 - WARNING: Unrecognized response. Retrying...
07-11-1998 03:21:26.08 - Session Statistics:
07-11-1998 03:21:26.08 -                    Reads : 55 bytes
07-11-1998 03:21:26.08 -                    Writes: 78 bytes
07-11-1998 03:21:26.08 - Courier V.Everything #3 closed.
07-11-1998 03:24:13.96 - Courier V.Everything #2 in use.
07-11-1998 03:24:14.00 - Modem type: Courier V.Everything
07-11-1998 03:24:14.00 - Modem inf path: MDMUSRCR.INF
07-11-1998 03:24:14.00 - Modem inf section: Modem29
07-11-1998 03:24:14.02 - 57600,N,8,1
07-11-1998 03:24:14.22 - 57600,N,8,1
07-11-1998 03:24:14.24 - Initializing modem.
07-11-1998 03:24:14.24 - Send: AT<cr>
07-11-1998 03:24:16.25 - Recv: <no response>
07-11-1998 03:24:16.25 - WARNING: Unrecognized response. Retrying...
07-11-1998 03:24:16.25 - Send: AT<cr>
07-11-1998 03:24:16.27 - Recv: <cr><lf>OK<cr><lf>
07-11-1998 03:24:16.27 - Interpreted response: Ok
07-11-1998 03:24:16.27 - Send: AT&F1&B1&C1&D2E0Q0V1&A3S0=<cr>
07-11-1998 03:24:16.49 - Recv: <cr><lf>OK<cr><lf>
07-11-1998 03:24:16.49 - Interpreted response: Ok
07-11-1998 03:24:16.49 - Send: ATS7=60S19=0M1&M4&K1&H1&R2&I0B0X4<cr>
07-11-1998 03:24:16.72 - Recv: <cr><lf>OK<cr><lf>
07-11-1998 03:24:16.72 - Interpreted response: Ok
07-11-1998 03:24:16.72 - Dialing.
07-11-1998 03:24:16.72 - Send: ATDT#######<cr>
07-11-1998 03:24:22.41 - Recv: <cr><lf>BUSY<cr><lf>
07-11-1998 03:24:22.41 - Interpreted response: Busy
07-11-1998 03:24:23.96 - Session Statistics:
07-11-1998 03:24:23.96 -                    Reads : 26 bytes
07-11-1998 03:24:23.96 -                    Writes: 78 bytes
07-11-1998 03:24:23.96 - Courier V.Everything #2 closed.
07-11-1998 03:24:28.01 - Courier V.Everything #2 in use.
07-11-1998 03:24:28.04 - Modem type: Courier V.Everything
07-11-1998 03:24:28.05 - Modem inf path: MDMUSRCR.INF
07-11-1998 03:24:28.05 - Modem inf section: Modem29
07-11-1998 03:24:28.06 - 57600,N,8,1
07-11-1998 03:24:28.26 - 57600,N,8,1
07-11-1998 03:24:28.27 - Initializing modem.
07-11-1998 03:24:28.27 - Send: AT<cr>
07-11-1998 03:24:29.44 - Hanging up the modem.
07-11-1998 03:24:29.44 - Send: <cr>
07-11-1998 03:24:30.81 - Recv: <cr><lf>OK<cr><lf>
```

```
07-11-1998 03:24:30.81 - Interpreted response: Ok
07-11-1998 03:24:30.81 - Send: ATH<cr>
07-11-1998 03:24:31.04 - Recv: <cr><lf>OK<cr><lf>
07-11-1998 03:24:31.04 - Interpreted response: Ok
07-11-1998 03:24:32.16 - Session Statistics:
07-11-1998 03:24:32.16 - Reads : 12 bytes
07-11-1998 03:24:32.16 - Writes: 8 bytes
07-11-1998 03:24:32.16 - Courier V.Everything #2 closed.
07-12-1998 06:47:00.58 - Courier V.Everything #2 in use.
07-12-1998 06:47:00.61 - Modem type: Courier V.Everything
07-12-1998 06:47:00.61 - Modem inf path: MDMUSRCR.INF
07-12-1998 06:47:00.61 - Modem inf section: Modem29
07-12-1998 06:47:00.65 - 57600,N,8,1
07-12-1998 06:47:00.84 - 57600,N,8,1
07-12-1998 06:47:00.86 - Initializing modem.
07-12-1998 06:47:00.86 - Send: AT<cr>
07-12-1998 06:47:03.03 - Recv: <no response>
07-12-1998 06:47:03.03 - WARNING: Unrecognized response. Retrying...
07-12-1998 06:47:03.03 - Send: AT<cr>
07-12-1998 06:47:03.04 - Recv: <cr><lf>OK<cr><lf>
07-12-1998 06:47:03.04 - Interpreted response: Ok
07-12-1998 06:47:03.04 - Send: AT&F1&B1&C1&D2E0Q0V1&A3S0=<cr>
07-12-1998 06:47:03.25 - Recv: <cr><lf>OK<cr><lf>
07-12-1998 06:47:03.25 - Interpreted response: Ok
07-12-1998 06:47:03.25 - Send: ATS7=60S19=0M1&M4&K1&H1&R2&I0B0X4<cr>
07-12-1998 06:47:03.41 - Recv: <cr><lf>OK<cr><lf>
07-12-1998 06:47:03.41 - Interpreted response: Ok
07-12-1998 06:47:03.41 - Dialing.
07-12-1998 06:47:03.41 - Send: ATDT#######<cr>
07-12-1998 06:47:10.13 - Recv: <cr><lf>BUSY<cr><lf>
07-12-1998 06:47:10.13 - Interpreted response: Busy
07-12-1998 06:47:11.80 - Session Statistics:
07-12-1998 06:47:11.80 -                 Reads : 26 bytes
07-12-1998 06:47:11.80 -                 Writes: 78 bytes
07-12-1998 06:47:11.80 - Courier V.Everything #2 closed.
07-12-1998 06:47:15.40 - Courier V.Everything #2 in use.
07-12-1998 06:47:15.43 - Modem type: Courier V.Everything
07-12-1998 06:47:15.43 - Modem inf path: MDMUSRCR.INF
07-12-1998 06:47:15.44 - Modem inf section: Modem29
07-12-1998 06:47:15.45 - 57600,N,8,1
07-12-1998 06:47:15.65 - 57600,N,8,1
07-12-1998 06:47:15.66 - Initializing modem.
07-12-1998 06:47:15.66 - Send: AT<cr>
07-12-1998 06:47:18.75 - Recv: <no response>
07-12-1998 06:47:18.75 - WARNING: Unrecognized response. Retrying...
07-12-1998 06:47:18.75 - Send: AT<cr>
07-12-1998 06:47:18.75 - Recv: <cr><lf>OK<cr><lf>
07-12-1998 06:47:18.75 - Interpreted response: Ok
07-12-1998 06:47:18.75 - Send: AT&F1&B1&C1&D2E0Q0V1&A3S0=<cr>
07-12-1998 06:47:18.93 - Recv: <cr><lf>OK<cr><lf>
07-12-1998 06:47:18.93 - Interpreted response: Ok
07-12-1998 06:47:18.93 - Send: ATS7=60S19=0M1&M4&K1&H1&R2&I0B0X4<cr>
07-12-1998 06:47:19.16 - Recv: <cr><lf>OK<cr><lf>
07-12-1998 06:47:19.16 - Interpreted response: Ok
07-12-1998 06:47:19.16 - Dialing.
07-12-1998 06:47:19.16 - Send: ATDT#######<cr>
07-12-1998 06:47:25.08 - Recv: <cr><lf>BUSY<cr><lf>
07-12-1998 06:47:25.08 - Interpreted response: Busy
07-12-1998 06:47:26.63 - Session Statistics:
```

```
07-12-1998 06:47:26.63 -                    Reads : 26 bytes
07-12-1998 06:47:26.63 -                    Writes: 78 bytes
07-12-1998 06:47:26.63 - Courier V.Everything #2 closed.
07-12-1998 06:47:30.12 - Courier V.Everything #2 in use.
07-12-1998 06:47:30.16 - Modem type: Courier V.Everything
07-12-1998 06:47:30.16 - Modem inf path: MDMUSRCR.INF
07-12-1998 06:47:30.16 - Modem inf section: Modem29
07-12-1998 06:47:30.17 - 57600,N,8,1
07-12-1998 06:47:30.38 - 57600,N,8,1
07-12-1998 06:47:30.38 - Initializing modem.
07-12-1998 06:47:30.38 - Send: AT<cr>
07-12-1998 06:47:33.42 - Recv: <no response>
07-12-1998 06:47:33.42 - WARNING: Unrecognized response. Retrying...
07-12-1998 06:47:33.42 - Send: AT<cr>
07-12-1998 06:47:33.42 - Recv: <cr><lf>OK<cr><lf>
07-12-1998 06:47:33.42 - Interpreted response: Ok
07-12-1998 06:47:33.42 - Send: AT&F1&B1&C1&D2E0Q0V1&A3S0=<cr>
07-12-1998 06:47:33.65 - Recv: <cr><lf>OK<cr><lf>
07-12-1998 06:47:33.65 - Interpreted response: Ok
07-12-1998 06:47:33.65 - Send: ATS7=60S19=0M1&M4&K1&H1&R2&I0B0X4<cr>
07-12-1998 06:47:33.81 - Recv: <cr><lf>OK<cr><lf>
07-12-1998 06:47:33.81 - Interpreted response: Ok
07-12-1998 06:47:33.81 - Dialing.
07-12-1998 06:47:33.81 - Send: ATDT#######<cr>
07-12-1998 06:47:39.17 - Recv: <cr><lf>BUSY<cr><lf>
07-12-1998 06:47:39.17 - Interpreted response: Busy
07-12-1998 06:47:50.06 - Session Statistics:
07-12-1998 06:47:50.06 -                    Reads : 26 bytes
07-12-1998 06:47:50.06 -                    Writes: 78 bytes
07-12-1998 06:47:50.06 - Courier V.Everything #2 closed.
07-12-1998 06:47:50.19 - Courier V.Everything #2 in use.
07-12-1998 06:47:50.22 - Modem type: Courier V.Everything
07-12-1998 06:47:50.22 - Modem inf path: MDMUSRCR.INF
07-12-1998 06:47:50.22 - Modem inf section: Modem29
07-12-1998 06:47:50.25 - 57600,N,8,1
07-12-1998 06:47:50.43 - 57600,N,8,1
07-12-1998 06:47:50.44 - Initializing modem.
07-12-1998 06:47:50.44 - Send: AT<cr>
07-12-1998 06:47:50.69 - Recv: <cr><lf>OK<cr><lf>
07-12-1998 06:47:50.69 - Interpreted response: Ok
07-12-1998 06:47:50.69 - Send: AT&F1&B1&C1&D2E0Q0V1&A3S0=<cr>
07-12-1998 06:47:50.92 - Recv: <cr><lf>OK<cr><lf>
07-12-1998 06:47:50.92 - Interpreted response: Ok
07-12-1998 06:47:50.92 - Send: ATS7=60S19=0M1&M4&K1&H1&R2&I0B0X4<cr>
07-12-1998 06:47:51.17 - Recv: <cr><lf>OK<cr><lf>
07-12-1998 06:47:51.17 - Interpreted response: Ok
07-12-1998 06:47:51.17 - Dialing.
07-12-1998 06:47:51.17 - Send: ATDT#######<cr>
07-12-1998 06:47:57.06 - Hanging up the modem.
07-12-1998 06:47:57.06 - Send: <cr>
07-12-1998 06:47:57.18 - Recv: <cr><lf>BUSY<cr><lf>
07-12-1998 06:47:57.18 - Interpreted response: Busy
07-12-1998 06:47:57.18 - Send: ATH<cr>
07-12-1998 06:47:59.20 - Recv: <no response>
07-12-1998 06:47:59.20 - WARNING: Unrecognized response. Retrying...
07-12-1998 06:47:59.20 - Send: ATH<cr>
07-12-1998 06:47:59.41 - Recv: <cr>\#60>lf\#62>OK<cr><lf>
07-12-1998 06:47:59.41 - Interpreted response: Ok
07-12-1998 06:48:00.52 - Session Statistics:
```

```
07-12-1998 06:48:00.52 -                    Reads : 32 bytes
07-12-1998 06:48:00.52 -                    Writes: 84 bytes
07-12-1998 06:48:00.52 - Courier V.Everything #2 closed.
```

I keep this information on file for my network purposes. You can use this as a guideline to what you should consider when you baseline your communication server.

11.5 Cayman HDSL Router Functionality

Digital subscriber line technology is different from an ordinary analog POTS modem. When an analog POTS modem connects to a data service, such as an Internet service provider (ISP), it connects through the telephone voice network, a circuit-switched network. Since the telephone network is essentially all digital, this is achieved by digitizing the modem analog signal into a 64-kbps digital data stream, utilizing 8-bit samples, 8000 times per second. This 8-kHz sampling rate limits the bandwidth on the analog telephone line to 4 kHz.

The wire which runs between the telephone central office and a subscriber's home can relay a signal as high as 1 MHz, provided the home is within 18,000 ft of the central office, and there is no unusual provisioning on the line. Since the existing telephone network cannot communicate more than 4 kHz, some special arrangements are required to allow the subscriber to use this line for faster communications. Using one version of DSL, the telephone company installs a special kind of modem in the telephone central office and one in the subscriber's home or business. These two modems utilize up to 500 kHz of bandwidth and communicate 784 kbps bidirectionally over a single twisted-pair copper cable. Utilizing two twisted pairs, this technology, called a *high-bit-rate digital subscriber line* (HDSL), is used to provision most new T1 lines in the United States. Consider Figure 11.5, which shows a typical HDSL installation with the local exchange and HDSL modem at each end. HDSL is a good technology, but it has some limitations that may or may not affect your situation. The technology is *baseband,* which means that it requires all the bandwidth from essentially 0 Hz to 500 kHz. This means that it cannot support simultaneous telephone service and high-speed digital communications over the same telephone line.

In the early 1990s, some telephone companies offered a new service, nicknamed "video dial tone." This meant that the telephone companies could get into the business of delivering video to consumers' homes. Some companies chose to use the existing telephone lines to deliver this service to their subscribers; but this required a second telephone line to the subscriber's home. However, at the time there were limitations with regard to the telephone network. To avoid this problem, DSL technology was needed that could provide high-speed communications over the existing telephone line connected to the subscriber's home.

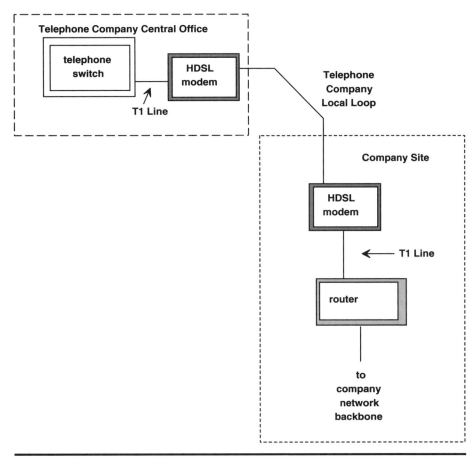

Figure 11.5   HDSL Implementation

A group of engineers at AT&T Bell Labs had such a technology. Bell Labs utilized essentially the same techniques as are used in analog Plain Old Telephone Service (POTS) modems, simply extending the bandwidth from 4 kHz to about 1 MHz. They developed this technique, and at that time digital signal processors (DSPs) were not as powerful as they are today. To lower the processing load, they used a modulation technique called *carrierless amplitude and phase* (CAP). This is essentially the same as *quadrature amplitude modulation* (QAM), but requires less multiplication. This technology is also known generically as the *asymmetric digital subscriber line* (ADSL). Hence, it allowed data rates from the central office to the home at rates of up to 1.5 Mbps, and from the home to the central office at 64 kbps.

I could include much more detail about xDSL technology, but suffice it to say that it is a technology that, if implemented correctly, can solve a lot of problems. Because of the technical depth of Cayman Systems staff, I recommend that you contact them at *www.cayman.com* and let them help you in your decisions.

11.6 How to Baseline Communication Servers and HDSL Routers

In order to get a good understanding of the functionality of the router and the communication server, I performed some traces with a stream of video through the system. For my purposes, this was the most important aspect. This type of scenario, in my environment, is the best way to load the network components and take an accurate sample reading.

First, consider some basic vital sign measurements. Afterward, consider the frames and details of those frames. I read this trace line by line and bold-faced those components which are important for my network. Your environment may vary in some aspects, but this level of detail is important.

```
                    TCP/IP Vital Signs Measurement
Frame Range: 80..432
                  Threshold   Current   Average    Peak      Total
Network Util %        10        0.39      0.33      0.42
IP Util %              5        0.36      0.31      0.39
Network Packets     1200         15        11        16        352
IP Packets           800         15        10        16        328
IP Broadcast          10          0         0         0          0
IP Fragment            5          0         0         0          0
ICMP Redirects         1          0         0         0          0
ICMP Unreach          10          0         0         0          0
Low TTL                1          0         0         0          0
IP Packet Size     18000        305       365       405
SNMP Get/Set Pkts     10          0         0         0          0
SNMP Trap Pkts        10          0         0         0          0
DNS Packets           10          0         0         0          0
ARP Packets           10          0         0         0          0
Low Window             5          0         0         0          0
Reset Connections      5          0         0         0          0
Routing Packets       50          0         0         0          0
Buffer Overwrites    100          0         0         0          0
Start Time:  Aug 7 98  @ 15:09:49
Sample Time: Aug 7 98  @ 15:10:19
```

The following is the trace of video traffic flowing through the routers and the communication server:

```
********************************************************************
**                                                          *****
**              HEWLETT PACKARD NETWORK ADVISOR             *****
**                                                          *****
**      Measurement:    Network Stack Decode                *****
**      Print Type:     All Frames                          *****
**      Open Views:     Summary Detailed                    *****
**      Display Mode:   Viewing All Frames                  *****
**      Print Date:     08/07/98                            *****
```

```
**    Print Time:    15:14:35                          *****
*********************************************************************
_____

1  13:54.529 220.100.100.172     220.100.100.178     TCP
    S = 1029 D = 10007    ACK = 13115331 WIN = 6096
```

Frame: 1   Time: Aug 07@15:13:54.5294367   Length: 64
***** DETAILED FORMAT *****

```
   TCP
```

Source port	**1029**	**User prog**
port		
Destination port	**10007**	**User prog.**
port		
Sequence number	2700475	
Ack number	13115331	Seqnum of next expected data
byte		
Data offset	5	Number of
32-bit words in		
header		
Reserved	....-0000-00..-....	
Flags:	..01-0000	
Urgent flag	..0.....	
Ack flag	...1....	Ack number field is
significant		
Push flag	....0...	
Reset flag	.....0..	
Syn flag	......0.	
Fin flag	0	
Window	6096	
Checksum	95-51	
Urgent pointer	0	Not used
> New address		
> State	**Data transfer**	
IP		
Version	4	
Internet header length	5	(32 bit words)
Precedence	000.-....	Routine
Delay	...0-....	Delay normal
Throughput	....-0...	Throughput normal
Reliability	....-.0..	Reliability normal
Total Length	**40**	
Identification	23147	
May / Do Not Fragment	.1..-....	Fragmentation not
allowed		
Last / More Fragments	..0.-....	Last fragment
Offset	0	
Time To Live	128	
Next Protocol	6	TCP
Checksum	1E-3D	
Source	**220.100.100.172**	
Destination	**220.100.100.178**	
> Data size	**20**	
Padding:		
00-00-00-00-00-00		
802.3/Ethernet		
Destination address	00-80-D4-00-EB-AA	Individual, global
Source address	00-60-08-98-1D-33	Individual, global
Type	08-00	IP
Frame check sequence	FA-A8-1C-D7	
> Data size	**46**	

```
2    13:54.535 220.100.100.178    220.100.100.172    TCP
     S = 10007 D = 1029    ACK = 2700475  SEQ = 13115331 LEN = 533
     WIN = 1536
```

Frame: 2   **Time: Aug 07@15:13:54.5356963 Length: 591**
                    ***** DETAILED FORMAT *****

TCP

Source port	**10007**	**User prog.**
port		
Destination port	**1029**	**User prog.**
port		
Sequence number	13115331	
Ack number	2700475	Seqnum of next expected data
byte		
Data offset	5	Number of
32-bit words in		
header		
Reserved	....-0000-00..-....	
Flags:	..01-1000	
Urgent flag	..0.....	
Ack flag	...1....	Ack number field is
significant		
Push flag	....1...	Sender requests immediate
delivery		
Reset flag	.....0..	
Syn flag	......0.	
Fin flag	0	
Window	1536	
Checksum	A5-82	
Urgent pointer	0	Not used
> Data size	**533**	
> New address		
> State	**Data transfer**	
IP		
Version	4	
Internet header length	5	(32 bit words)
Precedence	000.-....	Routine
Delay	...0-....	Delay normal
Throughput	....-0...	Throughput normal
Reliability	....-.0..	Reliability normal
Total Length	**573**	
Identification	58757	
May / Do Not Fragment	.0..-....	Fragmentation allowed
Last / More Fragments	..0.-....	Last fragment
Offset	0	
Time To Live	64	
Next Protocol	6	TCP
Checksum	11-0E	
Source	**220.100.100.178**	
Destination	**220.100.100.172**	
> Data size	**553**	
802.3/Ethernet		
Destination address	00-60-08-98-1D-33	Individual, global
Source address	00-80-D4-00-EB-AA	Individual, global
Type	08-00	IP
Frame check sequence	72-5D-C5-E3	
> Data size	**573**	

```
3    13:54.729 220.100.100.172    220.100.100.178    TCP
     S = 1029 D = 10007    ACK = 13115864 WIN = 5563
```

```
Frame: 3          Time: Aug 07@15:13:54.7296705  Length: 64
                       ***** DETAILED FORMAT *****
   TCP
Source port                 1029                    User prog.
port
Destination port            10007                   User prog.
port
Sequence number             2700475
Ack number                  13115864          Seqnum of next expected data
 byte
Data offset                 5                        Number of
32-bit words in
 header
Reserved                    ....-0000-00..-....
Flags:                      ..01-0000
 Urgent flag                ..0.....
 Ack flag                   ...1....           Ack number field is
 significant
 Push flag                  ....0...
 Reset flag                 .....0..
 Syn flag                   ......0.
 Fin flag                   .......0
Window                      5563
Checksum                    95-51
Urgent pointer              0                        Not used
> State                     Data transfer
   IP
Version                     4
Internet header length      5                        (32 bit words)
Precedence                  000.-....                Routine
Delay                       ...0-....                Delay normal
Throughput                  ....-0...                Throughput normal
Reliability                 ....-.0..                Reliability normal
Total Length                40
Identification              23403
May / Do Not Fragment       .1..-....          Fragmentation not allowed
Last / More Fragments       ..0.-....                Last fragment
Offset                      0
Time To Live                128
Next Protocol               6                        TCP
Checksum                    1D-3D
Source                      220.100.100.172
Destination                 220.100.100.178
> Data size                 20
Padding:
   00-00-00-00-00-00
   802.3/Ethernet
Destination address         00-80-D4-00-EB-AA        Individual, global
Source address              00-60-08-98-1D-33        Individual, global
Type                        08-00                    IP
Frame check sequence        F0-52-07-C6
> Data size                 46
_____
4    13:54.736 220.100.100.178   220.100.100.172        TCP
     S = 10007 D = 1029    ACK = 2700475 SEQ = 13115864 LEN = 749
     WIN = 1536
Frame: 4          Time: Aug 07@15:13:54.7363501  Length: 807
                       ***** DETAILED FORMAT *****
   TCP
Source port                 10007                   User prog.
```

```
port
Destination port          1029                    User prog.
port
Sequence number           13115864
Ack number                2700475          Seqnum of next expected data
 byte
Data offset               5                Number of
32-bit words in
 header
Reserved                  ....-0000-00..-....
Flags:                    ..01-1000
 Urgent flag              ..0.....
 Ack flag                 ...1....          Ack number field is
 significant
 Push flag                ....1...          Sender requests immediate
 delivery
 Reset flag               .....0..
 Syn flag                 ......0.
 Fin flag                 .......0
Window                    1536
Checksum                  C6-2F
Urgent pointer            0                 Not used
> Data size               749
> State                   Data transfer
  IP
Version                   4
Internet header length    5                 (32 bit words)
Precedence                000.-....          Routine
Delay                     ...0-....          Delay normal
Throughput                ....-0...          Throughput normal
Reliability               ....-.0..          Reliability normal
Total Length              789
Identification            58758
May / Do Not Fragment     .0..-....          Fragmentation allowed
Last / More Fragments     ..0.-....          Last fragment
Offset                    0
Time To Live              64
Next Protocol             6                 TCP
Checksum                  10-35
Source                    220.100.100.178
Destination               220.100.100.172
> Data size               769
  802.3/Ethernet
Destination address       00-60-08-98-1D-33   Individual, global
Source address            00-80-D4-00-EB-AA   Individual, global
Type                      08-00               IP
Frame check sequence      A4-77-F8-CE
> Data size               789
```

```
5    13:54.929 220.100.100.172     220.100.100.178TCP
          S = 1029 D = 10007    ACK = 13116613 WIN = 6096
Frame: 5            Time: Aug 07@15:13:54.9293546  Length: 64
                    ***** DETAILED FORMAT *****
TCP
Source port               1029                    User prog.
port
Destination port          10007                   User prog.
port
Sequence number           2700475
```

Ack number byte	13116613	Seqnum of next expected data
Data offset 32-bit words in header	5	Number of
Reserved	....-0000-00..-....	
Flags:	..01-0000	
Urgent flag	..0.....	
Ack flag significant	...1....	Ack number field is
Push flag	....0...	
Reset flag	.....0..	
Syn flag	......0.	
Fin flag	0	
Window	6096	
Checksum	90-4F	
Urgent pointer	0	Not used
> State	**Data transfer**	
IP		
Version	4	
Internet header length	5	(32 bit words)
Precedence	000.-....	Routine
Delay	...0-....	Delay normal
Throughput	....-0...	Throughput normal
Reliability	....-.0..	Reliability normal
Total Length	**40**	
Identification	23659	
May / Do Not Fragment	.1..-....	Fragmentation not allowed
Last / More Fragments	..0.-....	Last fragment
Offset	0	
Time To Live	128	
Next Protocol	6	TCP
Checksum	1C-3D	
Source	**220.100.100.172**	
Destination	**220.100.100.178**	
> Data size	**20**	
Padding: 00-00-00-00-00-00		
802.3/Ethernet		
Destination address	00-80-D4-00-EB-AA	Individual, global
Source address	00-60-08-98-1D-33	Individual, global
Type	08-00	IP
Frame check sequence	7C-F9-E9-5D	
> Data size	**46**	

6	13:54.935 220.100.100.178	220.100.100.172		TCP
	S = 10007 D = 1029	ACK = 2700475 SEQ = 13116613 LEN = 552		
	WIN = 1536			

Frame: 6   Time: Aug 07@15:13:54.9355334   Length: 610
***** DETAILED FORMAT *****

TCP		
Source port port	**10007**	**User prog.**
Destination port port	**1029**	**User prog.**
Sequence number	13116613	
Ack number byte	2700475	Seqnum of next expected data
Data offset	5	Number of

```
32-bit words in
 header
Reserved                    ....-0000-00..-....
Flags:                      ..01-1000
 Urgent flag                ..0.....
 Ack flag                   ...1....              Ack number field is
 significant
 Push flag                  ....1...              Sender requests immediate
 delivery
 Reset flag                 .....0..
 Syn flag                   ......0.
 Fin flag                   .......0
Window                      1536
Checksum                    2F-F3
Urgent pointer              0                     Not used
> Data size                 552
> State                     Data transfer
 IP
Version                     4
Internet header length      5                     (32 bit words)
Precedence                  000.-....             Routine
Delay                       ...0-....             Delay normal
Throughput                  ....-0...             Throughput normal
Reliability                 ....-.0..             Reliability normal
Total Length                592
Identification              58759
May / Do Not Fragment       .0..-....             Fragmentation allowed
Last / More Fragments       ..0.-....             Last fragment
Offset                      0
Time To Live                64
Next Protocol               6                     TCP
Checksum                    10-F9
Source                      220.100.100.178
Destination                 220.100.100.172
> Data size                 572
 802.3/Ethernet
Destination address         00-60-08-98-1D-33     Individual, global
Source address              00-80-D4-00-EB-AA     Individual, global
Type                        08-00                 IP
Frame check sequence        9F-5F-3B-3C
> Data size                 592
```

```
7    13:55.129 220.100.100.172    220.100.100.178          TCP
     S = 1029 D = 10007    ACK = 13117165 WIN = 5544
Frame: 7          Time: Aug 07@15:13:55.1295755  Length: 64
                    ***** DETAILED FORMAT *****
 TCP
Source port                 1029                  User prog.
port
Destination port            10007                 User prog.
port
Sequence number             2700475
Ack number                    13117165            Seqnum of next
expected data
 byte
Data offset                 5                     Number of
32-bit words in
 header
Reserved                    ....-0000-00..-....
```

```
Flags:                          ..01-0000
 Urgent flag                    ..0.....
 Ack flag                       ...1....              Ack number field is
 significant
 Push flag                      ....0...
 Reset flag                     .....0..
 Syn flag                       ......0.
 Fin flag                       .......0
Window                          5544
Checksum                        90-4F
Urgent pointer                  0                     Not used
> State                         Data transfer
  IP
Version                         4
Internet header length          5                     (32 bit words)
Precedence                      000.-....             Routine
Delay                           ...0-....             Delay normal
Throughput                      ....-0..              Throughput normal
Reliability                     ....-.0..             Reliability normal
Total Length                    40
Identification                  23915
May / Do Not Fragment           .1..-....             Fragmentation not allowed
Last / More Fragments           ..0.-....             Last fragment
Offset                          0
Time To Live                    128
Next Protocol                   6                     TCP
Checksum                        1B-3D
Source                          220.100.100.172
Destination                     220.100.100.178
> Data size                     20
Padding:
  00-00-00-00-00-00
  802.3/Ethernet
Destination address             00-80-D4-00-EB-AA     Individual, global
Source address                  00-60-08-98-1D-33     Individual, global
Type                            08-00                 IP
Frame check sequence            A8-A4-56-C8
> Data size                     46
```

```
8     13:55.136 220.100.100.178      220.100.100.172        TCP
      S = 10007 D = 1029     ACK = 2700475 SEQ = 13117165 LEN = 795
      WIN = 1536
```
Frame: 8   Time: Aug 07@15:13:55.1362022 Length: 853
***** DETAILED FORMAT *****

```
  TCP
Source port                     10007                 User prog.
port
Destination port                1029                  User prog.
port
Sequence number                 13117165
Ack number                       2700475                      Seqnum of next
expected data
 byte
Data offset                     5                     Number of
32-bit words in
 header
Reserved                        ....-0000-00..-....
Flags:                          ..01-1000
 Urgent flag                    ..0.....
```

```
Ack flag                    ...1....              Ack number field is
significant
Push flag                   ....1...              Sender requests immediate
delivery
Reset flag                  .....0..
Syn flag                    ......0.
Fin flag                    .......0
Window                      1536
Checksum                    59-3E
Urgent pointer              0                      Not used
```
> Data size   **795**
> State   **Data transfer**
```
  IP
Version                     4
Internet header length      5                      (32 bit words)
Precedence                  000.-....              Routine
Delay                       ...0-....              Delay normal
Throughput                  ....-0...              Throughput normal
Reliability                 ....-.0..              Reliability normal
```
Total Length   **835**
```
Identification              58760
May / Do Not Fragment       .0..-....              Fragmentation allowed
Last / More Fragments       ..0.-....              Last fragment
Offset                      0
Time To Live                64
Next Protocol               6                      TCP
Checksum                    10-05
```
Source   **220.100.100.178**
Destination   **220.100.100.172**
> Data size   **815**
```
  802.3/Ethernet
Destination address         00-60-08-98-1D-33      Individual, global
Source address              00-80-D4-00-EB-AA      Individual, global
Type                        08-00                  IP
Frame check sequence        E6-B8-43-59
```
> Data size   **835**

```
9    13:55.329 220.100.100.172      220.100.100.178          TCP
     S = 1029 D = 10007    ACK = 13117960 WIN = 6096
```
Frame: 9   **Time: Aug 07@15:13:55.3293556 Length: 64**
```
                   ***** DETAILED FORMAT *****
  TCP
```
Source port   **1029**   **User prog.**
port
Destination port   **10007**   **User prog.**
port
```
Sequence number             2700475
Ack number                  13117960               Seqnum of next expected data
  byte
Data offset                 5                      Number of
32-bit words in
  header
Reserved                    ....-0000-00..-....
Flags:                      ..01-0000
  Urgent flag               ..0.....
  Ack flag                  ...1....               Ack number field is
  significant
  Push flag                 ....0...
  Reset flag                .....0..
```

```
Syn flag                      ......0.
Fin flag                      .......0
Window                        6096
Checksum                      8B-0C
Urgent pointer                0                    Not used
> State                       Data transfer
  IP
Version                       4
Internet header length        5                    (32 bit words)
Precedence                    000.-....            Routine
Delay                         ...0-....            Delay normal
Throughput                    ....-0...            Throughput normal
Reliability                   ....-.0..            Reliability normal
Total Length                  40
Identification                24171
May / Do Not Fragment         .1..-....            Fragmentation not allowed
Last / More Fragments         ..0.-....            Last fragment
Offset                        0
Time To Live                  128
Next Protocol                 6                    TCP
Checksum                      1A-3D
Source                        220.100.100.172
Destination                   220.100.100.178
> Data size                   20
Padding:
   00-00-00-00-00-00
  802.3/Ethernet
Destination address           00-80-D4-00-EB-AA    Individual, global
Source address                00-60-08-98-1D-33    Individual, global
Type                          08-00                IP
Frame check sequence          A1-4B-8A-6D
> Data size                   46
```

```
10   13:55.337 220.100.100.178   220.100.100.172   TCP
     S = 10007 D = 1029   ACK = 2700475 SEQ = 13117960 LEN = 496
     WIN = 1536
```

Frame: 10   Time: Aug 07@15:13:55.3370648 Length: 554
***** DETAILED FORMAT *****

```
  TCP
Source port                   10007                User prog.
port
Destination port              1029                 User prog.
port
Sequence number               13117960
Ack number                    2700475              Seqnum of next expected data
  byte
Data offset                   5                    Number of
32-bit words in
  header
Reserved                      ....-0000-00..-....
Flags:                        ..01-1000
 Urgent flag                  ..0.....
 Ack flag                     ...1....             Ack number field is
 significant
 Push flag                    ....1...             Sender requests immediate
 delivery
 Reset flag                   .....0..
 Syn flag                     ......0.
 Fin flag                     .......0
```

```
Window                        1536
Checksum                      19-53
Urgent pointer                0                    Not used
> Data size                   496
> State                       Data transfer
  IP
Version                       4
Internet header length        5                    (32 bit words)
Precedence                    000.-....            Routine
Delay                         ...0-....            Delay normal
Throughput                    ....-0...            Throughput normal
Reliability                   ....-.0..            Reliability normal
Total Length                  536
Identification                58761
May / Do Not Fragment         .0..-....            Fragmentation allowed
Last / More Fragments         ..0.-....            Last fragment
Offset                        0
Time To Live                  64
Next Protocol                 6                    TCP
Checksum                      11-2F
Source                        220.100.100.178
Destination                   220.100.100.172
> Data size                   516
  802.3/Ethernet
Destination address           00-60-08-98-1D-33    Individual, global
Source address                00-80-D4-00-EB-AA    Individual, global
Type                          08-00                IP
Frame check sequence          A8-96-98-A8
> Data size                   536
```

```
11   13:55.539 220.100.100.172    220.100.100.178        TCP
     S = 1029 D = 10007     ACK = 13118456 WIN = 5600
```
Frame: 11   Time: Aug 07@15:13:55.5392769 Length: 64
```
                     ***** DETAILED FORMAT *****
  TCP
```
Source port   **1029**   **User prog.**
port
Destination port   **10007**   **User prog.**
port
```
Sequence number               2700475
Ack number                    13118456             Seqnum of next expected data
 byte
Data offset                   5                    Number of
32-bit words in
 header
Reserved                      ....-0000-00..-....
Flags:                        ..01-0000
 Urgent flag                  ..0.....
 Ack flag                     ...1....             Ack number field is
 significant
 Push flag                    ....0...
 Reset flag                   .....0..
 Syn flag                     ......0.
 Fin flag                     .......0
Window                        5600
Checksum                      8B-0C
Urgent pointer                0                    Not used
```
> State   **Data transfer**
```
  IP
```

```
Version                      4
Internet header length       5                          (32 bit words)
Precedence                   000.-....                  Routine
Delay                        ...0-....                  Delay normal
Throughput                   ....-0...                  Throughput normal
Reliability                  ....-.0..                  Reliability normal
Total Length                 40
Identification               24427
May / Do Not Fragment        .1..-....                  Fragmentation not allowed
Last / More Fragments        ..0.-....                  Last fragment
Offset                       0
Time To Live                 128
Next Protocol                6                           TCP
Checksum                     19-3D
```
Source   **220.100.100.172**
Destination   **220.100.100.178**
> Data size   **20**
```
Padding:
  00-00-00-00-00-00
  802.3/Ethernet
Destination address          00-80-D4-00-EB-AA          Individual, global
Source address               00-60-08-98-1D-33          Individual, global
Type                         08-00                       IP
Frame check sequence         B4-DA-B1-8A
```
> Data size   **46**

```
12   13:55.545 220.100.100.178   220.100.100.172          TCP
     S = 10007 D = 1029     ACK = 2700475 SEQ = 13118456 LEN = 796
     WIN = 1536
```
Frame: 12   **Time: Aug 07@15:13:55.5458853 Length: 854**
                     ***** DETAILED FORMAT *****
```
  TCP
```
Source port   **10007**   **User prog.**
port
Destination port   **1029**   **User prog.**
port
```
Sequence number              13118456
Ack number                   2700475                     Seqnum of next expected data
 byte
Data offset                  5                           Number of
32-bit words in
 header
Reserved                     ....-0000-00..-....
Flags:                       ..01-1000
 Urgent flag                 ..0.....
 Ack flag                    ...1....                     Ack number field is
 significant
 Push flag                   ....1...                     Sender requests immediate
 delivery
 Reset flag                  .....0..
 Syn flag                    ......0.
 Fin flag                    .......0
Window                       1536
Checksum                     D1-B4
Urgent pointer               0                           Not used
```
> Data size   **796**
> State   **Data transfer**
```
  IP
Version                      4
```

```
Internet header length   5                    (32 bit words)
Precedence               000.-....            Routine
Delay                    ...0-....            Delay normal
Throughput               ....-0...            Throughput normal
Reliability              ....-.0..            Reliability normal
Total Length             836
Identification           58762
May / Do Not Fragment    .0..-....            Fragmentation allowed
Last / More Fragments    ..0.-....            Last fragment
Offset                   0
Time To Live             64
Next Protocol            6                    TCP
Checksum                 10-02
```
Source   **220.100.100.178**
Destination   **220.100.100.172**
> Data size   **816**
```
 802.3/Ethernet
Destination address      00-60-08-98-1D-33    Individual, global
Source address           00-80-D4-00-EB-AA    Individual, global
Type                     08-00                IP
Frame check sequence     56-42-29-E8
> Data size              836
```

```
13   13:55.582 220.100.100.172   220.100.100.178        TCP
     S = 1029 D = 10007     ACK = 13119252 SEQ = 2700475 LEN = 47
     WIN = 6096
```
Frame: 13   **Time: Aug 07@15:13:55.5825635 Length: 105**
```
                  ***** DETAILED FORMAT *****
   TCP
```
Source port   **1029**   **User prog.**
port
Destination port   **10007**   **User prog.**
port
```
Sequence number          2700475
Ack number               13119252             Seqnum of next expected data
byte
Data offset              5                    Number of
32-bit words in
 header
Reserved                 ....-0000-00..-....
Flags:                   ..01-1000
 Urgent flag             ..0.....
 Ack flag                ...1....             Ack number field is
significant
 Push flag               ....1...             Sender requests immediate
delivery
 Reset flag              .....0..
 Syn flag                ......0.
 Fin flag                .......0
Window                   6096
Checksum                 09-32
Urgent pointer           0                    Not used
```
> Data size   **47**
> State   **Data transfer**
```
   IP
Version                  4
Internet header length   5                    (32 bit words)
Precedence               000.-....            Routine
Delay                    ...0-....            Delay normal
```

```
Throughput                 ....-0...            Throughput normal
Reliability                ....-.0..            Reliability normal
Total Length               87
Identification             25707
May / Do Not Fragment      .1..-....            Fragmentation not allowed
Last / More Fragments      ..0.-....            Last fragment
Offset                     0
Time To Live               128
Next Protocol              6                    TCP
Checksum                   14-0E
```
Source   **220.100.100.172**
Destination   **220.100.100.178**
```
> Data size                67
 802.3/Ethernet
Destination address        00-80-D4-00-EB-AA    Individual, global
Source address             00-60-08-98-1D-33    Individual, global
Type                       08-00                IP
Frame check sequence       97-BE-C2-9A
> Data size                87
```

```
14   13: 55.589 220.100.100.178   220.100.100.172        TCP
     S = 10007 D = 1029      ACK = 2700522 SEQ = 13119252 LEN = 209
     WIN = 1536
```
Frame: 14   **Time: Aug 07@15:13:55.5892311**   **Length: 267**
```
                      ***** DETAILED FORMAT *****
   TCP
```
Source port   **10007**   **User prog.**
port
Destination port   **1029**   **User prog.**
port
```
Sequence number            13119252
Ack number                 2700522              Seqnum of next expected data
 byte
Data offset                5                    Number of 32-bit
words in
 header
Reserved                   ....-0000-00..-....
Flags:                     ..01-1000
 Urgent flag               ..0.....
 Ack flag                  ...1....             Ack number field is
significant
Push flag                  ....1...             Sender requests immediate
 delivery
 Reset flag                .....0..
 Syn flag                  ......0.
 Fin flag                  .......0
Window                     1536
Checksum                   12-23
Urgent pointer             0                    Not used
```
> Data size   **209**
> State   **Data transfer**
```
   IP
Version                    4
Internet header length     5                    (32 bit words)
Precedence                 000.-....            Routine
Delay                      ...0-....            Delay normal
Throughput                 ....-0...            Throughput normal
Reliability                ....-.0..            Reliability normal
Total Length               249
```

```
Identification            58763
May / Do Not Fragment     .0..-....              Fragmentation allowed
Last / More Fragments     ..0.-....              Last fragment
Offset                    0
Time To Live              64
Next Protocol             6                      TCP
Checksum                  12-4C
```
Source   220.100.100.178
Destination   220.100.100.172
> Data size   229
```
 802.3/Ethernet
Destination address       00-60-08-98-1D-33      Individual, global
Source address            00-80-D4-00-EB-AA      Individual, global
Type                      08-00                  IP
Frame check sequence      99-28-52-B9
> Data size                249
```

```
15   13:55.589 220.100.100.172   220.100.100.178          TCP
       S = 1029  D = 10007    ACK = 13119461  SEQ = 2700522  LEN = 141
       WIN = 5887
```
Frame: 15   Time: Aug 07@15:13:55.5898057   Length: 199
```
                  ***** DETAILED FORMAT *****
   TCP
```
Source port   1029   User prog.
port
Destination port   10007   User prog.
port
```
Sequence number           2700522
Ack number                13119461               Seqnum of next expected data
 byte
Data offset               5                      Number of
32-bit words in
 header
Reserved                  ....-0000-00..-....
Flags:                    ..01-1000
 Urgent flag              ..0.....
 Ack flag                 ...1....               Ack number field is
significant
 Push flag                ....1...               Sender requests immediate
delivery
 Reset flag               .....0..
 Syn flag                 ......0.
 Fin flag                 .......0
Window                    5887
Checksum                  43-DC
Urgent pointer            0                      Not used
```
 Data size   141
> State   Data transfer
```
  IP
Version                   4
Internet header length    5                      (32 bit words)
Precedence                000.-....              Routine
Delay                     ...0-....              Delay normal
Throughput                ....-0...              Throughput normal
Reliability               ....-.0..              Reliability normal
Total Length              181
Identification            25963
May / Do Not Fragment     .1..-....              Fragmentation not allowed
Last / More Fragments     ..0.-....              Last fragment
```

```
Offset                      0
Time To Live                128
Next Protocol               6                   TCP
Checksum                    12-B0
Source                      220.100.100.172
Destination                 220.100.100.178
> Data size                 161
 802.3/Ethernet
Destination address         00-80-D4-00-EB-AA   Individual, global
Source address              00-60-08-98-1D-33   Individual, global
Type                        08-00               IP
Frame check sequence        F8-DF-91-8F
> Data size                 181
```

```
16    13:55.613 WellfleetE8-8F-1B 01-80-C2-00-00-00       LLC C
      S = 42  D = 42 UI
```
Frame: 16   **Time: Aug 07@15:13:55.6134195**   **Length: 64**

                   ***** DETAILED FORMAT *****

```
   802.2
```
Destination SAP   42   **Unknown SAP**
Source SAP   42   **Unknown SAP**
```
Command/Response            ....-...0            Command
Type                        03                   Unnumbered
Poll                        ...0-....
Modifier                    000.-00..            Information
 802.3/Ethernet
Destination address         01-80-C2-00-00-00    Group, global
Source address              WellfleetE8-8F-1B    Individual, global
Length 38
Padding:
  FF-FF-FF-55-55-55-55-55
Frame check sequence        64-97-18-44
> Data size                 38
```

```
17    13:55.663 220.100.100.178  220.100.100.172       TCP
      S = 10007  D = 1029    ACK = 2700663 SEQ = 13119461 LEN = 304
      WIN = 1536
```
Frame: 17   **Time: Aug 07@15:13:55.6633575**   **Length: 362**

                   ***** DETAILED FORMAT *****

```
   TCP
```
Source port   10007   **User prog.**
port
Destination port   1029   **User prog.**
port
```
Sequence number             13119461
Ack number                  2700663        Seqnum of next expected data
 byte
Data offset                 5              Number of
32-bit words in
 header
Reserved                    ....-0000-00..-....
 Flags:                     ..01-1000
 Urgent flag                ..0.....
Ack flag                    ...1....       Ack number field is
 significant
Push flag                   ....1...       Sender requests immediate
 delivery
 Reset flag                 .....0..
 Syn flag                   ......0.
```

```
  Fin flag                .......0
Window                    1536
Checksum                  2F-27
Urgent pointer            0                    Not used
> Data size               304
> State                   Data transfer
  IP
Version                   4
Internet header length    5                    (32 bit words)
Precedence                000.-....            Routine
Delay                     ...0-....            Delay normal
Throughput                ....-0...            Throughput normal
Reliability               ....-.0..            Reliability normal
Total Length              344
Identification            58764
May / Do Not Fragment     .0..-....            Fragmentation allowed
Last / More Fragments     ..0.-....            Last fragment
Offset                    0
Time To Live              64
Next Protocol             6                    TCP
Checksum                  11-EC
Source                    220.100.100.178
Destination               220.100.100.172
> Data size               324
  802.3/Ethernet
Destination address       00-60-08-98-1D-33    Individual, global
Source address            00-80-D4-00-EB-AA    Individual, global
Type                      08-00                IP
Frame check sequence      94-79-F8-B3
> Data size               344
```

```
18   13:55.849 220.100.100.172     220.100.100.178      TCP
     S = 1029 D = 10007     ACK = 13119765 WIN = 5583
Frame: 18          Time: Aug 07@15:13:55.8492738  Length: 64
                   ***** DETAILED FORMAT *****
  TCP
Source port               1029                 User prog.
port
Destination port          10007                User prog.
port
Sequence number           2700663
Ack number                13119765             Seqnum of next expected data
  byte
Data offset               5                    Number of
32-bit words in
header
Reserved                  ....-0000-00..-....
Flags:                    ..01-0000
  Urgent flag             ..0.....
  Ack flag                ...1....             Ack number field is
  significant
  Push flag               ....0...
  Reset flag              .....0..
  Syn flag                ......0.
  Fin flag                .......0
Window                    5583
Checksum                  85-44
Urgent pointer            0                    Not used
> State                   Data transfer
  IP
```

```
Version                    4
Internet header length     5                    (32 bit words)
Precedence                 000.-....            Routine
Delay                      ...0-....            Delay normal
Throughput                 ....-0...            Throughput normal
Reliability                ....-.0..            Reliability normal
Total Length               40
Identification             26219
May / Do Not Fragment      .1..-....            Fragmentation not allowed
Last / More Fragments      ..0.-....                Last fragment
Offset                     0
Time To Live               128
Next Protocol              6                    TCP
Checksum                   12-3D
Source                     220.100.100.172
Destination                220.100.100.178
> Data size                20
Padding:
   00-00-00-00-00-00
  802.3/Ethernet
Destination address        00-80-D4-00-EB-AA    Individual, global
Source address             00-60-08-98-1D-33    Individual, global
Type                       08-00                IP
Frame check sequence       8D-AD-7A-DD
> Data size                46
```

```
19   13:55.855 220.100.100.178   220.100.100.172       TCP
     S = 10007 D = 1029    ACK = 2700663 SEQ = 13119765   LEN = 493
     WIN = 1536
```

Frame: 19   Time: Aug 07@15:13:55.8556125   Length: 551
***** DETAILED FORMAT *****
```
  TCP
Source port                10007                User prog.
port
Destination port           1029                 User prog.
port
Sequence number            13119765
Ack number                 2700663              Seqnum of next expected data
 byte
Data offset                5                    Number of
32-bit words in
 header
Reserved                   ....-0000-00..-....
Flags:                     ..01-1000
 Urgent flag               ..0.....
 Ack flag                  ...1....             Ack number field is
 significant
 Push flag                 ....1...             Sender requests immediate
 delivery
 Reset flag                .....0..
 Syn flag                  ......0.
 Fin flag                  .......0
Window                     1536
Checksum                   96-E8
Urgent pointer             0                    Not used
> Data size                493
> State                    Data transfer
  IP
Version                    4
Internet header length     5                    (32 bit words)
```

Precedence	000.-....	Routine
Delay	...0-....	Delay normal
Throughput	....-0...	Throughput normal
Reliability	....-.0..	Reliability normal
Total Length	**533**	
Identification	58765	
May / Do Not Fragment	.0..-....	Fragmentation allowed
Last / More Fragments	..0.-....	Last fragment
Offset	0	
Time To Live	64	
Next Protocol	6	TCP
Checksum	11-2E	
Source	**220.100.100.178**	
Destination	**220.100.100.172**	
> Data size	**513**	
802.3/Ethernet		
Destination address	00-60-08-98-1D-33	Individual, global
Source address	00-80-D4-00-EB-AA	Individual, global
Type	08-00	IP
Frame check sequence	9E-D4-2B-0F	
> Data size	533	

---

20   13:56.055 220.100.100.172   220.100.100.178   TCP
     S = 1029 D = 10007   ACK = 13120258 WIN = 6096
Frame: 20   **Time: Aug 07@15:13:56.0551812 Length: 64**
              ***** DETAILED FORMAT *****

TCP		
Source port	**1029**	**User prog.**
port		
Destination port	**10007**	**User prog.**
port		
Sequence number	2700663	
Ack number	13120258	Seqnum of next expected data
byte		
Data offset	5	Number of
32-bit words in		
header		
Reserved	....-0000-00..-....	
Flags:	..01-0000	
Urgent flag	..0.....	
Ack flag	...1....	Ack number field is
significant		
Push flag	....0...	
Reset flag	.....0..	
Syn flag	......0.	
Fin flag	0	
Window	6096	
Checksum	81-56	
Urgent pointer	0	Not used
> State	**Data transfer**	
IP		
Version	4	
Internet header length	5	(32 bit words)
Precedence	000.-....	Routine
Delay	...0-....	Delay normal
Throughput	....-0...	Throughput normal
Reliability	....-.0..	Reliability normal
Total Length	**40**	
Identification	26475	

May / Do Not Fragment	.1..-....	Fragmentation not allowed
Last / More Fragments	..0.-....	Last fragment
Offset	0	
Time To Live	128	
Next Protocol	6	TCP
Checksum	11-3D	
Source	**220.100.100.172**	
Destination	**220.100.100.178**	
> Data size	**20**	
Padding:		
00-00-00-00-00-00		
802.3/Ethernet		
Destination address	00-80-D4-00-EB-AA	Individual, global
Source address	00-60-08-98-1D-33	Individual, global
Type	08-00	IP
Frame check sequence	B4-83-88-1A	
> Data size	**46**	

---

21   13:56.062 220.100.100.178   220.100.100.172   TCP
     S = 10007 D = 1029   ACK = 2700663 SEQ = 13120258 LEN = 498
     WIN = 1536

Frame: 21   **Time: Aug 07@15:13:56.0627936   Length: 556**
                ***** DETAILED FORMAT *****
   TCP

Source port	**10007**	**User prog.**
port		
Destination port	**1029**	**User prog.**
port		
Sequence number	13120258	
Ack number	2700663	Seqnum of next expected data
byte		
Data offset	5	Number of
32-bit words in		
header		
Reserved	....-0000-00..-....	
Flags:	..01-1000	
Urgent flag	..0.....	
Ack flag	...1....	Ack number field is
significant		
Push flag	....1...	Sender requests immediate
delivery		
Reset flag	.....0..	
Syn flag	......0.	
Fin flag	0	
Window	1536	
Checksum	3A-26	
Urgent pointer	0	Not used
> Data size	**498**	
> State	**Data transfer**	
IP		
Version	4	
Internet header length	5	(32 bit words)
Precedence	000.-....	Routine
Delay	...0-....	Delay normal
Throughput	....-0...	Throughput normal
Reliability	....-.0..	Reliability normal
Total Length	538	
Identification	58766	
May / Do Not Fragment	.0..-....	Fragmentation allowed

```
Last / More Fragments       ..0.-....              Last fragment
Offset                      0
Time To Live                64
Next Protocol               6                       TCP
Checksum                    11-28
Source                      220.100.100.178
Destination                 220.100.100.172
> Data size                 518
  802.3/Ethernet
Destination address         00-60-08-98-1D-33       Individual, global
Source address              00-80-D4-00-EB-AA       Individual, global
Type                        08-00                   IP
Frame check sequence        97-54-BE-C2
> Data size                 538
```

```
22    13:56.254 220.100.100.172      220.100.100.178           TCP
      S = 1029  D = 10007       ACK = 13120756  WIN = 5598
Frame: 22          Time: Aug 07@15:13:56.2542190  Length: 64
                        ***** DETAILED FORMAT *****
   TCP
Source port                 1029                   User prog.
 port
Destination port            10007                  User prog.
 port
Sequence number             2700663
Ack number                  13120756        Seqnum of next expected data
 byte
Data offset                 5                       Number of
 32-bit words in
  header
Reserved                    ....-0000-00..-....
Flags:                      ..01-0000
 Urgent flag                ..0.....
 Ack flag                   ...1....                Ack number field is
  significant
 Push flag                  ....0...
 Reset flag                 .....0..
 Syn flag                   ......0.
 Fin flag                   .......0
Window                      5598
Checksum                    81-56
Urgent pointer              0                       Not used
> State                     Data transfer
  IP
Version                     4
Internet header length      5                       (32 bit words)
Precedence                  000.-....               Routine
Delay                       ...0-....               Delay normal
Throughput                  ....-0...               Throughput normal
Reliability                 ....-.0..               Reliability normal
Total Length                40
Identification              26731
May / Do Not Fragment       .1..-...         Fragmentation not allowed
Last / More Fragments       ..0.-....               Last fragment
Offset                      0
Time To Live                128
Next Protocol               6                       TCP
Checksum                    10-3D
Source                      220.100.100.172
```

```
Destination                      220.100.100.178
> Data size                      20
Padding:
   00-00-00-00-00-00
 802.3/Ethernet
Destination address              00-80-D4-00-EB-AA        Individual, global
Source address                   00-60-08-98-1D-33        Individual, global
Type                             08-00                    IP
Frame check sequence             97-42-B8-7E
> Data size                      46
```

```
23   13:56.261 220.100.100.178    220.100.100.172        TCP
       S = 10007 D = 1029    ACK = 2700663 SEQ = 13120756 LEN = 696
       WIN = 1536
```

Frame: 23   Time: Aug 07@15:13:56.2617698 Length: 754
```
                 ***** DETAILED FORMAT *****
   TCP
```

```
Source port                      10007                   User prog.
port
Destination port                 1029                    User prog.
port
Sequence number                  13120756
Ack number                       2700663                 Seqnum of next expected data
 byte
Data offset                      5                       Number of
32-bit words in
 header
Reserved                         ....-0000-00..-....
Flags:                           ..01-1000
 Urgent flag                     ..0.....
 Ack flag                        ...1....                Ack number field is
significant
 Push flag                       ....1...                Sender requests immediate
delivery
 Reset flag                      .....0..
 Syn flag                        ......0.
 Fin flag                        .......0
Window                           1536
Checksum                         10-B0
Urgent pointer                   0                       Not used
> Data size                      696
> State                          Data transfer
 IP
Version                          4
Internet header length           5                       (32 bit words)
Precedence                       000.-....               Routine
Delay                            ...0-....               Delay normal
Throughput                       ....-0...               Throughput normal
Reliability                      ....-.0..               Reliability normal
Total Length                     736
Identification                   58767
May / Do Not Fragment            .0..-....               Fragmentation allowed
Last / More Fragments            ..0.-....               Last fragment
Offset 0
Time To Live                     64
Next Protocol                    6                       TCP
Checksum                         10-61
Source                           220.100.100.178
Destination                      220.100.100.172
```

> **Data size**	**716**	
802.3/Ethernet		
Destination address	00-60-08-98-1D-33	Individual, global
Source address	00-80-D4-00-EB-AA	Individual, global
Type	08-00	IP
Frame check sequence	03-28-19-F7	
> **Data size**	**736**	

---

24   13:56.459 220.100.100.172   220.100.100.178   TCP
    S = 1029 D = 10007   ACK = 13121452 WIN = 6096
Frame: 24   **Time: Aug 07@15:13:56.4591258 Length: 64**
                ***** DETAILED FORMAT *****

TCP		
Source port	**1029**	**User prog.**
port		
Destination port	**10007**	**User prog.**
port		
Sequence number	2700663	
Ack number	13121452	Seqnum of next expected data
byte		
Data offset	5	Number of
32-bit words in		
header		
Reserved	....-0000-00..-....	
Flags:	..01-0000	
Urgent flag	..0.....	
Ack flag	...1....	Ack number field is
significant		
Push flag	....0...	
Reset flag	.....0..	
Syn flag	......0.	
Fin flag	0	
Window	6096	
Checksum	7C-AC	
Urgent pointer	0	Not used
> **State**	**Data transfer**	
IP		
Version	4	
Internet header length	5	(32 bit words)
Precedence	000.-....	Routine
Delay	...0-....	Delay normal
Throughput	....-0...	Throughput normal
Reliability	....-.0..	Reliability normal
Total Length	40	
Identification	26987	
May / Do Not Fragment	.1..-....	Fragmentation not allowed
Last / More Fragments	..0.-....	Last fragment
Offset	0	
Time To Live	128	
Next Protocol	6	TCP
Checksum	0F-3D	
Source	**220.100.100.172**	
Destination	**220.100.100.178**	
> **Data size**	**20**	
Padding:		
00-00-00-00-00-00		
802.3/Ethernet		
Destination address	00-80-D4-00-EB-AA	Individual, global
Source address	00-60-08-98-1D-33	Individual, global

Type	08-00	IP
Frame check sequence	91-51-2F-22	
> Data size	**46**	

---

25   13:56.465 220.100.100.178   220.100.100.172   TCP
          S = 10007 D = 1029   ACK = 2700663 SEQ = 13121452 LEN = 809
          WIN = 1536

Frame: 25   **Time: Aug 07@15:13:56.4658357 Length: 867**
               ***** DETAILED FORMAT *****

TCP		
Source port port	**10007**	**User prog.**
Destination port port	**1029**	**User prog.**
Sequence number	13121452	
Ack number byte	2700663	Seqnum of next expected data
Data offset 32-bit words in header	5	Number of
Reserved	....-0000-00..-....	
Flags:	..01-1000	
Urgent flag	..0.....	
Ack flag significant	...1....	Ack number field is
Push flag delivery	....1...	Sender requests immediate
Reset flag	.....0..	
Syn flag	......0.	
Fin flag	0	
Window	1536	
Checksum	29-CD	
Urgent pointer	0	Not used
> Data size	**809**	
> State	**Data transfer**	
IP		
Version	4	
Internet header length	5	(32 bit words)
Precedence	000.-....	Routine
Delay	...0-....	Delay normal
Throughput	....-0...	Throughput normal
Reliability	....-.0..	Reliability normal
Total Length	**849**	
Identification	58768	
May / Do Not Fragment	.0..-....	Fragmentation allowed
Last / More Fragments	..0.-....	Last fragment
Offset	0	
Time To Live	64	
Next Protocol	6	TCP
Checksum	0F-EF	
Source	**220.100.100.178**	
Destination	**220.100.100.172**	
> Data size	**829**	
802.3/Ethernet		
Destination address	00-60-08-98-1D-33	Individual, global
Source address	00-80-D4-00-EB-AA	Individual, global
Type	08-00 IP	
Frame check sequence	C7-D9-7B-65	
> Data size	**849**	

11.7 Summary

The purpose of this chapter is to present some information that has been helpful to me, and which I believe will help you. The other purpose is to present some examples of information that can be important to have on hand when you start to troubleshoot your network.

Remember, troubleshooting takes time and tools. One of the best tools for troubleshooting is good documentation. This includes factory documentation as well as documentation that reflects the specifics of your site.

12

Network Switch
Baselining

The network switch is a key component in any network. It is equally important to have information about your switch in such a way that you have "known good records" of its implementation and operation. This chapter presents the OmniSwitch I selected to use in my network. I have included the information that I considered critical for me to have on hand; likewise, you should consider this level of detail for baselining your switch.

XYLAN's documentation and support get an A plus. For this reason I elected to include some information directly from XYLAN. The information is well written and explains the technology they created better than I could. Consider this as a starting-point guide when you baseline your network switch.

First, consider the logical view of my network as it relates to the network switch. See Figure 12.1, which shows a conceptual view of my network and the OmniSwitch. The functionality of the switch is such that it carries all the network payload; consequently, it is a most important network component.

12.1 The XYLAN Network Switch

XYLAN has very good documentation for all its equipment. The information included here is from some of that documentation.

OmniSwitch Cell Switching Modules

The OmniSwitch provides the flexibility needed to start as a pure LAN switch, gradually migrate to a hybrid LAN/ATM switch, and finally transform into a purely ATM switch capable of supporting multiple classes of service (CoSs) and robust traffic management. Making the transition from a LAN switch to an ATM switch requires only a change of interface modules; no backplane upgrade is necessary.

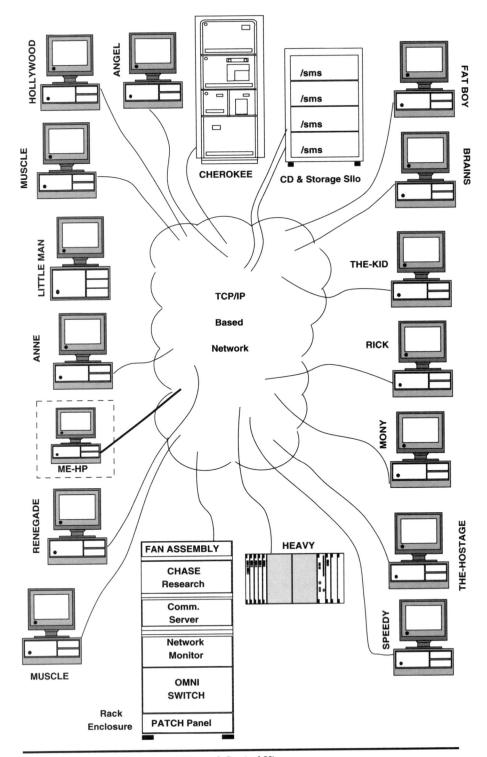

Figure 12.1   The OmniSwitch and Network Logical View

The OmniSwitch with ATM switching functionality is available in 5-slot and 9-slot versions. Each version supports the same management, frame switching, and cell switching modules. Each version also supports the same bus architecture.

Using a distributed architecture, the OmniSwitch enables you to increase the switching capacity as you add cell switching modules (CSMs). Each CSM provides enough capacity to handle the nonblocking load of its own ports. In this way, the OmniSwitch scales cost-effectively with the growth requirements of your ATM network.

Virtual circuits

Console and network management software allow you to configure and monitor permanent virtual circuits (PVCs) and soft PVCs. Switched virtual circuits (SVCs) are only monitored. Statistics are provided for all types of virtual circuits. Virtual circuits may be either virtual path connections (VPCs) or virtual channel connections (VCCs).

A variety of statistics are available at the port and virtual connection levels. These statistics provide information on cell loss priority (CLP) cell flows, cell discards, and actions taken as a result of leaky-bucket algorithms.

Dynamic input buffering with output control

The OmniSwitch uses a unique buffer management system that combines the scalability of input buffers and the control of output buffers. Cell buffers are located on input ports, but these buffers are actually controlled by output ports. Each output port sees the traffic destined for it and uses this knowledge to schedule traffic flow across the fabric. To effectively interconnect ATM networks with the bursty nature of LANs, the OmniSwitch uses very large cell buffers that can withstand massive inflows of LAN traffic.

Quality of service (QoS)

The OmniSwitch buffer management supports six (6) different CoS levels that are compatible and expand on ATM Forum QoS specifications. Each QoS level supports a different ATM traffic type (CBR, rt-VBR, nrt-VBR, ABR, or UBR) and supports different generic cell rate algorithms (GCRAs). The levels are organized by priority with additional granularity provided by 16 different user priority levels assignable at the virtual circuit level.

Partial packet discard (PPD) and random early detect (RED)

Partial packet discard (PPD) and random early detect (RED) are disabled by default for AAL5 traffic (i.e., unspecified bit rate and available bit rate). You can enable or disable these features at the virtual circuit level or through `mpm.cmd` file commands and statements. When these features are enabled,

AAL5 frames are discarded during congestion conditions to increase frame-level throughput.

When PPD is enabled, the switch can intelligently discard cells associated with AAL5 PDU during congestion conditions. This feature reduces the bandwidth used along the remaining downstream path. PPD can be enabled for a specific virtual circuit through the cvc command. You can also enable PPD for all new channels by adding the following statement to the switch mpm.cmd file:

```
aal5_dx = 1
```

Be sure that this statement comes before the cmInit line.

When RED is enabled, the switch will invoke PPD on logical connections in a round-robin fashion during congestion conditions. This feature smooths out the waves of congestion (retransmits) that occur when LAN frames are discarded. You can enable RED by adding the following statement to the switch mpm.cmd file:

```
sp_ccu_enable = 1
```

Be sure that this statement comes before the cmInit line.

Dual leaky buckets

Dual leaky buckets are set up on each virtual circuit, and policing algorithms can check for peak cell rate (PCR), sustained cell rate (SCR), and maximum burst size (MBS). Options for enforcement of the traffic contract can be static, dropping all cells in excess of the contract regardless of congestion or congestion-based conditions or enforcement. Congestion-based enforcement will tag or discard cells depending on the level of congestion on the connection and a cell's cell loss priority (CLP). The enforcement method is defaulted on the basis of traffic descriptors and is not user-selectable in this release.

Available-bit-rate traffic

The OmniSwitch supports explicit rate flow control for ABR traffic. Resource management (RM) cells are forwarded along virtual connections. In addition, the explicit forward congestion indicator (EFCI) is supported for all types of traffic. Currently SARs do not support ABR resource management. Therefore, ATM end systems supporting resource management are not available to test at this time, and this feature is not fully operational in this release.

High-speed module

Many switching modules that operate at speeds in excess of 10 Mbps are actually submodules that attach to a high-speed module (HSM). These switching modules include ATM, FDDI, Token Ring, and Frame Relay modules and some 100-Mbps Ethernet modules. The HSM provides the base memory and processing power for these high-throughput switching modules.

The HSM contains RISC processors, RAM for holding software image files, ASICs for performing switching, and content-addressable memory (CAM) for storing MAC addresses. The HSM is available in three versions: the HSM, HSM2, and HSM3. There is an option of factory installation of either one or two submodules on an HSM. Two submodules double the port count for a particular module. For example, a one-port ATM module contains one submodule attached to an HSM, and a two-port ATM module has two submodules attached to an HSM. With the HSM and attached submodule, you plug cable directly into a submodule, but it is the HSM module that connects to the switch backplane.

Content-addressable memory. Each switching module is supplied by XYLAN with 1, 2, or 4K of content-addressable memory (CAM). CAM is used to claim frames from the VBUS for forwarding to the ports on that switching module. Modules with 1K of CAM can store 1024 addresses, modules with 2K of CAM can store 2048 addresses, and modules with 4K of CAM can store 4096 addresses.

CAM is located directly on some Ethernet module boards; it is located on the HSM boards for ATM, FDDI, CDDI, Token Ring, and Frame Relay modules. Two CAM sockets are available for all 10-Mbps Ethernet modules and all HSM modules. In a configuration where all switching modules use the standard 1K of CAM, the OmniSwitch can actively manage up to 8192 MAC addresses in a 9-slot chassis, and up to 4096 addresses in a 5-slot chassis.

Because the CAM is actually a cache of most recently observed addresses and not all the addresses in the network, even a 1K CAM can often support networks with many more than 1024 stations. However, a module with only 1K of CAM can cause problems in networks with large shared media backbones in which more than 1024 addresses are simultaneously active.

The 2 and 4K CAM options address this limitation by allowing up to 2048 or 4096 addresses per switching module. This option provides a larger CAM for address recognition logic, which makes the OmniSwitch more robust in networks with large shared media backbones. This option is supported on most switching modules.

> **XYLAN Note:** ESM-U-6 modules must be at least Revision F1 to support the 2K CAM option. Older versions of the board do not contain an extra CAM socket.

The switch software recognizes if more than 1K of CAM is installed on a switching module. The switch can support up 16K of CAM among all switching modules. If you have more than 16K of CAM installed on all switching modules in your chassis, then you can view each module's CAM usage through the `camstat` command. In such configurations, you may also need to configure each slot's CAM usage through the `camcfg` command.

If you have 16K CAM or less, then no special configuration is required. The 2 or 4K CAM option is not normally required unless a port on that module is plugged into a backbone, such as an ATM backbone, in which a large number of addresses are simultaneously active. Each network is different, and the traffic patterns should be observed to best decide when this is used. Another alternative to greatly improve both CAM utilization and network performance is to split the backbone into multiple networks and switch between them.

Source learning and CAM capacity learning of source addresses are affected by the amount of space available in CAM. When CAM capacity is less than 85 percent (870 or fewer entries in a 1K CAM), normal source learning occurs. When CAM capacity is 85 percent or more (870 or more entries in a 1K CAM), the source addresses for broadcast frames are not learned; nonbroadcast frames are still learned. At the 95 percent level (972 or more entries in a 1K CAM), the CAM will not learn source addresses for frames sent to unknown destinations; frames destined to a known address are still learned.

XYLAN Note: Learning returns to normal once the CAM returns to below the 85 percent capacity.

Switch security

Using commands from the Security menu, you can configure system security parameters such as the password and logout time. The menu also provides a command for rebooting the switch. Enter Security at the prompt to enter the Security menu.

An authorized user can press the question mark (?) and see the following list of commands in the command security menu:

pw	Set a new password for a login account.
reboot	Reboot this system (allowed if the user is admin).
timeout	Configure Auto Logout Time.
Main File Summary	VLAN Networking
Interface Security	System Services Help

The pw, reboot, and timeout commands are described in the following sections. The software for authenticated groups displays the following list of commands in the command security menu:

pw	Set a new password for a login account reboot. Reboot this system (allowed if the user is admin).
timeout	Configure Auto Logout Time.
avlAddresses	Define an authentication router port address.
avlsAddresses	Show all the Authentication router port addresses.
avlBanner	Define the authentication port login banner.

`avlsBanner`	Display the Authentication port login banner.
`avlPorts`	Set a port to be a TELNET authenticated port.
`avlsPorts`	Show ports that are TELNET authenticated ports.

Commands with the `avl` prefix apply to authenticated groups.

12.2 The User Interface

The User Interface (UI) provides a means of configuring parameters and viewing real-time statistics from a terminal, such as a PC or UNIX workstation, using terminal emulation software. The UI is part of the MPM executable image. When a switch boots up, the boot monitor handles the loading of this executable image and system start-up. Once the image is loaded and initialized, the UI starts.

You access the UI through a connection with the switch. This connection can be made directly through the serial port, through a modem, or over a network via TELNET. You can have up to four simultaneous connections to an OmniSwitch or an OmniStack, and up to three simultaneous connections on a PizzaSwitch or PizzaPort. For TELNET access, you must first set up an IP address for the switch. In order to do this, you need XYLAN's *OmniSwitch: Getting Started Guide* for information on setting up an IP address and logging in. Once you log on, the following main menu displays.

Main menu commands

The following is an example of the user interface.

```
*********************************************************************
        Xylan OmniSwitch - Copyright (c) 1994-1998 Xylan Inc.
                      All rights reserved.
            OmniSwitch is a trademark of Xylan Corporation
       Registered in the United States Patent and Trademark Office.
*********************************************************************
System Name: IWI-SWITCH
Primary MPM
Command Main Menu
-------------------------------------------------------------------
File            Manager system files
Summary         Display summary info for VLANs,
                bridge, interfaces, etc.
VLAN            VLAN management
Networking      Configure/view network parameters
                such as routing, etc.
Interface       Enter the Physical Interface
                Configuration/Parameter sub-menu
Security        Configure system security parameters
System          View/set system-specific parameters
Services        View/set services parameters
Switch          View/set any to any switching
                parameters
Help            Help on specific tasks
```

```
Diag            Display diagnostic commands
Exit            (Logout) Log out of this session
?               Display contents of current menu
```

This menu provides a top-level view of all UI menus. The commands are grouped together in the form of submenus. Within each submenu there is a set of commands and/or another submenu.

XYLAN Note   Although the commands are grouped in a submenu structure, any command may be entered from any submenu. You are not restricted to the commands listed in the current submenu.

Main menu command summary.   The main menu command functions are described here.

File   Contains options for downloading system software, listing software files, copying files, editing files, and deleting files.

Summary   Provides very basic information on the physical switch, such as its name, MAC address, and resets. It also provides options for viewing the virtual interface and information on the MIB.

VLAN   The main menu for configuring groups, virtual ports, and AutoTracker VLANs. This menu also contains a submenu for configuring bridging parameters, such as Spanning Tree and Source Routing.

Networking   Contains menu options for managing internetworking protocols, such as SNMP and RMON, IP and IPX, and Next Hop Resolution Protocol (NHRP).

Interface   The main menu for configuring parameters and viewing statistics for switching modules. This menu has submenus for managing ATM, FDDI, Token Ring, Frame Relay, and Fast Ethernet switching modules. In addition, it includes a suboption for configuring SLIP.

Security   Contains options for changing a password and rebooting the system.

System   Contains a wide array of options for configuring and viewing information on a variety of switch functions. Options include displays of switch slot contents, configuring serial ports, and viewing CAM information. Commands used to configure User Interface display options are described in a submenu option. The System menu also includes a submenu option that provides additional commands for configuring the MPM module.

Services   Provides options for creating, modifying, viewing, and deleting ATM, FDDI, and Frame Relay services. ATM services include PTOP bridging and LAN emulation. FDDI services include Trunking and 802.10 Trunking. Frame Relay services include bridging, routing, and trunking.

Switch   Provides options to precisely define frame translations. A MAC layer type (Ethernet, Token Ring, etc.) may have more than one type of frame format, such as Ethernet or 802.3. But, by default, each MAC layer type defaults to a certain frame format on translation. This menu allows you to define translations for each frame format. This menu provides textual help on how to use the UI on each menu or submenu. For the item of interest, enter `help <sub-menu name>`.

Diag   This menu, fully available to the `diag login` account, contains commands to run diagnostic tests.

Exit   Logs you out of the UI. You can also enter `logout` to exit.

?   Displays the options for current menu.

12.3   OmniSwitch Switchwide Commands

The OmniSwitch provides commands to display and configure parameters on a switchwide basis. These commands are grouped into two menus: the Summary menu and the System menu.

Command Summary menu

The Summary menu consists of commands for displaying summary information about the switch. Enter `summary` at the prompt to enter the Summary menu. Press the question mark (?) to see the following commands.

ss   Display MIB-II system group variables
sc   OmniSwitch chassis summary
si   Current interface status

12.4   How to Display Basic System Information

To display basic information on the switch, enter `info` at the system prompt. The following display is an example.

System make	XYLAN OmniSwitch
System type	5-slot OmniSwitch
Description	`IWI SWITCH`
Backplane	`5 SLOT Bus Speed:` 640
Physical changes to the system since power-up or reset	2
Logical changes to the system since power-up or reset	0
Number of resets to this system	37
System base MAC address	`00:20:da:04:21:f0`
Number of free slots	`0`
Action on cold start	`Load & go`
Action on reset	`Restart`
Script file	`/flash/mpm.cmd`
Boot file	`/flash/mpm.img`
Ni image suffix	`img`

The attached MPM, slot 1, the Primary Automatic configuration synchronization, is enabled.

The fields displayed by the `info` command are described here:

`System Make`	Description of the specific type of chassis or device.
`System Type`	The OmniSwitch type.
`Description`	A description of the chassis and product. This field is set by the `syscfg` command.
`Backplane`	The style of backplane (3-slot, 5-slot, or 9-slot) used in this chassis.

Bus Speed   The speed of backplane, in megabits per second (Mbps), used in this chassis. This will be 640 Mbps unless you are using an MPM 1G or MPM 1GW, in which case it may be 960 Mbps.

The following changes are noted:

Physical changes to the system since power-up or reset: The number of physical changes that have occurred since the last reset or power-on.

Logical changes to the system since power-up or reset: The number of logical changes that have occurred since the last reset or power-on.

System menu

The System menu contains commands to view or set system-specific parameters. Enter system at the UI prompt to enter the System menu. If the system is not set in *verbose* mode, press the question mark (?), then press RETURN and the following System menu commands are shown:

info	Basic information on this system.
dt	Set system date and time.
ser	View or configure the DTE or DCE port.
mpm	Configure a management processor module.
slot	View slot table information.
systat	View system stats related to system, power, and environment.
taskstat	View task utilization stats.
memstat	View memory use statistics.
fsck	Perform a file system check on the flash file system.
newfs	Erase all files from /flash and create a new file system.
syscfg	Configure information related to this system.
camstat	View CAM information and usage.
camcfg	Configure CAM information and usage.
ver/ter	Enable/disable automatic display of menus on entry.
echo/noecho	Enable/disable character echo.
chpr	Change the prompt for the system.
Logging	View system logs.

How to display chassis summary

To display chassis summary information, enter sc at the system prompt. Something similar to the following will be displayed:

Type	Omni-5
Chassis ID	XYLAN
Description	THE-IWI-BACKBONE
Backplane	5 SLOT

```
Master MPM Serial No.    00000000
Physical Changes         7
Logical Changes          0
Number of Resets         26
Base MAC Address         00:20:da:02:04:80
Free Slots               0
```

Field descriptions

Type	The description of the specific type of chassis or device.
Chassis ID	The chassis ID for this OmniSwitch.
Description	The description of this chassis. This field is set by the `syscfg` command.
Backplane	The style of backplane (3-slot, 5-slot, or 9-slot) used in this chassis.
Master MPM Serial No.	The serial number for the primary MPM.
Physical Changes	The number of physical changes that have occurred since the last reset or power-on.
Logical Changes	The number of logical changes that have occurred since the last reset or power-on.
Number of Resets	The number of times this switch has been reset since the configuration file (`mpm.cnf`) was first removed.
Base MAC Address	The base MAC address for the primary MPM.
Free Slots	The number of front panel slots not occupied by a switching module.

12.5 OmniSwitch Implementation in the Author's Network

I integrated the OmniSwitch in my network and it is the backbone. Consider Figure 12.2, which shows the fiber-optic backbone which every device uses. It also highlights the OmniSwitch as the single-network backbone to move FDDI, Ethernet, ATM, and Token Ring traffic.

In order to conceptually understand the following material, consider Figure 12.3, which shows the OmniSwitch I have in my network lab. Consider the following information which I initially set aside when I began to record baseline information for my network.

12.6 Ethernet Interface

The ESM-100C can be configured with four or eight ports that connect to 100BaseTX devices. Each set of four ports is one collision domain that connects to a fifth internal port. This internal port connects directly to the switch backplane and has a unique MAC address. Each front panel port on the ESM-100C is capable of using the full 100 Mbps of dedicated bandwidth. However, when more than one connection is made to each set of four ports, those connections must share the 100 Mbps of bandwidth. Front panel ports receive

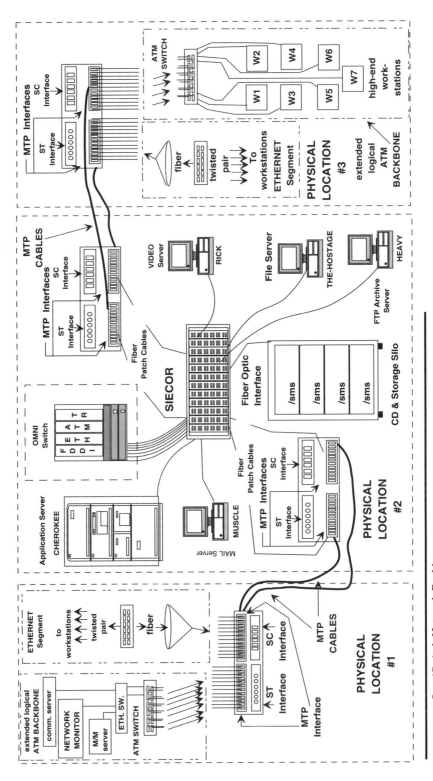

Figure 12.2 OmniSwitch Network Backbone

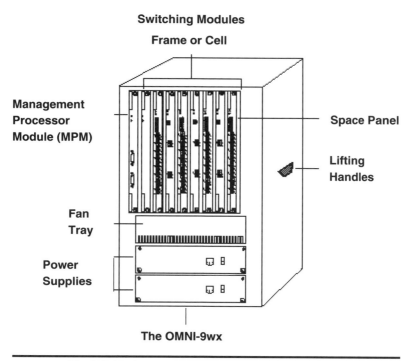

Switching Modules

Frame or Cell

Management Processor Module (MPM)

Space Panel

Lifting Handles

Fan Tray

Power Supplies

The OMNI-9wx

Figure 12.3   The XYLAN OmniSwitch

data from attached 100BaseTX devices and from the fifth internal port (which connects to the switch backplane). In addition, data received on any front panel port are automatically passed on to the other three ports that share their collision domain and to the internal port.

The internal switch port receives data from the switch backplane and the 100BaseTX front panel ports. This port passes data destined for the front panel ports (from other switch ports) in one direction, and passes data destined for other switch ports (from the front panel ports) in the other direction. This internal port has its own set of LEDs, separate from the front panel port LEDs.

Set of four 100BaseTX ports, switch backplane

Internal port

100BaseTX devices

12.7   FDDI Interface

The FSM-M FDDI switching module may contain one or two dual-attachment station (DAS) connections for support of dual FDDI rings. Each DAS connection is a set of A/B media interface connectors (MIC). The FSM-M supports multimode connections. (The FSM-S module supports single mode DAS connections.) In addition, each DAS connection has an optical bypass port that may be used to disconnect a port from the FDDI ring, or bypass this DAS connection.

The FSM-M is actually a submodule, or daughtercard, that attaches to a high-speed module (HSM). The HSM contains memory and processing power for switching modules that operate at speeds greater than 10 Mbps. You plug your fiber-optic cable directly into the FSM-M submodule, but it is the HSM module that connects to the switch backplane.

12.8   Token Ring Interface

The TSM-CD-6 contains six shielded ports that each may be separately configured as a station or lobe port. As a Station port, the TSM-CD-6 port plugs directly into an MAU; as a lobe port, the port acts as an MAU port and a Token Ring station plugs directly into the module. You configure the ports as station or lobe through the `tsc` command. By default, ports are configured as lobe ports.

Each port can support either unshielded twisted-pair (UTP) or shielded twisted-pair (STP) connections. No configuration is necessary to set up a port for UTP or STP. Each port supports a fully switched connection at either 4 or 16 Mbps. Ring speed is configurable through the `tpcfg` command. By default, ports are configured at 16 Mbps.

Automatic speed detection

Switch software will automatically modify the ring speed if there is a discrepancy with the ring to which the port is connected. A TSM-CD-6 port detects this difference in ring speed as it is inserted into the ring, then it resets itself and comes up in the new ring speed. (The new ring speed, however, is not saved in the system configuration file, `mpm.cfg`.) Once the port inserts into the ring, automatic ring speed detection is disabled (i.e., thereafter the port will not change speed automatically). Both station and lobe ports handle automatic speed detection this way. If a TSM-CD-6 port is the first device on the ring, then the ring speed is automatically set to the port's configured speed. If the port does not reset to match the ring speed, its speed becomes the ring speed. If the port is not the first device, then it will autodetect the ring speed and match that speed as described in the preceding paragraph.

The TSM-CD-6 is actually a submodule, or daughtercard, that attaches to a high-speed module (HSM). The HSM contains memory and processing power for switching modules that operate at speeds greater than 10 Mbps. You plug your cable directly into the TSM-CD-6 submodule, but it is the HSM module that connects to the switch backplane.

12.9   ATM Interface

ATM access switching modules allow you to connect the OmniSwitch to ATM servers, backbones, and switches. ATM modules support OC-3, DS-3, and E3 interfaces (155, 44.736, and 34.368 Mbps, respectively) and include the following:

- *ASM-155Fx:* One- or two-port fiber single-mode or multimode OC-3 switching module.

- *ASM2-155Fx:* One- or two-port fiber single-mode or multimode OC-3 switching module. This is a higher-performance version of the ASM-155Fx.

- *ASM-155C:* One- or two-port UTP OC-3 switching module.

- *ASM2-622F:* One- or two-port fiber single-mode or multimode OC-12 switching module.

- *ASM2-622FR:* Two- or four-port redundant fiber single-mode or multimode OC-12 switching module. Each port pair includes a primary port and a backup port.

- *ASM-DS3:* One- or two-port DS-3 switching module.

- *ASM-E3:* One- or two-port E3 switching module.

- *ASM-CE:* One ATM uplink port (OC-3, DS-3, or E3), two T1/E1 ports, and two serial ports supporting ATM circuit emulation.

The OC-3 modules are suited for connecting the switch to an ATM campus backbone or directly to an ATM server. Through the use of point-to-point bridging (RFC 1483), you can extend all LAN traffic over the ATM backbone. Several OmniSwitches could be connected over one or more backbones. In such a configuration, you combine the flexibility of the OmniSwitch any-to-any switching with the power and speed of the ATM backbone without the use of an ATM backbone switch.

If you are connecting the OmniSwitch directly to an ATM server, then all non-ATM devices in the LAN can communicate with the high-speed ATM server through the OmniSwitch. If your network uses ATM backbone switches, then the OmniSwitch ATM modules allow all non-ATM devices in the network to have access to the ATM network through the use of LAN emulation (LANE) or a XYLAN version of LANE called *XLANE,* or *VLAN Clusters.* XLANE connects OmniSwitches and PizzaSwitches together across ATM and legacy LAN networks to gain the benefits of LANE while eliminating interoperability issues. Classic IP (RFC 1577) may also be used to extend LAN traffic over ATM.

Remember: ASM2 modules do not support point-to-point bridging (PTOP) private configurations. However, they do support PTOP 1483 configurations.

The DS-3 and E3 modules are well suited for connecting the switch to ATM carrier services offered by telco service providers. Software controls on the switch allow you to control and monitor activity on ATM modules. On each ATM port, you can configure the connection type (SVC or PVC), virtual channel connections (VCCs), segment sizes, and loopback controls. On each VCC, you can configure *quality of service* (QoS), *best effort, traffic descriptor,* and *peak cell rate* variables. In addition, you can configure all ATM bridging and trunking services (point-to-point bridging, LANE, XLANE, classic IP).

12.10   How to View System Statistics

The systat command displays statistics related to system, power, and environment. To view these parameters, enter systat at the system prompt. A screen similar to the following will be displayed:

```
System uptime: 1 day, 12:09:22.64
MPM transmit overruns: 0
MPM receive overruns: 22
MPM total memory: 16 MB
MPM free memory: 6522536 bytes
MPM CPU utilization
     (5 s) : 5% (0% intr 0% kernel 3% task 95% idle)
MPM CPU utilization
     (60 s) : 5% (0% intr 0% kernel 3% task 96% idle)
Power supply 1 state: OK
Power supply 2 state: Not present
Temperature sensor: OK - Under threshold
Temperature alarm masking: Disabled
Temperature alarm masking delay: 5 min
```

The time since the last boot that the system has been running is displayed in days, hours, minutes, and seconds (to the nearest hundredth).

Statistics descriptions

MPM Transmit Overruns	The number of times a VSE transmit buffer could not be allocated by a task on the MPM.
MPM Receive Overruns	The number of times packets were dropped because the bus had more packets to deliver than the MPM could handle. This is a receive overrun condition which can happen when a storm occurs or when the switch is first powered up and many unknown MAC frames are being forwarded to the MPM.
MPM Total Memory	The amount of total memory installed on the MPM.
MPM Free Memory	The amount of free, or unused, memory available in the MPM. These data are also displayed by the memstat command.
MPM CPU Utilization (5 s)	The amount of time, by percent, the MPM processor actually worked during the last 5 s.

MPM CPU Utilization (60 s)	The amount of time, in percent, that the MPM processor actually did work during the last minute.
Power Supply (1-State)	Valid states are OK, Not Present, and Bad. A power supply that has been turned off will be in the Bad state. If not installed, it will be in the Not Present state.
Power Supply (2-State)	Valid states are OK, Not Present, and Bad. A power supply that has been turned off will be in the Bad state. If not installed, it will be in the Not Present state.
Temperature Sensor	Indicates whether the MPM temperature sensor detects overheating. Valid states are Under Threshold, Over Threshold, and Not Present.
Temperature Alarm Masking	Indicates whether temperature alarm masking is Enabled or Disabled. You enable masking through the maskta command.
Temperature Alarm Masking Delay	The amount of time after which the TEMP LED will turn off when alarm masking is partially enabled through the maskta command. This field will display only if the value is greater than zero.

Number of system resets

The number of times this switch has been reset since the last cold start. The info command will also display the number of MPMs, their location in chassis, and which one is the primary and which one is the secondary. In addition, it also displays whether automatic configuration synchronization is enabled.

System Base MAC Address	The base MAC address for the primary MPM in chassis.
Number of Free Slots	The number of slots not occupied by a module.
Action on Cold Start	The action taken when you switch the power on.
Action on Reset	The action taken when you reboot.
Script File	The name of the command file (mpm.cmd is the default) containing user-configurable commands.
Boot File	The boot file (mpm.img is the default) used by the switch when it boots up or reboots.
Ni Image Suffix	The name of the file extension (img is the default) indicating that the file is an executable binary file.

12.11   How to Obtain Baseline Reference

To baseline the XYLAN switch used in this network I decided to connect only three hosts to the switch:

- MUSCLE
- SPEEDY

■ THE-HOSTAGE

The following statistical information reflects interaction among these three systems. The first trace I ran shows two hosts and the new XYLAN switch.

```
***************************************************************
              HEWLETT-PACKARD NETWORK ADVISOR
            Node Discovery measurement
              Run started on Aug 22, 1998 @ 11:08:17
              Run stopped on Aug 22, 1998 @ 11:10:24
              2 nodes observed
            Display format: Observed Nodes
            Print:         All displayed records
***************************************************************
* New address observed on network
# Known address observed on network
~ New address-name mapping; no traffic observed
> Selected record
    Address              Layer       Type/ID       Comment/Name
  _____  _____  _____   _____

> MUSCLE
*>  Kingston-30-C2-43             Ethernet
*>  220.100.100.10                IP
*>  00000001-000000000001         IPX
*>  ADMINISTRATOR                 NetBIOS        ADMINISTRATOR
*     MUSCLE                      NetBIOS        MUSCLE
> THE-HOSTAGE
*>  00-60-08-98-1D-33             Ethernet
*>  220.100.100.172               IP
*>    THE-HOSTAGE                 NetBIOS        THE-HOSTAGE
> *NEW XYLAN-A76640
*>    XYLAN----A7-66-40           ETHERNET
> *NEW XYLAN-AC9EB5
*>    XYLAN----AC-9E-B5           ETHERNET
```

After completing this trace, I ran another one to show the functional addition of SPEEDY. Consider the following:

```
***************************************************************
              HEWLETT-PACKARD NETWORK ADVISOR
                Node Discovery measurement
            Run started on Sep 15, 2000 @ 11:16:48
            Run stopped on Sep 15. 2000 @ 11:17:18
              2 nodes observed
          Display format: Observed Nodes
          Print:         All displayed records
***************************************************************
* New address observed on network
# Known address observed on network
~ New address-name mapping; no traffic observed
> Selected record
    Address              Layer       Type/ID       Comment/Name
  _____  _____  _____   _____

> MUSCLE
*>  Kingston-30-C2-43           Ethernet
*>  220.100.100.10              IP
*>  00000001-000000000001 IPX
```

```
*>   ADMINISTRATOR          NetBIOS              ADMINISTRATOR
*    MUSCLE                 NetBIOS              MUSCLE
>  SPEEDY
*>   WstDigt—CF-08-F3       Ethernet
*>   220.100.100.111        IP
*>   SPEEDY                 NetBIOS              SPEEDY
>  THE-HOSTAGE
*>   00-60-08-98-1D-33      Ethernet
*>   220.100.100.172        IP
*>   THE-HOSTAGE           NetBIOS              THE-HOSTAGE
>  *NEW XYLAN-A76640
*>   XYLAN----A7-66-40      ETHERNET
>  *NEW XYLAN-AC9EB5
*>   XYLAN----AC-9E-B5      ETHERNET
```

With the new node (SPEEDY) working on the network, I took some additional snapshots (traces with the Internet Advisor). My first was a brief network stack decode:

```
**********************************************************************
*****                                                          *****
*****            HEWLETT PACKARD NETWORK ADVISOR               *****
*****                                                          *****
*****       Measurement:    Brief Network Stack Decode         *****
*****       Print Type:     All Frames                         *****
*****       Open Views:     Summary                            *****
*****       Display Mode:   Viewing All Frames                 *****
*****                                                          *****
****     Print Date:      08/22/98                             *****
*****     Print Time:     11:23:59                             *****
*****                                                          *****
*****                                                          *****
**********************************************************************
1    20:31.649 HP----21-08-A0 HP----21-08-A0          ARP R
     PA = [15.6.72.18] HA = 0060B02108A0
2    20:34.052 00000000-HP----210 00000000-Broadcast  SAP C
     Find general Unkn service
3    20:34.057 00000000-HP----210 00000000-Broadcast  SAP C
     Find general Unkn service
4    20:34.057 00000000-Kingst30C 00000000-HP----210   SAP R
     MUSCLE
5    20:34.061 00000000-HP----210 00000000-Broadcast  SAP C
     Find general Unkn service
6    20:34.065 00000000-HP----210 00000000-Broadcast  SAP C
     Find general Unkn service
7    20:34.104 220.100.100.111    220.100.100.255      SMB C
     Transaction name \MAILSLOT\BROWSE
8    20:34.104 00000000-WstDigCF0 00000000-Broadcast    IPX
     Type = 20 IPX WAN Broadcast LEN = 223
9    20:36.108 WstDigt----CF-08-F3 03-00-00-00-00-01   SMB C
     Transaction name \MAILSLOT\BROWSE
10   21:08.948 00000000-006008981 0000000—Broadcast   SAP C
     Find nearest file server
11   21:09.055 00000000-006008981 00000000-Broadcast  SAP C
     Find general file server
12   21:09.065 00000000-006008981 00000000-Broadcast  SAP C
     Find general file server
```

```
13   21:09.145 00000000-006008981 00000000-Broadcast   SAP C
     Find nearest file server
14   21:09.155 00000000-006008981 00000000-Broadcast   SAP C
     Find nearest file server
15   21:09.164 00000000-006008981 00000000-Broadcast   SAP C
     Find general file server
16   21:09.175 00000000-006008981 00000000-Broadcast   SAP C
     Find general file server
17   21:09.184 00000000-006008981 00000000-Broadcast   SAP C
     Find nearest file server
18   21:09.196 00000000-006008981 00000000-Broadcast   IPX NCP
     Unknown type = 0000
19   21:09.197 00000000-006008981 00000000-Broadcast   IPX RIP
     Request
20   21:09.648 220.100.100.10      Broadcast            BOOTP
     Request
21   21:10.800 00-60-08-98-1D-33 03-00-00-00-00-01     SMB C
     Transaction name \MAILSLOT\BROWSE
22   21:13.301 00000000-Kingst30C 00000000-Broadcast IPX RIP
     Response: 1 networks
23   21:17.064 00000000-006008981 00000000-Broadcast IPX RIP
     Request
24   21:20.022 00000000-006008981 00000000-Broadcast IPX RIP
     Request
25   21:20.333 220.100.100.10      Broadcast            BOOTP
     Request
26   21:22.653 00000000-006008981 00000000-Broadcast   SAP C
     Find general file server
27   21:27.084 00000000-Kingst30C 00000000-Broadcast   SAP R
     MUSCLE
28   21:33.913 HP----21-08-A0 H----21-08-A0      ARP R
     PA = [15.6.72.18] HA = 0060B02108A0
29   21:34.145 220.100.100.10      Broadcast            BOOTP
     Request
30   21:34.253 220.100.100.111 220.100.100.255        SMB C
     Transaction name \MAILSLOT\BROWSE
31   21:34.880 00000000-HP----210 00000000-Broadcast   SAP C
     Find general Unkn service
32   21:34.884 00000000-HP----210 00000000-Broadcast   SAP C
     Find general Unkn service
33   21:34.885 00000000-Kingst30C 00000000-HP----210   SAP R
     MUSCLE
34   21:34.892 00000000-HP----210 00000000-Broadcast   SAP C
     Find general Unkn service
35   21:34.899 00000000-HP----210 00000000-Broadcast   SAP C
     Find general Unkn service
36   21:36.257 WstDigt----CF-08-F3 03-00-00-00-00-01    SMB C
     Transaction name \MAILSLOT\BROWSE
37   21:52.164 220.100.100.10      Broadcast            BOOTP
     Request
38   22:00.163 HP----21-08-A0 HP----21-08-A0     ARP R
     PA = [15.6.72.18] HA = 0060B02108A0
39   22:00.683 00000000-HP----210 00000000-Broadcast   SAP C
     Find general Unkn service
40   22:00.687 00000000-HP----210 00000000-Broadcast   SAP C
     Find general Unkn service
41   22:00.688 00000000-Kingst30C 00000000-HP----210   SAP R
     MUSCLE
42   22:00.692 00000000-HP----210 00000000-Broadcast   SAP C
     Find general Unkn service
```

```
43   22:00.696 00000000-HP----210 00000000-Broadcast    SAP C
     Find general Unkn service
44   22:11.623 220.100.100.172    220.100.100.255        SMB C
     Transaction name \MAILSLOT\BROWSE
45   22:13.317 00000000-Kingst30C 00000000-Broadcast     IPX RIP
     Response: 1 networks
46   22:22.651 00000000-006008981 00000000-Broadcast     SAP C
     Find nearest file server
47   22:27.099 00000000-Kingst30C 00000000-Broadcast     SAP R
     MUSCLE
48   23:13.333 00000000-Kingst30C 00000000-Broadcast     IPX
     RIP
     Response: 1 networks
49   23:14.978 220.100.100.10      Broadcast              BOOTP
     Request
50   23:17.935 00000000-006008981 70001600-840565047     IPX
     Type = 20 IPX WAN Broadcast LEN = 228
51   23:22.649 00000000-006008981 00000000-Broadcast     SAP C
     Find general file server
52   23:24.239 Kingston-30-C2-43 03-00-00-00-00-01        NETB
     Name query SPEEDY
53   23:24.240 00000001-000000000 00000000-Broadcast     NETB
     Find Name SPEEDY
54   23:24.244 Kingston-30-C2-43    Broadcast             ARP C
     PA = [220.100.100.111]
55   23:24.781 00000001-000000000 00000000-Broadcast     NETB
     Find Name SPEEDY
56   23:25.132220.100.100.10       Broadcast             BOOTP
     Request
57   23:25.32200000001-000000000 00000000-Broadcast      NETBFind
     Name SPEEDY
58   23:27.115 00000000-Kingst30C 00000000-Broadcast     SAP R
     MUSCLE
```

I decided to take another trace of the ARPA stack; however, my purpose for doing so was to "catch" SPEEDY communicating. Examine the following trace data, which display this functionality in the XYLAN switch.

```
*******************************************************************
*****                                                       *****
*****           HEWLETT PACKARD NETWORK ADVISOR             *****
*****                                                       *****
*****      Measurement:      ARPA Stack Decode              *****
*****      Print Type:       Current frame 22               *****
*****      Open Views:       Detailed                       *****
*****      Display Mode:     Viewing All Frames             *****
*****      Print Date:       09/15/00                       *****
*****      Print Time:       11:19:53                       *****
*****                                                       *****
*******************************************************************
```

```
Frame: 22        Time: Aug 22@11:16:33.5805780 Length: 253
  SMB
Identifier              SMB
Command Code            25              Transaction Name
Error Class             00              Success
Reserved                00
Error Code              0000
                                        Success
```

```
Flags                            00000000              Good
  Response Request               0.......              Request
  Client Notification            .0......              Flag Not Set
  File Lock                      ..0.....              Flag Not Set
  Canonical Form                 ...0....              Flag Not Set
  Case Sensitive                 ....0...              Flag Not Set
  Reserved                       .....0..
  Rcv Buffer Posted              ......0.              Flag Not Set
  Subdialect                     .......0              Flag Not Set
Flags_2                          0000
Reserved (Truncated)             00-00-00-00-00-00-00-00-0
Authenticated Resource ID 0000
Callers Process ID               0000
Unauthenticated User ID          0000
Multiplex ID                     0000
Word Count                       17
Parameters                       0000
Parameters                       0027
Parameters                       0000
Parameters                       0000
Parameters (Truncated)           00-02-00-01-00-01-00-03-0
Buffer Count                     56
ASCII Data                       \MAILSLOT\BROWSE
Buffer Type                      01                    **Server Data**
Block
ASCII Data                       ^C`ΩSPEEDY
ASCII Data                       @ ^U^DU¬SPEEDY
  NetBIOS
Service Type :                                         Datagram Service
Packet Type :                                          Direct_Group Datagram
Msg_Type                         11
Flags                            1A                    See Bit Fields Below
  Reserved Bits                  0001....                Warning: Reserved
Bit Not
  Zero
  Source End-Node Type           ....10..              Mixed (M) node
  FIRST Flag                     ......1.              First Fragment
  MORE Flag                      .......0              Last Fragment
  DGM ID                         6
Source IP                         220.100.100.111      Source IP Address
Source Port                      138                   Source Port Number
DGM Length                       193
Packet Offset                    0
Name Length                      32
Source Name                      **SPEEDY**            NetBIOS Name
Name Length                      32
Destination Name                 INFO.COM       ^]     NetBIOS Name
User Data                                              SMB Data - See
SMB Decode
  UDP
Source port                      138                   NETBIOS
Destination port                 138                   NETBIOS
Length                           215
Checksum                         69-AF
> Data size                      207
> New address
  IP
Version                          4
Internet header length           5                     (32 bit words)
Precedence                       000.-....             Routine
```

```
Delay                        ...0-....           Delay normal
Throughput                   ....-0...             Throughput normal
Reliability                  ....-.0..            Reliability normal
Reserved                     ....-..00
Total Length                 235
Identification               1792
Reserved                     00..-....
May / Do Not Fragment        .0..-....           Fragmentation allowed
Last / More Fragments        ..0.-....           Last fragment
Offset                       0
Time To Live                 32
Next Protocol                17                  UDP
Checksum                     10-CB
Source                       220.100.100.111
Destination                  220.100.100.255
> Data size                  215
  802.3/Ethernet
Destination address          Broadcast           Broadcast
Source address                 WstDigt—CF-08-F3    Individual, global
Type                         08-00               IP
Frame check sequence         89-20-23-99
```

The following is a trace of the network stack decode for 39 frames. Note that the XYLAN switch Ethernet address shows up in the trace data as well as the following indicators:

- MUSCLE

- THE-HOSTAGE

- SPEEDY

- IP version 4

- The domain INFO.COM

- NETBIOS

- RIP

- IPX data

This level of detail is very helpful when troubleshooting. In order to use information like this in troubleshooting, one has to have information such as this on file. Consequently, consider this level of detail for baselining your switch:

```
************************************************************
*****                                                  *****
*****       HEWLETT PACKARD NETWORK ADVISOR             *****
*****                                                  *****
*****       Measurement:    Network Stack Decode        *****
*****       Print Type:     All Frames                  *****
*****       Open Views:     Detailed                    *****
*****       Display Mode:   Viewing All Frames          *****
*****       Print Date:     09/15/00                    *****
*****       Print Time:     11:27:58                    *****
*****                                                  *****
************************************************************
```

```
Frame: 1          Time: Aug 22@11:25:32.4611636  Length: 64
   ARP/RARP
Hardware                   1                        Ethernet
Protocol                   08-00                    IP
HW addr length             6
Phys addr length           4
Operation                  2                        ARP Reply
Sender HW addr             00-60-B0-21-08-A0
Sender internet addr       15.6.72.18
Target HW addr             00-00-00-00-00-00
Target internet addr       15.6.72.18
   802.3/Ethernet
Destination address        HP----21-08-A0     Warning:  Duplicate source
   and destination address
Source address             HP----21-08-A0     Warning:  Duplicate source
   and destination address
Type                       08-06                    ARP
Frame check sequence       F3-11-34-41
> Data size                46
> Protocol warning
```

```
Frame: 2          Time: Aug 22@11:25:34.1306347  Length: 64
   802.2
Destination SAP            42                       Unknown SAP
Source SAP                 42                       Unknown SAP
Command/Response           ....-...0                Command
Type                       03                       Unnumbered
Poll                       ...0-....
Modifier                   000.-00..                Information
   802.3/Ethernet
Destination address        01-80-C2-00-00-00        Group, global
Source address             XYLAN----AC-9E-B5        Individual, global
Length                     38
Padding:
   DC-B1-66-F8-AD-94-E3-36
Frame check sequence       B1-6C-E1-34
> Data size                38
```

```
Frame: 3          Time: Aug 22@11:25:34.3275052  Length: 244
   IPX
Checksum                   FFFF
IPX Length                 223
Transport Control          00
Packet Type                20                       Experimental
Destination Network        00000000
Destination Node           FFFFFFFFFFFF             Broadcast
Destination Socket         0553
Source Network             00000000
Source Node                0000C0CF08F3
Source Socket              0553
   802.2
Destination SAP            E0                       IPX
Source SAP                 E0                       IPX
Command/Response           ....-...0                Command
Type                       03                       Unnumbered
Poll                       ...0-....
Modifier                   000.-00..                Information
   802.3/Ethernet
Destination address        Broadcast                Broadcast
```

Source address	WstDigt—CF-08-F3	Individual, global
Length	226	
Frame check sequence	0F-D4-C0-72	
> Data size	226	

Frame: 4   Time: Aug 22@11:25:34.8463663   Length: 64
  802.2

Destination SAP	42	Unknown SAP
Source SAP	42	Unknown SAP
Command/Response	....-...0	Command
Type	03	Unnumbered
Poll	...0-....	
Modifier	000.-00..	Information

  802.3/Ethernet

Destination address	01-80-C2-00-00-00	Group, global
Source address	**XYLAN----AC-9E-B5**	Individual, global
Length	38	
Padding:		
DC-B1-66-F8-AD-94-E3-36		
Frame check sequence	B1-6C-E1-34	
> Data size	38	

Frame: 5   Time: Aug 22@11:25:36.8467995   Length: 64
  802.2

Destination SAP	42	Unknown SAP
Source SAP	42	Unknown SAP
Command/Response	....-...0	Command
Type	03	Unnumbered
Poll	...0-....	
Modifier	000.-00..	Information

  802.3/Ethernet

Destination address	01-80-C2-00-00-00	Group, global
Source address	Xylan----AC-9E-B5	Individual, global
Length	38	
Padding:		
DC-B1-66-F8-AD-94-E3-36		
Frame check sequence	B1-6C-E1-34	
> Data size	38	

Frame: 6   Time: Aug 22@11:25:38.8471699   Length: 64
  802.2

Destination SAP	42	Unknown SAP
Source SAP	42	Unknown SAP
Command/Response	....-...0	Command
Type	03	Unnumbered
Poll	...0-....	
Modifier	000.-00..	Information

  802.3/Ethernet

Destination address	01-80-C2-00-00-00	Group, global
Source address	**XYLAN----AC-9E-B5**	Individual, global
Length	38	
Padding:		
DC-B1-66-F8-AD-94-E3-36		
Frame check sequence	B1-6C-E1-34	
> Data size	38	

Frame: 7   Time: Aug 22@11:25:40.8477201   Length: 64
  802.2

Destination SAP	42	Unknown SAP
Source SAP	42	Unknown SAP

```
Command/Response            ....-...0              Command
Type                        03                     Unnumbered
Poll                        ...0-....
Modifier                    000.-00..              Information
  802.3/Ethernet
Destination address         01-80-C2-00-00-00      Group, global
Source address              XYLAN----AC-9E-B5      Individual, global
Length                      38
Padding:
  DC-B1-66-F8-AD-94-E3-36
Frame check sequence        B1-6C-E1-34
> Data size                 38
```

```
Frame: 8          Time: Aug 22@11:25:41.4800509  Length: 346
  BOOTP
Operation code              1                      Bootp Request
Hardware type               1                      Ethernet
Hardware address length     16
Hop count                   0
Transaction ID              961603691
Seconds since boot          5888
Client IP                   0.0.0.0
Gateway IP                  0.0.0.0
Hardware address (hex)      52-41-53-20-90-42-70-1D-
Host name (first 8 bytes)   00-00-00-00-00-00-00-00
Boot file name (hex)        00-00-00-00-00-00-00-00
Vendor magic cookie IP      99.130.83.99
  Host name                 MUSCLE
  UDP
Source port                 68                     BOOTPS
Destination port            67                     BOOTPS
Length                      308
Checksum                    25-A8
  IP
Version                     4
Internet header length      5                      (32 bit words)
Precedence                  000.-....              Routine
Delay                       ...0-....              Delay normal
Throughput                  ....-0...              Throughput normal
Reliability                 ....-.0..              Reliability normal
Total Length                328
Identification              58402
May / Do Not Fragment       .0..-....              Fragmentation allowed
Last / More Fragments       ..0.-....              Last fragment
Offset                      0
Time To Live                128
Next Protocol               17                     UDP
Checksum                    15-14
Source                      220.100.100.10
Destination                 Broadcast
> Data size                 308
  802.3/Ethernet
Destination address         Broadcast              Broadcast
Source address              Kingston-30-C2-43      Individual, global
Type                        08-00                  IP
Frame check sequence        B5-14-FE-4B
> Data size                 328
```

```
Frame: 9          Time: Aug 22@11:25:42.1361021  Length: 64
  Novell SAP
```

```
Service Adv. Protocol      0001                 General Service Query
Server Type                FFFF
   IPX
Checksum                   FFFF
IPX Length                 34
Transport Control          00
Packet Type                17                   NCP
Destination Network        00000000
Destination Node           FFFFFFFFFFFF         Broadcast
Destination Socket         0452                 Service Advertising
                                                Packet
Source Network             00000000
Source Node                0060B02108A0
Source Socket              4001
   SNAP
Organization code          00-00-00
Type                       81-37                IPX
   802.2
Destination SAP            AA                   SNAP
Source SAP                 AA                   SNAP
Command/Response           ....-...0            Command
Type                       03                   Unnumbered
Poll                       ...0-....
Modifier                   000.-00..            Information
   802.3/Ethernet
Destination address        Broadcast            Broadcast
Source address             HP----21-08-A0       Individual, global
Length                     42
Padding:
   00-00-00-00
Frame check sequence       F2-67-62-C1
> Data size                42
```

```
Frame: 10        Time: Aug 22@11:25:42.1403283  Length: 64
   Novell SAP
Service Adv. Protocol      0001                 General Service Query
Server Type                FFFF
   IPX
Checksum                   FFFF
IPX Length                 34
Transport Control          00
Packet Type                17                   NCP
Destination Network        00000000
Destination Node           FFFFFFFFFFFF         Broadcast
Destination Socket         0452                 Service Advertising Packet
Source Network             00000000
Source Node                0060B02108A0
Source Socket              4001
   802.2
Destination SAP            E0                   IPX
Source SAP                 E0                   IPX
Command/Response           ....-...0            Command
Type                       03                   Unnumbered
Poll                       ...0-....
Modifier                   000.-00..            Information
   802.3/Ethernet
Destination address        Broadcast            Broadcast
Source address             HP----21-08-A0       Individual, global
Length                     37
Padding:    00-00-00-00-00-00-00-00 00
```

```
Frame check sequence        23-51-92-A9
> Data size                 37
```

```
Frame: 11        Time: Aug 22@11:25:42.1410254  Length: 182
  Novell SAP
Service Adv. Protocol       0002              General Service Response
Server Type                 0640
Server Name                 MUSCLE
SAP Network Address         00000001
SAP Node Address            000000000001
SAP Socket Address          E885
Hops To Server              1
Server Type                 064E
Server Name                 MUSCLE!!!!!!!!!A5569B20A
SAP Network Address         00000001
SAP Node Address            000000000001
SAP Socket Address          4010
Hops To Server              1
  IPX
Checksum                    FFFF
IPX Length                  160
Transport Control           00
Packet Type                 17                NCP
Destination Network         00000000
Destination Node            0060B02108A0
Destination Socket          4001
Source Network              00000000
Source Node                 00C0F030C243
Source Socket               0452              Service Advertising Packet
  802.2
Destination SAP             E0                  IPX
Source SAP                  E0                  IPX
Command/Response            ....-...0           Command
Type                        03                  Unnumbered
Poll                        ...0-....
Modifier                    000.-00..           Information
  802.3/Ethernet
Destination address         HP----21-08-A0      Individual, global
Source address              Kingston-30-C2-43   Individual, global
Length                      164
Frame check sequence        E3-B7-41-28
> Data size                 164
```

```
Frame: 12        Time: Aug 22@11:25:42.1448953  Length: 64
  Novell SAP
Service Adv. Protocol       0001              General Service Query
Server Type                 FFFF
  IPX
Checksum                    FFFF
IPX Length                  34
Transport Control           00
Packet Type                 17                NCP
Destination Network         00000000
Destination Node            FFFFFFFFFFFF      Broadcast
Destination Socket          0452              Service Advertising Packet
Source Network              00000000
Source Node                 0060B02108A0
Source Socket               4001
  802.3/Ethernet
```

```
Destination address        Broadcast              Broadcast
Source address             HP----21-08-A0         Individual, global
Length                     34                     IPX
Padding:
  00-00-00-00-00-00-00-00 00-00-00-00
Frame check sequence       78-8A-D8-9A
> Data size                34
```

```
Frame: 13          Time: Aug 22@11:25:42.1491827  Length: 64
  Novell SAP
Service Adv. Protocol      0001                   General Service Query
Server Type                FFFF
  IPX
Checksum                   FFFF
IPX Length                 34
Transport Control          00
Packet Type                17                     NCP
Destination Network        00000000
Destination Node           FFFFFFFFFFFF           Broadcast
Destination Socket         0452                   Service Advertising Packet
Source Network             00000000
Source Node                0060B02108A0
Source Socket              4001
  802.3/Ethernet
Destination address        Broadcast              Broadcast
Source address             HP----21-08-A0         Individual, global
Type                       81-37                  IPX
Frame check sequence       93-E9-A4-48
> Data size                46
```

```
Frame: 14          Time: Aug 22@11:25:42.8481737  Length: 64
  802.2
Destination SAP            42                     Unknown SAP
Source SAP                 42                     Unknown SAP
Command/Response           ....-...0              Command
Type                       03                     Unnumbered
Poll                       ...0-....
Modifier                   000.-00..              Information
  802.3/Ethernet
Destination address        01-80-C2-00-00-00      Group, global
Source address             XYLAN----AC-9E-B5      Individual, global
Length                     38
Padding:   DC-B1-66-F8-AD-94-E3-36
Frame check sequence       B1-6C-E1-34
> Data size                38
```

```
Frame: 15          Time: Aug 22@11:25:44.8485252  Length: 64
  802.2
Destination SAP            42                     Unknown SAP
Source SAP                 42                     Unknown SAP
Command/Response           ....-...0              Command
Type                       03                     Unnumbered
Poll                       ...0-....
Modifier                   000.-00..              Information
  802.3/Ethernet
Destination address        01-80-C2-00-00-00      Group, global
Source address             XYLAN----AC-9E-B5      Individual, global
Length                     38
Padding:
  DC-B1-66-F8-AD-94-E3-36
```

```
Frame check sequence          B1-6C-E1-34
> Data size                   38
```

```
Frame: 16        Time: Aug 22@11:25:46.8490595  Length: 64
  802.2
Destination SAP               42                    Unknown SAP
Source SAP                    42                    Unknown SAP
Command/Response              ....-...0             Command
Type                          03                    Unnumbered
Poll                          ...0-....
Modifier                      000.-00..             Information
  802.3/Ethernet
Destination address           01-80-C2-00-00-00     Group, global
Source address                XYLAN----AC-9E-B5     Individual, global
Length                        38
Padding:
  DC-B1-66-F8-AD-94-E3-36
Frame check sequence          B1-6C-E1-34
> Data size                   38
```

```
Frame: 17        Time: Aug 22@11:25:48.8495315  Length: 64
  802.2
Destination SAP               42                    Unknown SAP
Source SAP                    42                    Unknown SAP
Command/Response              ....-...0             Command
Type                          03                    Unnumbered
Poll                          ...0-....
Modifier                      000.-00..             Information
  802.3/Ethernet
Destination address           01-80-C2-00-00-00     Group, global
Source address                XYLAN----AC-9E-B5     Individual, global
Length                        38
Padding:
  DC-B1-66-F8-AD-94-E3-36
Frame check sequence          B1-6C-E1-34
> Data size                   38
```

```
Frame: 18        Time: Aug 22@11:25:50.8498854  Length: 64
  802.2
Destination SAP               42                    Unknown SAP
Source SAP                    42                    Unknown SAP
Command/Response              ....-...0             Command
Type                          03                    Unnumbered
Poll                          ...0-....
Modifier                      000.-00..             Information
  802.3/Ethernet
Destination address           01-80-C2-00-00-00     Group, global
Source address                XYLAN----AC-9E-B5     Individual, global
Length                        38
Padding:
  DC-B1-66-F8-AD-94-E3-36
Frame check sequence          B1-6C-E1-34
> Data size                   38
```

```
Frame: 19        Time: Aug 22@11:25:52.8504332  Length: 64
  802.2
Destination SAP               42                    Unknown SAP
Source SAP                    42                    Unknown SAP
Command/Response              ....-...0             Command
Type                          03                    Unnumbered
```

```
Poll                       ...0-....
Modifier                   000.-00..              Information
  802.3/Ethernet
Destination address        01-80-C2-00-00-00      Group, global
Source address             XYLAN----C-9E-B5       Individual, global
Length                     38
Padding:
  DC-B1-66-F8-AD-94-E3-36
Frame check sequence       B1-6C-E1-34
> Data size                38
```

```
Frame: 20        Time: Aug 22@11:25:52.9576613   Length: 64
  ARP/RARP
Hardware                   1                      Ethernet
Protocol                   08-00                  IP
HW addr length             6
Phys addr length           4
Operation                  1                      ARP Request
Sender HW addr             00-C0-F0-30-C2-43
Sender internet addr       220.100.100.10
Target HW addr             00-00-00-00-00-00
Target internet addr       220.100.100.111
  802.3/Ethernet
Destination address        Broadcast              Broadcast
Source address             Kingston-30-C2-43      Individual, global
Type                       08-06                  ARP
Frame check sequence       53-2D-B4-10
> Data size                46
```

```
Frame: 21        Time: Aug 22@11:25:54.3223507   Length: 119
  IPX
Checksum                   FFFF
IPX Length                 98
Transport Control          00
Packet Type                4                      PEP
Destination Network        00000000
Destination Node           FFFFFFFFFFFF           Broadcast
Destination Socket         0551
Source Network             00000000
Source Node                0000C0CF08F3
Source Socket              0552
  802.2
Destination SAP            E0                     IPX
Source SAP                 E0                     IPX
Command/Response           ....-...0              Command
Type                       03                     Unnumbered
Poll                       ...0-....
Modifier                   000.-00..              Information
  802.3/Ethernet
Destination address        Broadcast              Broadcast
Source address             WstDigt—CF-08-F3       Individual, global
Length                     101
Frame check sequence       68-44-52-6C
> Data size                101
```

```
Frame: 22        Time: Aug 22@11:25:54.3302484   Length: 64
  ARP/RARP
Hardware                   1                      Ethernet
Protocol                   08-00                  IP
HW addr length             6
```

```
Phys addr length              4
Operation                     1                        ARP Request
Sender HW addr                00-00-C0-CF-08-F3
Sender internet addr          220.100.100.111
Target HW addr                00-00-00-00-00-00
Target internet addr          220.100.100.172
   802.3/Ethernet
Destination address           Broadcast                Broadcast
Source address                WstDigt—CF-08-F3         Individual, global
Type                          08-06                    ARP
Frame check sequence          02-18-9C-AA
> Data size                   46
```

```
Frame: 23       Time: Aug 22@11:25:54.3346122   Length: 65
   NetBIOS
Header Length                 44
Delimiter                     EFFF
Command                       0A                       NAME_QUERY
Optional Data 1               1A                       Warning:  Data in reserved
 field
  Name Type                   11                       Unique name type
  Session Number              00
Transmit Correlator           0000                     Reserved field
Response Correlator           0011
Destination Name              THE-HOSTAGE
Source Name                   SPEEDY
   802.2
Destination SAP               F0                       NetBios
Source SAP                    F0                       NetBios
Command/Response              ....-...0                Command
Type                          03                       Unnumbered
Poll                          ...0-....
Modifier                      000.-00..                Information
   802.3/Ethernet
Destination address           03-00-00-00-00-01        Group, local
Source address                WstDigt—CF-08-F3         Individual, global
Length                        47
Frame check sequence          2E-CF-0D-1B
> Data size                   47
```

```
Frame: 24       Time: Aug 22@11:26:00.1796446   Length: 346
   BOOTP
Operation code                1                        Bootp Request
Hardware type                 1                        Ethernet
Hardware address length       16
Hop count                     0
Transaction ID                961603691
Seconds since boot            10752
Client IP                     0.0.0.0
Gateway IP                    0.0.0.0
Hardware address (hex)        52-41-53-20-90-42-70-1D-
Host name (first 8 bytes)     00-00-00-00-00-00-00-00
Boot file name (hex)          00-00-00-00-00-00-00-00
Vendor magic cookie IP        99.130.83.99
  Host name                   MUSCLE
   UDP
Source port                   68                       BOOTPS
Destination port              67                       BOOTPS
Length                        308
Checksum                      12-A8
```

```
  IP
Version                        4
Internet header length         5                     (32 bit words)
Precedence                     000.-....            Routine
Delay                          ...0-....            Delay normal
Throughput                     ....-0...            Throughput normal
Reliability                    ....-.0..            Reliability normal
Total Length                   328
Identification                 4131
May / Do Not Fragment          .0..-....            Fragmentation allowed
Last / More Fragments          ..0.-....            Last fragment
Offset                         0
Time To Live                   128
Next Protocol                  17                   UDP
Checksum                       E9-13
Source                         220.100.100.10
Destination                    Broadcast
> Data size                    308
  802.3/Ethernet
Destination address            Broadcast            Broadcast
Source address                 Kingston-30-C2-43    Individual, global
Type                           08-00                IP
Frame check sequence           15-C7-AE-30
> Data size                    328
```

Frame: 25   Time: Aug 22@11:26:08.9609173   Length: 65

```
  NetBIOS
Header Length                  44
Delimiter                      EFFF
Command                        0A                   NAME_QUERY
Optional Data 1                17                   Warning:  Data in reserved
 field
  Name Type                    0F                   Unique name type
  Session Number               00
Transmit Correlator            0000                 Reserved field
Response Correlator            000F
Destination Name               MUSCLE
Source Name                    THE-HOSTAGE
  802.2
Destination SAP                F0                   NetBios
Source SAP                     F0                   NetBios
Command/Response               ....-...0            Command
Type                           03                   Unnumbered
Poll                           ...0-....
Modifier                       000.-00..            Information
  802.3/Ethernet
Destination address            03-00-00-00-00-01    Group, local
Source address                 00-60-08-98-1D-33    Individual, global
Length                         47
Frame check sequence           84-52-3B-16
> Data size                    47
```

Frame: 26   Time: Aug 22@11:26:11.7606845   Length: 195

```
  SMB
Identifier                     SMB
Command Code                   25                   Transaction Name
Error Class                    00                   Success
Reserved                       00
Error Code                     0000                 Success
Flags                          00000000             Good
```

```
        Response Request          0.......                    Request
        Client Notification       .0......                    Flag Not Set
        File Lock                 ..0.....                    Flag Not Set
        Canonical Form            ...0....                    Flag Not Set
        Case Sensitive            ....0...                    Flag Not Set
        Reserved                  .....0..
        Rcv Buffer Posted         ......0.                    Flag Not Set
        Subdialect                .......0                    Flag Not Set
Flags_2                           0000
Reserved (Truncated)              00-00-00-00-00-00-00-00-
Authenticated Resource ID         0000
Callers Process ID                0000
Unauthenticated User ID           0000
Multiplex ID                      0000
Word Count                        17
Parameters                        0000
Parameters                        002C
Parameters                        0000
Parameters                        0000
Parameters (Truncated)            00-02-00-01-00-01-00-03-
Buffer Count                      61
ASCII Data                        \MAILSLOT\BROWSE
Buffer Type                       01                          Server Data Block
ASCII Data                        ∝ô^D THE-HOSTAGE
ASCII Data                        C ^U^DU¬THE-HOSTAGE
  NetBIOS
Header Length                     44
Delimiter                         EFFF
Command                           08                          DATAGRAM
Optional Data 1                   00                          Reserved field
Optional Data 2                   0000                        Reserved field
Transmit Correlator               0000                        Reserved field
Response Correlator               0000                        Reserved field
Destination Name                  INFO.COM
Source Name                       THE-HOSTAGE
  802.2
Destination SAP                   F0                          NetBios
Source SAP                        F0                          NetBios
Command/Response                  ....-...0                   Command
Type                              03                          Unnumbered
Poll                              ...0-....
Modifier                          000.-00..                   Information
  802.3/Ethernet
Destination address               03-00-00-00-00-01           Group, local
Source address                    00-60-08-98-1D-33           Individual, global
Length                            177
Frame check sequence              DB-89-E3-1F
> Data size                       177
```

```
Frame: 27       Time: Aug 22@11:26:13.3800071   Length: 64
  Novell RIP
Routing Info. Protocol            0002                        Reply
Network Number                    00000001
Number Of Hops                    1
Number Of Ticks                   2
  IPX
Checksum                          FFFF
IPX Length                        40
Transport Control                 00
Packet Type                       1                           Routing Information Packet
```

```
Destination Network         00000000
Destination Node            FFFFFFFFFFFF        Broadcast
Destination Socket          0453               Routing Information Packet
Source Network              00000000
Source Node                 00C0F030C243
Source Socket               0453               Routing Information Packet
  802.2
Destination SAP             E0                 IPX
Source SAP                  E0                 IPX
Command/Response            ....-...0          Command
Type                        03                 Unnumbered
Poll                        ...0-....
Modifier                    000.-00..          Information
  802.3/Ethernet
Destination address         Broadcast          Broadcast
Source address              Kingston-30-C2-43  Individual, global
Length                      44
Padding:
  00-00
Frame check sequence        51-6F-D4-AD
> Data size                 44
```

```
Frame: 28        Time: Aug 22@11:26:22.6438210  Length: 64
  Novell SAP
Service Adv. Protocol       0003               Nearest Server Query
Server Type                 0004
  IPX
Checksum                    FFFF
IPX Length                  34
Transport Control           00
Packet Type                 17                 NCP
Destination Network         00000000
Destination Node            FFFFFFFFFFFF        Broadcast
Destination Socket          0452               Service Advertising Packet
Source Network              00000000
Source Node                 006008981D33
Source Socket               401C
  802.2
Destination SAP             E0                 IPX
Source SAP                  E0                 IPX
Command/Response            ....-...0          Command
Type                        03                 Unnumbered
Poll                        ...0-....
Modifier                    000.-00..            Information
  802.3/Ethernet
Destination address         Broadcast            Broadcast
Source address              00-60-08-98-1D-33    Individual, global
Length                      37
Padding:    00-04-00-04-00-04-00-04 00
Frame check sequence        FD-69-6C-C8
> Data size                 37
```

```
Frame: 29        Time: Aug 22@11:26:27.1631141  Length: 182
Service Adv. Protocol       0002               General Service Response
Server Type                 0640
Server Name                 MUSCLE
SAP Network Address         00000001
SAP Node Address            000000000001
SAP Socket Address          E885
Hops To Server              1
```

```
Server Type              064E
Server Name              MUSCLE!!!!!!!!!A5569B20A
SAP Network Address      00000001
SAP Node Address         000000000001
SAP Socket Address       4010
Hops To Server           1
  IPX
Checksum                 FFFF
IPX Length               160
Transport Control        00
Packet Type              4               PEP
Destination Network      00000000
Destination Node         FFFFFFFFFFFF    Broadcast
Destination Socket       0452            Service Advertising Packet
Source Network           00000000
Source Node              00C0F030C243
Source Socket            0452            Service Advertising Packet
  802.2
Destination SAP          E0              IPX
Source SAP               E0              IPX
Command/Response         ....-...0        Command
Type                     03              Unnumbered
Poll                     ...0-....
Modifier                 000.-00..        Information
  802.3/Ethernet
Destination address      Broadcast       Broadcast
Source address           Kingston-30-C2-43  Individual, global
Length                   164
Frame check sequence     CF-BB-1B-19
> Data size              164
```

```
Frame: 30        Time: Aug 22@11:26:34.2421174  Length: 253
  SMB
Identifier               SMB
Command Code             25              Transaction Name
Error Class              00              Success
Reserved                 00
Error Code               0000            Success
Flags                    00000000        Good
  Response Request       0.......        Request
  Client Notification    .0......        Flag Not Set
  File Lock              ..0.....        Flag Not Set
  Canonical Form         ...0....        Flag Not Set
  Case Sensitive         ....0...        Flag Not Set
  Reserved               .....0..
  Rcv Buffer Posted      ......0.        Flag Not Set
  Subdialect             .......0        Flag Not Set
Flags_2                  0000
Reserved (Truncated)     00-00-00-00-00-00-00-00-
Authenticated Resource ID  0000
Callers Process ID       0000
Unauthenticated User ID  0000
Multiplex ID             0000
Word Count               17
Parameters               0000
Parameters               0027
Parameters               0000
Parameters               0000
Parameters (Truncated)   00-02-00-01-00-01-00-03-
Buffer Count             56
```

ASCII Data	\MAILSLOT\BROWSE	
Buffer Type	01	Server Data Block
ASCII Data	^E∝ô^D SPEEDY	
ASCII Data	A ^U^DU¬SPEEDY	
NetBIOS		
Service Type :		Datagram Service
Packet Type :		Direct_Group Datagram
Msg_Type	11	
Flags	1A	See Bit Fields Below
Reserved Bits	0001....	Warning: Reserved Bit Not
Zero		
Source End-Node Type	....10..	Mixed (M) node
FIRST Flag	......1.	First Fragment
MORE Flag	0	Last Fragment
DGM ID	21	
Source IP	220.100.100.111	Source IP Address
Source Port	138	Source Port Number
DGM Length	193	
Packet Offset	0	
Name Length	32	
Source Name	**SPEEDY**	NetBIOS Name
Name Length	32	
Destination Name	INFO.COM	NetBIOS Name
User Data		SMB Data - See SMB Decode
UDP		
Source port	138	NETBIOS
Destination port	138	NETBIOS
Length	215	
Checksum	E4-F4	
IP		
Version	**4**	
Internet header length	5	(32 bit words)
Precedence	000.-....	Routine
Delay	...0-....	Delay normal
Throughput	....-0...	Throughput normal
Reliability	....-.0..	Reliability normal
Total Length	235	
Identification	4359	
May / Do Not Fragment	.0..-....	Fragmentation allowed
Last / More Fragments	..0.-....	Last fragment
Offset	0	
Time To Live	32	
Next Protocol	17	UDP
Checksum	06-C4	
Source	220.100.100.111	
Destination	220.100.100.255	
> Data size	215	
802.3/Ethernet		
Destination address	Broadcast	Broadcast
Source address	WstDigt—CF-08-F3	Individual, global
Type	08-00	IP
Frame check sequence	02-BC-97-FA	
> Data size	235	

Frame: 31   Time: Aug 22@11:26:36.2474343 Length: 190

SMB		
Identifier	SMB	
Command Code	25	Transaction Name
Error Class	00	Success
Reserved	00	

```
Error Code                      0000                          Success
Flags                           00000000                      Good
  Response Request              0.......                      Request
  Client Notification           .0......                      Flag Not Set
  File Lock                      ..0.....                      Flag Not Set
  Canonical Form                 ...0....                      Flag Not Set
  Case Sensitive                 ....0...                      Flag Not Set
  Reserved                       .....0..
  Rcv Buffer Posted              ......0.                      Flag Not Set
  Subdialect                     .......0                      Flag Not Set
Flags_2                         0000
Reserved (Truncated)            00-00-00-00-00-00-00-00-
Authenticated Resource ID       0000
Callers Process ID              0000
Unauthenticated User ID         0000
Multiplex ID                    0000
Word Count                      17
Parameters                      0000
Parameters                      0027
Parameters                      0000
Parameters                      0000
Parameters (Truncated)          00-02-00-01-00-01-00-03-
Buffer Count                    56
ASCII Data                      \MAILSLOT\BROWSE
Buffer Type                     01                            Server Data Block
ASCII Data                      ^E∝ô^D SPEEDY
ASCII Data                       A ^U^DU¬SPEEDY
  NetBIOS
Header Length                   44
Delimiter                       EFFF
Command                         08                            DATAGRAM
Optional Data 1                 00                            Reserved field
Optional Data 2                 0000                          Reserved field
Transmit Correlator             0000                          Reserved field
Response Correlator             0000                          Reserved field
Destination Name                INFO.COM
Source Name                     SPEEDY
  802.2
Destination SAP                 F0                            NetBios
Source SAP                      F0                            NetBios
Command/Response                ....-...0                     Command
Type                            03                            Unnumbered
Poll                            ...0-....
Modifier                        000.-00..                     Information
  802.3/Ethernet
Destination address             03-00-00-00-00-01             Group, local
Source address                  WstDigt—CF-08-F3              Individual, global
Length                          172
Frame check sequence            F9-8A-A4-55
> Data size                     172
```

```
Frame: 32        Time: Aug 22@11:27:00.9503546   Length: 65
  NetBIOS
Header Length                   44
Delimiter                       EFFF
Command                         0A                            NAME_QUERY
Optional Data 1                 1A                            Warning:  Data in reserved
  field
  Name Type                     12                            Unique name type
```

```
Session Number          00
Transmit Correlator     0000                 Reserved field
Response Correlator     0012
Destination Name        THE-HOSTAGE
Source Name             SPEEDY
  802.2
Destination SAP         F0                   NetBios
Source SAP              F0                   NetBios
Command/Response        ....-...0            Command
Type                    03                   Unnumbered
Poll                    ...0-....
Modifier                000.-00..            Information
  802.3/Ethernet
Destination address     03-00-00-00-00-01    Group, local
Source address          WstDigt—CF-08-F3     Individual, global
Length                  47
Frame check sequence    13-3C-63-3B
> Data size             47
```

```
Frame: 33       Time: Aug 22@11:27:08.9693520  Length: 64
  ARP/RARP
Hardware                1                    Ethernet
Protocol                08-00                IP
HW addr length          6
Phys addr length        4
Operation               1                    ARP Request
Sender HW addr          00-60-08-98-1D-33
Sender internet addr    220.100.100.172
Target HW addr          00-00-00-00-00-00
Target internet addr    220.100.100.10
  802.3/Ethernet
Destination address     Broadcast            Broadcast
Source address          00-60-08-98-1D-33    Individual, global
Type                    08-06                ARP
Frame check sequence    3D-DF-67-6B
> Data size             46
```

```
Frame: 34       Time: Aug 22@11:27:12.0436369  Length: 258
  SMB
Identifier              SMB
Command Code            25                   Transaction Name
Error Class             00                   Success
Reserved                00
Error Code              0000                 Success
Flags                   00000000             Good
  Response Request      0.......             Request
  Client Notification   .0......             Flag Not Set
  File Lock             ..0.....             Flag Not Set
  Canonical Form        ...0....             Flag Not Set
  Case Sensitive        ....0...             Flag Not Set
  Reserved              .....0..
  Rcv Buffer Posted     ......0.             Flag Not Set
  Subdialect            .......0             Flag Not Set
Flags_2                 0000
Reserved (Truncated)    00-00-00-00-00-00-00-00-
Authenticated Resource ID  0000
Callers Process ID      0000
Unauthenticated User ID 0000
Multiplex ID            0000
```

```
Word Count                  17
Parameters                  0000
Parameters                  002C
Parameters                  0000
Parameters                  0000
Parameters (Truncated)      00-02-00-01-00-01-00-03-
Buffer Count                61
ASCII Data                  \MAILSLOT\BROWSE
Buffer Type                 01                      Server Data Block
ASCII Data                  ∝ô^D THE-HOSTAGE
ASCII Data                   C^U^DU¬THE-HOSTAGE
  NetBIOS
Service Type :                                      Datagram Service
Packet Type  :                                      Direct_Group Datagram
Msg_Type                    11
Flags                       02                      See Bit Fields Below
  Reserved Bits             0000....
  Source End-Node Type      ....00..                Broadcast (B) node
  FIRST Flag                ......1.                First Fragment
  MORE Flag                 .......0                Last Fragment
DGM ID                      104
Source IP                   220.100.100.172         Source IP Address
Source Port                 138                     Source Port Number
DGM Length                  198
Packet Offset               0
Name Length                 32
Source Name                 THE-HOSTAGE             NetBIOS Name
Name Length                 32
Destination Name            INFO.COM      ^]        NetBIOS Name
User Data                                           SMB Data - See SMB
Decode
  UDP
Source port                 138                     NETBIOS
Destination port            138                     NETBIOS
Length                      220
Checksum                    F6-2D
  IP
Version                     4
Internet header length      5                       (32 bit words)
Precedence                  000.-....               Routine
Delay                       ...0-....               Delay normal
Throughput                  ....-0...               Throughput normal
Reliability                 ....-.0..               Reliability normal
Total Length                240
Identification              28937
May / Do Not Fragment       .0..-....               Fragmentation allowed
Last / More Fragments       ..0.-....               Last fragment
Offset                      0
Time To Live                128
Next Protocol               17                      UDP
Checksum                    46-7F
Source                      220.100.100.172
Destination                 220.100.100.255
> Data size                 220
  802.3/Ethernet
Destination address         Broadcast               Broadcast
Source address              00-60-08-98-1D-33       Individual, global
Type                        08-00                   IP
Frame check sequence        1E-67-FF-02
```

```
> Data size                   240
```

```
Frame: 35        Time: Aug 22@11:27:13.3956444  Length: 64
  Novell RIP
Routing Info. Protocol     0002                 Reply
Network Number             00000001
Number Of Hops             1
Number Of Ticks            2
  IPX
Checksum                   FFFF
IPX Length                 40
Transport Control          00
Packet Type                1              Routing Information Packet
Destination Network        00000000
Destination Node           FFFFFFFFFFFF   Broadcast
Destination Socket         0453           Routing Information Packet
Source Network             00000000
Source Node                00C0F030C243
Source Socket              0453           Routing Information Packet
  802.2
Destination SAP            E0             IPX
Source SAP                 E0             IPX
Command/Response           ....-...0       Command
Type                       03             Unnumbered
Poll                       ...0-....
Modifier                   000.-00..      Information
  802.3/Ethernet
Destination address        Broadcast      Broadcast
Source address             Kingston-30-C2-43  Individual, global
Length                     44
Padding:
  00-00
Frame check sequence       51-6F-D4-AD
> Data size                 44
```

```
Frame: 36        Time: Aug 22@11:27:21.4612320  Length: 346
  BOOTP
Operation code             1                   Bootp Request
Hardware type              1                   Ethernet
Hardware address length    16
Hop count                  0
Transaction ID             509547022
Seconds since boot         0
Client IP                  0.0.0.0
Gateway IP                 0.0.0.0
Hardware address (hex)     52-41-53-20-90-42-70-1D-
Host name (first 8 bytes)  00-00-00-00-00-00-00-00
Boot file name (hex)       00-00-00-00-00-00-00-00
Vendor magic cookie IP     99.130.83.99
  Host name                **MUSCLE**
  UDP
Source port                68                  BOOTPS
Destination port           67                  BOOTPS
Length                     308
Checksum                   2D-F7
  IP
Version                    4
Internet header length     5                   (32 bit words)
Precedence                 000.-....            Routine
```

```
Delay                      ...0-....              Delay normal
Throughput                 ....-0...              Throughput normal
Reliability                ....-.0..              Reliability normal
Total Length               328
Identification             54307
May / Do Not Fragment      .0..-....              Fragmentation allowed
Last / More Fragments      ..0.-....              Last fragment
Offset                     0
Time To Live               128
Next Protocol              17                     UDP
Checksum                   25-13
Source                     220.100.100.10
Destination                Broadcast
> Data size                308
  802.3/Ethernet
Destination address        Broadcast              Broadcast
Source address             Kingston-30-C2-43      Individual, global
Type                       08-00                  IP
Frame check sequence       A7-E1-49-70
> Data size                328
```

```
Frame: 37        Time: Aug 22@11:27:22.6418899   Length: 64
  Novell SAP
Service Adv. Protocol      0001                   General Service Query
Server Type                0004
  IPX
Checksum                   FFFF
IPX Length                 34
Transport Control          00
Packet Type                17                     NCP
Destination Network        00000000
Destination Node           FFFFFFFFFFFF           Broadcast
Destination Socket         0452                   Service Advertising Packet
Source Network             00000000
Source Node                006008981D33
Source Socket              401C
  802.2
Destination SAP            E0                     IPX
Source SAP                 E0                     IPX
Command/Response           ....-...0              Command
Type                       03                     Unnumbered
Poll                       ...0-....
Modifier                   000.-00..              Information
  802.3/Ethernet
Destination address        Broadcast              Broadcast
Source address             00-60-08-98-1D-3       Individual, global
Length                     37
Padding:    00-04-00-04-00-04-00-04 00
Frame check sequence       62-F7-57-24
> Data size                37
```

```
Frame: 38        Time: Aug 22@11:27:27.1779325  Length: 182
Service Adv. Protocol      0002                   General Service Response
Server Type                0640
Server Name                MUSCLE
SAP Network Address        00000001
SAP Node Address           000000000001
SAP Socket Address         E885
Hops To Server             1
Server Type                064E
```

```
Server Name                 MUSCLE!!!!!!!!!A5569B20A
SAP Network Address         00000001
SAP Node Address            000000000001
SAP Socket Address          4010
Hops To Server              1
  IPX
Checksum                    FFFF
IPX Length                  160
Transport Control           00
Packet Type                 4                  PEP
Destination Network         00000000
Destination Node            FFFFFFFFFFFF       Broadcast
Destination Socket          0452               Service Advertising Packet
Source Network              00000000
Source Node                 00C0F030C243
Source Socket               0452               Service Advertising Packet
  802.2
Destination SAP             E0                 IPX
Source SAP                  E0                 IPX
Command/Response            ....-...0           Command
Type                        03                 Unnumbered
Poll                        ...0-....
Modifier                    000.-00..          Information
  802.3/Ethernet
Destination address         Broadcast          Broadcast
Source address              Kingston-30-C2-43  Individual, global
Length                      164
Frame check sequence        CF-BB-1B-19
> Data size                 164
```

```
Frame: 39        Time: Aug 22@11:27:31.1044369  Length: 346
  BOOTP
Operation code              1                  Bootp Request
Hardware type               1                  Ethernet
Hardware address length     16
Hop count                   0
Transaction ID              509547022
Seconds since boot          2560
Client IP                   0.0.0.0
Gateway IP                  0.0.0.0
Hardware address (hex)      52-41-53-20-90-42-70-1D-
Host name (first 8 bytes)   00-00-00-00-00-00-00-00
Boot file name (hex)        00-00-00-00-00-00-00-00
Vendor magic cookie IP      99.130.83.99
  Host name                 MUSCLE
  UDP
Source port                 68                 BOOTPS
Destination port            67                 BOOTPS
Length                      308
Checksum                    23-F7
IP
Version                     4
Internet header length      5                  (32 bit words)
Precedence                  000.-....          Routine
Delay                       ...0-....          Delay normal
Throughput                  ....-0...          Throughput normal
Reliability                 ....-.0..          Reliability normal
Total Length                328
Identification              60195
May / Do Not Fragment       .0..-....          Fragmentation allowed
```

```
Last / More Fragments        ..0.-....
Last fragment Offset          0
Time To Live                 128
Next Protocol                17                     UDP
Checksum                     0E-13
Source                       220.100.100.10
Destination                  Broadcast
> Data size                  308
  802.3/Ethernet
Destination address          Broadcast              Broadcast
Source address               Kingston-30-C2-43      Individual, global
Type                         08-00                  IP
Frame check sequence         D3-1F-B1-72
> Data size                  328
```

I took another trace, which shows another view of a brief network stack decode. Note that the information presented here is similar to that shown with the previous network stack decode. This is because the same nodes are used on the network.

```
*****************************************************************
*****                                                     *****
*****        HEWLETT PACKARD NETWORK ADVISOR              *****
*****                                                     *****
*****    Measurement:    Brief Network Stack Decode       *****
*****    Print Type:     All Frames                       *****
*****    Open Views:     Summary                          *****
*****    Display Mode:   Viewing All Frames               *****
*****    Print Date:     08/22/98                         *****
*****    Print Time:     11:42:31                         *****
*****                                                     *****
*****************************************************************

1   40:46.700   HP----21-08-A0   HP----21-08-A0   ARP  R
PA = [15.6.72.18] HA = 0060B02108A0
2   40:50.382   00000000-HP----210  00000000-Broadcast SAP C
    Find
general Unkn service
3   40:50.386   00000000-HP----210  00000000-Broadcast SAP C
    Find general Unkn service
4   40:50.387   00000000-Kingst30C  00000000-HP----210 SAP R
    MUSCLE
5   40:50.391   00000000-HP----210  00000000-Broadcast SAP C
    Find general Unkn service
6   40:50.396   00000000-HP----210  00000000-Broadcast SAP C
    Find general Unkn service
7   41:12.811   00-60-08-98-1D-33   03-00-00-00-00-01   SMB C
    Transaction name \MAILSLOT\BROWSE
8   41:13.614   00000000-Kingst30C  00000000-Broadcast IPX RIP
    Response: 1 networks
9   41:19.334   Kingston-30-C2-43   03-00-00-00-00-01   SMB C
    Transaction name \MAILSLOT\BROWSE
10  41:19.343   00000001-000000000  00000000-Broadcast   NETB
    Find Name INFO.COM
11  41:19.884   00000001-000000000  00000000-Broadcast   NETB
    Find Name INFO.COM
12  41:20.425   00000001-000000000  00000000-Broadcast   NETB
    Find Name INFO.COM
```

```
13   41:20.967  00000001-000000000   00000000-Broadcast  IPX
     Type = 20 IPX WAN Broadcast LEN = 217
14   41:20.968  220.100.100.10       220.100.100.255     SMB C
     Transaction name \MAILSLOT\BROWSE
15   41:22.615  00000000-006008981  00000000-Broadcast   SAP C
     Find general file server
16   41:27.397  00000000-Kingst30C  00000000-Broadcast   SAP R
     MUSCLE1741:47.639  WstDigt—CF-08-F3  Broadcast
     ARP  C  PA = [220.100.100.172]
18   41:47.640  220.100.100.111      220.100.100.172     SMB C
     Tree connect
19   41:47.642  220.100.100.111      220.100.100.172     SMB C
     Transaction name \PIPE\LANMAN
20   41:47.644  WstDigt—CF-08-F3     03-00-00-00-00-01   NETB
     Name query THE-HOSTAGE
21   41:47.644  WstDigt—CF-08-F3     00-60-08-98-1D-33   LLC C
     S = F0 D = F0 SABME P
22   41:47.645  WstDigt—CF-08-F3     00-60-08-98-1D-33   LLC C
     S = F0 D = F0 RR NR = 0 P
23   41:47.646  WstDigt—CF-08-F3     00-60-08-98-1D-33   NETB
     S = 13 D = 10 Session init
24   41:47.646  WstDigt—CF-08-F3     00-60-08-98-1D-33   LLC R
     S = F0 D = F0 RR NR = 1 F
25   41:47.647  WstDigt—CF-08-F3     00-60-08-98-1D-33   SMB C
     Negotiate Protocol PC NETWORK PROGRAM 1.0
26   41:47.648  WstDigt—CF-08-F3     00-60-08-98-1D-33   LLC R
     S = F0 D = F0 RR NR = 2
27   41:47.649  WstDigt—CF-08-F3     00-60-08-98-1D-33   SMB C
     Session setup   Len = 34
28   41:47.650  WstDigt—CF-08-F3     00-60-08-98-1D-33   LLC R
     S = F0 D = F0 RR NR = 3
29   41:47.650  WstDigt—CF-08-F3     00-60-08-98-1D-33   SMB C
     Transaction name \PIPE\LANMAN
30   41:47.651  WstDigt—CF-08-F3     00-60-08-98-1D-33   LLC R
     S = F0 D = F0 RR NR = 4
31   41:49.434  220.100.100.10       Broadcast           BOOTP
     Request
32   41:58.797  220.100.100.10       Broadcast           BOOTP
     Request
```

****

The following trace is a baseline of the traffic load on the network as introduced by the Internet Advisor. It shows the performance of the switch itself. This information is helpful for gauging any possible aberrations that could exist in the future.

For example, with this traffic load and the hosts connected as presented here, it is easy to reproduce the conditions and actually test the switch itself. Much of troubleshooting network equipment involves being able to duplicate conditions. Consider this level of detail when you begin to baseline your switch.

```
**************ETHERNET TRAFFIC GENERATOR*****************
Added traffic Load:
        6% utilization
        7829 frames/second
        Inter-frame spacing: 0 ms.
```

```
Number of times to send activated frames: Continuous

Msg#  Message Type         Length       Source
Destination                FCS type
 1    802.3 Fox Message     76                   HP----21-08-A0
HP----14-02-01             Good
***********************************************************
```

.

12.12 Summary

The network switch is a key component in any network. It is preferable to have a baseline set up for the entire network, including all the protocols you use. I elected to use Ethernet here, for example; however, I do have similar baseline information about the OmniSwitch in my lab and all network protocols used with it, including FDDI, ATM, and Token Ring.

I recommend that you contact XYLAN technicians and let them assist you in making decisions about the most critical aspect of your network components. You can reach them at

XYLAN Corporation
26707 West Agoura Road
Calabasas, CA 91302
Phone: 818-880-3500
www.xylan.com

Glossary of
Wireless Technology

amplifier A device used to boost the strength of an electronic signal.

amplitude modulation (AM) The baseband signal causes variation of the amplitude or height of the carrier wave to create the desired information content.

analog A form of transmitting information characterized by continuously variable quantities, as opposed to digital transmission, which is characterized by discrete bits of information in numerical steps. An analog signal is responsive to changes in light, sound, heat, and pressure.

analog-to-digital conversion (ADC) Process of converting analog signals to a digital representation. DAC represents the reverse translation.

ANIK The Canadian domestic satellite system that transmits Canadian Broadcasting Corporation's (CBC) network feeds throughout the country. This system also carries long-distance voice and data services throughout Canada as well as some transborder service to the United States and Mexico.

antenna A device for transmitting and receiving radio waves. Depending on their use and operating frequency, antennas can take the form of a single piece of wire, a dipole or a grid such as a Yagi-Uda array, a horn, a helix, a sophisticated parabola-shaped dish, or a phase array of active electronic elements of virtually any flat or con-voluted surface.

aperture A cross-sectional area of the antenna which is exposed to the satellite signal.

apogee The point in an elliptical satellite orbit which is farthest from the surface of the earth. Geosynchronous satellites which maintain circular orbits around the earth are first launched into highly elliptical orbits with apogees of 22,237 mi. When the communication satellite reaches the appropriate apogee, a rocket motor is fired to place the satellite into its permanent circular orbit of 22,237 mi.

apogee kick motor (AKM) Rocket motor fired to circulate orbit and deploy satellites into geostationary orbit.

attenuation The loss in power of electromagnetic signals between transmission and reception points.

attitude control Orientation of the satellite in relationship to the earth and the sun.

audio subcarrier   The carrier between 5 and 8 MHz containing audio (or voice) information inside a video carrier.

automatic frequency control (AFC)   A circuit which automatically controls the frequency of a signal.

automatic gain control (AGC)   A circuit which automatically controls the gain of an amplifier so that the output signal level is virtually constant for varying input signal levels.

AZ/EL mount   Antenna mount that requires two separate adjustments to move from one satellite to another.

azimuth   The angle of rotation (horizontal) that a ground-based parabolic antenna must be rotated through to point to a specific satellite in a geosynchronous orbit. The azimuth angle for any particular satellite can be determined for any point on the surface of the earth given the latitude and longitude of that point. It is defined with respect to due north as a matter of easy convenience.

B-Mac   A method of transmitting and scrambling television signals. In such transmissions MAC (multiplexed analog component) signals are time-multiplexed with a digital burst containing digitized sound, video synchronizing, authorization, and information.

backhaul   A terrestrial communications channel linking an earth station to a local switching network or population center.

backoff   The process of reducing the input and output power levels of a traveling-wave tube to obtain more linear operation.

bandpass filter   An active or passive circuit which allows signals within the desired frequency band to pass through but impedes signals outside this passband from getting through.

bandwidth   A measure of spectrum (frequency) use or capacity. For instance, a voice transmission by telephone requires a bandwidth of about 3000 cycles per second (3 kHz). A TV channel occupies a bandwidth of 6 million cycles per second (6 MHz) in terrestrial systems. In satellite-based systems a larger bandwidth of 17.5 to 72 MHz is used to spread or "dither" the television signal in order to prevent interference.

baseband   The basic direct output signal in an intermediate frequency obtained directly from a television camera, satellite television receiver, or videotaperecorder. Baseband signals can be viewed only on studio monitors. To display the baseband signal on a conventional television set, a *modulator* is required to convert the baseband signal to one of the VHF or UHF television channels which the television set can be tuned to receive.

baud   The rate of data transmission based on the number of signal elements or symbols transmitted per second. Today most digital signals are characterized in bits per second.

beacon   Low-power carrier transmitted by a satellite which supplies the controlling engineers on the ground with a means of monitoring telemetry data, tracking the satellite, or conducting propagation experiments. This tracking beacon is usually a horn or omnidirectional antenna.

beamwidth   The angle or conical shape of the beam that the antenna projects. Large antennas have narrower beamwidths and can pinpoint satellites in space or dense traffic areas on the earth more precisely. Tighter beamwidths thus deliver higher levels of power and thus greater communications performance.

bird   Colloquial term for a communications satellite located in geosynchronous orbit.

bit   A single digital unit of information.

bit error rate   The fraction of a sequence of message bits that are in error. A bit error rate of 1×10^{-6} means that there is an average of one error per million bits.

bit rate   The speed of a digital transmission, measured in bits per second (bps).

blanking   An ordinary television signal consists of 30 separate still pictures or frames sent every second. They occur so rapidly that the human eye blurs them together to form an illusion of moving pictures. This is the basis for television and motion picture systems. The blanking interval is that portion of the television signal which occurs after one picture frame is sent and before the next one is transmitted. During this period of time special data signals can be sent which will not be picked up on an ordinary television receiver.

blockdown converter   A device used to convert the 3.7- to 4.2-kHz signal down to UHF (ultrahigh frequency) or lower frequencies (1 GHz and lower).

business television   Corporate communications tool involving video transmissions of information via satellite. Common uses of business television are for meetings, product introductions, and training.

C band   The band between 4 and 8 GHz. The 4- to 6-GHz band is used for satellite communications. Specifically, the 3.7- to 4.2-GHz satellite communication band is used as the downlink frequencies in tandem with the 5.925- to 6.425-GHz band, which serves as the uplink.

carrier   The basic radio, television, or telephony center of frequency transmit signal. The carrier in an analog signal. It is modulated by manipulating its amplitude (making it louder or softer) or its frequency (shifting it up or down) in relation to the incoming signal. Satellite carriers operating in the analog mode are usually frequency-modulated.

carrier frequency   The main frequency on which a voice, data, or video signal is sent. Microwave and satellite communications transmitters operate in the band from 1 to 14 GHz (1 GHz = 1 billion cycles per second).

carrier-to-noise ratio (C/N)   The ratio of the received carrier power and the noise power in a given bandwidth, expressed in decibels (dB). This figure is directly related to G/T and S/N; and in a video signal, the higher the C/N, the better the received picture.

Cassegrain antenna   The antenna principle that utilizes a subreflector at the focal point which reflects energy to or from a feed located at the apex of the main reflector.

CDMA   See **code division multiple access.**

channel   A frequency band in which a specific broadcast signal is transmitted. Channel frequencies are specified in the United States by the Federal Communications Commission (FCC). Television signals require a 6-MHz frequency band to carry all the necessary picture detail.

circular polarization   Unlike many domestic satellites which utilize vertical or horizontal polarization, the international Intelsat satellites transmit their signals in a rotating corkscrewlike pattern as they are downlinked to earth. On some satellites, both right-hand rotating and left-hand rotating signals can be transmitted simultaneously on the same frequency, thereby doubling the capacity of the satellite to carry communications channels.

clamp   A video processing circuit that removes the energy dispersal signal component from the video waveform.

Clarke orbit   That circular orbit in space 22,237 mi from the surface of the earth at which geosynchronous satellites are placed. This orbit was first postulated by the science fiction writer Arthur C. Clarke in *Wireless World* magazine in 1945. Satellites placed in these orbits, although traveling around the earth at thousands of miles per hour, appear to be stationary when viewed from a point on the earth, since the earth is rotating on its axis at the same angular rate with which the satellite is traveling around the earth.

C/No   Carrier-to-noise ratio measured either at the radio frequency (rf) or intermediate frequency (if).

code division multiple access (CDMA)   A multiple-access scheme where stations use spread-spectrum modulations and orthogonal codes to avoid interfering with one another.

codec   Coder/decoder system for digital transmission.

collocation   Ability of multiple satellites to share the same approximate geostationary orbital assignment frequently due to the fact that different frequency bands are used.

color subcarrier   A subcarrier that is added to the main video signal to convey the color information. In NTSC systems, the color subcarrier is centered on a frequency of 3.579545 MHz, referenced to the main video carrier.

common carrier   Any organization which operates communications circuits used by other people. Common carriers include the telephone companies as well as the owners of the communications satellites, RCA, Comsat, Direct Net Telecommunications, AT&T, and others. Common carriers are required to file fixed tariffs for specific services.

companding   A noise-reduction technique that applies single compression at the transmitter and complementary expansion at the receiver.

composite baseband   The unclamped and unfiltered output of the satellite receiver's demodulator circuit, containing the video information as well as all transmitted subcarriers.

Conus   Contiguous United States. In short, all the states in the United States except Hawaii and Alaska.

cross-modulation   A form of signal distortion in which modulation from one or more rf carrier(s) is imposed on another carrier.

C/T   Carrier-to-noise temperature ratio.

DAMA   See **demand-assigned multiple access.**

dBi   Decibel power relative to an isotropic source.

DBS   See **direct broadcast satellite.**

dBW   The ratio of the power to one watt (1 W) expressed in decibels.

decibel (dB)   The standard unit used to express the ratio of two power levels. It is used in communications to express either a gain or a loss in power between the input and output devices.

declination   The offset angle of an antenna from the axis of its polar mount as measured in the meridian plane between the equatorial plane and the antenna main beam.

decoder   A television set-top device which enables the home subscriber to convert an electronically scrambled television picture into a viewable signal. This should not be confused with a digital coder/decoder, known as a *codec,* which is used in conjunction with digital transmissions.

deemphasis   Reinstatement of a uniform baseband frequency response following demodulation.

delay   The time it takes for a signal to go from the sending station through the satellite to the receiving station. This transmission delay for a single-hop satellite connection is very close to one-quarter of a second (0.25 s).

demand-assigned multiple access (DAMA)   A highly efficient means of instantaneously assigning telephony channels in a transponder according to immediate traffic demands.

demodulator   A satellite receiver circuit which extracts or "demodulates" the "wanted" signals from the received carrier.

deviation   The modulation level of an FM signal determined by the amount of frequency shift from the frequency of the main carrier.

digital   Conversion of information into bits of data for transmission through wire, fiber-optic cable, satellite, or over-air techniques. This method allows simultaneous transmission of voice, data, or video.

digital speech interpolation (DSI)   A means of transmitting telephony 2.5 to 3 times more efficiently, based on the principle that people are talking only about 40 percent of the time.

direct broadcast satellite (DBS)   Service that uses satellites to broadcast multiple channels of television programming directly to home-mounted small-dish antennas.

dual spin   Spacecraft design in which the main body of the satellite is spun to provide altitude stabilization and the antenna assembly is despun by means of a motor and bearing system in order to continually direct the antenna earthward. This dual-spin configuration thus serves to create a spin-stabilized satellite.

earth station   The term used to describe the combination or antenna, low-noise amplifier (LNA), downconverter, and receiver electronics used to receive a signal transmitted by a satellite. Earth station antennas vary in diameter from 2 to 12 ft (65 cm to 3.7 m) used for TV reception to as large as 100 ft (30 m) in diameter sometimes used for international communications. The typical antenna used for Intelsat communication today is 40 to 60 ft (13 to 18 m).

echo canceler An electronic circuit which attenuates or eliminates the echo effect on satellite telephony links. Echo cancelers are largely replacing obsolete echo suppressors.

echo effect A time-delayed electronic reflection of a speaker's voice. This is largely eliminated by modern digital echo cancelers.

edge of coverage (EOC) Limit of a satellite's defined service area. In many cases, the EOC is defined as being 3 dB down from the signal level at beam center. However, reception may still be possible beyond the -3-dB point.

effective isotropic radiated power (EIRP) The strength of the signal leaving the satellite antenna or the transmitting earth station antenna; used in determining the C/N and S/N. The transmit power value in units of dBW is expressed by the product of the transponder output power and the gain of the satellite transmit antenna.

elevation The upward tilt to a satellite antenna measured in degrees required to aim the antenna at the communications satellite. When aimed at the horizon, the elevation angle is zero. If it were tilted to a point directly overhead, the satellite antenna would have an elevation of 90°.

encoder A device used to electronically alter a signal so that it can be viewed only on a receiver equipped with a special decoder.

Engineering Service Circuit (ESC) The 300- to 3400-Hz voice plus teletype (S+DX) channel used for earth station–to–earth station and earth station–to–operations center communications for the purpose of system maintenance, coordination, and general system information dissemination. In analog (FDM/FM) systems there are two S+DX channels available for this purpose in the 4000- to 12,000-Hz portion of the baseband. In digital systems there are one or two channels available which are usually convened to a 32- or 64-kbps digital signal and combined with the earth station traffic digital bit stream. Modern ESC equipment interfaces with any mix of analog and digital satellite carriers, as well as backhaul terrestrial links to the local switching center.

EOL End of life of a satellite.

equatorial orbit An orbit with a plane parallel to the earth's equator.

F/D Ratio of antenna focal length to antenna diameter. A higher ratio means a shallower dish.

FDMA See **frequency division multiple access.**

feed This term has at least two key meanings within the field of satellite communications. It is used to describe the transmission of video programming from a distribution center. It is also used to describe the feed system of an antenna. The feed system may consist of a subreflector plus a feedhorn or a feedhorn only.

feedhorn A satellite TV receiving antenna component that collects the signal reflected from the main surface reflector and channels this signal into the low-noise amplifier (LNA).

FM Frequency modulation: a modulation method in which the baseband signal varies the frequency of the carrier wave.

FM threshold   That point at which the input signal power is just strong enough to enable the receiver demodulator circuitry successfully to detect and recover a good-quality television picture from the incoming video carrier. Using threshold extension techniques, a typical satellite TV receiver will successfully provide good pictures with an incoming carrier noise ratio of 7 dB. Below the threshold a type of random noise called "sparkles" begins to appear in the video picture. In a digital transmission, however, signal is suddenly and dramatically lost when performance drops under the threshold.

focal length   Distance from the center feed to the center of the dish.

focal point   The area toward which the primary reflector directs and concentrates the signal received.

footprint   A map of the signal strength showing the EIRP contours of equal signal strengths as they cover the earth's surface. Different satellite transponders on the same satellite will often have different footprints of the signal strength. The accuracy of EIRP footprints or contour data can improve with the operational age of the satellite. The actual EIRP levels of the satellite, however, tend to decrease slowly as the spacecraft ages.

forward error correction (FEC)   The addition of unique codes to the digital signal at the source so that errors can be detected and corrected at the receiver.

frequency   The number of times that an alternating current goes through its complete cycle in one second of time. One cycle per second is also referred to as *one hertz* (1 Hz); 1000 cycles per second, *one kilohertz* (1 kHz); 1,000,000 cycles per second, *one megahertz* (1 MHz); and 1,000,000,000 cycles per second, *one gigahertz* (1 GHz).

frequency coordination   A process to eliminate frequency interference between different satellite systems or between terrestrial microwave systems and satellites. In the United States this activity relies on a computerized service utilizing an extensive database to analyze potential microwave interference problems that arise between organizations using the same microwave band. As the same C-band frequency spectrum is used by telephone networks and CATV companies when they are contemplating the installation of an earth station, they will often obtain a frequency coordination study to determine whether any problems will exist.

frequency division multiple access (FDMA)   The use of multiple carriers within the same transponder where each uplink has been assigned a frequency slot and bandwidth. This is usually employed in conjunction with frequency modulation.

gain   A measure of amplification expressed in decibels.

geostationary   Refers to a geosynchronous satellite angle with zero inclination so that the satellite appears to hover over one spot on the earth's equator.

geosynchronous   The Clarke circular orbit above the equator. For a planet the size and mass of the earth, this point is 22,237 mi above the surface.

gigahertz (GHz)   One billion cycles per second. Signals operating above 3 GHz are known as *microwaves*; above 30 GHz, as *millimeter waves*. As one moves above the millimeter waves, signals begin to take on the characteristics of lightwaves.

global beam   An antenna downlink pattern used by the Intelsat satellites which effectively covers one-third of the globe. Global beams are aimed at the center of the

Atlantic, Pacific, and Indian Oceans by the respective Intelsat satellites, enabling all nations on each side of the ocean to receive the signal. Because they transmit to such a wide area, global beam transponders have significantly lower EIRP outputs at the surface of the earth as compared to a U.S. domestic satellite system which covers just the continental United States. Therefore, earth stations receiving global beam signals need antennas much larger in size [typically ≥10 m (≥30 ft)].

gregorian dual-reflector antenna system   An antenna system employing a paraboloidal main reflector and a concave ellipsoidal subreflector.

G/T   A figure of merit of an antenna and low-noise amplifier (LNA) combination expressed in decibels, where *G* is the net gain of the system and *T* is the noise temperature of the system. The higher the number, the better the system.

guard channel   Television channels are separated in the frequency spectrum by spacing them several megahertz apart. This unused space serves to prevent the adjacent television channels from interfering with each other.

half-transponder   A method of transmitting two TV signals through a single transponder through the reduction of each TV signal's deviation and power level. Half-transponder TV carriers each operate typically 4 to 7 dB below single-carrier saturation power.

headend   Electronic control center—generally located at the antenna site of a CATV system—usually including antennas, preamplifiers, frequency converters, demodulators, and other related equipment which amplify, filter, and convert incoming broadcast TV signals to cable system channels.

hertz (Hz)   The name given to the basic measure of radio-frequency characteristics. An electromagnetic wave completes a full oscillation from its positive pole to its negative pole and back again in what is known as a *cycle*. A single hertz is thus equal to one cycle per second.

hub   The master station through which all communications to, from, and between microterminals must flow. In the future satellites with on-board processing will allow hubs to be eliminated as *mesh* networks are able to connect all points in a network together.

IBS   Intelsat Business Services.

inclination   The angle between the orbital plane of a satellite and the equatorial plane of the earth.

Inmarsat   A network of satellites, operated by the International Maritime Satellite Organization, for international transmissions for all types of international mobile services, including maritime, aeronautical, and land mobile.

Intelsat   A network of satellites for international transmissions operated by the International Telecommunications Satellite Organization.

interference   Energy which tends to interfere with the reception of the desired signals, such as fading from airline flights, radio-frequency interference from adjacent channels, or ghosting from reflecting objects such as mountains and buildings.

ISDN   Integrated Services Digital Network: a CCITT standard for integrated transmission of voice, video, and data. Bandwidths include basic-rate interface (BRI) (144 kbps; two B channels and one D channel) and primary rate interface (PRI) (1.544 to 2.048 Mbps).

isotropic antenna A hypothetical omnidirectional point-source antenna that serves as an engineering reference for the measurement of antenna gain.

ITU International Telecommunication Union.

JPEG ISO Joint Picture Expert Group standard for the compression of still pictures.

Ka band The frequency range from 18 to 31 GHz.

kbps Kilobits per second. Refers to transmission speed of 1000 bits per second (bps).

kelvin (K) The temperature measurement scale used in the scientific community. Zero K represents absolute zero, and corresponds to −459°F or −273°C. Thermal noise characteristics of LNA are measured in kelvins.

kilohertz (kHz) A unit of frequency equal to 1000 Hz.

klystron A type of high-power amplifier which uses a special beam tube.

Ku band The frequency range from 10.9 to 17 GHz.

L band The frequency range from 0.5 to 1.5 GHz. Also used to refer to the 950 to 1450 MHz frequency used for mobile communications.

leased line A dedicated circuit typically supplied by the telephone company.

low-noise amplifier (LNA) The preamplifier between the antenna and the earth station receiver. For maximum effectiveness, it must be located as near the antenna as possible, and is usually attached directly to the antenna receive port. The LNA is especially designed to contribute the least amount of thermal noise to the received signal.

low-noise block downconverter (LNB) A combination low-noise amplifier and downconverter built into one device attached to the feed.

MAC (A, B, C, D2) Multiplexed analog component color video transmission system. Subtypes refer to the various methods used to transmit audio and data signals.

margin The amount of signal in decibels by which the satellite system exceeds the minimum levels required for operation.

master antenna television (MATV) An antenna system that serves a concentration of television sets such as in apartment buildings, hotels, or motels.

megahertz (MHz) A frequency equal to one million hertz, or cycles per second.

microwave Line-of-sight, point-to-point transmission of signals at high frequency. Many CATV systems receive some television signals from a distant antenna location with the antenna and the system connected by microwave relay. Microwaves are also used for data, voice, and indeed all types of information transmission. The growth of fiber-optic networks has tended to curtail the growth and use of microwave relays.

microwave interference Interference which occurs when an earth station aimed at a distant satellite picks up a second, often stronger, signal from a local telephone terrestrial microwave relay transmitter. Microwave interference can also be produced by nearby radar transmitters as well as the sun itself. Relocating the antenna by only several feet will often completely eliminate the microwave interference.

modulation   The process of manipulating the frequency or amplitude of a carrier in relation to an incoming video, voice, or data signal.

modulator   A device which modulates a carrier. Modulators are found as components in broadcasting transmitters and in satellite transponders. Modulators are also used by CATV companies to place a baseband video television signal onto a desired VHF or UHF channel. Home videotaperecorders also have built-in modulators which enable the recorded video information to be played back using a television receiver tuned to VHF channel 3 or 4.

multiplexing   Techniques that allow a number of simultaneous transmissions over a single circuit.

National Television Standards Committee (NTSC)   A video standard established by the United States (RCA/NBC) and adopted by numerous other countries. This is a 525-line video with 3.58-MHz chroma subcarrier and a frequency of 60 cycles per second.

noise   Any unwanted and unmodulated energy that is always present to some extent within any signal.

noise figure (NF)   A term which is a figure of merit of a device, such as an LNA or receiver, expressed in decibels, which compares the device with a perfect device.

orbital period   The time that it takes a satellite to complete one circumnavigation of its orbit.

packet switching   Data transmission method that divides messages into standard-sized packets for greater efficiency of routing and transport through a network.

parabolic antenna   The most common satellite TV antenna, it takes its name from the shape of the dish described mathematically as a parabola. The function of the parabolic shape is to focus the weak microwave signal hitting the surface of the dish into a single focal point in front of the dish. It is at this point that the feedhorn is usually located.

phase alternation system (PAL)   The German-developed TV standard based on 50 cycles per second and 625 lines.

phase-locked loop (PLL)   A type of electronic circuit used to demodulate satellite signals.

polarization   A technique used by the satellite designer to increase the capacity of the satellite transmission channels by reusing the satellite transponder frequencies. In linear cross-polarization schemes, half of the transponders beam their signals to earth in a vertically polarized mode; the other half horizontally polarize their downlinks. Although the two sets of frequencies overlap, they are 90° out of phase, and will not interfere with each other. To successfully receive and decode these signals on earth, the earth station must be outfitted with a properly polarized feedhorn to select the vertically or horizontally polarized signals as desired. In some installations, the feedhorn has the capacity to receive the vertical and horizontal transponder signals simultaneously and route them into separate LNAs for delivery to two or more satellite television receivers. Unlike most domestic satellites, the Intelsat series use a technique known as left-hand and right-hand circular polarization.

polarization rotator   A device that can be manually or automatically adjusted to select one of two orthogonal polarizations.

polar mount   Antenna mechanism permitting steering in both elevation and azimuth through rotation about a single axis. While an astronomer's polar mount has its axis parallel to that of the earth, satellite earth stations utilize a modified polar mount geometry that incorporates a declination offset.

polar orbit   An orbit with its plane aligned in parallel with the polar axis of the earth.

Post Telephone and Telegraph Administration (PTT)   A group of agencies whose operation is directly or indirectly controlled by governments in charge of telecommunications services in most countries of the world.

pulse code modulation (PCM)   A time division modulation technique in which analog signals are sampled and quantized at periodic intervals into digital signals. The values observed are typically represented by a coded arrangement of 8 bits, one of which may be for parity.

quadrature phase shift keying (QPSK)   System of modulating a satellite signal.

quality butt time (QBT)   The unit of measurement used when calculating the hours spent by salespeople, installers, and field engineers in airplanes or automobiles.

rain outage   Loss of signal at Ku- or Ka-band frequencies due to absorption and increased sky-noise temperature caused by heavy rainfall. Can also affect C-Band networks in monsoon-type climates.

receiver (Rx)   An electronic device which enables a particular satellite signal to be separated from all others being received by an earth station, and converts the signal format into a format for video, voice, or data.

receiver sensitivity   Expressed in dBm (decibels > 1 mW); an index of the amount of power the detector must receive to achieve a specific baseband performance, such as a specified bit error rate or signal-to-noise ratio.

satellite   A sophisticated electronic communications relay station orbiting 22,237 mi above the equator moving in a fixed orbit at the same speed and direction of the earth (about 7000 mi/h east to west).

scalar feed   A type of horn antenna feed which uses a series of concentric rings to capture signals that have been reflected toward the focal point of a parabolic antenna.

scrambler   A device used to electronically alter a signal so that it can be viewed or heard only on a receiver equipped with a special decoder.

Secam   A color television system developed by the French and used in the former Soviet Union. Secam operates with 625 lines per picture frame and 50 cycles per second, but is incompatible in operation with the European PAL system or the U.S. NTSC system.

sidelobe   Off-axis response of an antenna.

signal-to-noise ratio (S/N)   The ratio of the signal power and noise power. A video S/N of 54 to 56 dB is considered to be an excellent S/N, that is, of broadcast quality. A video S/N of 48 to 52 dB is considered to be a good S/N at the headend for Cable TV.

single channel per carrier (SCPC)   A method used to transmit a large number of signals over a single satellite transponder.

skew   An adjustment that compensates for slight variance in angle between identical senses of polarity generated by two or more satellites.

slant range   The length of the path between a communications satellite and an associated earth station.

slot   That longitudinal position in the geosynchronous orbit in which a communications satellite is "parked." Above the United States, communications satellites are typically positioned in slots which are based at 2 to 3° intervals.

snow   A form of noise picked up by a television receiver caused by a weak signal. Snow is characterized by alternate dark and light dots appearing randomly on the picture tube. To eliminate snow, a more sensitive receive antenna must be used, or better amplification must be provided in the receiver (or both). Also, a manifestation of climate which, if present in the antenna, can cause lowered signal-to-noise performance over the satellite network.

solar outage   Solar outages occur when an antenna is looking at a satellite and the sun passes behind or near the satellite and within the field of view of the antenna. This field of view is usually wider than the beamwidth. Solar outages can be exactly predicted as to the timing for each site.

solid-state power amplifier (SSPA)   A VLSI (very large scale integrated circuit) solid-state device that is gradually replacing traveling-wave tubes in satellite communications systems because they are lighterweight and are more reliable.

spectrum   The range of electromagnetic radio frequencies used in transmission of voice, data, and television.

spillover   Satellite signal that falls on locations outside the beam pattern's defined edge of coverage.

spin stabilization   A form of satellite stabilization and attitude control which is achieved through spinning the exterior of the spacecraft about its axis at a fixed rate.

splitter   A passive device (one with no active electronic components) which distributes a television signal carried on a cable in two or more paths and sends it to a number of receivers simultaneously.

spot beam   A focused antenna pattern sent to a limited geographic area. Spot beams are used by domestic satellites to deliver certain transponder signals to geographically well-defined areas such as Hawaii, Alaska, and Puerto Rico.

spread spectrum   The transmission of a signal using a much wider bandwidth and power than would normally be required. Spread spectrum also involves the use of narrower signals that are frequency hopped through various parts of the transponder. Both techniques produce low levels of interference between the users. They also provide security in that the signals appear as though they were random noise to unauthorized earth stations. Both military and civil satellite applications have been developed for spread-spectrum transmissions.

SSPA   See **solid-state power amplifier.**

stationkeeping   Minor orbital adjustments that are conducted to maintain the satellite's orbital assignment within the allocated "box" within the geostationary arc.

subcarrier   A second signal "piggybacked" onto a main signal to carry additional information. In satellite television transmission, the video picture is transmitted over the main carrier. The corresponding audio is sent via an FM subcarrier. Some satellite transponders carry as many as four special audio or data subcarriers whose signals may or may not be related to the main programming.

synchronization (sync)   The process of orienting the transmitter and receiver circuits in the proper manner so that they can be synchronized. Home television sets are synchronized by an incoming sync signal with the television cameras in the studios 60 times per second. The horizontal and vertical hold controls on the television set are used to set the receiver circuits to the approximate sync frequencies of incoming television picture, and the sync pulses in the signal then fine-tune the circuits to the exact frequency and phase.

T1   The transmission bit rate of 1.544 millions bits per second (Mbps). This is also equivalent to the ISDN Primary Rate Interface for the United States. The European T1 or E1 transmission rate is 2.048 Mbps.

T3 channel (DS-3)   In North America, a digital channel which communicates at 45.304 Mbps.

TDMA   See **time division multiple access.**

terrestrial interference (TI)   Interference to satellite reception caused by ground-based microwave transmitting stations.

time division multiple access (TDMA)   A form of multiple access where a single carrier is shared by many users. Signals from earth stations reaching the satellite consecutively are processed in time segments without overlapping.

TLA   Three-letter acronym. Overly used by satellite and computer industry.

transmitter   An electronic device consisting of oscillator, modulator, and other circuits which produce a radio or television electromagnetic wave signal for radiation into the atmosphere by an antenna.

transponder   A combination receiver, frequency converter, and transmitter package, physically part of a communications satellite. Transponders have a typical output of 5 to 10 W, operate over a frequency band with a 36 to 72 MHz bandwidth in the L, C, Ku, and sometimes Ka bands or, in effect, typically in the microwave spectrum, except for mobile satellite communications. Communications satellites typically have between 12 and 24 on-board transponders, although the Intelsat VI at the extreme end has 50.

TVRO   Television receive-only terminals that use antenna reflectors and associated electronic equipment to receive and process television and audio communications via satellite. Typically small home systems.

tweaking   The process of adjusting an electronic receiver circuit to optimize its performance.

TWTA   Traveling-wave tube amplifier.

uplink   The earth station used to transmit signals to a satellite.

very small aperture terminal (VSAT)   A small earth station, usually in the 1.2- to 3.8-m range. Small-aperture terminals under 0.5 m are sometimes referred to as *ultra-small-aperture terminals* (USATs).

voltage standing-wave ratio (VSWR)   A measurement of mismatch in a cable, waveguide, or antenna system.

waveguide   A metallic microwave conductor, typically rectangular in shape, used to carry microwave signals into and out of microwave antennas.

X.25   A set of packet-switching standards published by the CCITT.

Bibliography

Abbatiello, Judy, and Ray Sarch, eds., 1987, *Telec Communications & Data Communications Factbook*, New York, N.Y.: Data Communications; Ramsey, N.J.: CCMI/McGraw-Hill.

Apple Computer, Inc., 1991, *Planning and Managing AppleTalk Networks*, Menlo Park, Calif.: Addison-Wesley.

Apple Computer, Inc., 1992, *Technical Introduction to the Macintosh Family*, 2d ed., Menlo Park, Calif.: Addison-Wesley.

Ashley, Ruth, and Judi N. Fernandez, 1984, *Job Control Language*, New York, N.Y.: Wiley.

Aspray, William, 1990, *John Von Neumann and the Origins of Modern Computing*, Cambridge, Mass.: MIT Press.

ATM Forum, The, 1993, *ATM User-Network Interface Specification*, Englewood Cliffs, N.J.: Prentice-Hall.

Bach, Maurice J., 1986, *The Design of the UNIX Operating System*, Englewood Cliffs, N.J.: Prentice-Hall.

Baggott, Jim, 1992, *The Meaning of Quantum Theory*, New York, N.Y.:, Oxford University Press.

Bashe, Charles J., Lyle R. Johnson, John H. Palmer, and Emerson W. Pugh, 1986, *IBM's Early Computers*, Cambridge, Mass.: MIT Press.

Berson, Alex, 1990, *APPC Introduction to LU6.2*, New York, N.Y.: McGraw-Hill.

Black, Uyless, 1989, *Data Networks Concepts, Theory, and Practice*, Englewood Cliffs, N.J.: Prentice-Hall.

Black, Uyless, 1991, *The V Series Recommendations Protocols for Data Communications over the Telephone Network*, New York, N.Y.: McGraw-Hill.

Black, Uyless, 1991, *The X Series Recommendations Protocols for Data Communications Networks*, New York, N.Y.: McGraw-Hill.

Black, Uyless, 1992, *TCP/IP and Related Protocols*, New York, N.Y.: McGraw-Hill.

Blyth, W. John, and Mary M. Blyth, 1990, *Telecommunications: Concepts, Development, and Management*, Mission Hills, Calif.: Glencoe/McGraw-Hill.

Bohl, Marilyn, 1971, *Information Processing*, 3d ed., Chicago: Science Research Associates.

Bradbeer, Robin, Peter De Bono, and Peter Laurie, 1982, *The Beginner's Guide to Computers*, Reading, Mass.: Addison-Wesley.

Brookshear, J. Glenn, 1988, *Computer Science: An Overview*, Menlo Park, Calif.: Benjamin/Cummings.

Bryant, David, 1971, *Physics*, London, U.K.: Hodder & Stoughton.

Campbell, Joe, 1984, *The RS-232 Solution*, Alameda, Calif.: SYBEX.

Campbell, Joe, 1987, *C Programmer's Guide to Serial Communications*, Carmel, Ind.: Howard W. Sams.

Chorafas, Dimitris N., 1989, *Local Area Network Reference*, New York, N.Y.: McGraw-Hill.

Comer, Douglas, 1988, *Internetworking with TCP/IP Principles, Protocols, and Architecture*, Englewood Cliffs, N.J.: Prentice-Hall.

Comer, Douglas E., 1991, *Internetworking with TCP/IP, Vol. I: Principles, Protocols, and Architecture*, Englewood Cliffs, N.J.: Prentice-Hall.

Comer, Douglas E., and David L. Stevens, 1991, *Internetworking with TCP/IP, Vol. II: Design, Implementation, and Internals*, Englewood Cliffs, N.J.: Prentice-Hall.

Dayton, Robert L., 1991, *Telecommunications: The Transmission of Information*, New York, N.Y.: McGraw-Hill.

Dern, Daniel P., 1994, *The Internet Guide for New Users*, New York, N.Y.: McGraw-Hill.

Digital Equipment Corp., 1991, *DECnet Digital Network Architecture (Phase V): Network Routing Layer Functional Specification*, EK-DNA03-FS-001, Maynard, Mass.: Digital Equipment Corp.

Digital Equipment Corp., 1993, *DECnet/OSI for OpenVMS: Introduction and Planning*, AA-PNHTB-TE, Maynard, Mass.: Digital Equipment Corp.

Digital Equipment Corp., 1993, *OpenVMS DCL Dictionary: A-M*, AA-PV5LA-TK, Maynard, Mass.: Digital Equipment Corp.

Digital Equipment Corp., 1993, *OpenVMS DCL Dictionary: N-Z*, AA-PV5LA-TK, Maynard, Mass.: Digital Equipment Corp.

Digital Equipment Corp., 1993, *OpenVMS Glossary*, AA-PV5UA-TK, Maynard, Mass.: Digital Equipment Corp.

Digital Equipment Corp., 1993, *OpenVMS Software Overview*, AA-PVXHA-TE, Maynard, Mass.: Digital Equipment Corp.

Edmunds, John J., 1992, *SAA/LU 6.2 Distributed Networks and Applications*, New York, N.Y.: McGraw-Hill.

Feit, Sidnie, 1993, *TCP/IP: Architecture, Protocols, and Implementation*, New York, N.Y.:, McGraw-Hill.

Forney, James S., 1989, *MS-DOS Beyond 640K Working with Extended and Expanded Memory, Blue Ridge Summit*, Pa.: Windcrest Books.

Forney, James S., 1992, *DOS Beyond 640K*, 2d ed., Blue Ridge Summit, Pa.: Windcrest/McGraw-Hill.

Fortier, Paul J., 1989, *Handbook of LAN Technology*, New York, N.Y.: Intertext Publications/Multiscience Press.

Gasman, Lawrence, 1994, *Broadband Networking*, New York, N.Y.: Van Nostrand-Reinhold.

Graubart-Cervone, H. Frank, 1994, *VSE/ESA JCL Utilities, Power, and VSAM*, New York, N.Y.: McGraw-Hill.

Groff, James R., and Paul N. Weinbert, 1983, *Understanding UNIX: A Conceptual Guide*, Carmel, Ind.: Que.

Hecht, Jeff, 1990, *Understanding Fiber Optics*, Carmel, Ind.: Howard W. Sams.

Hewlett-Packard Company, 1992, *HP OpenView SNMP Agent Administrator's Reference*, J2322-90002, Ft. Collins, Colo.: Hewlett-Packard.

Hewlett-Packard Company, 1992, *HP OpenView SNMP Management Platform Administrator's Reference*, J2313-90001, Ft. Collins, Colo.: Hewlett-Packard.

Hewlett-Packard Company, 1992, *HP OpenView Windows User's Guide*, J2316-90000, Ft. Collins, Colo.: Hewlett-Packard.

Hewlett-Packard Company, 1992, *Using HP-UX: Hp 9000 Workstations*, B2910-90001, Ft. Collins, Colo.: Hewlett-Packard.

Hewlett-Packard Company, 1991, *Using the X Window System*, B1171-90037, Ft. Collins, Colo.: Hewlett-Packard.

IBM Corp., 1980, *IBM Virtual Machine Facility: Terminal User's Guide*, GC20-1810-9, Poughkeepsie, N.Y.: IBM.

IBM Corp., 1983, *IBM System/370 Extended Architecture: Principles of Operation*, SA22-7085-0, Research Triangle Park, N.C.: IBM.

IBM Corp., 1985, *IBM 3270 Information Display System: 3274 Control Unit Description and Programmer's Guide*, GA23-0061-2, Research Triangle Park, N.C.: IBM.

IBM Corp., 1986, *JES3 Introduction*, GC23-0039-2, Poughkeepsie, N.Y.: IBM.

IBM Corp., 1987, *IBM System/370: Principles of Operation*, GA22-7000-10, Poughkeepsie, N.Y.: IBM.

IBM Corp., 1988, *IBM Enterprise Systems Architecture/370: Principles of Operation*, SA22-7200-0, Poughkeepsie, N.Y.: IBM.

IBM Corp., 1988, *3270 Information Display System: Introduction*, GA27-2739-22, Research Triangle Park, N.C.: IBM.

IBM Corp., 1989, *MVS/ESA Operations: System Commands Reference Summary*, GX22-0013-1, Poughkeepsie, N.Y.: IBM.

IBM Corp., 1990, *VM/ESA and Related Products: Overview*, GG24-3610-00, Poughkeepsie, N.Y.: IBM.

IBM Corp., 1990, *Enterprise Systems Architecture/390: Principles of Operation*, SA22-7201-00, Poughkeepsie, N.Y.: IBM.

IBM Corp., 1990, *Enterprise System/9000 Models 120, 130, 150, and 170: Introducing the System*, GA24-4186-00, Endicott, N.Y.: IBM.

IBM Corp., 1990, *IBM 3172 Interconnect Controller: Presentation Guide*, White Plains, N.Y.: IBM.

IBM Corp., 1990, *IBM VSE/ESA: System Control Statements*, SC33-6513-00, Mechanicsburg, Pa.: IBM.

IBM Corp., 1990, *IBM VSE/POWER: Networking*, SC33-6573-00, Mechanicsburg, Pa.: IBM.

IBM Corp., 1990, *MVS/ESA SP Version 4 Technical Presentation Guide*, GG24-3594-00, Poughkeepsie, N.Y.: IBM.

IBM Corp., 1990, *Virtual Machine/Enterprise Systems Architecture*, GC24-5441, Endicott, N.Y.: IBM.

IBM Corp., 1991, *Dictionary of Computing*, SC20-1699-8, Poughkeepsie, N.Y.: IBM.

IBM Corp., 1991, *Enterprise Systems Architecture/390 ESCON I/O Interface: Physical Layer*, SA23-0394-00, Kingston, N.Y.: IBM.

IBM Corp., 1991, *Enterprise Systems Connection*, GA23-0383-01, Kingston, N.Y.: IBM.

IBM Corp., 1991, *Enterprise Systems Connection: ESCON I/O Interface*, SA22-7202-01, Poughkeepsie, N.Y.: IBM.

IBM Corp., 1991, *Enterprise Systems Connection Manager*, GC23-0422-01, Kingston, N.Y.: IBM.

IBM Corp., 1991, *Installation Guidelines for the IBM Token-Ring Network Products*, GG24-3291-02, Research Triangle Park, N.C.: IBM.

IBM Corp., 1991, *NetView: NetView Graphic Monitor Facility Operation*, SC31-6099-1, Research Triangle Park, N.C.: IBM.

IBM Corp., 1991, *Systems Network Architecture: Concepts and Products*, GC30-3072-4, Research Triangle Park, N.C.: IBM.

IBM Corp., 1991, *Systems Network Architecture: Technical Overview*, GC30-3073-3, Research Triangle Park, N.C.: IBM.

IBM Corp., 1991, *Systems Network Architecture: Type 2.1 Node Reference*, Version 1, SC20-3422-2, Research Triangle Park, N.C.: IBM.

IBM Corp., 1991, *3174 Establishment Controller: Functional Description*, GA23-0218-08, Research Triangle Park, N.C.: IBM.

IBM Corp., 1991, *Virtual Machine/Enterprise System Architecture: General Information*, GC24-5550-02, Endicott, N.Y.: IBM.

IBM Corp., 1992, *APPN Architecture and Product Implementations Tutorial*, GG24-3669-01, Research Triangle Park, N.C.: IBM.

IBM Corp., 1992, *ES/9000 Multi-Image Processing, Vol. 1: Presentation and Solutions Guidelines*, GG24-3920-00, Poughkeepsie, N.Y.: IBM.

IBM Corp., 1992, *High Speed Networking Technology: An Introductory Survey*, GG24-3816-00, Raleigh, N.C.: IBM.

IBM Corp., 1992, *IBM Networking Systems: Planning and Reference*, SC31-6191-00, Research Triangle Park, N.C.: IBM.

IBM Corp., 1992, *MVS/ESA and Data in Memory: Performance Studies*, GG24-3698-00, Poughkeepsie, N.Y.: IBM.

IBM Corp., 1992, *MVS/ESA: General Information for MVS/ESA System Product Version 4*, GC28-1600-04, Poughkeepsie, N.Y.: IBM.

IBM Corp., 1992, *Sockets Interface for CICS—Using TCP/IP Version 2 Release 2 for MVS: User's Guide*, GC31-7015-00, Research Triangle Park, N.C.: IBM.

IBM Corp., 1992, *Synchronous Data Link Control: Concepts*, GA27-3093-04, Research Triangle Park, N.C.: IBM.

IBM Corp., 1992, *TCP/IP Version 2 Release 2.1 for MVS: Offload of TCP/IP Processing*, SA31-7033-00, Research Triangle Park, N.C.: IBM.

IBM Corp., 1992, *TCP/IP Version 2 Release 2.1 for MVS: Planning and Customization*, SC31-6085-02, Research Triangle Park, N.C.: IBM.

IBM Corp., 1992, *The IBM 6611 Network Processor*, GG24-3870-00, Raleigh, N.C.: IBM.

IBM Corp., 1992, *3172 Interconnect Controller: Operator's Guide*, GA27-3970-00, Research Triangle Park, N.C.: IBM.

IBM Corp., 1992, *3172 Interconnect Controller: Planning Guide*, GA27-3867-05, Research Triangle Park, N.C.: IBM.

IBM Corp., 1992, *3270 Information Display System: Data Stream Programmer's Reference*, GA23-0059-07, Research Triangle Park, N.C.: IBM.

IBM Corp., 1992, *VM/ESA: CMS Primer, SC24-5458-02*, Endicott, N.Y.: IBM.

IBM Corp., 1992, *VM/ESA Release 2 Overview*, GG24-3860-00, Poughkeepsie, N.Y.: IBM.

IBM Corp., 1992, *VSE/ESA Version 1.3: An Introduction Presentation Foil Master*, GG24-4008-00, Raleigh, N.C.: IBM.

IBM Corp., 1993, *IBM Network Products Implementation Guide*, GG24-3649-01, Raleigh, N.C.: IBM.

IBM Corp., 1993, *IBM VSE/Interactive Computing and Control Facility: Primer*, SC33-6561-01, Charlotte, N.C.: IBM.

IBM Corp., 1993, *LAN File Services/ESA: VM Guide and Reference*, SH24-5264-00, Endicott, N.Y.: IBM.

IBM Corp., 1993, *LAN File Services/ESA: MVS Guide and Reference*, SH24-5265-00, Endicott, N.Y.: IBM.

IBM Corp., 1993, *LAN Resource Extension and Services/VM: Guide and Reference*, SC24-5622-01, Endicott, N.Y.: IBM.

IBM Corp., 1993, *MVS/ESA: JES2 Command Reference Summary*, GX22-0017-03, Poughkeepsie, N.Y.: IBM.

IBM Corp., 1993, *MVS/ESA JES2 Commands*, GC23-0084-04, Poughkeepsie, N.Y.: IBM.

IBM Corp., 1993, *MVS/ESA: System Commands*, GC28-1626-05, Poughkeepsie, N.Y.: IBM.

IBM Corp., 1993, *NetView: Command Quick Reference*, SX75-0090-00, Research Triangle Park, N.C.: IBM.

IBM Corp., 1993, *NetView: Installation and Administration*, SC31-7084-00, Research Triangle Park, N.C.: IBM.

IBM Corp., 1993, *System Information Architecture: Formats*, GA27-3136, Research Triangle Park, N.C.: IBM.

IBM Corp., 1993, *System Network Architecture: Architecture Reference*, Version 2, SC30-3422-03, Research Triangle Park, N.C.: IBM.

IBM Corp., 1993, *The Host as a Data Server Using LANRES and Novell NetWare*, GG24-4069-00, Poughkeepsie, N.Y.: IBM.

IBM Corp., 1993, *Virtual Machine/Enterprise Systems Architecture*, SC24-5460-03, Endicott, N.Y.: IBM.

IBM Corp., 1993, *VM/ESA: CMS Command Reference*, SC24-5461-03, Endicott, N.Y.: IBM.

IBM Corp., 1993, *VM/ESA: CP Command and Utility Reference*, SC24-5519-03, Endicott, N.Y.: IBM.

IBM Corp., 1993, *VTAM: Operation*, SC31-6420-00, Research Triangle Park, N.C.: IBM.

IBM Corp., 1993, *VTAM: Resource Definition Reference Version 4 Release 1 for MVS/ESA*, SC31-6427-00, Research Triangle Park, N.C.: IBM.

IBM Corp., 1994, *LAN Resource Extension and Services/VM: General Information*, GC24-5618-03, Endicott, N.Y.: IBM.

IBM Corp., 1994, *LAN Resource Extension and Services/MVS: General Information*, GC24-5625-03, Endicott, N.Y.: IBM.

IBM Corp., 1994, *LAN Resource Extension and Services/MVS: Guide and Reference*, SC24-5623-02, Endicott, N.Y.: IBM.

Jain, Bijendra N., and Ashok K. Agrawala, 1993, *Open Systems Interconnection*, New York, N.Y.: McGraw-Hill.

Kessler, Gary C., 1990, *ISDN*, New York, N.Y.: McGraw-Hill.

Kessler, Gary C., and David A. *Train,* 1992, *Metropolitan Area Networks Concepts, Standards, and Services*, New York, N.Y.: McGraw-Hill.

Killen, Michael, 1992, *SAA and UNIX IBM's Open Systems Strategy*, New York, N.Y.: McGraw-Hill.

Killen, Michael, 1992, *SAA Managing Distributed Data*, New York, N.Y.: McGraw-Hill.

Kochan, Stephen G., and Patrick H. Wood, 1984, *Exploring the UNIX System*, Indianapolis, Ind.: Hayden Books.

McClain, Gary R., 1991, *Open Systems Interconnection Handbook*, New York, N.Y.: Intertext Publications/Multiscience Press.

Madron, Thomas W., 1988, *Local Area Networks: The Next Generation*, New York, N.Y.: Wiley.

Martin, James, 1989, *Local Area Networks Architectures and Implementations*, Englewood Cliffs, N.J.: Prentice-Hall.

Meijer, Anton, 1987, *Systems Network Architecture: A Tutorial*, London, U.K.: Pitman; New York, N.Y.: Wiley.

Merrow, Bill, 1993, *VSE/ESA Performance Management and Fine Tuning*, New York, N.Y.: McGraw-Hill.

Merrow, Bill, 1994, *VSE/ESA Concepts and Facilities*, New York, N.Y.: McGraw-Hill.

Nash, Stephen G., ed., 1990, *A History of Scientific Computing*, New York, N.Y.: ACM Press.

Naugle, Matthew G., 1991, *Local Area Networking*, New York, N.Y.: McGraw-Hill.

Naugle, Matthew, 1994, *Network Protocol Handbook*, New York, N.Y.: McGraw-Hill.

Nemzow, Martin A. W., 1992, *The Ethernet Management Guide: Keeping the Link*, 2d ed., New York, N.Y.: McGraw-Hill.

O'Dell, Peter, 1989, *The Computer Networking Book*, Chapel Hill, N.C.: Ventana Press.

Parker, Sybil P., ed., 1984, *McGraw-Hill Dictionary of Science and Engineering*, New York, N.Y.: McGraw-Hill.

Pugh, Emerson W., Lyle R. Johnson, and John H. Palmer, *IBM's 360 and Early 370 Systems*, Cambridge, Mass.: MIT Press.

Pugh, Emerson W., 1984, *Memories That Shaped an Industry*, Cambridge, Mass.: MIT Press.

Ranade, Jay, and George C. Sackett, 1989, *Introduction to SNA Networking Using VTAM/NCP*, New York, N.Y.: McGraw-Hill.

Rose, Marshall T., 1990, *The Open Book: A Practical Perspective on OSI*, Englewood Cliffs, N.J.: Prentice-Hall.

Rose, Marshall T., 1991, *The Simple Book: An Introduction to Management of TCP/IP-Based Internets*, Englewood Cliffs, N.J.: Prentice-Hall.

Samson, Stephen L., 1990, *MVS Performance Management*, New York, N.Y.: McGraw-Hill.

Savit, Jeffrey, 1993, *VM/CMS Concepts and Facilities*, New York, N.Y.: McGraw-Hill.

Schatt, Stan, 1990, *Understanding Local Area Networks*, 2d ed., Carmel, Ind.: Howard W. Sams.

Schlar, Serman K., 1990, *Inside X.25: A Manager's Guide*, New York, N.Y.: McGraw-Hill.

Seyer, Martin D., 1991, *RS-232 Made Easy: Connecting Computers, Printers, Terminals, and Modems*, Englewood Cliffs, N.J.: Prentice-Hall.

Sidhu, Gursharan S., Richard F. Andrews, and Alan B. Oppenheimer, 1990, *Inside AppleTalk*, 2d ed., Menlo Park, Calif.: Addison-Wesley.

Spohn, Darren L., 1993, *Data Network Design*, New York, N.Y.: McGraw-Hill.

Stallings, William, 1987–1988, *Handbook of Computer-Communications Standards*, Vols. 1–3, New York, N.Y.: Macmillan.

Stallings, William, 1989, *ISDN: An Introduction*, New York, N.Y.: Macmillan.

Stamper, David A., 1986, *Business Data Communications*, Menlo Park, Calif.: Benjamin/Cummings.

Tang, Adrian, and Sophia Scoggins, 1992, *Open Networking with OSI*, Englewood Cliffs, N.J.: Prentice-Hall.

Umar, Amjad, 1993, *Distributed Computing: A Practical Synthesis*, Englewood Cliffs, N.J.: Prentice-Hall.

White, Gene, 1992, *Internetworking and Addressing*, New York, N.Y.: McGraw-Hill.

Zwass, Vladimir, 1981, *Introduction to Computer Science*, New York, N.Y.: Barnes & Noble Books.

Trademarks

Trademarks are listed alphabetically, followed (in parentheses) by their trademark (T) or registered trademark (R) designations, then proprietor (company, institute, etc.) names (DEC = Digital Equipment Corp.; IBM = International Business Machines Corp.; IEEE = Institute of Electrical and Electronic Engineers; MIT = Massachusetts Institute of Technology).

ACF/VTAM (R: IBM)

ACMS (T: DEC)

AIX (T: IBM)

AIXwindows (T: IBM)

ALL-IN-1 (T: DEC)

Alpha AXP (T: DEC)

APDA (T: Apple Computer, Inc.)

Apollo (R: Apollo Computer, Inc.)

Apple and Apple logo (R,R: Apple Computer, Inc.)

AppleColor (R: Apple Computer, Inc.)

Apple Desktop Bus (T: Apple Computer, Inc.)

AppleShare (T: Apple Computer, Inc.)

AppleTalk (R: Apple Computer, Inc.)

Apple IIGS (R: Apple Computer, Inc.)

AS/400 (R: IBM)

A/UX (R: Apple Computer, Inc.)

AXP and AXP logo (T,T: DEC)

Bookreader (T: DEC)

CDA (T: DEC)

CDD (T: DEC)

CDD/REpository (T: DEC)

CI COHESION (T: DEC)

CICS (R: IBM)

CICS/ESA (R: IBM)

CICS/MVS (R: IBM)

Cisco (R: Cisco Systems, Inc.)

DATABASE 2, DB2 (R,R: IBM)

DEC (R: DEC)

DEC ACCESSWORKS (T: DEC)

DEC GKS (T: DEC)

DEC MAILworks (T: DEC)

DEC PHIGS (T: DEC)

DEC Rdb for Open VMS (T: DEC)

DEC RTR (T: DEC)

DEC VTX (T: DEC)

DEC VUIT (T: DEC)

DECalert (T: DEC)

DECamds (T: DEC)

DECdecision (T: DEC)

DECdesign (T: DEC)

DECdtm (T: DEC)

DECforms (T: DEC)

DECmcc (T: DEC)

DECmessageQ (T: DEC)

DECnet (R: DEC)

DECNIS (T: DEC)

DECperformance Solution (T: DEC)

DECplan (T: DEC)

DECprint (T: DEC)

DECquery (T: DEC)

DECram (T: DEC)

DECscheduler (T: DEC)

DECserver (T: DEC)

DECset (T: DEC)

DECtalk (T: DEC)

DECterm (T: DEC)

DECthreads (T: DEC)

DECtp (T: DEC)

DECtrace (T: DEC)

DECwindows (T: DEC)

DECwrite (T: DEC)

DFSMS, DFSMS.MVS (R,R: IBM)

Digital and Digital logo (T,T: DEC)

DNA (T: DEC)

EDT (T: DEC)

80386, 80386SX, 80486, 80486SX (T,T,T,T: Intel Corp.)

Enterprise System/3090, ES/3090 (R,R: IBM)

Enterprise System/4381, ES/4381 (R,R: IBM)

Enterprise System/9000, ES/9000 (R,R: IBM)

Enterprise Systems Architecture/ 370, ESA/370 (R,R: IBM)

Enterprise Systems Architecture/390, ESA/390 (R,R: IBM)

Enterprise Systems Connection Architecture, ESCON, ESCON XDF (R,R,R: IBM)

EtherCard PLUS (T: Western Digital Corp.)

Etherlink (T: 3Com Corp.)

Ethernet (R: Xerox Corp.)

eXcursion (T: DEC)

Finder (T: Apple Computer, Inc.)

GDDM (R: IBM)

Hardware Configuration Definition (R: IBM)

Hiperbatch (R: IBM)

Hiperspace (R: IBM)

HP (R: Hewlett-Packard Co.)

HSC (T: DEC)

HyperCard (R: Apple Computer, Inc.)

HYPERchannel (R: Network Systems Corp.)

IBM (R: IBM)

IBMLink (R: IBM)

ImageWrite (R: Apple Computer, Inc.)

IMS (R: IBM)

IMS/ESA (R: IBM)

Information Warehouse (R: IBM)

Intel (R: Intel Corp.)

Internetwork Packet eXchange (R: Novell, Inc.)

IPX (R: Novell, Inc.)

KanjiTalk (T: Apple Computer, Inc.)

Kerberos (R: MIT)

LaserWriter (R: Apple Computer, Inc.)

Lat (T: DEC)

LattisNet (R: SynOptics Communications, Inc.)

LinkWorks (T: DEC)

Lisa (R: Apple Computer, Inc.)

MacApp (R: Apple Computer, Inc.)

MacDraw (R: Claris Corp.)

Macintosh (R: Apple Computer, Inc.)

MacPaint (R: Claris Corp.)

MacWorks (R: Apple Computer, Inc.)

MacWrite (R: Claris Corp.)

Madge (T: Madge Networks Ltd.)

Microsoft (T: Microsoft Corp.)

Microsoft C (R: Microsoft Corp.)

Microsoft Windows (R: Microsoft Corp.)

MPW (T: Apple Computer, Inc.)

MSCP (T: DEC)

MS-DOS (R: Microsoft Corp.)

MultiFinder (T: Apple Computer, Inc.)

MVS, MVS/DFP, MVS/ESA, MVS/SP, MVS/XA (R,R,R,R,R: IBM)

NAP (R: Automated Network Management, Inc.)

NCP (R: IBM)

NCS (R: Apollo Computer, Inc.)

NETMAP (R: SynOptics Communications, Inc.)

NetView (R: IBM)

NetWare (R: Novell, Inc.)

Network Computing System (R: Apollo Computer, Inc.)

Network File System, NFS (R,R.: Sun Microsystems, Inc.)

Novell (R: Novell, Inc.)

NuBus (T: Texas Instruments)

OpenEdition (R: IBM)

OpenVMS (T: DEC)

OSF, OSF/Motif (R,R: Open Software Foundation, Inc.)

OS/2 (R: IBM)

PATHWORKS (T: DEC)

PC-AT (T: IBM)

PC-NFS (R: Sun Microsystems, Inc.)

POLYCENTER (T: DEC)

Portmapper (R: Sun Microsystems, Inc.)

POSIX (T: IEEE)

PostScript (R: Adobe Systems, Inc.)

Presentation Manager (R: IBM)

Processor Resource/Systems Manager, PR/SM (R,R: IBM)

Proprinter (T: IBM)

PSF (R: IBM)

PS/2 (R: IBM)

PS2/2 (T: IBM)

RACF (R: IBM)

Reliable Transaction Router (T: DEC)

RISC System/6000 (T: IBM)

RS6000 (R: IBM)

RT (T: IBM)

rtVAX (T: DEC)

SANE (R: Apple Computer, Inc.)

SDLC (R: IBM)

SNA (R: IBM)

Sun (R: Sun Microsystems, Inc.)

SunOS (R: Sun Microsystems, Inc.)

Switcher (T: Apple Computer, Inc.)

Sysplex Timer (R: IBM)

SystemView (R: IBM)

System/370 (R: IBM)

3090 (R: IBM)

TMSCP (T: DEC)

Trellis (T: DEC)

TURBOchannel (T: DEC)

ULTRIX (T: DEC)

UNIX (R: UNIX System Laboratories, Inc.) (UNIX was originally developed in the 1970s by AT&T and Bell Laboratories)

VAX (R: DEC)

VAX Ada (T: DEC)

VAX APL (T: DEC)

VAX BASIC (T: DEC)

VAX BLISS-32 (T: DEC)

VAX C (T: DEC)

VAX COBOL (T: DEC)

VAX DATATRIEVE (T: DEC)

VAX DBMS (T: DEC)

VAX DIBOL (T: DEC)

VAX DOCUMENT (T: DEC)

VAX DSM (T: DEC)

VAX FORTRAN (T: DEC)

VAX LISP (T: DEC)

VAX MACRO (T: DEC)

VAX Notes (T: DEC)

VAX OPS5 (T: DEC)

VAX Pascal (T: DEC)

VAX RALLY (T: DEC)

VAX RMS (T: DEC)

VAX SCAN (T: DEC)

VAX SQL (T: DEC)

VAX TEAMDATA (T: DEC)

VAXcluster (T: DEC)

VAXELN (T: DEC)

VAXft (T: DEC)

VAXmail (T: DEC)

VAXshare (T: DEC)

VAXsimPLUS (T: DEC)

VAXstation (T: DEC)

VIDA (T: DEC)

VM/ESA (R: IBM)

VM/XA (R: IBM)

VMS (T: DEC)

VTAM (R: IBM)

VT100, VT220, VT330 (T,T,T: DEC)

Windows (T: Microsoft, Inc.)

Word for Windows (T: Microsoft, Inc.)

WPS (T: DEC)

WPS-PLUS (T: DEC)

Xerox (T: Xerox Corp.)

XNS (T: Xerox Corp.)

X/Open (R: X.Open Co., Ltd.)

XUI (T: DEC)

XWindow (R: MIT)

X-Windows (T: MIT)

Index

ABOUT THE AUTHOR

Ed Taylor is founder and chief network architect for Information World, Inc. and former network architect for IBM.

Some of Mr. Taylor's consulting experience includes work for NEC, Orange County, CA, BASF, Chrysler, Hewlett-Packard, Dow Jones, Ore-Ida Foods, Mutual of New York (MONY), and IBM Education.